WITHDRAWN

ENCYCLOPEDIA OF

CELL TECHNOLOGY

VOLUME 2

WILEY BIOTECHNOLOGY ENCYCLOPEDIAS

Encyclopedia of Bioprocess Technology: Fermentation, Biocatalysis, and Bioseparation
Edited by Michael C. Flickinger and Stephen W. Drew

Encyclopedia of Molecular Biology
Edited by Thomas E. Creighton

Encyclopedia of Cell Technology
Edited by Raymond E. Spier

Encyclopedia of Ethical, Legal, and Policy Issues in Biotechnology
Edited by Thomas J. Murray and Maxwell J. Mehlman

ENCYCLOPEDIA OF CELL TECHNOLOGY
EDITORIAL BOARD

ENCYCLOPEDIA OF
CELL TECHNOLOGY

VOLUME 2

Raymond E. Spier
University of Surrey
Guildford, Surrey
United Kingdom

A Wiley-Interscience Publication
John Wiley & Sons, Inc.
New York / Chichester / Weinheim / Brisbane / Singapore / Toronto

This book is printed on acid-free paper. ⊗

Copyright © 2000 by John Wiley & Sons, Inc.

All rights reserved. Published simultaneously in Canada.

No part of this publication may be reproduced, stored in a retrieval system or transmitted in any form or by any means, electronic, mechanical, photocopying, recording, scanning or otherwise, except as permitted under Sections 107 or 108 of the 1976 United States Copyright Act, without either the prior written permission of the Publisher, or authorization through payment of the appropriate per-copy fee to the Copyright Clearance Center, 222 Rosewood Drive, Danvers, MA 01923, (978) 750-8400, fax (978) 750-4744. Requests to the Publisher for permission should be addressed to the Permissions Department, John Wiley & Sons, Inc., 605 Third Avenue, New York, NY 10158-0012, (212) 850-6011, fax (212) 850-6008, E-Mail: PERMREQ@WILEY.COM.

For ordering and customer service, call 1-800-CALL-WILEY.

Library of Congress Cataloging in Publication Data

Encyclopedia of cell technology / [edited by] Raymond E. Spier.
    p.   cm.
    ISBN 0-471-16123-3 (cloth : set : alk. paper) — ISBN (invalid) 0-471-16643-X (v. 1 : alk. paper). — ISBN 0-471-16623-5 (v. 2 : alk. paper).
    1. Animal cell biotechnology Encyclopedias.   2. Plant cell biotechnology Encyclopedias.   3. Cell culture Encyclopedias.
4. Cytology Encyclopedias.   I. Spier, R. (Raymond)
TP248.27.A53E53   2000
660.6 — dc21   99-25295

Printed in the United States of America.

10 9 8 7 6 5 4 3 2 1

ENCYCLOPEDIA OF

CELL TECHNOLOGY

VOLUME 2

D

DICOTYLEDONS

Margaret M. Ramsay
Royal Botanic Gardens
Kew, Richmond, Surrey
United Kingdom

OUTLINE

INTRODUCTION

Dicotyledons are the larger of the two angiosperm classes with over 150,000 species of trees, shrubs, and herbaceous plants. Since experimental work with carrot (*Daucus carota*) and tobacco (*Nicotiana tabacum*) indicated the totipotency of plant tissue and demonstrated that entire plants could be regenerated from small pieces of tissue and isolated cells, *in vitro* culture has been widely used for plant breeding, propagation, biotechnology, and conservation of crop genetic resources in both agriculture and horticulture. In addition, these techniques have been adapted for use with a wide range of wild species. Vegetative propagation through axillary and adventitious shoots, callus, or somatic embryogenesis has been applied to crop plants (potato, tomato, sugar beet); ornamental horticultural plants (*Chrysanthemum, Rosacea, Saintpaulia, Gerbera*); woody species and trees (*Malus, Pyrus, Prunus, Tilia, Quercus*); and to a lesser extent, medicinal plants (*Matricaria, Dictamnus, Diascorea, Digitalis*), and these methods will be summarized in this article. Other *in vitro* techniques include production of haploids and triploids; *in vitro* pollination, fertilization, and embryo rescue; protoplast isolation and somatic hybridization; and genetic modification and production of secondary metabolites. Most of them were originally developed for dicot species and cultivars.

Culture of woody plant species presents particular problems compared to herbaceous species, genetic variation is generally greater, sterilization of material is more difficult, toxic exudates may be produced, and dormancy and juvelinity of material may play a greater role. Nevertheless, many of these problems have been overcome, and new techniques have been developed.

With the development of slow growth and cryopreservation procedures, it is now possible to secure *in vitro* germplasm of crop plants and cultivars and their wild relatives and also of endangered species, effectively and economically on a long-term basis.

SEED GERMINATION

As seeds arise through sexual reproduction, they maintain a wider genetic base than clonal material, an important consideration for species of conservation concern although not if uniform offspring is required. The main application of *in vitro* seed germination is to overcome dormancy or other germination requirements and to provide aseptic material as explants for shoot cultures.

Trochetiopsis erythroxylon (St. Helena redwood) and *T. melanoxylon* (St. Helena ebony) are endangered trees in the Sterculiaceae and are endemic to St. Helena. Work at Kew has shown that removal of the testa from seed of this species under sterile conditions greatly increased the percentage germination and allowed the successful establishment of plants *ex vitro* (1). Similar techniques have been applied to *Sophora toromira*, an endemic plant from Easter Island, now extinct in the wild.

Carnivorous plants are another group threatened by habitat destruction and overcollection of wild plants. Using *in vitro* seed germination, followed in many cases by proliferation, many species have been raised, including representatives of *Droseraceae, Lentibulariaceae, Nepenthaceae*, and *Sarraceniaceae*.

MICROPROPAGATION

The main application of micropropagation is mass clonal multiplication of desirable genotypes of plants. For some crop plants that produce few if any viable seeds, vegetative multiplication is the only method possible. Stages have been defined by Murashige (2) in the *in vitro* multiplication of plants that describe procedural steps and also points at which the culture environment needs to be changed. The preparative stage involves preparing of donor plants to provide quality explants for aseptic culture. This may involve exposing stock plants to suitable light, temperature, and growth regulator regimes and growing under greenhouse conditions to minimize contamination problems.

Stage I: Initiation of cultures involves selecting an explant that depends largely on the multiplication procedure to be adopted. This can take the form of a vegetative bud, a meristem tip, an immature zygotic embryo, or explants derived from other plant parts that have the capacity to form adventitious buds. A number of different sterilants can be used to start an aseptic culture. Particular care is required for field-derived material.

Stage II *in vitro* multiplication is achieved through four main approaches: axillary shoot production, adventitious bud formation, callus, and somatic embryogenesis.

Stage III rooting of shoots can be carried out *in vitro* although many commercial laboratories prefer to treat the shoots as microcuttings and root them *in vivo*. Axillary and adventitious shoots grown in the prescence of cytokinins generally lack roots and must be transferred to a rooting medium to achieve this.

Stage IV transplantation of *in vitro* plants can be problematic because of their poor control of water loss and their heterotrophic means of nutrition, and plants need to be acclimatized gradually from conditions of high humidity using such systems as fogging and misting.

AXILLARY SHOOT PRODUCTION

In axillary shoot production, cytokinins are normally used to overcome apical dominance and stimulate the lateral buds to grow directly into shoots. This process can be repeated several times to produce a mass of branches from the initial explant and can be carried out almost indefinitely if those shoots are excised and planted on fresh medium. Because cells of the shoot apex are diploid and less susceptible to genotypic change during culture, this is the method of choice for clonal propagation of crop plants such as potato (3), for endangered wild material, and for the commercial production of many ornamental plants.

Techniques developed at Kew (4) for succulent plants are based on inducing shoot formation from dormant meristems in the areole of cacti or from axillary buds in other succulents. These have been used most successfully with members of *Asclepiadaceae* and succulent species of *Aizoaceae* and *Crassulaceae*. Species of *Cactaceae* and succulent *Euphorbias* have proved more problematic because the meristematic areas are embedded in the areole tissue. Removal of woody spines can damage this tissue or allow it to be damaged by the sterilant.

ADVENTITIOUS BUD FORMATION

Adventitious buds are those that arise directly from a plant organ or explant other than the shoot apex or leaf axil. The rate of adventitious bud development can be considerably enhanced *in vitro* for plants where vegetative propagation through adventitious buds is already routinely applied using standard horticultural practice. These include adventitious buds arising from leaf tissue of *Begonia*, *Peperomia*, *Saintpaulia*, and from roots of raspberry and blackberry. Where adventitious shoots do not occur naturally, they can nevertheless be artificially induced. Examples include the propagation of some grape cultivars from adventitious bud formation at the base of shoot-tip fragments and de novo production of shoots on the petioles of sugar beet leaves. Although this method generally produces true-to-type plants, somaclonal variants have been detected in some cases.

CALLUS AND CELL SUSPENSION

The ability of plants to regenerate shoots and roots from somatic, as well as reproductive tissues (totipotency), has been utilized in callus and cell culture. Callus can be initiated by placing explants on media containing growth regulators which stimulate the active division of cells and result in new tissue made up of meristematic and unspecialized cell types. Callus is hugely variable in its color, appearance, friability, and morphogenic potential, even from a single explant, and can be manipulated in a number of ways through the use of careful subculturing and the use of different media. Whole plant regeneration from cells in culture can take the form of shoot differentiation or somatic embryogenesis. Although in some plants, such as tobacco, almost all explants are amenable to this process, in others some tissues, mainly young and meristematic tissue, may have more potential than others. Several factors influence the ability of callus and cells to regenerate: the size and physiological state of the explant, orientation, and inoculation density on the media, as well as hormonal manipulation of the medium itself. Organogenic differentiation in response to these factors is a multistep process involving induction and then commitment of cells to a particular developmental pathway.

The isolation and culture of single cells have many advantages compared with intact organs and whole plants for studying cell metabolism and the effects of chemicals on them and allow easy application and withdrawal of substances. Single-cell culture also allows extending the techniques of microbial genetics to higher plants for crop improvement and for the production of phytochemicals through large scale cultivation. Cells can be isolated from intact plant organs by mechanical or enzymatic methods but are normally extracted from cultured tissues through repeated subculture of friable callus and agitation of cell aggregates in liquid medium. There are two main types of suspension cultures: batch cultures and continuous cultures. Batch cultures are characterized by constant change in the pattern of cell growth and metabolism and the composition of the nutrient medium which means that there is not a period of steady-state growth. Continuous culture may be of the closed or open type: as growth proceeds in closed systems, the cell biomass continues to increase, whereas in the open type, medium flowing in is equal to the volume of culture (medium and cells) harvested, and thus cultures may be maintained at a constant, submaximal growth rate. The two main types of vessels for open continuous culture are the chemostat and turbostat. Plant-cell reactors are designed with different considerations from those of microbial fermentors because of the differences in the nature and growth of the two types of cells. Plant cells are more sensitive to shear forces because of their large size, rigid cellulose wall, and extensive vacuole. They also tend to form aggregates of 2–200 cells, and thus efficient mixing at very low agitation speeds is required . The bioreactors most commonly used for suspension cultures of plant cells are stirred-tank, bubble-column, air-lift, rotating-drum, and immobilized plant-cell reactors. Despite intense investigations into the use of cell culture to produce useful chemicals, only two products, shikonin and ginseng cells, have been produced on a commercial scale, and cell culture has not yet become a cost-effective technology.

SOMATIC EMBRYOGENESIS

The specialized physical and chemical environment required by embryos to develop and mature can be supplied using tissue culture techniques so that, provided irreversible differentiation has not taken place, any cell has the potential to develop an embryo-like structure and produce a complete plant. The number of species for which somatic embryos can be produced is increasing all the time. *Daucus carota* has been widely used to investigate the different parameters involved with *in vitro* somatic embryogenesis (5) although other plants studied in some detail include *Citrus* sp. which display natural polyembryony (6). Somatic embryogenesis consists of three steps: induction of embryogenesis, embryonic development, and embryonic maturation. Factors that affect these include the choice of explant (particularly important for recalcitrant species such as grain legumes) and a genotypic effect, as shown in studies of alfafa where somatic embryogenesis is a genetically controlled process (7). Most somatic embryogenesis systems require a synthetic auxin for induction, followed by transfer to auxin-free media for differentiation. The auxin most commonly used is 2,4-D although others such as Picloram have also been used. The form of nitrogen in the medium also significantly affects somatic embryogenesis, in particular the presence of reduced nitrogen, usually NH_4^+ in the induction stage. The presence of amino acids have also been found beneficial for converting and maturing of somatic embryos and there is some evidence that polyamines may also be involved in the process (8). Selective subculture can also have a big impact because often only a small number of cells within an explant exhibit distinct embryogenic tissue which may not develop further if transferred with the rest of the calli. Although somatic embrogenesis has been reported for many crop species, it often does not result in high quality plants because they have not gone through a maturation phase, specifically the accumulation of food reserves and proteins that impart desiccation tolerance. A number of factors are being investigated, in particular the role of abscisic acid (ABA) in maturation of somatic embryos.

Somatic embryogenesis offers a potential system for large-scale plant propagation in automated bioreactors because multiplication and development can take place in a liquid medium. However at present there are few articles published. Some problems encountered include shear damage and asynchronous cultures.

LIMITATIONS: CONTAMINATION, HYPERHYDRICITY, RECALCITRANCE AND OXIDATIVE BROWNING

Shoot-tip culture continues to play an important role in the production of disease-free plants particularly in the horticulture industry despite the potential of genetic engineering to breed virus-resistant plants. However, disease and microbial contamination remain the major causes of ecomomic losses in the micropropagation industry. The most likely sources of contamination are pathogens of crops, endophytic microorganisms, and laboratory contaminants. Because it is recognized that truly axenic cultures are rare due to the problem of cryptic contaminants, the management of contamination is emphasized now (9). Attention must be given to selecting healthy source stocks, establishing and multiplying propagules with thorough contaminant screening, and producing vigorous shoots able to withstand damping-off disease. The use of beneficial bacterial and mycorrhizal associations with microplants *in vitro* and *in vivo* are also being explored.

Hyperhydricity (previously called vitrification) is a phenomenon noted particularly during intensive shoot production where the plants show abnormalities such as leaves and stems with a water-soaked, glassy appearance, often thick and brittle with short internodes (10). Altered biochemical characteristics include reduced lignin and cellulose and changes in enzyme activity. Shoots generally grow poorly and become necrotic or turn into callus and show low survival on acclimatization mainly due to inadequately developed stomata and reduced surface wax. The physical and chemical environment within the culture vessels are thought to be responsible for this phenomenon. Liquid medium causes more hyperhydration than solid medium and Phytogel causes more problems than agar. Media rich in minerals such as (MS) Murashige and Skoog medium and high cytokinin concentrations are also implicated as are conditions of poor gaseous exchange which allow a buildup of humidity and accumulation of gases. Hyperhydricity can be reduced by lowering humidity in vessels through increased aeration and the amount of agar used, diluting MS media and lowering NH_4^+ concentrations, and reducing the levels of cytokinins used. The addition of the chemicals phlorizin and phloroglucinol have also been found beneficial in some cases.

Many tree species are propagated vegetatively by woody cuttings and specialized layering procedures. These are usually slow and labor-intensive, and because many forest trees and orchard crops are managed on a 20–25 year rotation, rapid multiplication of elite clonal material is desirable. Juvenility is of major significance in relation to the vegetative propagation of trees by conventional and *in vitro* methods. Explants of axillary and apical buds and shoots are generally taken when trees are in this phase of very active growth. In the case of mature specimens, the rejuvenated types of growth can be induced by treatments such as grafting of shoots on seedlings, shoot pruning, the maintenance of high fertilizer levels, or spraying with cytokinins (11). Buds may be excised before opening, and the apical tip is dissected out. Episodic growth in culture is another problem encountered with some temperate hardwood species.

Woody plants can contain high concentrations of phenolic substances which are oxidized when cells are wounded or senescent. Isolated tissue then becomes brown or black and fails to grow. Several different methods have been used to overcome this problem (12), including keeping the cultures initially in the dark and rapidly transferring explants to fresh medium or within the same vessel. The addition of antioxidants, such as ascorbic acid or citric acid, to the culture media or compounds, such as PVP (polyvinylpyrrolidone), to adsorb phenolic compounds have also proved effective in some cases.

PLANT GENETIC ENGINEERING

Besides giving invaluable information on the role of individual genes within plant genomes, recombinant DNA technology offers the possibility of expanding plant breeding beyond traditional barriers and allowing the introduction of traits from nonrelated plant species and even from other organisms.

In genetic modification, the genetic material or DNA sequencing for a desirable trait is located in the donor organism, extracted using restriction endonucleases, and then introduced into the recipient plant cells via a vector by one of several possible methods. Plants are then regenerated from these cells.

The use of the Ti-plasmid of *Agrobacterium tumefaciens* as a vector has been studied in great detail along with a number of other vectors developed from it. Early studies involved the cocultivation of protoplasts with the bacteria. This had limited application for many crop plants because protoplast isolation and regeneration were required. The development of the explant cocultivation method, where small pieces of tissue such as leaf discs, proembryos, microspores, etc., were cocultivated with *Agrobacterium*, resulted in the production of many transgenic plants, although largely restricted to dicots which exhibit a strong wound response. After cocultivation, explants are transferred to media containing antibiotics to kill the bacteria. Under selection conditions, transformed cells grow and form callus and then undergo standard tissue culture techniques. *Agrobacterium rhizogenes*-mediated transformation (hairy root cultures) has also been used in some circumstances.

The main route for transformation other than by using *Agrobacterium* is by direct gene transfer. Some chemicals such as polyamines and polyethylene glycol (PEG) can be used to stimulate DNA uptake into protoplasts. Other methods used are electroporation, in which an electric field is used to make protoplasts temporarily permeable to DNA, and microinjection, where DNA is directly injected into protoplasts and cells after immobilization. However, the most widely used direct gene transfer technique is the particle bombardment method. This method overcomes many problems of host specificity of *Agrobacterium* and regeneration of complete plants from protoplasts because DNA can be introduced into organized morphogenic tissues such as seeds, embryos, and meristems by using particle bombardment—microscopic gold or tungsten particles forced into cells at high velocity using a variety of ballistic "guns". The genetic selection, identification, and recovery of transformed plants are important components of transformation systems as are field performance trials for commercial applications.

So far, genetic engineering has been applied mainly to produce crop plants with a high degree of tolerance and resistance to pests (viruses, fungi, bacteria, and insects) and diseases and with tolerance to herbicides (mainly "Roundup" or Glyphosate). Potentially useful transgenic plants of potato, cotton, soybean, rapeseed, and the tomato cf "Flavr Savr" (13) have been generated, and many papers have been published about species that have been transformed and regenerated into complete transgenic plants, as reviewed by Fisk and Dandakau (14).

Although the list of transgenic crop species continues to grow, their commercialization and marketing, particularly of genetically modified (GM) foods, has been the subject of much debate. Considerable public concern has been expressed about food safety and issues of labeling, as well as possible environmental hazards.

CRYOPRESERVATION

Germplasm storage is crucial in preserving cultivars and wild relatives of crop plants, as well as in wider plant genetic diversity. Conventionally, this is achieved through the use of seed banks because seeds can be stored at low temperatures for many years in a relatively small space. This method, however, is not efficient for short-lived and recalcitrant seed (e.g., those that are desiccation-intolerant or lack a dormancy mechanism), for apomictic species, or for vegetatively propagated crops such as potato. Therefore, *in vitro* storage of genotypes has been investigated with the possibility of regeneration from somatic and gametic cells and from shoot apices.

In theory, plants can be maintained by serial subculture at 4–8 week intervals for indefinite periods. However the genetic makeup of the cells and their regeneration potential may change over time, thus risking the stability of the germplasm. Short- and medium-term storage methods (reduced temperature and growth limiting) aim to reduce growth and increase the intervals between subcultures, but for long-term storage, cryopreservation, storage at ultralow temperatures, is the method used. In this technique, plant material is frozen at the temperature of liquid nitrogen (around −196 °C) where the cells are maintained in an inactive state.

Cells in culture are not the ideal system for germplasm storage, other than for preservation of cell lines used in producing secondary metabolites, because of their genetic instability and in some cases reduced totipotency. Therefore the emphasis has been on organized structures such as shoot apices and embryos. Most of these structures are sensitive to freezing injury because most contain high amounts of cellular water and are often not naturally freeze-tolerant. Thus cells must be dehydrated artificially to protect them from damage caused by ice crystal formation. The classical approach to cryopreservation, slow cooling followed by rapid immersion in liquid nitrogen, has been applied to a range of *in vitro* plant-culture systems, particularly for homogenous cultures of small units, such as protoplasts, or exponential growth phase suspension cultures. This approach is less successful for plant material made up of a mixture of cell sizes and types, such as shoot tips or mature somatic embryos, due to the problems of achieving uniform dehydration, for which vitrification procedures are more effective. In these procedures, intracellular ice formation is avoided through cell dehydration by exposing material to concentrated cryoprotectants and/or air desiccation followed by rapid cooling.

Six different vitrification procedures have been identified and assessed by Engelmann (15): encapsulation–dehydration, vitrification, encapsulation-vitrification, desiccation, pregrowth, and pregrowth-desiccation. The encapsulation-dehydration technique is based on artificial seed technology where explants are encapsulated in alginate beads, pregrown in sucrose-enriched media, partially desiccated, then frozen rapidly, and has been applied successfully to apices of temperate species such as apple, pear, grape, and eucalyptus (16). Shoot-tip encapsulation of the endangered plant *Cosmos atrosanguineus* has been achieved using alginate strips which allows greater precision in positioning the explant, a major concern when dealing with limited amounts of material (17).

Vitrification involves the use of highly concentrated cryoprotectants, then rapid freezing, and has been applied to cell suspensions, apices, and somatic embryos, particularly of woody species. Encapsulation-vitrification is a combination of the above techniques. Desiccation is used mainly for freezing zygotic embryos or embryonic axes dissected from seeds and consists of dehydrating explants, then freezing rapidly by direct immersion. This simple technique has been applied successfully to embryos of a large number of intermediate and recalcitrant species (18,19).

Pregrowth-desiccation procedures combining pregrowth with dehydration steps, then rapid freezing, are under development for species with problematic zygotic and somatic embryos.

BIBLIOGRAPHY

1. M.F. Fay, E. Bunn, and M.M. Ramsay in B.G. Bowles, ed., *A Colour Atlas of Plant Propagation and Conservation*, Manson Publishing, London, 1999, pp. 97–107.

2. T. Murashige, *Annu. Rev. Plant Physiol.* **25**, 135–166 (1974).

3. J.H. Dodds, D. Silva-Rodriguez, and P. Tovar, in Y.P.S. Bajaj, ed., *Biotechnology in Agriculture and Forestry*, Vol. 19, Springer, Berlin, 1992, pp. 91–106.

4. J. Gratton and M.F. Fay, *Methods Mol. Bio.* **111**, 135–140 (1999).

5. J.L. Zimmerman, *Plant Cell* **5**, 1411–1423 (1993).

6. S.S. Bhojwani and S.P. Bhatnagar, *The Embryology of Angiosperms*, Vikas, Delhi, 1990.

7. G.A. Kielly and S.R. Bowley, *Genome* **35**, 474–477 (1992).

8. A. Altman, B.L. Nadel, Z. Falash, and N. Levin, in H.J.J. Nijkamp et al., eds., *Progress in Plant Cellular and Molecular Biology*, Kluwer Academic Publishers, Dordrecht, The Netherlands, 1990, pp. 454–459.

9. A.C. Cassells, ed., *Pathogen and Microbial Contamination Management in Micropropagation*, Kluwer Academic Publishers, Dordrecht, The Netherlands, 1997.

10. T. Gaspar, in Y.P.S. Bajaj, ed., *Biotechnology in Agriculture and Forestry*, Vol. 17, Springer, Berlin, 1991, pp. 116–126.

11. T.A Thorpe, I.S. Harry, and P.P Kumar, in P.C. Debergh and R.H. Zimmerman, eds., *Micropropagation: Technology and Application*, Kluwer Academic Publishers, Dordrecht, The Netherlands, 1991, pp. 311–336.

12. J.E. Preece and M.E. Compton, in Y.P.S. Bajaj, ed., *Biotechnology in Agriculture and Forestry*, Vol. 17, Springer, Berlin, 1991, pp. 169–189.

13. P. Christou, *In Vitro Cell. Dev. Biol.* **29P**, 119–124 (1993).

14. H.J. Fisk and A.M. Dandakau, *Sci. Hortic.* **55**, 5–36 (1993).

15. F. Engelmann, in B.V. Ford-LLoyd, H.J. Newbury, and J.A. Callow, eds., *Biotechnology and Plant Genetic Resources: Conservation and Use*, CABI, Wallingford, U.K., 1997, pp. 119–162.

16. J. Dereuddre, in Y. Datee, C. Dumas, and A. Gallais, eds., *Reproductive Biology and Plant Breeding*, Springer-Verlag, Berlin, 1992, pp. 291–300.

17. T. Wilkinson, A. Wetton, and M.F. Fay, *Cryo-Letters* **19**, 293–302 (1998).

18. V.C Pence, *Cryobiology* **27**, 212–218 (1990).

19. V.C. Pence, *Cryobiology* **29**, 391–399 (1992).

See also ACCLIMATIZATION; CRYOPRESERVATION OF PLANT CELLS, TISSUES AND ORGANS; CULTURE ESTABLISHMENT, PLANT CELL CULTURE; GERMPLASM PRESERVATION OF IN VITRO PLANT CULTURES; MICROPROPAGATION OF PLANTS, PRINCIPLES AND PRACTICES; MONOCOT CELL CULTURE.

DISEASE RESISTANCE IN TRANSGENIC PLANTS

MARY ROBISON
K. PETER PAULS
Ontario Agricultural College
University of Guelp
Guelp Ontario, Canada

OUTLINE

Introduction

The Plant Resistance Response

Resistance from *R* Genes

Resistance from Manipulation of Reactive Oxygen Species

Resistance from Cell Death

Resistance from Pathogenesis-Related Proteins

Resistance from Phytoalexins

Resistance from Antimicrobial Peptides and Proteins

Pathogen-Derived Resistance

Resistance from Novel Sources

Conclusions

Bibliography

INTRODUCTION

Approximately 80,000 diseases, caused by a wide variety of pathogenic fungi, bacteria, and viruses, affect cultivated plants grown world-wide and result in economic

Table 1. Examples of Severe Losses Caused by Plant Diseases

Host/disease	Pathogen	Crop losses due to pathogens
Rice	All	15% ($33 b) worldwide, 1988–1990
Rice blast	*Magnaporthe grisea*	Up to 30% loss
Wheat	All	12.4% ($14 b) worldwide, 1988–1990
Wheat rusts	*Puccinia* spp.	Up to 100% loss in certain epidemics
Barley	All	10.1% ($1.9 b) worldwide, 1988–1990
Powdery mildew	*Erysiphe graminis*	Up to 9% loss
Maize	All	10.9% ($7.8 b) worldwide, 1988–1990
Potatoes	All	16.3% ($9.8 b) worldwide, 1988–1990
Late blight	*Phytophthora infestans*	Up to 30% loss
Potato soft rot	*Erwinia caratovora*	Up to 30% loss
Potato virus X		Up to 75% loss
Soybeans	All	9% ($3.2 b) worldwide, 1988–1990
Cotton	All	10.5% ($4.3 b) worldwide, 1988–1990
Coffee	All	14.8% ($2.8 b) worldwide, 1988–1990

Source: Adapted from Ref. 1.

losses totalling approximately $70 (U.S.) billion annually (Table 1) (1). A single crop may be attacked by more than one pathogen; for example, tomato is susceptible to infection by 80 species of fungi, 11 species of bacteria, and 16 different viruses. Conversely, a pathogen may be able to infect only one or several different plant species. Disease results from a compatible interaction between a pathogen carrying an avirulence gene (*avr*) and a susceptible host plant (*r*). Disease resistance may result from either (*1*) an incompatible interaction between the same pathogen (*avr*) and a host plant with a matching resistance (*R*) gene (specific resistance), or (*2*) the interaction between a microorganism that is pathogenic on a certain plant(s) and a plant that is not normally infected by that pathogen (nonhost resistance). The complexities of both specific and nonhost resistance are just beginning to be understood at the cellular and molecular levels. This article describes how this knowledge may be exploited in strategies that use recombinant DNA and plant transformation technologies to increase disease resistance in plants.

THE PLANT RESISTANCE RESPONSE

The plant resistance response is the sum result of a wide variety of defense responses that vary in specificity, timing, magnitude, and localization, depending on the plant–pathogen interaction (Fig. 1). Within minutes of inoculation, an "oxidative burst," which is an increase in intracellular levels of superoxide anion ($O_2^{\bullet-}$) and H_2O_2, is observed. Subsequently, one or more of the following may occur: an accumulation of phenolics at the infection site; induction of antimicrobial compounds such as phytoalexins and so-called pathogenesis-related (PR) proteins (e.g., chitinases, glucanases); the construction of physical barriers through lignification and production/cross-linking of hydroxyproline-rich glycoproteins (HRGP); localized cell death at the site of infection (called the hypersensitive response or HR), which limits the spread of the pathogen; and induction of systemic acquired resistance

(SAR), which acts nonspecifically throughout the plant and provides plants with resistance to a variety of pathogens for several days. The degree of success of these responses determines the level of resistance expressed by the plant. Thus addition or modulation of any of these responses within a plant may increase its level of resistance to disease. This assumption underlies the following transgene approaches to increase plant disease resistance.

RESISTANCE FROM *R* GENES

The gene-for-gene model of disease resistance in plants, first proposed by H.H. Flor in 1940, describes the genetic basis for resistance identified in many plant–pathogen interactions (2). A normally compatible disease interaction between a susceptible host plant and an infective pathogen may become incompatible as a result of the evolution of a single dominant resistance (*R*) gene in the plant population. However, in a situation analogous to an "arms race," this resistance is only effective against pathogens carrying a specific avirulence (*avr*) gene and may be broken down by the appearance of a dominant virulence (*vir*) gene in the pathogen population. Thus each *R* gene appears to "match" a specific *avr* gene, and each *vir* gene appears specifically to overcome a particular *R* gene. Most studies of plant defense responses have been based on this type of incompatible interaction between a resistant (*R*) plant and an avirulent (*avr*) pathogen.

Molecular analysis of *R* genes from several plant–pathogen systems has revealed that they fall into one of four structural, and presumably functional, classes. Members of the largest class have receptor-like features, including leucine-rich repeats (LRRs) and nucleotide-binding sites (NBS). Another class has features of transmembrane receptors, including potential extracellular LRRs and a transmembrane domain. The *Pto* gene from tomato that confers resistance to *Pseudomonas syringae* pv. *tomato* defines another class with features of a serine–threonine

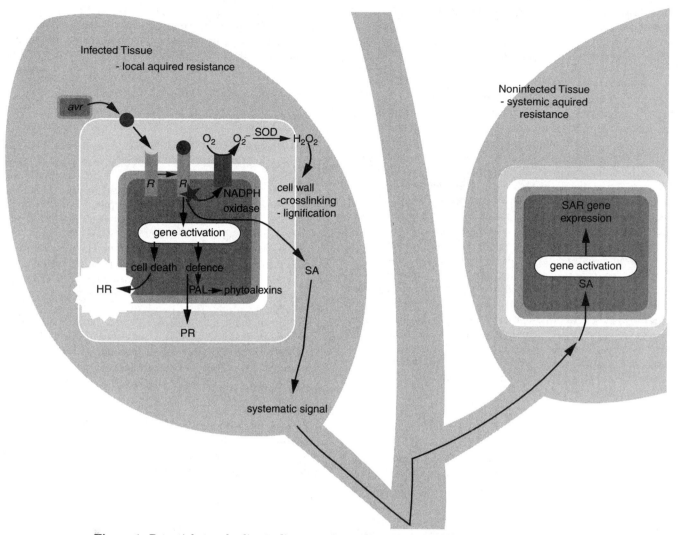

Figure 1. Potential steps leading to disease resistance in an incompatible interaction between a pathogen and a plant. At the infection site, the *avr* gene product from the pathogen interacts with the *R* gene product from the plant to trigger a cascade of events that can include: modification of the *R* gene product, synthesis of activated oxygen species like superoxide and hydrogen peroxide, activation of genes involved in the hypersensitive reaction (HR), and activation of defense-related genes coding for pathogenesis-related (PR) proteins and enzymes for phytoalexin synthesis. Signaling from the infected tissue, which includes the synthesis of salicylic acid (SA), induces systemic acquired resistance in noninfected tissue.

kinase. Finally, a fourth class encodes proteins with both receptor and kinase-like features. Thus *R* genes appear to encode products involved in recognition of the pathogen signal or immediate transduction of that signal along a defense response pathway. Few commonalities among *avr* gene products can be identified, and it is believed that their primary function in the pathogen is unrelated to their role of signaling in resistant host plants (3).

The potential for transfer of an *R* gene across species lines was successfully demonstrated when the *Pto* gene of tomato that confers resistance to *Pseudomonas syringae* pv. *tomato* made *Pto*-transformed tobacco resistant to bacteria carrying the same avirulence gene. It appears that the components of the defense systems with which *R*

genes interact are conserved across several genera, thus making this a technically feasible strategy. However, *R* gene transfer across species is unlikely to be of major importance for improving the resistance of agricultural commodities unless the identical pathogen (with the same *avr* gene) is a major problem in more than one crop. To increase the utility of *R* gene-based resistance, a two-component (*R–avr* gene pair) system has been proposed. In a two-component system, the plant would be transformed with both an *R* gene and the corresponding *avr* gene, but expression of the *avr* gene would be controlled by a promoter that responds quickly and locally to a broad spectrum of pathogens. As a result, any pathogen challenge would trigger the disease resistance response (4).

RESISTANCE FROM MANIPULATION OF REACTIVE OXYGEN SPECIES

The "oxidative burst" is produced in reaction to pathogens, elicitors, and many stresses. An initial, short-lived, increase in reactive oxygen species, such as H_2O_2, occurs immediately after plant–pathogen contact, for both compatible (disease) and incompatible (resistant) reactions. A subsequent massive and prolonged increase in reactive oxygen species occurs in resistant reactions. The primary defense functions of the bursts are generally thought to be twofold: (1) direct antimicrobial action of the increased levels of $O_2^{\cdot-}$ and H_2O_2, and (2) oxidative cross-linking of tyrosine-rich structural proteins in the cell wall that increase its resistance to microbial digestion. H_2O_2 may also function indirectly as a signal for the induction of PR-proteins, phytoalexins, and peroxidases. Increased resistance of potato to *Erwinia carotovora* (soft rot) has been obtained by introducing a fungal gene for glucose oxidase (which catalyzes the reaction of glucose with O_2 to produce gluconate and H_2O_2) into the plant, thereby causing an increase in intracellular levels of H_2O_2. However, elevated H_2O_2 may also initiate cell death in the HR by stimulating Ca^{2+} influx and lipid peroxidation, and so strict regulation of expression may be required to make this strategy applicable to other systems (5).

RESISTANCE FROM CELL DEATH

The HR is characterized by rapid death of most cells around the site of infection and is a feature of incompatible ($R-avr$) resistance reactions. It is possible that the HR functions to prevent pathogen spread from the point of infection via controlled cell death (6). An attempt has been made to mimic the HR by engineering controlled cell death into plants. Potatoes were transformed with (1) barnase (a ribonuclease of bacterial origin that will kill any cell in which it is expressed) under the control of a pathogen-induced promoter, and (2) a specific inhibitor of barnase under the control of a constitutive promoter to prevent background expression of barnase in uninfected cells. Necrotic lesions formed around infection sites of *Phytophthora infestans*, the causal agent of late blight disease, and sporulation of the fungus on infected tissue was inhibited (7).

RESISTANCE FROM PATHOGENESIS-RELATED PROTEINS

Pathogenesis-related proteins include several families of plant proteins that accumulate after pathogen attack or in response to certain stresses (e.g., β-1,3-glucanases and cutinases). Some of these proteins have antimicrobial activity in vitro, and this may be their primary role in defense. Secondarily, they may cause the induction of other defense-related compounds, such as phytoalexins, by releasing elicitors from pathogen walls. Transgenic plants overexpressing certain PR proteins have been shown to have increased resistance to diseases. For example, β-1,3-glucanase overexpression in tobacco increases resistance to *Phytophthora megasperma*, *Alternaria alternata*, and *Rhizoctonia solani*. However, coordinated expression of several PR proteins may be required for increased resistance in other plants. Coexpression of tobacco chitinase and glucanase genes in carrot leads to high levels of resistance to both *Alternaria* and *Cercospora* in the field (8).

RESISTANCE FROM PHYTOALEXINS

Phytoalexins are low-molecular-weight antimicrobial compounds that are produced by many plants in response to pathogen attack, pathogen-derived elicitors, and other stresses. Biosynthesis is complex and may involve steps in one or more of the phenylpropanoid, isoflavonoid, or sesquiterpenoid pathways. Phytoalexins are effective antimicrobial agents in vitro and may play important roles in nonspecific disease resistance. However, dramatically increasing phytoalexin production in plants can be stressful and cause stunting. An alternative strategy has been to produce a novel phytoalexin in a heterologous host. For example, tobacco plants transformed with the gene for stilbene synthase from grape, which utilizes the precursors malonyl-CoA and *p*-coumaroyl-CoA (found in most plants) to produce the phytoalexin resveratrol, had enhanced resistance to *Botrytis cinerea*. The same strategy has been successfully applied in tomato and rice to increase resistance to *Phytophthora infestans* and *Pyricularia oryzae*, respectively. Other single-step syntheses of novel phytoalexins from common precursors or modifications of natural phytoalexins into more pathotoxic forms may be possible, but extensive manipulation of phytoalexin biosynthesis may be limited in applicability because of the complexity of most biosynthetic pathways for these compounds (9).

RESISTANCE FROM ANTIMICROBIAL PEPTIDES AND PROTEINS

Defensins are short antimicrobial peptides (12–45 amino acids long) that are produced by a wide variety of plants and animals, either constitutively or as a result of pathogen attack. Many are rich in the cationic residues lysine or arginine, and their antimicrobial action may result from their ability to interact with and disrupt membranes, particularly anionic bacterial membranes. Seeds are the richest sources of defensins in plants, although they are also found in the epidermises of vegetative structures. Expression of plant or animal defensins in heterologous hosts has led to increased resistance to bacterial or fungal pathogens in several cases. For example, increased resistance to bacterial pathogens has been obtained in tobacco transformed with either hordothionon from barley or cercropin isolated from the silk moth (10).

Ribosome inactivating proteins (RIPs) from plants disrupt ribosome structure, and thus protein synthesis, through N-glycosidic cleavage of the 28S rRNA. The most commonly known RIP is the toxic component of the castor bean, ricin, but other RIPs have been isolated from several families of dicots and monocots. These enzymes can be used to protect plants from fungal attack because they do not interfere with the function of self ribosomes. For example, tobacco transformed with a barley-derived RIP gene under the control of a pathogen-inducible promoter grew more vigorously in soil inoculated with *Rhizoctonia solani* than nontransformed control plants (11).

PATHOGEN-DERIVED RESISTANCE

An effective means of developing virus-resistant plants has been to transform them with a portion of the viral genome encoding important components of the viral replication cycle, such as viral coat proteins, replicases, or movement proteins. Coat protein-mediated viral resistance was first demonstrated in tobacco plants transformed with the tobacco mosaic virus coat protein gene under the control of a constitutive promoter. Plants expressing high levels of the coat protein are thought to interrupt the natural infection cycle of the virus through inhibition of the disassembly step of the cycle. This approach has since been used to incorporate virus resistance into several species, and the first generation of coat protein-mediated virus resistant plants are currently for sale (12). Expression of mutated or antisense viral genes in transformed plants may also increase virus resistance. These transgenics may interrupt the normal infection cycle through the production of nonfunctional molecules that compete with the viral genome, or its protein products, during replication or movement steps, or by gene silencing mechanisms (13,14) (Fig. 2).

RESISTANCE FROM NOVEL SOURCES

Other strategies for increasing the disease resistance of plants have concentrated on genes that are not involved in plant–pathogen interactions. Human or bacteriophage T4-derived lysozymes, which can cleave the glycosidic bonds of peptidoglycans found in bacterial cell walls and chitins found in fungal cell walls, have been incorporated into plants and provide broad-spectrum resistance to a variety of bacterial and fungal diseases (15). The ability of plants to express functional antibodies from animal genes has been used to create tobacco plants that are resistant to tobacco mosaic virus. Antibodies may provide protection against disease through agglutination of pathogens or blockage of epitopes required for infection (16). Finally, some dsRNA viruses of pathogenic fungi encode peptides that are toxic to related pathogens lacking the dsRNA, and so expression by plants of these toxin genes in the intercellular fluid of the plant may inhibit growth of the pathogen (17).

CONCLUSIONS

Genes that mediate interactions between plants and pathogens may be exploited to produce transgenic plants that are less susceptible to disease. Several of these transgenics are currently in open release trials for efficacy in agricultural settings. These are remarkable achievements considering that the first transgenic plants were produced in the early 1980s and the first disease resistance genes were not cloned until the early 1990s.

BIBLIOGRAPHY

1. B. Baker, P. Zambryski, B. Staskawicz, and S.P. Dinesh-Kumar, *Science* **276**, 726–733 (1997).
2. H.H. Flor, *Annu. Rev. Phytopathol.* **9**, 275–296 (1971).
3. J.D.G. Jones, *Curr. Opin. Biotechnol.* **7**, 155–160 (1996).
4. P.J.G.M. Dewit, *Annu. Rev. Phytopathol.* **30**, 391–418 (1992).
5. C. Lamb and R.A. Dixon, *Annu. Rev. Plant Physiol. Plant Mol. Biol.* **48**, 251–275 (1997).
6. J.L. Dangl, R.A. Dietrich, and M.H. Richberg, *Plant Cell* **8**, 1793–1807 (1996).
7. G. Strittmatter, J. Janssens, C. Opsomer, and J. Botterman, *Bio/Technology* **13**, 1085–1089 (1995).
8. L. Sticher, B. Mauch-Mani, and J.P. Métraux, *Annu. Rev. Phytopathol.* **35**, 235–270 (1997).
9. J. Kuć, *Annu. Rev. Phytopathol.* **33**, 275–297 (1995).
10. R.E.W. Hancock and R. Lehrer, *Trends Biotechnol.* **16**, 82–88 (1998).
11. J. Logemann et al., *Bio/Technology* **10**, 305–308 (1992).
12. D.M. Shah, C.M.T. Rommens, and R.N. Beachy, *Trends Biotechnol.* **13**, 362–368 (1995).
13. M. Fuchs and D. Gonsalves, *Bio/Technology* **13**, 1466–1473 (1995).
14. D.C. Baulcombe, *Plant Cell* **8**, 1833–1844 (1996).
15. H. Nakajima, T. Muranaka, F. Ishige, and K. Akutsu, *Plant Cell Rep.* **16**, 674–679 (1997).
16. E. Franken, U. Teuschel, and R. Hain, *Curr. Opin. Biotechnol.* **8**, 411–416 (1997).
17. C.-M. Park, J.O. Berry, and J.A. Bruenn, *Plant Mol. Biol.* **30**, 359–366 (1996).

Figure 2. Resistance to mixed infections of transgenic squash expressing the coat protein genes of zucchini yellow mosaic virus and watermelon mosaic virus 2. The pile of squash in the foreground includes fruit from nontransgenic controls and transgenics expressing a single coat protein gene. The squash in the background are from plants expressing both coat protein genes. All plants were inoculated with a mixture of zucchini yellow mosaic virus and watermelon mosaic virus 2 (from Ref. 13).

See also CONTAMINATION DETECTION AND ELIMINATION IN PLANT CELL CULTURE; TOXIN RESISTANT PLANTS FROM PLANT CELL CULTURE AND TRANSFORMATION; TRANSFORMATION OF PLANTS; VIRUS REMOVAL FROM PLANTS.

E

EMBRYOGENESIS IN ANGIOSPERMS, SOMATIC

WAYNE A. PARROTT
The University of Georgia
Athens, Georgia

OUTLINE

Introduction: Defining a Somatic Embryo
Somatic Embryogenesis from Plant Cells in Culture
    Origin of Somatic Embryos
    Somatic Embryo Developmental Biology
Repetitive Embryogenesis
    Uses of Repetitive Embryogenesis
Androgenesis and Gynogenesis
Summary
Bibliography

INTRODUCTION: DEFINING A SOMATIC EMBRYO

As in most higher organisms, new individuals of angiosperms (i.e., flowering plants) start life as a zygote that undergoes successive mitotic divisions to form a proembryo, and then an embryo. The developmental patterns of such zygote-derived embryos have been well characterized, and barring minor derivations, are remarkably consistent within groups of flowering plants (1,2). However, to first place the process of embryogenesis in context, a brief review of angiosperm reproduction is necessary.

Within the female organs of a flower, archegonial cells undergo meiosis to form megaspores. Megaspores in turn divide mitotically to form a multicellular female gametophyte, also known as the megagametophyte or the embryo sac. The latter term is a misnomer, as embryos are not present in it. One of the cells in the female gametophyte is the egg cell, which upon fertilization by a sperm cell becomes the zygote. The female gametophyte is in turn surrounded by one or two layers of cells, known as integuments, and by additional tissue known as the nucellus. Together, they comprise all the tissues within an ovule.

However, in angiosperms, embryos do not necessarily have to originate from zygotes. Instead, these can originate from a variety of different types of somatic cells (i.e., body cells not associated with reproduction), and are consequently referred to as somatic embryos. The process through which a somatic embryo forms and develops is then termed *somatic embryogenesis*.

One of the best-known examples of such naturally occurring somatic embryogenesis is known as adventive embryony (1), whereby somatic embryos form directly from mitosis of a cell or cells in the integuments or the nucellus around the female gametophyte. As such, adventive embryogenesis is also considered to be a form of apomixis, a process whereby embryos are obtained without fertilization of an egg cell.

Other forms of apomixis exist as well. In one case, termed *apospory* (i.e., without a spore), somatic cells first give rise to female gametophytes via mitosis, and then the egg cell within the female gametophyte divides to form an embryo. In a second type of apomixis, meiosis fails during megasporogenesis, giving rise to a diploid egg cell within the female gametophyte, which can in turn develop into an embryo without first being fertilized. This type of apomixis is termed *diplospory* (i.e., diploid spore). Finally, haploid cells within the gametophyte, such as the synergids, can also undergo mitosis to produce haploid embryos. This type of apomixis is termed *apogamety* (i.e., without a gamete). Although the female gametophyte in apospory comes from a somatic cell rather than from a spore, embryos derived from apospory, diplospory, and apogamety, though of asexual origin, are not somatic embryos in a strict sense, as they come from cells of a female gametophyte, rather than from somatic cells.

Finally, naturally occurring somatic embryogenesis of angiosperms need not be limited to tissues found within an ovule. The orchid *Malaxis paludosa* forms somatic embryos on its leaf tips, while some succulents from *Bryophyllum* spp. form somatic embryos on their leaf margins (3).

It is also possible to obtain somatic embryos from cultured plant cells. In contrast to somatic embryos formed *in planta*, somatic embryos formed in vitro are not surrounded by maternal tissues and can be propagated in large numbers. This makes the use of somatic embryos feasible for the study of embryogenesis (4), for mass propagation, and most recently, for genetic transformation of plants. Hence, as currently used, the term somatic embryo almost invariably refers to an embryo formed in vitro rather than *in planta*.

SOMATIC EMBRYOGENESIS FROM PLANT CELLS IN CULTURE

Somatic embryogenesis is but one of two pathways whereby cells in culture can regenerate into whole plants in the absence of meristematic cells. The second pathway is referred to as organogenesis, and is characterized by the formation of roots or of shoot meristems, which elongate into shoots. Such shoots can be rooted, and whole plants obtained. In contrast, somatic embryos lack vascular connections to the cultured plant tissues, but contain both root and shoot meristems, and therefore germinate into plantlets.

That plant cells in culture could divide to produce embryos was first hinted at during the late 1950s, and proven by the early 1960s. Since then, the observation has been extended to a wide range of plant species. At last count, somatic embryogenesis had been achieved in over 130 species of plants, including both angiosperms and gymnosperms (5). Nevertheless, various species of plants remain for which somatic embryogenesis has never been reported. Even for those species in which somatic embryogenesis is possible, somatic embryos can usually only be obtained from certain tissues at certain growth stages, or from certain genotypes within a species. The relative ability of a given tissue from a given genotype to form somatic embryos is known as *embryogenic competence*.

Origin of Somatic Embryos

In the simplest scenario, somatic embryos can be obtained from cultured immature plant zygotic embryos in a process sometimes referred to as *embryo cloning*. The cells within embryonic tissues of a zygotic embryo can be stimulated to divide and form somatic embryos. In this case, somatic embryogenesis is said to be direct, as preexisting cells divide directly to form a somatic embryo. The term *pre-embryogenic determined cells* (PEDCs) has been used to refer to this situation.

At the opposite end of the spectrum, tissues from mature plants, which have long since lost their embryonic status, can undergo repeated mitosis under inducing conditions, until these cells obtain the ability to form somatic embryos. In this case, preexisting cells divide to form callus, and callus can in turn become embryogenic. In this case, somatic embryogenesis is said to be indirect, and the term *induced embryogenic determined cells* (IEDCs) has been used to describe this phenomenon.

PEDCs and IEDCs represent two ends of a continuum, and differently aged plant tissues can fall anywhere between the two extremes. Nevertheless, once IEDCs are obtained, they are functionally equivalent to PEDCs. However, the word *determined*, as used in these acronyms, is somewhat misleading, as somatic embryos are not inevitably produced from these tissues. Consequently, the term *embryogenic cells* (ECs) is a more accurate way to refer to tissues with the ability to form somatic embryos (6). The term *embryogenic tissue* is synonymous to ECs.

Thus the treatments necessary to obtain somatic embryos can depend on whether the explant is a PEDC or an IEDC, as traditionally defined. In the former, cells are already embryogenic, and merely need to be permitted to divide independently of other cells in the surrounding tissue. The use of a cytokinin alone is frequently sufficient to accomplish the task.

When nonembryonic tissues are involved, the presence of an auxin is usually required to induce an embryogenic state. However, several other factors have been effective in somatic embryo induction, including heat shock, exposure to heavy metals, desiccation stress, and tissue disruption leading to isolation of cells or cell groups. It is not known if all these have a common mode of action, but one possibility is that all these treatments have the ability to induce a general stress response and terminate ongoing gene expression within the cells. Furthermore, high auxin levels are known to lead to DNA methylation. Since somatic cells in tissue becoming embryogenic have been shown to undergo meiosis and even show structural elements in common with egg cells, it might be possible that cells react to a termination of existing gene expression patterns by initiating the gene expression patterns associated with

sporogenesis and gametogenesis (7,8). Once a cell with spore or gamete-like features is obtained, the formation of somatic embryos might not be that different from apomixis, as described earlier.

A second factor that appears to be important for embryogenesis is isolation, by tissue maceration, necrosis of surrounding tissue, or formation of a cuticle layer around cells destined to become an embryo. Presumably, such isolation permits the isolated cells to function as an independent organism, as opposed to cells acting as part of a tissue (8). While zygotic embryos are invariably derived from a single-celled zygote, neither apomictic adventitious embryos nor somatic embryos suffer from this limitation. It is possible for a group of cells to grow collectively into a somatic embryo (9).

Embryogenic tissue is characterized by cells that are small, richly cytoplasmic, and asymmetrical. Cells within embryogenic tissues will continue to divide and maintain their embryogenic nature as long as they are in the presence of an auxin. As these tissues grow, they tend to from clumps, which have been called proembryogenic masses (PEMs), proembryonal complexes, or embryogenic clusters.

Somatic Embryo Developmental Biology

Once the level of auxin in the culture medium is reduced below a threshold level, embryogenic cells begin a process termed *histodifferentiation*. Embryos undergoing histodifferentiation grow through cell division, and proceed through the same stages of development as zygotic embryos. The first stage of development is known as the globular stage, consisting of cells arranged in a spherical configuration. The developing embryo then acquires a bilateral symmetry as it reaches the heart stage. After further elongation, the embryo reaches the torpedo stage, and then the cotyledonary stage (2,10).

Polarity in transport of endogenous auxin is apparently essential if a developing somatic embryo is to make the transition between the globular and heart stages. These internal auxin gradients can be upset or overwhelmed by the presence of exogenous auxin. Consequently, the presence of residual auxin in the culture medium during histodifferentiation, even at a level below the threshold level for histodifferentiation to occur, will interfere with normal histodifferentiation, preventing the attainment of bilateral symmetry and development of the apical meristem (8). However, even under ideal culture conditions, it is not uncommon for somatic embryos to have a variable number of cotyledons or other anomalies.

As described in the preceding paragraph, the stages of histodifferentiation apply only to embryos from the *Dicotyledoneae*. Embryos from the *Monocotyledoneae* undergo analogous stages of histodifferentiation, but differ markedly in appearance due to the presence of a single cotyledon. The stages of histodifferentiation of monocotyledonous embryos are consequently designated as globular, scutellar, and coleoptilar (11).

Following histodifferentiation, zygotic and somatic embryos start their maturation phase, during which growth occurs due to cell expansion. Early stages of maturation are characterized by the accumulation of storage reserves, and the late stages are characterized by the acquisition of desiccation tolerance, which is analogous to physiological maturity in a seed. The osmotic potential of the culture medium appears to be the most important factor to induce proper maturation. Following desiccation, embryos will germinate (12). Those somatic embryos that germinate and then grow into plants are said to be "converted," and the transition from a germinating somatic embryo to a plant is known as "conversion."

Histodifferentiation, maturation, desiccation, germination, and conversion of angiosperm somatic embryos can occur in the absence of all exogenous growth regulators. However, many existing protocols for somatic embryogenesis omit one or more of these stages and use unnecessary growth regulators or suboptimal culture conditions. The net result is somatic embryos that require the application of growth regulators (usually a cytokinin, abscisic acid, or gibberellin) before they will germinate and covert into plants. Precociously germinated embryos can physiologically resemble both a maturing embryo and a germinating embryo simultaneously. Such precociously germinating embryos are known as *emblings*, for embryonic seedlings. Finally, somatic embryos, like their zygotic counterparts, may experience a period of dormancy, and thus require a dormancy-breaking treatment, such as vernalization, before they are capable of germination.

REPETITIVE EMBRYOGENESIS

As mentioned previously, embryogenic tissue will form globular-stage embryos below a threshold level of exogenous auxin. This threshold level is very species-specific. Nevertheless, once a globular-stage embryo is formed, the level of exogenous auxins will determine its subsequent development. In the absence of auxins, histodifferentiation will proceed normally. In the presence of auxin levels within the threshold level that permits histodifferentiation, histodifferentiation will proceed abnormally. As exogenous auxins are increased, they reach a new level in which histodifferentiation beyond the globular stage of development is arrested altogether. In this case, new globular-stage embryos will bud off the older embryo, and the process of new globular-stage embryos forming on older ones can be repeated indefinitely, as long as the level of exogenous auxin is high enough. This process has been variously termed repetitive, recurrent, accessory, or secondary embryogenesis. A mass of repetitive embryos is often called an *embryogenic callus*, but this term is incorrect, as no callus is involved in the process.

Once the level of exogenous auxin is lowered below the threshold necessary to maintain repetitive embryogenesis, the cycle of repetitive embryogenesis is broken, and the globular-stage embryos complete histodifferentiation and develop into mature embryos. There are deviations from this overall scheme. For some species, somatic embryos can reach the heart, torpedo, or cotyledonary stage, or even begin germinating, before undergoing another round of repetitive embryogenesis (13). In other species, repetitive embryogenesis can occur in the absence of all exogenous auxins, in which cases it may be difficult, if not impossible, to break the cycle of repetitive embryogenesis. The term

autoembryony has been used to describe repetitive somatic embryogenesis in the absence of exogenous auxins (8).

Uses of Repetitive Embryogenesis

The ability to propagate embryogenic tissue or repetitive embryo cultures leads to the ability to use somatic embryos for mass propagation, which is the topic of another article within this *Encyclopedia*. Because somatic embryo technology can produce essentially unlimited numbers of propagules that can germinate into whole plants without additional rooting steps, somatic embryo technology can be especially useful to propagate elite but heterozygous plants that do not breed true from botanical seed. Somatic embryo technology is equally useful to propagate elite but otherwise sterile genotypes, such as seedless grapes (14). Furthermore, the potential exists to encapsulate somatic embryos of elite genotypes for use as synthetic seeds (15). In theory, encapsulating somatic embryos makes them easier to handle, increases their shelf life, and facilitates embryo germination under a greater range of environmental conditions by incorporating fertilizers and pesticides into the encapsulating material.

Both embryogenic tissue and repetitive embryos have proven to be excellent targets for genetic transformation, making genetic transformation possible for those crop species that do not regenerate via organogenesis. While ECs have been amenable to a variety of DNA delivery techniques, ECs are especially good targets for microprojectile-mediated transformation, as their lack of prominent vacuoles increases the chances that a microprojectile will hit the cell nucleus. Genetic transformation is ultimately a single-cell phenomenon. In the simplest scenario, a transgenic cell can divide to form a transgenic somatic embryo. The transgenic embryo can then be converted to obtain a transgenic plant, or the transgenic embryo can be propagated, via repetitive embryogenesis, to form multiple somatic embryos prior to plant regeneration.

However, as mentioned previously, somatic embryo formation can be a multicellular event. In this case, the resulting somatic embryo will be chimeric for the transgene, and only those cells derived from the one transgenic cell, out of all the cells that gave rise to the embryo, will be transgenic. In this case, a completely transgenic embryo can be obtained once a repetitive embryo forms from the transgenic sector of the original embryo (14).

ANDROGENESIS AND GYNOGENESIS

There is a final category of embryos that are obtained from microspores in culture (androgenesis), which are either isolated or which remain within an anther, or from cultured ovules (gynogenesis). Since microspores and cells within an embryo sac are not somatic cells, these embryos technically are not somatic embryos. Nevertheless, other than their origin, which is exclusively unicellular, they exhibit the same developmental features that somatic embryos do. The recovery of embryos from cultured microspores is also known as haploid embryogenesis, gametic embryogenesis, microspore embryogenesis, or pollen embryogenesis. The latter term should not be used, as embryogenesis occurs before the microspores become mature pollen grains.

The most important distinction between an androgenic or gynogenic embryo and a somatic embryo is that the former, being derived from a haploid cell, is itself haploid. Doubling of the chromosome number of the resulting plant, either spontaneously or through the use of colchicine, will result in an "instant inbred" that would otherwise take 6 to 8 generations of self-pollination to produce. Thus the use of such "doubled haploid" plants saves considerable time, but denies the plant breeder an opportunity to select for desirable genotypes segregating out during the inbreeding phase of a plant breeding program.

Much more is known about androgenesis than gynogenesis in vitro, as incidences of the latter are exceedingly rare. Essentially the same factors that induce somatic embryos will also induce formation of androgenic embryos. During normal microgametogenesis, the microspore divides mitotically to form two asymmetric cells, the vegetative cell and the generative cell. The generative cell then divides mitotically to form two sperm cells. Under inducing conditions, androgenesis is known to proceed via two pathways. In the first one, either the vegetative or the generative cell will continue to divide mitotically, leading to the formation of a proembryo, which continues development into an embryo, as described previously for somatic embryogenesis. In the second pathway, the first mitotic division of the microspore divides

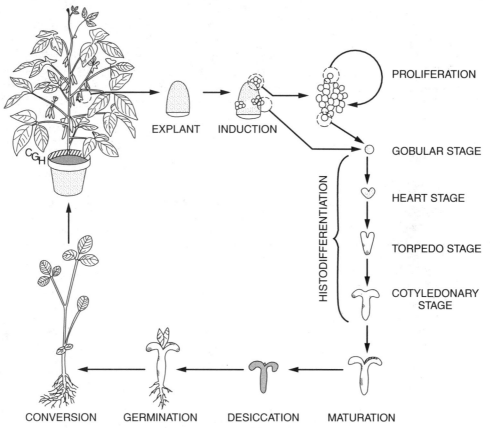

Figure 1. Somatic embryogenesis. This figure illustrates the typical sequence of events that can take place during somatic embryogenesis, using soybean, *Glycine max* (L.) Merrill, as an example. In the case of soybean, only cotyledons from immature embryos exhibit embryogenic competence (top left). When these immature cotyledons (the explant tissue) are dissected out and cultured in the presence of high auxin levels, somatic embryos are induced. These somatic embryos are arrested at a globular stage of development due to the presence of a high level of auxin. These globular-stage embryos can undergo a proliferation phase, which will last indefinitely as long as the auxin levels are sufficiently high (top right). In the absence of exogenous auxins, the globular-stage embryos can begin the process of histodifferenciation (right side), whereby they gain bilateral symmetry and go through stages known as heart, torpedo, and cotyledonary. Cotyledonary-stage embryos will then begin a process of maturation, whereby they acquire their storage reserves and acquire desiccation tolerance (bottom right). Physiologically mature embryos can be desiccated, much like a seed that naturally desiccates prior to harvest (bottom, center). Desiccated embryos will germinate once moisture and temperature conditions are appropriate. If the germination process continues, plantlets form, and the embryos are said to be converted (bottom left). When the plantlets reach reproductive maturity, they cycle can be repeated. Illustration by Carol G. Hahn.

to produce two identical daughter cells instead of a vegetative and a generative cell. The daughter cells then continue dividing mitotically to form a proembryo, and then an embryo (16).

Overall, plants with androgenic ability are far fewer than those with somatic embryogenic ability. At last count, plants have been recovered via androgenesis from only 34 species, and the majority of these were solanaceous, cruciferous, or graminaceous species. As with somatic embryogenesis, both developmental stage and genotype play a crucial role in embryogenic competence (8). Furthermore, it is not known with certainty whether every microspore has embryogenic capacity (8) or embryogenic capacity is limited to certain microspores exhibiting feminized features (17).

SUMMARY

During the past 35 years we have acquired the ability to obtain embryos from a variety of plant tissues grown in culture from an ever-increasing number of plant species, and the various stages of somatic embryogenesis have been defined. Figure 1 summarizes the various possible steps in an embryogenic protocol. The availability of such embryos has facilitated the study of embryogenesis by providing abundant, readily accessible sources of study material. In vitro embryogenesis has also assisted plant breeding programs by facilitating the production of transgenic plants, and to a lesser extent, by providing "instant inbreds." For angiosperms, the best-known example of mass propagation via somatic embryogenesis is the propagation of elite genotypes of oil palm in Southeast Asia. The use of somatic embryogenesis in mass propagation will inevitably increase as protocols for somatic embryogenesis become more advanced and can produce somatic embryos that are developmentally normal, not subject to somaclonal variation (i.e., mutations that can occur during the cell culture process), and exhibit uniform germination. While the culture requirements necessary to normalize somatic embryogenesis exhibit many similarities across species, important differences exist, making it essential to optimize protocols for each individual species.

BIBLIOGRAPHY

1. P. Maheshwari, *An Introduction to the Embryology of Angiosperms*, McGraw-Hill, New York, 1950.

2. V. Raghavan, *Embryogenesis in Angiosperms*, Cambridge University Press, New York, 1986.

3. A.P. Mordhorst, M.A.J. Toonen, and S.C. de Vries, *Crit. Rev. Plant Sci.* **16**, 535–576 (1997).

4. V.L. Dodeman, G. Ducreux, and M. Kreis, *J. Exp. Bot.* **48**, 1493–1509 (1997).

5. T.A. Thorpe, *Anim. Plant. Sci.* **1**, 81–88 (1988).

6. J.G. Carman, *In Vitro Cell Dev. Biol.* **26**, 746–753 (1990).

7. M. Terzi and F. LoSchiavo, in S.S. Bhojwani, ed., *Plant Tissue Culture: Aplications and Limitations*, Elsevier, Amsterdam, 1990, pp. 54–66.

8. T.A. Thorpe, *In Vitro Embryogenesis in Plants*, Kluwer Academic Publishers, Dordrecht, The Netherlands, 1995.

9. E.G. Williams and G. Maheswaran, *Ann. Bot. (London)* **57**, 443–462 (1986).

10. J.L. Zimmerman, *Plant Cell* **5**, 1411–1423 (1993).

11. D.J. Gray and A. Purohit, *Crit. Rev. Plant. Sci.* **10**, 33–61 (1991).

12. A.R. Kermode, in J. Kigel and G. Galili, eds., *Seed Development and Germination*, Dekker, New York, 1995, pp. 273–332.

13. S.A. Merkle, W.A. Parrott, and E.G. Williams, in S.S. Bhojwani, ed., *Plant Tissue Culture: Applications and Limitations*, Elsevier, Amsterdam, 1990, pp. 67–101.

14. W.A. Parrott, S.A. Merkle, and E.G. Williams, in D.R. Murray, ed., *Advanced Methods in Plant Breeding and Biotechnology*, CAB International, Wallingford, U.K., 1991, pp. 158–200.

15. K. Redenbaugh, *SynSeeds: Applications of Synthetic Seeds to Crop Improvement*, CRC Press, Boca Raton, Fa., 1993.

16. T.L. Reynolds, *Plant Mol. Biol.* **33**, 1–10 (1997).

17. E. Heberle-Bors, *Planta* **156**, 396–401 (1982).

See also CULTURE ESTABLISHMENT, PLANT CELL CULTURE; GERMPLASM PRESERVATION OF IN VITRO PLANT CULTURES; MICROPROPAGATION OF PLANTS, PRINCIPLES AND PRACTICES; SOMACLONAL VARIATION.

ENRICHMENT AND ISOLATION TECHNIQUES FOR ANIMAL CELL TYPES

P. MARLENE ABSHER
University of Vermont
College of Medicine
Colchester, Vermont

OUTLINE

INTRODUCTION

The successful isolation of homogeneous cell population depends on numerous factors relating to tissue and cell type, method of isolation, and procedures for purifying and enriching the population. There are diverse methods for isolating homogeneous populations of cells with varying degrees of success that use biological, physical, chemical, and mechanical means often in combination (Table 1). The technology for cell isolation and enrichment procedures has advanced markedly in the past several years with the advent of flow cytometry, selective adherence techniques, magnetic-bead separation, the availability of highly selective immunological reagents, and refined centrifugation techniques using various types of gradients.

METHODS OF CELL SEPARATION AND ENRICHMENT

Isolation of Cells from Tissues

One of the earliest methods used to obtain cells from solid tissues took advantage of the ability of some types of cells in the tissues to migrate away from the explanted tissue fragment and proliferate. Most solid tissues are comprised of multiple cell types, but generally only epithelial and fibroblastlike cells or smooth muscle cells readily migrate from tissues and replicate in *in vitro* culture (1). Fibroblasts tend to migrate more readily from explants than other cell types and tend to have a higher rate of proliferation which allows them to become eventually the predominant cell type in a mixed population. Upon repeated subcultivation, the fibroblasts continue to proliferate at a rate higher than other cells in the population and eventually a population consisting only of fibroblasts is achieved.

Table 1. Methods of Cell Separation

Method	Basis for Separation
Cloning	Growth from single cell isolation
Selective adherence	Time for attachment to matrix
Sedimentation velocity at unit gravity	Cell Size
Isokinetic gradient centrifugation	Cell size, cell density, and cell configuration
Isopycnic gradient centrifugation	Cell density
Density gradient electrophoresis	Cell-surface charge
Elutriation centrifugation	Cell size and density
Affinity methods	Cell-surface connstituents
Panning	Antibodies to surface antigens
Lectin binding	Binding to surface carbohydrates moieties
Coated magnetic beads	Antigen binding to antibody-coated magnetic microspheres

The most commonly used technique to obtain single cell populations from tissues employs dissociation of tissues with proteolytic enzymes, such as collagenase, trypsin, and elastase alone or in combination. The enzymes break down the matrix materials that surround the cells in the tissues and thus free the cells from the tissue fragments. Tissue fragments are minced to approximately 1 mm^3 and are placed in a solution of enzyme at $37\,^{\circ}\text{C}$. However, prolonged incubation at lower temperatures has also been used for cells too fragile to withstand the higher temperatures. To aid in the digestive process, the tissue fragments are gently shaken during the enzyme dissociation incubation period. Depending on the tissue type, multiple rounds of successive dissociation steps may be required. For example, adult lung tissue may involve five dissociation steps of 45 minutes each, whereas dissociation of fetal heart tissue may utilize eight to ten dissociation steps, each 10 minutes long. The action of the enzyme is stopped by placing the cell suspension in a culture medium containing serum or by using specific enzyme inhibitors. The resulting free cells are placed in an appropriate culture medium and allowed to proliferate. Then, a variety of techniques may be used to obtain pure or enriched populations of cells from the mixture of cells in the tissue digest.

Selective Medium for Enrichment or Depletion of Specific Cell Types

The selection of appropriate culture medium makes it possible to further manipulate the selection of specific cell types (1). The use of selective media favors the growth of one cell type over another and has been used notably to enhance the growth of epithelial cells in mixed populations, as well as to suppress fibroblast growth (Table 2) (2–10). The limitation of this application for animal cells is that there are basic similarities in nutrient requirements for most cell types. Cell replication requires the presence of growth factors in the culture medium, and the most commonly used source of these factors is serum which tends to override the selective properties of the culture medium. Several serum-free medium formulations have been developed that do allow preferential growth of epithelial cells (11–13). Because fibroblast overgrowth is a common problem in populations of mixed cell types, many medium formulations have been designed to inhibit fibroblast growth, including amino acid analogs, such as *cis*-proline, deletion of a required amino acid, specific toxins, cytotoxic antibodies, and nucleic acid analogs, such as bromodeoxyuridine (BrDU).

Selective Adhesion Methods

The differential affinities of cells for culture substrate have been used to select for specific cell types. Different cell types have different rates of attachment on a substrate, and specific cell types in a mixed population can be selected for by multiple transfers of cells from one culture dish to another over a few hours in primary culture (1). Fibroblasts tend to adhere to plastic more rapidly than epithelial cells, and this feature can be used to enrich a population of fibroblasts or epithelial cells. A mixed

Table 2. Reagents Selective for Different Types of Cells

Reagent	Example	Selects Against	Selects For	Reference
Nucleic acid analogs	Bromodeoxyuridine	Prototrophs	Auxotrophs	2
	Bromodeoxyuridine	Fibroblasts	Myocardicocytes	3
Amino acid annalogs	cis-Proline	Fibroblasts	Epithelial cells	4
	cis-Hydroxyproline	Fibroblasts	Epithelial cells	5
	D-Valine	Fibroblasts	Epithelial cells	6
Amino acid deficient	Glutamine	Fibroblasts	Myocardiocytes	3
	Arginine	Fibroblasts	Hepatocytes	7
Polyamines	Putrescine	Fibroblasts	Epithelial cells	8
	Spermine	Fibroblasts	Epithelial cells	9
calcium	Low calcium	Fibroblasts	Smooth muscle cells	10

Table 3. Cell Adhesion to Matrix Molecules

Cell Type	Matrix Molecules	Enhancement Factors	Reference
Epithelial	Denatured collagen		14,15
Epithelial	Matrigel		16
Alveolar epithelial	Fibronectin, collagen IV, and laminin	Manganese (Mn^{2+})	17
Fibroblast	Fibrinogen		18
Fibroblast	Fibronnectin, chondroitin sulfate, and heparin sulphate		19
Fibroblast	Collagen, fibronectin		20
Fibroblast	Laminin, collagen I	Magnesium ((Mg^{2+})	21
Smooth muscle cell	Collagen I and IV, laminin, and Fibronectin		22
Endothelial Cell	Von Willebrand factor	Arg-Gly-Asp	23
Endothelial cell	Collagen I, III and IV		24
Dendritic cell	Fibronectin, laminin, and collagen I, III and IV	Fibronectin enhanced by Ifn-γ and TNF-α	25
T-lymphocyte	Laminin, fibronectin, and collagen IV	Induced by IL-2	26

Notes: Ifn-γ (Interferon-Gamma); TNF-α (tumor necrosis factor-Alpha); IL-2 (Interleukin-2); Arg-Gly-Asp (arginine, glycine, and aspartate).

population of fibroblasts and epithelial cells are plated for one to two hours during which time the fibroblasts attach to the plastic substrate. Then, the nonadherent epithelial cells are removed from the plate, transferred to a fresh plate, and the epithelial cells attach over a period of several hours. A variety of matrix materials coated on the culture vessel have been effectively used to further enhance adherence of specific cell types (Table 3) (14–26). These include fibronectin, laminin, and collagens type I, III, or IV used alone or in combination. Growth of epithelial cells is favored when plated on collagen-coated surfaces. Selective adhesion combined with a selective medium may be used to enhance a given population of cells. For example, isolation of enriched populations of myocardiocytes from enzymatically dissociated cardiac tissue containing cardiac fibroblasts can be achieved by allowing the fibroblasts to adhere to a plastic culture dish, removing the nonadherent myocardiocytes, and replating the latter on a collagen-coated culture dish in a selective culture medium which lacks glutamine and contains BrDU to inhibit the proliferation of any residual fibroblasts (3). Enriched populations of macrophages in mixtures of leukocytes or inflammatory cells is relatively easy using differential adherence techniques. Macrophages readily adhere to plastic culture vessels within 15 to 30 minutes after which nonadherent cells may be washed off. Any adherent polymorphonuclear leukocytes that remain on the original plate generally do not survive more than 24 hours, whereas macrophages can be maintained in are appropriate, pure culture medium for several days to weeks.

Cloning Techniques

A population of cells derived from a single cell is the most homogeneous of cultures. Such a population can be established by cloning techniques (Fig. 1). There are, however, serious limitations to cloning: (1) most animal cells exhibit very poor cloning efficiency (sometimes less that 1%); and (2) the limited life span of most diploid cells in cultures (27). By the time the clones are established and have grown to a sufficient number to be used, the cells have gone through enough generations that they may be no longer useful for experimentation or may even be senescent. Twenty generations are required to obtain one million cells derived from a single cell. Two general cloning techniques are used: (1) dilution cloning where a suspension of cells is diluted so that a culture well contains a single cell from which progeny arise; and (2) limited dilution on a cell culture dish plate (Fig. 1). In the latter, approximately 100 cells are seeded into a 100 mm diameter dish, and after the clones begin to expand they can be isolated by using cloning rings. A small cylinder is placed around a clone, and cells in the clone are enzymatically dissociated and transferred to a new culture vessel. Most cells grow poorly when

Cell cloning methods

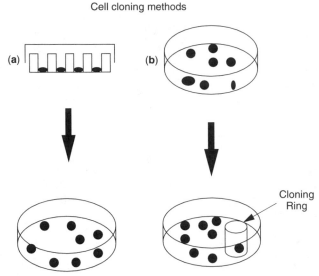

Figure 1. Methods of cell cloning. In part A, cells are diluted and seeded into 96-well culture plates so that several wells have a single cell. The wells that have a single cell are marked, and the cells that arise from that single cell are allowed to proliferate, after which they are enzymatically dissociated, transferred to a larger culture dish, and allowed to grow to a monolayer. The method shown in part B relies on seeding a plate (e.g., 60-mm dish) with a low number of cells, approximately 100 or fewer cells. As the clones begin to proliferate, they are marked, and a sterile cloning ring (cylinder) is secured around the clone with sterile silicon grease. An enzyme solution (trypsin or collagenase) is added to the cylinder, and when the cells disperse, they are removed with a Pasteur pipet, transferred to a fresh growth plate, fed complete growth medium, and allowed to grow to confluence.

isolated as single cells or in sparsely seeded cultures and require a nutrient mixture with appropriate growth factors to establish proliferating clones. Ham and colleagues developed a series of media formulations that promote cloning efficiency in different cell types (28–30). Medium MCDB 110 is designed for fibroblasts (28), and Ham's F-12 or MCDB 302 for Chinese hamster ovary cells (29,30). Hormones including insulin (30) and dexamethasone (31) have been used to increase the plating efficiency of several types of cells. Other metabolites that have been used as supplements to cell culture medium to enhance cell proliferation include pyruvate, α-ketoglutarate (32,33), and nucleosides (34).

PHYSICAL AND BIOLOGICAL METHODS OF CELL SEPARATION

Physical methods of cell separation use the characteristics of cell size, cell density, and the unique chemistry of the cell surface that permits binding of the cell to molecules, such as lectins, specific antibodies, or other substances (35).

Density Gradient Electrophoresis

Density gradient electrophoresis is a useful method for preparations for separating cells. High-resolution separation with high rates for recovering large numbers of cells can be achieved simultaneously preserving the

functional and structural integrity of the cells (36). The surfaces of mammalian cells are electrically charged and thus can be separated electrophoretically based on the surface density charge. In physiological pH solution, mammalian cells are negatively charged so that the outer layer of ions surrounding a cell is positively charged. Thus, the apparent surface charge is the potential at the outer part of the layer formed by the cell surface and the surrounding ions. The mobility of a cell in an electric field depends on this apparent surface density charge.

To minimize the effects of sedimentation on migration velocity, the density gradient is selected to be equivalent to the density of the cells, so that the cells are separated on the basis of their surface charge.

To avoid the effects of heat, use electric fields of low strength and buffers of low conductivity and carry out procedure at 4 °C. Overloading of cells must be avoided because this results in aggregates of cells rather than single cells. Buffers need to be of low ionic strength and must be made isotonic by adding nonionic carbohydrates, such as sucrose (36). Osmolarities should be between 200 to 400 mOsm to sustain cell viability and must be in a density range of (1.04 to 1.08 g/mL at 4 °C). Compounds used in density gradients must have low specific conductivity, a small charge to mass ratio, must preserve the viability and structural and functional integrity of the cells, and should not interact with the cells or be phagocytosed (37). Ficoll is better than Hypaque, colloidal silica, or sucrose/dextran for cell electrophoresis. Hypaque has too high a specific conductivity, dextran increases the zeta potential of cells, and colloidal silica may be toxic to some cells (37).

Density gradient electrophoresis is carried out in a vertical column which is surrounded by a cooling jacket and an inner cooling piece. In the center of the cooling piece is a glass tube through which the cells are collected after electrophoresis. The apparatus has an upper electrode reservoir which is filled with 6.8% sucrose in the electrophoresis buffer. Supporting the density gradient in the lower part of the column is a hollow plug immersed in the lower electrode reservoir which contains 5.1% sucrose. The solution at the bottom (floor) of the gradient column contains 10% Ficoll and 5.1% sucrose in the electrophoresis buffer, and the density gradient is layered over the floor at a constant rate of 2 mL per minute. The cells are suspended in 10 mL of 2% Ficoll and 6.44% sucrose. The system is kept at a constant temperature of 4 °C inside the column, and electrophoresis is carried out at a constant current of 20 mA for 4.5 hours. Cells are collected in a fraction collector using a peristaltic pump (36).

Density gradient electrophoresis has been effective for separating blood cells, human and murine splenic lymphocytes, human bone marrow cells, and human leukemia cells. The apparatus is relatively inexpensive, and the method permits high resolution of large numbers of cells with recovery rates of 70 to 90% without losing the functional and structural integrity of the cells (36).

Velocity Sedimentation

Velocity sedimentation separates cells based on cell size and cell density (Fig. 2). The basic techniques of velocity

Velocity sedimentation

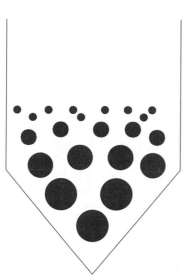

Figure 2. Velocity sedimentation. Cells of mixed sizes in a fluid sediment to the bottom of the tube according to the the cell size. The largest cells sediment to the bottom of the tube, and the smallest cells appear on the top.

sedimentation include sedimentation by gravity (which is sedimentation of cells through a density gradient in a gravitational field), sedimentation in an isokinetic or isopycnic gradient, and elutriation or counterflow centrifugation (38).

The sedimentation of cells in a centrifugal field is described by the equation,

$$\frac{dr}{dt} = \frac{a^2(D_c - D_m)\omega^2 r}{k_\eta}$$

where r is the distance of the cell from center of revolution, a is the diameter or radius of the cell, D_c is the cell density, D_m is the density of the gradient at the location of the cell, ω is the angular velocity, η is the viscosity of the gradient at the location of the cell, and k is a constant. Cell diameter and cell density are important in determining the velocity of sedimentation.

Both unit gravity sedimentation and isopycnic gradient centrifugation offer the advantages of cell separation under sterile conditions, a high degree of reproducibility, and economy (39). Because of the broad overlap in the size and density of cells from most tissues, it is more difficult to achieve the desired purity of cell populations by sedimentation alone. Common problems associated with gradient centrifugation include cell aggregation, overloading the capacity of the gradient, adherence of cells to the walls of the centrifuge tube, turbulence, and mixing of bands. Separation of cells or particles of identical size but different densities can be achieved effectively by velocity sedimentation. However, isopycnic sedimentation is most commonly used to sediment particles of different densities.

Isopycnic sedimentation is centrifugation in a continuous gradient at a centrifugal force that allows the cells to arrive at a location in the gradient where the density of the cell is identical to that of the gradient (40). In isopycnic gradient a density gradient is formed in a centrifuge tube, and upon centrifugation cells sediment in the gradient until they reach their buoyant density (40).

Cells sedimented by velocity sedimentation are generally more purified than cells isolated by isopycnic sedimentation. Isopynic sedimentation requires a higher centrifugal force than velocity sedimentation and thus may be more injurious to the cell. The most effective gradients for velocity sedimentation are those whose densities are distinct from the densities of the cells.

A variety of commercially available gradient materials, such as serum albumin, dextran, metrizamide, Ficoll, and Percoll, can be used at specified g forces to sediment cells to a level of the same density as the gradient.

Percoll, a widely used gradient material, is a colloidal suspension of silica whose particles have been coated with polyvinyl pyrrolidine to reduce their surface charge (41). It has a density of 1.13 g/mL. Percoll has essentially no osmotic activity. Thus, solutions at all density ranges used can be made iso-osmolar by a choice of buffers. It has been successfully used to separate cells, cellular organelles, and viruses. Percoll has several advantages over pure colloidal silica: it is stable at physiological ionic strength and pH, whereas pure silica tends to aggregate; it does not contain salt and has a low osmolality; it can be diluted with physiological buffers; it has a sufficient density for the formation of gradients that accommodate most cell types; and its viscosity is low compared with other density gradient media of comparable density, so that it is easier to use. The colloidal silica, Percoll, can be made iso-osmotic, allowing cells to sediment and form a band at their physiologic densities, whereas in gradients of sucrose, albumin, or metrizamide, cells tend to exhibit higher buoyant densities. Percoll gradients may be preformed by high speed centrifugation and then used at a low g force for isopycnic banding (41). Percoll is stable and can be stored for several months.

Cells can be recovered from Percoll gradients by pumping heavy fluid through the bottom of the centrifuge tube and collecting the fraction from the top. Alternatively, cells may be recovered from the bands by drawing them into a syringe with a long needle. Once recovered, Percoll is removed from the cell suspensions by repeated washing in a physiological buffer or appropriate cell culture medium. Percoll gradient separations usually result in high cell yields.

Cells suspensions of up to 50×10^6 cells in 1 mL are layered on a 5 mL gradient. Higher numbers of cells result in aggregation and reduced cell recovery. Cells may also adhere to the walls of the centrifuge tubes, particularly in tubes of small diameter. To minimize sticking, serum or albumin may be added to the cell suspension. Thin wall polycarbonate tubes give the highest recovery of cells. It is important that the cell suspension be at the same temperature as the gradient. Because cells may aggregate at low temperature, it is best to work at 20 °C. Percoll is nontoxic for most cell types.

Damaged cells and debris have a low density in Percoll. Thus Percoll can be used to separate viable cells from

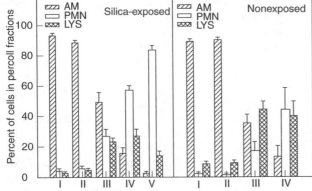

Figure 3. Separation of lung alveolar cells on a discontinuous Percoll gradient. Three-step discontinuous gradients were prepared by sequentially layering 5 mL volumes of 55% up to 35% Percoll. Lung cells were suspended in 4 mL of 20% Percoll, layered onto the 35% layer, and centrifuged at 400 g for 30 minutes at 20 °C. Then the gradients were divided into five layers. The data show good separation of alveolar macrophages (AM) in fractions I and II and of polymorphonuclear leukocytes (PMN) in fraction V of silica exposed lungs, but lymphocytes (LYS) were not well separated. In sham air-exposed lungs, there was good separation of AM but not of PMN or LYS.

dead cells and debris by layering the cells on top of Percoll in a centrifuge tube and allowing the cells to penetrate the Percoll and pellet on the bottom while the debris and dead cells remain at the top of the tube. Figure 3 shows a Percoll gradient separation of alveolar inflammatory cells isolated from lungs of rats that had been exposed to aerosols of the silica, α-cristobalite, or sham exposed to air. Three-step discontinuous gradients were prepared by sequentially layering 5 mL volumes of 55% up to 35% Percoll in Beckman ultraclear centrifuge tubes (42). Lung cells were suspended in 4 mL of 20% Percoll layered onto the 35% layer and centrifuged at 400 g for 30 minutes at 20 °C. Then, the gradients were divided into five layers (Fig. 3). The data show good separation of alveolar macrophages (AM) in fractions I and II and of polymorphonuclear leukocytes (PMN) in fraction V of silica-exposed lungs, but lymphocytes (LYS) were not well separated. In sham air-exposed lungs, there was good separation of AM but not of PMN or LYS (42).

Percoll gradients have also been used for velocity sedimentation (41). Cells are layered on top of the gradient and allowed to sediment in a gravitational field. This has been used effectively to isolate pancreatic islets from collagenase-digested tissue at unit gravity. The method has also been used to isolate specific population of lymphocytes by rosetting with cells that have specific surface markers. The rosettes sediment through the Percoll and leave other lymphocytes behind.

Ficoll is a nonionic synthetic polymer of sucrose that has a molecular weight of approximately 400,000. The Ficoll gradient is designed so that the cells sediment at almost constant velocities due to an increasing centrifugal

force and a proportional increase in the velocity of sedimentation (40,43). As the distance of the cell from the center of resolution increases, the increases in viscosity and density of the gradient are counterbalanced with the result that accelerating and decelerating forces cancel one another, and thus the cells sediment at constant velocity. A disadvantage of Ficoll is that it is highly viscous and hyperosmotic and thus can damage cells.

Hypaque is sodium diatrizoate whose chemical formula is (3,5-bis[acetylamino]-3,4,6-triiodobenzoic acid, sodium) and whose molecular weight is 635.9. Ficoll and Hypaque are frequently combined (marketed commercially as Histopaque) to isolate peripheral blood leukocytes. It is commercially available as Histopaque 1077 with a density of 1.077 g/mL, Histopaque 1083 with a density of 1.083 g/mL, and Histopaque 1119 with a density of 1.119 g/mL.

Metrizamide is a nonionic derivative of metrizoate and is less dense than Percoll or Ficoll at high density (44). The chemical formula for metrizamide is (2-[3-acetamido-5-N-methylacetamido-2,4,6-triiodo-benzamidol]-2-deoxy-D-glucose). It has a molecular weight of 789.1, is iso-osmotic, and at 37% (w/v) it has a density of 1.192 g/mL.

Nycodenz, a nonionic density gradient material is a triiodinated derivative of benzoic acid which is nontoxic to cells (44). Its chemical formula is 5-(N-2,3-dihydroxy-propylacetamido)-2,4,6-triiodo-N,N'-bis(2,3-dihydroxypropyl) isothalamide and it has a molecular weight of 821.1.

Iodixanol, another iodinated gradient material, is a new nonionic density gradient medium (45). It is effectively a dimer of Nycodenz, and it has two significant advantages over previous iodinated density gradient media in that its aqueous solutions are iso-osmotic up to a density of 1.32 g/mL [at 30% (w/v) its density is 1.159 g/mL], and it can form self-generating gradients in 1 to 3 h. It has very low toxicity toward biological material, and enzyme assays can be carried out in its presence. The chemical formulation of Iodixanol is 5,5'-[(2-hydroxy-1,3-propanediyl)-bis(acetylimino)]bis-[N,N'-bis(2,3-dihydroxypropyl)-2,4,6-triiodo-1,3-benzene dicarboxamide].

Viscosity is the major determinant of sedimentation in a gradient. High molecular weight carbohydrates, such as Ficoll and dextran, are less ideal because at the concentrations used for gradients, sucrose solutions are highly viscous and hyperosmotic leading to slower sedimentation rates and loss of water from sub cellular organelles.

Ideally, gradient materials need to be iso-osmolar to avoid cell shrinkage or swelling. Iodinated density gradient materials, such as metrizamide, Nycodenz, Iodixanol, and the colloidal silica, Percoll, have lower osmolality and lower viscosity and are generally more suitable for gradient cell separation.

Gradients are either continuous or discontinuous. Discontinuous gradients are formed by layering different concentrations of the gradient material on top of each other generally by using a syringe and long needle. After centrifugation, cells of the same density can be recovered at the interfaces between the layers. In continuous gradients, cells sediment to the point of their exact densities and

Density gradient centrifugation

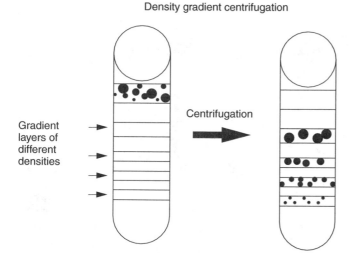

Figure 4. Density gradient centrifugation. Gradient materials at different densities are layered into centrifuge tubes, and a suspension of cells that have different densities are layered on to the top of the gradient (left panel). After centrifugation, the cells sediment to the level in the gradient that equals their own densities (right panel).

form distinct bands. Continuous gradients may be formed by stirring discontinuous gradients with a glass rod to smooth out interfaces or by self-generating gradients by centrifuging the gradient materials at a high g force. Gradients may also be formed by using a variety of commercial gradient makers.

Most populations of cells vary in density which results in banding at different locations in the centrifuge tube (Fig. 4). With discontinuous gradients there is more contamination by other cell populations which have partly overlapping densities. Therefore, continuous gradients yield higher purity of cell populations.

Elutriation or Counterflow Centrifugation

Elutriation or counterflow centrifugation uses a specially designed centrifuge rotor in which a suspension of cells is pumped into a separation chamber while the rotor is running (35,46) (Fig. 5). The rotor is operated at speeds appropriate for the specific types of cells being isolated. The rotor speed selected varies with cell volume, cell density, and the viscosity of the medium. Prior to elutriation, the volumes of the cells in the population must be determined, and this can be achieved by using a Coulter counter and a multichannel analyzer (46). Centrifugal sedimentation of the cells is opposed by the centripetal flow of medium in which the cells are suspended. The centripetal flow of the medium counterbalances the centrifugal force creating a gradient of cells of different sizes. Thus, the rate of sedimentation is determined by the sum of the centrifugal force and the countercentripetal flow (46).

Samples are pumped from a medium/buffer reservoir into the sample mixing chamber by a peristaltic pump. The centrifugal force moves the cells away from the center of the rotor. Medium is pumped through the chamber counter to the centrifugal force at a rate approximating

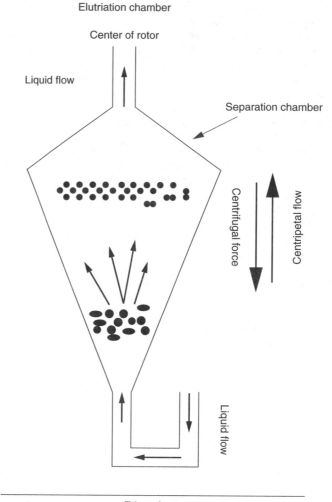

Figure 5. Elutriation or counterflow centrifugation. The figure depicts diagrammatically the structure of the elutriation chamber which is a specially designed centrifuge rotor in which a suspension cells are pumped into a separation chamber while the rotor is running. The rotor is operated at a speed ranging from 800 to 2500 rpm. The rotor speed depends the specific type of cell being isolated. Centrifugal sedimentation of the cells is opposed by the centripetal flow of medium in which the cells are suspended. The centripetal flow of the medium counterbalances the centrifugal force, creating a gradient of cells of different sizes. Thus, the rate of sedimentation is determined by the sum of the centrifugal force and the countercentripetal flow. The centrifugal force moves the cells away from the center of the rotor while medium is pumped through the chamber counter to the centrifugal force at a rate approximating the sedimentation rate of the cells. Differences in the size and density of the cells cause them to sediment at different rates and to reach equilibrium at different positions in the separation chamber. By increasing the flow rate of the medium, the cells are then pumped out of the chamber into collecting vessels. Smaller cells are recovered first, and the largest cells are recovered last.

the sedimentation rate of the cells. Thus, differences in cell size and density cause them to sediment at different rates and to reach equilibrium at different positions in the separation chamber. By increasing the flow rate of the medium, the cells are then pumped out of the chamber into collecting vessels. Smaller cells are recovered first, and the largest cells are recovered last.

Counterflow centrifugation offers several advantages: among them are high resolution and large cell capacity (up to 10^9 cells). Good separations can be achieved in a relatively short period of time. Another advantage is that cells can be separated in a physiological medium, thus avoiding the deleterious effects on cells that some gradient materials have. The main disadvantage of elutriation is the cost of the machine.

It is important that single cell suspensions be used because cells that are clumped together will effectively be larger and therefore elute at a rate different from single cells, thus compromising both purity and yield. Cells effectively can be separated at a range of temperatures between 4 °C and 30 °C depending on cell type. When cells are elutriated at 4 °C, the choice of elutriation medium is less important because the cells are not metabolically active. However, it is a good practice to use a medium that assures high cell viability. Generally, the best choice is the same medium that is used for culturing the particular cell type. Supplementing the medium with protein in the form of BSA or a low concentration of fetal bovine serum prevents sticking of the cells.

Good cell recovery can be achieved over a wide range of cell concentrations. Cell recoveries of 80 to 90% have been found using cell loads between 5×10^6 to $>10^8$. However, at higher loads ($>10^8$ cells), the cells are pumped out of the chamber at a lower flow rate, and more cells are elutriated in the early fractions. When large numbers of cells are in the chamber, the cross-sectional area available for fluid flow is reduced. The flow rate for eluting the cells can be maintained by either a peristaltic pump or by hydrostatic pressure. Fractions may be collected by increasing the flow rate while maintaining a constant rotor speed or by decreasing the rotor speed and maintaining a constant flow rate. It is generally preferable to use increased flow rate and constant rotor speed because of the time required for the rotor to slow down and tendency for the centrifuge to drop to a speed lower than set. The choices of flow rates and rotor speed are determined by the types of cells being separated. The first fraction to be eluted is composed of dead cells and cell debris, and the last fraction is composed of the largest cells in the population. Thus, rates of flow and rotor speed must be set to span the range of cell sizes in the population.

Affinity Binding

Specific cell surface moieties can be used advantageously for separating different populations by affinity binding. Most cells exhibit an array of distinct cell-surface carbohydrates. A variety of biologically active molecules, called ligands, bind with high affinity to cell surfaces (Fig. 6). These ligands may be antibodies, lectins, hormones, toxins, enzyme inhibitors, drugs, or chemical transmitters. The ligands most commonly used for separating cells are specific antibodies and a variety of lectins.

Affinity Binding with Lectins. Compounds were discovered several years ago that could agglutinate erythrocytes (47). Subsequently, other compounds were found

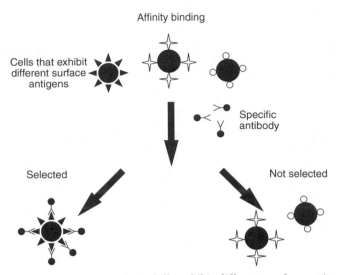

Figure 6. Affinity binding. Cells exhibit different surface antigenic binding sites. When mixed cell populations are exposed to an antibody which is specific for a given cell antigen, a complex forms between the antibody and the cell. Cells that possess different surface antigens do not form such complexes and therefore are not selected.

that could selectively aggregate different types of blood cells. These compounds, are called lectins and are sugar-specific, cell-agglutinating proteins found in various plants, animals, viruses, and other microorganisms. All lectins are oligomeric proteins or glycoproteins that have two or more sugar-binding sites per molecule. They combine noncovalently with mono- and oligosaccharides in the same way that antibodies bind antigens. However, lectins bind more weakly than antibodies and can be removed under mild conditions by competing sugars. Each lectin is specific for a particular carbohydrate structure; some lectins bind to mannose, to glucose, or to galactose. The affinity of the lectin for its receptor may vary due to small changes in the structure of the carbohydrate. Glycoconjugates are present on all biological membranes. Thus, lectins can be used to study all organisms.

Common plant lectins include concanavalin A, peanut agglutinin, leukoagglutinin (PHA-L), phytohemagglutinin (PHA-P), and wheat germ agglutinin. Lectin binding has been used to identify and separate cells that bind differentially to sugar moieties on the cell surfaces. Certain lectins are blood-type-specific and can be used to separate leukocytes from erythrocytes. Different lectins have been discovered that specifically bind to and agglutinate murine lymphocyte subpopulations (Table 4) (48–50). By selective agglutination with lectins that bind to specific cell types, complexes are formed that can be isolated by unit gravity in a viscous medium containing serum or BSA. Both agglutinated and unagglutinated cells can be recovered with good yield and viability. By using affinity chromatography, lectins can be immobilized on a solid support column, such as agarose, Sepharose, or plastic, through which a suspension of cells is passed and the unbound cells are washed out with buffer (Fig. 7). Then, ligand-bound cells are eluted by competitive binding with an excess of the lectin-specific carbohydrate.

Table 4. Lectin Binding to Murine Lymphocytes Subpopulations

Lectin	Cell Type	Reaction	Reference
Soybean agglutinin (SBA)	Nude mouse splenocyte	Agglutinates B cells and mature lymphocytes	48
Soybean agglutinin (SBA)	Thoracic duct T lymphocyte	No agglutination	48
Soybean agglutinin (SBA)	Splenocyte	Seperates B cells and T cells	49
Wheat germ agglutinin (WGA)	Nude mouse splenocyte	Agglutinates B cells but not mature T cells	50
Wheat germ agglutinin (WGA)	Thoracic duct T lymphocyte	No agglutinatiion	48
Peanut agglutinin (PNA)	Thymocyte	Separates cortical and medullary thymocytes	50

Affinity binding on immobilized matrix

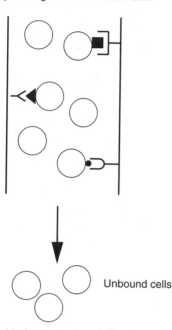

Unbound cells

Figure 7. Affinity binding on an immobilized matrix. Cell-specific antibodies (or lectins) are immobilized on a solid support matrix of material such as Sepharose or Agarose. Cell suspensions are applied to the column, and cells that possess the appropriate surface moiety are retained by the column. Unbound cells pass through the column and may be collected. A change of buffer allows removing the specifically bound cells.

The procedure has the advantage of gentleness because enzymatic treatment is not required to elute the cells and the cell yields are high. Fluorochromes can be also be conjugated to lectins and used for fluorescent-activated cell sorting (FACS).

Affinity Binding with Antibodies. Cells can be labeled and separated by immunospecific binding (Fig. 6). Cell separation is based on differences in the cell-surface antigen to which specific antibodies bind. "Panning"is a simple method of immunobinding in which plastic tissue culture dishes are coated with cell-specific antibodies. A mixture of cells is added to the plate. Cells that have the corresponding surface antigenic sites bind to the plate, and unbound cells are removed by washing and decantation.

Antibodies can be immobilized by cross-linking to a variety of solid matrices, including dextran, glass, agarose or polyacrylamide (Fig. 7). Cells are incubated with the immobilized antibody, and those cells that possess the specific antigen to which the antibody is directed adhere to the antibody-linked resin. Unbound cells are eluted by repeated washes with buffer. A change of buffer allows removing the specifically bound cells. For effective separation the solid matrix material should have limited or no nonspecific binding, should be stable against aggregation, should be capable of binding ligands through covalent binding, should have high affinity specific binding, and should possess the chemical and physical properties to allow separating labeled and unlabeled cells. The sensitivity of the primary antibody is increased by using an indirect immunoaffinity approach. Cells are premixed with the primary antibody and then incubated with a secondary antibody that has been immobilized on a solid support. Antibody-bound cells adhere to the solid support and can subsequently be separated by altering the buffer conditions or by enzymatic dissociation.

Cell Separation with Magnetic Beads

Antibodies or lectins specific for a cell surface moiety are conjugated with ferritin beads. The cells are mixed with the beads, and the suspension is passed by a magnet that attracts the cells that are adherent to the beads (51,52) (Fig. 8). The cells can subsequently be separated from the

Cell separation using magnetic beads

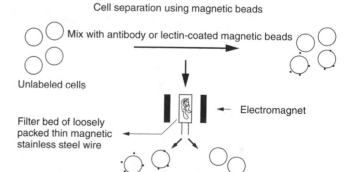

Mix with antibody or lectin-coated magnetic beads

Unlabeled cells

Filter bed of loosely packed thin magnetic stainless steel wire

Electromagnet

Figure 8. Cell separation using magnetic beads. Magnetized beads are coated with antibodies or with lectins and mixed with cell mixtures that possess a corresponding antigenic site or carbohydrate moiety on the cell's surface. The cell-bead mixtures are passed through a column with a filter bed of loosely packed, thin, magnetic stainless steel wire. An electromagnet is applied to the column, and the complexes of specific cells and coated magnetic beads are retained, whereas unbound cells pass through the column. The electromagnets are removed, and then the bound cells are collected.

ferritin beads by trypsinization and placed in a culture medium.

Magnetic cell sorting utilizes ferromagnetic particles to which antibodies, lectins, or other materials have been coupled. Cells that bear the specified antigen or other moiety attach to the magnetic particles and then can be removed by passing the cell suspension through a magnetic field in which the labeled cells are selectively attracted toward the magnet. Cells not attached to magnetic particles pass through the column and can be discarded or collected (51,52).

Because ferromagnetic particles are attracted to themselves they must be coated with materials that allow complexing of the desired ligand while inhibiting self-aggregation. Various polymerization methods have been used to coat ferrofluid particles which then can be covalently attached to ligands, such as antibodies and lectins. The surface charge of the particles needs to be sufficiently strong to overcome the magnetic attraction between the particles. Kronick (53) used a polymeric matrix of hydroxyl ethyl methylate N,N'-methylene bisacrylamide and methacrylic acid. Margel (54) prepared polyglutaraldehyde coated magnetic spheres. Rembaum (55) coated polyacrolein onto magnetic polystyrene microspheres. Widder (56) prepared an emulsion polymerization of ferrofluid particles with a mixture of albumin, protein A, and cottonseed oil. Molday (57) prepared ferromagnetic iron dextran particles.

The basic apparatus for high gradient magnetic filtration is simple (Fig. 8). A glass column less than 1 cm in diameter is loosely packed with fine stainless steel wire (25 μm in diameter. The glass column is placed between poles of an electromagnet that can produce a field of 1 to 10 kilogauss. The field magnetizes both the stainless steel wire and the labeled cells. The use of a very small diameter wire allows a large field gradient to be created with ordinary magnets of a few kilogauss. Cells or organelles labeled with magnetic microspheres that have been coupled to specific antibodies, lectins, or other cell-selective materials are pumped through the column with a peristaltic pump. The fraction of unlabeled cells passes through the column and is collected. Then the column is removed and the cells are eluted with buffer to release those retarded by the magnetic field.

For the most successful separation of cells or other biological materials, the superparamagnetic beads must exhibit fast magnetic separation, must be easily coupled to the specific ligand, must be compatible with a variety of buffers and other biological mixtures, and must separate cells efficiently over a distance of at least 5 cm. Vector Laboratories has developed magnetic particles with these properties. SCIGEN M100 particles are composed of 50:50 magnetite:cellulose, have a mean diameter of 3.5 μm, and contain 3×10^8 particles per mg. The cellulose has a large surface area which leads to fast reaction kinetics. In addition to use for cell separation, these magnetic beads can also be used for mRNA isolation, immunoassays, protein purification, and enzyme immobilization.

Flow Cytometry

Within the past several years many antibodies have been developed against specific cell-antigenic moieties that have revolutionized our ability to select for and separate multiple types of cells by a variety of immunoaffinity methods. These antibodies have made flow cytometry one of the most useful techniques for separating cells, cell organelles, and other biological particles (58,59). Flow cytometry has become a sophisticated tool for analyzing the chemical and physical properties of cells and subcellular organelles. Flow cytometry is also a rapid, objective, and quantitative method for analyzing and selecting cells (60). It has become the standard tool for hematology, including blood cell counting and differential detection of leukocytes and has been particularly important for typing the numerous subclasses of lymphocytes.

Flow cytometry in its simplest form distinguishes cells based on differences that are detectable by light scattering. In this technique a single stream of cells is projected through a laser beam. When the cells pass the laser beam, light scattering from the cells is detected by a photomultiplier, and cells that have the same light scattering properties are diverted into a collection vessel. Cells of differing size have different light scattering properties. Living and dead cells can be distinguished because dead cells have lower forward light scattering (60). For example, forward and side scattering signals distinguish blood lymphocytes from other blood cells. Near forward light scattering correlates with cell volume, whereas right-angle scattering correlates with granularity. Thus, the combination of forward and side scattering distinguishes lymphocytes, monocytes, and granulocytes.

Most applications in flow cytometry rely on measuring fluorescent dyes bound to nuclear or cytoplasmic protein or conjugated with cell-specific antibodies to cell-surface antigens (60). Cells are labeled with fluorescent-tagged molecules that bind specifically to the constituents to be measured. For example, monoclonal antibodies conjugated with fluorescein isothiocyanate (FITC), phycoerythrin or a fluorescent label, such as propidium iodide. Other dyes used include acridine orange, phycocyanin, and rhodamine. The use of a variety of fluorescent detectors with different wavelength filters allows simultaneous analysis of multiparameters (61). For example, fluorescein-conjugated antibodies show maximum excitation at 495 nm, and maximal emission is at 515 nm, whereas sulforhodamine excites at 595 NM and emits at 615 NM. Sulforhodamine produces a bright red fluorescence, whereas fluorescein produces a green fluorescence that makes these two fluorochromes ideally suited for measuring two parameters on a cell simultaneously.

The three main components of the flow cytometry system are the sample flow, the laser beam, and the optical detection device (58,59). The laser light is focused on a sample by lenses, and the focus must allow for high sensitivity and high resolution. The system may have one or two lasers. With two lasers, cells may be excited sequentially at two different wavelengths. Thus, one can measure two cell components with different dyes that require different excitation wavelengths. The detection limit is determined by the intensity of fluorescence and light scattering and by the efficiency of collection and conversion to electrical signals. The detection limit depends on the number of molecules per cell that produce light pulses large enough to be distinguished from background noise.

The cells are carried by a stream of fluid and pass through an intense beam of excitative light in the flow cytometer. As each cell passes through the light beam, it produces a flash of fluorescence whose intensity is proportional to the cellular concentration of the fluorescent-labeled constituent. The optics of the system focus the light on a sensitive detector and transform the light flash into an electrical pulse which is measured by an electronic device and recorded in the computer. The fluorescent emission is detected by a second photomultiplier tube. The intensity of light scattering is a function of the size, shape, and structure of the cell. Scattered light is recorded by a separate detector. Cell size, shape, and structure are recorded. Based on the characteristics of the cell, coordinates can be set so that the cell can be deflected by passing it between two oppositely charged plates and into a receiving vessel (Fig. 9). Cells can be sorted to collect fractions according to the parameters

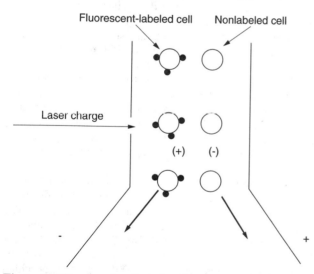

Fluorescent-Activated cell sorting (FACS)

Figure 9. Fluorescent-activated cell sorting (FACS). Cells are labeled with fluorescent-tagged molecules that bind specifically to the constituents to be measured, for example. monoclonal antibodies conjugated with fluorescein isothiocyanate (FITC), phycoerythrin, or with a fluorescent label, such as propidium iodide. The laser light is focused on the sample by lenses, and the focus must allow for high sensitivity and high resolution. The cells are carried by a stream of fluid and pass through an intense beam of excitation light in the flow cytometer. As each cell passes through the beam of light, it produces a flash of fluorescence whose intensity is proportional to the cellular concentration of the fluorescent-labeled constituent. The optics of the system focus the light on a sensitive detector and transform the light flash into an electrical pulse which is measured by an electronic device and recorded in the computer.

set. For each individual cell, the cellular content labeled with dyes fluoresces at different wavelengths. The ability to measure single cells makes it possible to distinguish subpopulations of cells in a mixture, and several thousand cells per second can be measured. It is possible to measure several parameters on each individual cell. Particles as small 0.1 μm can be measured, and the technique is sufficiently sensitive to detect 10^{-18} g of a specific substance per cell. The high sensitivity and rapidity of measurement also allows detecting cells that are in low frequency in a population (61). However, multiple rounds of cell sorting may be required to recover highly purified cells that are in low frequency in the original population (60).

APPLICATIONS OF PURIFICATION AND ENRICHMENT TECHNIQUES FOR DIVERSE CELL TYPES BY IMPLEMENTING A COMBINATION OF METHODS

Yamaguchi et al. (62) report a simple method for propagating and purifying gamma delta T ($\gamma\delta$T) cells from the peripheral blood of glioblastoma patients using solid-phase anti-CD3 antibody and soluble IL-2. Because $\gamma\delta$T cells represent only 1 to 10% of peripheral white blood cells, it has been difficult to study their role in regulating tumor growth. Enrichment procedures for $\gamma\delta$T cells have been difficult. Negative selection procedures using anti-CD4 and anti CD8 antibodies yielded a population of 90% $\gamma\delta$T cells, but this method requires a large amount of peripheral blood. Using a monoclonal antibody along with complement to remove $\alpha\beta$T cells has been partially successful in enriching the population of $\gamma\delta$T cells. Multistep panning using several antibodies has also been used to enrich for $\gamma\delta$T cells. Cloning methods have also been used but this requires the presence of feeder cells, as well as stimulation with IL-2. Large amounts of blood are required in all of these procedures.

In their study, Yamaguchi and colleagues (62) devised a method for obtaining large numbers of $\gamma\delta$T cells from 5 mL of blood from glioblastoma patients. They achieved a 1000 to 1500-fold increase in total cell numbers in about two weeks. The $\gamma\delta$T cells were enriched by about 30% and the yield was a total of approximately 10 to 15 × 10^8 $\gamma\delta$T cells.

Their approach was first to isolate the PBM (Peripheral Blood Mononuclear) cells from heparinized blood using Ficoll-Hypaque density gradient centrifugation. Cells were collected from the interface and subsequently cultured on plastic dishes coated with OKT3 monoclonal antibody. After a period of culture in the presence of IL-2, the cell population expanded, and then the cells were transferred to a culture vessel that contained growth medium with the OKT3 antibody.

In the next step magnetic beads were coated with sheep anti-mouse IgG, removed from the cell suspension using a magnet, and then incubated with mouse anti-CD16 monoclonal antibody. Then, the coated magnetic beads were mixed with PBM cells. Rosetted cells and free cells were removed with a magnet. The nonrosetted cells were cultured with OKT3 antibody, and CD4 and CD8 cells were removed with beads coated in two successive steps with anti-CD4 and anti-CD8 antibodies.

Lastly, the population of cells was analyzed by flow cytometry using FITC-labeled anti-TCR $\gamma\delta$ monoclonal antibody. After removing the CD4, CD8, and CD16 cells, the population contained greater than 95% $\gamma\delta$T cells which had cytotoxic activity against K562 target cells and autologous glioblastoma cells, expressed receptors for IL-2, and were stimulated to proliferate in the presence of IL-2. Thus, this study provides an excellent example of combining gradient centrifugation, magnetic bead separation, and flow cytometry to markedly enrich a population of cells that have low frequency in peripheral blood, starting with only 5 mL of blood.

Isolation and culture of human dendritic cells from precursor cells employed two types of density gradient centrifugation (63). Dendritic cells are antigen-presenting cells that capture antigens at body surfaces and in tissues which are exposed to the environment and then migrate to the lymphoid organs via lymph and blood. They express a variety of adhesion molecules and integrins and also express all of the major histocompatibility antigens.

Isolation from peripheral blood was achieved by separating mononuclear cells on Ficoll-Hypaque and subsequently removing T cells by sheep red blood cell rosetting. Then the Fc-bearing monocytes were removed by layering on immobilized human immunoglobulin, after which the cells were passed over a metrizamide column to separate the high-density B and NK cell fractions from the low-density dendritic cells. The cells were Further enriched by incubating them on immobilized anti-CD45R to remove any remaining T cells. Approximately 3×10^6 dendritic cells 80 to 90% pure were isolated from about 5×10^8 white blood cells.

Scott and Bicknell isolated endothelial cells from microvascular beds (64). Obtaining pure cultures of endothelial cells requires selective techniques including the use of a medium that promotes their growth (such as a serum-free medium containing VEGF (Vascular endothelial growth factor) which is specific for endothelial cells) while inhibiting the growth of other cells, particularly smooth muscle cells. Endothelial cells were removed from their competitive environment by cloning and subsequent mechanical removal using mesh filters whose pore size permitted passage of endothelial cells while retaining contaminants. Next, magnetic beads coated with lectins which react with endothelial cells were used to further enrich the endothelial cells.

Another technique used FACS sorting using diI-Ac-LDL to label cells (64). Acetyl-LDL is taken up by endothelial cells and macrophages. Because macrophages do not proliferate in culture, pure populations of endothelial populations may be obtained. The best results were achieved if density gradient centrifugation using Percoll was carried out first. Additionally, elutriation has also been successfully used for separating endothelial cells to provide substantial quantities of pure cells.

Speirs and Cutz have provided an overview of culture and isolation methods for in vitro studies on pulmonary neuroendocrine cells (65). Pulmonary neuroendocrine cells (PNEC), present in very low frequency in the lung, occur along the basement membrane between adjacent epithelial cells or in small clusters scattered throughout the airways. In all they represent only about 0.1% of the total epithelial cells. Their method of isolation first used a collagenase digestion of lung tissue followed by a pronase digest, followed by density gradient centrifugation using a single-step gradient of 50% Percoll. Next, they used immunomagnetic separation with an antibody (MOC-1) derived from a human small cell lung carcinoma that is also expressed on the surface of PNEC of human and rabbit lung. MOC-1 is related to the neural cell adhesion molecule N-CAM. Magnetic beads were made of polystyrene containing 20% iron conjugated to the antibody. PNEC that express the antigen formed a complex with the beads and were removed with a magnet. The authors found that this method yielded two to three times better recovery than density gradient centrifugation alone.

Carbonari and colleagues measured apoptotic cells in peripheral blood (66). Apoptosis is classically determined by microscopic detection of typical morphological changes and analysis of in situ end labeling of fragmented DNA. The terminal transferase-mediated dUTP-biotin nick end-labeling (TUNEL) technique measures degraded DNA in apoptotic cells.

Flow cytometry methods measure permeability of plasma and nuclear membranes to DNA binding dyes (ethidium bromide, propidium iodide, and actinomycin D). It is difficult to distinguish apoptosis from necrosis on the basis of differential permeability. Using flow cytometry, apoptotic lymphocytes were detected by their high binding to merocyanine 540 which detects decreased plasma membrane phospholipid packing. Further, reduced expression of surface CD45 antigen is associated with apoptotic lymphocytes and distinguishes them from viable and necrotic lymphocytes which can be detected by flow cytometry.

CD8^{bright} and CD8^{dim} lymphocyte populations were prepared using two positive selection methods in tandem (67). CD8^{bright} cells largely represent a CD3+ subset that have MHC-restricted cytolytic activity and suppressive activity for antibody production. CD8^{dim} cells express non-MHC-restricted cytolytic activity, as well as natural killer activity.

The method employed magnetic beads which were coated with anti-CD8, and the captured cells were recovered using a sheep anti-mouse Fab reagent. The selected cells were more than 94% CD8$^+$ cells and were enriched for CD8^{bright} cells by 77 to 85%. In the next phase cells were placed in flasks coated with anti-CD8, and the recovery was more than 90% CD8$^+$ cells which were modestly enriched for CD8^{dim} cells, mononuclear populations were first incubated with anti-CD8-coated magnetic beads to obtain a CD8^{bright} population. Then, the uncaptured cells were incubated with anti-CD4-coated magnetic beads, and the uncaptured cells from this step were incubated in flasks coated with anti-CD8. The recovered flask selected population was highly enriched for CD8^{dim} cells.

Markiewicz and colleagues used an immunomagnetic method to separate CD34(+) cells (68). Mononuclear cells were incubated with mouse anti-CD34 antibody and then washed to remove unbound antibody. Polystyrene paramagnetic microbeads 4.5 μm in diameter were covalently linked with sheep anti-mouse IgG. CD34(+) cells sensitized with anti-CD34 antibody formed rosettes with the coated magnetic spheres and were captured with a magnet. Following separation, the cells were released from the magnetic beads with chymopapain. Yields were between 37 and 70%, and purity was between 38 and 83%.

Davies and co-workers compared the use of two immunomagnetic microspheres for secondary purification of pancreatic islets (69). They used MIMS and Dynabeads and either lectins or monoclonal antibodies to coat the magnetic beads. MIMS are biodegradable magnetic-inducible microspheres, whereas Dynabeads are nonbiodegradable. The results showed that MIMs coated with lectin and Dynabeads coated with antibody removed 80% of the acinar contamination with a yield of 70% pancreatic islets.

A combination of immunomagnetic cell sorting and the enzyme-linked immunospot assay) (ELISPOT) was used for the phenotypic characterization of specific antibody-forming cells by Lakew and colleagues (70). The authors reported an enrichment of specific antibody-forming cells with a rapid and simple method to identify SFC (SPOT-forming cells) based on expression (or lack) of surface markers. Cell separation used magnetic beads coated with antibodies to a given surface marker. Using ELISPOT assay, the phenotype of SFC could be determined.

Zwerner et al. reported a simple and rapid method for removing specific cell populations from whole blood by using antibodies specific for cell-surface antigens that enable removing cells from a mixed population that expresses specific markers (71). Using antibody-labeled dense particles attached to cells, the cells were separated by gravity settling. It is a simple and rapid method for recovering specific cells. Dense nickel particles with a diameter of 8 µm were labeled with antibody to CD4 and CD8. Whole blood was added to the particles and mixed after which tubes were set vertically, and particles were allowed to settle for 4 min. Particle pellets were held in the bottom of the tube with a magnet, and the depleted blood was removed.

The method yielded a 97% depletion of CD4 cells when anti-CD4 antibody was used and 96% depletion when anti-CD8 antibodies were used. The advantage of this method is that all of the cells are effectively bound to the particles in only 4 minutes of mixing, and the cells settle to the bottom more rapidly than in a magnetic column or centrifugal separation without trapping other cells present in the system.

McKnight and co-workers employed an isotype-directed enrichment of B cells by magnetic beads in generating immuno reactive human monoclonal antibodies (72). Lymphocytes plus a biotinylated murine monoclonal antibody directed against human IgG$_4$ were used and added to streptavidin-conjugated magnetic beads. Unseparated pooled lymphocytes were 1.5% IgG$_4$$^+$ cells, and magnetically separated cells were 20% IgG$_4$$^+$. Fusion experiments with unseparated lymphocytes yielded one clone out of 481 generated hybridomas that had detectable IgG4, whereas the magnetically separated cells generated 21 clones out of 101 hybridomas that secreted IgG4. The method

demonstrates that cells of rare isotypes can easily be isolated from a heterogenous population by magnetic beads.

Sun and colleagues performed a large scale and clinical grade purification of syndecan-1$^+$ malignant plasma cells from the bone marrow of patients who had multiple myelomatosis (73). Mouse antibodies B-B4 and MI 15 both recognize syndecan-1 which is present on myeloma cells only in tumor samples. They incubated the cells with B-B4 or MI 15 monoclonal antibody and reacted them with magnetic beads coated with sheep anti-mouse IgG which then were captured with a magnet. Then, cells were released from the magnetic beads with chymopapain. The result yielded a homogenous population of syndecan-1 positive cells without affecting cell viability and growth.

Jareo and co-workers used magnetic cell sorting to isolate blood neutrophils from rats (74). They compared density gradient centrifugation separation with magnetic cell sorting for rat leukocytes. The leukocyte fraction from whole rat blood was layered over Ficoll-Hypaque (Histopaque) of 1.077 g/mL density. Erythrocytes were removed by a 10-second exposure to distilled water.

In the second strategy, magnetic beads were coated with streptavidin-conjugated superparamagnetic microbeads 50 nm in diameter. Leukocytes were labeled with biotinylated anti-rat granulocyte monoclonal antibody. This antibody reacts with antigen found on all granulocytes and some monocytes. Then, leukocytes were mixed with the streptavidin-conjugated beads. Labeled neutrophils were separated from non labeled cells by passing them through a column of a magnetized steel wool matrix. The unlabeled cells passed through the column, and the neutrophils were retained. Then column was removed from the magnet, and the neutrophils were flushed from the column.

Their results showed that separation on Histopaque yielded approximately 70% neutrophils with a viability of greater than 94%, and 1.0 to 1.6 × 10^6 cells were recovered from a 250 g rat. Using magnetic bead separation, cell viability was greater than 95%, purity, was 78–84% and 3.8 to 11 × 10^6 cells were recovered. The major contaminant was monocytes probably due to some cross-reactivity with the antibody used. An advantage of magnetic bead separation is that it does not require lysis of RBCs (red blood cells) with water.

Radbruch and Recktenwald reviewed methods for detecting and isolating rare cells (75), and they optimized the method using flow cytometry. The nonrare cells were labeled with a mixture of antibodies tagged with one fluorophore, and they stained the rare cell type with a specific antibody that was conjugated with a different fluorophore. Gross (76) used antibodies to CD3, CD4, CD7, CD8, CD15, CD41a, and CD 42b to label the non rare cells and antibodies to CD10 and used CD19 to detect the rare pre-B cells in a population of peripheral blood lymphocytes.

Rare cells were positively enriched by high-gradient magnetic cell sorting. Magnetic labeling was done with superparamagnetic beads less that 100 nm in size conjugated with antibodies. Cells were separated in a high-gradient magnetic field. Cell numbers as high as 10^{10} could be used, and the rare cells were collected in a small volume. This technique has been used successfully to isolate rare cells, such as hematopoietic stem cells from peripheral blood, fetal cells in maternal blood, memory B lymphocytes, and IgA1 expressing cells that occur at frequencies of 0.5% or less in peripheral blood.

Bhat and co-workers compared a triple gradient with a one-step method for isolating and enriching nucleated red blood cells (RBC) (77). The triple gradient [consisting of Histopaque 1119 (bottom), 1083 (middle) and 1077 (on the top)] yielded a 25-fold enrichment compared with the one-step method using Histopaque 1077. The third gradient allows further separation of CD71$^+$ (transferrin receptor) erythroblasts from granulocytes and mature or immature RBC that are CD71$^-$. In the single-step gradient, mononuclear and nucleated RBCs banded together, whereas in the triple gradient, the mononuclear and nucleated RBCs were well-separated.

Kossovsky and colleagues prepared high-purity resident tissue macrophage isolates from human synovium and periprosthetic tissues using immunomagnetic techniques (78). They used murine monoclonal antibody directed against CD68 which is a phagocyte-specific marker and sheep anti-mouse IgG antibodies bound to polystyrene-coated magnetic microspheres. The system was used to retrieve CD68$^+$ cells from collagenase-digested synovial tissues and fluids. They recovered in excess of 80% of the cells with approximately 80% viability. Density gradient centrifugation cell yields and purity were an order of magnitude less than those achieved by the immunomagnetic technique.

Griwatz and co-workers applied an immunological enrichment method to epithelial cells from peripheral blood (79). Primary tumors metastasize leading to circulating carcinoma cells (epithelial). A two-layer density gradient was used in which the epithelial cells formed a single density band. Peripheral blood target cells were initially separated from blood erythrocytes, granulocytes, and lymphocytes using Polymorphprep and Nycoprep gradient. The second stage of enrichment was achieved with a secondary antibody bound to superparamagnetic beads. Rat anti-mouse IgG2a$^+$b antibody was coupled to the magnetic microbeads. Human cytokeratin antibody was linked to the cells. The maximal level of cancer cells in peripheral blood is about 2 in 10^7 leukocytes. An enrichment factor greater than 10,000 was required to separate the epithelial-derived cells from peripheral blood. The first step was to use density gradient centrifugation to remove leukocytes and erythrocytes and then use superparamagnetic beads using cytokeratin antibodies to cytokeratins 8 and 18 because they have superior sensitivity and specificity. Loading the enriched cells onto the magnetic column achieved a recovery rate of 30% and a maximal total enrichment of about 200,000. Density gradient centrifugation yielded a 20-fold enrichment, and the immunomagnetic separation gave a 10,000-fold enrichment starting with 5 × 10^9 leukocytes.

Romero and colleagues studied the ionic calcium content of light and dense human red blood cells separated by Percoll density gradients (80). Two methods using Percoll were carried out to separate light and dense erythrocytes. A discontinuous Percoll with 6% meglumine diatrizoate was used to prepare five layers and Percoll concentrations to obtain densities from 1.080 to 1.150 g/mL. The second system employed preformed gradients of Percoll plus sodium diatrizoate and glucose with Percoll densities ranging from 1.080 to 1.120 g/mL. The gradients were self-formed by centrifuging at 26,500 g for 10 min. The results showed that the auto-formed gradients allowed more stringent separation of light erythrocytes with closely related density values that were not observed with discontinuous gradients.

DISCUSSION

In the past few years researchers have increased their activity seeking to refine and improve on the various techniques of cell enrichment. Combinations of cell separation and enrichment procedures have significantly improved the ability to isolate viable populations of cells with high purity and in high yield. The production of an abundance of monoclonal antibodies directed against a broad assortment of cellular antigens has fundamentally revolutionized the ability to detect and isolate cells that occur with rare frequency in populations of cells. The use of flow cytometry has been exceptionally significant in this regard.

BIBLIOGRAPHY

1. M.E. Kaighn and J.F. Lechner, in T.G. Pretlow, II and T.P. Pretlow, eds., *Cell Separation: Methods and Selected Applications*, Vol. 3, Academic Press, New York, 1984, pp. 285–306.

2. F.-T. Kao and T.T. Puck, *Methods Cell Biol.* **8**, 23–29 (1974).

3. S.A. Fisher and M. Absher, *Am. J. Physiol.* **268**, C910–C917 (1995).

4. W.W.-Y. Kao and J. Prockop, *Birth Defects, Orig. Artic. Ser.* **16**, 53–59 (1980).

5. L.A. Liotta et al., *Nature (London)* **272**, 622–624 (1978).

6. B.R. Migeon, *Birth Defects, Orig. Artic. Ser.* **16**, 239–247 (1980).

7. H.L. Leffert and D. Pau, *J. Cell Biol.* **52**, 559–568 (1972).

8. G.D. Stoner et al., *In Vitro* **16**, 399–406 (1980).

9. M.M. Webber and D. Chaproniere-Rickenberg, *Cell Biol. Int. Rep.* **4**, 185–193 (1980).

10. M. Absher et al., *In Vitro Cell Dev. Biol.* **25**, 183–192 (1989).

11. R.G. Ham, *Handb. Exp. Pharmacol.* **57**, 13–88 (1981).

12. R.G. Ham, *Cold Spring Harbor Conf. Cell Proliferation* **9**, 39–60 (1981).

13. R.G. Ham and W.L. McKeehan, in H. Kasuta, ed., *Nutritional Requirements of Cultured Cells*, Japan Scientific Societies Press, Tokyo, 1978, pp. 63–115.

14. A.E. Freeman, H.J. Igel, B.J. Herrman, and K.L. Kleinfield, *In Vitro* **12**, 352–362 (1976).

15. I.H. Lillie, D.K. MacCallum, and A. Jepsen, *Exp. Cell Res.* **125**, 153–165 (1980).

16. M.C. Kibbey, L.S. Royce, M. Dym, and B.J. Baum, *Exp. Cell Res.* **198**, 343–351 (1992).

17. S.L. Sigurdson and J.S. Lwebuga-Mukasa, *Exp. Cell Res.* **213**, 71–79 (1994).

18. D.H. Farrell and H.A. al-Mondhiry, *Biochemistry* **36**, 1123–1128 (1997).

19. A.S. High and P.A. Robinson, *Arch. Oral Biol.* **39**, 387–393 (1994).

20. F. Grinnell and M.H. Bennett, *J.Cell Sci.* **48**, 19–34 (1981).

21. T.S. Lange et al., *Exp. Cell Res.* **214**, 381–388 (1994).

22. P.M. Absher et al., *Atherosclerosis* **131**, 187–194.

23. E. Dejana et al., *J. Cell Biol.* **109**, 367–375 (1989).

24. H. Rixen et al., *Exp. Cell Biol.* **57**, 315–323 (1989).

25. T.C. Tsao et al., *Pathobiology* **62**, 120–126 (1994).

26. A. Ariel et al., *J. Immunol.* **161**, 2465–2472 (1998).

27. R.I. Freshney, *Culture of Animal Cells: A Manual of Basic Technique*, 3rd ed., Wiley-Liss, New York, 1994, pp. 161–178.

28. R.G. Ham, in D.W. Barnes, D.A. Sirbasku, and G.H. Sato, eds., *Cell Culture Methods for Molecular and Cell Biology*, Vol. 3, Alan R. Liss, New York, 1984, pp. 249–264.

29. R.G. Ham, *Exp. Cell Res.* **29**, 515 (1963).

30. W.G. Hamilton and R.G. Ham, *In Vitro* **13**, 537–547 (1977).

31. R.I. Freshney, in D.G.T. Thomas and D.I. Graham, eds., *Brain Tumours, Scientific Basis, Clinical Investigation and Current Therapy*, Butterworth, London, 1980, pp. 21–50.

32. J.B. Griffiths and G.J. Pirt, *Proc. R. Soc. London, Ser. B.* **168**, 421–438 (1967).

33. W.L. McKeehan and K.A. McKeehan, *J. Cell Physiol.* **101**, 9–16 (1979).

34. C.I. Stanners, G.L. Eliceri, and H. Green, *Nature (London), New Biol.* **230**, 52–54 (1971).

35. R.I. Freshney, *Culture of Animal Cells: A Manual of Basic Technique*, 3rd ed., Wiley-Liss, New York, 1994, pp. 179–195.

36. C.D. Platsoucas, in T.G. Pretlow, II and T. P. Pretlow, eds., *Cell Separation: Methods and Selected Applications*, Vol. 2, Academic Press, New York, 1983, pp. 145–182.

37. R.C. Boltz, P. Todd, M.J. Streibel, and M.K. Louie, *Prep. Biochem.* **3**, 383–401 (1973).

38. I. Bertoncello, in T.G. Pretlow, II and T. P. Pretlow, eds., *Cell Separation: Methods and Selected Applications*, Vol. 5, Academic Press, New York, 1987, pp. 89–108.

39. T.G. Pretlow, II and T.P. Pretlow, in T.G. Pretlow, II and T.P. Pretlow, eds., *Cell Separation: Methods and Selected Applications*, Vol. 1, Academic Press, New York, 1982, pp. 41–60.

40. T.G. Pretlow, II and T.P. Pretlow, in N. Catsimpoolas, ed., *Methods of Cell Separation*, Plenum, New York, 1977, pp. 171–191.

41. H. Pertoft and T.C. Laurent, in T.G. Pretlow, II and T.P. Pretlow, eds., *Cell Separation: Methods and Selected Applications*, Vol. 1, Academic Press, New York, 1982, pp. 115–152.

42. M. Sjöstrand et al., *Am. Rev. Respir. Dir.* **143**, 47–52 (1991).

43. T.G. Pretlow, II and T.P. Pretlow, in T.G. Pretlow, II and T.P. Pretlow, eds., *Cell Separation: Methods and Selected Applications*, Vol. 5, Academic Press, New York, 1987, pp. 281–309.

44. G. Alpini, J.O. Phillips, B. Vroman, and N.F. LaRusso, *Hepatology* **20**, 494–514 (1994).

45. T. Ford, J. Graham, and D. Rickwood, *Anal. Biochem.* **220**, 360–366 (1994).

46. M.L. Meistrich, in T.G. Pretlow, II and T.P. Pretlow, eds., *Cell Separation: Methods and Selected Applications*, Vol. 2, Academic Press, New York, 1983, pp. 33–61.

47. N. Sharon, in T.G. Pretlow, II and T.P. Pretlow, eds., *Cell Separation: Methods and Selected Applications*, Vol. 3, Academic Press, New York, 1984, pp. 13–23.

48. H.P. Schnebli and P. Dukor, *Eur. J. Immunol.* **2**, 607–609 (1972).

49. Y. Reisner, A. Ravid, and N. Sharon, *Biochem. Biophys. Res. Commun.* **72**, 1585–1591 (1976).

50. Y. Reisner, M. Linker-Israeli, and N. Sharon, *Cell. Immunol.* **25**, 129–134 (1976).

51. R.S. Molday, in T.G. Pretlow, II and T.P. Pretlow, eds., *Cell Separation: Methods and Selected Applications*, Vol. 3, Academic Press, New York, 1984, pp. 237–263.

52. C.S. Owen and P.A. Liberti, in T.G. Pretlow, II and T.P. Pretlow, eds., *Cell Separation: Methods and Selected Applications*, Vol. 5, Academic Press, New York, 1987, pp. 259–275.

53. P.L. Kronick, G. Campbell, and K. Joseph, *Science* **200**, 1074–1076 (1978).

54. S. Margel, S. Zisblatt, and A. Rembaum, *J. Immunol. Methods* **28**, 341–353 (1979).

55. A. Rembaum, R.C.K. Yen, D.H. Kemper, and J. Ugelstad, *J. Immunol. Methods* **52**, 341–351 (1982).

56. K.J. Widder, A.E. Senyei, H. Ovadia, and P.Y. Paterson, *J. Pharm. Sci.* **70**, 387–389 (1981).

57. R.S. Molday and D. MacKenzie, *J. Immunol. Methods* **52**, 353–367 (1982).

58. M.R. Melamed, P.F. Mullaney, and H.M. Shapiro, in M.R. Melamed, T. Lindmo, and M.L. Mendelsohn, eds., *Flow Cytometry and Sorting*, 2nd ed., Wiley-Liss, New York, 1990, pp. 1–9.

59. H.B. Steen, in M.R. Melamed, T. Lindmo, and M.L. Mendelsohn, eds., *Flow Cytometry and Sorting*, 2nd ed., Wiley-Liss, New York, 1990, pp. 11–25.

60. F.I. Preffer and R.B. Colvin, in T.G. Pretlow, II and T.P. Pretlow, eds., *Cell Separation: Methods and Selected Applications*, Vol. 5, Academic Press, New York, 1987, pp. 311–347.

61. C.D. Jennings and K.A. Foon, *Cancer Invest.* **15**, 384–399 (1997).

62. T. Yamaguchi et al., *J. Immunol. Methods* **205**, 19–28 (1997).

63. R. Jaffe, *Pediatr. Pathol.* **13**, 821–837 (1993).

64. P.A. Scott and R. Bicknell, *J. Cell Sci.* **105**, 269–273 (1993).

65. V. Speirs and E. Cutz, *Anat. Rec.* **236**, 35–40 (1993).

66. M. Carbonari, M. Cibati, and M. Fiorilli, *Cytometry* **22**, 161–167 (1995).

67. H.E. Prince, S. Bermudez, and S. Plaeger-Marshall, *J. Immunol. Methods* **165**, 139–48 (1993).

68. M. Markiewicz et al., *Transplant. Proc.* **28**, 3526–3527 (1996).

69. J.E. Davies et al., *Transplantation* **62**, 1301–1306 (1996).

70. M. Lakew, I. Nordstrom, C. Czerkinsky, and M. Quiding-Jarbrink, *J. Immunol. Methods* **203**, 193–198 (1997).

71. R.K. Zwerner, R.J. Schmittling, and T.R. Russell, *J. Immunol. Methods* 199–202 (1996).

72. M.E. McKnight et al., *Hybridoma* **15**, 255–261 (1996).

73. R.X. Sun et al., *J. Immunol. Methods* **205**, 73–799 (1997).

74. P.W. Jareo, L.C. Preheim, M.U. Snitily, and M.J. Gentry, *Lab. Anim. Sci.* **47**, 414–418 (1997).

75. A. Radbruch and D. Recktenwald, *Curr. Opin. Immunol.* **7**, 270–2733 (1995).

76. H.J. Gross et al., *Cytometry* **14**, 519–526 (1993).

77. N.M. Bhat, M.M. Bieber, and N.N. Teng, *J. Immunol. Methods* **158**, 277–280 (1993).

78. N. Kossovsky et al., *Clin. Orthop. Relat. Res.* **297**, 262–268 (1993).

79. C. Griwatz, B. Brandt, G. Assmann, and K.S. Zanker, *J. Immunol. Methods* **183**, 251–265 (1995).

80. P.J. Romero, E.A. Romero, and M.D. Winkler, *Biochem. Biophys. Acta* **1323**, 23–28 (1997).

See also ANIMAL CELL CULTURE MEDIA; CELL AND CELL LINE CHARACTERIZATION; CELL DIFFERENTIATION, ANIMAL; SOMACLONAL VARIATION.

EQUIPMENT AND LABORATORY DESIGN FOR CELL CULTURE

M. BUTLER
University of Manitoba
Winnipeg, Manitoba
Canada

OUTLINE

INTRODUCTION

The purpose of this article is to review some of the basic requirements for setting up a small-scale culture laboratory for handling animal cell cultures. This will include a description of a suitable laboratory environment in which to manipulate such cells and some of the basic laboratory equipment needed. There are a number of excellent reference books available on this topic, and some of these are included in the bibliography (1–9).

LABORATORY DESIGN

A cell culture laboratory should facilitate the handling of cells in culture with an undectable level of contamination. The growth rate of bacterial or fungal cells is usually much greater than that of mammalian cells, so that any level of contamination cannot be tolerated in an animal cell culture. However, it is impractical to design a laboratory that is totally free of potentially contaminating microorganisms. The laboratory is generally designed to minimize the risk of contamination for an experienced worker. Thus the maintenance of noncontaminated (axenic) cultures is as much a product of good experimental technique as a clean germ-free environment.

In the development of animal cell culture techniques during the 1920s and 1930s, Alexis Carrel used methods borrowed from surgical practices employed in hospital operating rooms. This included full gowning with surgical dress in a sterile room. However, now these methods would be regarded as rather extreme and are not normally considered necessary in a modern laboratory. To minimize the risks of contamination, several features can be incorporated into the designated "clean" laboratory (10).

An important feature of the laboratory should be an effective physical separation of the sterile handling area from the areas for washup and sterilization. Ideally these may be separated in different labs. Cell culture facilities are often located in small rooms where there is minimal traffic of personnel. A small room containing a standard class II laminar flow cabinet is ideal because the air flow through the sterile exhaust of the cabinet should maintain a low particle count in the environment. The laminar flow cabinet (hood), microscope, and incubator should be positioned close together so that physical transfer of cultures will be minimized. When it is not possible to have an independent sterile handling laboratory, it is at least necessary to ensure that the sterile handling area of a larger laboratory is positioned in a region where there is minimal movement of people. The area used for nonsterile work such as the washing-up facility and disposal of used culture flasks should be positioned at the other side of the laboratory from the clean area. A typical plan for a cell culture laboratory is shown in Figure 1. This is a self-contained lab suitable for use by two or three people. In a larger facility it would be essential to include separate rooms for the clean area and washup area.

The incoming air into the laboratory may be filtered through a particle filter (HEPA or electronic) that may be incorporated into the ceiling space. The incoming air pressure may be increased to cause a slight positive pressure within the laboratory. Air cooling ("conditioning") may often be necessary because of the heat generated by the incubators and other electronic equipment in the laboratory. Such measures will reduce the level of potential airborne contaminants in the lab environment. Sterile handling of cultures is generally carried out in a laminar flow cabinet into which only the operator's arms enter the sterile work area. This reduces air currents and the potential for contamination carried by laboratory workers and minimizes the potential of contaminants entering opened culture flasks. Other areas of the laboratory should be maintained clean by removal of unnecessary clutter and application of antiseptic cleaning agents at regular intervals.

WASHING REUSABLE GLASSWARE

The general use of presterilized tissue-culture-grade plasticware has meant a decrease in the amount of washing necessary in an average research laboratory involved in cell culture. It is difficult and time consuming to wash glassware sufficiently so that it is free of potentially

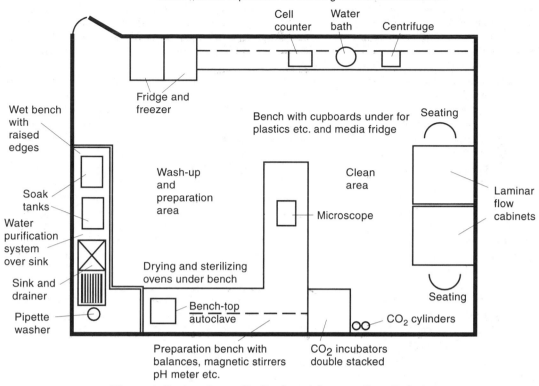

Glass-fronted cupboards for sterile glassware above bench

Figure 1. Design of a small cell culture laboratory (from Ref. 1).

cytotoxic detergent to enable reproducibility in cell culture. The advantages of single-use plastic culture vessels include a consistency in operation as well as a decreased preparation time. Nevertheless there is still a need for an adequate washing facility in most laboratories to prepare the spinner flasks, beakers, and measuring cylinders that are used routinely. These all require a scrupulous washing regime prior to use or prior to sterilization. Any failure in the washing operation allows the possibility of the introduction of contaminants (e.g., traces of heavy metal) into the cultures and would likely result in a cytotoxic effect, causing lowered cell growth or an altered metabolism.

It is necessary to soak all reusable glassware in a hypochlorite solution (Chloros) as soon as possible after use. This will prevent the possibility of a buildup of dried protein residues that are difficult to remove. It is desirable to have access to a sink deep enough to accommodate all the dirty glassware at one time and to allow the complete immersion of the largest glass items. Generally a sink depth of around 45 cm is suitable. If the washingup area is outside the culture laboratory, then the glassware may be stored in a bucket next to the work area before removal to the main sink. Prior to immersion in the soak tank, it is advisable to rinse under a cold tap, remove any tape, and remove any marker pen labelling with acetone. Soaking should be for several hours or preferably overnight.

In many laboratories a suitable washing machine (e.g., Lancer) is available for washing after the initial soaking. The desired procedure, either manually or by machine, is to wash with a detergent and rinse with a dilute

acid. Washing machine manufacturers have recommended conditions for this as appropriate for a particular machine. These procedures are followed by repeated sequential washes in tap water and then distilled or reverse osmosis water.

The glassware should be dried in a hot air oven at around 100 °C before use or sterilization (11). Items that are not immediately sterilized should be kept covered or inverted on a clean surface until required.

Although individually packed presterilized plastic pipettes are available, many laboratories choose to reuse standard glass pipettes in cell culture operations. These may be washed and sterilized by following a similar procedure to that recommended for other glassware. Pipettes may be washed in a free-standing cylindrical pipette washer, which is generally made of polypropylene. After removal of the cotton plug from each pipette, they should be placed tip uppermost into the cylinder container of the pipette washer for overnight soaking in a hypochorite solution. This is then followed by 4 to 6 hours of washing using the siphon-type automatic washer. Initially this should be done with tap water and then with distilled or reverse osmosis water. The pipettes are then dried in an oven before replugging with cotton wool and sorting pipettes of the same size into metal cans. These may be sterilized by dry heat (160 °C for 1 h).

BIOSAFETY CABINETS

Sterile operations in a cell culture laboratory are normally undertaken in cabinets (commonly called hoods), which serve the purpose of minimizing the chance of culture contamination and ensure the safety of the operator.

For media preparation, or when handling nonprimate cell lines, culture manipulations can be conducted in a small front-opening cabinet. The cabinets are relatively cheap and are equipped with a UV light source to prevent contamination of the cabinet surface when not in use but may not have an internal air flow. Alternatively, a sterile working area can be provided by a horizontal flow hood, which allows filtered air to blow from the back of the cabinet and through the contained space. Good technique will ensure that cultures do not become contaminated, but it must be noted that these systems do not offer operator protection against possible pathogens.

If human or other primate cells are used, then some protection is required against the possibility of transmission of infectious agents. For this purpose most cell culture laboratories have an open-fronted laminar flow cabinet in which only the operator's arms enter the sterile area. The cabinet offers a space containing a vertical flow of filtered air and a horizontal working surface that can be disinfected. The most commonly used cabinet for cell culture is 4 ft long and designated as Class II (Fig. 2). The classification is a measure of the biological safety as reviewed in the article "Aseptic Techniques In Cell Culture."

A Class II cabinet is suitable for work with low to moderate toxic or infectious agents. There is an inward flow of air drawn into the sterile working area of the cabinet through a high-efficiency particulate air (HEPA) filter. The direction of flow offers personnel protection. Most of the air (70–80%) is recirculated to form an air curtain, which serves to maintain a sterile space for

culture manipulation. The exhausted air is also forced through a HEPA filter, and this serves to protect the surrounding environment from any potential pathogens or toxic compounds. The design of the Class II cabinet is such that there is free access for the operator's hands, but a Perspex cover prevents the operator breathing over the working surface. The HEPA filters are designed to trap extraneous airborne particles or aerosols. They are constructed of a continuous sheet of submicrometer glass fiber folded back and forth over a corrugated spacer as a support. The common HEPA filter in Class II cabinets ensures a 99.99% efficiency of entrapment of 0.3-μm particles. The cabinet should be located in a corner of the laboratory free from draughts and air movement. A source of UV light is an optional feature that can be built into these cabinets. The purpose is that the UV light may be used to maintain sterility when the cabinet is not in use. It is also advisable to spray and wipe the horizontal working surface of the cabinet with 70% ethanol before use.

The Class III cabinet is a totally enclosed system found in specialized laboratories designed to handle high-risk pathogens. This type of cabinet is completely sealed and contains glove pockets to facilitate the manipulation of the cultures. The exhausted air from the cabinet is filtered through at least two HEPA filters to ensure the complete removal of all pathogens. All equipment entering the cabinet is passed through an air lock and removed directly into an autoclave. The Class III cabinets are required for handling highly pathogenic material such as virus-producing human cell lines or tissue samples carrying known human pathogens.

INCUBATORS

Incubators are a basic necessity for maintaining a constant temperature during cell culture, usually at 37 °C for mammalian cells. These incubators may range from temperature-regulated boxes to more elaborate systems that can control temperature, humidity and CO_2 (Fig. 3). These three parameters are essential for maintaining the consistency of culture conditions as well as preserving the viability of the cells. A slight decrease in temperature from the optimal may slow the cell growth rate, but an increase in temperature is likely to be far more detrimental to the cells. Cells will survive at 39 °C for only a few hours, and they will die rapidly at a temperature above 40 °C. Maintenance of a humidified atmosphere is essential to prevent loss of medium by evaporation in nonsealed culture systems such as Petri dishes and multiwell plates or in T-flasks without an airtight cap.

An enriched CO_2 atmosphere of the incubator chamber is usually maintained as a buffering system, which involves an equilibration with the bicarbonate contained in the culture medium. The required level of CO_2 to maintain a culture pH at around 6.9 to 7.4 will depend upon the bicarbonate concentration of the medium (Table 1). Most growth media are rated for either 5% or 10% CO_2, and this necessitates a constant supply of CO_2 into the incubation chamber.

Abnormal CO_2 levels in the incubator are reflected by a change in pH of the culture medium, as observed by the

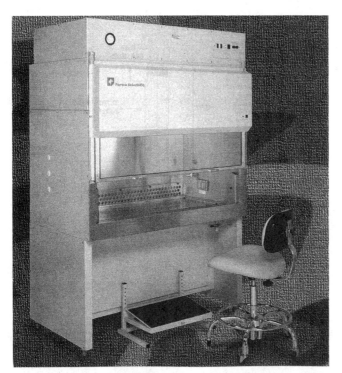

Figure 2. A Class II laminar flow cabinet.

Figure 3. A CO_2 incubator.

Table 1. Recommended Levels of CO_2 in Incubators with Different Media

Bicarbonate in medium (mM)	Recommended CO_2 in incubation chamber	Example of medium
4	Atmospheric	Hank's BSS
26	5%	RPMI 1640
44	10%	DMEM

color. Too low a level of CO_2 causes an increase in culture pH, whereas too high a level of CO_2 causes a decrease in pH. The CO_2 level can be monitored by a Fyrite test kit. In this simple apparatus a gas sample is pumped manually into an absorbing liquid by a rubber bulb. The level the liquid rises in the glass column indicates the percent CO_2.

The disadvantage of the bicarbonate–CO_2 buffer system is that cultures may become alkaline quickly when removed from the incubator. It is also possible to use an organic buffer to maintain culture pH. HEPES (N-2-hydroxyethylpiperazine-N'-2-ethanesulfonic acid; $pK_a = 7.3$ at $37\,°C$) or MOPS (morpholinopropane sulfonic acid; $pK_a = 7.0$ at $37\,°C$) at a concentration of $10-20$ mM will maintain culture pH without an enriched CO_2 atmosphere. In the presence of HEPES the CO_2 level can be reduced to around 2% with a concomitant decrease

in bicarbonate concentration. The organic buffers may be used in addition to the bicarbonate–CO_2 buffering system when a high degree of pH control is required. The disadvantage of using organic buffers is that the medium becomes expensive, and therefore they are not generally used for routine culture.

The CO_2 incubator, in which a fixed CO_2 tension is maintained in a humidified atmosphere, has now become a standard piece of equipment in a cell culture laboratory. In a small lab the CO_2 cylinders are secured to a rack alongside the incubator. Gas is fed via a reducing valve on the cylinder head through pressure tubing to an intake port that passes through a filter before entering the incubation chamber. For older CO_2 incubators there is a constant flow of a CO_2/air mixture, with each gas supplied separately from a different cylinder and mixed to set proportions via gas burettes. This has the disadvantage of excessive usage of CO_2, and if the CO_2 supply runs out, then the constant air flow flushes out any remaining CO_2 from the incubator.

In a modern system two CO_2 cylinders are mounted alongside each incubator. Each cylinder has two regulator valves. One is a high-pressure gauge that measures the pressure in the cylinder with a range of $0-2000$ psi, and the second is a low-pressure gauge ($0-30$ psi) measuring the gas pressure into the incubator. Pressure tubing connects the low-pressure gauges of the two cylinders to a switching device, which if automated will switch the CO_2 supply from cylinder one to cylinder two if the pressure falls below a certain level (typically 4 psi). This automated switchover unit is essential to ensure a constant CO_2 supply (Fig. 4).

The percent CO_2 in the incubation chamber is controlled by a valve governed by intermittent readings of an infrared gas analyzer. Such a sensor system is built into the control box of the incubator and is capable of maintaining a constant CO_2 level to an accuracy of $\pm 0.1\%$. The infrared controller measures the CO_2 level independently of humidity and incorporates a correction for temperature.

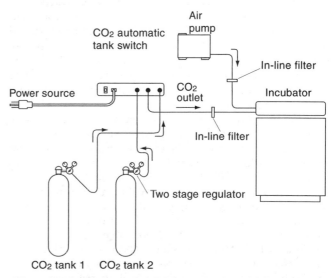

Figure 4. An automated switchover unit for a CO_2 incubator.

Air is normally pumped into the incubation chamber by a small pump via a filter. The circulation of air ensures an even temperature throughout the chamber. The chamber temperature is effectively controlled by a large jacket through which the circulation of water can ensure a uniform temperature of $\pm 0.2\,°C$. Other temperature control devices can be used, but traditionally they have been assumed to be not as good as water jackets in ensuring an even chamber temperature. However, modern direct-heat CO_2 incubators are available with heating elements on all sides of the outer chamber wall. Microprocessor control can ensure thermal stability in these incubators at least as well as in the water-jacketed type. The main advantage of the direct-heat incubators is that they are considerably lighter than the water-jacketed type.

The inner volume of a CO_2 incubator is typically 60 to 220 L. The inner chamber of the incubator is normally sealed by a glass door, and in order to prevent excessive condensation on the glass, a source of radiant heat is provided in the outer door. A water tray in the bottom of the incubator over which air is circulated maintains the humidity. It is important to prevent microbial growth in this water reservoir by the addition of a low concentration of a disinfectant detergent. Routine maintenance requires regular cleaning and disinfection of the inner walls and trays of the chamber, which are made of stainless steel. In some incubator models (e.g., Cytoperm from Heraeus) an automated disinfection routine involves the introduction of hot air at $180\,°C$. For many labs double-cabinet incubators are useful. One chamber is stacked above the other, but they are independently regulated.

LABORATORY-SCALE CULTURE VESSELS

In the past, culture flasks were made of borosilicate glass. The flasks were recycled and required washing and autoclaving before use—a process that could give rise to contamination. However, presterilized plastic flasks suitable for cell culture are now commercially available and are used by most laboratories. The plastic is polystyrene, which is treated to produce a surface amenable for cell attachment and growth. The tissue-grade plastic flasks are sterilized by gamma irradiation and are suitable for single use. The use of presterilized and disposable plastic flasks has significantly reduced any contamination arising from the culture vessels. There is no need for an extensive washing process, which is critical to ensure the complete removal of cytotoxic contaminants from glass containers.

Whatever material is used, the surface charge density is critical for the attachment of cells. Thus the physical and chemical treatment of surfaces has a considerable effect on cell adhesion. New borosilicate glass flasks or bottles often show poor cell adherence, but this can be improved by washing, sterilization, and chemical treatment. An appropriate charge can be placed on the glass by alkali treatment. Typically, this involves addition of 0.1 M EDTA in 0.025 M NaOH at $122\,°C$ for 30 min, followed by washing with sodium carbonate. The negative charge on the surface of the glass can be manipulated by the extent of alkali treatment. The effect of alkali treatment is to rupture the Si—O—Si bonds of the silica network, forming SiO^- residues with counterions of Na^+ on the surface structure. The depth of penetration of Na^+ depends on the extent of treatment. The state of the surface can be quantitatively assessed by the extent of adsorption of the positively charged quaternary ammonium dye, crystal violet (12). Cell attachment can be improved by increasing the negative charge to a level specific for each cell type.

The attachment of the negatively charged cell surface to a negatively charged substratum requires the presence of a divalent cation such as Ca^{2+} and Mg^{2+} in the culture medium. Electron microscopic analysis of the cell–surface interface also shows the presence of a 50 Å protein layer between the cells and the substratum (13). These may originate as surface-active proteins secreted by the cells or from a serum supplement in the growth medium.

The polystyrene used to make most plastic containers is unsuitable as a surface for cell attachment because it is hydrophobic and has no charge. The "tissue-culture-grade" plasticware available from commercial sources is generally made of polystyrene, which is treated to present a negative surface charge. This provides a surface chemistry that is hydrophilic, wettable, and negatively charged. The charge may be provided by sulfonation, which involves short exposure of the polystyrene to sulfuric acid. An alternative is the usual commercial process, corona-oxidation, in which the plastic is exposed to a high-voltage electric arc. This also leads to a surface with a layer of negatively charged groups. The structure of the chemically modified polystyrene is shown in Figure 5. There has been shown to be an optimal surface charge for cell attachment at a negative charge density of $2-10 \times 10^{14}$ charges per cm^2 (14). The polystyrene growth surface may be further modified by applying a variety of anionic and cationic groups, as shown in Figure 5(c). These surfaces may be optimal for the growth of certain specialized cell lines. Sterilized culture flasks of this type are available as Primaria products (Falcon).

Cells have also shown an ability to attach to various positively charged polymers. These include DEAE-dextran, polyacrylamide, polylysine, polyornithine, polyarginine, polyhistidine, and protamine (15). Thus, although the charge density on the surface appears to be a critical parameter, the charge may be positive or negative. Poly-D-lysine of molecular weight in the range 30,000 to 300,000 kD has been used extensively as coating polymer for certain applications to provide a positive charge on glass or plastic (16). Washing a flask with a polylysine solution (10 µg/mL) is generally sufficient to apply the polymer coating. This may be useful to encourage the attachment of cells that usually grow in suspension. The surface charge density can also be manipulated by choosing a selected molecular weight of the polymer.

The choice of culture vessel for the growth of cells is dependent on the scale of operation and whether suspension or anchorage-dependent cells are required. Culture volumes from 10^{-5} to 10^4 L are possible with existing commercially designed equipment. The smaller-volume vessels (Table 2) are generally not equipped with control devices, and it is accepted that pH and oxygen

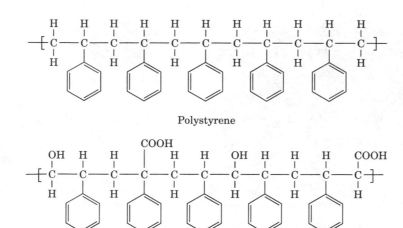

Polystyrene

Traditional Tissue Culture

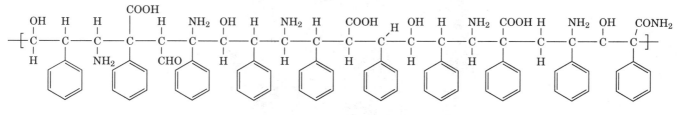

PRIMARIA

Figure 5. The surface chemistry of polystyrene plasticware.

Table 2. Typical Culture Vessels Suitable for Cell Growth

Culture vessel	Number of culture wells/unit	Max. culture volume (mL)	Vessel size	Growth surface (cm²)	Material
Multiple-well plate	96	0.37	10.8 × 6.4 mm (Dxdia.)	0.32	plastic
	24	3.4	17.6 × 15.5 mm	1.88	plastic
	12	6.9	17.6 × 22.1 mm	3.8	plastic
	6	16.8	17.6 × 34.6 mm	9.4	plastic
Medical flat bottle		10	125 mL	22	glass
		15	250 mL	30	glass
Roux bottle		50	500 mL	200	glass
T-flask, 25		5.0	50 mL	25	plastic
75		15–30	250 mL	75	plastic
150		75	600 mL	150	plastic
175		50–100	750 mL	175	plastic
Roller bottle		100–200	1250 mL	490	plastic
		100–250	2200 mL	850	plastic
		100–500	4900 mL	1750	plastic
Spinner flask		100	250 mL		glass
		250	500 mL		glass
		500	1000 mL		glass
		1000	2000 mL		glass
Cell factory, Nunc		1800		6000	plastic

concentrations in culture may fluctuate during cell growth. However, the advantages of these vessels are that they can be handled in replicates, and they are suitable for insertion into CO_2-enriched incubators. Most of these vessels offer a flat surface for cell attachment, although cells may be grown in suspension or surface attached.

The most popular forms of plastic culture containers are multiwell plates, Petri dishes, and flasks (usually referred to as tissue culture flasks or T-flasks) made of tissue-culture-grade polystyrene (Fig. 6). The multiwell plates can accommodate many replicates of small-volume cultures [Fig. 6(a)]. The 24-well plates hold 3 mL per well and are well suited for cell growth experiments, for example, to test for toxicity or stimulatory activity. The 96-well plates hold a volume of 0.3 mL per well and are suitable for cloning. Rapid dispensing of solutions into the

(a)   **(b)**

(c)

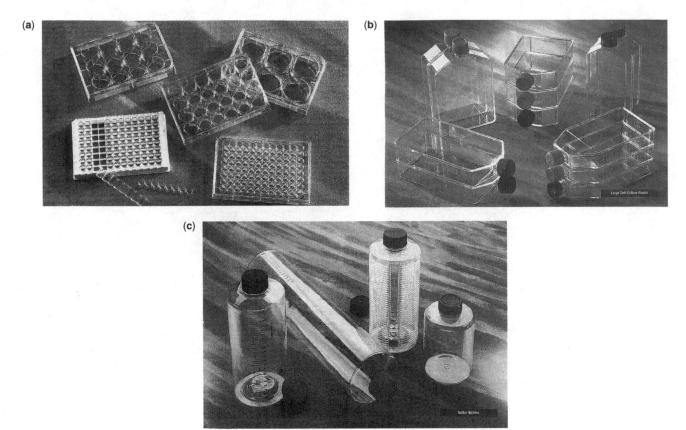

Figure 6. Typical plastic culture vessels: (**a**) multiwell culture plates; (**b**) T-flasks of various sizes; (**c**) roller bottles.

96-well plate is made easy by use of a multiwell pipettor. For some applications porous inserts for multiwell plates are available. These have polycarbonate or polyethylene terephthalate membranes of various pore sizes (0.4–8 μm). Cells can grow over the membrane provided. This may be useful to study cell polarity, as access is provided to the basolateral and apical sides of the cell layer.

The Petri dishes and T-flasks can accommodate cultures of 2–100 mL and are suitable for both anchorage-dependent and suspension cells. The T-flasks are designated by the surface area available for cell attachment [Fig. 6(b)]. Thus T-25, T-75, T-150, and T-175 flasks have growth areas of 25–175 cm^2. A canted (angled) neck is provided so that sterile manipulation is easy. It is important to allow an equilibrium to develop between the gas phase of the flask and the atmosphere of the incubator chamber. The T-flask caps can be adjusted to fit loosely to allow gas exchange with the environment of the incubator. The caps should be closed tightly once the flasks are removed from the incubator. Some T-flasks have a ring of 5 holes in the plastic caps to allow gas exchange through an inner permeable membrane.

Spinner bottles are straight-sided glass flasks containing a suspended central Teflon paddle containing a magnet, which turns and agitates the culture when placed on a magnetic stirrer (Fig. 7). The stirring should be stable over a long period at a rotation speed of between 10 and 300 rpm. The bottle (or flask) is usually fitted with one

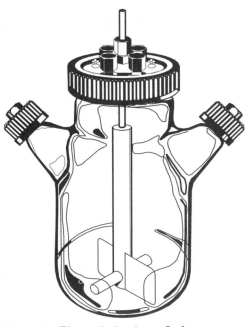

Figure 7. A spinner flask.

or more side arms. These are useful for sampling or as ports for probes or tubing. Spinner bottles can be designed up to a capacity of 5 to 10 L. Cultures above this volume require a top-driven motor for stirring. The spinner bottles are suited for growing suspension cells, although they can be adapted for anchorage-dependent cells by the use of microcarriers. The spinner flasks are usually siliconized to prevent undue attachment of cells to the inner glass surface. This may be performed by application of dimethyldichlorosilane (Repelcote from Sigma).

An appropriately designed stirring base is required for operation of the spinner bottles. Most laboratory stirring bases used for chemical operations are unsuitable because they have an inaccurate speed control and cause excessive heating. The stirring bases used for cultures are required to maintain good speed control for long time periods and without excessive heating. The stirring bases are normally fitted with a tachometer for an accurate indication of the stirring rate. Although these cultures are often established in warm rooms, many CO_2 incubators will also accommodate such a stirring base—the power line may be fitted through a sealable hole provided at the side of the incubator. However, prolonged use of stirring bases in a humidified incubator can cause corrosion of the internal mechanical drives. This problem has been solved by some advanced stirrer modules (e.g., Bellco), which are sealed units placed inside the humidified incubator. A separate master controller, which may control more than one stirrer module is placed outside.

A larger surface area for cell growth is offered in roller bottles, which are cylindrical plastic or glass containers that are placed on their side onto mechanical rollers [Fig. 6(c)]. The rolling mechanism allows the bottles to be rotated gently and the culture medium to flow continuously over the inner surface. On inoculation into the culture medium, the cells attach and grow over the entire inner surface. The bottles are positioned to turn slowly along the long axis at between 5 and 60 rph. The volume of medium added should be just sufficient to provide a shallow covering of the cell monolayer. After each complete turn of a bottle the entire cell monolayer is transiently exposed to the medium. It is important to ensure that the rotation platform is perfectly horizontal, otherwise cells at the high end of a flask will not be in contact with medium.

Roller bottle systems offer the possibility of high yields of anchorage-dependent cells in replicate cultures. They were originally developed for the large-scale culture of anchorage-dependent cells used in the commercial production of viral vaccines. Equipment is available to accommodate up to 30,000 bottles each of 1 L capacity. However, the process is labor intensive, as each roller bottle must be handled individually for media changes or cell harvest. In commercial operations, the bottles may be handled in batches of up to 18 as described by Pania (17) for an operating vaccine production plant in Brescia, Italy. Microcarrier cultures offer an alternative means of producing large quantities of anchorage-dependent cells, and these have now been adopted in most commercial processes for vaccine production.

An alternative culture vessel for producing a large yield of cells on a laboratory scale is the multitray unit called the cell factory (Nunc). This is a plastic container that incorporates 10 large plastic trays sealed together. The total growth surface area is 6000 cm^2. No rolling is

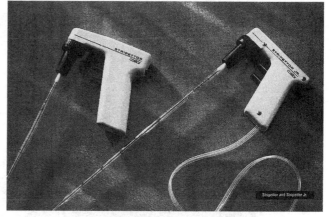

Figure 8. Pipette aid.

required, and a maximum yield of over 10^9 anchorage-dependent cells can be expected. The system is designed for single use.

Transfer of media or cell suspensions from culture vessels can be made with presterilized pipettes, which are available in various sizes and individually wrapped. These liquid manipulations under sterile conditions are conducted with a pipette aid that is lightweight and normally has an adjustable speed setting. These pipette aids are designed for use with sterile pipettes (Fig. 8).

MICROSCOPE

An inverted microscope is essential for examination of a cell culture at regular intervals to monitor the health and growth of cells [Fig. 9(a)]. The design of this microscope with the light source at the top and a long-working-distance condenser allows cells in flasks or even roller bottles to be viewed. Changes in the cell morphology, granularity, and degree of spreading are all indicators that can be monitored by such regular examination.

A standard microscope with a movable side holder is required to count cells in a counting chamber [Fig. 9(b)]. In addition to this, it is worthwhile to inspect cultures under a microscope to determine if there are any significant changes to the appearance of the cells. Both types of microscope are essential for routine monitoring of cells in culture.

CENTRIFUGATION

A low-speed centrifuge is a requirement to harvest cells from culture (Fig. 10). In general, a centrifugal force of $150-200\,g$ for $5-10$ min should be sufficient to separate out cells from culture medium. Higher forces or longer times may cause damage to the cells by compacting them on the bottom of the centrifuge tube. Once centrifugation is completed, the supernatant should be decanted and the cells resuspended. Typically swing-out buckets in a bench centrifuge will accommodate 50 or 15 mL plastic centrifuge tubes. The bucket size required will depend upon the volume of culture to be handled.

(a)   (b)

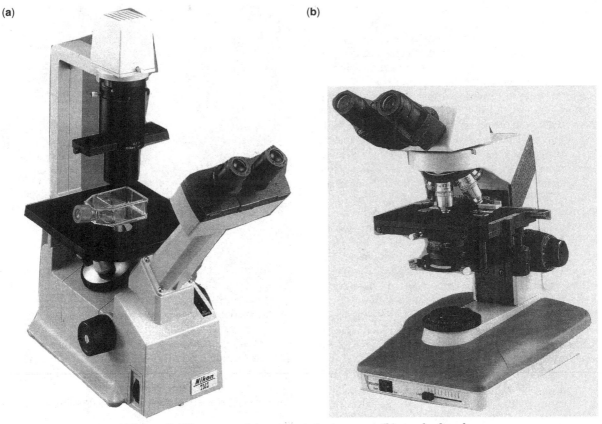

Figure 9. Microscopes: (**a**) an inverted microscope; (**b**) standard mode.

(a)   (b)

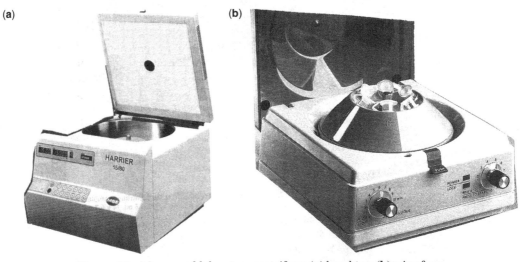

Figure 10. A low-speed laboratory centrifuge: (**a**) benchtop; (**b**) microfuge.

For reasons of safety the centrifuge rotor or individual buckets should be sealable to contain any spillage or breakage. Also, the centrifuge chamber should be sealed. Fine control of braking is desirable, particularly if isolating cells from a concentration gradient. Gentle braking prevents disruption of the separated bands.

A benchtop microfuge may also be useful for higher-speed centrifugation of small volumes of reagents or media samples. These may develop precipitates after freezing.

Also, many analytical techniques performed on cell culture media require precipitation of proteins prior to analysis.

LIQUID NITROGEN STORAGE

Cells can be stored for long periods at subzero temperatures. This permits cell stocks of non-primary cells to be maintained in laboratories without having to resort to primary animal tissue. The maintenance of a cell stock guards against loss of a cell line by contamination or by genetic change. For cells that are grown continuously it is often desirable to store cells after various passages so that any genetic change can be monitored.

For a valuable cell line it is common to maintain a two-tiered cell bank—a master cell bank and a working cell bank. The master bank is a store of cells at early passage and established soon after receiving the original cells. The cells in this bank are thoroughly examined for freedom from contamination and identity. The working bank is a store of cells formed by growth for several passages of one of the master bank samples. Future cell samples are taken from the working cell bank, and the master cell bank is accessed only when absolutely necessary. This practice is common in industrial production when the lifespan of the cell banks is carefully monitored.

Cells can be stored in a suspension (10^7 cells/mL) in a freezing medium that is dispensed into plastic ampoules (typically 2 mL). The freezing medium consists of growth medium or serum supplemented with a cryoprotectant such as 10% glycerol or dimethylsulphoxide (DMSO), which will protect the cells from disruption during the freezing and thawing process. The cells are stable almost indefinitely in the cryoprotectant when held under liquid nitrogen ($-196\,°C$) or in the gas phase above the liquid nitrogen at ($\leq -136\,°C$). Most cell culture laboratories will have liquid nitrogen storage canisters for such a purpose.

The method of freezing and thawing is important to maintain a high viability of the stored cells. Slow freezing and rapid thawing is recommended for maximum cell survival. The cell suspension can be frozen by placing the ampoules containing the cells in a polystyrene box held at $-70\,°C$ overnight. This ensures an initial freezing rate of about $1\,°C/min$, after which time the ampoules are placed directly into liquid nitrogen. Programmable coolers are available to control the rate of cooling. These are based on a slow infusion of liquid nitrogen at a rate determined by the preset cooling program. However, they are not widely used in research labs because of the expense and the fact that there is no great advantage unless it is required to vary the rate of cell freezing. For recovering cells, the ampoules are transferred as quickly as possible from liquid nitrogen to a water bath at $37\,°C$. The water bath should be covered for safety because there is a possibility that a damaged ampoule may explode if liquid nitrogen has penetrated the seal.

A liquid nitrogen freezer can range in capacity from 25 to 500 L and may be narrow necked or wide necked. The freezers require regular addition of liquid nitrogen to replace losses due to evaporation. The wide neck type of freezer has the advantage of easy access, but the rate of liquid nitrogen evaporation is higher. The cells are stored in plastic vials (1–2 mL), which are lowered into liquid nitrogen for long-term storage. These are placed in large drawers (for wide-necked freezers) or attached to metal canes (for narrow-necked freezers). Depending on the size of the freezer, the storage capacity will vary between 250 to 15,000 plastic vials (or ampoules). A capacity for 1200 to 1500 vials is more than adequate for most research labs. Cryogenic plastic vials have strong seals to prevent leakage that could result from large temperature

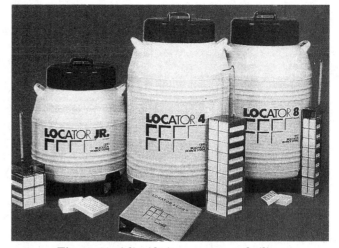

Figure 11. A liquid nitrogen storage facility.

fluctuations. The liquid nitrogen reservoir needs to be monitored at regular intervals, so that the stored vials of cells are maintained frozen. This may be performed with a dipstick. However, many modern freezers are fitted with an automatic indicator with an alarm, which sounds if the liquid nitrogen level gets too low. This lowers the risk of damaging important cell stocks by inadvertently allowing the liquid nitrogen level to drop.

Figure 11 shows typical laboratory cell storage units of different capacities. The cryogenic vials are contained in the plastic boxes, which are stacked in the metal racks before lowering into the liquid nitrogen.

CELL COUNTING

Growth in cultures is normally determined by counting cells at regular intervals—at least once a day. The two direct methods commonly used are manual counting through a microscope or electronic counting by a particle counter. Both methods depend upon obtaining a sample of an even distribution of cells in suspension. Therefore, it is extremely important to ensure that the culture is well mixed by stirring or shaking before taking a sample.

HEMOCYTOMETER

This is a thick glass plate that fits onto the adjustable stage of a microscope. The design most commonly used is the improved Neubauer hemocytometer. A grooved calibrated grid is observed through the microscope on the hemocytometer surface (Fig. 12). This consists of 9 large squares with 1 mm sides. The central square is subdivided into 25 squares, each of which is further subdivided into 16 squares of 0.05×0.05 mm. A cell suspension enters the grid space by touching the end of a capillary tube (or Pasteur pipette) at the edge of a specially designed cover slip placed on the upper surface of the hemocytometer. The position of the cover slip forms a chamber, the sides of which are the calibrated edges of the slide raised exactly 0.1 mm above the ruled surface. The volume contained

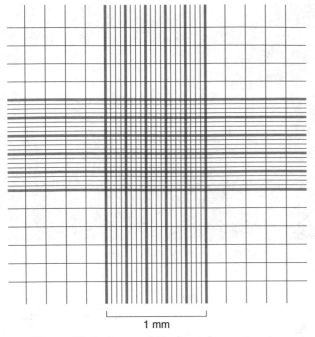

1 mm

Figure 12. An improved Neubauer hemocytometer.

in each of the 9 large squares is $1 \times 1 \times 0.1 = 0.1$ mm^3 ($= 0.1$ μL). The cells are then counted in a standard volume (usually 5×0.1 μL) as defined by the area of the grid. In this case

$$\text{cells per ml} = (\text{total count} \times 10^4)/5$$

A standard microscope at low magnification of $\times 40$ to $\times 100$ is required for viewing the cells. A handheld tally counter helps in counting.

Trypan blue is often added to the cell suspension before counting (18). The dye penetrates the membrane of nonviable cells, which are stained blue and can therefore be distinguished from viable cells. This is the most commonly used assay for cell viability (see article on "Measurement of Cell Viability").

A modification of this method involves counting nuclei. Incubation of cell samples in a mixture of citric acid and crystal violet causes cells to lyse and the released nuclei to stain purple (19). Nuclei counting is well suited for the determination of anchorage-dependent cells, for example, when attached to microcarriers. However, care must be taken in interpreting nuclei counts, as cells can become binucleated, particularly when growth is arrested. As a result the nuclei concentration may be higher than the cell concentration (20).

The hemocytometer counting method is simple and effective but can be laborious if many samples are being analyzed. The expected determined error in cell concentration is around 10%. This can arise from variability in sampling, dilution, mixing, filling the chamber, or counting.

Electronic Counting

The principle of an electronic cell counter (or Coulter counter) is that a predetermined volume (usually 0.5 mL)

of a cell suspension diluted in buffered saline is forced through a small hole (diam. 70 μm) in a tube by suction. As the cells (or any particles) move through the hole, they cause a measurable change in electrical resistance as detected by two electrodes, one inside and one outside the glass tube. This produces a series of pulses recorded as a signal on an oscilloscope. Several thousand particles per second may be counted and sized with accuracy.

The major advantage of this method is the speed of analysis and is therefore suitable for counting a large number of samples. It is also reasonably accurate within an expected counting error of less than 5%. However, the method is based upon the number of particles contained in suspension, and consequently, the proportion of viable cells in the sample cannot be determined. Also it must be ensured that cell aggregates are not present in the sample; otherwise the cell count will be underestimated. Cell suspensions above 10^4 per mL should be diluted, otherwise two or more cells passing through the counting zone at the same time will cause coincidence errors. A standard protocol is to dilute a cell suspension ($\times 20 - \times 40$) in a saline solution (Isoton).

In the simplest instrument (e.g., Coulter model D Industrial) a lower size threshold of counting may be set electronically (Fig. 13). Thus particles smaller than cells (dust or cell fragments) can be eliminated from the count. The largest particle size is determined by the size of the orifice in the tube, which is normally 75 or 100 μm. For routine counting the Coulter Industrial D is more than adequate. In more complex instruments (e.g., Coulter model ZB) lower and upper size thresholds, ("gates") can be set electronically. This allows the size distribution of a cell population to be determined. This requires a size calibration with a standard suspension of particles such as latex beads or pollen grains.

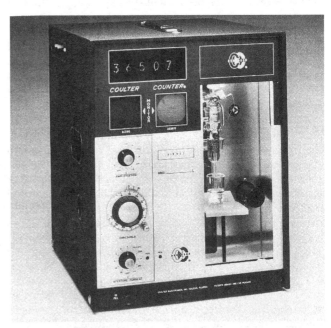

Figure 13. A simple Coulter counter.

OSMOMETER

An important parameter of cell culture medium is the osmotic pressure expressed as osmolarity (number of particles per liter) or osmolality (number of particles per kilogram). Most measuring devices will determine the osmolality, which approximates to the osmolarity in dilute solution. The effect of each component in the medium to the overall osmolarity is additive and dependent upon its dissociation. Therefore, 15 mM glucose will increase the osmolarity by 15 mOsm/L whereas 15 mM NaCl will increase the osmolarity by 30 mOsm/L.

The osmolarity of standard culture medium is approximately 300 mOsm/L and is optimal for most cell lines. Cells can normally tolerate variations within 10% of this value. However, care should be taken in adding supplements to the media, as the osmolarity may be adversely affected.

The osmolarity of a culture may increase during cell growth as a result of the production of low-molecular-weight metabolites such as ammonia and lactic acid. An offline measurement of the osmolarity of the culture may be made with a simple benchtop osmometer. The most common type is based on the measurement of the freezing point of the liquid. The principle is that the freezing point is lowered as the total number of all dissolved particles (ionic and nonionic) is increased. Water has a freezing point of $0\,°C$, whereas a saline solution with an osmolality of 1 Osmol/kg has a freezing point of $-1.858\,°C$. Osmometers will measure the freezing point of a solution in comparison to that of water to an accuracy of $\pm0.001\,°C$. Most models will measure within a range of 0–3000 mOsm/kg. Variations between different models of osmometers include the degree of automation for measuring multiple samples and the sample size required. In a micro-osmometer a sample size of 20–50 µL would be sufficient, whereas samples sizes for a standard instrument are 0.2–2 mL.

BIBLIOGRAPHY

1. J.M. Davis, ed., *Basic Cell Culture: A Practical Approach*, Oxford University Press, Oxford, U.K., 1994.

2. M. Clynes, ed., *Animal Cell Culture Techniques*, Springer-Verlag, Berlin, 1998.

3. A. Doyle and J.B. Griffiths, eds., *Cell and Tissue Culture: Laboratory Procedures in Biotechnology*, Wiley, New York, 1998.

4. N. Jenkins, ed., *Animal Cell Biotechnology: Methods and Protocols*, Humana Press, Clifton, N.J., 1999.

5. S.J. Morgan and D.C. Darling, *Animal Cell Culture*, Bios Scientific, Oxford, U.K., 1993.

6. R.I. Freshney, *Culture of Animal Cells: A Manual of Basic Technique*, Alan R. Liss, New York, 1994.

7. M. Butler, *BASICS: Mammalian Cell Culture and Technology*, Oxford University Press, Oxford, U.K., 1996.

8. M. Butler and M.M. Dawson, eds., *Cell Culture: Labfax*, Bios Scientific, Oxford, U.K., 1992.

9. M. Butler, ed., *Mammalian Cell Biotechnology: A Practical Approach*, Oxford University Press, Oxford, U.K., 1991.

10. C. Wigley, in J.M. Davis, ed., *Basic Cell Culture: A Practical Approach*, Oxford University Press, Oxford, U.K., 1994, pp. 1–26.

11. P.L. Roberts, in J.M. Davis, ed., *Basic Cell Culture: A Practical Approach*, Oxford University Press, Oxford, U.K., 1994, pp. 27–55.

12. C. Rappaport, J.P. Poole, and H.P. Rappaport, *Exp. Cell Res.* **20**, 465–510 (1960).

13. F. Grinnell, *Int. Rev. Cytol.* **53**, 65–144 (1978).

14. N.G. Maroudas, *J. Cell. Physiol.* **90**, 511–519 (1977).

15. W.L. McKeehan, K.A. McKeehan, and R.G. Ham, in Waymouth, et al., eds., *Requirements of Vertebrate Cells In Vitro*, Cambridge University Press, Cambridge, U.K., 1981, pp. 118–130.

16. W.L. McKeehan and R.G. Ham, *J. Cell Biol.* **71**, 727–734 (1976).

17. G.E. Panina, in R.E. Spier and J.B. Griffiths, eds., *Animal Cell Biotechnology*, Vol. 1, Academic Press, London, 1985.

18. M.K. Patterson, *Methods Enzymol.* **58**, 141–152 (1979).

19. K.K. Sanford et al., *J. Natl. Cancer Inst. (U.S.)* **11**, 773–795 (1951).

20. J.M. Berry, E. Huebner, and M. Butler, *Cytotechnology* **21**, 73–80.

See also ASEPTIC TECHNIQUES IN CELL CULTURE; CONTAMINATION DETECTION AND ELIMINATION IN PLANT CELL CULTURE; CONTAMINATION DETECTION IN ANIMAL CELL CULTURE; MICROPROPAGATION OF PLANTS, PRINCIPLES AND PRACTICES; PLANT CELL CULTURE, LABORATORY TECHNIQUES; STERILIZATION AND DECONTAMINATION.

ETHICAL ISSUES IN ANIMAL AND PLANT CELL TECHNOLOGY

R.E. SPIER
University of Surrey
Guildford, Surrey
England

OUTLINE

Ethics Overview

    Ethics

Types of Ethics

Ethics as the Set Point in a Control System

Modulating Human Behaviour

Ethical Systems

Resolving Ethical Conflicts

Ethics, Science, and Engineering

Ethical Issues Common to Both Animal and Plant Cell Technology

    Disaster Scenarios

    Naturalness

    Superseding Deities

    Commercial Exploitation

Ethical Issues Arising from Plant Cell Technology

Ethical Issues in Animal Cell Technology: Overview

ETHICS OVERVIEW

When the *Tour de France* cycle race is brought to a standstill (1) because of a biopharmaceutical made by genetically engineered animal cells in culture, one can begin to appreciate the seriousness of the ethical issues that are engendered through the practice of animal cell technology. Other ethical issues have been construed to justify the uprooting of experimental crops that are known to be based on genetically engineered plant cells (2) National and international legislative assemblies have been actively engaged in enacting legislation that would outlaw the cloning of humans by processes involving the growth of adult human cells in culture prior to extracting an appropriate nucleus that is transferred into an anucleate human ovum creating a preembryo. Biopiracy is a newly defined practice whereby a developed country acquires, by illegal or unethical means, plant materials that, through processes involving plant cell technology, may be converted into profitable biopharmaceuticals. There are many other such issues stemming from activities in the animal and plant cell technology areas. It therefore behooves practitioners and others interested in this area of endeavor to become familiar with the ethical implications of their activities. This is because, in the not too distant past, the society at large has been subjected to the reckless production and distribution of new biopharmaceuticals (e.g., Thalidomide) and foods (e.g., BSE in meat) from which damage has resulted.

Ethics

To appreciate the finer ramifications of the use of the term *ethical implications* it is useful to examine what we mean when we invoke the word *ethics* or its congeners. There are many connotations of the word *ethics*, which include: a dictionary definition of ethics as "Relating to morals; the science of morals; the department of study concerned with the principles of human duty" (Oxford English Dictionary (O.E.D.) 1993). Nevertheless, the word is often used in association with other words such as morals, laws, values, good, right, and benefit. So it would serve us well in this overview section to examine the relationship of ethics to these other concepts.

The O.E.D. definition of *moral* is "Of or pertaining to character or disposition, considered as good or bad, virtuous or vicious; of or pertaining to the distinction between right and wrong, or good and evil, in relation to

the actions; volitions or character of responsible beings; ethical." Its relationship to ethics may be determined from the etymology of the two words. In the Oxford Dictionary of Etymology (O.D.E.), 1966: L. *moralis*, translates to Gr. ηθικος (ethikos), ethical. While some philosophers and writers seek to maintain a distinction in meaning between the two words (ethics being more abstract and theoretical while morals pertains to a person's views of right and wrong, or the teachings of one's conscience), in a work such as this I would hold that the two words, ethics and morals (and their derivatives) may be used interchangeably and connote virtually identical meanings.

A useful way of thinking about ethics is as 'verbal guidelines that are intended to modulate human behavior' (also see the following).

Law is a verbal expression of what a social institution requires with regard to our behavior in relation to other members of the community and their properties. When behavior is in default of the law, sanctions can be expected to result. The laws themselves may be subdivided into categories such as civil, ecclesiastical, and criminal, each with its further subdivisions. Other verbal guidelines for behavior emerge as rights, rules, regulations, statutes, guidelines, codes, injunctions, commandments, traditions, or customs. It is clear, however, that there are ethical guidelines that exist in areas not covered by laws, in any of the latter's manifestations. For example, we do not have laws denoting that people should be totally honest with one another in their conversation and some might indeed be "economical with the truth." However, I would also contend that all that is denoted by laws is also contained within ethics. One might regard the death penalty as unethical but legal, but it is necessary to remember that a majority of the society think otherwise. Although acceptability is not necessarily grounds for ethicality, it is often used as such. Again, there are different ethical systems whose resulting guidelines may be in conflict; so, what is ethical in one ethical system may be unethical for another such system (see the section on ethical systems).

A "right" is that for which one can properly make a claim. In this sense it is part of ethics, as it denotes a suite of ethically acceptable actions. Similarly ethically approved actions may be considered right, while ethically endorsed things or objects may be described as good. While most laws proscribe actions, rights provide entitlements. Thus in the United Nations Declaration of Human Rights of 1948, Article 12 has it that:

No one shall be subject to arbitrary interference with his privacy, family, home or correspondence, nor to attacks upon his honor and reputation. Everyone has the right to the protection of the law against such interference or attacks.

Many such rights are now embodied in laws. Yet these ideational "rights" may be waived by criminal investigation agencies, who have satisfied members of the judiciary that they have a due cause, while engaged in the pursuit of alleged criminals. Declared rights (e.g., ... the right to keep and bear arms ... as in the United States; Article I, Section 9 #13) are legal rights as they are a component part of the Constitution, which provides the legal framework for the operation of the whole society. It should also be noted and stressed that when in receipt of rights, individuals are required to exercise responsibilities. The immunity of the family to violation should be matched by a corresponding pattern of behavior that does not put the wellbeing of society at risk. The right to be armed requires following a gun code that provides for the safety of citizens.

It is also useful to examine the concept of value. Some individuals regard ethics as being dependent on values, whereas the reverse is a more sustainable position. The word *value* comes from the Latin verb *valere*, which means be strong, healthy, effective, worth(y). This leaves open the question of how values are assigned. When, as infants, we begin to perceive the world, the objects and actions we encounter have preassigned values. Those with a high positive value are encouraged and vice versa. Clearly, values are assigned by adults to objects and actions on the basis of what it is that they wish to encourage and promote. In this regard the seemingly ridiculous values placed on rare works of art or jewelry do not so much signify the value of the item *per se*; rather they act as a signal to society of the wealth (status) of the possessor of such items. Hence they are instruments in establishing a dominance hierarchy that seems to be akin to the behavior patterns of our primate forebears. It is in this way that they acquire their value, but it is the ethics of heirarchy formation that enables the worth of the items to be scaled.

TYPES OF ETHICS

It is both customary and confusing to recognize at least three different uses of the word *ethics*. We may, for instance, consider that the determination of the principles of ethics as one such use. As such considerations sit outside most ethical discourse, this area is often referred to as *meta-ethics*. Examples of meta-ethical thinking occur whenever we seek to establish a principle from which we can derive the detailed prescriptions of our day-to-day behavior. If our meta-ethics directed us towards a communitarian course, then we would espouse those patterns of behavior that most benefited the community of which we were a part. If, on the other hand, we adopted a more individualistic mien, then we could expect a greater influence on our behavior to come from such sources as conscience, instincts, emotions, or personal drives.

On a day-to-day basis, we use verbal expressions of how to behave as the matter of our ethics. Such expressions are termed *normative ethics*. Examples of this type of ethics may be gleaned from statements like: do not steal; do not murder; help the less well off. These statements are often derived from some meta-ethical principle. Two kinds of principle may be discerned; the one being *absolute* while the other is *relative*. Absolute ethics are based on texts that are invariant. They are handed down with great care to prevent modifications from generation to generation; the Jewish *Torah*, the Christian *New Testament*, and the Muslim *Koran* are examples of such texts. In the case of relative ethics, the principles are modified to meet with the circumstances. It may therefore be permissible to steal if life-threatening circumstances can, as a result of a theft, be alleviated.

A third kind of ethics is seen when people portray the way other people behave. This is called *descriptive ethics*. Ethologists and ethnologists study the way people behave as either individuals or as members of a racial group, respectively. From such descriptions one may be able to perceive what could be construed as normal or acceptable behavior. This could then go on to form the basis of the way people might be encouraged to behave. It is often found that when panels adjudicating on whether some new biotechnological tool may be used (as, for example, in the use of animal cells in human transplantation), the ethical stance that is taken is based on what the panel thinks is likely to be acceptable to most of the people in the immediate society. Such an approach to ethics is fraught with dangers. From time to time select communities have concurred in the genocide of specific ethnic groups. We have seen ethnic cleansing in the former Yugoslavia as well as in several African countries in recent times. Nevertheless, for issues whose impact is relatively slight (that is, does not involve the wholesale destruction by violent means of established communities), descriptive ethics may be a way to achieve progress and examine in a careful and pragmatic way the potential of the new biotechnological tools that have recently been devised.

ETHICS AS THE SET POINT IN A CONTROL SYSTEM MODULATING HUMAN BEHAVIOUR

The behavior of living organisms is controlled by a variety of mechanisms. At the microscopic level, bacteria and protozoa control the directions in which they move, the way they feed and grow, and how they reproduce. Much is known about the way genes are switched on and off. With multicellular organisms additional chemical elements enter into the control arena, such as hormones. In addition to these ostensibly molecular or chemical methods of controlling behavior, an explanation for the complex behavior of animals is to assert that they are responding to their instincts, where these constitute "An innate propensity in organized beings (esp. in the lower animals), varying with the species, and manifesting itself in acts which appear to be rational, but are performed without conscious adaptation of means to ends" (The Shorter O.E.D, 1933). The building of a hive by bees or an anthill by ants, the nesting/mating activities of birds, and the hunting strategems of wild hyenas and lions may be said to be based on instinctive behaviors. "Conscious adaptation of means to ends" may be identified in the higher mammals and in particular the primates. Hence we now have another source of stimuli for action that is based on the coordinated activity of brain neurons. Humans are unique in that they are able to communicate with one another via the use of words (originating orally/aurally some 100,000–200,000 years ago and represented by tangible symbols about 5,000–6,000 years ago), in sharp contrast to the less precise calls, tweets, barks, howls, squeaks, bellowings, shrieks, etc. of the nonhuman animals. Some such word compositions are used to control human behavior. Words used in this way constitute our ethics and ethical systems.

The verbal formulation of an ethical guideline serves as a "set point" in both the feedforward (quality assurance) and feedback (quality control) systems operating in contemporary societies (3). These set points are derived from answers to meta-ethical programs of discovery. In this they may be influenced by considerations based on theistic systems whose doctrines encourage individuals to seek "salvation" or a life of charity and piety so that they, or their spirit, may, after death, exist in a state of grace or bliss. An alternative, atheistic system, based on the biological nature of humans, would hold that behavior should be based on the objective of human survival. In stating this goal it is most important to note that the concept of human survival is complex. It is not solely based on the survival of individuals, but rather it is most appropriately considered in terms which include the survivability of related or socially connected individuals. This is also to assert that babies and those adults whose means are so slender that they are in danger of starvation naturally consider their personal survival to be paramount. However, for the most part, human survival is to be considered in groups (both multiple and overlapping) that differ in size, complexity, and cohesiveness as time and circumstances dictate.

ETHICAL SYSTEMS

Philosophers who have focused on ethical issues have approached this subject area from a number of contrasting standpoints. Some of the leading contenders for the provision of the principles whereby we decide how to behave are summarized as:

- Golden Rulers assert that "you should do unto others as you would have others do to you". This is a similar position to that taken by Emmanuel Kant (1724–1804), who proposed that you should only do that which you would wish to become a general practice for the society at large (the categorical imperative). Alternative expressions such as "you should not do unto others what you would not wish others to do to you" also hold considerable sway. It may be that the latter formulation is the more prevalent statement.

- Virtue ethicists hold that one should behave according to the dictates of one's conscience, emotions, desires, or instincts. One should seek to acquire a sense of empathy or sympathy with one's fellow citizen and act to protect whatever harmony is engendered by such feelings. It would be easy to confuse this view of virtue ethics with that of a more classical origin. This maintains that one should behave in a manner as defined by the cardinal virtues set out by Greek philosophers (allegedly Socrates) during the classical period. The prime virtues are those of prudence, temperance, fortitude, and justice. To these the apostle Paul added the Christian virtues of faith, hope, and love/charity, where charity has the sense of "love of fellow human." In modern medicine virtue ethics has taken the form of the adoption by a substantial proportion of the medical ethics community of the four principles approach based on the virtues of autonomy, beneficence, nonmaleficence, and justice (4).

- Utilitarians assert that you should do what is most useful or makes you happiest. This is often paraphrased as "the greatest good or greatest happiness for the greatest number" and, as it seems that this is ascertainable by objective means, it becomes a way to solve ethical problems, which is particularly useful to engineers. It is also referred to as consequentialism, as one looks to the consequences of a proposed act before commiting oneself to that act.

- Eudaemonists assert that you should do what makes you and or the community happiest. This derives from Aristotle's dictum that the basis of all behavior is the goal of personal happiness. It may be that the improvement of one's personal or communal chance of survival is a route via which one can obtain happiness, but it would seem that a variety of alternative ends, such as the acquisition of power, money, or sexual profligacy are the ways in which some individuals allege that they find happiness. In this latter case, the survival value of these excesses is more dependent on the determination of the position of that individual in a dominance hierarchy than the actual possession of the goods, which the power or money can achieve.

- Communitarians assert that actions should be determined by what most benefits the community. A subprinciple of this ethic would be that the power to determine how the community acts should be held at that scale of communal operation that is the most suitable. Such power would be devolved to larger groupings of people in such cases as communal defense or policing, or the establishment of a communication system that would unite people over a wide and diversified area.

- Survivalists might assert that you should do that which most promotes survival of yourself and/or your family or tribe and/or other communities and/or other biotic entities. The determination of how this system works is dependent on the variables of wealth (in terms of multiples of the amount of wealth required for survival) and age. Circumstances determine the size, composition, and cohesiveness of the groups, which can be both overlapping and multifarious.

- Concordance (majoritarian, acceptability, democratic, consensus, referendal) ethics requires you to find out what is acceptable to all/the most/a majority and put that agreement into practice. The determination of acceptability may be achieved through questionnaires (referenda) or a group of individuals may take a view of what is, or what is likely to become, acceptable. It should be noted that people are generally resistant to changes in the status quo or of things or situations that are foreign (xenophobia) (5).

- Rights-based ethics; recently we have seen the promulgation of a series of declarations of human rights. The first such may be part of the amended American Constitution of 1791, while a further declaration was issued in 1948 from the United Nations. The Council of Europe (some 40+ nation states) also issued a set of human rights that have been adopted by many of the states of the European Union. These rights are often used as the basis for ethical discussions, as they define the envelope of permitted behaviors.

It is clear that there are a wide variety of principles from which to choose when making an ethical decision. While this may not matter when the outcome is the same, when the outcome is different, it is necessary to resolve the ensuing dispute before the situation becomes uncontrollable.

RESOLVING ETHICAL CONFLICTS

Where protagonists seem to adopt irreconcilable positions, there are a series of practices that can be put in place to aid the resolution of ethical (and other) issues. These reduce to a set of actions, which can include one or more of the following:

- Define the issue over which there is a dispute so that both parties have the same view of the differences between them
- Make sure that what are stated to be the "facts" of the case are indeed those concepts in which people have the greatest sense of confidence
- By examination of the extreme requirements of each protagonist, it may be possible to move to some compromise position in the middle where neither protagonist obtains all that they originally desired
- By the application of the method of *casuistry*, which requires that one of the two ends of the possible action spectrum be taken by a solution that is evidently right while the other end is occupied by a solution that is evident to all to be wrong; we can then move to a solution by interpolating additional cases whose rightness or wrongness are not quite as well defined but on which some agreement can be obtained so as eventually to narrow down the differences to a position on which the agreed action may be based
- Find a technical solution that solves the ethical dilemma (6); for example, were it possible to provide a vaccine that would protect people against infection with the virus that causes AIDS, then this would be a solution to the behavioral problem that would otherwise require people to modify their behavior and use condoms and safe sex in order to prevent infection
- Agree to share the burden that could result from a compromise resolution to the conflict, so that others accept their share of any costs incurred as a result of, say, a newly perceived need to improve performance specifications
- In the event that there are a number of ethical issues, it is useful to come to some agreement as to which of these issues might be considered the most important; the resolution of that concern often opens the door to the elimination of the other differences

- Calculate the consequences of the outcomes of the alternative solutions in a common medium (money, lives, dignity) and agree on a way to maximize the level of this parameter
- Require each protagonist to stand outside the system and view it as if they were a member of an independent arbitration tribunal; compare results and move from this position rather than the *ab initio* situation
- Obtain the agreement of the disputants that the resolution of the difference will provide mutual benefits that could not otherwise be obtained; once this has been ascertained, the examination of the issues may begin afresh
- Enclose the disputants in a confined space and coerce them to resolve their differences (decrease the temperature, quality of the food and beverages, amount of space available ... as for the procedures used for the selection of a new Pope).

The most difficult disputes to solve are those that involve the lives of humans or animals. For some who stand on absolute principles, it is not enough to equate the value of a human life at £750,000 for a road user, and £2,000,000 if a railway user (7) or the comparatively paltry assessment of the courts when awarding damages of £20,000–£1,000,000 (based on a calculation of lifetime earnings foregone) until November 1998, when an award of £3.9 million was made to a 17 year old damaged in an operation at age 5. Others will not, or cannot, put a price on a life saved. All lives are considered to be infinitely valuable, including those of some (all) animals. Therefore, they would argue, it *is* justified to spend all our resources to save the life of a one cat, canary, or child. For these individuals, balloon or life raft debates would result in the loss of all lives rather than the sacrifice of one or other life for the survival of the remaining human beings.

In practice we do not behave in this way. Each structure we build, each car or airplane we construct, or each bridge we design can fail under unforeseen conditions of weather, loading, or part defect. To guard against, and prevent, all putative disaster possibilities would require infinite resources; so risks are taken. Thus we can be seen to value our lives in proportion to the level of risk to which we voluntarily expose ourselves (Table 1). So, by an examination of the ways in which we actually behave, it should be possible to reach an accommodation with even those absolutists, who assert that the Deity made all his creatures of equal value. This can be done by asking them some pointed questions about how they would *actually* behave in particular situations as opposed to how they *would like* to behave, as they do not, in reality, possess infinite resources.

ETHICS, SCIENCE, AND ENGINEERING

It is implicit in the development of animal and plant cell technology that both new knowledge and new practical manifestations of that knowledge will be created. There are many ethical issues that have emerged as a result

Table 1. Disasters in Perspective

	Deaths/100K popln/annum (U.K.) (1980s)
Rail	0.2
Home fires	1
Homicide	1.2
Manufacturing industry	2
AIDS	7
Household accident	8
of which falls	3.2
Road transport	10
of which alcohol	2
Agriculture industry	10
Mining	20
Lung cancer in 55–64 year olds	100

From Social Trends, HMSO, London.

of scientists and engineers having been engaged in these innovative processes (8,9).

For example, scientists have been known to falsify data, to invent data, and to steal data from others (plagiarism) or to publish the same work in a variety of journals. Other areas of scientific misconduct have included the exploitation of students and the sexual harassment of co-workers. Issues of authorship (particularly "gift" authorship to individuals who have not made any contribution to the investigation or its publication) and taking advantage of having privileged information contained in a paper under review, or a grant application that has been submitted, are less well-documented deviations from proper behavior. The deliberate withholding of data or its selective transmission is also fraught with opportunities for inappropriate behavior. This has led to the setting up of an "Office of Research Integrity" in the U.S. and to the requirement for universities to establish Ethics Committees to vet projects for the prospects of malpractice and conflicts of interest. While much of this misconduct is not made public, there are documented sources that report on those cases that have become notorious (10–12).

Similar issues to the preceding appear in engineering institutions, but here, as the work is nearer the marketplace, issues of whistleblowing occur. In these cases the whistleblower's career is severely jeopardized, and while attempting to raise social behavior to a higher moral plane, the whistleblower is categorized as a sort of pariah by the colleagues of the person whose misdeeds have been made public. There are also many malpractices that occur as a result of "conflicts of interest," so much so that it is becoming increasing common for journals to insist on the authors of articles reporting the sources of their funding. Coupled with the need to comply to commercial pressures, engineers may present the prospects of their future successes in terms that belie realities. Dishonesty in such communications is often at the base of much "overselling" of both projects and persons. Judgements of product or process safety and hazard are often subject to commercial considerations, as are activities that may lead to unacceptable or even illegal pollution of the environment (13,14).

ETHICAL ISSUES COMMON TO BOTH ANIMAL AND PLANT CELL TECHNOLOGY

There are four ethical issues that are commonly used to challenge the continuing development of the modern biotechnologies. These are:

- That in modifying the genomes of cells and organisms we will, unpredictably, create a doomsday monster resulting in a major disaster
- That it is not natural deliberately to alter the genomes of organisms
- That one would usurp the function of a deity in creating living beings with characteristics based on human designs
- Industry will benefit most while people in developing countries will suffer

Disaster Scenarios

The media is replete with articles evoking the image conjured up by Mary Shelley in 1818 of the large and ugly humanoid entity both created and deserted by the fictional character Victor Frankenstein. This entity was a conglomeration of oversized human parts that, as a result of a lack of courage and understanding on the part of its creator, caused a number of fatalities before remorse set in, which led to its demise. The genetic modification of animal and plant cells is often alleged to be about to give rise to a doomsday organism that, through an all-pervasive plague, causes the end of humanity. To support such contentions we are led to envisage a takeover of arable farmland by a noxious weed that is resistant to all forms of chemical weed killer. An alternative scenario is that by transferring cells from one species of animal to another (xenotransplantation), the endogenous defective and latent viruses would be revived by their juxtaposition with genes from the host organism that are not defective. This could create a new virus that could have effects similar to, or worse than, the epidemic caused by the human immunodeficiency virus, HIV.

It is facile to beat a drum to the tune of the unforeseen disaster. The future is unpredictable because we do not have, nor will we ever have, the necessary knowledge to make the required calculations (this follows from Heisenberg's Uncertainty Principle of 1927, which may be paraphrased "that the position and the velocity of an object cannot both be measured exactly, at the same time, even in theory"). Asteroids, earthquakes, volcanic eruptions, tornadoes, tsunamis, floods, and sunspot cycles all provide unpredictable elements of *major* consequence to life on earth. By contrast, we have, more or less, been able to cope with the translocation of various biological species to new habitats (15). And this includes the introduction of the rabbit to Australia, the potato to the eastern world, water hyacinth into Papua and Aswan, and Africanized killer bees into the Americas. In each of these cases where the newly introduced organisms became a pest, our response has been to find another biological organism that can limit the growth of the pest without itself becoming a nuisance.

Nevertheless, we seek to protect ourselves against future distress by the implementation of *regulatory processes.*

Regulatory Processes. In the determination of those aspects of behavior that are likely to affect our societies, we establish special rules and regulations to control otherwise unbridled practices. For food, pharmaceuticals, the products of commerce and manufacturing industries, most countries have a well-developed set of laws and statues governing behavior. For animal and plant cell technologists there are well-established regulatory agencies (see the section on Good Manufacturing Practice and Licensing) to provide licences for companies and individuals to produce and market products to those who are willing to buy. In the case of animal cell products used as pharmaceuticals, the work involved in providing the necessary data via a three-stage process may amount to $200–600 million over a period of 3–10 years. These expenditures, which are primarily directed at the establishment of product safety, efficacy, and consistency of the production process, may well be criticized as they drive up the cost of the final product to the customer. This means that poorer people who are not protected by health-care schemes will not be able to avail themselves of the most advantageous materials for their health care. This is particularly acute in developing countries. There is therefore an ethical case to reduce the certainty that the products are as safe as it is possible to make them, in exchange for a greater availability at lower cost to a greater number. However, the regulatory agencies that operate in these areas are not constituted easily to determine how much risk society is prepared to accept; perhaps this is one area for future examination and development. For plant cell products the process is shorter and less costly, but nonetheless it takes years and involves animal feeding experiments as well as field test studies.

But regulation is not a once and for all time activity. There is a constant need to monitor the situation in the field. This requires the establishment and operation of specialized laboratories, trained personnel, and the necessary legislative authority to travel, gain access, and take samples from whatever might be judged indicative of the way a pharmaceutical or genetically engineered crop plant is behaving in use. These operations and practices have been ongoing for many years, but it is clear the public, as a whole, has not been well informed of these safeguards. Much of the recent criticism of modern biotechnology stems from a poorly informed public coupled to the pressing requirements of media personnel to highlight the new and the controversial aspects of any discovery or invention. This often leads them to present with an equal weighting (time allocated) both sides of the argument even though it is clear to most reasonable people that one view of events should prevail. This even-handedness has provided many nongovernmental organizations with platforms to present opinions (or soundbites) that emphasize those aspects of the issue that are intended to lead to an increase in the fear or distaste of listeners, viewers, or readers to the more progressive or advanced developments in, say, biotechnology. It now becomes part of the ethically driven aspects of being a scientist and/or engineer to engage more

effectively in presenting to the public the advantages and safeguards that are inherent with any development of the product profile of the area. Openness, communication, availability are becoming the hallmark of the way the new ethic is permeating the field. This, coupled with appropriately labeled products, could begin to forge a new relationship between those who are riding the tidal wave of new developments in the biotechnologies and the people to whom these benefits are directed.

Ethical Issues in Clinical Trials. Before a licence to market a drug, pharmaceutical, or vaccine can be obtained, extensive trials occur in three or more phases (see Regulatory Processes). This requirement follows from the disasters caused by the incautious distribution and use of Thalidomide, a drug that, when taken by pregnant women to calm their headaches, damaged the fetus *in utero.* In proceeding with these phased trials it is necessary to conduct experiments on humans. But following the Nuremberg trials of the mid-1940s, which brought to light the atrocious experiments conducted on prisoners of the Third Reich, a series of laws were agreed internationally to govern the conditions for future experiments with human subjects. It is now the case that when human patients are involved in such trials it is obligatory to acquire the informed consent of such individuals. While most trials proceed on the basis of a patient's willingness to be an experimental subject, in other instances the patient is asked to participate in a pretrial review of the implications of his/her involvement. This may be followed up by some written statement or multiple choice questionnaire to determine whether the putative patient has understood the implications of the engagement. Additionally, the subjects have to show that they do not need to be on the trial (financially) and do not benefit excessively by their involvement. Cases where prospective trial subjects are not in a fit condition to give informed consent (babies, the mentally sick, the unconscious, or comatose) may be introduced into trials by responsible adults who have an official guardianship or legal authority to make such decisions. A more recent relaxation of the informed consent guideline occurs when a doctor wishes to test an experimental procedure, which is under development as a therapeutic process, on people who are presented under emergency conditions.

Randomly selected subjects, in double blind (neither the patients nor the doctors know whether the subject is being treated with the test material, placebo, or the best available alternative from current practice) controlled trials are the basis on which trials proceed. Data from tests on the people involved are collected and at the *end of the trial* the key to which subject received what treatment is added into the data set so that the appropriate comparisons and correlations can be made. However, those conducting the trial are not insensitive to the progress of the trial, and their prior knowledge of the likely outcomes may predispose them to guess as to how the trial is progressing. For example, if it is clear that the test material is efficacious and the people on the placebo are running the risk of catching a disease or facing the worsening of a disease state, then it would not be ethical to proceed with the trial and deny to the placebo arm of the trial the advantages of the test material. Most trials are not so clear cut, and it is often necessary to keep them going for several years to assure the investigators and the regulators that the long-term effects or side reactions of the test materials are not such as to cause problems.

As the therapeutic and vaccinal materials are applied to humans and may ameliorate health, the substances involved may acquire considerable value. This attracts unscrupulous individuals and companies to promote these materials and to effect trials in such a manner as to give the greatest likelihood of a health-promoting outcome. This has led to a distinction between the determination of efficacy (done under carefully controlled conditions designed to enhance the differences between the test material *vis à vis* alternatives) and efficiency (which is the effect of the test material when it is used by people under uncontrolled conditions and subject to the vicissitudes of external influences). Additional bias may be introduced into such studies when companies commission work in academic establishments. The latter may benefit financially from such contracts with a consequence that the chief scientist on the project might find it convenient to present the best possible picture to the industrial contractor. This could involve careful selection of which data to present and the manner of that presentation. It could also involve the inclusion in trials of people who do not meet the criteria of selection which were agreed to by the local ethics committee. Inconvenient data points may be discounted as being "untypical of the experiment." There are also instances where the academics have wished to present data that are damaging to a company's product and have been forbidden to do so by the company. When companies contract out their product evaluations, the possibilities of bias in the resulting reports are not insignificant. Recent experiences may lead to the conclusion that data production and analysis with the least bias may be most effectively achieved when socially sponsored laboratories are engaged to evaluate such products. Under these conditions the financial well being of neither the laboratory nor the investigating scientists is involved in the examination; so one might expect a result with the least bias and hence the greatest social value (16).

Another consideration has emerged in the past 20 years, when a large number (several hundred) of small biotechnology companies have been founded. Many of these companies are engaged in generating products for the human health-care market using animal and plant cell technology. They are subject to intense pressure to succeed by their share holders and financial backers. As they normally start with a vision and some basic technology or "product in embryo," the initial cash flow of these companies is highly negative. Whether they can succeed will depend on how quickly they can convert this negative cash flow to a positive income stream of substantial magnitude. This, in turn, depends on how their products fare in the type of clinical trial discussed. To keep the investors from withdrawing funds, the company feels compelled to make statements to the press on the progress of the product lines it is seekinga to commercialize or

license. There are cases where the material of such press releases is less than revealing of the actual situation. There are also situations where the personnel of the companies, fortified with internal information as to the likely outcome of a clinical trial, have dealt in the shares of the company to their own benefit. Some such instances have come to the attention of the wider public, with a consequence that the value of companies operating in the same area has been depressed. These disservices to the developing biotechnologies may be prevented were the company executives better educated and informed of their ethical and legal responsibilities. The virtues of honesty, openness, fairness, and prudence have to become pervasive and characterize behavior in this area.

Naturalness

Naturalness has, for some, become a guiding principle. Individuals criticize genetically engineered organisms for being "unnatural." But is this the case? There is some confusion in the application of this term to events that happen in the world. We do define a category of activities we call "artificial" or as a transliteration "made by the application of art." The word *art* has the connotations of skill, craft, ability, or aptitude. But in its usage, artificial has come to mean false, fake, counterfeit, as well as unreal and unnatural. Yet if naturalness directs us to examine what is in nature, and what is other than miraculous or spiritual, then we find that artificial entities are just as much a part of this natural world as are bird's nests, anthills, or beehives, in which case the designation of a genetically engineered cell as unnatural is insecure.

Indeed, "nature" has been doing genetic engineering for as long as living organisms have existed. Viruses act as a transportation system, shuttling whole genes from one organism to another. But the origin of animal and plant cells by the amalgamation of a number of different types of prokaryotic cell is also a way that cells can incorporate whole genomes and make revolutionary changes as part of the evolutionary process. (This process may account for rates of evolution vastly in excess of what could be achieved by single base mutations that are held to provide the minute variations called for in Darwin's theory of evolution by natural selection. Such wholesale mergings of genomes may, in part, account for the step changes in evolution designated as punctuated evolution.) The key difference that delineates the human genetic engineer from the natural processes is that in the case of the former there is an attempt to achieve a deliberately designed end, whereas in the latter case, nature does not have a particular end in view. However, the insertion of a particular gene into a cell is fraught with uncertainties as to where that gene will become incorporated in the genome and how many copies will be made when the cell replicates. Such position effects are crucial to the timing and efficacy of the expression of the exogenous gene. So the engineers resort to the selection, from a number of engineered cells, of the particular cell that gives the result closest to the objectives sought. This increases the rate of production of novel organisms having properties considered desirable. But it can hardly be called an unnatural process, relying, as it does, on the "natural" biochemical components and reactions that have been changing and evolving for the past 4 billion years.

A corrollary to the charge that genetic engineering is not natural is that it is contrary to the notional wishes of planet Earth. Since the establishment of the Gaia model in the 1970s by the British chemist James E. Lovelock about the way the Earth performs, it has become commonplace for individuals to assert that what humans are doing could in some way prevent the Earth from achieving its goals, one of which is the maintainance of an environment suitable for the existence of life. This approach is still controversial and is difficult to maintain, as the Earth is not in control of its macroenvironment, which is more determined by its position in a particular solar system and by the way the nuclear reactions of the Sun are likely to progress as that star ages and runs out of fuel.

Superseding Deities

The Old Testament states that God created the plants, animals, and the man Adam. From Adam he took some cells (a rib; Genesis 2:21–22) and made the woman Eve. (If true, this would have been the first cloning process and would have resulted in another man—in the absence of environmental chemicals.) He also created man in his own image (Genesis 1:26). Are we not, therefore, usurping a function of the deity by deliberately making changes to that which was "created in his image"? (17). But many men shave their beards, cut their hair, and become circumcised (as commanded; Genesis 17:10–14); women have used makeup and pared their fingernails since recorded history. The dogs, cows, horses, camels, and turkeys we have today are not like their historical progenitors of 10,000 years ago. Indeed, if we accept the alternative story to account for the origin of humans by the process of evolution, we have to imagine that some 4–8 million years ago the ancestor of the modern human would have looked like a member of the ape/chimpanzee/bonobo assemblage. Some 750 to 1,500 mutations later *Homo sapiens sapiens* emerged. It would be difficult not to conceive a similar, if not greater, change taking place over the next 4 or so million years. In the future it is possible to envisage the origination of a new species of hominid, given our ability to use genetic vectors (based on modified viruses grown in animal cells in culture) to alter the genome of contemporary humans. A new suite of ethics is needed to handle this imminent manifestation of our newfound biotechnological art. It could be the most challenging task that has ever been presented to the human species. Yet, perhaps this is what God intended. There is little doubt that the creation of a being with human abilities would result in those endowments being used to lead to the development of the next stage of evolutionary progress.

Commercial Exploitation

The fourth argument is that the main beneficiary for genetically engineered organisms is the company that produces them. Is this something that requires ethical examination? Industry's functions include the need to survive, to provide a workplace for its employees and

profits for the shareholders. Should this be objectionable, then there would be dissension against all industrial activity and not just at that fraction that deals with genetically engineered organisms. That industry seeks to obtain monopoly positions should also not be surprising. The patent system provides limited-period monopolies for inventions in exchange for the complete disclosure of the invention in a manner that can be replicated by someone "skilled in the art." Patents promote inventiveness; they do not provide ownership of intellectual property beyond the time for which the monopoly is granted (16–20 years). Any transformation of this system requires a radical overhaul of the basic political structure of our societies, a task that is beyond the scope of this entry.

There are, however, weighty considerations pertaining to the use of genetically engineered plants, which may be so modified that where once they would only grow in a developing country they may now grow in a developed country. This means that the developing country is deprived of income from the export of such plant materials. The development of plant varieties to meet local conditions has become so effective that the yields of most crop plants, including those grown in developing countries, has multiplied considerably in recent years. There is, therefore, reason to believe that genetically modified crops will also provide their share of benefit to the developing world as they will for the developed world: Such outcomes are not mutually exclusive.

An additional consequence of advances in the productivity of food-yielding plants is that farms become more efficient and expand, with a resulting displacement of less efficient farmers who often operate smaller holdings. This seeming job decrease may be compensated by increase in jobs in other sectors of the economy. In the UK at the turn of the twentieth century some 70% of the labor force was employed on the land, whereas, at the close of the same century that number had dropped to less than 2% (18). It is clear that the redeployment of labor is a consequence of increases in the standard and quality of life.

ETHICAL ISSUES ARISING FROM PLANT CELL TECHNOLOGY

The battery of techniques, tools, and facilities that have been described in other parts of this encyclopedia enable us to make genetically modified plants. These can be used in both traditional applications and also for some nontraditional purposes, such as the manufacture of animal or human vaccines that will protect against diseases caused by viruses and other microorganisms. These new possibilities and the ethical problems they engender will be dealt with in the subsection on ethical issues raised by vaccines. In general, it is possible to catagorize the three leading uses of genetically engineered plants as (1) modification of plant enzymes to increase the shelf life of plant food materials, (2) the production of new plant cell lines such as rape seed lines, which do not produce human toxins, and (3) plants that are resistant to herbicides or pesticides or both.

From the diversity of the different ethical systems, it is clear that people who cleave to one such viewpoint may have differences of opinion to others who adopt a contrasting ethical system. In practice there are methods for the resolution of disputes between such individuals, but in this exposition of the issues, it is not useful to show how each system will deal with the new and problematic area. However, for each of the cases presented it is important to show the extent to which there is a really new problem and to endeavor to establish the probability of its occurrence and its magnitude. Once these parameters have been ascertained it would be possible to determine the likely acceptability of the new development. This process has two facets. The one relates to the process of implementation of the new departure, while the second concerns the nature of the novel entity.

Most people would agree that a careful, prudent, and pragmatic approach to the introduction of new technologies is to be preferred. This requires that we base our actions and behaviors on what we observe to be the case, coupled with a suite of understandings derived from immediately relevant experiments, rather than on notions that predict from fundamental theoretical reasonings what ought to be the outcome: These latter rationalizations are rarely of predictive value in practice. It also means that we move in small steps and at each stage of the operation we make sure that we can control all foreseeable developments, especially those that could negate any benefits we hope to accrue.

The consequences of the introduction of a novel product into the marketplace cannot be predicted with a high degree of certainty. Again, we can adopt a careful, prudent, and pragmatic approach and watch what happens with such insertions. In the absence of consumer acceptance the feedback to the producer will be wholly negative and the product will no longer be made. When, however, there is a strong and unsatisfied consumer demand, we have to ask whether, in spite of its clear acceptance by the customer, the product is making a beneficial contribution to the life and wellbeing of the community. Plant-derived opiates may be in demand by some sections of the community, but they are outlawed by the society at large because of the alleged negative effects that would result were they freely available. (It should be noted that such drugs were only outlawed in the early years of this century; before that, they were purchasable as any other commodity.) (The principal U.S. legislation has been the Harrison Narcotics Act of 1914, the Opium Poppy Control Act of 1942, and the Narcotic Drug Control Act of 1956; the Drug Abuse Control Amendment of 1965 added controls over depressant, stimulant, and hallucinogenic drugs not covered under the other narcotic control acts (19). Nevertheless, in the absence of clear evidence of harmful effects (generally to health, but there could also be ecological damage) in either the short term or the long term, it is likely that there will be a general acceptance of the product.

This approach to the ethicality of new developments in plant cell biotechnology is clearly based on the ethical principle, that "what is accepted can be progressed." All we have to do is to determine the acceptability (or otherwise). While this ethic is in itself a pragmatic response to a need to make a practical determination in the face of changing circumstances, it does not mean that this is either the only

approach or even the correct approach. Perhaps when our judgmental systems increase in sophistication, we may ask questions more relevant to the beneficial aspects of new products. But before we do that we have to have a clear notion of what we mean by beneficial, and that is still in dispute. This author would advance the notion that a developed interpretation of a survivalist objective would provide such answers, but not all would agree.

Ethics and New Plant Foods. The thought that the genetic composition of our food materials may have been deliberately altered has inspired many to examine the issues of the genetic engineering of plants thoroughly (20). In November 1994 a consensus conference was held in London to examine the concerns of a wide cross section of people on plant biotechnology (21). This was an acute issue at this time as the "flavor-saver" tomato, based on a construct designed to express an enzyme that delayed ripening, had just received its distribution licence. The outcome of this conference was that the lay panel wanted genetically engineered food to be clearly labeled as such, with the ready availability of comprehensive information on the changes that had been engineered into each product. (In such labeling it would be difficult to communicate the concept that the additional enzyme is but one of 10,000–100,000 proteins and is indistinguishable from them except by sophisticated biochemical techniques.) The food distributors at the time held that the special labeling might stigmatize the product so that people would be reluctant to purchase it (as had been the case, uniquely in the UK, when γ-ray-sterilized foods appeared on supermarket shelves). However, recent experience has shown that the labeling of tomato puree as being derived from a genetically engineered tomato had increased sales (although a contributory factor could have been a marginally lower price).

While the present concerns have centered on the newly engineered variants of common food plants, over the past century there has been a continual change in the genetics of these plants through a concerted mutation, crossing, and selection process that has resulted in much higher-yielding types of crop plants. Such plants may have smaller stems and dispose of more of their resources to the edible components. They also account for our ability to keep up with an expanding world population. So there is an illogicality in an objection to newly genetically engineered plants because they have been so modified. Rather we have to look for other reasons for the basis of the strength of the rejectionists views (22). One ethical objection made to such developments is that the companies supplying the seeds for such modified plants obtain a monopolistic position such that they can exploit the market. A corollary to this is that such plants may be engineered to yield sterile seeds. However, while a battery of genes (terminator genes) may confer this (23), an international research group has recommended to its 16 research institutes that the terminator technology is banned. Other ethical aspects are dealt with in sections on ethical issues common to animal and plant cell technology and the ethical issues on patents.

Were developed nations to become so competent that they were able to produce all the food and plant materials they wanted from indigenous plants and their genetically engineered variants, then there could be knock-on negative effects to the developing world that once supplied this market. For example, a company called RiceTech has invested a new rice they claim is indistinguishable from Indian-grown Basmati rice. While it is difficult to see how they can market the rice under a "Basmati" label, it would not be impossible to persuade an American public to purchase a home-grown *equivalent* to the Indian variety (24). Efforts have to be directed towards some form of compensation for market losses of this nature.

Other ways in which the markets for food and plant-sourced commodities may be jeopardized is through the genetic engineering of indigenous plants to produce the materials that were once the exclusive capability of plants grown only in developing countries. For example, it is possible to engineer plants that normally grow in temperate climates to produce cocoa butter and palm oil. This would have profound economic effects for African and Asian farmers. However, the magnitudes of such effects and their longevity may be exaggerated as plant species indigenous to one country have been cultivated elsewhere on many occasions in the past (e.g., potato, rice, rubber trees, mulberry trees, oil palms, grape vines, etc.). Nevertheless, we have a duty of care to ascertain that any such transposition is effected with the minimum harm to the indigenous communities coupled with appropriate schemes for compensation and crop diversification.

The incorporation of genetically engineered soya beans into a stored mass of nonengineered soya beans has aroused considerable concern recently (25). The ethical issue here is that people assert the right to choose the food they eat, and if they have objections to eating genetically engineered food for the general reasons set out in in the section on ethical issues common to both animal and plant cell technology, then they would wish to exercise the right not to have to eat products made from soya beans that could contain a proportion of the genetically engineered material. In the complex contemporary market place, many hundreds of derivative products may contain soya bean derivative inclusions. These would be regarded as forbidden to those with objections. As the material quality of such foods would be indistinguishable from foods that did not contain any material from a genetically engineered plant source (except when sophisticated biotechnological techniques are deployed), it is not reasonable that a minority of individuals, who are uncompromising in their views, exercise a stranglehold on the emergence of new technologies, particularly as the new materials are just as benign as the old variety.

The addition of the toxin gene from *Bacillus thuringiensis* (Bt) to plants to make them resistant to attack by insects is an effective way of increasing yields and decreasing the uses of insecticides. However, the protein involved is an animal (albeit, insect) toxin; so other animals that eat the insects that have fed on the modified plants may also become sick. This would result in a reassortment of the species inhabiting the locality; a process that is not unusual in most ecosystems.

There is also the prospect that strains of insect will be selected that are resistant to the toxin material made by the plant. To counter this eventuality, it is advised that crops modified with the Bt addition constitute less than 80% of any one ecosystem. This will enable normal populations of insects to outnumber the resistant variants and prevent the establishment of the variant as the dominant species.

Other efforts to produce insect- and fungus-resistant plants have relied on the transposition of the genes that code for plant lectins. Some such materials are highly toxic: The lectin ricin from castor oil plants is a human toxin with a lethal dose that will kill 50% of mice of 100 ng/kg. The examination of food materials that could contain such a protein will need to be extensive. Clearly, the cooked/uncooked state of the material is a determinant of its safety to humans; and we are well aware that many ordinary plant products need to be processed before they can be eaten safely. It is essential, therefore, that information to the public about such experiments be full and comprehensive and that judgment should await the outcome of the regulatory agency investigation as to the suitability of such products for the domestic market.

Ethics and Biodiversity. Biodiversity, or the number of species per unit area, is a parameter whose value has varied throughout biological time. Over the past 250 million years the number of species on this planet (as judged by the fossil record) has fluctuated considerably. There have been about five occasions when some 70–90% of all the then present species became extinct (26). The last such was the event 65 million years ago that led to the demise of the dinosaurs and the emergence of the mammals. So a result of the disappearance of old species is to provide new species opportunities to take the ecological niches vacated by the species that passed on. Therefore, the world-wide ecosystem is already conversant with wild changes in the number of species.

As new plant variants come on stream, they tend to dominate the agricultural practice of the day and, as monocultures, they are uniformly susceptible to particular pests or viruses. However, they tend to be backed up by other variants, which, although, not as productive are less susceptible to these attacks. Another safeguard against crop annihilation is to so engineer them that they become resistant to all the known pathogens. Whether it causes more benefit than harm to proceed in this way is still an open question. It is clear that increases in agricultural efficiency stemming from the monoculture approach is of value, but this is achieved at the expense of the decrease in the opportunities for improvement that could have resulted from an unknown variant that was not provided with a chance to express its capabilities to the full. At this time the balance of benefit is with the monoculturists, but it is essential that we bear in mind the inherent weaknesses of this approach and prepare ourselves to respond rapidly and overcome the problems resulting from wipeouts.

A second aspect of biodiversity is based on a decrease in the number of species of plants in those parts of the tropical rain forests that have been denuded of trees to make way for other forms of agriculture. The loss of these plants is thought to result in a decrease in the possibilities for the discovery of medicinals: a serious consideration, as some 80–90% of our current pharmaceutical drug list is derived from plant-based products. Nevertheless, there has been a revolution in strategies of the pharmaceutical companies who use their knowledge of the three-dimensional molecular structures of existing biomolecules as the source of information for "rational" drug design. Additionally, they have recently learned to make and examine millions of alternative molecular structures for biological effects (the combinatorial approach to drug discovery). Yet the screening of native organisms for natural products still occupies a considerable proportion of research budgets, and while this has opened fields such as the algae and fungi, the need to examine both native and exotic plants continues. The exploitation of the flora of other, often developing, countries has to be effected through appropriate agreements with those countries, so that benefit, possibly in the form of a royalty, may accrue to the country of origin of the source material.

As an aid to retaining as much biodiversity as possible, national and international agencies have established seed banks to archive as much nonperishable material as possible from the plant kingdom. Second, the genetically engineered plants themselves constitute an increment in the amount of biodiversity available. When the hundreds and thousands of differently engineered experimental plantlets in each of many hundreds of laboratories across the world are taken into account, it would be difficult to sustain an objection to this activity on the grounds that it decreases biodiversity.

Ethical Implications of Genetically Engineered Pollen Movements. That the pollen from a transgenic crop can travel several kilometers and fertilize related plants should not surprise (27). But whether such fertilized plants will become pests is a less likely event. Field experiments in the United States have shown that the characteristic of herbicide resistance may be transferred to a related plant (in the *Brassica* or oilseed rape family), which then became a weed that could not be eliminated by the herbicide (28). An even less likely scenario is that the gene for herbicide resistance becomes incorporated into the genome of an unrelated plant that is a natural weed (29). These eventualities would provoke a need to respond with a newly engineered crop plant resistant to another herbicide. The danger from chemically resistant transgenic plants is twofold. On the one hand, it is possible that the weed targeted by the herbicide, to which the transgenic plant has been made resistant, will mutate and no longer succumb to the chemical. This means that the plant to be protected will have to be reengineered to be resistant to another herbicide to kill the weeds that have become resistant to the first herbicide. Multiple cycles of this nature may be anticipated. Whether combinations of resistant genes coupled with mixtures of herbicides will be a longer-lasting answer has not been determined, but there is little doubt that this way of improving crop yields will be explored in all its aspects. What applies

to the plants that have been genetically engineered with exogenous herbicide resistance genes is also applicable to plants engineered with insect-, fungus-, or virus-resistant genes. In each of these cases variants of the pests will emerge for which a different transgene will have to be introduced into the plant. In practice the use of genetically resistant plants has led to a decrease in the number of applications of both herbicides and pesticides. This has resulted in less expensive produce as well as decreasing the load of pollutants washed into nearby waterways.

Organic farmers object to the possibility that the plants they are producing might become contaminated by herbicide-resistant pollen. Such farmers do not use chemicals to help fertilize or protect their crops against weeds, fungi, or insects. It is also held that they may lose their special licence to produce such crops if they become so modified. However, recently a UK court decided that the likelihood of pollen contaminating such crops at a distance of 2 km was negligible, and the motion to uproot the engineered crop was not sustained (30).

Ethics and the Production of Animal Proteins in Plants. The addition of selected animal genes for expression in food plants may also present problems, especially when the origin of the genes is from animals Jews and Moslems are forbidden to eat, such as pigs. Others, such as vegetarians, might object to the introduction of any animal gene into a plant that is used as a food for humans. While the previous conditions may indeed be effected, it is most unlikely that the exact gene that originated in an animal would be inserted into a plant in an unmodified form: It would be shorter with exons removed, with expression control promoters or with some of the redundant third bases changed. (Were those bases of a porcine insulin gene that were different from the human insulin gene replaced with the appropriate human bases, does the resulting gene still retain its porcine-ness?). It should also be noted that plants do not have the same post-translational modification systems as animals. So we might expect differences in glycosylation to occur when such animal-derived genes are expressed in plants. Nevertheless, for some purposes this is not consequential, and the advantages of a plant-produced product may make this the preferred production system.

As the reason for the rejection of food animals is based on the nature of the whole animal and/or the processes undertaken to render it suitable for eating, a gene taken from such an animal does not evoke either of these situations and therefore may be considered in a different light. However, any exploitation of an animal, including the extraction of its genetic material, might be considered unacceptable. In this case a synthetic gene could be constructed that would never have experienced the animal environment.

These may be technical fixes to obviate ethical dilemmas, but they do put the magnitude of the ethical questions raised into perspective so that reasonable people might come to acceptable and pragmatic conclusions about their actions regarding plants genetically engineered with animal genes.

Ethics and Plant-Derived Infectious Agents. The agent that effects the genetic engineering of the plant may be a type of DNA that can have an independent existence, in the form of a virus or bacterium. It is held that such agents may leave the plant and transform other species. Were they, for example, to transport an antibiotic resistance gene (a gene normally contained in these vectors because it enables the modified organism to be selected for further use) to a pathogenic bacterium found in nature, then some people believe that humans might be put at risk of contracting disease. But as the gene coding for Kanamycin resistance is often used for this purpose (because the antibiotic Kanamycin is not used to cure humans of bacterial disease as it is too toxic), it is not a matter of concern if bacteria become Kanamycin resistant. A Kanomycin-resistant pathogen would be treated with a different antibiotic, one to which it had been deemed sensitive by laboratory tests.

The release of genetic material from plants cannot be considered a new event. Pollen has been distributed by wind and water for eons. Were one or other of the vectors used to genetically engineer the plant cells become dispersed in nature, then it is unlikely that it would result in a fruitful interaction with another genome. However, should such an interaction occur, any progeny that form would have to contend for their survival with the indigenous plants. That humans may injest the nucleic acids from the vectors may be discounted as a source of danger, as humans are capable of processing the DNA and RNA of their food materials in such a manner that they do not suffer a known genetic damage.

Ethics and the Patenting of Genetically Engineered Plants. A recent (May 1998) ruling of the European Parliament has endorsed the Patent Directive of the Council of Ministers establishing two crucial provisions: The first is that discoveries of the sequence of bases of the genes of a living organism are not in themselves patentable. Inventions that incorporate the base sequence of genes that are identical to those found in living organisms may be patentable providing an industrial application has been specified. This means that the discovery of the sequence of bases in the genes of existing living organisms cannot be patented, so that foods, plants, and animals cannot be monopolized merely because somebody has managed to sequence the bases of one or more genes of those entities. Indeed *varieties* of plants may be protected as intellectual property if they are uniform, can be identifiably differentiated, and possess a stable modification; but this does not tie up the use of the parent plants whose genomes might have been used in the novel construct. A genetically engineered plant may be rightfully considered an invention. It had not previously occurred in nature and could be regarded as a novel addition to the biosphere.

Another danger is that companies supplying both the herbicide and the genetically resistant plant will so exploit their monopoly position as to render the new technology unavailable to any other than the already prosperous. There could also be some coercion in that a purchaser of a particular herbicide-resistant plant might be constrained into making a further purchase from the same source of the matching herbicide. Of course, patent monopoly rights only last some 16–20 years, after which any supplier may mimic and market the inventions, yet the problems inherent in making a herbicide (special chemical synthesis) and transgenic plant (resistance gene and transfection process) preclude an easy entry into the field, even in an effort to copy what has already proven successful.

Increases in the yield of crop plants have been obtained by creating hybrids that grow and produce vigorously but do not generate fertile seeds. These are made by a seed company from the two parent strains of the hybrid. Control of this process enables companies to assert a dominant position in the marketplace, as the farmers have to come back to them each year for a new supply of seeds. This arrangement seems to have been successful in developed economies, where the increase in yield more than compensates for the increased costs of the seed materials (see the preceding section on ethics and new plant foods for comments on terminator genes). However, it is exclusive, and farmers in developing countries would have difficulty in acquiring the necessary funding to engage in this process. The disparity in the distribution of wealth, which results from these activities, is an ethical issue. However, as the countries of the world are beginning to share an increasingly common culture, pressures will be generated to decrease the magnitude of wealth differences.

ETHICAL ISSUES IN ANIMAL CELL TECHNOLOGY: OVERVIEW

While plant cell technology generates ethical issues in the areas of food and the ecosystem, the animal cell technologist contends with a diverse array of concerns in the therapeutic and prophylactic areas of human and animal medicine. As there is a more direct connectivity between human cells in culture and human beings, the use of such cells throws up a welter of ethical issues to consider. Also, while plant cells enrich human populations via their modification into foods, flowers, or pharmaceuticals, animal cells provide a basis for the production of viruses for vaccines and gene vectors for use in the modification of the human genome, and in recent months animal cells in culture have been used to initiate clones, which has caused the reissue of the concern about the establishment of cloned populations of humans (31).

Animal cells in culture are used for an ever-widening range of applications (see the section on animal cell products). Whereas the initial uses were based on attempts to understand the way the human body differentiated from a fertilized embryo to an adult, in the 1950s animal cells in culture began to be used to produce virus vaccines (polio, followed in the 1960s by mumps, measles, and rubella), in which position they stayed until in the 1970s, when additional uses were discovered (see the section on the history of animal cell technology). These included the manufacture of monoclonal antibodies, the production of cytokines and immunoregulators, the generation of therapeutically active enzymes and hormones, and the making of human organs from cells grown in bioreactors. Most recently animal cell cultures have been used to provide the cells destined for the cloning of animals (32,33). Further developments of these techniques could be used to clone humans, were the legal regulations and ethical guidelines construed to permit this development. The use of virus vectors, grown in animal cells in culture, for somatic and possibly gametic genetic modification of humans and animals, presents a further set of concerns. Genome changes effected by these agents need not be confined to therapeutic applications, but can also be used to enhance the character or performance of people and animals.

As a result of these developments, many questions have to be answered as to how we use these potent product materials and, in particular, whether we continue to focus on the therapeutic approach to medicine or to give greater emphasis to the prophylactic and diagnostic aspects of human and animal health care. The use of modified viruses as biowar agents is also a cause for concern, and the recently reported developments in the extraction of pluripotent stem cells from human embryos for the later production of homogeneic organs may prove to be an advance that will obviate the need for allogeneic organs in human transplant surgery (34).

ETHICS AND VIRUS VACCINES

Below I examine some of the ethical issues produced by recent advances in the field of vaccines and vaccination. It will touch on the matter of the putative autonomy of the individual when faced with the need to achieve universal vaccination, and ways we will have to reassess the cost = ((risk* the magnitude of the damage) + cost of manufacture and distribution + surplus) to benefit relationship. Issues derived from the effect of vaccines on the size of populations will be followed by an examination of the transcultural issues raised when vaccines are tested in societies different from the ones in which the vaccine is manufactured and for which it is designed. Under such conditions the concept of informed consent may need to be considered for modification. The use of vaccines to obviate behavioral changes (technical fixes), generate transcendental concerns, and provide new threats via biological warfare agents will also be considered. There are also vaccines in development that are likely to protect people from non-infectious disease. The implications of the widespread use of such prophylactics, which would include an increase in the average lifespan of individuals, requires examination, as it has profound implications on the structure and operation of our societies.

Vaccines and the Ethic of Autonomy. It is part of current medical practice when dealing with patients to extol four basic ethical principles: autonomy, beneficence, nonmaleficence, and justice. However, when we consider issues related to vaccination, the principle of autonomy (self-determination, freedom from interference unless the act harms others (J.S. Mill), as in U.N. or Council of Europe declarations on human rights) is challenged. The principle of autonomy may be assailed from a number of different facets, such as the competence of an individual to

provide informed consent, the rights of a fetus if a pregnant mother decides to be immunized, or the connotations of the social contract entered into when an individual chooses to dwell in a particular society.

It is well known that when a high proportion of a population is vaccinated, those who have not been immunized are less threatened by disease due to the decrease in the level of the pathogenic organism prevalent in the society (the herd effect). The question this poses is: Do those who have opted against vaccination have the right to benefit from the expense and the risks of vaccine-induced damage accepted by those who have been vaccinated? Not only that, but such unvaccinated individuals pose a threat to the vaccinees as they serve as a reservoir in which the disease can be maintained and propagated. Were the society to collectively determine that all its citizens should receive the vaccine, then the principle of patient autonomy is infringed. An intermediate position might be to levy a special cash buy-out dispensation, or an equivalent contribution to the society, from those who refuse vaccination. This would be in compensation for the costs incurred by those who have accepted the risks of vaccine-induced damage. Whatever the outcome in any particular society, it is clear that vaccination poses a challenge to accepted ethical positions of personal autonomy, the resolution of which will be dependent on the degree of social coherence and commitment.

Notwithstanding the ethical support for socially mandated vaccination, individual mothers or physicians may take the view that, as it is possible there may be collateral damage or discomfort from the vaccine, the requirement to be vaccinated should be resisted. Clearly, people who have a family history of disease or whose children have demonstrated a propensity to succumb to infection may be granted a dispensation not to be vaccinated. Members of a religious sect that bases its ethics on traditional mores to the exclusion of the advances made in modern technology may resist vaccination. Additionally, people who are ill-informed or misinformed about vaccines and their benefits may also object to being subject to something they do not understand. Whether mothers have had first- or second-hand experience of the infectious disease is also a determinant in the acceptability of some vaccines with some mothers. For each such situation the provision of accurate and relevant information to all involved with the vaccination programs is essential. The crucial data about the deaths and disabilities that have been caused by the disease for which people are being asked to take preventive (vaccinal) measures have to be available and have to be reliable. This, when contrasted with the low costs of the vaccination, should be presented to the putative vaccinee and his/her parent(s). Educated physicians, public health nurses, and educational programs at all levels of society (to include the people who produce material for the media) are a necessary prerequisite for the moderation of the ethical issues that arise when societal representatives or regulations for school admission coerce individuals into becoming vaccinated. It is ironic that when people are compelled to be vaccinated, they take the view that vaccines are important, and comply with the regulations; when the vaccines are not so mandated, they are more inclined to refuse vaccination, as it is clearly not important. Another paradox is apparent in the response of mothers to the prospects of vaccines in that they recognize the need to be vaccinated against diseases that have been highlighted in the media as causing death (meningitis), even though such deaths are relatively rare. But these self-same mothers are reluctant to have their children vaccinated against diseases for which they have no information on the dangers of those diseases, because those diseases have been all but eliminated by previous vaccination campaigns (e.g., polio).

To ease the situation where vaccination is compulsory, it is possible to institute a compensation scheme to cover the unusual and putative occurrence of vaccine-caused damage. In the United States the National Vaccine Injury Compensation Program has been established. The usual tests whereby vaccine damage compensation may be claimed are if the damage has lasted longer than 6 months, if the onset of the damage can be held to have occurred within 15–30 days of the child's vaccination, and if there are any other supporting indications of a causal relationship between the damage and the vaccination. This is a no-fault system of payments, and boards have been liberal in their assessment of damage worthy of compensation. It is important to realize that the assessing body does not have to see a proof of causality beyond reasonable doubt; rather they have to judge, on the balance of probabilities, whether compensation is merited. This means that payments may well have been made in many cases where the damage was not due to a vaccination. It also means that if this is widely accepted, then people who have damaged children but who cannot possibly associate that damage with a vaccination incident might consider themselves deprived for not having received the same treatment as those who allege vaccine-caused damage. Two issues arise from this situation: One involves the principle of causation, while the other involves fairness and justice.

Courts of law or their pared-down counterparts (commissions, boards, tribunals) provide settings in which a determination can be made as to how to proceed in a particular case. They do not (generally) pretend to establish the truth; although much is said to assert that such and such is both factual and truthful, including the verbal evidence of witnesses; this may be considered window-dressing in the greater cause of case winning. Science, however, is concerned less with winning than with proffering a view of the world that is reliable and can lend itself to progress. Causation, therefore, in these two arenas is quite different; in the legal arena one is interested in an outcome of a contest whereby a judge or jury is, on balance, convinced one way or the other by the evidence. In the scientific area, we perform test after test to determine the level of confidence we may have in the guesses that we call hypotheses. In each arena we have to deal with the proposition that A caused B as opposed to A is coincidental with B. In the cases that come before compensation boards, it is generally enough to fit the alleged vaccine-caused damage in with

the *time constraints* for causation. This is not the concept of causation, which satisfies the stringent criteria generally adopted by working scientists.

Having obviated the need for a rigorous determination of causation, the way is open for compensation for "seeming" vaccine damage. Others who cannot construe their cases in this way claim that they are being dealt with unfairly. Does the state have a responsibility to compensate all those who give birth to damaged children? Those societies with national health systems do provide considerable support, and even when there is not a universal health care system, provision is often made for the poor to receive some support. Under these circumstances one might conclude that families in distress due to the diseases of their children receive adequate compensation either via the special schemes for vaccinated children or by socially financed health care projects.

The most important measure of the success of compensation schemes is that if, in spite of abuses, there is an increase in those seeking vaccination, then the scheme may be deemed a success. To date, in view of the increases in the numbers of people seeking vaccination, the National Vaccine Injury Compensation Program, operating in the United States may be considered successful.

Vaccines, Immigrants, and Discriminatory Practices. Travel is rapidly becoming a feature of life at the end of the twentieth century. Taking the UK as an example, the 57 million inhabitants made 42 million international visits, and the country received an incoming 24 million visitors in 1996; there was also a net inflow of 50,000 immigrants. Such cross-border movements are diverse:

- Tourists (for days, weeks and occasionally months)
- Business/commercial people (ditto)
- Professionals in the arts and sciences (ditto)
- Diplomatic and government/military officials (ditto)
- Students (for months and a small number of years)
- Pensioners (wintering in a different country)
- Workers or self-employed entrepreneurs or traders and distributors (months to many years if not permanent change of country of residence)
- Families of workers, etc. (ditto)
- Illegal migrants/sex workers/vagrants
- Refugees seeking asylum (months to many years)
- Transport systems staffs and operators (railway personnel, sailors, flight attendants, airline personnel) (days to weeks)
- Annual agricultural migrant workers (months)

And as borders between countries are dissolved (as is happening between some of the countries of Europe in the late 1990s), more such movements might be expected.

The disease threats to indigenous populations from external sources have both real and perceived components. The black death, caused by the bacterium *Yersinia pestis*, spread by deliberately infected people (an early example of biological warfare) escaping from a besieged city in the Crimea (in 1346, Caffa, now Feodosija), caused the premature death of over 30% of the European population. The Spanish influenza epidemic probably started in a military institution in the United States in 1918. It caused between 20 and 40 million deaths across the world. Other waves of influenza have swept across the world, and the vaccines that are commissioned to protect local populations are based on the strains of the virus that are prevalent in the Far East at the time when the vaccine is produced. Other human diseases have been associated with the international movement of people, for example, syphilis, measles, gonorrhoea, herpes simplex, papilloma virus cancers, human immunodeficiency virus/AIDS, malaria, yellow fever, dengue, cholera, hepatitis (A, B, C, +), typhus, and typhoid.

There are commonly held views that migrants and visitors from poorer countries are also sources of disease. Within a country there is little doubt that poorer (low socioeconomic class) people are more susceptible to disease, and the economic stratification and distribution of people in the society reflects the disease prevalence distribution. Sex workers who arrive in a country illegally or legally are also thought to be the purveyors of disease. Recently, tourists and business people have been held to be the transporters of the virus that causes AIDS from its African origin to the new world. Habitual travellers and transportation system employees are also implicated in cross-border transmission of disease-causing organisms.

This situation poses both practical and ethical problems. On the practical side, there is the question of what measures can be taken to limit, control, and reduce the incidence of exotic diseases. There would then have to be an examination of the ethicality of the measures proposed. The requirement for vaccinations and vaccination certificates, the possibilities of introducing quarantine, the administration of vaccines at a border, and the need to undertake a medical examination before or after travelling are all procedures that could be adopted. One might also consider the differential treatment of people dependent on their country of origin or on the basis of the countries through which they have passed and the time they have spent there. The socioeconomic status might also be taken into account, as might the family situation and the reasons for the cross-border travel. People who are neither citizens nor travellers, such as the families of visiting workers whose children are indistinguishable from the children of citizens, may yet be treated differently with regard to vaccination. Such variances might apply to the vaccination regimen that is applicable to these individuals. Were these features of travellers and/or immigrants to provide the rationale for the differential treatment of cross-border travellers, then they could be construed as contrary to international declarations of human rights which "... apply without distinction of any kind, such as race, colour, sex, language, religion, political or other opinion, *national or social origin*, property, birth or other status." (U.N. Declaration of Human Rights, Art 2, *author's italics*.)

The ethical issues are not easily resolved. The assertion of such rights could put an acceptor country at a higher risk of importing a debilitating infectious disease. This might be seen as the denial of the rights of a country to operate basic controls as to who does, or does not, enter that state. While this does not appear as a documented "right," individuals and communities may determine with whom they consort. And in the matter of disease control (which ultimately becomes a survival issue) it would be unusual to give up these aspects of self-determination, whether or not that was discriminatory. Once accepted as a member of the society, issues of discrimination take on a different hue. Now the group sinks or swims as a unit, and although the various abilities and properties of individuals may be engaged differentially, the terms of that involvement are more likely to be applied in accordance with U.N. perceptions of rights.

Vaccines and Animal Movement Controls. The control of highly infectious diseases such as foot-and-mouth disease by the use of vaccines is a triumph of modern methods of animal health improvement. One of the key aspects of the control program is the use of certificates of vaccination to validate the vaccine status of animals that could be designated for transportation either within a country or between countries. The incentive for such movements is the higher profits that can be acquired from the selective marketing of the animals. To support the certificated vaccination status of the animals, border posts are used to inspect incoming animals, and national legislatures pass laws that forbid the ingress of nonvaccinated animals. Each of these provisions, however is an opportunity for illegal or illicit activities. It is not uncommon for vaccination certificates to be forged, for vaccines to be used past their recommended date, for vaccines to be diluted or adulterated, for border controllers to be bribed, for the secret movement of cattle along unpatrolled and unregulated cross-border pathways, and for higher officials to be persuaded to look the other way. In short, wherever a regulation is put in place that prevents the monetary gains of a trader, methods will be sought to obviate the superposed hurdles. Here the technologist who makes the vaccines is an instrument in the process whereby people may be led to behave in an unfitting manner. There is, therefore, a need to reflect on these issues and build into all societies a comprehensive respect for law and order, coupled with a nationwide sense of social fairness, particularly when the wealth of the community is distributed.

Vaccine Costs and Benefits. For much of the past 350 years, commercial companies have been required to provide products to the marketplace, and society's judgment on the company has been via the acceptability of the product at the price demanded. The function of the company was to accumulate profits for its shareholders and top managers (incentives), and society did not interfere with the way the product was made, nor with the product spectrum on offer. This ethic, too, is in need of review. Vaccines are a clear benefit to the society as a whole. However, there is a risk of vaccine-induced long-term and severely debilitating damage [well recognized for polio vaccines and less well established for any other vaccine, cf. swin fever (inactivated influenza) vaccines and Guillain–Barré syndrome], which is especially poignant when incurred after the vaccination of a 3-month-old healthy infant. Under present conditions the manufacturing company may be sued for damages (both actual and punitive, if willful negligence is proven). But is this the appropriate ethic? May not the society, in accepting the benefit of widespread vaccination, compensate those who suffer damage at a level commensurate with the damage? In recent years the United States has established a National Vaccine Injury Compensation Program. Of course, were the manufacturer culpably negligent in a procedural matter, then compensation would also be due from that source.

Resulting from this liability situation, vaccine manufacturers are reluctant to venture into vaccine projects. Also, as the cost of obtaining a product license is estimated to be some $200–600 million, the implications for the cost of a dose of vaccine is more driven by the cost of the regulatory procedure than the production cost (which rarely exceeds the cost of the bottle plus label). The ethical issue here is whether the regulatory hurdle that has to be overcome is really operating in society's best interests. Nothing we eat or do is without the risk of incurring damage. Vaccines are not different in that respect. Yet the cost of obtaining a license to manufacture and distribute implies that the price of the vaccine has to be many dollars merely to recoup the costs involved. Does this mean that the rich should pay a high price for a vaccine and thus subsidize the provision of cheap vaccines to the poor? Or is it the job of the elected representatives of the people to act as purchaser on behalf of the poor and provide the vaccine manufacturer compensation through the tax system or other fiscal dispensation?

The development and manufacture of vaccines for diseases that afflict few people (orphan vaccines) are not a commercial proposition unless communal support is provided. Vaccines that lead to a decrease in the need for over the counter or prescribed medicaments are also unlikely to be made by commercial concerns. The reluctance of pharmaceutical companies to produce a vaccine for *Helicobacter pylori*, which would prevent the recurrence of stomach ulcers and hence stomach cancers, is evident from the research programs of those companies that make antiulcer drugs. Research on vaccines that would prevent the common cold (caused by a combination of *Rhinoviruses*, *Coronaviruses*, and *Adenoviruses*) is also conspicuous by its absence. But prophylaxis as an approach to healthcare is also underfunded by the society at large. Therapeutic research receives over ten times the funding of prophylaxis, and this is particularly difficult to understand when there are many inexpensive ways of achieving prophylaxis, of which vaccination, which affects the immune system, is but one. Other methods of prevention focus on the protection of the immune system to decrease the probability that it will be overwhelmed by an endogenous or exogenous pathogen; such procedures may be termed "fence vaccines" (35).

It is difficult to determine reliable cost–benefit relationships. Such calculations tend to restrict their scope to the monetary balances of what is paid out in the production and use of a vaccine and what monies are saved by decreased expenses at the doctor or hospital.

But the assessment of benefit has to be broader than mere monetary considerations. When a child is able to complete a school program without having to have time off to combat an infectious disease, s/he is in an advantageous position to benefit from having completed the full educational program. In later life the sense that one need not suffer from a debilitating disease may result in feelings of optimism and confidence in the future. This could lead to increases in personal investment and saving, thus increasing social wealth and wellbeing, a situation that could well lead to further health improvements.

Ethical Issues from the Decreased Death Rates Caused by Vaccination. An ethical argument that is proscriptive of the use of vaccines in the developing and less developed world (containing 79% of the world's 6.1 billion people) is that they will lead to an increase in an already unsustainable population. This will have sequellae via an increase in suffering from malnourishment, population migrations, and war. However, recent figures published by UNESCO refute these projections and show that the average number of children born to a woman of the developing world throughout the period of her fertility has dropped from 6.06 to 3.75 between 1960 and 1994. This would indicate that more, rather than fewer, vaccines are required; and indeed vaccines protective against the diarrhoeal and respiratory diseases (causing upward of 2 million deaths per annum) of childhood are in test in the field, while candidate vaccines aimed at controlling malaria (about 1 million deaths per annum) languish in laboratory refrigerators. At present there is a campaign to rid the world of polio. This is likely to succeed by the early years of the next millennium, with the prospect of a similar demise for measles to follow. In 1998 malaria was made a target for worldwide healthcare by WHO. However, it seems that the focus will be on the therapeutic side rather than the prophylactic.

Population may not only be affected by a decrease of infant mortality but also by an increase in the average age of the community. As the level of communicable disease wanes, people live longer and the society then has to adjust its working conditions such that there are productive positions for the older people to occupy. It clearly has to become practicable to provide for protracted retirements; so the emphasis on life-long learning, skill changing, job flexibility, and part-time working will become the norms of future social development (see the section on ethical issues pertaining to the development and use of vaccines protective against noninfectious diseases).

Using Vaccines as a Technical Fix is an Ethical Issue. Is it appropriate to use a technical fix when an almost cost-free change of behavior will achieve the same effect? Such an ethical problem is thrown up by the willingness of our communities to spend billions of dollars to provide therapeutic and prophylactic agents to control the spread and effects of the human immunodeficiency virus (HIV). Yet this disease would be eliminated were people to engage in safe, condom-protected, intercourse in their pre- or extramarital sexual relationships, especially where the prospective partners have not been thoroughly tested for the presence of serum antibodies to the virus. This provision also applies to the transmission of the virus that cause hepatitis B, genital herpes, as well as the cancers wrought by the *Papilloma* virus. As a corollary to the practice of safe sex, it might also be expected that gonorrheal infections would decline as would those caused by *Treponema syphilis* and the yeast *Candida*.

Many of the food and water-borne diseases caused by the bacteria of the *Salmonella*, *Escherichia*, *Shigella*, *Listeria*, *Campylobacter*, and *Vibrio* groups would be eliminated were drinking and washing water to be prepared according to the highest standards prevalent in most developed countries. However, the engineering requirements to achieve this in the short term are daunting. Whereas the prospects for the development of orally deliverable vaccines which would provide protection against the diseases caused by the above pathogenic bacteria is a task which may be brought to a successful conclusion within the next decade.

A further case where vaccines are used to preclude the expenditure of monies is to protect people from the effects of the diseases of propinquity; typhus and tuberculosis. Both of these diseases flourish when people are housed in crowded insanitary conditions. It may be that the vaccination route is cost-effective in monetary terms but this should not be used as a way of avoiding the social improvements which would enhance the dignity of citizens as well as improving their health.

It is also possible that the new vaccine protective against Hepatitis A would be rendered superfluous were travelers to wash their hands thoroughly and take more care of their cleanliness.

Ethics of Testing Vaccines Abroad. We are presented with a situation in which tests of vaccines in Developing Countries can be effected at considerably less expense than in a Developed Country. This has led to a series of ethical issues which are exacerbated by the differences in the cultures of the people who may be engaged in the vaccine trials. For example, is it possible to obtain the informed consent of a person who is illiterate and who does not understand the implications of something like a vaccine with which s/he is totally unfamiliar? A second issue might be that the removal of blood or tissue for sampling might be regarded as an attempt to capture the spirit of the sampled individual. Additionally there may be taboos about removal of blood via venipuncture and in some cultures the insertion of needles into bodies may have overtones not foreseen in Western cultures.

On removal of a sample containing cellular material from the body of an individual (generally a tissue responsible for a pathogenic effect) one obtains the opportunity to work with a highly selected and unique genome. Were the genes of that cell to be used to make a pharmaceutical to particularly benefit people in the Developed World what sort of compensation should accrue to the source of the cell line from which the gene was obtained? Current thinking by the Nuffield Ethics Committee (a non-governmental organisation) would have it that the cell provider has not contributed to the inventive step in the drug or prophylactic development and therefore

is not to be compensated (36). However, if advantage is taken of the uniqueness of the material derived from a person of the Developing World then it would be churlish not to recognize this through some financial contribution to the individual and his/her community.

One might ask to what extent is a prophylactic trial in the developing world relevant to the circumstances prevalent in the developed world? Are the conditions leading to infection and the challenge organisms relevant? Are the people in whom the vaccine is tested likely to respond in an immunologically equivalent manner when the history of the exposure of their immune systems to disease is dissimilar in many ways to a person of the developed world? In the event that there is damage to an individual as a result of exposure to vaccine in trial, what are the levels of compensation and who pays? And indeed, is it ethical that a person in the vaccine-producing country should enjoy the benefits which have been won at the expense of the risktaking of a person in less privileged circumstances? It is clear that there is not a legal requirement for compensation, unless such a provision has been written into the contract with the leaders of the people who will be engaged in the experimentation. But, having exposed the test subjects to unknown (although previous experiments in animals would have given indications that the risks of vaccine damage were vanishingly small, if not nonexistent), it would not be unreasonable to make the final vaccine available under favorable terms (free) to the population that provided the test data.

Ethics, Vaccine Testing, and Placebos. In situations where it is believed that an effective vaccine already exists, it would not be an acceptable ethic to effect trials with placebo controls that did not provide the best possible protection. Similarly, it would be counterproductive to use vaccines whose safety was an issue and where a less damaging vaccine could be made available, albeit at greater expense. In addition, there is the overriding consideration that if nothing is attempted, then there would be a known tally of deaths and disease and our efforts to combat that embody a justification for effecting vaccine experimentation.

Yet the strongest case for the use of a vaccine is when it provides a significantly improved protection against infection when compared with the inactive placebo controls. But the people who are the controls do not know whether or not they have been vaccinated and might, as a result, increase their risky behavior, which could result in disease. This ethical dilemma tends towards resolution when the people effecting the trials compromise on the clarity of the result they obtain in exchange for a way of dealing with the unvaccinated (or inactive placebo) controls that does not increase the risk of such individuals becoming infected as a consequence of taking part in the trials. For example, in a trial of a vaccine directed towards protection against the onset of AIDS, it may be thought ethical to treat the control group with a variety of HIV-inhibiting drugs that is the most efficacious alternative to the possible full protection afforded by the vaccine. In recent (1998) deliberations on this issue in UNAIDS, an interim conclusion is that when conducting AIDS vaccine trials in developing countries, the tests should be placebo controlled and the subjects be engaged following "informed consent." Following the regular monitoring of the subjects, those known to have become infected would be provided with the highest level of treatment available in that country. (It is recognized that this will not necessarily involve the triple drug treatment available in developed countries at a cost of about $15,000 per patient per annum.) The use of placebo controls was justified in that it will lead to an effective vaccine in less time than an uncontrolled trial, and although there may be a cost in human lives, that cost will be less than the cost of doing less well-controlled trials over a longer period, during which many more people would die as a result of natural infection. Such trials would be effected as a collaborative partnership between the trial proposer representatives of the indigenous population under the persistent scrutiny of local ethics committees.

In testing a vaccine designed to be protective against the development of the AIDS condition (though it is not necessary to protect against the infection by HIV, which causes this condition), it is essential to provide to the test subjects counselling about how to behave in sexual situations. This would advise subjects to use condoms in their sexual activities and to refrain from multiple partnering and other profligate practices. Both the test subjects and the placebo or comparison arms of the trial are exposed to this counselling. Clearly, if the subjects take notice of the admonitions, then neither they nor their unvaccinated controls need become infected, a situation that would not test the efficacy of the vaccine. To omit the counselling would be regarded as callous and contrary to the ethic that seeks to act beneficently to all patients and subjects. How this can be related to effecting tests in countries where the disease poses a serious risk of infection and where the availability of counsellors is rare are still controversial question, but it will lead to an increase in the number of subjects incorporated into the trials as the incidence of infection is likely to be severely lowered with a concomitant decrease of the challenge to the vaccine.

Ethics, Vaccines, and the Transcendental. A definition of the transcendental might be "that which is outside the cause-and-effect system," where the latter relates specifically to the interactions between those entities we recognize as being made up of matter and/or energy. For example, ghosts, fairies, trolls, spirits, angels, jinn, and souls are described in such a way that they perform their tasks with scant regard for the properties of matter and energy. The same may be said of the panoply of deities that have been posited as having creative and control capabilities with regard to the workings of the world and the affairs of humans. Nevertheless, such considerations cannot be obviated when we review the reactions of community members to the production and use of vaccines, particularly when some of the most emphatic proscriptive reactions emanate from the leadership of recognized deistic religions.

In Kirkpatric's book on inoculation published in 1761, there is the astonishing report of the abreaction of the church to inoculation with treated material taken from patients who were suffering from smallpox. This is because there would be a small, but finite, possibility of dying from inoculated material; so it could be alleged that the individual, ostensibly seeking protection, was actually seeking to commit suicide. This was sinful. Recently, in 1995 (37), there was a series of reports and letters in the U.K. media about the activities of the Catholic church, which was seeking to prevail on its disease-susceptible female members to forego vaccination protective against rubella, as the vaccine was prepared from the cells of an aborted human fetus: Human abortion is contrary to the *teachings* of that church.

On a more esoteric plane, it is possible to argue that, through the use of vaccines, mankind has developed a capability that may eventually rid the world of those infectious microorganisms, which have been the bane of our struggle to survive. This depletion in the deistic armamentarium may be construed as seeking to deny deities of one of their controlling effector systems; viz, the threat of divine retribution through the causation of plagues. Alternatively, it may be held with equal rectitude that the deity ordained us to discover and use vaccines as part of its (undisclosed) master plan. Consonant with this latter controversy, there are those who assert that it is unnatural to disturb the ways of nature and as vaccines are a creation of mankind they are not natural and are therefore to be condemned. Nevertheless, it can be argued that, as vaccines exist in nature (however they got there), they are natural, as has been argued in more detail in a preceding section on ethical issues common to both animal and plant cell technology.

Now that it is practicable to identify a defective gene in an adult, child, or even embryo, techniques are in development to repair, exchange, or inactivate that gene specifically. These methods imply the existence of "genetic vaccines." However, these self-same methods may be used not just to correct defects but also to enhance characteristics we may desire to accentuate.

As the word *disease* is defined as a state of being in which one is *not at ease*, it is not difficult to use the word to describe a situation where a person (or a parent) is not at ease with their (or their child's) height, intelligence, physical prowess, or color. This raises the ethical question of the use of genetic vaccines to prevent the disease resulting from such deeply held feelings. There is little doubt that the remediation and/or prevention of situations that cause physical pain is encouraged and applauded by the society. The same cannot be asserted where the pain may be psychological. Nevertheless, this latter pain is just as actionable as the physical pain (indeed it is physical, but of the activities of the brain as opposed to muscle). So, not only would we relieve suffering, but we might also achieve a human being who is more functionally capable of making a more extensive contribution to society, a feature not given to all pain-killing remedies. That such measures might be construed as interfering with some transcendental plan cannot be denied, but the ethic of beneficence might be applied to progress the use of these genetic vaccines in all their manifestations (see also the section on ethical issues in the genetic enhancement of humans).

Ethics and Contraceptive Vaccines. Animal cells in culture can be specifically engineered to overproduce hormones, or antigens associated with the trophoblast, whose introduction into an animal or human female would result in the generation of a contraceptive state. By selection of a suitable delivery system it should soon be possible to achieve an orally deployable contraceptive, based on one or two applications. Ethical considerations will then be evoked to determine the way in which such a powerful tool for population control might be used. This would be an advance on the steroid hormone pills, which need to be taken daily.

The deliberate contamination of drinking water supplies with a contraceptive vaccine would act counter to the autonomy principle of ethics and could be held to be an affront to the dignity of humans in denying them control over their own fertility. Notwithstanding this clear ruling, it is possible to conceive of conditions in which a decrease in population levels is an urgent necessity and the use of an orally delivered contraceptive vaccine might be the only way of achieving that end without recourse to widespread sterilization. As with any other tool, we have to adopt an ethic that permits appropriate uses; what we need to do ahead of time is to discuss and debate what those circumstances might be.

On the basis of a majoritarian or acceptability ethic, a population might openly decide to apply an orally effective contraceptive to a drinking water supply. The objective would be to decrease the overall fertility of the society. However, it is clear that individuals who are not part of the majority and who can afford bottled water or untreated water may be able to obviate the need to decrease population size. Alternatively, it may be possible to remove the contraceptive by physical or chemical means. This would provide people with additional choices of whether or not they would wish to limit the size of their families by using raw modified water. Other ethical arguments may center upon the adaptation of this practice to introduce into water supplies materials that could, for example, modify the state of an individual's mind, or shorten his/her life. So the possibly acceptable use for contraceptive purposes may be perverted to unacceptable and surreptitious uses by unscrupulous individuals or groups. As in many such cases, the construction and implementation of adequate control and regulatory systems enables citizens to have confidence in the materials they receive or acquire from other agencies in the society.

Ethical Concerns when Making Vaccines to Protect Against Putative Biological Warfare Agents. Measles, ebola, Lassa fever, and influenza viruses have, among others, been proposed as agents of human destruction in the context of international and intranational conflict. Both smallpox and measles have been implicated in the (advertent or inadvertent) decimation of the indigenous populations of the Americas during the colonization processes beginning in the 1500s. Vaccines protective against these diseases, therefore, become defensive devices that would have to be surmounted by a would-be aggressor. Perhaps, of more serious consequence, would be the engineering-out of the epitopes (those parts of the virus structure that evoke a response by the immune system; this could be as few as a sequence of 6 amino acids or a smaller number of carbohydrate monomers), which excite the immune system to produce virus-neutralizing antibodies. When this occurs, epitopes that heretofore were immunosuppressed become immunodominant. However, if, as will be suggested in the following, cross-protective vaccines are made that react with the immunosubdominant epitopes, then it should be possible to continue to make effective vaccines.

In addition to the manipulation of the epitopic profile of a virus, developments occur in the methods for the dissemination of the agents. While it is possible to conjure scenarios of contaminated water supplies and recognize that the air-handling systems of large buildings may constitute a means of agent distribution, the mechanisms for the protection of such seemingly open targets are well in place already. For we do treat water supplies with inactivants, and it is recognized that the circulation of air within air conditioned buildings is fraught with problems if people's natural illnesses are circulated by air-handling equipment devoid of high-performance filtration systems. To meet the contingencies of the distribution a pathogenic virus, the stratagem of *fence vaccination* (35) may be applied.

The cycle of measure/countermeasure, with which we are familiar in the area of conventional and nuclear weapons, has echoes in the area of biological warfare. That we have a duty to defend the lives of our peoples is an ethical principle few would dispute. In the context of this article, the pursuit of vaccines to existing and potential biological warfare agents is not just a job done in response to real or perceived threats, but it should become a mission whose importance ranks so highly that it has to be included with the strategic planning we have to undertake to survive. As in other areas of defensive reaction, we might expect the vaccine production techniques to be enhanced with regard to both the ability rapidly to manufacture high-quality immunogenic preparations and also with respect to the design and engineering of those immunogens.

The immune system of animals responds primarily to the most dominant of the epitopes presented to it by a pathogenic virus. When such epitopes change, it is necessary to make a new vaccine. As the immunodominance of these epitopes is partly achieved through their position on the outer extremities of the virus, it is clear that changes in their molecular structure do not cause collateral changes to the fundamental or basic virus structure. However, when these dominant epitopes are removed or replaced with anodyne substitutes, the immune system responds to the otherwise immunosuppressed epitopes on other parts of the virus whose integrity is vital to virus reproduction and pathogenicity. These epitopes, by contrast, cannot be readily changed; so vaccines that evoke antibodies or cytotoxic T-cells to the newly exposed epitopes continue to be effective, whatever changes are made to the previously immunodominant epitopes inhabiting the outer extremities of the virus. They thereby become cross-protective vaccines, whose utility is considerably enhanced over the conventional vaccines, which are produced by unmodified viruses.

These abilities will have spinoff effects with regard to our ability to produce vaccines protective against the pathogenic biological agents that pose threats from natural sources, such as influenza viruses whose type changes require us to make immunogenically unique vaccines on a year-by-year basis. We have also to take note of the emergent infectious agents (ebola, hantavirus, HIV) that have achieved a degree of notoriety in recent years. Our ability to respond to such agents has been slow, cumbersome, disorganized, and paltry in relation to the importance of the testing situation these agents proffer. Our ethics require that we improve on this performance.

Serious thinkers have also contemplated the possibility of designing a biowarfare agent that can differentiate between similar ethnic groups. From our knowledge of genetically determined diseases and the way different ethnic groups have a propensity for certain red blood cell surface components (blood group antigens), it may be possible to build an viral agent that uses such specific structures for attachment and infection (38). Although such ideas may, at this time, seem far-fetched, it becomes more urgent to devote a higher proportion of social resources to meeting the potentially highly damaging prospect such possibilities embody.

Ethical Issues Pertaining to the Development and Use of Vaccines Protective against Noninfectious Diseases. Cancers and atherosclerotic conditions account for some 43% and 52% of years of life lost to females and males up to the age 65, respectively. During the past 10 or so years there have been many indications that it will be possible to interfere with, and possibly prevent, these diseases by modulating the actions of the immune system. The vaccines, made from genetically engineered animal cells and viruses grown in culture, which will effect this redirection of the immune system, will be instruments used to decrease the death rates of people above the age of 35, where some 75% of the total deaths are caused by such noninfectious conditions. Other noninfectious diseases (Table 2) may also succumb to this approach to prophylactic medicine. This will have two major consequences for society. First, there will be an increase in the number of people who will be available for work, and second, we can expect an increase in the number of people who have retired from their major field of endeavor and who will be drawing on state (where applicable) and private pensions. There could be additional drains on social resources, for, as people live longer, they would have more opportunities to obtain costly services from healthcare organizations.

The changes that will ensue from the increase in the numbers of people and the increased age to which people might be expected to live are multifarious. Many alterations to the way we behave might be expected, and such behavioral changes will occur within the family as well as within the broader society. Thus families may expect to have elderly parents present for longer times, which will mean that inheritances will not be passed on as quickly, yet the older people may become a font of useful guidance to younger generations, if, and only if, they keep up with the technologies of the times. A further benefit of the presence of older but fitter parents (grand and great-grand) will

Table 2. Disease Targets

Cancer	Diabetes mellitus
Lung	Genetic diseases
Colon	Huntingdon's chorea
Breast	Cystic fibrosis
Liver	Phenylketonuria
Melanoma	Albinism
Stomach	Mucopolysaccharidoses
Sarcomas	Thalasaemia
Brain	Tay–Sachs disease
Osteosarcoma	Drug addiction
Atherosclerosis	Alzheimer
Arthritis	
Myasthenia gravis	
Multiple sclerosis	

be the provision of a reliable baby-sitting service, which will enable the younger generations to face the world of work with greater confidence and commitments.

Changes will be needed to capacitate the requirements and the abilities of an increased number of older people in our societies. The world of work may be extended, so that after a retirement from a regular position an individual may still wish to make a contribution to society. We may need to rethink the kinds of activities that may be best effected by trained individuals who would value the work more for the pleasure it generates than for either the exercise of power, or remuneration at a level that would support the raising of children. A new superstratum of goods and services would also find economic viability. Entertainment, culture, travel, gardening, house refurbishment, food, and sport/leisure activities would need some additional special facilities and could provide exciting opportunities for young and old alike. Also, educational facilities (such as the University of the Third Age, U3A, started in France), would be needed that would not only cater for leisure learning, but would be involved in retaining for a third age (50+) career.

A crucial and often neglected aspect of analyses of the benefit side of increased life span is the change in a person's attitude to him/herself and the rest of society. It would not be unreasonable to expect that if a person knows that s/he is likely to live longer, then such an individual is more likely to think about investing for the future. There is an optimism that is in contradistinction to the thoughts engendered by the imminence and inevitability of a premature death. As more people will save and invest more, economic activity, which is dependent on the availability of investment monies, could flourish and a virtuous cycle of saving, investment, and growth is promoted. However, we have to return to the issues of increasing the size of the population and the cost to the society of an increased number of people drawing their pensions.

Recent data published in a UNICEF report for 1996 (39) indicate that the number of children born to a woman throughout the period of her fertility has dropped between the years 1960 and 1994, in the developed world from 2.8 to 1.7 and in the developing world, comprising some 79% of the world's population, from 6.06 to 3.75. Additional efforts to decrease these rates even further is under intensive examination, and the development of immunoactive oral contraceptives may give a boost to population control in the decades ahead (see the section on ethics and contraceptive vaccines), so much so, that it is likely that the world's population could well top out at some 7+ billion people by the middle of the next century and then drop, through natural causes, in subsequent years. In this light, it is not envisaged that an increase in the *number* of older people will be of major significance in relation to the total world's population, but it may be that the *proportion* of older people could produce some difficulties.

Perhaps the most pervasive argument about the promotion of a society of people who are getting older is that the state (that is, the people as a collective) will have to pay out large amounts of money for healthcare services and/or as pensions. This could be such a drain on resources that there would not be funds available for other socially necessary expenditures for education, housing, etc. This, too, may be an unfounded reservation. We have already seen major increases in life expectancy within the past 100 years. For example, the life expectancy of a person born in the United States in the year 1900 was 47 years; a person born in the year 2000 might be expected to live to about 75. So an increase in life span has not brought about a social disaster; the contrary is the case. Additionally, during the years when people work to acquire the necessary monies to bring up and educate their children, they also put away money in insurance schemes to pay for their healthcare and pensions; such expenditures normally become due later in a person's life. This money is invested and so serves the society as funds that can grow and contribute to the future wealth of the society. It should be noted that the payment of pensions and healthcare monies serves as an incentive for younger people to join such insurance schemes and make investments in their, and the society's, future wellbeing. Again this is a virtuous cycle. People who save, and whose savings are deployed to create additional wealth for the society, are making a commitment to a future world. So, as the state withdraws from the payments of pensions, and leaves it to the private sector to draw up the necessary insurance schemes, which are constructed in such a way that the insurance companies are likely to return a profit to their investors, we can anticipate that the cost of keeping people provided with pension funds is unlikely be a serious drain on the resources of the society.

In conclusion, it would seem that a decrease in the number of deaths due to cancer, atherosclerosis, and other noninfectious diseases is not likely to cause a major increase in the costs of running a society. Rather the additional contribution from these older and wiser people is likely to enrich the society and make serious contributions to the benefit side of the cost–benefit analysis.

ETHICS AND MONOCLONAL ANTIBODIES

Monoclonal antibodies are monomolecular antibody preparations made from a selected clone of antibody-secreting animal cells. They are used as components of diagnostic kits, for preparative processes based on affinity chromatography methods, for the delineation of cancerous tissue, and/or for the attack of such tissue by bifunctional reagents; they may even be used for their enzymatic properties (abzymes). Few ethical issues pertain to these reagents though the intellectual property disputes in the early days of their use were not insignificant. Otherwise, as these antibodies may be used as hormones, in that they can be targeted to hormone receptor molecules, issues that pertain to hormones can be raised for these antibodies (see the section on ethics and hormones).

There are, however, issues of an ethical nature, which are raised with regard to diagnosis. Although this may be more acute in those cases where inheritable, genetic defects are found and that normally would be expected to ensue from the determination of the sequence of bases in the human genome or modifications to chromosome structure or number, the use of monoclonal antibodies in a diagnostic mode may also provide ethical conundrums for those who are involved. The detection of α-fetoprotein in either amniotic fluids or maternal serum can be achieved through the use of specifically reactive monoclonal antibodies. A positive reaction in this test may indicate that the neural tube of the fetus remains unsealed and that a baby could be born that would suffer from Down's syndrome.

The ethical question posed by such a diagnosis is: What action should one take? It may be possible to take the fetus to full term, in which case either the family would take care of the sick baby or alternatively the baby might be lodged in a social institution where the society would look after the diseased child. In both of these cases a considerable cost would be elicited either in terms of the decreased amount of time the parents could devolve to other children (or their procreation) or in the increased use of social resources. The alternative course of action, which is to procure an abortion, may be contrary to a religiously based ethic. In practice, in most countries, where such information is available, many people elect not to carry the fetus to full term. In some such cases there may result some psychological damage, which, in time, often heals. However, in the 1990s, there is little evidence of wisespread distress, even though some 200,000+ abortions occur in the UK per annum, out of some 5 million abortions annually, worldwide.

A corollary to the discovery of a propensity for a genetically inherited disease is that this knowledge of a future likelihood provides an individual with an unfair advantage when negotiating a premium for, say, a life-insurance policy. It also may be used to the disadvantage of others when accepting certain employments or when entering contractual situations. Legislative assemblies are currently engaged in devising laws to meet this type of contingency. Whatever the outcome of such deliberations, there are ethical issues that need to be addressed. One such provision is that one deals fairly with other members of the community. In presenting one's situation, it is incumbent on individuals to provide, without intentional deception, all relevant information. As we move into a data-dominated era, decisions about whether or not to acquire information about one's genetic make up become more pressing; in some cases it is not clear that the acquisition of such details is to the advantage of the possessor.

ETHICS AND THE USE OF VIRUSES TO MODIFY HUMAN AND ANIMAL GENOMES

Animal cells in culture can be used to produce the vaccinia, herpes, and adenoviruses that are commonly used to attempt to introduce exogenous genes into the human genome. As the adenovirus targets the lung and the disease cystic fibrosis results from the genetically caused formation of an abnormal mucin, it is logical to use this vector to infect lung cells with an adenovirus virus that has been engineered to carry the gene for normal mucin production. To date, attempts at this kind of viral therapy have only been partially successful, in that relief has been obtained for a limited period amounting to several months. Nevertheless, such efforts do mark the way we may achieve progress.

Most regulatory authorities and legislative assemblies condone the use of such vectors to achieve the genetic modification of the somatic cells of humans for therapeutic purposes but do not sanction the modification of the gametic cells (spermatozoa and ova). The ethical position taken is that we may help a diseased individual, but we may not develop the techniques necessary to modify, in an inheritable way, the human species. While it is necessary to point out that we lack the basic knowledge to enable us to achieve human gametic genetic modification in a safe and beneficial way, it is also useful to note that if we do not attempt to accomplish such a goal, we are unlikely ever to be successful. (The production of genetically engineered strains of mice and other animals is a growing commercial activity; here the carrier of the transgene is applied to the embryo and as most of the embryonic cells are infected, the transgene becomes incorporated into the cells that make the gametes. It would seem that this technique could be applicable to humans. However, it may be necessary to have knowledge of the nature of the embryo before embarking on a transformation that may not have been necessary.) There are over 5,000 genetically inherited diseases, each caused by single different deleterious mutation. It would seem worthwhile, therefore, to work towards the elimination of such impediments from the families so stricken, once and for all.

A similar case may be made for the re-engineering of humans to be able to resist all known pathogens without going through the process of vaccination. It is conceivable that this may be accomplished by the addition to the human genome of genes coding for the antibodies and chemicals that evoke those T-cell responses that would have been induced as a result of the inoculation of an exogenous immunogen. This procedure can also be applied to animals, which would obviate difficult and expensive vaccination campaigns. Again such modifications might be most advantageously introduced into the germ line. Were this to cause the eventual elimination of the pathogenic organism (*qua* smallpox), then humans could applaud this decrease in the risk of pathogenic infections. However, this would also represent a decrease in the amount of biodiversity, which would be regarded by some as a loss. A way a round the latter position would be to determine the full sequence of the bases of the genes of the pathogen, such that, were the revival of that organism regarded as worthwhile, its genes could be synthesised *de novo* (from the electronic or paper copy stored formula), and following an infection process, the previously extinct pathogen could be made to re-emerge.

The present-day legislative block on human gametic genetic engineering may be more directed at the prevention of the deliberate production of humans with exceptional abilities. We must note, however, that from some 750 to 1,500 random gene mutations and gene incorporations, eliminations, and transpositions, etc., the human species has emerged from its chimpanzee or bonobo-like condition over a period of 4–8 million years. It would, therefore, be likely that an equivalent transition would occur naturally in the next 4–8 million years. But, having acquired the ability deliberately to modify the genes in the human genome, we might expect such changes to occur over a considerably shortened time period of, say, hundreds of years as opposed to millions (see also the section on ethical issues in the genetic enhancement of humans). As we do not know for certain in what directions we should move with regard to such changes, it would be prudent and pragmatic to move, in small steps, in many directions at the same time, and, having evaluated the consequences, determine a general bearing for further investigation. It may be that in this process, individuals would arise who would be disadvantaged as a result of the implementation of the gene modification program. Such people would need to be treated with compassion and care so that their dignity was not impugned and their contribution to the progress of humanity was recognized and rewarded.

ETHICS AND HORMONE TREATMENTS

A wide range of hormones can be made from animal cells in culture. These include growth hormone, erythropoietin, insulin, follicle stimulating hormone, leutenizing hormone, somatostatin, prolactin, nerve cell growth hormone (NCGH), and others. These substances can control the nature of the animals into which they are injected. Additionally, it is possible to use the genes that code for these hormones, when incorporated into a viral vector, as a means of generating transfected animals and humans that permanently secrete larger amounts of the hormone than normal. This may lead to larger animals, or cows with increased milk yields, or animals deliberately rendered sterile. A consequence of effecting such changes is that the economics of particular industries may be affected, with the displacement of groups of farmers (for example) from the workforce. There is also a series of concerns based on the production of unusual animals. However, the latter eventualities may be likened to the selective breeding programs that have been used for dogs, camels, turkeys, or horses, whereby breeds have emerged that are incapable of survival except through the offices of human carers. As each development is novel, it may be most appropriate to deal with the issues that arise on a case-by-case basis.

Many hormone treatments deal with attempts to ameliorate disease situations. Others relate to efforts to enhance the nature of humans and may only be considered as disease alleviators were psychological discomfort to be considered a disease. Ethically, it is generally acceptable to treat physical disease by the most appropriate means. However, society generally has mixed feelings about the use of psychoactive treatments (with the notable exceptions of nicotine, alcohol, barbiturates, Prozac, Vallium, etc.). Similar proscriptions apply to those who wish to enhance aspects of their body or performance. This latter subject is dealt with in greater detail in the next section.

Hormone Applications to Enhance Human Performance. One case that has generated considerable media attention recently has been the use of growth hormone and/or erythropoietin by athletes and others engaged in sport (40). It surfaced in the recent (1998) *Tour de France*, when members of several of the leading teams were arrested and their living quarters searched for these materials. But attempts to enhance the performance of athletes through hormone treatements is a feature of the competitive events of the past 50 years. In particular, some former East German sports trainers were alleged to have dosed their young athletes with body-enhancing drugs without having gained the prior informed consent of the youngsters. Many of the so-treated contestants, who have survived into the present world, have spoken of their experiences and provide living evidence of the potential for damage that can be caused by the uncontrolled use of such materials. It is also thought that Flo-Jo (Florence Griffith-Joyner), an American female runner who holds the current world records for the 100 and 200 m, sprints took advantage of body-enhancing drugs; she died from heart seizure in 1998 at the age of 38 (41).

There are two ethical considerations. On the one hand, if the laws or regulations governing the conduct of participants in the sport specifically delineate the nonuse of "prowess enhancers," then clearly people who use the newly available hormones are in breach of these rules and can be banned from the competition. However, as the two hormones delineated are normal components of the body, it is difficult to effect a blood test and then conclude that the individual has been in receipt of enhancing hormonal treatments. (The erythropoietin is most advantageously administered some 6 weeks before the competition and is only detectable in the blood for a few days after injection.) There are two responses to this contingency. The one requires the manufacturer of the hormone to adulterate the material with a detectable component to act as a marker, while the other examines the level of red blood cells in the athlete, and were there to be over 50% above a recognized norm, then it would be concluded that enhancers had been used and the athlete would be disqualified. That athletes carefully control their diet and include in their food intake many additives of a vitamin, amino acid, or lipidic nature is well known. Thus it is difficult to draw a line between the added hormone and these special food supplements, particularly if techniques of oral administration of the hormones become commonplace.

On the other hand, the rules may be altered to allow the use of enhancers. This generates another series of ethical questions. Would it be permissible for athletes to use enhancers (hormones) to the point that would either put them at risk of damaging themselves while competing or in the aftermath of the competition? As our knowledge of the likely consequences of enhancement are relatively sparse, would we be justified in doing these experiments on, albeit willing, individuals in search of riches and glory? Would richer athletes be allowed to express their financial advantage through the purchase of the most expensive enhancers applied by qualified personnel under strict supervision? Do we want to observe a competition based on the relative abilities of those who are engineering the enhancement of the athlete? Should the athlete then become an agent of the enhancement system, and should not the enhancers share in the prize, etc.? Would it be sensible to run a two-tier sport system, where one goes all out for a maximized performance while the other is based on what the trained human body can achieve in the absence of added non-nutrient chemical or biochemicals? It may be that the genie of enhancement is out of the box: How we exploit the potential of such agents in sport has yet to be decided, but it is not unlikely that our curiosity of the potential of such materials will override our ethical concerns, and we may be able carefully to explore the new envelope of human ability that is unlocked through such facilities.

Hormonal enhancement of the growth of children who are suffering from "dwarfism" is now a generally acceptable way of providing therapy to such individuals. It is also used, more questionably, by parents who believe their children to be too small. But it is clear that were we to use other hormones, for example, nerve cell growth factor (NCGF), to extend the size of the brain, then further ethical questions are in order. It is well known that the size of a brain *per se* does not necessarily provide for greater intelligence. However, the increase in brain size as we moved from the apes to the humans from, say, 500 to 1,500 ml is associated with an intelligence enhancement. Assuming that we could achieve a further extension to the intelligence of an individual by the application, from birth, of NCGH, then the ethical issues we would have to consider would seek to delineate how we might proceed. Would the application of this type of hormone lead to incurable immediate or latent injuries, and how might such disadvantaged people be treated? Who should receive such brain extension treatments? How might we educate or deploy these people? How many people should be treated? Would this create an elite, and would this elite seek to be self-limiting and perpetuating? How might the socialization of these people be achieved? Are there any political/geopolitical issues that need to be addressed? What effect would it have on ethnic and racial matters? Would such people have a special status and be differentiated from those not so treated? Would the pronouncements of these individuals be listened to with greater belief, and what would be the consequences of such attention? We do not have a body of understanding that would enable us to answer these questions. Nor do we have theories that can reliably predict the outcome of such experiments. Adopting a trial and error approach will lead to mistakes but will also provide insights as to how to proceed to maximize the benefits.

Our societies are quite clear on what they regard as desirable. It is not only the monetary value and incomes of sports people, stars of the stage and screen, and purveyors of popular music that can provide the clues as to the way society values particular personal properties, but there are equivalent rewards for shrewdness in business, artistic flair, and ruthless determination. Other attributes, such as height, strength, mental ability, hair/eye/skin color, and symmetry may be taken as elements in the construction of an individual who can excel in these or other denoted areas. The question that falls from these considerations is whether we would wish to produce more people with attributes of higher value as depicted previously? Another way of phrasing this question is to ask whether we would wish to construct our mating (status) hierarchies on the basis of the parameters delineated? How we proceed in this matter will depend upon the establishment of the necessary control systems and upon the careful, sensitive, and open way by which we engage in society-wide experimentation with alternative forms of using the techniques which have been made available to us via the production of animal cells in culture.

Ethical Issues in the Genetic Enhancement of Humans. Humans may be enhanced as a result of incorporating new genes into their chromosomes. These would be delivered by viruses that integrate some or all of their genomes in the cellular organelles. When the viruses are genetically engineered to contain genes coding for human hormones, we might expect similar effects as the repetitive addition of hormones by mouth or injection. The ethical issues raised by these procedures are dealt with in the section on ethics and human hormone treatments. In what follows the focus will be on the essential inheritability of the newly incorporated genes.

In modifying the human genome in a directed way and with genes whose expression products will have major influences on the nature of the human form and its capabilities, we must pause and consider the implications. There is the prospect of creating the equivalent of a new race of individuals who might have properties that would lead to their dominance over the present species of humans. Should such an operation get out of control, then the disaster scenarios of a subset of the futurists may become realized. There is little doubt that the Neanderthals were superseded by the *Homo sapiens* group. Whether this was a painful transition is unknown, but judging from the totality of the event, it may be that in the competition between the two species, the successful one completely eliminated those who were less well endowed. Would this process be repeated in a future species takeover? May we develop the ethical guidelines that would enable us to proceed with a deliberately engineered species replacement, not through the process of physical annihilation, but by

a process based on benign, phased, and compliant replacement? Alternatively, could we build into the new species of *Homo* that we make features that require it to form a symbiotic union with the existing species of *Homo*? But it is clear that if we do not think such events through ahead of time, we are more likely to be taken by surprise, and under such circumstances we may not make decisions that would enable a pacific outcome.

ETHICS AND ENZYMES

Using animal cell cultures to produce enzymes such as tissue-plasminogen activator, blood clotting factor VIII, or DNAase may seem to be unburdened with ethical problems; the three enzymes are therapeutically active and useful. However, there are issues that relate to the most cost-effective treatment of blood clots in heart attacks, where substances such as aspirin and the relatively inexpensive bacterial product asparaginase may also be efficacious. A new suite of over 40 immunomodulatory proteins/glycoproteins has been discovered in the past 20 years. Manipulation of the composition and concentration of these chemicals can be used to improve the immune response to vaccines, infections, cancers, and autoimmune diseases such as the rheumatic disorders. Again the main ethical issue that emerges is the affordability and availability of these materials.

While present techniques focus on the development in drug form of the enzyme therapeutics made by animal cells in culture, it should be possible in the future to provide the same therapy via the use of an infecting virus, which was furnished with the controllable expression gene coding for the therapeutic enzyme protein. It should be noted that repetitive drug treatments are expensive, while one-off infections are much less costly (once the expenditures of obtaining a licence to produce and market the product have been covered; see the section on regulatory processes).

Ethical Tests Using Animal Cell Cultures to Replace Animals. Millions of rats, mice, rabbits, guinea pigs, and, to a much lesser extent, cats, dogs, and monkeys, are used annually in toxicity tests and efficacy tests for a variety of drugs, vaccines, and foods. In a few such cases the relationship between the toxicity to the animal and the human has been determined, but in many other cases this relationship remains obscure. These tests are time consuming, use expensive facilities, yield results with large variances, and in the final analysis may or may not be relevant. As techniques for the growth of animal cells in culture have developed, it has become possible to produce cell lines that retain many of the differentiated characteristics of the original tissues. Such cell cultures, derived from different organs and a wide variety of animals, may be used to determine the toxicity and, in some cases, the efficacy of food, drugs, and vaccines. In so far as it is possible to store and aliquot the cells made in the cultures, it becomes practicable to effect repeat tests and with multiples of samples in a rapid and reproducible manner. Statistically significant results, therefore, become more likely. However, it is not always clear that observations on cells in culture reflect the effects of the material under test in the target animal: the human. It is possible to obtain correlations between the effects of a substance on any of the animal models and the effects of the same substance in a cell culture alternative system. Although this in itself requires the extensive use of animals, it may be condoned, as the intention is eventually to omit the animal test and proceed solely with the cell culture equivalent.

The wholesale slaughter of millions of small mammals in the search for the protection of humans from the toxic effects of biopharmaceuticals and foods is an activity that is unlikely to be completely eliminated. Although the relationship between these tests and effects on humans is limited and sometimes misleading (penicillin is toxic to cats but does not affect humans at doses that eliminate sensitive bacteria), they determine whether of not permission is granted to try materials on humans. Through the establishment of the necessary correlations with changes in appearance, metabolism, surface adhesiveness, response to selective stains, or other observable parameters, it should become possible, and would be more acceptable, were animal cell cultures to be used in place of the animal tests. Nevertheless, as part of the regulatory procedures, a cautious pragmatic approach is adopted whenever new materials are applied to, or provided for, humans.

Ethical Aspects of Producing Agents Others Might Consider Valuable in Biological Warfare. Viruses have been used as agents of war or genocide. Whereas the historical sources of such viruses were once diseased humans or cadavers, modern technology can produce copious quantities of potentially lethal viruses from animal cells in culture. While these agents would be useless when applied to a vaccine-protected population, in the absence of such prophylaxis untold damage could result. Also, through the use of genetic engineering techniques, new viruses may be deliberately constructed whose pathogenic properties may be both predictable and enhanced when compared with viruses that can be isolated from diseased individuals.

Not only may the pathogenicity of such agents be extended, but the hardiness of the organisms may be sufficiently enhanced to enable the distribution of the agent to be achieved under physical and environmental conditions that would normally be lethal to that pathogenic virus. Thus viruses that are stable to desiccation, high temperatures, the sun's ultraviolet radiation, and extremes of pH, might be engineered.

Biological warfare conventions, which forbid the production and use of biological agents or their derivatives in any conflict situation, do not prohibit the production of agents or vaccines that would be protective against putative biological warfare agents. However, this results in a conundrum. To produce an agent to be a prophylatic against a potential viral pathogen, one would have to have produced the pathogen ahead of time. This latter entity would be a biological warfare agent, but produced with the specific *intent* of generating its vaccinal antidote. Therefore, the determination of the *intent* of the pathogen producer is crucial to the ethicality of the productive activity. It is the objective of current thinking by those who are negotiating the treaties that are focused on the prevention of biological warfare to define conditions under which such research may or may not take place.

The determination of the intentions of a nation state, or the secretive leader thereof, is held to be ascertainable through both direct and indirect methods. The former would consist of the right to unannounced inspection of any facility that was thought to harbor a virus production operation that was not oriented to vaccine or therapeutic applications. This approach suffers from the disadvantage that industrial ventures do not like people surveying, and asking questions about, what they hold to be their commercially valuable secrets. Indirect methods would have to rely on the observation of the flow of funds, the ordering of relevant equipment, the training and movements of people who were thought capable of a virus production operation and a careful monitoring of the information flow to and from potentially active institutions. As it is difficult to detect the production of biological weapons at a distance, it is necessary to acquire information from the people actively engaged in their production. Such reports might be acquired were attractive rewards and informant protection programs made available. Another suggestion is for all those trained as microbiologists of fermentation technologist to be required to swear an oath committing them to use their knowledge and skill to protect and preserve human life (42).

While it is possible to set out ethical guidelines for behavior in regard to the production of viruses of increased utility in a war situation, it would also be ethically justified to set about rapidly acquiring the abilities to develop the necessary vaccines that would protect against any such agent. Although this may seem like an impossible task, particularly as we bear in mind the hypervariability of the HIV or influenza virus, there are yet many indications that we can make effective vaccines to the immunosubdominant epitopes, which are much less variable that the immunodominant epitopes that have commanded our attention until this time. Were this possible, then through the production of a relatively few vaccines we would be able to protect against a wide range of viruses, irrespective of the particular composition or configuration of their principal point of interaction with the immune system.

In demanding the development of radically new types of vaccines to counter potential threats of hostile virus use, it is possible to produce agents that can protect human populations against the infectious and pathogenic organisms that occur in nature. In this way we may be able better to protect ourselves as a species against viral attack. So the threat of biological warfare, waged with pathogenic viruses, is not wholly without ethically redeeming features. But these benefits will most positively accrue only if the threat of biological war is not activated.

ETHICAL ISSUES CONTINGENT ON *IN VITRO* FERTILIZATION

Since 1978, when Steptoe, and Edwards demonstrated that it was possible to obtain the fertilization of a human ovum by spermatozoa in a Petri dish, the applications and developments of this new technique have been manifold. To collect the maximum number of mature ova from females, hormone treatments are used, and to increase the success (up from 5 to 20%) of the technique a number (a maximum of 5 in the U.S.) of viable embryos are implanted into either the hormonally prepared womb of the ova provider or a willing surrogate mother. A recent variant (which obviates the defective mitochondrial genes of one of the mothers) involved the use of two ova from different females, where the nucleus was taken from one ovum and inserted into the anucleated ovum from the second female. This hybrid was fertilized by spermatozoa in the normal way. This results in an embryo with three genetic parents. Consequent on the use of these techniques we have situations in which a woman may have her ova fertilized by the spermatozoa of a dead man, who may or may not have been willing to procreate. A new technique enables the spermatozoa-generating cells of a healthy male to be transplanted into a male whose testicular tissues have been damaged due, for example, to an irradiation treatment to cure cancer. Also the viable embryos of such procedures may be cryopreserved for 5–10 years or more. During this time the parties to the production of the embryo may have separated or their circumstances may have changed such that their need for the embryo has ceased; on occasion the putative parents have disappeared. Under these eventualities, the laboratory effecting the fertilization may either use the embryo for limited research or it is destroyed. While it has been common practice with animals to separate the cells of a growing embryo and create from each cell a new embryo, the same technology may be used to create clones of humans. The times when such embryos may be implanted could lead to the birth of identical brothers or sisters over an extended period. By manipulating the sperm, it is possible to enhance the production of male or female embryos, or alternatively, it is relatively simple to examine the sex of the embryo and discard those embryos that are not of the desired sex. A further motive for this method of conception is the production of a child at a time in a woman's career after she has reached her highest level of professional development and has also moved into the menopause. These techniques have been most helpful in providing for otherwise infertile couples the children they have desperately sought.

The cell culture techniques outlined have led to a number of changes in behavior and thereby a new series of ethical questions. To what extent is the genetic provenance of an embryo a factor in the birthing and raising of children? How may surrogate mothers be prepared for their ordeal and reimbursed for their pains? What is the effect of establishing a market in unfertilized ova? May spermatozoa from one individual be sought after and used repeatedly? (There are reports of one doctor surreptitiously siring over 60 embryos with his own sperm before he was called to task.) What is the ethical position on a woman's desire to produce a child with the spermatozoa of a notable or famous person? Are "designer" babies, if permissible, desirable? Is it justified to require the hormonally enhanced increase in the frequency of ovulation and the procedure of ova extraction to be undertaken by females who do not wish to have children themselves but are prepared to provide ova to others? How will the ability to select the sex of a child reflect on social and family developments? What will the parent–child relationship be like were the parenting to take place much later in the life of the parents? How would single parenting or the parenting of children by people who are not heterosexual affect the profile of individuals in the society? Would it be ethical deliberately to seek the production of clones? (see the section on ethical issues raised by the possibilities of cloning humans). What are the implications for the fostering and adoption of children as the number of suitable homes for these youngsters decreases? What is it prudent to tell children of such origins about their parents?

There is great sympathy for the childless couple who have tried every available means to procreate and who have failed. This extends to the mature, and now infertile, parents who have lost only children in perilous circumstances or through disease. From the wide suite of options available, it is now possible to provide these individuals with the offspring they seek. Nevertheless, the questions posed apply as much to a future world as the present. We do not know how the manifestations of the new *in vitro* tools to provide fertility and an enhanced degree of control of the nature of the children created will affect our future collective well-being. Although we do have some experience of attempting to change the sex ratio using infanticide as the method, and many of the questions raised in the preceding paragraph have been tested in the courts of some countries, the new laboratory techniques provide a novel departure from traditional practices, which could lead the accentuation of such otherwise rare occurrences. Under these conditions we can only proceed by a process of trial and error, unless we adopt a more stringent set of ethics that does not permit such "tinkering" with the lives of humans. To delimit procreation to primeval coital techniques restricts human development. As has been the case in the past, we may gain more from grappling with the challenge of the new, not by its elimination, but by seeking ways whereby it may be beneficially exploited.

ETHICAL ISSUES RAISED BY THE POSSIBILITIES OF CLONING HUMANS

The techniques pioneered by Wilmut and others (32,33), which have led to the development of the cloning of mammals by the use of nuclear transfer, may be considered as providing engineers and scientists with a new tool. Whenever a fresh tool appears on the horizon, people express concern over the possible uses to which it might be applied. They are well aware that when the capability of amplifying the actions of humans through the use of implements becomes practicable, there is a corresponding increase in the capability to perform both beneficial and harmful acts. A hammer may be used to curtail life (43), just as it can be used to embed nails; a pen may be used to flatter or defame; fire may sterilize food, harden spear points, bake clay vessels for cooking and storage, and keep predators at bay, and rustle prey to a lethal ambush while causing death by burning.

Taking a historical perspective, it is clear that many tools that have come to be esteemed and highly valued have had periods in their relationship with humankind where they were regarded as dangerous and reviled. Humans are the only animals to use fire deliberately. One can imagine that the first fire users often died as a result of the infections resulting from burn wounds. Nevertheless, persistent application to the techniques whereby the fire might be tamed and used with confidence must have taken a considerable time. During this learning period, the early humans would have developed rules (or guidelines for behavior; *viz.* ethics), the use of language would have become more valuable, and the education of novices would become a necessity. Once mastery over the fire-tool had become the norm, the wide diversity of its uses could be explored. The same procedures might have been applied to the development of explosives, the techniques of mining, travel by boat or air. What these histories have in common is that when presented with potentially dangerous tools, humans have been able to suppress the disadvantageous aspects and enhance the advantages. Although such procedures may have presented difficulties *ab initio*, through a trial and error approach, a suite of rules with the corresponding controls was derived. This enabled those experienced in the art of the new tool use to proceed to glean the benefits and also to teach succeeding generations the secrets and mysteries of the properties of the new tools.

Tools, therefore, are powerful adjuncts for the human condition. It is good that we are wary of the prospective uses of new tools. This is particularly germane when we consider the potential uses of genetic engineering and cloning. The cloning tool is viewed with some alarm. Are we to permit the cloning of individuals because people want to avail themselves of the "right to reproduce"? (U.N. Declaration of Human Rights: ... Art. 3 "Everyone has the right to life ..." and at Art. 16, "Men and women of a full age ... have the right to marry and found a family ...."). And, on *a priori* grounds, cloning, for the establishment of a family that cannot otherwise be formed, cannot be excluded either. However, the cloning tool may also be used for eugenic ends, which some people would find objectionable.

The application of cloning techniques to achieve eugenic ends is one of the greater fears of those who have been impressed by the failed efforts in human eugenics, which have peppered the historical canvas of the past 1000 years or more. Societies have sought their betterment by limiting the reproductive abilities of those members who are sick, incapable of looking after themselves, or mentally deficient. Other positive eugenic campaigns have sought to increase the chances of the more "desirable" members of society establishing the next generation. Sometimes

the society is stratified through a caste system; other times a monetary gradation in used; a further way is to define an aristocracy or power-based subset of the society to further the breeding ambitions of those who seek to improve the quality of the societal "blood stock." In the recent past we have witnessed attempts to deny the reproductive activities of selected individuals in the United States, Sweden, and Nazi Germany (44–46), while today we observe similar efforts at social control in China. These policies are contrary to many ethical guidelines. The need for fairness, the proscription of discrimination, the denial of the basic rights to set up a family and reproduce, and the removal of personal autonomy are all ethical norms that often have counterparts in documents outlining human rights. However, contrary rulings may be obtained from consensus ethics or from communitarian or survivalistic teachings. One possible way ahead is not to eliminate eugenic thinking altogether, but to consider ways in which one might proceed, while protecting the dignity and sense of self-worth of anybody affected by the activity. This matter has not been resolved, but will need great care were it progressed, as it readily excites memories of previous disasters and human suffering on unprecedented scales.

But it is clear that the use of tools whose development lies in the future cannot be evaluated with regard to benefits and harms accrued. Rather we must seek to use the guidelines afforded by our ethical systems to answer the question as to what rules we can apply to the future tools to maximize the benefit and minimize the harm that might be expected from their use. We can proceed with such an examination on the basis of a theoretical evaluation of benefit and harm, or we might take a more practical approach, as will be described in the following.

Theoretical Approaches to the Regulation of a Future Tool Use. In the contemporary literature on the use of the cloning tool, the major schools of ethical thinking are used by those who seek to ground their objections on what might be respectable philosophical bases. Thus we have the American President (W. Clinton) asserting that "... human cloning would have to raise deep concerns, given our most cherished concepts of faith and humanity. Each human life is unique, born of a miracle that reaches beyond laboratory science." This might be regarded as exemplifying the application of virtue ethics: a process of deriving guidelines for behavior from one's emotional (gut) reactions to ethical questions or one based on the virutes of faith, humanity, and the desire to maintain the uniqueness of the individual. The consequentialists (utilitarians, teleologists) who hold that the outcome of the act determines its value rather than the way the act comes into being do not hold much sway either, because we do not know the outcomes of the cloning activity. Medical ethicists (bioethicists) who adhere to the principles of "autonomy, beneficence, nonmaleficence, and justice" might regard cloning as an extension of autonomy (in enabling the nonfertile to have offspring), or as a decline in autonomy, as the offspring do not have an equivalent chance of being as different from their parents as is usual in human sexual reproduction. Some of those who adhere to an absolute ethics based on holy texts and their interpretation by hermeneuts may come out in favor of cloning cells or genes for the use in saving lives but balk at the cloning of whole humans for other than the obviation of the problems of infertility in married couples. Other religious groups have advocated a complete ban on the cloning technology (47). However, they would do well to reconsider the Adam and Eve story as the first depiction of human cloning. Were we to look to biology for our ethics, then we can perceive many examples where cloned animals succeed and where similar species of animals persist as sexually reproducing entities. One could conclude that biology demonstrates that any way in which a species may reproduce may have survivalistic advantages in particular niches, and that variations in the reproductive method are of value so that as many niches as possible may be colonized by that animal family.

However, most of the discussion of the ethics of the human cloning tool have arisen from the declaration of the rights of individuals to be unique and to have identities that pertain to themselves alone (The Universal Declaration on the Human Genome and Human Rights of November, 1997, the UNESCO document claims at Art 2b. "That dignity makes it imperative not to reduce individuals to their genetic characteristics and to respect their uniqueness and diversity."). Making a human clone is an attempt at making a human as alike as an identical twin to another human. We are well aware that identical twins are as similar to one another as it is possible for humans to achieve. Yet it is well known that in the most rigorous identical twin studies only some 70% or so of the responses to intelligence tests are equivalent. When other characteristics are measured, the correlation between identical twins is less impressive. Whatever we do in the cloning of humans, it would be virtually impossible to produce identical people. Experiences in the womb, the mitochondrial DNA of the ovum used, environmental influences post-parturition are such that, even if one were specifically to set about the production of identical (unable to distinguish in any way) humans, the task would probably never be achieved.

The second argument, which is based on the impugning of the dignity of a human, is also flawed. It may seem that were one to clone an individual for personal or social reasons, that such humans have become commodified (dehumanized) as a result of the process. But then we all have resulted from the desire of our parents to reproduce. Not only that, many parents take an active role in bringing their children up to be a particular kind of person, of imbuing them with respect and manners and even the rudiments of a career. Traditionally, children were regarded a resource for running a farm and providing sustenance for ageing parents. Are such children thereby commodified? It would be reckless to think that one can raise children so that they are free from the influences of the environment in which they are housed. Yet in seeking to control the way they develop we do not assert that they have been dehumanized. In extreme cases, where such teachings are ineffective and punitive acts are applied, we may consider that the efforts in control have "gone too

far" and that the rights of the child to be as they wish should be given greater scope. Thus at the appropriate time and under suitable conditions control devolves from parents to children. It is difficult to appreciate why this should not also pertain in the case of cloned individuals. So the invocation of the UNESCO declaration by Federiko Mayor (48) to declaim human cloning is not a particularly effective way to achieve this object.

Practical Approaches to New Tool Uses. When early humans were experimenting with clubs, scrapers, spears, and fire, they were generally bereft of theories of nature or deities. Indeed, they could not have had notions as to how such tools might be used in a future far beyond that encompassed by their relatively short life spans. Nevertheless, they persevered with their devices and developed mechanisms for their beneficial use. Today, we have more sophisticated procedures to ensure that tools old, new, or future have the maximum chance of generating the most benefit. We can establish regulations that limit and legitimize tool uses. Hammers may not be used for murder, as the latter is outlawed; spoons cannot administer poison for the same reason. To make sure that we have appropriate guidelines we set up committees, authorities, and bodies of regulators to make and administer laws, rules, and regulations. To back up such bodies we have a public address system under the guise of the press and media. Their efficacy is assured when we are open and transparent in our dealings with them, especially when something new has burst upon the scene. In transmitting data and evidence about the nature of new tools and their powers, the media used in public communication provide a service that enables us to examine exhaustively each new development in the light of people's opinions and in the views of appropriate experts. In this way we become forewarned as to potential disbenefits and have the opportunity to put in place the necessary strictures to prevent discomfort before it becomes disaster.

The second way in which tool use is contained to personal and social benefit is through education. This may be delivered via parents in the first instance followed by educational establishments and then there is on-the-job training. As a final check the public is capable of making its collective will felt through lobbying the legislature and through legislation. The pressure of opinion as delivered by person-to-person contact and as influenced by the media is also a factor in the education process.

Unburdened by notions of theory or ethics, our ancestors developed and used tools. As we can observe in contemporary situations, children and primates learn to use tools through a trial and error approach. This pragmatism is obviously most applicable when we do not know how to use tools for benefit. A cautious pragmatism prevents great harms from happening. A pragmatism enriched by theoretical notions of prospective dos and don'ts is even more likely to result in human gains with minimal costs or losses. While pragmatism may be characterized by "learning from action," it is salutary to review the steps one might take before embarking on the introduction of a new tool. The listing to follow provides one such reference resource:

- Estimate the hazards (albeit theoretical) before commencing any practical work, and either decreasing them or making provision for observing harmful deviations, or setting aside the ability to correct the operation before it has a chance of effecting harm
- Begin the experimentation by making the smallest possible and relevant changes to the existing *status quo*
- Take time to observe the results of the initial experiments before commencing the next experiment
- Operate in situations in which one can isolate the consequences of a failed experiment
- Develop and make available antidotes to conjectured malfunctions
- Design into the experiment those monitoring and control systems to enable the maximum amount of information to be acquired and to retain the ability to redirect the operation at any time during the course of the test
- Recognize the *precautionary principle* ("one shall take action to avoid potentially damaging impacts on nature even when there is not enough scientific evidence to prove beyond reasonable doubt a causal link between emissions and effects" (49)
- Obtain approval by the relevant committees or review boards
- Adopt a strategy of open communication with colleagues and the public via the media
- Have available the resources to restore any ensuing damage

However we approach the use of the cloning tool, we have a duty of care to proceed with caution and openness. There will be advantages to be gained from different societies operating in different ways. From such divergent approaches we may better perceive the ways in which we might proceed with the likelihood of generating maximized benefits.

On the verge of a new development, we are in the position of the pioneers of the twentieth century who demonstrated the petrol engine, a method for moving heavier than air machines off the ground, radio communication, and simple computers. Only this time the developments are in the area of biology and the subject of those advances is the nature of humankind itself. It would be regressive to claim that we are all that we could be and cannot be improved. Just what those changes are likely to be, and what effect they will have on the human form and character are impossible to predict with any surety. All we can assert at this time is that it is likely there could be many beneficial changes to humanity as we know it. As we differ from our non human primate ancestors, it should not cause us to complain if future descendants of humans are as distinguishable from their progenitors as we are from ours; this is fully in keeping with the 4 billion-year-old tradition that is life.

BIBLIOGRAPHY

1. D. Walsh, W. Franke, and J. Wilcockson, *The Sunday Times (U.K.)* Section 2, August 2, pp. 8–9 (1998).
2. J. Walsh and N. Planck, *Time*, August 24, pp. 40–48 (1998).
3. R.E. Spier, *Sci. Eng. Ethics.* **2**, 259–262 (1996).
4. T.L. Beauchamp and J.E. Childress, *Principles of Biomedical Ethics*, 4th ed., Oxford University Press, Oxford, 1994.
5. R.E. Spier, *Sci. Eng. Ethics.* **2**, 291–306 (1996).
6. R.E. Spier, *Vaccine* **7**, 381–382 (1989).
7. Editorial, *The Economist*, March 16, p. 29 (1996).
8. R.E. Spier, *Encyclo. Appl. Ethics* **4**, 9–28 (1998).
9. C. Crossen, *Tainted Truth: Manipulation of Fact in America*, Simon & Schuster, London, 1994.
10. W. Broad and N. Wade, *Betrayers of the Truth*, Simon & Schuster, New York, 1982.
11. L. Grayson, *Scientific Deception*, The British Library, London, 1995, p. 107.
12. L. Grayson, *Scientific Deception*, an update, The British Library, London, 1997, p. 71.
13. C.E. Harris, Jr., M.S. Pritchard, and M.J. Rabins, *Engineering Ethics, Concepts and Cases*, Wadsworth, London, 1995, p. 411.
14. S. Unger, *Controlling Technology; Ethics and the Responsible Engineer*, 2nd ed., Wiley, New York, 1994, p. 35.
15. M. Williamson, *Biological Invasions*, Chapman & Hall, London, 1996.
16. S. Lock and F. Wells, eds., *Fraud and Misconduct in Medical Research*, BMJ Publishing Group, London, 1993.
17. HRH, the Prince of Wales, *The Daily Telegraph*, August 6 (1998), p. 16.
18. *Social Trends*, HM Stationery Office, London, 1993, p. 23.
19. *Encyclopedia Britannica*, CD Rom version, 1998.
20. J. Rifkin, *The Biotech Century*, Victor Golancz, London, 1998, pp. 80–90.
21. L.P.M. Lloyd-Evans, *Sci. Eng. Ethics* **1**, 93–96 (1995).
22. E. Perrenboom, *Nat. Biotechnol.* **16**, 130 (1998).
23. R.F. Service, *Science* **282**, 850–851 (1998).
24. K.S. Jayaraman, *Nature (London)* **391**, 728 (1998).
25. R. Hoyle, *Nat. Biotechnol.* **14**, 1628 (1996).
26. R.A. Kerr, *Science* **266**, 28–30 (1994).
27. A.M. Timmons et al., *Nature (London)* **380**, 487 (1996).
28. A. Coghlan and K. Kleiner, *New Sci.* **149**, 5 (1998).
29. A.-M. Chevre, F. Eber, A. Beranger, and M. Renard, *Nature (London)* **389**, 924 (1997).
30. E. Masood, *Nature (London)* **394**, 212 (1998).
31. R.E. Spier, *Sci. Eng. Ethics* **3**, 106–108 (1997).
32. I. Willmut et al., *Nature (London)* **385**, 810–813 (1997).
33. T. Wakayama et al., *Nature (London)* **394**, 369–374 (1998).
34. K. Patel, *The Times Higher*, November 13 (1998), p. 5.
35. R.E. Spier, in S. Cohen and A. Shafferman, eds., *Novel Strategies in Design and Production of Vaccines*, Plenum, New York, 1996, pp. 183–189.
36. *Human Tissue/Ethical and Legal Issues*, Nuffield Council on Bioethics, London, p. 153.
37. See articles/letters in *The Times (London)*, November 2, (1995), p. 5; November 5 (1995), p. 19; November 7 (1995), p. 16; November 9 (1995), p. 19.

38. U. Mahnaimi and M. Colvin, *The Sunday Times (London)*, November 15 (1998), p. 1.

39. UNICEF, *The State of the World's Children*, Oxford University Press, Oxford, 1996, p. 103.

40. R. Gareau et al., *Nature (London)* **380**, 113 (1996).

41. J. Bryant, *The Times (London)*, September 24 (1998), p. 5.

42. R.M. Atlas, *ASM News* **64**, 383–389 (1998).

43. P. Wilkinson, *The Times (London)*, January 14 (1998).

44. D.J. Kelves, *In the name of Eugenics*, University of California Press, Berkeley, 1986.

45. P. Weingart, Osiris 2 **5**, 260–282 (1989).

46. A.D. Smith and M. Zaremba, *The Observer*, August 24 (1997), p. 6.

47. P. Hirschberg, *The Jerusalem Rep.* **7** (25) 33–36 (1998).

48. F. Mayor, *The Times: Higher Education Supplement*, February 6 (1998).

49. L. Buhl-Mortensen, S. Welin, and *Sci. Eng. Ethics* **4**, 401–412 (1998).

See also ANIMAL CELL PRODUCTS, OVERVIEW; CELL PRODUCTS—ANTIBODIES; CELL PRODUCTS—IMMUNOREGULATORS; CELL PRODUCTS—VIRAL GENE THERAPY VECTORS; DISEASE RESISTANCE IN TRANSGENIC PLANTS; GENETIC ENGINEERING: ANIMAL CELL TECHNOLOGY; HERBICIDE-RESISTANT PLANTS, PRODUCTION OF; PRODUCT DEVELOPMENT, QUALITY AND REGULATORY ISSUES; TRANSFORMATION OF PLANTS; VIRAL INACTIVATION, EMERGING TECHNOLOGIES FOR HUMAN BLOOD PRODUCTS.

F

FLOW CYTOMETRY OF PLANT CELLS

N.W. BLACKHALL
J.B. POWER
K.C. LOWE
M.R. DAVEY
School of Biological Sciences
University of Nottingham
Nottingham, United Kingdom

OUTLINE

INTRODUCTION

Flow cytometry facilitates the automated analysis of the optical properties of individual cells within large populations (1). Cells or organelles, after suitable preparation and staining, are passed individually in a liquid stream through a focused beam of light, typically from either a laser or an arc lamp (Fig. 1). The scattered light and fluorescence emissions from the cells are collected by lenses and mirrors, subdivided on the basis of their wavelength (color), and passed to one or more detectors. Voltage signals from the detectors are converted into a digital format and used to construct histograms of the intensity of fluorescence or scattered light. Such histograms are displayed on the computer screen of the instrument and form the basis of the analytical system. Populations of cells are identified as peaks on the fluorescence histograms and may be selected for further analysis or sorting. When the instrument is configured for sorting, the stream of liquid containing the cells is broken into droplets that are passed between two charged plates. The computer is able to determine whether individual droplets contain cells that are in the sorted population previously identified in the histograms. It is possible, by charging the individual droplets, to select and to isolate specific cells from a population.

The majority of commercial flow cytometers have been constructed, primarily, for clinical work (2) and are usually located in a hospital/medical research environment, where they are used routinely for diagnostic procedures. In the case of humans and animals, it is relatively simple to obtain a suspension of single cells either from blood samples or by enzymatic and/or mechanical disruption of tissues. However, with plant material, it is more difficult to obtain a suspension of single cells. Consequently, most studies to date have used either isolated protoplasts or isolated organelles.

ANALYSIS AND SORTING OF PLANT PROTOPLASTS

The analysis of mixtures of protoplasts was among the first flow cytometric studies to be undertaken with plants (3–5). The conventional sheath fluid for flow cytometry as developed for animal cells, based on 0.9% (w/v) saline solution (pH 7.4), was replaced with a solution of higher osmotic pressure, such as CPW salts solution (6) supplemented with $130 \, \text{g} \, \text{l}^{-1}$ mannitol, at pH 5.8, in order to preserve the integrity of the osmotically fragile protoplasts. Changes in the operating parameters of the instrument were also necessary because of the larger size of plant protoplasts (10–60 µm in diameter) compared with the size of animal cells (5–20 µm) (7). The ability of flow cytometers to sort plant protoplasts, while maintaining their viability, was first reported in 1984 (8). However, certain difficulties were experienced in the procedure. For example, using protoplasts from suspension cultures of *Nicotiana tabacum* cv. Xanthi, it was observed that the large size of the protoplasts (36 µm in diameter) reduced the efficiency of the sorting process to 50% compared with that of 10-µm-diameter fluorescently labeled calibration beads. The viability of the flow-sorted protoplasts was also reduced, being 50% of that of unsorted (control) protoplasts. Nevertheless, these experiments demonstrated that it was feasible to apply procedures developed for animal cells to plant cell systems.

Attempts were made to use this instrumentation to select heterokaryons resulting from the fusion of protoplasts from different genera and/or species in somatic hybridization experiments. The details relating to the fusion of isolated plant protoplasts, the generation of heterokaryons that develop into hybrid cells and tissues, and the relevance of somatic hybridization to plant improvement programs are discussed elsewhere in this volume. In early experiments (9) to select heterokaryons by flow cytometry, hypocotyl-derived protoplasts of *Glycine argyrea* were fused with cotyledon-derived protoplasts of *G. clandestina*, the latter being stained with fluorescein diacetate (FDA) (10). The green hypocotyl-derived protoplasts exhibited red auto-fluorescence from chlorophyll, while the cotyledon-derived protoplasts, which lacked chlorophyll in their plastids, emitted green fluorescence arising from cleavage of the FDA molecules to fluorescein within the viable protoplasts. Heterokaryons were identified in the flow cytometer by their bifluorescence and sorted into centrifuge tubes. All other material, including homokaryons and unfused parental protoplasts, remained in the main stream of liquid and passed into the waste container.

In other studies, red and green fluorochromes have been used to differentially label morphologically identical parental protoplasts, that is, two populations of protoplasts isolated from chlorophyll-containing tissues or two protoplast populations from cell suspensions. For example, rhodamine isothiocyanate, which fluoresces red

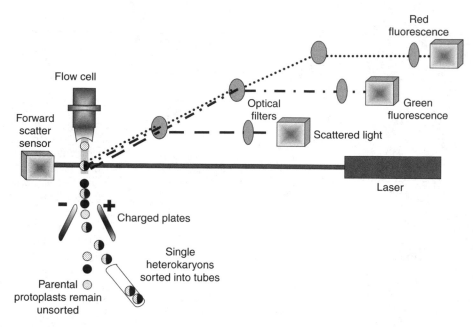

Figure 1. The basic components of a flow cytometer as used for selecting heterokaryons resulting from the fusion of green and red fluorescently labelled plant protoplasts.

but at a different wavelength to chlorophyll, was used to label protein moieties on the surface of protoplasts isolated from leaves of *N. tabacum* cv. Xanthi, while FDA was used to label a second protoplast population from leaves of a nitrate reductase-deficient, streptomycin-resistant mutant of *N. tabacum* (9).

The percentage of the heterokaryons that are retained after sorting varies from 10 to 60%, depending upon the parental species employed in their production. This yield is lower than expected, probably because of the fragility of the heterokaryons, as well as the disruption of the sorting process of the instrument by the protoplasts and the remains of burst protoplasts. In spite of these problems, it has been possible, in an 8-h session, to sort ca. 4×10^6 heterokaryons formed by the fusion of protoplasts of *Brassica oleracea* var. *botrytis* with those of *Raphanus sativus*. Of these heterokaryons, 2.4×10^6 were selected and cultured using a nurse cell system, leading to the production of 12 somatic hybrid plants. Additionally, flow cytometry and cell sorting have been exploited to isolate heterokaryons following the fusion of protoplasts between *B. tournefortii* and *B. napus* (11), from which, after culture, somatic hybrid plants were regenerated. These somatic hybrids exhibited resistance to *Phoma lingam*, demonstrating that a trait of agronomic importance had been transferred from *B. tournefortii* to *B. napus* by protoplast fusion.

In general, sorting of heterokaryons by flow cytometry would only be considered when it is possible to produce and to fuse large numbers of protoplasts (more than 5×10^7) of each parental population. Other procedures have been used for the selection of heterokaryons when the number of protoplasts that can be isolated is limited. For example, manual selection with micropipettes has been employed to select heterokaryons between protoplasts of *Medicago sativa* and *M. falcata*, prior to the regeneration of somatic hybrid plants from heterokaryon-derived tissues (12). The same method of dual fluorescent labeling was also used

in these studies, protoplasts of *M. sativa* being labeled with FDA and those of *M. falcata* with rhodamine isothiocyanate. Although micromanipulation of individual heterokaryons is both time consuming and tedious, it is technically relatively straightforward and is a reliable method for somatic hybrid production.

ANALYSIS OF NUCLEAR DNA CONTENT

Determination of the ploidy of plants is an essential requirement in breeding and genetic manipulation programs. Historically, cytological techniques involving the harvesting of cells during mitosis and/or meiosis, followed by the preparation of cell/tissue squashes and the counting of chromosomes, have been used to determine the ploidy status of plants. Such procedures are time consuming and laborious and depend on the generation of metaphase spreads of chromosomes. In comparison, analysis of the nuclear DNA content of cells by flow cytometry is straightforward and provides a rapid indication of ploidy.

The DNA content per genome varies considerably within plants, ranging from less than 1 pg per 2C nucleus (e.g., *Aphanes arvensis*, 0.6 pg) to 254 pg in *Fritillaria acmopetala*. Knowledge of such variation has been useful for studies of plant taxonomy and evolution (13). Numerous investigations have shown that the DNA content per genome is usually constant and, consequently, is characteristic for each species. Several techniques have been developed to determine DNA content. Principally, these involve physio-chemical estimations after bulk extraction from a large number of cells (14) or *in situ* microphotodensitometry of nuclei stained by the Feulgen method (15). A comprehensive list of DNA amounts per nucleus has been compiled and updated (16).

In the application of flow cytometry to analyze DNA content, simple procedures have been described for isolating nuclei from intact leaves (17,18) in which 0.1–0.5 g fresh weight of leaf material is chopped in a buffer containing 25–100 mg l^{-1} of the DNA binding fluorochrome propidium iodide. The samples are introduced into the instrument following their passage through a 30-μm filter to remove larger debris. The nuclei are passed sequentially through a 488-nm laser beam, and the red fluorescence emissions are collected and quantified. Two populations of nuclei can be identified with different levels of fluorescence for each sample. These populations are in the G_0/G_1 and the G_2/M phases of the cell cycle. The ploidy is determined by comparison of the position of the G_0/G_1 peak with that of seed-derived diploid material of the same species. In this way, large populations of plants from breeding programs or procedures involving tissue culture-based technologies can be screened to detect variation in ploidy between individuals. The use of calibration standards, consisting of nuclei isolated from the leaves of plants with a known quantity of DNA per nucleus, such as *Hordeum vulgare* cv. Sultan (11.12 pg), *Pisum sativum* cv. Minerva Maple (9.73 pg), and *Senecio vulgaris* (2.94 pg), allows estimation of the total DNA content per genome in the material under investigation.

The choice of fluorochrome in estimations of nuclear DNA content is governed by the application and by the availability of a suitable light source for excitation. The fluorochrome propidium iodide intercalates into the helical structure of DNA molecules independently of the actual base composition. Alternative staining procedures have been described using 4,6-diamidino-2-phenylindole (DAPI) and the bisbenzimide dyes Hoechst 33258 and Hoechst 33342 (19), which frequently result in more precise DNA staining and improved resolution during flow cytometric analysis. However, DAPI and the Hoechst dyes bind to the minor groove of DNA at adenine (A) and thymine (T) rich sites; they require at least 4 AT pairs and possess a marked affinity for 5 or 6 pairs in a sequence (20,21). Consequently, propidium iodide is considered to be the most suitable fluorochrome when determinations are being made of the total DNA content per nucleus. DAPI and the bisbenzimide dyes are more suitable for detecting small changes in DNA content between samples with the same overall AT content.

Flow cytometry of fluorochrome-labeled DNA has proved to be useful for determining the ploidy and, hence, the taxonomic relationships between *Glycine* species (22). Other applications relate to assessments of the ploidy of tissue culture-derived plants (23) and somatic hybrids generated during protoplast fusion (24), assessing the stability of ploidy in *Solanum* species after recovery from cryopreservation (25) and detecting any ploidy changes in the seed progeny of transgenic plants, such as those of rice (26).

ANALYSIS AND SORTING OF CHROMOSOMES

Numerous studies have been undertaken to analyze and to sort plant chromosomes by extending the procedures developed for intact nuclei (27). Chromosomes are released by lysis of protoplasts using hypotonic buffers or by mechanical disruption of the protoplast membranes by passage through a hypodermic needle. It is essential to increase the mitotic index of the source material in order to have an adequate number of chromosomes and to be able to identify the chromosomes on the fluorescence histogram. Combined treatments of cell suspension cultures with DNA synthesis inhibitors, such as hydroxyurea and colchicine, can be used to enhance the mitotic index in protoplasts subsequently isolated enzymatically from such cells.

Chromosomes released from isolated protoplasts are stained by DNA-specific fluorochromes, as described for the analysis of nuclear DNA content, before being characterized by their fluorescence intensity in order to produce histograms (flow karyotypes). Chromosomes generate individual peaks when the fluorescence of each chromosome is distinct, or composite peaks when the fluorescence intensity reveals the DNA content of different chromosomes to be similar. Flow cytometry presents the capability to analyze statistically large populations of chromosomes as compared to classical cytology, which is based upon cell-by-cell analysis. It has been possible, with the availability of multilaser instruments, to excite simultaneously multiple fluorochromes on single chromosomes (multivariate analysis). For example, greater resolution can be obtained than is possible with single fluorochrome analysis by employing two fluorochromes, Chromomycin A3 (guanine and cytosine binding) and Hoechst 33258 (adenine and thymine binding), simultaneously (28). Such multivariate procedures are now considered commonplace (29).

In recent years, chromosome analysis and sorting have been given a considerable boost by the availability of PCR-based procedures for amplification and labeling of specific fragments of DNA. Thus a strategy has been described (30) for sorting chromosomes, differing in size by less than 2% of the genome DNA content, in which chromosomes are labeled by PCR with a fluorescent nucleotide. The PCR labeling results in fluorescence signals attached to a specific position and at a specific intensity for each chromosome when a primer that recognizes a tandemly repetitive sequence is employed. Such procedures, although technically demanding, have considerable potential for isolating individual chromosomes and chromosome fragments.

CONCLUDING REMARKS

Flow cytometry of plant cells has benefited from the developments in medical applications of this technology, especially in relation to the analysis of nuclei and chromosomes. As discussed previously, sorting of plant protoplasts, while possible theoretically, is technically still demanding and usually results in heterokaryons being dispersed in large volumes of solution. This necessitates extensive handling, often accompanied by centrifugation, to concentrate the protoplasts to an optimum density for culture. Clearly, the most useful application of flow cytometry to plant material is in the analysis of nuclear DNA content, together with the analysis and sorting of chromosomes and chromosome fragments.

BIBLIOGRAPHY

1. M.A. Van Dilla, P.N. Dean, O.D. Laerum, and M.R. Melamed, *Flow Cytometry: Instrumentation and Data Analysis*, Academic Press, London, 1985.

2. H.M. Shapiro, *Practical Flow Cytometry*, 3rd ed., Wiley-Liss, New York, 1995.

3. K. Redenbaugh, S. Ruzin, J. Bartholme, and J.A. Bassham, *Z. Pflanzenphysiol.* **107**, 65–80 (1982).

4. K.R. Harkins and D.W. Galbraith, *J. Physiol. Plant.* **60**, 43–52 (1984).

5. R.G. Alexander, E.C. Cocking, P.J. Jackson, and J.H. Jett, *Protoplasma* **128**, 52–58 (1985).

6. E.M. Frearson, J.B. Power, and E.C. Cocking, *Dev. Biol.* **33**, 130–137 (1973).

7. J.H. Jett and R.G. Alexander, *Cytometry* **6**, 484–486 (1985).

8. K.R. Harkins and D.W. Galbraith, *Physiol. Plant.* **60**, 43–52 (1984).

9. N. Hammatt et al. *Protoplasma* **154**, 34–44 (1990).

10. J.M. Widholm, *Stain Technol.* **47**, 189–194 (1972).

11. J.-H. Liu, C. Dixelius, I. Eriksson, and K. Glimelius, *Plant Sci.* **109**, 75–86 (1995).

12. M.H. Mendis, J.B. Power, and M.R. Davey, *J. Exp. Bot.* **42**, 1565–1573 (1991).

13. H.J. Price and K. Bachmann, *Am. J. Bot.* **62**, 262–267 (1975).

14. R.F. Lyndon, *J. Exp. Bot.* **14**, 419–430 (1963).

15. J. McLeish and N. Sunderland, *Expl. Cell Res.* **24**, 527–540 (1961).

16. M.D. Bennett and I.J. Leitch, *Ann. Bot. (London)* [N.S.] **76**, 113–176 (1995).

17. J. Dolezel, P. Binarova, and S. Lucretti, *Biol. Plant.* **31**, 113–120 (1989).

18. D.W. Galbraith et al., *Science* **220**, 1049–1051 (1983).

19. A.M.M. de Laat, W. Gohde, and M.J.D.C. Vogelzang, *Plant Breed.* **99**, 303–307 (1987).

20. J. Portugal and M.J. Waring, *Biochim. Biophys. Acta* **949**, 158 (1988).

21. M.E.A. Churchill and M. Suzuki, *EMBO J.* **8**, 4189–4195 (1989).

22. N. Hammatt, N.W. Blackhall, and M.R. Davey, *J. Exp. Bot.* **42**, 659–665 (1991).

23. A. Tibok, N.W. Blackhall, J.B. Power, and M.R. Davey, *Plant Sci.* **110**, 139–145 (1995).

24. W.C. Otoni et al., *J. Exp. Bot.* **46**, 777–785 (1995).

25. A.C.W. Ward et al., *Cryo-Letters* **14**, 145–152 (1993).

26. W. Schuh et al., *Plant Sci.* **89**, 69–79 (1993).

27. J. Conia and P. Muller, in A. Yen, ed., *Flow Cytometry: Advanced Experimental and Clinical Applications*, Vol. 1, CRC Press, Boca Raton, Fl. 1989, pp. 143–164.

28. K. Arumuganathan, J.P. Slattery, S.D. Tanksley, and E.D. Earle, *Theor. Appl. Genet.* **82**, 101–111 (1991).

29. T. Schwarzacher et al., *Theor. Appl. Genet.* **94**, 91–97 (1997).

30. U. Pich et al., *Plant J.* **7**, 1039–1044 (1995).

See also CELL AND CELL LINE CHARACTERIZATION; CELL CYCLE EVENTS AND CELL CYCLE-DEPENDENT PROCESSES; CELL CYCLE SYNCHRONIZATION; OFF-LINE ANALYSIS IN ANIMAL CELL CULTURE, METHODS; OFF-LINE IMMUNOASSAYS IN BIOPROCESS CONTROL.

FLUX ANALYSIS OF MAMMALIAN CELL CULTURE: METHODS AND APPLICATIONS

HENDRIK P.J. BONARIUS
Novo Nordisk Ltd.
Gentofte, Denmark

CORNELIS D. DE GOOIJER
JOHANNES TRAMPER
Wageningen Agricultural University
Wageningen, The Netherlands

OUTLINE

Introduction

Metabolic Fluxes in Cultured Mammalian Cells: Some Lessons from Tumor Cell Physiology

Metabolism of Industrially Useful Cell Lines

Flux-Balance Models: Methods

    1. Reduction of Complexity

    2. Identification of Linear-Dependent Reactions

    3. Measure Biomass Composition and Metabolic Rates

    4. Calculate Determinable Fluxes

    5. Making the Underdetermined Determined

    6. Modeling Isotopic Distributions

Flux-Balance Models: Applications in Mammalian Cell Culture

    Balancing Medium Composition with Requirements for Biosynthesis

    Studying Cellular Physiology

Outlook

Conclusion

Bibliography

INTRODUCTION

The metabolism of mammalian cell lines used to produce glycoproteins is inefficient and suboptimal for industrial scale because the nutrient uptake is not sufficiently tuned to the needs of biosynthesis. Mammalian cells take up more amino acids and glucose than they actually require for cellular processes. As a result waste products, such as lactate, bicarbonate, carbon dioxide and ammonia, are secreted and their accumulation inhibits process yields (1).

Mammalian cells have long been cultivated in "minimal essential media," such as developed by Eagle (2). Only since the demand for optimal bioprocesses for glycoproteins have efforts been undertaken to balance the medium composition with the actual growth and energy requirements of mammalian cells (3–8).

Here we review studies on glucose and amino acid metabolism of mammalian cells. First, a brief survey is given on the metabolism of malignant cells. The metabolism of cancer cells shares many characteristics with the metabolism of continuous cell lines used to produce biologicals. It will be shown that these characteristics (which among others result in the previously-mentioned problems in mammalian cell culture) have certain selective advantages for metastatic tumor cells. Secondly, reports on the metabolism of industrial cell lines will be discussed and similarities with tumor cell metabolism are shown. Then, the analysis of intracellular fluxes of mammalian cell culture is surveyed. In particular, methods and applications of flux balances are discussed. It is shown that flux-balancing techniques have been applied successfully to trace potential sites for metabolic engineering, to determine metabolic capabilities, to study overflow metabolism, and to design optimal medium compositions and feeding strategies. Finally, an outlook is given on research that will lead to further improvement of low-cost, high-yield, cell-culture processes by the manipulation of cell metabolism.

METABOLIC FLUXES IN CULTURED MAMMALIAN CELLS: SOME LESSONS FROM TUMOR CELL PHYSIOLOGY

Most of our knowledge of carbohydrate and amino acid metabolism of mammalian cells stems from physiological studies of malignant cells. Apart from the ability to proliferate and the lack of differentiation, both tumor cells and cultured mammalian cells share various properties with respect to their metabolism (9). In contrast to normally proliferating mammalian tissue, transformed cell lines do not regulate the uptake of nutrients strictly to the needs of biosynthesis and maintenance processes. For example, glucose uptake is high and not tuned to the requirements for energy and growth, which causes the production of lactate. The high rate of glycolysis combined with elevated lactate production observed in tumor cells initially gave rise to the postulation of impaired respiratory capabilities as a specific property of malignant cells (10). Later, a number of observations led to the concept that the differences in carbohydrate metabolism in tumor cells compared to normal tissue were "selective" alterations that allowed tumor cells to proliferate under changing conditions with respect to glucose levels and oxygen pressure and in the absence of sufficient metabolic control (for a review, see Ref. 11).

Several characteristics of the metabolism of tumor cells are shown in Figure 1, and the proposed relevance for selection advantage is indicated. For example, high glycolytic activity allows tumor cells to generate energy in hypoxic areas (12). When sufficient oxygen is available, the glycolytic activity and lactate production rate in tumor cells also remain high. There is no feedback inhibition by ATP on phosphofructokinase (reaction 3, Fig. 2a), as in normal, nonmalignant cells (Pasteur effect). Although this seems inefficient with respect to energy metabolism, it has been suggested that the high glycolytic rate ensures the availability of precursors for biosynthesis: the intracellular pools of glycolytic intermediates between glucose-6-phosphate (G6P, Fig. 1) and pyruvate (PYR) increase, thus supplying substrates for the biosynthesis of nucleotides, triglycerides, and glycoproteins. This mechanism allows tumor cells to proliferate (because

precursors for biosynthesis are available) and generate energy (because pyruvate kinase and pyruvate oxidation remain active) at a relatively high rate and independent of the oxygen pressure (13).

It has been established that lactate is generated by glycolysis and also derives to a large extent from glutamine metabolism in malignant cell lines (14). Glutaminolysis may theoretically yield nine ATP equivalents per mole of glutamine consumed and allows tumor cells to proliferate at low glucose concentrations. It is likely that the carbon of glutamine in tumor cells, and also that of other amino acids emerges in TCA-cycle intermediates and provides a significant amount of energy.

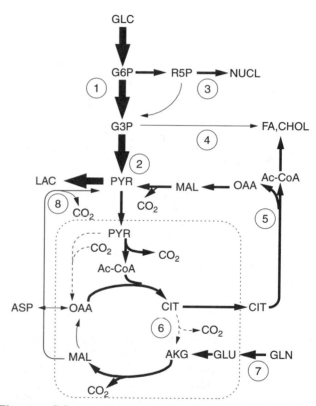

Figure 1. Selective advantages of tumor-cell metabolism. The regulation of glucose and amino acid uptake in tumor cells is relatively poor compared to cells in normal tissue. Although this results in the secretion of toxic waste products, such as lactate and ammonia, several selective advantages are associated with the low level of metabolic control. The high glycolytic rate enables tumor cells to proliferate in hypoxic areas (1). As a result, intracellular concentrations of the glycolytic intermediates between hexokinase and pyruvate kinase (2) remain high, and the availability of precursors for nucleic acid (3) and triglyceride synthesis (4) is ensured. Tumor cells synthesize relatively high amounts of cholesterol (5), as a result of which the isocitrate-dehydrogenase flux (6) is low. This is an advantage for cells proliferating in areas with low concentrations of antioxidants because isocitrate dehydrogenase is particularly sensitive to oxidative stress. TCA-cycle intermediates are replenished via glutamine degradation (7). If glucose levels are low, glutamine can be the major energy source. In that case, a relatively large amount of lactate is be derived from the malate shunt (8). (See also the main text for further details.) The dotted line represents the mitochondrial membrane.

In addition to enhanced glycolysis and glutaminolysis, tumor cells show little sensitivity to variation in oxygen concentrations, a lower requirement for antioxidants (15), a reduced (iso)citrate decarboxylation (x_{14}) (16), and enhanced nucleic acid (x_{28}, x_{29}) (17) and lipid synthesis (x_{19}) (18). The low isocitrate — dehydrogenase activity may be an advantage for tumor cells because isocitrate dehydrogenase is relatively sensitive to oxidative stress. Another possible advantage for a low isocitrate — dehydrogenase flux has been suggested by Coleman and Lavietes (16). They hypothesized that the high lipid synthesis rates "truncate" the TCA cycle. To fuel lipid synthesis with carbon sources, the citrate — synthase reaction (x_{13}) is supplied with oxaloacetate from TCA-cycle intermediates that are replenished by products from amino acid degradation. The relevance of these characteristics for the metabolism of rapidly proliferating cells is further outlined in Figure 1.

METABOLISM OF INDUSTRIALLY USEFUL CELL LINES

Mammalian cells have been used since the early 1980 to produce heterologous glycoproteins. It appeared that their metabolism was similar to that of tumor cells: cultured mammalian cells do not adequately regulate the uptake of glucose and amino acids to the actual metabolic requirements for growth and energy (1). Therefore, cultured hybridoma, BHK, and CHO cells produce large amounts of lactate, even if sufficient oxygen is available. At low oxygen concentrations, glucose uptake rates increase to offset the reduced energy production from glutamine oxidation (19), resulting in more lactate production. At low glucose concentrations, glutamine uptake rates and ammonia production rates increase (20,21). When adequate amounts of glucose are available, glutamine consumption is also abundant, which results in the accumulation of various glutamate-derived amino acids (3,22).

Because of the lack of *cellular* regulation, the culture environment has to be controlled to regulate nutrient uptake and to reduce waste product formation. Flux-balancing techniques have been applied to determine the actual nutrient requirements for energy, growth, and glycoprotein production. This has led to improved media and feeding strategies and significantly higher yields (7,8). Further, metabolic flux analysis gives a quantitative understanding of the physiology of cultured mammalian cells and provides clues for metabolic engineering. Various methods of flux analysis are discussed in the following sections, and applications to mammalian cell culture are reviewed.

FLUX-BALANCE MODELS: METHODS

An overview of the different steps that should be carried out to quantify the metabolic flows in mammalian cells is shown in Table 1. Below, these steps are discussed in more detail.

1. Reduction of Complexity

Metabolism is a large network of reaction pathways that enables (micro)organisms to convert substrates into

Table 1. Phases in Flux Analysis

1. Set up stoichiometric matrix.
2. Identify determinable fluxes (see "Intermezzo Matrix Rank").
3. Measure biomass composition and metabolic rates (Table 2).
4. Calculate determinable fluxes (least-squares analysis, Fig. 3)
5. Select isotopic tracer experiments (Table 3).
6. Calculate remaining fluxes from data generated at phase 4 and 5 by applying numerical methods, such as described in Ref. 50–52.

biomass, energy, and, in selected cases, certain valuable products. The metabolic network of mammalian cells contains in the order of 10^3 enzymatic reactions for the synthesis and/or degradation of carbohydrates, fatty acids, lipids, amino acids, proteins, and nucleic acids. The first step in metabolic flux analysis is to reduce the metabolic network to a manageable set of stoichiometric equations by selecting relevant pathways and by lumping complex subnetworks. For example, mammalian cells lack the pathway for synthezing essential amino acids, and most cultured mammalian cells generate neither glycogen nor urea, although the original species possess the enzymes for glycogen and urea synthesis. Therefore, these synthesis pathways are omitted in a flux-balance model for cultured mammalian cells.

Further reduction of the complexity is achieved by "lumping" linear reaction pathways. This simplification is based on assuming that the intracellular accumulation rate of intermediate metabolites is negligible with respect to the uptake rate of substrates and the accumulation of (end) products. For example, complete fatty acid synthesis machinery can be lumped into one reaction if the fractions of different fatty acids in triglycerides in mammalian cells are known. Figure 2a shows a flux model that describes the metabolism of hybridoma cells after the previously-mentioned reductions.

2. Identification of Linear-Dependent Reactions

The second step in formulating flux-balance models involves identifying determined and underdetermined subnetworks. Many fluxes can be estimated solely by metabolite-balancing techniques. For example, the alanine aminotransferase flux (x_{20} in Fig. 2a) is calculated from the extracellular alanine production rate and the (intracellular) alanine requirements for biomass. In contrast, most fluxes in cyclic pathways (for instance x_{14} and x_{15} in Fig. 2a) cannot be determined independently by mass balancing techniques alone. In the set of mass balance equations such fluxes cause linearly dependent relationship (23). Linear-dependent fluxes can be determined by measuring the rank of the stoichiometric matrix (24).

Intermezzo: Matrix Rank. The "rank" of the stoichiometric matrix is the maximum number of linear-dependent

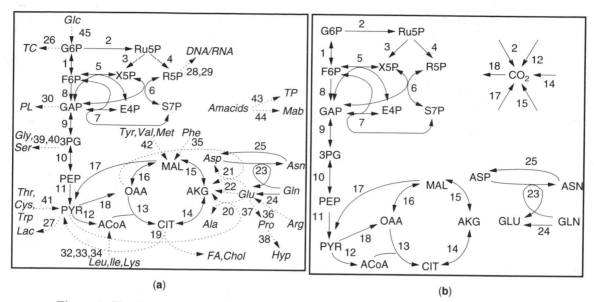

Figure 2. Flux-balance models. The first step in designing a flux-balance model is reduction, which leads from a complex to a simple network (**Fig. 2a**). Later, linearly dependent fluxes are identified, which leads to a network, such as shown in **Figure 2b**.

metabolite balances (the rows in matrix S). The metabolic network is "rank deficient" if the rank is smaller than the number of metabolic reactions (the columns in matrix S). In complex networks, linear dependent reactions can be traced by determining the rank of the matrix after sequential deletion of the reactions. Below, a simple example is given to explain this procedure. In this example, matrix **S** numerically represents the stoichiometry of the metabolic network shown. The network contains three metabolites A, B, and C, that are connected by three reactions (indicated by the arrows). The rows of matrix **S** are associated with mass balance equations, and the columns with stoichiometric reactions or fluxes, respectively.

$$S = \begin{bmatrix} -1 & 0 & 0 \\ 1 & -1 & -2 \\ 0 & 1 & 2 \end{bmatrix}$$

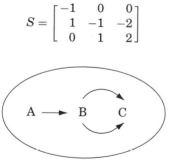

The rank of matrix **S** is 2 because there are two linearly dependent rows (and columns) in this 3×3 matrix. Sequential deletion of columns 1, 2 and 3 leads to a 3×2 matrix with rank 1, 2 and 2, respectively. In contrast to the first column, columns 2 and 3 do not affect the rank when deleted and are thus assigned as "linearly dependent reactions."

To reduce the number of linearly dependent reactions, futile cycles are often neglected. The result of futile cycling is dissipation of energy, whereas the net flux remains unchanged. For example, when flux-balance

models are used to determine the requirement for carbon and nitrogen sources for anabolic processes, it is not necessary to include certain futile cycles. However, many cyclic pathways cannot be neglected for applications such as described here. Constraints other than the metabolite balances are required to estimate fluxes in a remaining underdetermined network, such as shown in Figure 2b. Examples of constraints that have been applied to flux analysis in mammalian cell culture are reviewed below.

3. Measure Biomass Composition and Metabolic Rates

Table 2 lists the metabolites that have been measured to estimate the major metabolic flows in mammalian cell

Table 2. Metabolites Measured for Flux Analysis

Metabolite	Method
Glucose	Enzymatic assay
Lactate	Enzymatic assay
Ammonia	Ion-selective electrode
Oxygen	Mass spectrometry
Carbon dioxide	Infrared gas analysis
Amino acids	HPLC
Fatty acids	Gas chromatography
Cholesterol	Gas chromatography
Total lipid fraction	Weight (after extraction)
Total protein	Biuret assay
Amino acid composition of total protein	HPLC (after hydrolysis)
Total carbohydrate fraction	Phenol reaction
RNA and DNA	Absorbance at 260 nm
Monoclonal antibody (product)	ELISA

Note: As described in Refs. 7 and 25.

culture together with the appropriate methods (7,25). It is critical to measure the biomass composition for each cell line because cell lines differ significantly in biomass compositon (7,25).

Turnover of Macromolecules. A problem in estimating biomass requirements is caused by the fact that most macromolecules can be synthesized via two different pathways, often designated as de novo and *salvage* pathways. *De novo* pathways refer to the biosynthesis of macromolecules via the complete biochemical pathways from basic nutrients, such as essential amino acids or (derivatives of) glucose, to the end products. Salvage reactions are simpler, much less costly, and include only the assembly of pre formed building blocks which accumulate as a result of turnover of macromolecules. Implementation of both pathways in flux-balance models renders underdetermined networks: the different fluxes cannot be determined by the measurement of the end product alone because the reactions are linearly dependent (see also late). When the need for new biomass material is high, for example, at high growth rates, de novo synthesis is most likely prevalent. Therefore, salvage pathways are often neglected in metabolic flux analysis of industrial microorganisms and mammalian cells. An exception is the metabolic model described

by Savinell and Palsson (26), in which the turnover rate of RNA in hybridoma cells is estimated from mRNA and rRNA degradation rate constants. The reuse of the free bases produced can be calculated from these values. Preferably, the substrate requirements for macromolecules are determined experimentally. For example, Mancuso et al. (27) determined the *de novo* synthesis of fatty acids by incorporating ^{13}C into triglycerides of cultured hybridoma cells.

4. Calculate Determinable Fluxes

The principle of metabolic flux balancing techniques is shown in Figure 3 for an (over)determined metabolic network. In this example the network is "overdetermined" because it contains three independent constraints (mass balance equations) and only two unknowns (fluxes). If the uptake and secretion rates of the relevant metabolites (for example r_A, r_B and r_C in Fig. 3) have been measured, the reaction rates (x_1 and x_2 in the figure) can be determined using the appropriate mass balance equations. A reaction network is shown for which one unique solution for the variables x_1 and x_2 can be estimated by least squares analysis of mass balances A, B, and C. The example shows that intracellular fluxes can be quantified by measuring only the uptake and secretion rates of

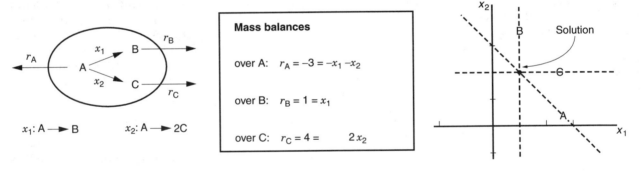

(i)   (ii)   (iii)

Figure 3. Principles of metabolic-flux balancing. **i.** Metabolic model and reaction stoichiometry of flux x_1 and x_2. **ii.** Mass balance equations for metabolites A, B, and C in the model (numerical values are chosen arbitrarily). **iii.** Plot of flux values x_1 and x_2. The mass balances are given as dotted lines. Metabolic-flux balancing techniques are based on relatively simple linear algebra. If the stoichiometry of the relevant intracellular reactions and the cellular composition are known, and the uptake and secretion rates of the relevant metabolites (e.g., r_A, r_B and r_C in the figure) have been measured, the reaction rates (x_1 and x_2 in the figure) can be determined by using the appropriate mass balance equations. A reaction network is shown for which one unique solution for the variables x_1 and x_2 can be estimated by least squares analysis of mass balances A, B, and C. The least squares method, which is used here because there are more constraints (mass balances) than unknowns (fluxes), is calculated by (pseudo)inverting stoichiometric matrix S (23):

$$Sx = r \Leftrightarrow S^T Sx = S^T r \Leftrightarrow x = (S^T S)^{-1} S^T r$$

For the stoichiometry and measured metabolic rates given in the figure, this equation reads

$$\begin{bmatrix} -1 & -1 \\ 1 & 0 \\ 0 & 2 \end{bmatrix} \cdot \begin{bmatrix} x_1 \\ x_2 \end{bmatrix} = \begin{bmatrix} r_A \\ r_B \\ r_C \end{bmatrix} \Leftrightarrow \begin{bmatrix} x_1 \\ x_2 \end{bmatrix} = \frac{1}{9} \begin{bmatrix} 5 & -1 \\ -1 & 2 \end{bmatrix} \cdot \begin{bmatrix} -1 & 1 & 0 \\ -1 & 0 & 2 \end{bmatrix} \cdot \begin{bmatrix} -3 \\ 1 \\ 4 \end{bmatrix} = \begin{bmatrix} 1 \\ 2 \end{bmatrix}$$

This shows that intracellular fluxes can be quantified by measuring only the uptake and secretion rates of the relevant metabolites.

the relevant metabolites, provided that the network is (over)determined.

5. Making the Underdetermined Determined

The minimal number of extra constraints that are necessary to solve an underdetermined set of mass balance equations depends on how many sets of linear-dependent reactions are present. The metabolic network shown in Figure 2b contains three sets of linear-dependent reactions, for each of which an additional constraint is required. In the example these three sets are fluxes 1–16, fluxes 16–18, and fluxes 23–25. The determination of one flux out of each set is sufficient to solve the mass balance equations. Preferably, these are derived from isotope balances (27–29). Figure 4 shows an example of the metabolic fate of isopotic label at the first atom of glucose. It is apparent that fluxes in the pentose shunt, the malic shunt, and the TCA cycle can be assessed when the label distribution of the appropriate intermediates or end products is determined.

If isotopic tracer data are not available, other constraints which have been proposed for estimating fluxes in mammalian cells can be used instead (25,26,30). In Table 3 the possible methods that have been applied for flux analysis in mammalian cell culture are outlined.

Radioactive Isotopes. Katz and Wood (31) and Bontemps et al. (32) developed methods to determine metabolic fluxes of the pentose shunt, TCA cycle, and glycolysis in tumor cell lines based on scintillation counting of labeled end products (CO_2 or H_2O). Recently, these methods were applied to analyze hybridoma cell metabolism (33–35) and other industrially used cell lines (36). Methods that apply radiolabeled isotopes are sensitive and have been proven useful in providing experimental evidence of certain (relative) biochemical effects. For example, Jan and co-workers (34) showed that the relative flux of glucose through the pentose phosphate pathway increased at higher oxygen level. Fitzpatrick and co-workers (33) showed that a large fraction of glutamine (~36%) was oxidized to CO_2, which emphasizes the importance of glutamine as an energy source. Petch and Butler (35) estimated from flux data obtained by radio labeled isotopes, that 41% of the ATP produced in hybridoma cells is provided by glutamine.

No or insignificant amounts of glucose or pyruvate-derived carbon entering the TCA cycle could be detected by the $^{14}CO_2$ release from 6-^{14}C-glucose (33,35,36). This, however does not agree with flux analysis by other techniques. The detection of glucose-derived fatty acids measured by in vivo ^{13}C-NMR (27,28) and on-line measured $^{13}CO_2$ from 6-^{13}C-glucose-fed hybridomas (29)

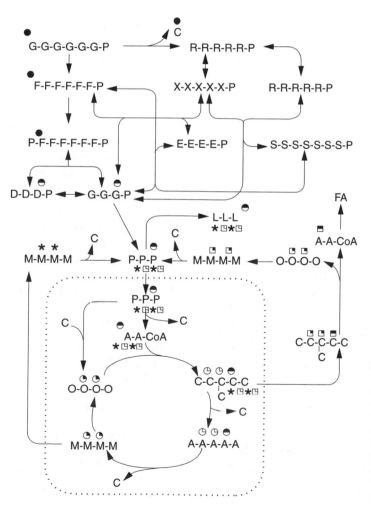

Figure 4. The metabolic fate of 1-^{13}C-glucose [Adapted from Mancuso et al. (27).] Glycolytic labeling (circles), malate shunt labeling (stars), and malate/pyruvate shuttle labeling (squares) are shown. Reductions of 25 or 50% in filling of symbols indicate 25 or 50% reductions, respectively, in labeling associated with reaction stoichiometry. The dashed line indicates a mitochondrial membrane. Gray symbols indicate label transfer associated with interconnected pathways. Capitals indicate C atoms of metabolites, except for the capital P which indicates either a phosphate group or the C atoms of pyruvate and FA which denotes fatty acids. A acetyl-CoA, C carbon dioxide or citrate; D dihydroxyacetonephosphate; E erythrose-4-phosphate; F fructose-6-phosphate or fructose1,6-biphosphate; G glucose, glucose-6-phosphate, or glyceraldehyde 3-phosphate; L lactate; M malate; O oxaloactetate; P pyruvate; R ribose-5-phosphate or ribulose-5-phosphate; S S7P sedoheptulose-7-phosphate; X xylulose-5-phosphate.

Table 3. Determination of Fluxes in Underdetermined Networks

	Advantage	Disadvantage	When to use
1. Isotopic-tracer experiments			
a. Radioactive isotopes	Sensitive small amounts sufficient	Radioactive Possible experimental bias because cells are incubated in new medium	Relative changes in fluxes are sufficient
b. Stable isotopes NMR spectroscopy	In situ possible In vivo possible	Insensitive Metabolites/cells need to be concentrated	Absolute flux values are required
c. Stable isotopes mass spectroscopy	In situ possible Sensitive		Absolute flux values are required
2. Metabolic modeling			
a. Addition of mass balances NAD(P)H balance ATP balance	Nonlaborious	Error-sensitive	Estimation of relative changes is sufficient
b. Numerical methods Linear optimization	Nonlaborious	Error-sensitive May give relatively accurate values when biochemical effects are well established	Estimation of relative changes is sufficient

both indicate that a small but significant amount of glucose enters the TCA cycle.

A disadvantage of assays based on radio isotopic tracers for analyzing metabolic fluxes in bioprocesses is that cells are incubated in a new metabolic environment. Thus, fluxes cannot be assessed *in situ* by this method. Therefore, when absolute flux values of cells cultured in bioreactors are required, data from scintillation experiments should be interpreted carefully. *In situ* flux data can safely be obtained by using stable isotopes combined with mass or NMR spectrometry.

Stable Isotopes. Stable isotopes that can be analyzed by NMR spectrometry or mass spectrometry (^{13}C or ^{15}N) have been used to determine metabolic fluxes of cultured mammalian cells *in situ* in bioreactors. Zupke and Stephanopoulos (37) used 1-^{13}C-glucose to assess the fraction of carbon entering the pyruvate branch point via the malate shunt by measuring the fractional labeling of lactate. Bonarius et al. (29) combined ^{1}H-NMR analysis of the ^{13}C-enrichment in secreted lactate and *on-line* ^{13}CO$_2$-mass spectrometry to determine the pentose and malate shunts of continuously cultured hybridoma cells. These data were used to estimate the optimal glucose consumption rates, that is the minimum amount of glucose that should be consumed without limiting energy supplies. A step further to on-line flux analysis was taken by Sharfstein et al. (28) and Mancuso et al. (27), who exploited the fact that mammalian cells cultures in hollow-fiber bioreactors are sufficiently dense to allow in vivo measurement of (labeled) metabolites by relatively insensitive NMR spectroscopy. They showed, for example that high lipid synthesis rates in hybridoma cells "truncate" the TCA cycle (see also Fig. 1) and that the pentose shunt activity was only 4% of the glucose uptake, which is low compared to the pentose shunt flux in cells grown in a CSTR (20% of the glucose uptake; Ref. 29). In addition, NMR spectrograms of hollow-fiber cultures can

be used to assess the kinetics of uptake and incorporation of nutrients.

An alternative to the relatively insensitive NMR spectrometry is mass spectrometry, which is not limited only to metabolites that evaporate into the gas phase. By GC-MS, this technique can also be applied to metabolites secreted in the culture medium (38). This powerful technique has not yet been used to study the metabolism of industrially useful cell lines.

NAD(P)H Balance in Metabolic Flux Analysis. For industrial applications, it is desirable to determine intracellular fluxes by mass balancing techniques alone. Various alternative constraints have been suggested to estimate fluxes without information from isotopic tracer experiments. The NADH and NADPH balance has been used in flux-balance models to determine flux ratios at particular nodes in the metabolism of microorganisms (e.g., Ref. 23,39,40). The rank, and thus the observability, of stoichiometric networks increases after addition of the NAD(P)H balance (25,41). Although the requirements for NADPH in anabolic processes can be estimated and the amount of NADH that is oxidized can be determined by measuring the oxygen uptake rate, certain fluxes are overly sensitive to these mass balances. Even if the transhydrogenase activity, which generates a metabolic cycle in NADH and NADPH metabolism, is taken into account, relatively small deviations in the NAD(P)H balance result in large differences in certain fluxes. For example, it has been shown for both *Bacillus subtilis* (42) and hybridoma cells (29) that the estimated pentose shunt flux is very sensitive to changes in the NAD(P)H balance.

Linear Optimization Techniques. Instead of assuming that the NAD(P)H balance can be closed, NAD(P)H stoichiometry can be used to formulate biochemically meaningful objective functions (30). In certain cases, the requirement for or surplus of one of these reduction equivalents may determine the metabolic flux distribution of the cell. This is the case, for instance, for adipose tissue, which requires large amounts of NADPH for triglyceride synthesis (30), for oxygen-limited mammalian cells, which have NADH in surplus (43), or artificially, for mammalian cells that are incubated with non natural electron acceptors, such as PMS, and consequently require large amounts of both NADH and NADPH (44). Other objective functions were proposed by Savinell and Palsson (26), who assumed that hybridoma cells maximize intracellular ATP levels, and by Bonarius et al. (25), who assumed that cell metabolism strives to minimize the net flow. Recently, a number of these objective functions were compared to flux values that were determined by isotopic tracer experiments. The flux distributions found using two objective functions, that is, maximize ATP and maximize NADH, were relatively similar to the distribution determined by using 1-^{13}C-glucose (29). This is consistent with the results obtained by Savinell and Palsson (26), who estimated that hybridoma cells produce more ATP and NADH than the cells actually need. In addition, this suggests that hybridoma cells are similar to other cancer cells in being metabolically hyperactive and in the fact that they consume nutrients regardless of energy requirements.

6. Modeling Isotopic Distributions

Because metabolic pathways are complex, in particular when data from istopic tracer experiments are included to determine intracellular flows, computational methods are indispensable. For example, various simple, nonnumerical methods have been proposed to evaluate data from isotopic tracer experiments to determine the pentose shunt flux in mammalian cells or tissue (31,45,46). However, none of these nonnumerical methods can correct completely for inaccuracies due to recycling of (labeled) products in the pentose shunt, to the dilution of labeling by other (endogenous) carbon sources, or to assumptions with respect to the stoichiometry (47). Instead, computational methods make it possible to dissect the complexity of stoichiometric networks and isotope distributions and to perform calculations that cannot be carried out manually. In numerical algorithms, mass balances of single atoms can be combined with mass balances of entire molecules to yield solutions that are free of assumptions with respect to recycling or dilution of labels (48,49). Recently, Zupke and Stephanopoulos (50) and Marx and co-authors (51) developed noninvasive numerical algorithms for this purpose. In contrast to other methods in which mass balance equations for each single atom have to be derived (48), this approach requires only atom-mapping matrices (AMMs), in which the reaction stoichiometry is encapsulated. The resulting network is conveniently arranged, easier to understand, requires less algebraic manipulation, and modifications do not require new derivations of atom balances (50).

Bidirectional Fluxes. Any reversible reaction can proceed in both directions simultaneously. In isotopic tracer experiments "bidirectional reactions" cause scrambling of labels and complicate their interpretation. Computational methods that include bidirectional fluxes are available

(48,52) but have been applied only to a limited extent to mammalian tissue (53,54). This may be due to the fact that the method is laborious because it requires the incubation of different isotopic tracers in parallel experiments and the extraction of metabolic intermediates.

FLUX-BALANCE MODELS: APPLICATIONS IN MAMMALIAN CELL CULTURE

Balancing Medium Composition with Requirements for Biosynthesis

Metabolic flux analysis has already been proven a useful tool for analyzing the requirements for energy and biomass synthesis. Using linear optimization techniques to analyze data of hybridoma cell metabolism, Savinell and Palsson (26) calculated that neither the maintenance demand for ATP nor the antibody production rate limits the growth rate of these cells. They also estimated that hybridoma cells use their nutrients with only 57 to 78% efficiency under normal conditions. Apart from this theoretical work, several experimental studies have been carried out to investigate "overflow metabolism" of glucose and amino acids at an intracellular level. These are discussed later.

Flux balances have been used to improve the medium composition of cell culture. Ferrance and co-workers (55) examined amino acid balances in developing insect-cell culture media. They distinguished "balanced" versus "unbalanced" amino acids in a batch culture of Sf9 cells. A certain amino acid was designated "balanced" when the total amount of amino acid measured after 10 days of cultivation (in the culture medium plus in the hydrolyzed cell extract) differed by less than 20% different from the amount in the medium. In contrast, "unbalanced" amino acids are converted in catabolic processes for more than 20%. It was found that the unbalanced amino acids are alanine and serine (which are produced in catabolism) and arginine, asparagine, glutamate, glutamine, glycine, and threonine (which are consumed in catabolism).

The determination of "net catabolic rates" is a similar concept (25). The net catabolic rate of metabolite X is the production rate of X corrected for incorporation in biomass. The fraction of amino acids required for biosynthesis was determined by measuring amino acids in (hydrolyzed) cell protein and measurement of nucleic acid content. In hybridoma cells, the amino acids aspartate, asparagine, alanine, (hydroxy)proline, and serine were produced in catabolic processes. Arginine, glutamate, glutamine, isoleucine, leucine, and lysine were consumed and used to generate carbon for TCA-cycle intermediates. In other words, alanine, aspartate, asparine, proline, and serine are waste products of amino acid catabolism, and their formation can be reduced by balancing arginine, glutamate, glutamine, etc., to the requirement for anabolic processes.

Sharfstein et al. (28) used mass balances to complement ^{13}C-NMR data from hybridoma cells cultured in hollow-fiber bioreactors. It was found that at both low and high glutamine concentrations a significant fraction of amino acids entered the TCA cycle at acetyl-CoA (e.g., isoleucine, leucine, lysine) and succinyl-CoA (isoleucine, methionine, and valine). At low glutamine concentrations, only 24% of the amino acids entered the TCA cycle via α-ketoglutarate (which is mainly glutamine). These data show that it is important to balance glutamine and also other amino acids for optimal process conditions.

A systematic and successful approach to reduce the production of lactate, ammonia, and amino acids, while avoiding substrate limitation for biomass synthesis and energy generation, has been proposed by Xie and Wang (7,8). Based on stoichiometric analysis and mass balancing techniques, they designed a process control strategy to meet the requirements for energy and growth of fed, batch-cultured hybridoma cells. The ratio of lactate to glucose and the ratio of ammonia to glutamine was only 0.067 and 0.15, respectively, compared to 1.33 and 0.40 in a conventional batch culture. As a result, the final antibody titer was 2.4 g/L, almost 50 times as high as in conventional batch cultivations (8). It would be interesting to compare the efficiency of nutrient consumption of these optimized, fed, batch cultures to cultures studied by Savinell and Palsson (26).

Studying Cellular Physiology

In addition to the studies described above, mass balances have been used to estimate intracellular fluxes in mammalian cell culture. For example, it has been shown that almost all glutamate enters the TCA cycle via transaminases (x_{20} and x_{21}) and not by the glutamate—dehydrogenase flux (x_{22}) in cultured hybridoma cells (25,43), most likely to avoid producing additional ammonia. Indeed, when hybridoma cells are ammonia stressed, the transaminase activity is higher, and the glutamate–dehydrogenase flux is in the direction of glutamate production, thereby detoxifying a fraction of ammonia (see also Fig. 5 and Ref. 56). This suggests that ammonia-resistant cells can be engineered by the overexpression of glutamate dehydrogenase.

The effect of culture conditions on intracellular fluxes has been estimated with balancing techniques, even for underdetermined metabolic subnetworks. For instance, it has been shown that the TCA-cycle activity is low under oxygen-limiting conditions (43). This agrees with the low pyruvate oxidation activity found in other cultured cell lines (15). Recently, we demonstrated by metabolite balancing techniques that the pentose shunt

flux (x_2) in hybridoma cells increases after addition of a growth-stimulating component (25), which agrees with the biochemical function of the oxidative branch of the shunt to supply NADPH for anabolic processes. These results suggest that mass balancing techniques are useful for the analysis of effects of toxic compounds on cellular physiology, even if the metabolic network under investigation is underdetermined.

OUTLOOK

In the near future, metabolite balancing techniques may be used to study areas of mammalian cell metabolism other than energy (26), glucose (7,25,43) or amino acid (7,56) metabolism. A few studies of those committed to optimizing the production of glycoproteins by mammalian cells have already proceeded this direction. Bibila and Flickinger (57) used a structured model to study the pathway dynamics of antibody synthesis and suggested that the antibody assembly in the ER may be rate-limiting in rapidly growing hybridoma cells. Recently, Bailey et al. (58) used mass balance techniques to predict the fraction of biantennary glycoforms of a glycoprotein product produced by CHO cells, as a function of β-N-acetyl glucosaminyl transferase III activity. Whiteley et al. (59) described a model to quantify the effect of coexpression of the chaperone BiP on the secretion of IgG in insect cells. These studies consider only a fraction of the secretory pathway. When more quantitative in vivo data are available, it may be possible to determine rate-limiting steps in protein synthesis of mammalian cells by mass balance techniques.

CONCLUSION

Stoichiometric and flux analyses have been shown useful for optimizing cell-culture processes and for designing flux distributions with optimal nutrient uptake and a minimum of waste product synthesis. It has been demonstrated that a large fraction of metabolic fluxes in mammalian cells can be estimated by mass balancing techniques alone. Isotopic-tracer experiments remain indispensable for the determination of fluxes in cyclic pathways. However, relative trends in intracellular metabolic fluxes upon changes

Figure 5. Proposed mechanism of ammonia detoxification by cultured mammalian cells, as analyzed by mass balancing techniques. (**a**) Under normal conditions, the flux through glutamate dehydrogenase is insignificant relative to aminotransferases. (**b**) Under ammonia stress, ammonia levels are reduced by converting it and α-ketoglurate into glutamate, which is subsequently channeled back into the TCA cycle by aminotransferases. The intensity of the solid lines qualitatively represents the magnitudes of the fluxes.
Abbreviations: ALA alanine; ASP aspartate; TCA cycle tricarboxylic acid cycle; GLU glutamate; GLN glutamine; NH$_3$ Ammonia; OAA oxaloacetate; PRO proline.

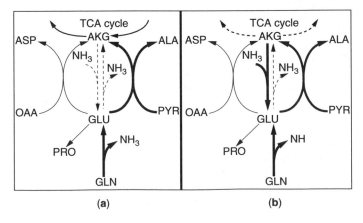
(a)   (b)

in extracellular conditions can be determined solely by mass balancing techniques, even if the metabolic network is principally underdetermined. The *combination* of flux-balance models and isotopic tracer studies will be the future tool for quantitative flux analysis of complex metabolic networks.

BIBLIOGRAPHY

1. M.W. Glacken, *Bio/Technology* **6**, 1041–1050 (1988).
2. H. Eagle, *Proc. Soc. Exp. Biol. Med.* **89**, 362–378 (1965).
3. J. Ljunggren and L. Haggström, *Cytotechnology* **8**, 45–56 (1992).
4. U.S. Pat. 5,122,469 (1992), J.P. Mather and M.C. Tsao.
5. Eur. Pat. 0,653,487 A1 (1995), F. Messi.
6. WO Pat. 95/12664 (1995), S.R. Adamson, D. Drapeau, Y.-T. Luan and D. Miller.
7. L. Xie and D.I.C. Wang, *Cytotechnology* **15**(1–3), 17–29 (1994).
8. L. Xie and D.I.C. Wang, *Biotechnol. Bioeng.* **51**, 725–729 (1996).
9. C.H. Leist, H.P. Meyer, and A. Fiechter, *J. Biotechnol.* **15**, 1–46 (1990).
10. O. Warburg, *Science* **123**, 309–314. (1956).
11. E. Eigenbrodt, P. Fister, and M. Reinacher, in R. Breitner, (ed.), *Regulation of Carbohydrate Metabolism*, Vol. 2. CRC Press, Boca Raton, Fla., 1985, pp. 141–169.
12. D.E. Epner et al., *Cancer Res.* **53**, 1995–1997 (1993).
13. E. Eigenbrodt et al., *Crit. Rev. Oncog.* **3**, 91–115 (1992).
14. L.J. Reitzer, B.M. Wice, and D. Kennel, *J. Biol. Chem.* **254**, 2669–2676. (1979).
15. P.J. Hornsby and G.N. Gill, *J. Cell. Physiol.* **109**, 111–123 (1981).
16. P.S. Coleman and B.B. Lavietes, *CRC Crit. Rev. Biochem.* **11**, 341–393 (1981).
17. R.C. Jackson et al., *Cancer. Res.* **40**, 1286–1291 (1980).
18. H. Engeser, *Exp. Cell Res.* **139**, 396–400 (1982).
19. W.M. Miller, C.R. Wilke, and H.W. Blanch, *J. Cell. Phys.* **132**, 524–530 (1987).
20. W.M. Miller, C.R. Wilke, and H.W. Blanch, *Biotechnol. Bioeng.* **33**, 477–486 (1989).
21. J.J. Meijer and J.P. Van Dijken, *J. Cell. Phys.* **162**, 191–198 (1995).
22. G. Schmid and T. Keller, *Cytotechnology* **9**, 217–229 (1992).
23. J.J. Vallino and G. Stephanopoulos, in S.K. Sikdar, M. Bier, and P. Todd, eds., *Frontiers in Bioprocessing*, CRC Press, Boca Rotan, Fla., 1989.
24. H.P.J. Bonarius, G. Schmid, and J. Tramper, *Trends Biotechnol.* **15**, 308–314 (1997).
25. H.P.J. Bonarius et al., *Biotechnol. Bioeng.* **50**, 299–318 (1996).
26. J.M. Savinell and B.O. Palsson, *J. Theor. Biol.* **154**, 421–454. (1992).
27. A. Mancuso et al., *Biotechnol. Bioeng.* **44**, 563–585 (1994).
28. S.T. Sharfstein et al., *Biotechnol. Bioeng.* **43**, 1059–1074 (1994).
29. H.P.J. Bonarius, B. Timmerarends, C.D. De Gooijer, and J. Tramper, *Biotechnol. Bioeng.* **58**, 258–262 (1998).
30. D.A. Fell and J.A. Small, *Biochem. J.* **238**, 781–786 (1986).
31. J. Katz and H.G. Wood, *J. Biol. Chem.* **238**, 517–523 (1963).
32. F. Bontemps, L. Hue, and H.-G Hers, *Biochem. J.* **174**, 603 612 (1978).
33. L. Fitzpatrick, H.A. Jenkins, and M. Butler, *Appl. Biochem. Biotechnol.* **43**, 93–116 (1993).
34. D.C.H. Jan, D.A. Petch, N. Huzel, and M. Butler, *Biotechnol. Bioeng.* **54**, 153–162 (1997).
35. D. Petch and M. Butler, *J. Cell. Phys.* **161**, 71–76 (1994).
36. J. Neermann and R. Wagner, *J. Cell. Phys.* **166**, 152–169 (1996).
37. C. Zupke and G. Stephanopoulos, *Biotechnol. Bioeng.* **45**, 292–303 (1995).
38. Y.Y. Lin, W.B. Cheng, and C.E. Wright, *Anal. Biochem.* **209**, 267–273 (1993).
39. W.M. Van Gulik and J.J. Heijnen, *Biotechnol. Bioeng.* **48**, 681–698 (1995).
40. H. Jørgensen, J. Nielsen, J. Villadsen, and H. Møllgaard, *Biotechnol. Bioeng.* **46**, 117–131 (1995).
41. A. Goel, J. Ferrance, J. Jeong, and M.M. Ataai, *Biotechnol. Bioeng.* **42**, 686–696 (1988).
42. U. Sauer et al., *Appl. Environ. Microbiol.* **62**, 3687–3696 (1996).
43. C. Zupke, A.J. Sinskey, and G. Stephanopoulos, *Appl. Microbiol. Biotechnol.* **44**, 27–36 (1995).
44. J.S. Hothershall, N.Z. Baquer, A.L. Greenbaum, and P. McLean, *Arch. Biochem. Biophys.* **198**, 478–492 (1979).
45. A. Willis, W.F. Williams, and T. Schleich, *Biochem. Biophys. Res. Commun.* **138**, 1068–1073 (1986).
46. P.B. Kingsley-Hickman, B.D. Ross, and T. Krick, *Anal. Biochem.* **185**, 235–237 (1990).
47. M.G. Larrabee, *J. Biol. Chem.* **264**, 15875–15879 (1989).
48. J.J. Blum and R.B. Stein, in R.F. Goldberger, ed., *Biological Regulation and Development*, Vol. 3A, Plenum, New York, (1982), pp. 99–124.
49. J.-C Portais, R. Schuster, M. Merle, and P. Canioni, *Eur. J. Biochem.* **217**, 457–468 (1993).
50. C. Zupke and G. Stephanopoulos, *Biotechnol. Prog.* **10**, 489–498 (1994).
51. A. Marx et al., *Biotechnol. Bioeng.* **49**, 111–129 (1996).
52. W. Wiechert and A.A. De Graaf, *Biotechnol. Bioeng.* **55**, 101–117 (1997).
53. J.C. Chatman, J.R. Forder, J.D. Glickson, and E.M. Chance, *J. Biol. Chem.* **270**, 7999–8008 (1995).
54. M. Rabkin and J.J. Blum, *Biochem. J.* **225**, 761–786 (1985).
55. J.P. Ferrance, A. Goel, and M.M. Ataai, *Biotechnol. Bioeng.* **42**, 697–707 (1993).
56. H.P.J. Bonarius et al., *Biotechnol. Bioeng.* **57**, 447–453 (1998).
57. T. Bibila and M.C. Flickinger, *Biotechnol. Bioeng.* **41**, 682–682 (1993).
58. J.E. Bailey et al., in M.J.T. Carrondo et al., eds., *Animal Cell Technology*, Kluwer Academic Publishers, 1997, pp. 489–495.
59. E.M. Whiteley, T.A. Hsu, and M.J. Betenbaugh, *Biotechnol. Bioeng.* **56**, 106–116 (1997).

See also CELL METABOLISM, ANIMAL; PHYSIOLOGY OF PLANT CELLS IN CULTURE.

G

GENETIC ENGINEERING: ANIMAL CELL TECHNOLOGY

Richard M. Twyman
John Inness Centre
Norwich
United Kingdom

Bruce Whitelaw
Roslin Institute
Roslin
Midlothian
United Kingdom

OUTLINE

INTRODUCTION

Genetic engineering can be defined as a deliberate attempt to alter the genotype of a cell or organism by introducing foreign DNA. In this context, *foreign* DNA is any exogenously supplied DNA, and does not necessarily have to be derived exclusively from a heterologous source. The ability of mammalian cells to take up DNA from their surrounding medium was first shown in the early 1960s (1). However, gene transfer to animal cells had been appreciated even since the 1940s, when viruses were first shown to carry their own nucleic acid. It is now known that animal cells can take up DNA naturally from a variety of sources, such as from incompletely hydrolyzed DNA molecules in the digestive tract (2). However, the *predetermined* genetic manipulation of animal cells only became possible at the beginning of the recombinant DNA era. This saw the development of a range of tools and techniques for the cloning and in vitro manipulation of particular DNA fragments, permitting the construction of *recombinant DNA* molecules containing novel combinations of sequences from diverse sources. Such techniques facilitated the design of *vectors*, purpose-constructed delivery vehicles used to introduce and establish foreign DNA sequences in animal cells. This, and the inclusion of transcriptional and translational control sequences in vectors to drive foreign gene expression, forms the basis of genetic engineering in animal cells.

The applications of this technology are manifold. In most cases, the underlying aim of a particular gene transfer experiment is to express a protein, either for commercial or research purposes, or for gene therapy. The expressed protein is usually referred to as a *recombinant protein* because it is encoded by a recombinant vector, not necessarily because the open reading frame itself is recombinant at the DNA level. If the open reading frame is recombinant, that is, represents two or more heterologous coding regions joined together in-frame, the protein is defined as a *fusion protein*. In many cases, the recombinant protein is not typically synthesized by the host cell (e.g., it may be a protein from a different species, or a protein that is normally restricted to a different cell type), in which case it may be described as a *heterologous protein*. Alternatively, it may be an endogenous protein, but the aim may be to overexpress it, or express it under unusual circumstances. Finally, the recombinant protein may be a particular mutant form of an endogenous protein, or one that has been modified so it is targeted to a different intracellular compartment. The expression of recombinant proteins in animal cells is now a well-established technology and has been used in a huge variety of experimental systems. As a commercial approach to protein production, large-scale cultures of engineered mammalian cells have been used to synthesize antibodies, hormones, growth factors and cytokines, blood clotting factors, and the surface proteins of numerous viruses for use as recombinant vaccines (3). More recently, the same gene transfer technology has been used to alter endogenous gene expression or make targeted genome rearrangements in host cells. Vectors producing antisense RNA can be used to inhibit the expression of specific endogenous genes. Novel vectors can also be used as insertional mutagens, and to facilitate the identification and cloning of genes by reporting their expression patterns. Others can replace endogenous genes by homologous recombination, and can even generate specific chromosome rearrangements. The scope of such experiments may be limited to animal cells in culture, but if fertilized eggs, early embryos, or embryonic stem cells are used as host cells for gene transfer, it is possible to regenerate chimeric or fully transgenic animals expressing recombinant proteins or carrying specific germline alterations. The reintroduction of engineered cells into living animals, and gene transfer to animal cells in vivo, are also becoming established as technologies for gene therapy and the generation of chimeric animals for research.

OVERVIEW OF ANIMAL CELL TECHNOLOGY

Animal Cells Used for Genetic Manipulation

The use of cells to analyze gene function and gene regulation plays a pivotal role in many molecular biology studies. For the analysis of animal genes, it is usually beneficial, and in many cases essential, to use animal cells as hosts. Animal cells alone provide the correct genetic and biochemical background for such studies. Furthermore, animal proteins expressed in animal cells are more likely to be correctly processed and modified compared to those expressed in bacteria or microbial eukaryotic systems. For these reasons, there has been an intense effort over the past twenty years to develop efficient vectors and DNA transfer procedures for use with animal cells. Generally, this means *mammalian* cells and cell lines, because this is where most resources have been directed. However, other vertebrate cells are used for specialized purposes (e.g., the chicken DT40 cell line for homologous recombination). Furthermore, insect cell lines are used for the highly efficient baculovirus-based transient expression system, and since they are cheap to maintain, insect cells have recently emerged as hosts for recombinant protein expression in their own right (4). One exception to this apparently polarized exploitation of the diversity within the animal kingdom is in the field of transgenesis. The eggs and early embryos of many animals—nematodes, mollusks, annelids, insects, fish, amphibians, birds, and mammals—have been subjected to gene transfer procedures to produce animals containing transient episomal foreign DNA or carrying stable germline modifications. Additionally, the large oocytes and eggs of the South African clawed frog *Xenopus laevis* have been widely exploited as a transient heterologous expression system for the analysis of protein function (5).

Protein Expression

For protein expression, the DNA sequence to be expressed is typically cloned in a bacterial host and then introduced into animal cells either by transfection (direct DNA transfer) or transduction (carried within a virus particle). In each case, cloning and transfer involve the use of specialized vectors carrying all the DNA sequences required for transcription and translation. There are many reasons for doing this type of experiment (Table 1). Sometimes such a strategy is chosen because the foreign sequence cannot be expressed in any other host (e.g., if it contains introns that are incorrectly spliced in microbial systems). Characterizing the properties of cloned genes by expression in mammalian cells may also be one route to isolating a particular gene or cDNA sequence from a DNA

Table 1. Reasons for the Genetic Manipulation of Animal Cells

Protein expression	(i) For the production of large amounts of a protein that is either naturally scarce or the completely novel product of recombinant DNA technology; especially applicable for the production of biologically active proteins with specific forms of post-translational modification, which are carried out incorrectly in microbial expression systems
	(ii) For confirmation of the identity of a cloned gene by immunological assay of its product
	(iii) For the study of protein function, transport, localization, etc. within animal cells
	(iv) For the comparison of normal and mutant proteins
	(v) For the expression of proteins from genomic sequences containing introns, which are not spliced or incorrectly spliced in microbial systems
	(vi) For gene augmentation therapy, the expression of proteins in animal cells in order to correct a genetic defect in a live animal
	(vii) For the production of transgenic animals expressing a foreign protein
Regulatory analysis	(i) For transient analysis of gene regulatory sequences in cells using reporter constructs
	(ii) For the analysis of gene regulatory sequences using reporter constructs in transgenic animals
	(iii) For the cloning and analysis of higher-order function elements (origins, centromeres, matrix attachment regions, boundary elements, etc.)
Gene inhibition	(i) For the inhibition of endogenous gene function using antisense RNA, ribozymes, intrabodies, or dominant negative alleles either for functional analysis in cells/transgenic animals, or for gene inhibition therapy
Mutagenesis and targeting	(i) For untargeted gene mutation by random insertional mutagenesis
	(ii) For mutagenesis screening and cloning by tagging or plasmid rescue
	(iii) For the entrapment of genes or regulatory elements
	(iv) For targeted disruption of an endogenous gene (gene knockout)
	(v) To introduce a subtle mutation (allele replacement)
	(vi) To replace one gene with another (gene knock in)

library, an approach termed *expression cloning*. In many cases, cloned sequences are introduced into animal cells in order to be subjected to some kind of functional analysis, such as testing various mutant forms of a protein or regulatory element for their activity. Alternatively, protein production may itself be the goal, allowing biochemical and structural analysis, or in the biotechnology industry, commercial production for research, industrial, or medical use. The exploitation of animal cells as "protein factories" is particularly important if correct post-translational modification is required for efficient protein activity or if the product is intended for human therapeutic use, since incorrect modification often renders recombinant human proteins immunogenic. In research, recombinant protein synthesis is a means to investigate a particular biological system, and this is usually the major factor determining the choice of suitable host cells. Gene delivery therefore has to be optimized to fit these parameters. However, where protein synthesis is itself the ultimate aim, a small number of cell lines have been specially developed to complement particular vectors, such as COS-7 cells for SV40-derived replicons, HEK 293 cells for adenoviral vectors, and Sf9 cells for baculovirus vectors. Gene transfer procedures for such cells have been carefully optimized and are routine in many laboratories.

Many of the strategies discussed require only transient protein expression. The foreign DNA need only remain intact and functional in the host cell for a short time, or the host cell itself need only survive transiently. This type of system is sufficient for protein harvesting if a large amount of protein can accumulate over a short period of time. It is also sufficient for many types of functional analysis, because the given assay can be completed rapidly. In other situations, however, it may be necessary to generate a cell line producing recombinant protein on a long-term basis. This approach is used where a continuous supply of protein is required or where the cell line is used as a basis for further study. Such applications require foreign genes to be stably and permanently maintained in their animal cell hosts. This can be achieved in two ways: first by stable integration of foreign DNA into the genome, and second by the use of stably maintained episomal vectors. Stable maintenance and long-term expression are also required where manipulated cells are used to generate transgenic animals, or as part of a gene therapy program. Like engineered cells, transgenic animals may be used purely for functional analysis, or as novel strains for exploitation in further experiments. Transgenic animals can also be used as living factories, producing correctly modified commercially valuable proteins, for example in their milk. This approach is euphemistically termed "animal pharming."

Recent Advances in Gene Transfer Technology

While protein expression remains the predominant use for animal cells, attention has recently switched to a powerful set of novel applications that exploit the same gene transfer techniques directly to modify animal genomes, or the expression of endogenous genes. *Gene targeting* is the replacement of one allele with another by homologous recombination, leaving the rest of the genome unchanged.

This technique facilitates allele replacement and gene disruption (gene knockout) to create tailor-made mutant cells. The expression of endogenous genes can also be influenced by using expression constructs to generate antisense RNA, sometimes associated with ribozymes. These interact with and destroy cellular mRNAs, and hence block gene expression at the post-transcriptional level. Both gene targeting and antisense RNA strategies are extremely powerful when combined with current methods for generating transgenic animals, because they allow the creation of specific mutants with particular genes interrupted, replaced, altered by subtle mutation, or inhibited. The random insertion of cloned DNA also has many applications, for example, saturation mutagenesis, gene cloning by tagging or plasmid rescue, and the trapping of endogenous genes and regulatory elements using randomly inserted reporter gene constructs. Once again, this technology is at its most powerful when used in transgenic animals, allowing the isolation of genes and regulatory elements with specific expression patterns, or the isolation of genes associated with particular mutant phenotypes.

The technology associated with gene expression and genome modification is now quite sophisticated, and is advancing rapidly. This reflects the free use of well-characterized genetic systems from simpler organisms as genetic tools, and the trend towards designing and customizing them to make them unique and fully controllable. Of particular interest is the use of site-specific recombination systems from bacteriophage and yeast to control gene expression and generate targeted genome rearrangements, often in an inducible or regulated fashion. The design of fully synthetic or hybrid inducible gene expression systems should eventually allow the experimenter to exercise complete and predictable control over foreign genes transferred to animal cells and in transgenic animals. It will not be long before it is possible to generate cell lines and animals in which particular genes can be disrupted or activated in specific cell types or at specific developmental stages at the whim of the investigator.

Transfer and Fate of DNA Introduced into Animal Cells

DNA can be introduced into cultured animal cells by two routes. The first exploits the natural ability of animal viruses to infect cells and deliver the viral genome either to the cytoplasm (most RNA viruses) or nucleus (most DNA viruses). Recombinant viruses carrying foreign DNA can thus be used to transfer foreign genes into the cell, a process termed *transduction*. Most DNA viruses, as well as the retroviruses (which have a DNA stage of the replication cycle), have been used to deliver foreign genes to the nucleus. Some replicate episomally (e.g., herpes viruses), while others integrate (e.g., retroviruses). Exceptionally, the poxviruses are DNA viruses that replicate in the cytoplasm. They, and some RNA viruses, have been exploited for cytoplasmic gene delivery and expression, which can be advantageous in certain experiments (e.g., for producing antisense RNA). The general advantage of transduction as a gene delivery method is its high efficiency: In certain systems every cell in a culture dish can receive foreign DNA. It is also possible to exploit the natural tropism of a virus to infect particular cells in a tissue; for example, Epstein—Barr virus is lymphotropic. On the down side, there is often a complex series of manipulations involved in the preparation of recombinant viruses. Most viruses also exhibit cytopathic effects, and there are safety concerns over the use of recombinant human viruses. The alternative and simpler strategy is direct DNA delivery, where the cell is forced to internalize DNA present in the surrounding medium, or where there is direct physical delivery of DNA into the nucleus, such as by microinjection. These unnatural DNA uptake routes are grouped under the term *transfection*. Direct delivery is by far the most commonly used strategy due to its simplicity and the requirement for only small, easily manipulable vectors. However, it is much less efficient, and strong selection systems must be used to identify successfully transfected cells.

The fate of DNA introduced into cells depends on the vector system being used. Many viruses, and plasmids derived from them, carry *cis*-acting elements that facilitate episomal replication, allowing the DNA to be replicated and expressed without integration. Alternatively, foreign DNA may integrate into a random chromosomal site and replicate as a normal part of the genome. Integration generally represents a permanent modification, while episomal maintenance may be permanent or transient, depending on the nature of the replicon and its effect on the cell. Genes carried on vectors with no capacity for episomal maintenance may also be expressed transiently, but are soon diluted from the cell population. In some cases, the use of nonreplicating vectors, or even simple donor DNA without vector, ensures that only cells which have stably integrated the DNA will be selected.

The sections to follow have been written to provide an overview of the technology associated with gene transfer to animal cells. The following two sections describe the construction and use of direct transfer vectors and viral vectors, respectively. The next two sections discuss the factors controlling heterologous gene expression in animal cells. The subsequent section introduces the more recent

technological advances of genome manipulation, including the use of antisense RNA and gene targeting. The final section describes how transgenic animals are produced from manipulated animal cells, and discusses the impact of this relatively new technology.

PLASMID EXPRESSION VECTORS FOR ANIMAL CELLS

Classes of Expression Vector and Common Modular Components

An expression vector contains regulatory elements allowing the expression of any foreign DNA it carries. The simplest expression vectors, *transcription vectors*, allow transcription but not translation of cloned foreign DNA, and are designed for in vitro use [Fig. 1(a)]. They allow the production of large quantities (up to 100 μg per reaction) of recombinant RNA and are often equipped with dual, opposing promoters allowing both message sense and antisense RNA to be synthesized, for example, for use as probes in hybridization experiments. Significantly, such vectors utilize the very specific promoters from *E. coli* bacteriophages such as T3, T7, and SP6, which do not function in animal cells. More complex vectors can therefore be designed to incorporate this in vitro transcription system without interfering with the function of eukaryotic transcription units in animal cells. Simple transcription vectors lack other regulatory sequences, including transcriptional termination sites. RNA of specified length can therefore be produced from such vectors only by linearization (run-off transcription). Although designed for in vitro use, transcription vectors play an essential role in certain protein expression systems (e.g., see the later section on Sindbis virus and Semliki Forest virus vectors).

Typical *protein expression vectors* allow both the transcription and translation of cloned DNA, and thus facilitate the production of recombinant protein [Fig. 1(b)]. Such vectors are equipped with transcriptional regulatory sequences and sequences that control RNA processing and protein synthesis (6). They are designed for use both in cell culture and in vivo. In cases where the objective

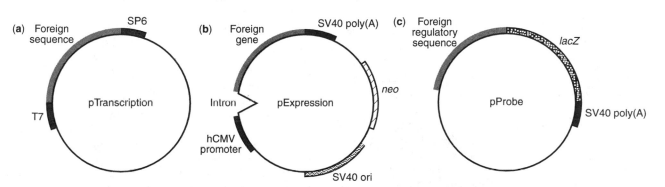

Figure 1. Generic maps of different types of expression vector: (**a**) a transcription vector, which carries promoters allowing the in vitro transcription of foreign DNA; (**b**) a protein expression vector, which contains the regulatory elements (promoter—enhancer, intron, polyadenylation site) allowing the transcription and translation of foreign DNA; such vectors may also carry a marker gene for selection of transformants, or a viral origin of replication for episomal maintenance; (**c**) a regulatory probe vector, which carries a reporter gene and allows the characterization of cloned regulatory elements.

of the expression experiment is simply to produce as much protein as possible, *overexpression vectors* are used, which are designed to maximize both transcription and translation. Where more moderate protein expression levels are appropriate for the experiment, or where large amounts of protein would be toxic to the cells, inducible regulatory elements may be used. Proteins may be expressed as native polypeptides or fusion proteins, the latter often to facilitate protein purification or analysis. A common fusion strategy is to express recombinant proteins with an N-terminal signal peptide. This allows secretion from host cell, so that the protein can be purified from the growth medium without resorting to cell lysis.

Further expression vectors are designed not for the analysis of cloned gene products, but cloned regulatory elements (7). Such *regulatory probe vectors* carry a screenable marker gene such as *lacZ*, and allow the insertion of putative regulatory elements that can be used to drive marker gene expression [Fig. 1(c)]. Different vectors are available for the analysis of different types of *cis*-acting element. *Promoter probe vectors* carry a reporter gene with an initiation codon but no upstream regulatory sequences, and are used for the identification and dissection of putative promoters. *Enhancer probe vectors* carry a reporter gene driven by a minimal promoter, allowing analysis for the upregulation of basal activity. There are also vectors available for the analysis of transcriptional terminator/polyadenylation sites and splice signals. Specialized probe vectors called *entrapment vectors* are used for the identification and isolation of novel regulatory elements following random integration into the genome. These are discussed in more detail in a later section.

There are now hundreds of different expression vectors available commercially, and many more that have been designed for specific experimental purposes. Despite this overwhelming diversity, all expression vectors carry a number of common modular components and differ only in their versatility and applicability to particular experimental systems and host cell types. The typical modular components of an expression vector for animal cells are discussed in the following, and can be divided into five major categories (6):

- *Plasmid backbone sequences.* Those sequences required for cloning in bacteria and for in vitro manipulation
- *Plasmid maintenance sequences.* Many vectors also carry sequences of viral origin that allow episomal replication in animal cells
- *Components of the animal gene transcription unit.* Those sequences used for the efficient expression of foreign genes, including promoter and enhancer elements, a polyadenylation site, an intron, sequences for translational control, and sequences for protein targeting in the host cell
- *Marker genes.* Either for visible quantification or characterization of gene expression, or for selection of transfected cells
- *Sequences to simplify protein purification.* In overexpression vectors there may be additional sequences

encoding a signal peptide (to facilitate secretion), a protein tag (to allow, e.g., affinity purification of the fusion protein), and a protease cleavage site (to remove the tag after purification)

Plasmid Backbone Sequences

All expression vectors for use in animal cells are *shuttle vectors*; that is, they can be propagated in cells of more than one species. In most cases, the alternative host is *Escherichia coli*, allowing large quantities of plasmid DNA to be prepared and isolated from bacterial culture (c.f. yeast artificial chromosome vectors in the following section). Such vectors contain an origin of replication derived from the naturally occurring plasmid ColE1, and a dominant marker for selection in bacterial cells. This marker is usually an antibiotic resistance gene because the selective regime is simple. However, suppressor tRNAs are used in some host–vector systems.

In addition to these basic maintenance sequences, other backbone sequences include those used for in vitro manipulation (8). The most important of these is the *multiple cloning site*, a cluster of unique restriction enzyme sites allowing the insertion of foreign DNA, using a variety of subcloning strategies, at a site that does not disturb vector functions. For many vectors, recombinant screening is facilitated by locating the multiple cloning site within a marker gene so that recombinants can be screened for loss of marker activity. The simplest and most popular system is *blue-white selection*. This is based on the marker gene *lacZ*, whose product β-galactosidase converts the chromogenic substrate X-gal (5-bromo-4-chloro-3-indolyl-β-D-galactopyranoside) into a blue pigment. Recombinant vectors, in which the marker is interrupted, lack β-galactosidase activity. Therefore, on X-gal supplemented medium, recombinant colonies appear white and nonrecombinant colonies blue. The best contemporary vectors are extremely versatile and contain a bacteriophage f1 (or similar) origin of replication, facilitating the production of single stranded DNA for sequencing, in vitro mutagenesis, etc., and opposed bacteriophage promoters allowing the synthesis of sense and antisense RNA corresponding to the insert (e.g. for in situ hybridization).

Generally, the bacterial and animal components of shuttle vectors are functionally segregated. The animal DNA does not function in bacteria, and therefore does not interfere with cloning. Similarly, the *E. coli* backbone sequences are not intended for use once the plasmid has been introduced into animal cells, and they do not interfere with maintenance or expression. However, certain plasmid sequences have been shown to inhibit vector function in mammalian cells. The first example was a fragment of the pBR322 backbone that inhibited the activity of the SV40 origin of replication in monkey cells (9). Such *poison sequences* are often poorly defined, but they may be responsible for the varying efficiencies of otherwise similar expression vectors. Occasionally, eukaryotic insert sequences can interfere with cloning in bacteria—this usually involves rearrangement of the insert due to the presence of repetitive DNA sequences, but can also result in nonrecovery of recombinant vectors from bacterial culture. Some contemporary vectors are designed to use certain sequences both in bacterial and animal cells. A recent series of expression vectors from Invitrogen utilizes a single dominant selectable marker for resistance to the antibiotic Zeocin. This can be selected in bacteria and mammalian cells because the gene is controlled by dual tandem promoters (a synthetic bacterial promoter and the human cytomegalovirus promoter), and hence significantly reduces the size of the vector allowing the propagation of larger inserts. Bacterial promoters, such as the T7 promoter and the *E. coli lac* promoter, have also been used as part of animal gene transcription units. They have been exploited as heterologous inducible promoters, allowing efficient inducible expression of cloned genes if the appropriate transcription factors are provided in *trans*. Such systems are discussed in more detail later.

Plasmid Maintenance Sequences

The transfection of animal cells with bacterial plasmids results in a low frequency of transformation due to stable integration of the DNA into the host genome. Such vectors are not maintained episomally because the bacterial ColE1 origin does not function in eukaryotes. Any extrachromosomal DNA is rapidly diluted and degraded in nontransformed cells. Certain mammalian viruses, however, propagate their genomes as episomal plasmids on either a long-term (latent) or a short-term (lytic) basis. The inclusion of viral origins in recombinant plasmids allows expression vectors to be propagated in the same manner.

Lytic origins, such as the SV40 *ori* and Epstein–Barr virus *oriLyt*, can promote massive extrachromosomal replication of expression vectors if appropriate regulatory proteins are supplied in *trans*. This prolific amplification of the foreign DNA allows high-level recombinant protein synthesis, but this rapidly becomes toxic to the host cell, resulting in cell death within a few days. Vectors with lytic origins are thus suitable for transient expression, but not for long-term protein synthesis. Conversely, latent origins, such as Epstein–Barr virus *oriP* and the bovine papillomavirus origin, allow stable maintenance of expression vectors at a low copy number. This is not toxic to the cell, and such vectors are suitable for long-term propagation and facilitate the stable expression of recombinant proteins. Expression vectors carrying papovavirus and Epstein–Barr virus origins are discussed in more detail later.

Regulatory Sequences

All protein expression vectors carry a transcription unit containing the sequences required for efficient gene expression. These comprise transcriptional regulatory sequences, RNA processing signals, and sequences for protein synthesis and targeting. The major components are outlined briefly in the following section and discussed more fully in subsequent sections.

- *Promoter and enhancer sequences.* The promoter is the site where RNA polymerase II binds to the transcription unit, and *cis*-acting elements upstream of the promoter also control its cell type specificity and induction in response to external signals. Enhancers are *cis*-acting elements that work with endogenous promoters to increase their transcriptional activity; they may also impart cell type and inducible specificity upon gene expression. The promoter and enhancer elements chosen for particular expression strategies depend on the experimental parameters. There are three types of system: (*1*) endogenous systems; (*2*) promiscuous viral systems; and (*3*) inducible systems. Where a particular level or pattern of gene expression is required (e.g., when directing gene expression to specific tissues in transgenic mice), an endogenous promoter/enhancer system may be employed because many highly specific systems have been characterized. Where high-level expression and versatility are required, the strong and promiscuous regulatory elements found in mammalian viruses are often used. These include the SV40 early promoter and enhancer, the human cytomegalovirus promoter/enhancer, and the Rous sarcoma virus long terminal repeat (LTR) promoter/enhancer. These widely used elements function in many cell types, often beyond the scope specified by the host range of the virus, allowing the same expression vectors to be transfected into a range of different cell lines. Where precise control of gene expression is desired, or where the recombinant protein is toxic to the cells, inducible systems may be used. These may be of endogenous origin (e.g., heat induction), in which case endogenous genes may also be activated. Alternatively, they may be heterologous systems that have to be activated by supplying appropriate transcriptional regulators in *trans* (e.g., *E. coli lac* and *tet* systems, the *Drosophila melanogaster* ecdysone system). Both endogenous and heterologous systems may suffer from leakage (high background expression) or a low induction ratio, so there has been an intense effort in recent years to develop hybrid or completely artificial induction systems, allowing precise control of foreign gene expression.

- *RNA processing sequences.* These include a transcriptional termination/polyadenylation site and often an intron. Termination and polyadenylation sites are essential for stable RNA production. Introns are not necessary for the efficient expression of all genes, but in many cases the inclusion of an intron has been shown to improve protein expression levels. For some genes, this may be because splicing is required for continued transcription or RNA stability. Alternatively, the recruitment of particular proteins during splicing may facilitate translation when the mRNA is exported from the nucleus.

- *Sequences for efficient translation and protein targeting.* By far the most important consideration here is the Kozak consensus, a sequence surrounding the initiation codon whose context sponsors efficient ribosome scanning and initiation. The size of the 5′ untranslated region (UTR) is also kept as short as possible, as secondary structure in the transcript can inhibit translation. If a 3′ UTR is included in the vector, AU-rich instability sequences are avoided. A further sequence included in some vectors is a picornaviral internal ribosome entry site, allowing the production and translation of polycistronic mRNAs. Sequences may also be included that target recombinant proteins to particular cellular compartments. Nuclear localization sequences are used to target proteins to the nucleus. Signal peptides target proteins to the secretory pathway, which may be essential for correct post-translational modification. KDEL retention signals (KDEL specifies a tetrapeptide sequence in the single letter amino acid code) may be used to favor intracellular protein accumulation.

Marker Genes

A *marker gene* is one conferring a readily identifiable phenotype. Many expression vectors carry marker genes, or are introduced with a second vector carrying a marker gene. Such genes can be divided into two classes serving distinct functions.

First, *visible or screenable markers (reporter genes)* provide visible evidence of transfection and gene expression. Under the control of a constitutive promoter, reporter genes can be used to determine transfection efficiency. Such vectors are often used for cotransfection with a series of experimental vectors to provide an internal experimental control. If a reporter gene is linked to a heterologous regulatory element, it can be used to quantify the expression levels and patterns associated with that regulatory element. If a reporter gene is joined to a foreign gene and expressed as a fusion protein, it can be used as a flag to determine protein localization, or exploited for protein purification (see next section). Entrapment vectors, which integrate into the genome and reveal the attributes of proximal genes and regulatory elements by reproducing their expression patterns, can exploit both these principles.

Second, *selectable markers* encode products conferring resistance (positive selection) or sensitivity (negative selection or counterselection) to a particular treatment. These are used to select stably transfected cells from a background of nontransfected cells, or other rare products of transfection (e.g., cells that have undergone homologous recombination as opposed to those that have integrated the DNA randomly).

Sequences to Simplify Protein Purification

The synthesis and accumulation of recombinant protein in the cytoplasm of stably transfected cells has several disadvantages, including toxicity effects and dependence on cell lysis for protein isolation. However, by expressing recombinant proteins with an N-terminal signal peptide, proteins can be secreted from the cell and purified from the medium, reducing toxicity and allowing long-term protein production by repeated passaging. Traditional methods for the purification of overexpressed proteins involve time-consuming gel filtration or ion-exchange chromatography procedures. Only if the protein has a natural ligand,

or if an antibody is available, can it be purified by the simpler techniques of affinity chromatography or immunoprecipitation. Many current expression vectors include sequences incorporated specifically to simplify the purification of overexpressed proteins (10). These sequences fall into three classes: fusion polypeptides, fusion epitopes, and oligo(amino acid) tails. Each provides a tag with which to purify the protein product of any gene expressed using that vector (Table 2). Fusion polypeptides include β-galactosidase, glutathione-S-transferase, and staphylococcal protein A. In each case, there is a particular ligand to which this polypeptide binds, allowing the

Table 2. Sequences Included in Mammalian Expression Vectors to Simplify the Purification of Overexpressed Proteins

Sequence	Comments
Secretion	
Signal peptide	An N-terminal 15–30 amino acid peptide which, by interacting with a signal recognition particle, causes ribosomes to attach to the ER membrane and pass the nascent polypeptide into the ER lumen for secretion; many signal peptides have been characterized and some exploited in mammalian expression vectors; e.g., the mouse Ig kappa chain signal peptide is used in the Invitrogen vector pSecTag
Fusion polypeptides	
β-galactosidase	Approximately 120-kDa polypeptide, binds to APTG
Glutathione-S-transferase	Approximately 30-kDa polypeptide, binds to glutathione
Staphylococcal protein A	Approximately 30-kDa polypeptide, binds to IgG and elutes at low pH
Fusion epitopes	
c-Myc	11 amino acid epitope, recognized by mouse monoclonal antibody 9E10; elutes at low pH
FLAG	Hydrophilic 8 amino acid epitope recognized by commercially available antibody anti-FLAG M1/M2
Oligo(amino acid) tails	
$(His)_6$	Purified by metal chelate affinity chromatography, or anti-$(His)_6$ antibodies
$(Cys)_4$	Purified by affinity to thiopropyl groups
Cleavage sites	
Collagenase	Cleavage site is -Pro-xxx-↓-Gly-Pro-xxx-↓
Enterokinase	Cleavage site is -$(Asp)_4$—Lys-↓
Factor Xa	Cleavage site is -Ile-Glu-Gly-Arg-↓ at pH 8.0

Abbreviations: APTG, *p*-aminophenyl-β-D-thiogalactopyranoside; ER, endoplasmic reticulum; FLAG, amino acid one-letter code for residues within the "FLAG" epitope.

recombinant fusion protein to be captured and then eluted. Fusion epitopes are short peptides providing a single epitope of a particular protein, such as c-Myc, for recognition by a monoclonal antibody. The advantage of epitopes is that their small size and surface location usually does not interfere with the native folding or activity of the recombinant protein, which is sometimes a problem using the larger fusion polypeptides. Similarly, a short oligo(amino acid) tail provides an unobtrusive tag allowing purification by simple chromatographic procedures, or again using antibodies. The tail is usually 2–20 residues in length. A further sequence often included in such vectors is a consensus cleavage site allowing the overexpressed protein to be separated from its fusion tag. A number of simple sequences may be chemically or enzymatically cleaved (e.g., cyanogen bromide cleaves after methionine residues). More complex cleavage sites, such as the motif recognized by enterokinase, are useful because they are unlikely to appear within the recombinant protein by chance.

OTHER DIRECT TRANSFER VECTORS FOR ANIMAL CELLS

Yeast Artificial Chromosome Expression Vectors

Simple engineering strategies, such as protein synthesis and transient analysis, can be performed with cDNAs or minigene constructs cloned in plasmid or viral vectors. Although such constructs provide the essential information for protein structure, it is well established that endogenous gene expression is influenced not just by local regulatory elements, but also distant sites that may exert a direct regulatory influence, or may control chromatin structure or the extent of DNA methylation. Hence, to reproduce the native expression characteristics of an endogenous gene fully, a transgene may need to be bracketed by hundreds of kilobase pairs of flanking sequence. Inserts greater than 50 kbp cannot be cloned in standard plasmid, cosmid, or viral vectors due to packaging constraints, instability resulting from recombination, the selection of spontaneous deletion mutants, and the likelihood of shearing the DNA during in vitro manipulation.

Such limitations have been overcome by developing yeast artificial chromosome (YAC) vectors (11). These are linear vectors carrying the essential *cis*-acting elements of a yeast chromosome, and are stably propagated in yeast cells at a low copy number. The components required are a yeast centromere (*CEN*), an origin of replication (autonomous replicating sequence, *ARS*) and telomeres (*TEL*). The vectors also carry a multiple cloning site for the insertion of foreign DNA, and selectable markers for stable maintenance (such markers generally restore prototrophy to an auxotrophic yeast strain). Of the various large-capacity vectors developed for use in bacterial and mammalian cells (reviewed in Ref. 11), YAC vectors have many advantages, including their capacity (theoretically up to 2 Mbp, which should enable even the largest mammalian genes to be cloned) and the amenability of yeast for homologous recombination. This allows yeast vector sequences to be replaced by mammalian selectable

markers prior to transfection, a process termed *retrofitting*. It also allows specific mutations to be introduced into the foreign DNA. Recombinant YAC clones are fragile and subject to shear, but several methods have been developed for their efficient transfection into mammalian cells, including lipofection, fusion with yeast spheroplasts, and microinjection into the pronuclei of fertilized eggs (see later). Embryonic stem (ES) cells have been the predominant targets for YAC transfection, and such techniques yield transgenic mice with at least the same efficiency as obtained using more traditional and smaller transgenes.

The generation of YAC-transgenic mice is not a trivial process, since recombinant YAC DNA is difficult to purify intact, and is highly susceptible to fragmentation once inside the cell. Typically, transgenic animals integrate several YACs, some with terminal deletions reflecting intracellular fragmentation events. Despite these difficulties, YACs have been used to study the expression of a number of human and mouse genes in a transgenic environment, using constructs ranging in size from 40 kbp to over 1 Mbp (11). In most cases, transgene expression was shown to closely mirror the expression of the endogenous gene, suggesting that the inclusion of flanking material can isolate transgenes from position effects, which often influence basic expression constructs. The applications of this technology are manifold, including mutational analysis, the generation of animal models for human disease, the analysis of *cis*-acting elements in their natural context, and the analysis of higher-order genome function (e.g., genomic imprinting and X-chromosome inactivation). YACs have also been used as the basis of one class of mammalian artificial chromosome (MAC), as discussed later.

Targeting Vectors

Whatever the ultimate aim of a gene transfer experiment, most vectors are designed primarily to express *something*, be it a recombinant protein, a reporter gene under the control of a cloned regulatory element, or an antisense RNA molecule. Some plasmid vectors, however, do not carry the typical components of a eukaryotic transcription unit, and are therefore not strictly expression vectors. There are two uses for such constructs: gene targeting and random integration.

Gene targeting is the replacement of specific target DNA sequences with foreign DNA carried in a vector by homologous recombination and/or gene conversion (12). *Targeting vectors* are used for two purposes, first to replace genomic DNA sequences, and second to replace sequences in viral genomes already in the cell, to generate recombinant viral vectors (see later). Like expression vectors, targeting vectors carry plasmid backbone sequences and selectable markers, but they lack eukaryotic maintenance sequences because the vectors are not designed for amplification or recovery—their sole purpose is delivery of the foreign DNA to the homologous target. For this reason, such vectors are often termed *gene delivery vectors*, or *suicide vectors*. The most important feature of a targeting vector is the region of homology with the intended target, as this is an absolute requirement for homologous recombination. The design of the homology region allows either insertion by single crossover or transplacement by double crossover (targeting vectors and strategies for gene targeting are discussed in more detail later). Note that gene targeting and protein targeting are *not* related terms: The former refers to the introduction of particular mutations into specific genes by homologous recombination, while the latter refers to controlling the intracellular (or extracellular) destination of a protein once it has been synthesized. The purposeful alteration of protein structure by introducing specific mutations into its gene is termed *protein engineering*.

Plasmid Vectors for Insertional Mutagenesis and Entrapment

The use of vectors for random integration into genomic DNA serves two purposes. First, integrating vectors can be used to generate mutants. Mutagenesis in classical genetic analysis traditionally involves exposing a population of organisms to high levels of a mutagen, and then recovering mutant offspring by suitable selection and screening. The mutagens employed are either chemical (e.g., ethylmethane sulfonate added to food) or physical (e.g., bombardment with X-rays). More recently, *biological* mutagens have been exploited. These are based on transposable elements, DNA sequences that naturally jump from site to site in the genome, often happening to interrupt genes. Transposable elements cloned in plasmid vectors can be introduced into animal cells and will jump to random sites in the genome resulting in insertional mutagenesis. This strategy has been widely used to generate *Drosophila* mutants: vectors carrying recombinant *Drosophila* transposons called P elements have been microinjected into eggs, leading to the recovery of mutant offspring (13). Transposable elements require both *cis*-acting sequences and *trans*-acting enzymes for mobilization. The strategy used to control P element mutagenesis in *Drosophila* is to coinject eggs with two plasmids, one containing a defective P element (lacking the *trans*-functions) and another containing a helper P element, which has been rendered nonmobilizable by deleting its *cis*-functions (these are termed "wings-clipped" elements). This enables the defective P element to jump once, from the plasmid to a random location in the genome, and then remain stably integrated. Insertional mutants have also been generated in mice, initially by the chance integration of transgenes or retroviral vectors designed for other purposes, and later by specially dedicated integration vectors (14).

Second, integrating vectors can be used as *entrapment vectors* to identify local genes and regulatory elements [Fig. 2(a)]. In this case, the transposable element contains a reporter gene that responds to local promoter or enhancer elements at the site of integration. The classic example of this type of vector is the original *Drosophila enhancer trap* (15). A recombinant P element transferred to the *Drosophila* germline, as discussed, carries *lacZ* under the control of a minimal promoter. The randomly integrated cassette is then influenced by any local enhancers, and the reporter gene expression pattern reveals the expression parameters of the gene normally controlled by the enhancer. *Gene traps* use the same strategy to identify genes. In this case, the reporter gene may be located downstream from an AUG codon or a splice acceptor site. The first type of gene trap is activated upon insertion into the first exon of an endogenous gene, while the other is activated if inserted into an intron. Entrapment strategies are widely used in *Drosophila* to identify novel genes on the basis of their expression parameters. More recently, the same approach has been used in other animals, including mice (16), where libraries of ES cells carrying reporter insertions can be used to generate transgenic animals (17). ES cells are the preferred target for such experiments as the interpretation of insertional mutation phenotypes generated by the pronuclear injection of mouse eggs may be complicated by the extensive genome rearrangements that often accompany this procedure. More refined approaches can be used to identify specific classes of genes, for example, the use of a reporter gene that requires an N-terminal signal sequence for expression effectively selects for mutations in genes that encode secreted proteins. Also, a gene trap comprising two selectable markers and designed to express the site-specific recombinase Cre will induce a permanent switch between the markers when integrated adjacent to a constitutive promoter (Cre recombinase is discussed in more detail later). This approach can be used to identify genes expressed in a temporally restricted manner through the generation of a cell autonomous marker (no switching of marker genes). The integration of a gene trap vector is generally mutagenic, and depending on the gene, the mutant phenotype may be observed in heterozygotes or homozygotes. Such vectors thus serve a dual role — interesting new genes can be identified both by their reporter expression pattern and by their mutant phenotype. Note that retroviruses (see later) are often used for insertional mutagenesis and trapping in mammals. Their unusual mode of replication allows them to be classed as transposable elements as well as viruses; so their activity is very similar to *Drosophila* P element vectors.

Basic integrating vectors do not require any special sequences in addition to the plasmid backbone, and even this can be dispensed with — insertional mutants in mice can be generated by introducing foreign DNA fragments into fertilized eggs without a vector. Entrapment vectors require a marker gene and minimal regulatory elements, but both basic integrating vectors and entrapment vectors lack eukaryotic maintenance sequences, because they are not deigned for amplification or recovery. However, careful design of such vectors can prove very useful. One consideration is the uniqueness of the introduced sequence. In *Drosophila*, the introduction of single P elements into fly strains normally lacking P elements enables genes identified by insertional mutagenesis to be cloned by *tagging*. Simply, this involves screening a genomic library generated from the mutant line for the unique sequence of the integrated element [Fig. 2(b)]. Any clones isolated by this technique would contain the integrated foreign DNA and surrounding genomic DNA. This could then be used to screen genomic and cDNA libraries from wild-type flies to identify and isolate the noninterrupted version of the gene. This is an extremely convenient reverse genetics approach in the study of gene

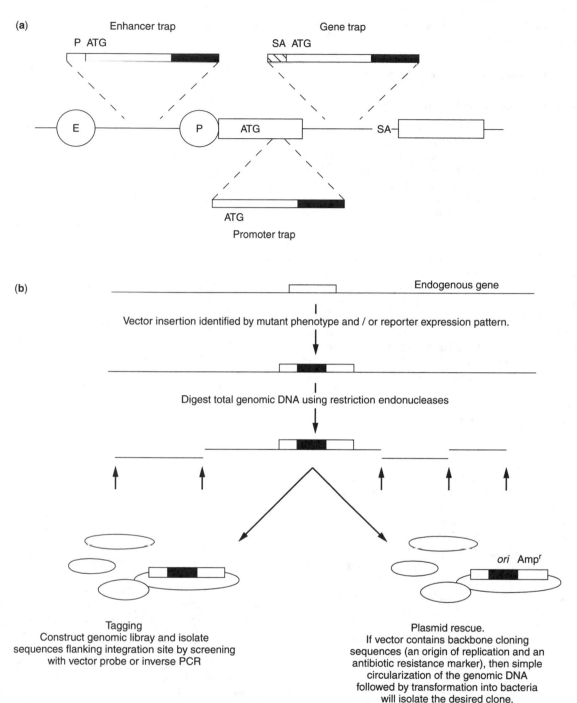

Figure 2. Insertional mutagenesis and entrapment vectors: (**a**) different forms of entrapment vector. The enhancer trap vector carries a minimal promoter, and gene trap vectors may carry a "naked" start codon (this type of vector is also known as a promoter trap) or a splice acceptor. (**b**) insertional mutagenesis and entrapment vectors may be used to clone local genes either by tagging or plasmid rescue.

function, based on an original strategy devised by Lowry and colleagues (18).

An even more elegant refinement is the technique of *plasmid rescue* (19). In this case, the vector is designed so that the sequence that integrates into the genome contains certain plasmid backbone elements: the origin of replication and a bacterial selectable marker. The isolation of flanking DNA can then be achieved without library construction: Genomic DNA from the mutant line is digested with a restriction endonuclease cutting at a single site in the vector, and the resulting genomic DNA fragments are ligated to form circles. These can be introduced into bacterial cells *en masse*, but only those carrying a plasmid origin and marker will replicate under the selective regime [Fig. 2(b)]. Bacterial colonies growing on selective media thus contain circularized genomic fragments carrying the inserted DNA sequence and flanking genomic DNA.

DIRECT DNA TRANSFER TO ANIMAL CELLS

Overview of Animal Cell Transfection

The direct transfer of DNA into animal cells can be accomplished by a number of techniques that either force the cells to take in DNA by breaching the cell membrane or exploit the natural ability of cells to internalize certain molecules in their environment. The DNA introduced into cells by transfection may be maintained transiently or permanently. In transient transfection, the DNA may be nonreplicative, in which case it is diluted and lost from the population of cells over a few hours, depending on its stability. For plasmids containing an SV40 origin of replication, episomal replication occurs in certain simian cells, but the high replication rate eventually causes cell death. In both cases, foreign genes may be expressed transiently, with a rapid onset of protein synthesis, but for a limited duration. Transient transfection is therefore useful for strategies such as expression cloning, rapid assays for protein activity, and establishing the potential of different promoters. Transient transfection is not an efficient method for the overexpression and purification of recombinant proteins on a long-term basis and cannot be used to generate transgenic animals. For stable transfection (also termed *transformation* because the genotype of the cell is altered), foreign DNA must be maintained permanently in the cell. If the exogenous DNA is nonreplicative, stable transfection must occur by integration of the DNA into the genome. Alternatively, the foreign DNA may be carried in an episomal vector, whose moderate replication rate does not cause cell death. Stable transfection is required for the long-term production of foreign proteins, for gene silencing by antisense RNA synthesis, and for the generation of transgenic animals. It is also highly desirable in many gene therapy applications.

What governs whether a given DNA molecule will transiently or stably transfect a cell? Partly, this depends on the type of vector. Those carrying episomal maintenance sequences control their own fate: SV40-based vectors kill simian host cells by high-level episomal replication; so stably transfected cells are not recovered. However, vectors carrying the Epstein–Barr virus latent origin are stably maintained in permissive cells because their replication rate is moderate and is tolerated by the host. For nonreplicating DNA, however, both transient and stable transfection occur concurrently. The efficiency of transient transfection varies considerably among different cell types and according to the transfection method, but is always several orders of magnitude higher than that of stable integration. Thus, in transient transfection experiments, a small number of cells will also be stably transfected, but these will not generally be noticed in the short experimental time scale. In stable transfection experiments, many cells are initially transiently transfected, but the DNA is soon diluted and destroyed. Selection is used to identify the rare cells where foreign DNA has integrated into the genome,

and by this time, the "transient" DNA is no longer present. Stable integration is thought to occur by illegitimate recombination—end joining between broken chromosomal DNA and vector DNA. In some cells, an alternative to illegitimate recombination is homologous recombination. The efficiency of this process is extremely low in most cells, and even in particularly amenable cells (such as ES cells and the DT40 line), it is still a rare process and occurs several orders of magnitude less frequently than random integration. Homologous recombination occurs only if the vector carries a homology region, where ectopic pairing can occur between the genome and the vector, facilitating crossing over or gene conversion. Due to the rarity of this event and the relative frequency of random integration, very powerful selective strategies must be employed to identify targeted cells, as discussed later.

Transient Transfection with Nonreplicating Vectors

In transient transfection, DNA is not integrated into the genome. Instead, when taken up by cells, it is transferred to the nucleus, where it remains for a short period of time in an extrachromosomal state (6,20). Almost any vector and any cell line can be used for this type of transient transfection, and recombinant proteins can be synthesized as long as the vector contains a mammalian expression cassette. The onset of protein expression is rapid, but the yield depends not only on the regulatory elements in the vector, but also on the transfection efficiency (i.e., how much DNA is taken into each cell) and the stability of the extrachromosomal DNA (i.e., how long it lasts once inside). Covalently closed circular plasmid DNA survives 12–48 hours in many cell lines before it is degraded and diluted, allowing the transient expression of foreign genes from simple vectors lacking eukaryotic maintenance sequences. Some cell lines are renowned for the stability of transfected DNA, allowing survival and foreign gene expression for over 80 hours. One example is the adenovirus-transformed human embryonic kidney line 293 (21). Covalently closed and supercoiled plasmid DNA is required for efficient transient transfection. Relaxed DNA (i.e., nicked circles or linear DNA) is a poor template for transcription, and is prone to exonucleolytic degradation. Ideally, high-quality plasmid DNA, prepared using either cesium chloride equilibrium density gradient ultracentrifugation or anion exchange chromatography, should be used for transient transfection experiments.

Transient Transfection with Runaway Polyomavirus Replicons

The polyomaviruses are a genus of small DNA viruses from the papovavirus family. Each virion comprises a nonenveloped, icosahedral capsid and a circular double-stranded DNA genome of approximately 5 kbp. The best-characterized species is simian virus 40 (SV40), whose productive host range is limited to certain permissive monkey cells. SV40 was the first animal virus to be exploited as a vector because, like bacteriophage λ, it was considered a model system and its molecular biology was studied in great detail. The first SV40-based vectors were viral transduction vectors, and the life cycle of SV40 and its development as a viral vector are discussed later. Despite many successes, however, the use of such vectors has been severely curtailed by the limited capacity for foreign DNA (maximum insert size 2.5 kbp), reflecting the small size of the capsid.

A breakthrough came with the discovery that plasmids containing a polyomavirus origin of replication were propagated in the same way as the virus genome, that is, as episomal replicons in permissive cells (22). Replication also requires the presence of a viral-encoded *trans*-acting regulator termed the *T antigen*. However, since the polyomavirus replicon is not packaged into viral capsids, there is no effective limit to insert size. A number of polyomaviruses have been exploited to develop episomal vectors, including SV40 for monkey cells, murine polyomavirus for mouse cells, and BK virus for human cells. The related bovine papillomavirus (BPV) has also been used. BK virus and BPV-derived replicons can be maintained episomally at a moderate copy number and allow long-term protein expression: These vectors are discussed later. Conversely, the replication of SV40- and murine polyomavirus-derived vectors is uncontrolled. In permissive cells, with readily available T antigen, such vectors can replicate to an astonishingly high copy number (up to 10^5 vector molecules per cell). This facilitates high-level recombinant protein synthesis, making such host–vector systems among the most efficient available. Unfortunately, this prodigious replication and gene expression cannot be sustained by the host cell, and cell death occurs within a few days. SV40 and polyomavirus replicons are therefore suitable only for transient transfection, not in this case because the DNA is lost, but because so much DNA is synthesized that the cell cannot survive.

In some polyomavirus vectors, the T-antigen coding sequence is included, enabling propagation in any permissive cell line. Other vectors lack the T antigen, which must then be supplied in *trans*. The development of the COS cell line simplified the use of SV40-based vectors. This is a derivative of the African Green Monkey cell line CV-1, which is stably transformed with a partial SV40 genome (hence COS: CV-1, origin, SV40). The integrated SV40 origin is mutated and nonfunctional, but the early transcription unit is functional, allowing constitutive expression of the T antigen. This can stimulate the replication of any SV40 replicon in the same nucleus, and therefore allows the episomal propagation of SV40 vectors lacking their own T-antigen transcription unit (22). A whole series of SV40-based expression vectors has been designed for use in COS cells, some also utilizing SV40 transcriptional regulatory elements, others containing heterologous elements. It would be impossible to discuss all these vectors in detail; so the interested reader is advised to consult Ref. 20 for a review of early vector development, and recent product catalogues from biotechnology companies such as Invitrogen for descriptions of contemporary vectors. Cell lines have also been developed for the propagation of murine polyomavirus replicons, such as the mouse cell line MOP-8 (23). Some of the most versatile transient expression vectors contain both SV40 and murine polyomavirus origins (e.g., the pcDNA1 vector series from Invitrogen). Notably, while the SV40 origin of replication may function only in certain permissive monkey cells, the promoter and enhancer sequences of this and other viruses are extremely promiscuous. SV40 replicons can therefore be used for transient transfection of any mammalian cell type, although protein yields are much lower than for monkey cells because there is no episomal replication. In nonpermissive cells, SV40 DNA may also integrate into the genome resulting in stable transformation, and allowing the development of cell lines. More recently, it has been possible to generate permissive monkey cell lines stably transformed with episomal SV40-based vectors by using conditionally expressed or temperature sensitive T antigens, which sponsor more moderate and tolerable replication rates (24,25).

Reporter Genes in Transfection Analysis

Transient transfection is often used to study gene expression, function, and regulation in animal cells because it is rapid, repeatable, and simple to perform, allowing the comparative analysis of many different expression constructs simultaneously. The alternative strategy of producing cell lines for each construct is laborious and expensive. Additionally, as discussed later, the integrated foreign DNA is subject to random position and dosage effects that may obscure the true relationship between different constructs. Following the introduction of foreign DNA into animal cells, it is possible to study gene expression directly, for example, by northern blot, nuclease protection, RT-PCR, immunological assay, or assay for protein activity. This strategy suffers several disadvantages, however, including the time-consuming assays required, the requirement for gene-specific probes, and the fact that if the transfected gene is similar to an endogenous gene, it may be impossible to discriminate between them.

One way to avoid these problems is to study gene activity indirectly, by fusing the appropriate regulatory sequences to a reporter gene (7). A reporter gene is a screenable marker gene, that is, a gene whose product is easily detected using a simple assay. Reporter genes are often used to detect and characterize gene regulatory elements by inserting the putative elements upstream of the marker in specialized regulatory probe vectors. The recombinant vectors are then introduced into one or more types of animal cell, and quantitative assays for the reporter molecule allow the experimenter indirectly to gauge the level of transcriptional activity conferred by the regulatory elements (26). In the same way, inducible regulatory elements can be tested for their response to particular stimuli by measuring the induction of reporter gene expression. Cell type or developmental specificity can be assayed by causing cells to differentiate in vitro, or by testing reporter constructs in transgenic animals known as *reporter transgenics*. A common strategy is to generate a series of mutated versions of a given reporter construct to narrow down particular *cis*-acting motifs in regulatory elements. Upstream signaling events can also be studied, for example by addressing the response of reporter genes to the perturbation of specific signaling pathways.

Reporter genes are not used only to analyze regulatory elements. By fusing a reporter gene to the coding region of a second foreign gene, a fusion protein may be generated that generally retains reporter activity. This can be used to study protein localization in the absence of a specific antibody, or, as discussed previously, to simplify protein purification. One of the most important uses of reporter genes in transient transfection is to normalize data for transfection efficiency. As discussed, the yield of protein obtained from a dish of transiently transfected cells is highly dependent on transfection efficiency, which can vary widely within an experiment according to the transfection method used. When comparing the activities of different constructs, it is necessary to discriminate between variation caused by genuine functional differences between constructs, and that caused by fluctuations in transfection efficiency. A reporter gene hitched to a constitutive viral promoter can provide an excellent internal control.

There are many different reporter genes used in animal systems, each with specific advantages and disadvantages (Table 3) (27–36). Reporter molecules also differ greatly in their half-lives, an important consideration where researchers wish to study rapid inductive responses and longer-term effects. General properties that make ideal reporter genes include the following:

- The availability of rapid, sensitive, and inexpensive assays for the product
- Minimal background activity in animal cells
- The reporter assay should be quantitative and have a broad linear range, allowing the experimenter to detect both major and minor differences in activity
- The reporter gene should have a small coding region, so that expression vectors and fusion proteins are kept to reasonable sizes
- The product should not be toxic or otherwise affect the host cell physiology

Stable Transfection Using Nonreplicating DNA

In stable transfection, transformed *cell lines* are produced in which recombinant proteins are synthesized on a long-term basis, lasting months to years. Stable transfection thus requires foreign DNA sequences to be maintained on a long-term basis and in such a manner that the cell can otherwise function normally (5,20,37). This can occur in two ways. First, foreign DNA may integrate into the genome, where it is maintained as a new chromosomal locus by endogenous DNA replication. Second, foreign DNA can be maintained episomally on a vector that replicates at a moderate rate and hence does not affect cell viability. In both cases, transformed cells may be maintained under a selective regime, ensuring that the foreign DNA is still present.

The most popular strategy for generating stable cell lines is the integration of foreign DNA into the genome. This strategy does not require specialized vectors, as the integration mechanism involves illegitimate recombination, where any DNA sequence can serve as a substrate. A foreign gene that has integrated into the host genome is termed a *transgene*. Stable integration has been achieved with many different types of vector, including those with no eukaryotic maintenance sequences. Even linear foreign DNA fragments without a vector are suitable substrates for integration. In fact, in contrast to transient transfection, which is more efficient using supercoiled plasmids, the frequency of stable integration is increased using linear DNA because this is a better substrate for illegitimate recombination. The integration mechanism is extremely inefficient, that is, three to four orders of magnitude less efficient than transient transfection and viral gene transfer. Transformants are typically recovered at a frequency of 10^{-5} to 10^{-6}. For this reason, selectable markers must be used to identify and selectively propagate the rare, stably transformed cells (such markers are discussed in the next section).

Another important factor in stable transfection by integration is the random nature of the integration event. It is thought that the position of integration reflects the adventitious use of randomly occurring chromosome breaks in the target cell population, and that the foreign DNA is erroneously used as a substrate by end-joining enzymes that exist to repair such breaks. Typically, multiple copies of the transfected DNA integrate at a single donor site, following end-to-end ligation to form a transient low-complexity structure termed a *transgenome*. Some transfection methods allow a degree of control over copy number (e.g., electroporation parameters can be set to favor single copy integration), while others, such as calcium phosphate–mediated transfection, are not controllable. The position of integration and the number of transgene copies integrated are therefore highly variable, and both can influence transgene expression. This results in varying expression levels between independently derived transformed clones, and the phenomenon of transgene silencing, where even cells with stably integrated and intact transgenes fail to express recombinant proteins. The causes of these effects and strategies to overcome them are discussed in a later section.

Selectable Markers for Use in Mammalian Cell Lines

Under some circumstances, the foreign DNA introduced into a cell may confer a phenotype that can itself be selected or used as a visible assay for stable transfection. This is unusual, however; so a selectable marker gene is normally introduced along with the nonselectable foreign DNA to allow transformed cells to be propagated under conditions where the high background of nontransformed cells will die. Initially, selectable markers were included on the same vector as the nonselectable foreign DNA, so that the two would cointegrate and selection for the marker would necessarily identify cells carrying the nonselectable gene of interest. However, it was shown that two discrete plasmids cotransfected into mammalian cells also resulted in a high frequency of *cotransformation* (i.e., where the initially unlinked genes were integrated together, usually at the same locus) (38). Typically, a 10 : 1 ratio of nonselectable to selectable vector is used, so that cells transformed with the marker are highly likely to be

Table 3. Properties of Genetic Reporter Systems Used in Animal Cells

Reporter gene (product)	Comments
lacZ (β-galactosidase)	*Source: E. coli* *Activity*: Catalyzes the hydrolysis of β-galactosides, e.g., lactose and many specialized derivative substrates for different assay formats *Assays*: β-galactosidase assays are nonisotopic. In vitro assay formats based on colorimetric (with substrate ONPG) or fluorometric (with substrate MUG) detection systems lack sensitivity, but chemiluminescent systems using 1,2-dioxetane derivatives are highly sensitive. High-resolution in vivo histological assays are also available. The chromogenic substrate X-gal can be used for fixed tissue, and the fluorescent substrate FDG can be used for live cells. *Advantages*: Versatile, sensitive and many assay formats available. *Disadvantages*: Some mammalian cells have high endogenous β-galactosidase activity *Other comments*: β-galactosidase is a stable protein *References*: 27,28
cat (chloramphenicol acetyltransferase)	*Source: E. coli* transposon Tn9 *Activity*: Catalyzes the transfer of acetyl groups from acetyl coenzyme A to chloramphenicol. *Assays*: In vitro assays are isotopic, involving chromatogrpahic separation of acetylated and nonacetylated forms of ^{14}C-chloramphenicol. Such assays have low sensitivity and are expensive, but more recently developed immunological and fluorometric assays are better. In vivo CAT assays rarely used due to low resolution. *Advantages*: Minimal background activity in mammalian cells *Disadvantages*: Low sensitivity, expense, reliance on isotopic assay format *Other comments*: CAT is a highly stable protein *Reference*: 29
SEAP (secreted alkaline phosphatase)	*Source*: Truncated form of human *PLAP* *Activity*: Removes phosphate groups from a variety of substrates *Assays*: Nonisotopic, sensitive in vitro assays using either colorimetric, fluorometric or chemiluminescent formats to detect secreted protein. Not used for in vivo assays. *Advantages*: Secreted protein can assayed in growth medium without lysing cells, allowing multiple assays for the same culture and further manipulation of cells following assay *Disadvantages*: High endogenous levels of alkaline phosphatase in some mammalian cells (although SEAP is heat tolerant, allowing endogenous enzyme to be inactivated by heat treatment). Reporter system depends on correct function of the secretory pathway. *References*: 30,31
luc (firefly luciferase)	*Source*: The firefly *Photinus pyralis* *Activity*: Light produced in the presence of luciferase, its substrate luciferin, oxygen, magnesium ions, and ATP *Assays*: Nonisotopic bioluminescent assays are used in vitro and in vivo. These are highly sensitive and can be performed in live cells, using lipophilic luciferin esters. *Advantages*: Sensitive, minimal background activity in mammalian cells *Disadvantages*: Requires expensive detection equipment, some assay formats have limited reproducibility *Other comments*: Luciferase has a high turnover rate and is thus useful for the study of inducible systems. *References*: 28,32,33
GFP (green fluorescent protein)	*Source*: The jellyfish *Aequorea victoria* *Activity*: Intrinsic ability to fluoresce under blue or UV light *Assays*: Nonisotopic. Used for in vivo assays in live animals. Allows monitoring of changes of gene expression in real time, and fusion GFPs allow protein sorting events to be followed. *Advantages*: Intrinsic activity (no substrate requirements), sensitivity, use in live organisms *Disadvantages*: The signal from *A. victoria* GFP is not intense enough for some systems. *Other comments*: Improved GFPs with stronger emission, and emission at different wavelengths, have been generated by mutation allowing multiple studies in a single cell. *References*: 33–36

Abbreviations: ATP, adenosine 5'-triphosphate; CAT, chloramphenicol acetyltransferase; FDG, fluorescein di-β-D-galactopyranoside; GFP, green fluorescent protein; MUG, 4-methylumbelliferyl-β-D-galactoside; ONPG, o-nitrophenyl-β-D-galactopyranoside; PLAP, human placental alkaline phosphatase; SEAP, secreted alkaline phosphatase; UV, ultraviolet; X-gal, 5-bromo-4-chloro-3-indolyl-β-D-galactopyranoside.

cotransformed with the nonselectable DNA. The markers are used to select founder cells that give rise to stably transformed cell lines. Cells are allowed to grow under the appropriate selective regime for about 10 generations. At this point, individual clones of surviving cells are isolated and used to found new lines.

The first selectable marker to be widely used was *Tk*, encoding the enzyme thymidine kinase (TK) (39). This is an *endogenous marker*; that is, it represents an activity already present in most mammalian cells, and therefore requires a *tk⁻* cell background for positive selection. Like most endogenous markers, *Tk* encodes a nonessential enzyme involved in nucleotide biosynthesis. Such markers have been developed because there are two alternate nucleotide biosynthesis pathways in mammalian cells, allowing viable mutant cells for each pathway to be isolated, and chemical inhibitors of each pathway to be identified. Under normal growth conditions, TK is not required because dTTP can be synthesized from carbamyl phosphate (the *de novo pathway*). However, if cells are grown in medium containing the inhibitor aminopterin, the de novo pathway is blocked and dTTP must be synthesized from thymine (the *salvage pathway*), which requires TK. Other endogenous markers are listed in the first part of Table 4, and their role in nucleotide biosynthesis is summarized in Figure 3. The problem with

such markers is that the number of cell types available for transfection is limited to those where appropriate mutant lines have been developed. Thus, although *tk⁻* mutant cells are themselves easily selected using 5-bromodeoxyuridine, there has been a drive to develop new markers that can be used in all mammalian cells.

Such *dominant selectable markers* (dominant because they are derived from an exogenous source and there is no competing activity in any mammalian cell) are often drug resistance genes of bacterial origin (3,6,20,37). Cells can be propagated in normal medium and then transformed cells can be positively selected by adding the drug at the appropriate concentration. Commonly used dominant selectable markers are listed in the second part of Table 4. One disadvantage of these bacterial markers is that the concentration range over which the selective agents are active tends to be narrow. Such markers are therefore not suitable for stepwise selection for increased transgene copy number. As discussed in more detail in the following section, in situ transgene amplification is one way to overcome position effects and generate high-yield transformed cell lines, but this requires markers than can be selected in a stepwise manner over a range of selective conditions (40,41). The predominant example of this type of *amplifiable marker* is *Dhfr*, which encodes the enzyme dihydrofolate reductase (DHFR). Increasing

Table 4. Selectable Markers Used in Animal Cells: Endogenous Markers; Dominant Selectable Markers; Amplifiable Markers; Reviews and Further References for the Development and Use of Selectable Markers can be Found in Refs. 3, 6, 20, 37, 40 and 41

Endogenous markers

These markers are involved in nonessential endogenous biosynthetic pathways. Most of the markers are enzymes involved in the nucleotide biosynthesis salvage pathway, and such markers can be used both for positive and negative selection. Positive selection is achieved using salvage pathway mutant cell lines in combination with drugs that block the de novo nucleotide biosynthesis pathway. Negative selection is achieved using toxic base analogs that are incorporated into DNA only if the salvage pathway is used. Alternative endogenous markers are expressed at a low level in animal cells, and can be used for selection in the presence of a certain inhibitor. The endogenous functions of the markers and the activity of the inhibitors are summarized in Figure 3.

Marker	Product and function	Principles of selection
Ada	adenosine deaminase; converts adenosine to inosine	Xyl-A (9-β-D-xylofuranosyl adenosine) is an adenosine analog, which is toxic if incorporated into DNA. ADA detoxifies Xyl-A added to the growth medium by converting it to Xyl-I, its inosine equivalent. There is a low background of ADA activity in most mammalian cells and 2′-deoxycoformycin, an ADA inhibitor, is therefore included in the selection medium.
Aprt	adenine phosphoriboyl-transferase; converts adenine to AMP	Positive selection: Adenine, and azaserine, to block de novo dATP synthesis, so only cells using salvage pathway survive. Negative selection: Toxic adenine analogs (e.g., 2,6-diaminopurine) which are incorporated into DNA only in cells with APRT activity.
Cad	carbamyl phosphate synthase; aspartate transcarbamylase; dihydro-oroatase. These are the first three steps in de novo uridine biosynthesis.	Positive selection: PALA (N-phosphonacetyl-L-aspartate) inhibits the aspartate transcarbamylase activity of CAD
Dhfr	dihydrofolate reductase; converts folate to dihydrofolate and then to tetrahydrofolate	Positive selection: DHFR is required for several reactions in de novo and salvage nucleotide/amino acid biosynthesis; hence selection is carried out in nucleotide-free medium. However, *Dhfr* is typically used as an amplifiable marker with the inhibitor methotrexate (see third section of table).

Table 4. *Continued*

Marker	Product and function	Principles of selection
Hgprt	hypoxanthine–guanine phosphoribosyl-transferase; converts hypoxanthine to IMP and guanine to GMP	Positive selection: Hypoxanthine and aminopterin, to block de novo IMP synthesis; so only cells using salvage pathway survive. Selected on HAT medium*. Negative selection: Toxic guanine analogs (e.g., azaguanine) which are incorporated into DNA only if there is HGPRT activity in the cell.
Tk	thymidine kinase, converts thymidine to dTMP	Positive selection: Thymidine, and aminopterin to block de novo dTTP synthesis; so only cells using salvage pathway survive. Selected on HAT medium* Negative selection: Toxic thymidine analogs (e.g., 5-bromodeoxyuridine, gancyclovir) which are incorporated into DNA only if there is TK activity in the cell.

Dominant selectable markers

These markers are derived from a different species and confer an alien drug-resistance phenotype upon the transfected cell.

Marker	Product (and source species)	Principles of selection
AS	asparagine synthase (*E. coli*)	Bacterial enzyme uses ammonia as amide donor unlike mammalian equivalent. Hence cells transformed with *AS* grow on asparagine-free medium containing the toxic glutamine analog albizziin
ble	glycopeptide-binding protein (*Streptoalloteichus hindustantus*)	Confers resistance to glycopeptide antibiotics bleomycin and pheomycin (and its derivative, Zeocin™)
gpt	guanine–xanthine phosphoribosyltransferase (*E. coli*)	Analogous to *Hgprt* in mammals, but possesses additional xanthine phosphoribosyltransferase activity allowing survival in medium containing aminopterin and mycophenolic acid (Fig. 3)
hisD	histidinol dehydrogenase (*Salmonella typhimurium*)	Confers resistance to histidinol
hpt	Hygromycin phosphotransferase (*E. coli*)	Confers resistance to hygromycin-B
neo	neomycin phosphotransferase (*E. coli*)	Confers resistance to aminoglycoside antibiotics (e.g., neomycin, kanamycin, G418)
pac	puromycin N-acetyltransferase (*Streptomyces alboniger*)	Confers resistance to puromycin
trpB	Tryptophan synthesis (*E. coli*)	Confers resistance to indole

Markers used for in situ gene amplification

These markers can be amplified in situ by increasing the concentration of a competitive inhibitor in the medium. Many amplifiable markers are also used as endogenous or dominant selectable markers, but in some cases, the drug used for amplification may not be the same as that used for standard selection.

Marker	Product	Amplifying selective drug
Ada	adenosine deaminase	deoxycoformycin
AS	asparagine synthase	β-aspartylhydroxamate
Cad	aspartate transcarbamylase	N-phosphonacetyl-L-aspartate
Dhfr	dihydrofolate reductase	methotrexate
gpt	xanthine–guanine phosphoribosyltransferase	mycophenolic acid
GS	glutamine synthase	methionine sulfoximine
Hgprt	hypoxanthine–guanine phosphoriboosyltransferase	aminopterin
Impdh	inosine monophosphate dehydrogenase	mycophenolic acid
Mt-1	metallothionein 1	Cd^{2+}
M^{res}	multidrug resistance: P-glycoprotein 170 gene	adriamycin, colchicine, others
Odc	ornithine decarboxylase	difluoromethylornithine
Rnr	ribonucleotide reductase	hydroxyurea
tk^-	thymidine kinase	aminopterin
Umps	uridine monophosphate synthase	pyrazofurin

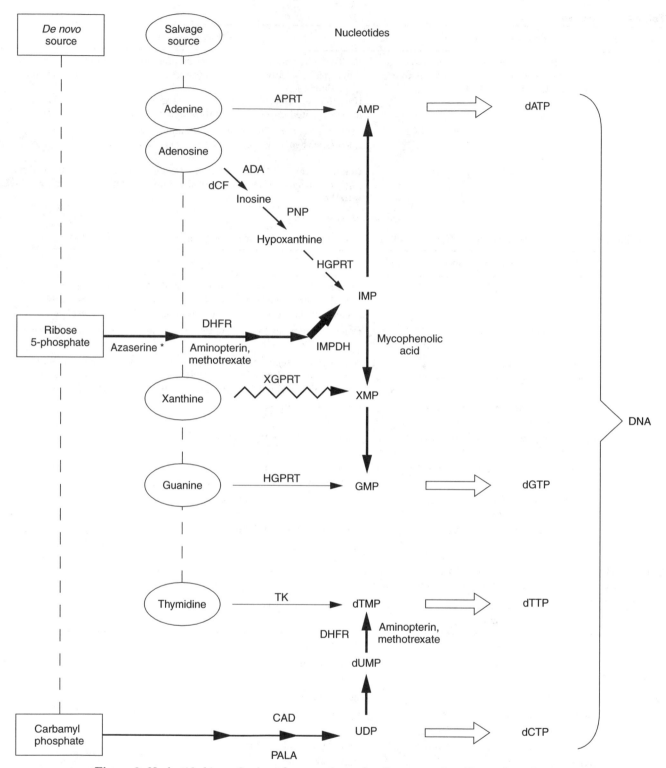

Figure 3. Nucleotide biosynthesis and commonly used endogenous selectable markers. De novo nucleotide synthesis begins with the boxed precursors and follows the thick arrows. In the absence of de novo substrates, or where the de novo pathway is blocked, the cell can use pyrimidine and purine salvage pathways, beginning with the circled precursors and following the thin arrows. Mammalian cells cannot convert xanthine to XMP, but this reaction is carried out by the *E. coli* enzyme XGPRT, encoded by the *gpt* gene, allowing this to be used as a dominant selectable marker in mammalian cells (zigzag arrow). Eventually, the nucleotides are converted into dNTPs (open arrows) and incorporated into DNA. The salvage enzymes are not required for cell growth when de novo substrates are available; so salvage pathway mutants are viable under normal growth conditions. However, if the de novo pathway is blocked using any of the inhibitors (shown in bold), genes encoding salvage pathway enzymes can be used as selectable markers when salvage

resistance to methotrexate, a competitive inhibitor of DHFR, usually correlates to increased *Dhfr* gene copy number, and coamplification of the nonselected donor gene. Amplifiable markers are highly efficient, but *Dhfr* is endogenous, and the background of wild-type cells that express and amplify their wild-type *Dhfr* locus can be a problem. For this reason, such markers tend to be used in mutant cell lines, which again restricts the number of cell types available for transfection.

Maximizing Transgene Expression by Gene Amplification

When cultured cells are exposed to toxic concentrations of certain drugs, rare individual cells survive because they happen to have undergone a mutation that confers drug resistance. The first such system to be investigated in detail was resistance to the folic acid analog methotrexate, which is a competitive inhibitor of DHFR (reviewed in Ref. 42). Resistant cells were shown to fall into three classes: those with reduced methotrexate uptake; those with point mutations in the *Dhfr* gene, making the enzyme less susceptible to inhibition; and those carrying multiple copies of the *Dhfr* locus, allowing the production of enough enzyme to out-compete the inhibitor. This latter class can be selected stepwise by successive increases in drug dosage, resulting in the propagation of clones with highly amplified *Dhfr* gene arrays, and allowing cell growth in concentrations of methotrexate up to 10^5 times greater than the dose lethal to wild-type cells. The amplified copies may be maintained as large intrachromosomal tandem repeat units known as *homogeneously staining regions* (HSRs), or as small extra chromosomes termed *double minutes*. It is important to note that the drug does not *induce* gene amplification, but facilitates the selection of rare cells that have undergone random amplification.

Cloned copies of the *Dhfr* gene and its cDNA, reintroduced into cells by transfection and randomly integrated into the genome, are also amplified by drug selection. However, it is not just the essential coding region that is amplified. Extensive flanking sequences of up to 10^6 bp of DNA may be coamplified, emphasizing the random nature of the amplification process. It is this amplification of nonselected flanking material that can be exploited in gene transfer experiments. Vectors have been constructed in which a gene such as *Dhfr* is included adjacent to the multiple cloning site where the nonselectable foreign gene is inserted. The stable transfection of this construct allows tandem cointegration of the amplifiable marker and the nonselected gene. Alternatively, the *Dhfr* vector can be cotransfected with a second vector carrying nonselectable foreign DNA. As discussed, cotransfected vectors tend to cointegrate at the same locus. Cointegration is followed by a regime of intensifying drug selection, resulting in the propagation of cells containing highly amplified arrays of both the marker and nonselected transgenes (40,41).

This strategy facilitates high-level recombinant protein synthesis, and can overcome position-dependent transgene silencing because amplification can continue until there are so many transgene copies that the amount of mRNA synthesized is no longer the limiting factor for protein expression. Alternatively, a specific regime of drug treatment can be used to select for transformants where the transgene is not subject to negative position effects. However, since *Dhfr* is an endogenous marker, drug selection can amplify the endogenous *Dhfr* gene as well as transfected copies. *Dhfr* is therefore most advantageous when used in a *dhfr⁻* cell line, so that nontransfected cells are not coselected on the basis of endogenous gene amplification. Several derivatives of the CHO (Chinese hamster ovary) cell line have been described that lack DHFR activity. These include DUKX-B11 (DXB-11), which has one active *Dhfr* gene (43), and DG44, which is a homozygous null cell line (44). Two strategies have been used to extend the range of cell lines available for DHFR selection. First, a mutant form of the *Dhfr* gene, which is highly resistant to methotrexate, can be used to select for methotrexate resistance even in cells carrying two normal copies of the normal *Dhfr* gene. However, the level of amplification is restricted because large doses of methotrexate are required to inhibit the endogenous genes. Second, the *Dhfr* marker can be cotransfected with a dominant selectable marker such as *neo*. Thus cells can be treated with increasing concentrations of methotrexate, and also selected with constant levels of G418, to counterselect wild-type cells (which would otherwise survive through amplification of the endogenous

Figure 3. (*Continued*) precursors are also provided. For example, *Tk* can be used to circumvent aminopterin-inhibited de novo dTMP synthesis if the salvage precursor, thymidine, is included in the growth medium. Alternatively, de novo and salvage inhibitors can be overcome by amplifiable selection, e.g., PALA, an inhibitor of de novo UDP synthesis, can be overcome by amplification of the *Cad* gene, and methotrexate, an inhibitor of several de novo and salvage reactions, can be overcome by amplification of the *Dhfr* gene. Salvage pathway markers can also be counterselected using toxic base or nucleoside analogs. These are toxic when incorporated into DNA via the salvage pathway, but innocuous if nucleotides are synthesized de novo. For example, 5-bromodeoxyuridine (bdUr) is a thymidine analog incorporated into DNA following conversion into a nucleotide by TK. In the absence of TK, bdUr is not phosphorylated and is not incorporated into DNA. Azaserine blocks several de novo reactions, the most important of which is shown. Abbreviations of enzymes and inhibitors: APRT, adenine phosphoribosyltransferase; ADA, adenosine deaminase; CAD, carbamyl phosphate synthase/aspartate transcarbamoylase/dihydroorotase; dCF, deoxycoformycin; DHFR, dihydrofolate reductase; HGPRT, hypoxanthine–guanine phosphoribosyltransferase; IMPDH, inosine monophosphate dehydrogenase; PALA, N-phosphonacetyl-L-aspartate; PNP, purine nucleoside phosphorylase; TK, thymidine kinase; XGPRT, xanthine–guanine phosphoribosyltransferase.

Dhfr gene). *Dhfr* was the first selectable marker to be used for amplification, and remains the most popular. Other markers, listed in the third part of Table 4, have also been used, but suffer from disadvantages such as the prevalence of nonamplified resistance mutants, or cytotoxicity at high drug concentrations. Only glutamine synthase has been used anywhere near as frequently as *Dhfr*.

Stable Transfection Using Episomally Maintained Vectors

Replicating, extrachromosomal vectors for stable transfection possess a number of distinct advantages over integrating vectors. First, recombinant proteins are expressed at a moderate level, which is uniform among independently derived clonal lines. This is because there are no position effects (the construct does not integrate) and no dosage effects (the plasmid reaches a stable episomal copy number, regardless of initial transfection efficiency). Second, stable transfection by episomal maintenance is equivalent in efficiency to transient transfection, that is, up to 10^5 times more efficient than stable transfection by integration. Finally, because the vectors are episomal, they can be separated easily from chromosomal DNA: This is particularly advantageous in techniques such as expression cloning, which rely on the recovery of cloned DNA. While nonreplicating plasmids suffice for stable transfection by integration, episomal plasmids require maintenance sequences derived from viruses whose genomes are also maintained episomally. Novel strategies based on controlling the runaway replication of SV40-derived vectors have already been discussed. Three other viruses that have been widely exploited to construct episomal vectors are bovine papillomavirus (BPV), BK virus (a human polyomavirus), and Epstein–Barr virus (EBV).

The papovavirus family includes the polyomavirus and papillomavirus genera. SV40 and the related murine polyomavirus have been used to develop a range of transient expression vectors that replicate to high copy number and eventually cause cell death. The human BK polyomavirus is stably maintained at a moderate copy number (approximately 500 copies per cell) in human cells. Plasmid vectors carrying the BK virus origin of replication are similarly maintained as long as the BK virus T antigen is available, and cell lines stably transformed with such vectors have been continuously propagated for over a year (45). BK virus-derived replicons contain a selectable marker (e.g., *neo*) as well as plasmid backbone sequences, BK virus functions, and the mammalian transcription unit. This allows high-level recombinant protein expression to be achieved by increasing the drug concentration in the medium and hence selecting for increased copy number. In this way, stable cell lines carrying up to 9,000 copies of the vector can be generated, although the copy number falls when selection is removed. This vector system is extremely versatile: Variants have been described with different promoters and selectable markers, and a number of different host cell lines have been used, including HeLa, COS-7, and 293 (45,46).

The papillomaviruses are related to the polyomaviruses but possess larger, more complex genomes and encode proteins on only one DNA strand. They infect higher vertebrates, including man, and cause benign growths called papillomas or warts. Bovine papillomavirus can infect cultured mouse cells, but cannot produce progeny virions. Instead, 50–100 copies of the genome are maintained episomally as plasmids, and it is this property that has been exploited to develop a series of episomal expression vectors. Like SV40 and other polyomaviruses, the early functions of BPV cause growth transformation. The earliest BPV-derived vectors therefore comprised the entire BPV genome cloned in a bacterial plasmid with a mammalian expression cassette, and transfected cells were identified by their transformation to a continuously proliferative state. The early functions are carried on a 5.5-kbp sector of the BPV genome, which is termed the 69% transforming fragment (BPV$_{69T}$), and this appears to be sufficient for establishment and maintenance of the episomal state (47). This fragment forms the basis of a more versatile series of expression vectors that also contain a mammalian selectable marker to extend the range of possible host cells (reviewed in Ref. 48). The ability of BPV$_{69T}$ vectors to replicate efficiently is increased in some but not all cells by certain mammalian genomic sequences, which are included, for example, in the BV-1 vector series (reviewed in Ref. 49). BPV vectors can establish long-term, moderate-level foreign gene expression in a broad range of mammalian cell types, although 3T3 and C127 fibroblasts are the most popular hosts. There is no limit to insert size, allowing both cDNAs and full genes to be expressed. However, BPV vectors suffer from several limitations. First, although the viral genome is small in comparison to, for example, herpes virus or vaccinia virus, it is still too large (>10 kbp) to manipulate easily in vitro, and lacks the cloning versatility of other plasmids. Second, there are problems with vector stability (50). Recombinant vectors may undergo recombination or deletion, resulting in the loss of foreign DNA, and in certain cell lines the vector may integrate into the genome. Recombination between vectors can occur, so that either single plasmids or oligomers may be propagated. These effects are largely unpredictable, depending on multiple parameters such as cell line, vector type, and insert structure. The same parameters also affect replication efficiency; so the episomal copy number may vary from very low (20 plasmids per cell) to over 300 copies.

Due to the instability of BPV replicons, many researchers have turned to Epstein–Barr virus as an episomal expression vector (51). EBV is a human herpes virus whose productive host range is limited to primates and a few other mammals (e.g., dogs). The virus is naturally lymphotropic and commonly infects B cells, causing infectious mononucleosis. The virus has a large, double-stranded linear DNA genome that circularizes shortly after penetration by interaction between terminal repeat sequences. In culture, the virus can cause lytic infection, resulting in cell death, but most infected cells are transformed into a proliferative state and the virus genome is maintained as a latent, episomally replicating plasmid, with a copy number under 1000. Although the tropism of the virus is limited by its interaction with a specific receptor found on very few cell types, the circular EBV genome is maintained in many primate cells following transfection, and thus shows great potential as a broad cellular host-range expression vector. However, the species host range is still limited to primate and dog cells — rodent cell lines are not permissive for episomal EBV replication. Only two regions of the EBV genome are essential for the establishment and maintenance of latent replication: the bipartite origin of replication *oriP*, and the gene encoding the *trans*-acting regulator of transcription and replication, EBV nuclear antigen-1 (*EBNA-1*). These sequences form the basis of EBV latent expression vectors, which are maintained at a copy number of 2–50 per cell. A distinct origin, *oriLyt*, and a different regulator termed ZEBRA, are required for lytic replication, thus *oriP*/EBNA-1 vectors do not amplify in cells undergoing lytic EBV infection. More recently developed EBV vectors containing both origins can be maintained as low-copy-number vectors in latently infected B-cell lines, and amplified approximately 500-fold when cells are transfected with constitutively expressed *BZLF-1* (the ZEBRA gene) to induce lytic replication. EBV vectors may contain *oriP* only (in which case EBNA-1 must be supplied in *trans*) or both *oriP* and the EBNA-1 coding region driven by a mammalian promoter (in which case the vectors are helper independent). EBV vectors must also carry a selectable marker, because (*1*) transformation efficiency, while much higher than for stable integration, is still less than 10%, and (*2*) in the absence of selection, both *oriP* and *oriP*/EBNA-1 vectors are passively lost at the rate of 2–6% of cells per generation. A number of markers have been successfully used, including *Tk*, *neo*, and *gpt*. Many foreign genes have been successfully expressed using EBV vectors, including those encoding enzymes, growth factors and receptors, structural proteins, and heterologous viral proteins (51, and references therein). In addition to their use as "standard" mammalian expression vectors, EBV replicons can be recovered intact from mammalian cells, facilitating their use for expression cloning. The EBO series of vectors has been designed for this purpose (52). Furthermore, because of their large capacity, the inclusion of bacteriophage λ cohesive end (*cos*) sites allows such vectors to be maintained in *E. coli* as cosmids (53). The most recent advance in EBV-replicon technology is the development of EBV vectors as human artificial episomal chromosomes. Such vectors represent one of a number of strategies for the design of mammalian artificial chromosomes, and can carry up to 350 kbp of genomic DNA (reviewed in Ref. 54).

TRANSFECTION METHODS

Overview of Transfection Strategies

The term *transfection* was originally coined to describe the introduction of bacteriophage genomic DNA into bacterial cells via the same route as plasmid DNA (the latter process being known as transformation). The term was meant to convey the unusual nature of DNA uptake, contrasting with the natural infection route. In the same way, forcing animal cells to take up DNA from the surrounding medium using a variety of chemical and physical methods is also termed transfection, and can be a highly efficient way to

introduce DNA either transiently or stably into cultured cells, or indeed cells in vivo. When the term *transformation* is applied to animal cells, it usually refers to a stable change of genotype brought about, as discussed, either by incorporation of the transfected DNA into the genome, or its long-term episomal maintenance. However, the same term is also used to indicate *oncogenic* transformation (growth transformation), that is, the change in phenotype resulting from the activation of an oncogene, causing for example, loss of substrate dependence, uncontrolled proliferation in the absence of growth factors, and abnormal differentiation.

When DNA transfer to cultured animal cells was first demonstrated (1), the uptake mechanism was unknown. Later it was shown to depend on the formation of a calcium phosphate–DNA coprecipitate, and this was the first of many "chemical transfection" techniques to be described, where cells take up DNA complexed with another molecule by endocytosis. Generally, these techniques result in a significant frequency of transgene mutation due to passage of the DNA through acidic endosomes. Over the years, a number of alternative transfection strategies have been devised (6,20,55) (Fig. 4). *Fusion transfection* involves cells taking up DNA by fusion with a natural or artificial lipid

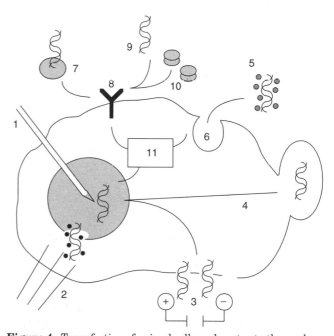

Figure 4. Transfection of animal cells and routes to the nucleus. Microinjection (*1*) and particle bombardment (*2*) facilitate the direct delivery of DNA to either the nucleus or cytoplasm. Electroporation (*3*) or fusion transfection (e.g., protoplast fusion, liposome fusion (*4*)) result in the delivery of DNA to the cytoplasm, and its subsequent transfer to the nucleus by an unknown mechanism. Chemical transfection methods (*5*) result in the uptake of DNA–chemical complexes by endocytosis (*6*). Similarly, ligand-conjugated DNA (*7*) is taken up by receptor-mediated endocytosis (*8*), which is also thought to be the case for naked DNA (*9*) having first interacted with unknown extracellular proteins (*10*). Following endocytosis, the DNA is transferred to the nucleus through the endosomal pathway in an unknown manner (*11*). This delivery mechanism is made more efficient using adenoviral capsid proteins, which cause endosomal disruption.

membrane containing foreign DNA. *Poration transfection* involves the creation of small pores in the cell membrane through which DNA can be imported. *Physical transfection* involves a mechanical breach of the cell membrane, and the direct delivery of DNA either to the cytoplasm or nucleus. All these mechanisms result in direct delivery, and avoid endosomal processing of the DNA. Additionally, by conjugating DNA to a suitable ligand, it can be introduced into specific cell types by receptor-mediated endocytosis (this strategy is particularly applicable for cell targeting in gene therapy). These different transfection mechanisms are discussed in more detail in the following section, and are summarized in Table 5.

The successful transfection of animal cells in culture is dependent on many parameters. Some are universally important, such as the quality of the foreign DNA and the health of the target cells, which should both be maximized. Other parameters are cell type specific; thus different cells are transfected with differing efficiencies, and not all cells respond to the same transfection methods. Primary cells are particularly resilient to transfection, and some cannot be transfected efficiently using standard methods. Cells that grow as monolayers are easier to transfect than those growing in suspension or as clumps, and quiescent or postmitotic cells are more recalcitrant than rapidly dividing cells. The efficiency of chemical transfection often depends on the composition of the growth medium; for example, the presence of serum tends to inhibit transfection using cationic lipid preparations. Chemical transfection in particular tends to have the most adverse effects. Some cells are badly affected by calcium phosphate transfection because they respond poorly to the precipitate adhering to their surfaces. Conversely, cationic lipids appear to be better tolerated and are suitable for many cells traditionally regarded as difficult to transfect. The major cell lines used for recombinant protein expression (e.g., CHO, COS-7, HEK 293, Sf9) are well characterized, and transfection protocols have been optimized to enable many researchers to use them. Unfortunately, cell lines for transfection cannot always be chosen purely for the ease of DNA transfer. The choice is often made according to other properties, such as the ability of cells to express certain proteins or to use specific regulatory elements efficiently, the ability of cells to differentiate or respond to particular inductive treatments, or because a particular form of post-translational modification is carried out. Therefore, the first step in a transfection strategy is often to optimize transfection efficiency using a range of protocols and testing the parameters within each transfection method.

Transfection with Locally Applied Naked DNA

Naked DNA transfects cultured cells very inefficiently when added to the growth medium, due both to degradation and poor internalization. Similarly, uncomplexed DNA administered intravenously to live animals is rapidly degraded following hepatic uptake (56). Unlikely as it may seem, however, the injection of uncomplexed plasmid DNA in vivo into muscle results in high-efficiency gene transfer and expression (57). This can be exploited to raise a protective immune response against viral and other pathogenic antigens and against tumor proteins (58). The application of naked DNA to other tissues has also resulted in successful transfection, (e.g., using balloon catheters to coat the internal walls of arteries) (59). DNA has also been injected into the blastocoel cavity of mouse embryos, resulting in the generation of transgenic mice, albeit with much lower efficiency than pronuclear microinjection. The mechanism by which naked DNA is taken into, for example, muscle cells is entirely unknown. It is thought that the extracellular DNA may become coated with certain extracellular

Table 5. Examples and Properties of the Major Categories of Transfection Method Used to Introduce DNA into Animal Cells

Category[a]	Examples	Method of uptake	Route	Transgene structure
Chemical	Calcium phosphate, DEAE–dextran, Polybrene, lipofection	Endocytosis of DNA complexes	Via endosome	Multiple arrays[b]
Poration	Electroporation, laser transfection	Diffusion through transient pores in cell membrane	Directly into cytoplasm	Single transgenes or multiple arrays; highly controllable
Fusion	Liposome/virosome delivery, protoplast fusion	Fusion of DNA-containing lipid vesicle with cell membrane	Directly into cytoplasm	Multiple arrays
Physical	Particle bombardment, microinjection	Mechanical direct transfer of DNA into cell	Directly into cytoplasm or nucleus	Multiple arrays
Receptor mediated	Conjugation to various ligands, naked DNA transfection?	Receptor mediated endocytosis	Via endosome	?

[a]Note that some methods are suitable for both transient and stable transfection (e.g., calcium phosphate transfection, lipofection), whereas others tend to favor transient transfection (e.g., DEAE–dextran transfection, protoplast fusion) and others tend to favor stable transfection (e.g., nuclear microinjection).
[b]Transgene structure following chemical transfection is dependent on method. Calcium phosphate generates large random arrays if there is carrier DNA, but smaller, concatemeric arrays are generated by other methods. For more details see later section "Fate of foreign DNA and structure of the transgenome".

proteins, and that these may facilitate receptor-mediated endocytosis.

Transfection with Calcium Phosphate

Calcium phosphate transfection was first used in 1973 to introduce adenovirus DNA into mammalian cells (60). The first mammalian cell lines stably transfected with nonviral DNA were also produced using this technique and were described in 1978 (61). Calcium phosphate transfection is probably still the most widely used gene transfer technique, and this reflects its numerous advantages: The procedure is inexpensive, highly repeatable, and suitable for both the transient and stable transfection of a wide range of cells (61a,61b). In transient calcium phosphate–mediated cotransfection, the molar ratio of different plasmids used in the transfection mix appears to be faithfully reproduced in the transfected cell population (62).

There are many variations on the original technique, but all involve mixing DNA, a HEPES-buffered phosphate solution, and calcium chloride, resulting in the immediate formation of a fine DNA/calcium phosphate coprecipitate. This settles onto the cells and is internalized. Originally, it was thought that coprecipitated particles might be taken up by phagocytosis, but it is now suggested that endocytosis results in the transfer of calcium phosphate–DNA complexes to the nucleus (63).

Since cells need to be coated by the coprecipitate, calcium phosphate transfection is particularly suitable for cells that grow as monolayers, as opposed to cells growing as clumps or in suspension. An alternative technique, using a BES buffer, which allows the precipitate to form gradually over several hours, is up to 100-fold more efficient for stable transfection with high-quality plasmid DNA, although equivalent in efficiency to the original HEPES-buffered method for transient transfection, or for stable transfection with linear DNA (64,65). The efficiency of transient transfection using the original method may be enhanced by chemical shock, as will be discussed in the following section. However, this does not increase the efficiency of the BES-buffered method.

Transfection with DEAE–Dextran

A major disadvantage of the calcium phosphate transfection technique is that certain cell lines are adversely affected by the precipitate, resulting in extensive cell death. A mixture of DNA and DEAE–dextran (diethylaminoethyl-dextran), a *soluble* polycationic carbohydrate, allows the transfection of many cells that respond poorly to calcium phosphate–DNA coprecipitates. Like calcium phosphate transfection, the DEAE–dextran technique was originally devised to facilitate the transfer of viral DNA into animal cells and was later adapted as a plasmid transfection method (64,65). Contemporary DEAE–dextran transfection protocols are based on improved strategies devised by Lopata et al. (66) and Sussman and Milman (67), which include chemical shock treatments to increase the efficiency of DNA uptake (see the following section). The DEAE–dextran technique is highly reproducible and simple to carry out.

DNA is simply mixed with 10 mg ml^{-1} DEAE–dextran and added to the cells. The mixture is presumed to contain complexes that increase the efficiency of endocytosis, and compared to calcium phosphate transfection, a much smaller amount of DNA is required. Plasmid DNA introduced into cells by DEAE–dextran adopts the nucleosome structure typical of endogenous chromosomes, whereas most of the estimated 1 Mbp of DNA entering cells as calcium phosphate coprecipitates remains in an aggregated form (68). However, because less DNA is introduced into cells using DEAE–dextran, this method is useful only for transient transfection, not for the generation of stably transfected cell lines.

Enhancing Transient Transfection Efficiency

In some transient transfection systems, cotransfection with a plasmid carrying the RNA polymerase III–dependent adenoviral VA$_I$ gene results in an increased efficiency of foreign gene expression (69). VA$_I$ is thought to act at the level of protein synthesis by restoring the activity of the host translational initiation factor eIF2. This factor is inhibited by a protein kinase activated in the presence of double-stranded RNA, which can sometimes arise from dual-strand transcription of transfected plasmid DNA. The adenoviral VA$_I$ gene product is an RNA molecule that specifically interacts with and represses this kinase, the dsRNA-activated inhibitory protein kinase (DAI kinase), and is used to stimulate viral protein synthesis during adenovirus infections. Vectors carrying the adenoviral VA genes are commercially available (e.g., pAd-VAntage, which is marketed by Promega).

A number of chemical treatments have also been described that enhance the efficiency of transient transfection, perhaps by increasing the rate of DNA uptake or improving the stability of DNA in the cell. A commonly used procedure is to expose cells to an osmotic shock following transfection, which increases the amount of DNA taken up from the surrounding medium. The shock involves brief exposure of transfected cells to 10–30% solutions of glycerol or dimethylsulfate (66,67). As with other transfection parameters, the optimal concentration and exposure time must be determined empirically. Another transfection enhancer is chloroquine, which inhibits acidification of endosomal vesicles and thus probably protects DNA from degradation (70). Chloroquine is moderately cytotoxic, however, and cells may be exposed to this chemical either during or after transfection, but only for a few hours. Sodium butyrate is also used to increase transfection efficiencies and may be used in conjunction with an osmotic shock (71). The treatment involves adding sodium butyrate (final concentration 10 mM) to the growth medium after the shock, and leaving cells in contact with it for 24 hours.

Electroporation and Laser Transfection

Electroporation is the transfection of cells in culture by exposing them to a transient electric field. This causes nanometer-sized pores to open briefly in the cell membrane, allowing uptake of free DNA from the surrounding medium. This method is ideal for many cells recalcitrant to chemical transfection methods. It is efficient, highly reproducible, and suitable for both stable and transient transfection, and has the added advantage that transgene copy number can be controlled (72). Electroporated DNA is transferred directly into the cytoplasm without processing through endocytotic vesicles (73), and for this reason the observed frequency of mutation is much lower than for chemical transfection methods (74). Electroporation is applicable to most cell types, and once optimal conditions have been determined, is a very simple procedure — cells are suspended in electroporation buffer in a cuvette and exposed to a brief, high-voltage electrical pulse. The exact magnitude and duration of the pulse are the critical parameters, and these must be determined empirically for different cells. Many cells are efficiently electroporated by a brief high-voltage pulse (800–1500 V), but others, especially primary cells, may be killed by such treatment and respond better to a longer lasting pulse of 100–300 V. The highest transfection efficiencies typically occur when there is about 50% cell death. The technique was first carried out in 1982 using mouse fibroblasts (75), but was soon adapted to many other cell types (76). Among the few disadvantages of this technique are the requirement for specialized capacitor discharge equipment capable of accurately controlling pulse length and voltage, and the requirement for larger numbers of cells and higher DNA concentrations than for other procedures. A number of electroporation instruments are commercially available and are discussed extensively by Potter (77). More recently, the technique has been adapted for in vivo gene transfer (78).

Another transfection technology, which has not become widely used, is transfection following laser treatment (79). This technique has been grouped with electroporation because it involves a similar DNA uptake mechanism. Free DNA is taken up directly from the surrounding medium through transient pores created by a finely focused laser beam. Like microinjection (see the following section) this strategy can be applied only to a small number of cells at a time, but with optimal DNA concentration can result in stable transfection frequencies of greater than 0.5%.

Liposomes, Virosomes, and Lipofection

Gene transfer mediated by liposomes was first described in 1980 (80). *Liposomes* are unilaminar phospholipid vesicles into which DNA can be packaged. When mixed with cells in culture, the vesicles fuse with the cell membrane and deliver DNA directly into the cytoplasm (81), a mechanism similar to that of protoplast fusion (see the following section). The original liposome transfection techniques were no more efficient than calcium phosphate transfection and suffered the further disadvantage that the preparation of DNA-containing liposomes was complicated and labor intensive. One particular advantage of the method, however, was the ability to transform cells in vivo by injecting liposomes into the bloodstream (reviewed in Ref. 82). The efficiency of liposome-mediated gene transfer can be enhanced by incorporating viral proteins that facilitate the active fusion between viral envelopes and cell membranes.

Such fusogenic particles have been termed *virosomes*. For example, virosomes have been prepared from the envelopes of Sendai virus allowing the delivery of DNA to astroglial cultures (83).

A breakthrough came with the development of cationic/neutral lipid mixtures, which spontaneously associate with negatively charged DNA to form complexes (84). Residual positive charge in the complexes then interacts with negatively charged molecules on the cell surface, causing the DNA to be internalized. Technically, this is one of the simplest transfection protocols. Lipid–DNA complexes are prepared simply by mixing DNA with the lipid preparation in serum-free medium, then the mixture is added to the cells. This facilitates rapid and efficient DNA uptake, and is gentle enough to be applicable to both conventional plasmid vectors and YACs (11). The uptake mechanism was originally thought to be similar to liposome fusion (84), but more recent experiments suggest that endocytosis of DNA–lipid complexes occurs (85,86). *Lipofection*, as this technique has become known, is highly reproducible and extremely efficient for both transient and stable transfection. It allows up to 90% of cells in culture to be transiently transfected, and demonstrates stable transfection efficiencies up to 20-fold greater than standard chemical transfection methods. One drawback to this approach is that the lipids are usually difficult to prepare in the laboratory. They must therefore be purchased from a commercial source, and they are very expensive. There are now many different lipid preparations available, varying in price, efficiency, and suitability for different cell lines. A number of formulas have been compared (87), but new ones are entering the market all the time.

Polybrene-Mediated Transfection

Another polycationic chemical, the detergent Polybrene, has been used to mediate the transfection of certain cell lines, for example, CHO cells, which resist transfection by calcium phosphate (88). Like DEAE–dextran, Polybrene is soluble and may form complexes with DNA to facilitate uptake by endocytosis. For other cell lines, Polybrene has been shown to be no more efficient than calcium phosphate as a transfection mediator, and it has not gained widespread use.

Cell or Protoplast Fusion

Certain chemicals, such as polyethylene glycol (PEG), act as fusogens, agents that cause cell membranes to fuse together. This can be exploited to transfect animal cells by mixing them with other cells containing large amounts of plasmid DNA. Schaffner first successfully used bacterial protoplasts to transfect mammalian cells in culture by treating bacterial cells with chloramphenicol to amplify the plasmid DNA content, and lysozyme to remove the cell wall. The protoplasts were then centrifuged onto a layer of mammalian cells and induced to fuse with them, thus delivering the DNA directly into the cytoplasm (89). This is a highly efficient method for transient transfection, but poor for stable transfection and cotransfection. Similarly, some investigators have used the hemoglobin-free ghosts of erythrocytes for gene delivery (90). In both cases, the complexities involved in preparing and delivering the donor cells have hindered the widespread adoption of the method. However, the technique is gentle, allowing it to be applied to the transfection of ES cells with fragile YAC vectors and human chromosome fragments. For YAC delivery, yeast spheroplasts containing recombinant YAC vectors are induced to fuse with ES cells in culture, facilitating the introduction of YAC vector DNA and the eventual generation of YAC transgenic mice. One drawback to this method of YAC transfection is that all the endogenous yeast chromosomes are also introduced into the mouse cells, and these may have unpredictable effects (11). The largest DNA molecules currently transferred to mouse cells are human chromosome fragments, a process involving microcell-mediated gene transfer (91).

Microinjection

The direct microinjection of DNA into the cytoplasm or nuclei of cultured cells is sometimes used as a transfection method, but although highly efficient on an individual cell basis, this procedure is time consuming, and only a small number of cells can be treated. Originally, this technique was used for the transformation of cells that were resistant to any other method of transfection (92). Stable transfection efficiencies are extremely high, in the order of 20%, and very small quantities of DNA are sufficient. Another major advantage of this technique is that direct nuclear delivery avoids exposing the foreign DNA to any cytoplasmic organelles; so it is delivered intact. Microinjected DNA therefore suffers less mutation than DNA delivered by most chemical transfection methods. The most significant use of microinjection is the introduction of DNA into the oocytes and eggs of animals, either for transient expression analysis (e.g., in *Xenopus*) or to generate transgenic animals. It is suitable for the introduction of YAC vectors into the pronuclei of fertilized mouse eggs, but since DNA delivered in this manner must be very pure, painstaking preparation of the DNA must be carried out to avoid fragmentation. Shearing can also occur in the delivery needle, and YAC DNA is often protected by dissolving it in a high salt buffer and/or mixing it with polyamines. The production of transgenic animals by microinjection is considered in more detail later.

Transfection By Particle Bombardment

Particle bombardment (also known as microballistic or microprojectile transfection) is a relatively recent addition to the range of transfection techniques available to scientists working with animal cells. The procedure involves coating micrometer-sized gold or tungsten particles with DNA and then accelerating the particles into cells or tissues using a blast of high-pressure helium gas or an electrical discharge. The size and total mass of the particles and the force of the bombardment are important parameters that balance efficient penetration against cell damage. The technique was developed for the transformation of maize (93) and is now a method of choice for generating transgenic cereal plants. For animal cells, the technique has been less widely used

because it is usually simpler to transfect cultured cells by alternative well-established methods. However, the technique has found a role in the transfection of whole organs and tissue slices (94,95), and more recently for the transfer of DNA to surface organs in gene therapy (96). In a variation of the technique, Vahlsing et al. (97) have used a pneumatic gun to drive DNA *solutions* through skin and into muscle. This technique, which is much less efficient that the traditional injection route to in vivo muscle transfection, has nevertheless allowed the robust expression of several viral and bacterial antigens, resulting in a particular immune response.

Receptor-Mediated Transfection

A recent development in transfection technology, suitable for gene therapy applications, is the delivery of DNA to particular cells by conjugation to a specific ligand. The ligand interacts with receptors on the cell surface, allowing both it and the attached DNA to be internalized. This strategy was first used to deliver plasmid DNA to liver cells by targeting the liver-specific asialoglycoprotein receptor (98). Plasmid DNA was conjugated to the ligand, asialoorosomucoid protein, using a polylysine bridge. The conjugate was added to cultured cells, and plasmid reporter gene activity was observed in liver cells but not other cell types. Since then, many similar experiments have been performed, and the efficient receptor-mediated transfection of many cell types using various ligands has been reported (reviewed in Ref. 58). One problem associated with this technique is that the ligand–DNA complexes are internalized via endocytotic vesicles that generally fuse with lysosomes, resulting in degradation of the DNA and consequent failure of gene expression. Some DNA escapes this fate and finds its way to the nucleus to be expressed, but the mechanism by which this occurs is not understood. A greater than 1000-fold enhancement of gene expression occurs if the ligand–DNA complexes are joined to adenoviral particles, which are known to disrupt endosomes as part of their infection strategy (99). More recently, adenovirus-derived peptides have been used for the same purpose, because these are less toxic and are less likely to provoke an immune response after in vivo delivery. Receptor-mediated transfection is highly efficient in cell culture, resulting in the transfection of up to 90% of cells carrying the appropriate receptor. Less success has been observed for in vivo gene transfer, partly because the ligand–DNA complexes are degraded in serum, and partly because the size of the particles appears to be a critical parameter for the transfection of different cell types. The attachment of peptides to DNA molecules can serve other purposes in gene delivery. Recently, plasmid DNA has been conjugated to the SV40 T-antigen nuclear localization signal (100), resulting in the accumulation of transfected DNA in the nucleus.

VIRAL EXPRESSION VECTORS FOR ANIMAL CELLS

General Properties of Viral Vectors

Viruses are natural gene delivery vehicles; so it was inevitable that they should be exploited as vectors. The development of viral vectors for DNA transfer to animal cells reflects seven advantageous characteristics of animal viruses:

- They have evolved efficient mechanisms to adsorb to the surface of and gain entry into cells without damaging them. Transfection, by comparison, is very inefficient and can be destructive.
- They deliver their nucleic acid intact because it is initially packaged in a proteinaceous capsule. Conversely, DNA delivered by transfection is exposed, and hence often suffers damage leading to mutation.
- They tend to block host cell protein synthesis to favor the expression of viral genes (including transduced foreign genes), which simplifies the recovery of recombinant proteins.
- Viral genomes contain strong and promiscuous regulatory elements that can be exploited to drive high-level foreign gene expression.
- Many animal viruses have a broad host range and can thus replicate in diverse cell types from a large number of species.
- During lytic infection, viruses replicate to a high copy number and hence facilitate similar amplification of any foreign genes they carry.
- Many viruses can stably transform cells by integration or latent episomal replication, becoming quiescent in the process and allowing the production of cell lines. The integrated form of a viral genome is a *provirus*, and the same term is sometimes used to describe the plasmid-like latent episomal form of a virus.

Many animal viruses have been exploited as vectors, mostly for foreign gene expression in cultured cells, but more recently as gene therapy vectors both in vitro and in vivo. Four classes of viral vector to be discussed—adenovirus, adeno-associated virus, herpes simplex virus, and retrovirus—have been used in phase 1 clinical gene therapy trials (reviewed in Ref. 101).

Like foreign genes integrated in cellular genomes, foreign genes inserted into a viral genome are termed *transgenes*. There are three strategies for the incorporation of foreign genes into viral genomes. In two of these strategies, the resulting virus is known as *helper independent* or *replication competent*, meaning that the recombinant virus is able to propagate, even though it carries foreign DNA. First, foreign DNA can be *added* to the entire viral genome without loss of viral genomic sequences. Vectors designed on this principle are termed *insertion vectors*, and typically the foreign DNA is inserted between functional viral genes, or at the edge of a linear genome. Second, foreign DNA can be used to replace a nonessential viral gene (nonessential, at least, for productive infection in cell culture). Vectors designed on this principle are termed *replacement vectors*, and the wild-type viral DNA fragment that is replaced is termed the *stuffer fragment*. The third strategy also involves replacement, but in this case one or more *essential* viral genes is replaced with foreign DNA. This renders

the recombinant vector *helper dependent* or *replication defective*, and missing essential functions must be supplied in *trans*.

Helper-dependent vectors are especially important for gene therapy applications because an obligatory viral infection accompanying gene transfer would be extremely undesirable. The *trans*-functions may be supplied (*1*) using a *helper virus* (a virus carrying the essential functions, which is co-introduced with the vector) or (*2*) using a helper plasmid, which is transfected into the cells infected by the vector. Alternatively (*3*) dedicated cell lines sometimes termed *packaging lines* or *complementary lines* can be used to propagate the vector. These cells are transformed with a deficient viral genome that is itself incapable of replication, but supplies helper functions in *trans* to the vector. The extreme form of this strategy uses derivatives that are sometimes termed *amplicons* and sometimes described as *gutted* (or *gutless*): All viral coding sequences are deleted, leaving behind only those *cis*-acting elements required for replication, packaging, and/or proviral integration. The choice of strategy depends on many factors, including genome size, the availability of packaging lines, the number and nature of nonessential genes, and the packaging capacity of the viral capsid.

Many viruses (e.g., papovaviruses) package DNA into a preformed capsid and thus have a strictly defined packaging capacity that limits the size of foreign DNA. Others (e.g., the baculoviruses) form the capsid around the genome, and no such limitation exists. There are a number of techniques for placing foreign DNA into viral genomes. The two most popular are ligation and homologous recombination. In the ligation strategy, restriction enzymes are used to prepare vector and foreign DNA and the two elements are joined in vitro using DNA ligase. In the homologous recombination strategy, a plasmid carrying the foreign DNA within a viral homology region is transfected into cells infected with the parental vector, and recombinants are generated by crossing over within the homology region. The homologous recombination strategy is favored for viruses with large genomes, which are difficult to manipulate directly (e.g., baculovirus, herpes virus, vaccinia virus). In both cases, various screening and selection strategies may be employed to isolate recombinant vector molecules, as discussed for individual viruses in the following section. The use of helper viruses that are themselves replication defective or that carry mutations allowing counterselection is useful for preparing pure stocks of recombinant vector. Contemporary systems are also designed so that two or more entirely independent recombination events are required to generate replication-competent, wild-type virus genomes. Novel strategies involving site-specific recombination and transposition have also been used to generate recombinant viruses.

Adenovirus Vectors

Overview. The adenoviruses are a family of DNA viruses characterized by a nonenveloped, icosahedral capsid and a double-stranded, linear genome of approximately 36 kbp. They are well known for causing upper respiratory tract diseases in humans, and display a broad species and cellular host range in mammals. Two unrelated cellular receptors that mediate viral interaction with target cells have recently been identified. Over 50 distinct serotypes of human adenovirus have been isolated, but most adenovirus vectors are derivatives of Ad2 and Ad5.

The major advantages of adenoviruses as vectors are the high titer (10^{12}–10^{13} pfu ml^{-1}), the efficiency of gene transfer (approaching 100%), the broad species and cellular host range (including postmitotic cells), and the ease of in vitro manipulation (102,103). Adenovirus vectors in current use can accommodate up to 8 kbp of foreign DNA, although the theoretical maximum is approximately 30 kbp. One disadvantage of adenoviral vectors is the low efficiency of transformation (10^{-5}). They are therefore useful as transient expression vectors, but not for efficient stable gene transfer. This, together with their tendency to provoke an immune response, may limit their utility for human gene therapy. The potential use of adenoviral vectors for gene therapy has generated much interest in prolonging the expression of adenoviral transgenes, reducing cellular and humoral immune responses, and targeting gene transfer to particular cells. Progress in these areas is discussed in two recent reviews (104,105).

Quite apart from their use as vectors, adenoviruses are, as discussed earlier, exploited in two other areas of gene transfer technology. First, plasmids expressing the adenoviral VA genes may be used to increase foreign gene expression following transient transfection with plasmid vectors. This is because the RNA products of these genes inhibit the activity of DAI protein kinase, an enzyme that blocks protein synthesis in the presence of dsRNA. Second, the presence of adenoviral capsids during receptor-mediated transfection has been shown to increase the efficiency of transgene expression up to 2000-fold. This is because DNA taken up by receptor-mediated endocytosis is delivered to lysosomes, wherein it is degraded, but since adenovirus disrupts endosomes as a normal part of its infection strategy, the addition of adenovirus particles can increase the survival of internalized DNA and increase foreign gene expression.

Adenovirus Molecular Biology. There are approximately 10 transcription units in the linear adenovirus genome, but the number of gene products produced is increased by complex patterns of alternative splicing and protein processing (102,103). Genes are expressed in two phases, early genes before replication and late genes after replication. There are six early transcription units, which from left to right on the adenovirus gene map are E1a, E1b, E2a, E2b, E3, and E4 [Fig. 5(a)]. E1a proteins are transcriptional regulators. E1b proteins control mRNA export and the inhibition of host cell protein synthesis. E2a and E2b encode proteins for viral DNA replication. E3 proteins help to evade the host immune response, and E4 encodes further transcriptional regulators. All regions except E3 are essential for viral propagation

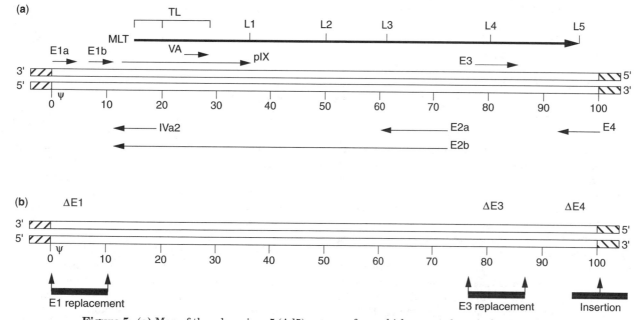

Figure 5. (a) Map of the adenovirus 5 (Ad5) genome, from which many adenoviral vectors have been developed. The genome is divided into 100 map units, each representing 360 bp, with inverted terminal repeats (hatched boxes). Arrows represent transcripts, the early transcripts E1–E4, the intermediate transcripts pIX and IVa2, and the major late transcript (MLT). The position of the RNA polymerase III–dependent VA genes is also shown. The major late transcript is differentially spliced to yield five families of mature transcripts (LI–L5), each beginning with the tripartite leader (TL) and ending where indicated. (b) Strategies for vector development. Foreign genes can be inserted adjacent to the E4 region, or used to replace either E1 or E3. E1 replacement vectors are the most widely used, and their capacity may be increased by also deleting the E3 and E4 regions. A further strategy is to delete all internal sequences except the packaging site (ψ), generating an amplicon vector.

in cultured cells. Replication occurs by a displacement mechanism, and begins at inverted repeats at the termini of the viral genome, where it is primed by terminal, nucleotide-binding proteins. After replication, early gene expression is switched off and transcription initiates from the single *major late promoter*, producing five major families of transcripts. All these late transcripts begin with a sequence termed the *tripartite leader*, an untranslated region containing two introns, which increases the efficiency of protein synthesis. Each transcript family also has a common 3′ end, and individual members differ with respect to internal splicing patterns. Further genes within the E1b, E2a, and E2b transcription units are expressed during the late phase. There are also several intermediate genes, (e.g., pIX and the set of *VA genes*) transcribed by RNA polymerase III. These enhance late gene expression by inhibiting DAI protein kinase, which otherwise blocks protein synthesis during late infection. Late genes encode viral structural proteins and proteins involved in their processing and assembly to form the mature virion.

Although stable integration of adenovirus DNA occurs at low frequency, one of the major reasons for interest in the adenoviruses is their ability to transform cells. The adenoviruses are divided into several subgroups based on their oncogenicity, with subgroup A being the most oncogenic, usually causing tumors when injected into newborn mice. Subgroup B is weakly oncogenic, and subgroups C–F induce tumors only occasionally. All adenoviruses can transform cultured cells, however, and invariably this involves stable integration of at least the leftmost 11% of the viral genome. This fragment of the genome contains the E1a and E1b transcription units. Certain products from this region are oncogenic because they inhibit the activity of host cell cycle regulators. E1a inactivates the retinoblastoma protein, whose function is to prevent S-phase transcription, and E1b inhibits the activity of p53, which blocks the cell cycle in response to DNA damage and other signals.

Construction of Recombinant Adenovirus Vectors. Both replication-competent and replication-deficient adenoviral vectors have been developed (102,103) [Fig. 5(b)]. The replication-competent vectors include E3 replacement vectors and insertion vectors (where foreign DNA is added at the right-hand edge of the linear gene map just upstream of the E4 transcription unit). The most widely used adenovirus vectors, however, are replication defective due to deletion of the E1a and E1b transcription units. These E1 replacement vectors are propagated in the complementary human embryonic kidney cell line 293, which is transformed with the leftmost 11% of the adenovirus genome and hence supplies the missing functions. E1 replacement vectors may also lack the E3 transcription unit, which increases the maximum capacity of the vector to approximately 8 kbp (106). The further deletion of the E4 region allows foreign DNA of up to 11 kbp to be inserted, and has the further advantage of removing adenoviral functions that interfere with host cell physiology. The theoretical maximum capacity of an adenoviral vector is 30 kbp. This requires the deletion of all adenoviral coding DNA, leaving just the *cis*-acting

elements required for packaging and replication—a so-called *adenovirus amplicon*. Packaging lines like HEK 293 cannot be prepared for amplicons because the overexpression of adenoviral late proteins is cytotoxic. Current strategies therefore use helper viruses, although there remain problems separating the recombinant vector and helper, and with vector instability. Amplicon vectors have been used successfully to prepare vectors carrying the cystic fibrosis transmembrane receptor cDNA (107) and dystrophin cDNA (108) in 293 cells either cotransfected or coinfected with helper vectors, but yields of the recombinant vector are so far very low.

Wild-type adenovirus genomes are difficult to manipulate because of their size and lack of conveniently placed restriction sites. The production of recombinant adenoviral vectors by homologous recombination is therefore a popular strategy, and a series of plasmid vectors has been produced, containing adenoviral sequences interrupted by a multiple cloning site (102,103). The alternative strategy of recombinant vector production in vitro has been facilitated by the development of derivatives of the wild-type adenovirus genome containing unique restriction sites for insertion, or paired sites for excision of E1 or E3 stuffer fragments and their replacement with foreign DNA (102,103). Recombinant adenoviral genomes produced as discussed earlier are infectious and can be introduced into permissive cells by transfection. Evidence of viral infection is seen within a few days, and cell lysates can then be used to infect fresh cells, resulting in the formation of plaques representing viral clones. These can be purified and the DNA analyzed for the presence of the foreign insert by PCR. It is desirable to check for sequence loss and rearrangements, especially if the insert is large and the recombinant genome approaches the maximum packaging size of the virus.

Adeno-Associated Virus Vectors

Overview. The parvovirus family of single-stranded DNA viruses is divided into the autonomous and dependovirus subgroups. The latter includes adeno-associated virus (AAV), which is naturally *defective*, that is, unable to complete its replication cycle in the absence of a helper virus. In this instance, the term *helper virus* does not refer to a replication-competent derivative of the same species. Rather, the dependoviruses require functions supplied by a different virus species for their propagation. Adenovirus is a suitable helper virus, hence "adeno-associated" but herpes virus is also competent to supply the required functions, and to a lesser extent so is vaccinia virus. The AAV virion is small, with a nonenveloped icosahedral capsid. Either DNA strand is packaged with equal efficiency, and both strands are infectious. AAV has a biphasic infection cycle. In adenovirus-infected cells it enters the lytic cycle and replicates to a high copy number. In other cells it enters a latent state where it does not replicate, but instead integrates into the genome. It is this latent state that is currently being exploited for gene transfer, due to the potential for long term transgene expression. However, if a transformed cell is subsequently infected with adenovirus, the AAV provirus is excised (*rescued*) and lytic infection commences.

AAV has numerous properties that make it a valuable gene transfer and expression vector, particularly for gene therapy (109,110). First, stable integration occurs with great efficiency, and proviral transgenes can be expressed using either AAV or heterologous promoters. Second, the virus has an impressive host range that includes nonproliferating cells. Third, the virus is unusual in that even the wild type does not cause any disease symptoms. Fourth, it is very safe to use: Recombinant AAV vectors lacking replication functions require two helper viruses, a helper AAV to supply missing AAV functions, as well as adenovirus. Finally, there is no superinfection immunity; so cells can be transduced with different AAV vectors as many time as necessary. This allows the addition of multiple traits to cells through successive transformations. The host range of AAV has not been fully explored, but it appears to infect and replicate efficiently in all mammalian cell lines if a suitable helper virus is used. The helper virus is the primary determinant of which cells can be productively infected. Conversely, integration efficiencies vary from species to species, with human cells the most efficient hosts. This may reflect the specificity of the proviral insertion site — most integration events involving wild-type virus appear to occur within a relatively small region of chromosome 19 (19q13.1-qter), suggesting specific sequences may be involved that are endogenous to humans. This specific targeting could be an advantage in gene therapy, but recombinant AAV vectors tend to integrate randomly, suggesting the site specificity is conferred by AAV *trans*-functions. AAV has been shown to integrate into the DNA of all human cell lines tested, although the potential of primary cells has not been widely examined. One problem with AAV is the low titer of recombinant viral stocks. Initially, this was as low as 10^4-10^5 transducing units per milliliter, although by careful optimization of preparation methods, this has increased to 10^9.

AAV Molecular Biology. The AAV genome is approximately 5 kbp in length. The unique central region of the genome is flanked by 145-bp inverted terminal repeats, which are required for several functions including replication, gene regulation, and proviral integration (109). The internal region of the genome has been divided into two large sections by genetic analysis [Fig. 6(a)]. The *rep* region encodes nonstructural proteins, and mutations within this region generate a replication-deficient phenotype that also lacks certain transcriptional functions. The *cap* region encodes the structural proteins of the capsid, and mutations within this region generate a packaging-deficient phenotype. There are three promoters in the AAV genome, named according to their map positions (p5, p19, p40). Rep proteins arise from mRNAs transcribed from the p5 and p19 promoters, while capsid proteins arise from mRNAs transcribed from the p40 promoter. All transcripts share a common intron and polyadenylation site. The polyadenylation site is adjacent to the origin of replication and *cis*-acting elements required for packaging, integration, and rescue.

The regulation of AAV gene expression is complex, involving both helper virus and AAV functions (109). In the

absence of helper virus, no AAV genes are expressed. In the presence of adenovirus, transcription begins from the p5 and p19 AAV promoters, resulting in the synthesis of AAV Rep proteins. This in turn induces high-level transcription from all three AAV promoters, heralding the lytic cycle. The adenovirus E1a protein plays the major role in this process, as it is the initial transactivator of p5 and p19 transcription. However, further adenovirus gene products are also required for productive AAV infection (hence the 293 cell line is not permissive for AAV replication). In fact E1b, E2a, E4, and VA genes are also required for the efficient accumulation and productive splicing of AAV mRNAs.

Construction of Recombinant AAV Vectors. The first AAV vectors, produced in 1984, were *cap*-replacement vectors. Initially, the *cap* region was replaced with the *E. coli neo* gene. The integrated *neo* gene was expressed at a low level from the endogenous AAV p40 promoter, but levels were sufficient to allow G418 selection of transduced cells. Major improvements to AAV-mediated gene delivery came with the development of vectors where all internal reading frames were deleted, leaving just the polyadenylation site and the *cis*-acting sequences for packaging, integration, and rescue in addition to the terminal repeats (109,110) [Fig. 6(b)]. The maximum capacity of the AAV capsid is 110% wild-type genome size; thus amplicon vectors of this nature allow the insertion of approximately 4.5 kbp of foreign DNA. The removal of the *rep* region provided an additional advantage: AAV Rep proteins control transcription as well as replication, and have been shown to interfere with endogenous promoters and enhancers in AAV vectors. However, *rep⁻* vectors are not affected in this manner and have been used with several constitutive and inducible eukaryotic promoters, and the patterns of cell type-specific and inducible expression have been faithfully reproduced. Vectors with intact Rep functions are less predictable, although some promoters appear unaffected (e.g., the adenovirus E4 promoter).

One disadvantage of AAV expression vectors is the laborious procedure for producing stocks of recombinant

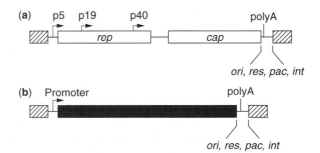

Figure 6. (a) Simplified map of the AAV genome showing the *rep* and *cap* regions, the three promoters (p5, p19, and p40), the polyadenylation site, the cluster of *cis*-acting sites at the right-hand site of the map (origin of replication, rescue, packaging, integration), and the inverted terminal repeats (hatched boxes). (b) A recombinant AAV vector. The viral coding sequences have been removed and replaced by a foreign gene under the control of a heterologous promoter. The *cis*-acting sites remain in situ.

virus. Since both a helper virus (adenovirus) and a helper AAV are required to provide missing functions in *trans*, there are two types of contaminant to remove. Wild-type AAV can be used as a helper, but the resulting recombinant stock contains adenovirus and wild-type AAV contaminants, the latter often in great excess to the recombinant virus. Much effort has been expended on developing procedures for the removal of contaminants. Adenovirus can be inactivated by heating (lysates are heated to 60 °C for 2 hours) and effectively removed by CsCl density centrifugation or other physical methods. Several strategies have been employed to restrict the propagation of wild-type AAV, including the use of packaging-deficient AAV strains, the use of helper plasmids transfected into the cells infected with the parental AAV vector and adenovirus, the use of cell lines with integrated AAV genomes lacking functional rescue sequences, and the use of conditional lethal AAV mutants as helpers. These strategies have reduced the proportion of wild-type virus in the resulting stocks, although the level can still reach 10–50% due to recombination between the recombinant and helper AAV genomes. There is little chance of generating true AAV packaging lines because the overexpression of AAV genes is cytotoxic and, as discussed in the previous section, so is the overexpression of adenoviral helper functions. The current method for producing essentially pure recombinant AAV is to use two plasmids, one carrying the recombinant AAV genome with all *cis*-acting sites intact but all *trans*-functions replaced by foreign DNA, and the other carrying the *rep* and *cap* functions, but lacking any *cis*-acting elements. These are cotransfected into cells infected with adenovirus. There is no homology between the two plasmids, preventing the production of wild-type AAV by homologous recombination, but with all the required functions supplied in *trans*, the recombinant AAV vector is rescued from the plasmid and packaged. Contaminating adenovirus is then removed as discussed, leaving the recombinant AAV vectors.

AAV vectors are newcomers in the field of gene transfer, and much remains to be learned of their suitability for stable gene expression especially in gene therapy. In particular, issues that need to be addressed include the nature and efficiency of vector transduction and transgene activity in vivo. A number of such studies have been carried out recently, and are reviewed in Ref. 110.

Alphavirus Vectors

Overview. The alphaviruses are a group of single-stranded positive-sense RNA viruses with a broad host range including insects and mammals (111). The wild-type genome has two genes, the 5′ gene encoding viral replicase and the 3′ gene encoding a self-cleaving polyprotein containing all the capsid structural proteins. The genome acts as a direct substrate for translation, but initially only the replicase gene can be translated because it is associated with the typical 5′ cap required for eukaryotic protein synthesis, while the start of the structural gene is internal and lacks such a cap. Naked viral RNA is infectious because the replicase gene is translated efficiently by host ribosomes. The replicase produces a full-length negative-sense "antigenomic strand" that is used as a template to generate both full-length daughter genomes and a subgenomic RNA carrying the structural proteins gene. This subgenomic RNA is also capped, hence allowing translation of the structural proteins.

Alphaviruses have several properties making them suitable as transient expression vectors (111,112). First, they have a broad host range and cell tropism, facilitating gene delivery to many cell types. Second, recombinant alphaviruses deliver their RNA to the cytoplasm, where it is efficiently self-replicated and expressed to yield high levels of recombinant protein (however, alphavirus genomes can also be cloned as cDNA and expressed from a normal expression vector, resulting in the export of recombinant viral RNA from the nucleus). Third, because the viral structural proteins are encoded on a separate subgenomic RNA, this region can be replaced by foreign DNA without rendering the vector replication defective. Fourth, the delivery of recombinant vector RNA ensures that the virus never integrates into the genome, making this system particularly useful for short-term gene therapy (e.g., cancer therapy). Finally, the two best-characterized alphaviruses—Semliki Forest virus (SFV) and Sindbis virus (SIN)—are transmitted in an asymptomatic manner, so they express foreign DNA in cell culture and in vivo without causing cytotoxic effects or disease symptoms. The alphaviruses have been developed as vectors only recently, and are so far the only RNA viruses (excluding the retroviruses, which have a DNA stage in their replication cycle) to be commercially exploited as expression vectors. The use of RNA viruses is advantageous for certain experimental strategies because there is no chance of proviral integration, and hence no danger of mutation or transformation. A number of negative-strand RNA viruses have also shown potential for vector development, although at this time the number of successful gene transfer and expression experiments are limited (for a recent review, see Ref. 113). One potential disadvantage with the use of RNA viruses is the generally low fidelity of the viral replicase enzymes, which results in a higher level of transgene mutation than seen with DNA viruses.

Molecular Biology of SFV and Sindbis Virus. SFV, Sindbis, and other alphaviruses infect cells by receptor-mediated endocytosis. The spike glycoprotein of the virus envelope then causes the viral and endosome vesicles to fuse, releasing the viral nucleocapsid into the cytoplasm. Proteins such as Sindbis spike glycoprotein have been exploited to enhance the efficiency of liposome-mediated transfection by catalyzing the fusion of liposomes and their target cells — such fusogenic DNA-containing particles are known as virosomes, and have already been discussed in more detail. Following entry into the cytoplasm, the genomic RNA is released from the nucleocapsid and is immediately translated to yield the viral replicase [Fig. 7(a)]. This enzyme produces progeny genomes by first synthesizing a negative-sense antigenomic strand, and then using this as a template to generate positive-sense genomic strands. The replicase also transcribes the subgenomic RNA from an internal promoter, and as

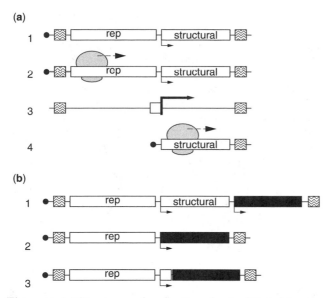

(a)

(b)

Figure 7. (**a**) Structure and replication of a simplified alphavirus genome. (*1*) There are two genes, one encoding replicase and the other encoding structural proteins. The genome is flanked by replicase binding sequences (wavy lines) and is capped at the 5′ end (black circle). (*2*) The 5′ cap allows ribosome binding, resulting in translation of the replicase gene (broken arrow). (*3*) Replicase copies the genomic RNA to generate an antigenomic strand. This contains an internal promoter (thick arrow shown on antigenomic strand, small arrow shown on genomic strand). (*4*) replicase initiation at the internal promoter facilitates transcription of the subgenomic RNA, which is capped and translated to yield the structural proteins. (**b**) Design of alphavirus vectors. (*1*) Addition vector, where a gene can be added to the full genome under a second internal promoter. (*2*) The structural genes can be replaced by foreign DNA. (*3*) The foreign DNA can be fused to part of the structural polyprotein gene to take advantage of a translational enhancer.

discussed, this encodes a polyprotein containing the viral structural proteins. The polyprotein is cleaved by capsid protein C, which has chymotrypsin-like autoproteolytic activity. The viral proteins associate with naked genomic RNA, and the new nucleocapsids migrate to the cell surface, where they are released by budding, generating new lipid envelopes with spike proteins.

Construction of Recombinant SFV and Sindbis Virus Vectors. The alphavirus replicase initiates transcription of the subgenomic RNA at an internal promoter, and one strategy for expressing recombinant proteins from alphavirus vectors is to add a second promoter either upstream or downstream of the structural genes, allowing the insertion of a foreign gene and its expression as an additional subgenomic RNA (111,112). All subgenomic RNAs are capped and can be translated. Alternatively, the insertion of an IRES element between the structural genes and the transgene allows internal translation of the transgene, albeit at a lower efficiency compared to cap-dependent translation. Such strategies produce vectors that are not only replication competent, but also competent to produce infectious viral progeny. Since this is not always desirable, a second strategy is to replace

the structural genes with foreign DNA. Such constructs are more efficient than the addition-type vectors, which tend to be unstable (111). Structural gene replacement does not affect replication, but it prevents the formation of infectious virions, and can result in extremely high levels of recombinant protein synthesis, up to 50% total cellular protein. Foreign DNA can be used to replace the entire structural coding region, but the first 40 amino acid residues include a strong enhancer of protein synthesis, which significantly increases the yield of recombinant protein. In many expression systems, this region is included in the vector, so that the foreign gene is expressed as an N-terminal fusion protein. Alternatively, the entire capsid C protein region can be included. In this case, foreign genes are initially expressed as N-terminal fusion proteins, but autocatalytic cleavage results in the production of native protein. These strategies are summarized in Figure 7(b).

Since SFV and Sindbis are RNA viruses, in vitro manipulation and recombinant vector construction must involve the use of cDNA genome copies (111). These can be used to produce infectious RNA in vitro, which can be transfected into cells using many of the methods traditionally used for DNA transfection. For example, Sindbis expression vectors are marketed by Invitrogen. The vector pSinRep5 is a plasmid containing bacterial backbone elements, the Sindbis replicase genes and packaging site, and an expression cassette featuring a Sindbis subgenomic promoter, a multiple cloning site, and a polyadenylation site. There is an SP6 promoter upstream of the replicase genes and expression cassette for generating full-length in vitro transcripts. There is a second set of restriction sites downstream from the polylinker, allowing the vector to be linearized prior to in vitro transcription. Foreign DNA is cloned in the expression cassette, the vector is linearized and transcribed, and the infectious recombinant Sindbis RNA thus produced is transfected into cells and expressed to generate high levels of recombinant protein. A different approach is to clone the entire alphavirus vector as an expression unit in a conventional plasmid expression vector under the control of a typical mammalian promoter, such as the SV40 promoter. In this case, DNA is transfected into the cell as normal and alphavirus RNA is produced as mRNA and exported to the cytoplasm. Here it replicates as a virus and produces large amounts of recombinant protein. In both the RNA and DNA transfection strategies, helper functions are not required and recombinant virus particles are not produced.

The introduction of recombinant RNA into cells is unsuitable for certain experiments, especially for gene delivery in vivo. In these cases, viral infection of cells is used for gene transfer. The propagation of infectious recombinant viruses requires helper functions (i.e., structural genes) to be supplied in *trans*. A binary approach has been used successfully to produce recombinant viruses. A vector such as that described above is used in concert with a second vector carrying the structural genes (111,112). Two in vitro transcription reactions are performed and target cells are cotransfected with two RNAs, one expressing replicase and the transgene, and one the structural proteins. This facilitates one round of replication and packaging and the production of recombinant viral particles that can be used to infect other cells. There is a risk of replication-competent viruses assembling by promiscuous replication, involving switching between the alternative RNA templates. This has been addressed by developing helper viruses with conditional lethal mutations, but the risks are at present too great for alphaviruses to be considered safe for human gene therapy.

Baculovirus Vectors

Overview. The baculoviruses are a diverse group of double-stranded DNA viruses whose productive host range is limited to insects and other arthropods (114). There are no known vertebrate hosts; thus vectors derived from baculoviruses are among the safest to use in the laboratory. However, baculoviruses are taken up by mammalian cells in culture, and recent studies have shown them capable of expressing foreign genes under the control of mammalian viral promoters (115). Baculoviruses are therefore potential vectors for gene therapy, and it is likely that this relatively unexplored aspect of their molecular biology will be studied in great detail and exploited in the future.

The mainstream role of baculovirus vectors, however, is the high-yield transient expression of foreign proteins in insect cells (116–118). The usefulness of baculoviruses as vectors stems from the unusual infection cycle of one particular subfamily, known as the *nuclear polyhedrosis viruses*. The baculoviruses are divided into three subfamilies: the nuclear polyhedrosis viruses (NPVs), the granulosis viruses, and the nonoccluded viruses (114). The NPVs are potentially the most suitable vectors because they produce *nuclear occlusion bodies*, where mature virions are embedded in an abundant proteinaceous matrix. The matrix allows virions to survive in a harsh environment such as the external surface of leaves. The two important features of this system (as concerns vector development) are: (*1*) The matrix consists predominantly of a single virus protein, *polyhedrin*, which is expressed at very high levels; and (*2*) the nuclear occlusion stage of the infection cycle is nonessential for viral propagation in insect cell lines. The polyhedrin coding region can therefore be replaced with foreign genes, allowing prodigious heterologous gene expression from the polyhedrin promoter, and such replacement vectors are replication competent.

Due to the simple procedures involved in laboratory handling and propagation, vector development has concentrated on two species of virus (117,118). For the production of recombinant proteins in insect cells, the multiple nuclear polyhedrosis virus from the alfalfa looper *Autographa californica* has been extensively utilized. This virus (AcMNPV) is propagated in several insect cell lines, the most popular of which are derived from *Spodoptera frugiperda* (e.g., Sf9, Sf21). Alternative hosts include cell lines derived from *Estigmene acrea*, *Mamesta brassicae*, and *Trichoplusia ni* (e.g., High Five™). A related virus (BmNPV), which infects the silkworm *Bombyx mori*, has been used for the production of recombinant protein in live silkworm larvae.

The baculovirus expression system has two other important advantages in addition to its safety, convenience, and yield. First, the rod-shaped viral capsid is completed after genome packaging, so that the size of the capsid is determined by the length of the genome. This means that any amount of foreign DNA can be accommodated, and multiple genes can be expressed in tandem (119). Second, many types of post-translational protein modification have been documented in insect cell lines, including proteolytic cleavage, formation of disulfide bonds, N-linked and O-linked glycosylation, and fatty acid acylation (119). Baculoviruses are therefore ideal for overexpressing mammalian proteins, especially those intended for therapeutic use. However, there is some variation in the nature of protein modification, particularly with respect to N-linked glycosylation, between mammalian cells and the popular baculovirus host cell line Sf9. It has been reported that glycosylation patterns in an alternative cell line derived from *E. acrea* are similar to those in mammalian cells (120). Furthermore, mammalian glycosylation enzymes have been coexpressed with target foreign proteins using baculovirus vectors in Sf9 cells, and this strategy has successfully altered the specificity of the glycosylation pathway to generate correct modifications typical of mammalian proteins (120). For cellular localization studies, it is also notable that most proteins expressed in insect cells using baculovirus vectors are correctly targeted.

Molecular Biology of AcMNPV. *A. californica* multiple nuclear polyhedrosis virus (AcMNPV) replicates with a biphasic cycle in susceptible insect cells and produces two distinct forms of virus (119). The early cycle results in the production of *extracellular budded viruses* (EBVs), single-enveloped virions that are released by budding from the cell membrane and go on to infect other cells. This first phase of the lytic cycle occurs within 20 hours following infection and involves the expression of three sets of viral genes. The immediate early (alpha) genes and the delayed early (beta) genes are expressed before DNA replication. The alpha genes are expressed immediately after the infecting virus is uncoated, and expression requires no viral gene products; hence transfected naked AcMNPV genomic DNA is infectious. The beta genes are expressed after the alpha genes, and their expression is dependent upon alpha gene products. The late (gamma) genes are expressed after the onset of replication and are thought to encode products involved in ECV structure and assembly. Most of the alpha, beta, and gamma genes are essential for productive infection.

After 20 hours post-infection, the production of ECVs is dramatically reduced. This corresponds to reduction of the transcription of alpha, beta, and gamma genes, and the induction of a fourth set of very late (delta) genes. Partially assembled virions in the nucleus at this stage are enclosed within envelopes and then trapped in a paracrystalline matrix consisting mainly of a single protein, polyhedrin. The resulting structures are termed occlusion bodies, and function to protect the virus from temperature fluctuation and desiccation. The occlusion bodies are ingested by insects, and dissolve in the high pH of the digestive system, freeing the trapped viruses to infect the cells of their host.

Several delta genes have been characterized, including the polyhedrin gene itself, the p10 gene whose function is unknown, and several genes encoding components of the occlusion body envelope. Importantly, these genes can be regarded as nonessential for productive infection in insect cell lines, although they are essential for the spread of the virus in nature. This establishes a containment system for laboratory-constructed baculovirus vectors.

Construction of Recombinant Baculovirus Vectors. Most baculovirus vectors involve replacement of the polyhedrin or p10 coding regions (reviewed in Ref. 119). As discussed, the nonessential nature of these delta gene functions has made them desirable targets for replacement with foreign DNA. There are also vectors that use early promoters, particularly for the production of proteins known to be toxic to insect cells, and more recently for baculovirus surface display technology (reviewed in Ref. 120).

Polyhedrin replacement vectors are most popular due to the prodigious expression of polyhedrin in the late part of the replication cycle (accounting for up to 25% of total cellular protein, or 1 mg per 10^6 cells) and the ease with which recombinant vectors can be identified (see the following section). The polyhedrin upstream promoter and 5′ untranslated region are important for high-level foreign gene expression, and these are included in all polyhedrin replacement vectors. Initially, the highest levels of recombinant protein expression were obtained as fusions with at least the first 30 amino acids from the N-terminal region of the polyhedrin protein. This would appear at first to reflect optimization of protein stability, but in fact reflects the presence of additional regulatory elements located downstream of the polyhedrin translation start site. For the production of native proteins, vectors are available where the natural polyhedrin initiation codon is mutated, so that these important "downstream" sequences become part of the 5′ untranslated region of the foreign gene. However, it has been reported that initiation may still occur at this mutated site; so cloned foreign genes must be trimmed of their own untranslated regions, and the start codon should be out of frame with respect to the natural polyhedrin start codon.

The original method for identifying recombinant polyhedrin-replacement clones was screening plaques for lack of occlusion bodies. Wild-type virus produces occlusion bodies, which cause plaques to appear opalescent under an oblique light source. Conversely, recombinant plaques lack occlusion bodies (OB⁻) and therefore appear clear. Such analysis must be carried out using a light microscope as baculovirus plaques are very small. The major disadvantage of p10 replacement vectors is that p10 mutants are not OB⁻ and have no easily scorable phenotype. Plaques of both polyhedrin and p10 replacement vectors can be screened for the presence of the insert by hybridization or immunological detection of foreign protein. More recently, a number of powerful visual screening strategies have been developed as well as systems for *selecting* recombinant viruses. The *E. coli* *lacZ* gene has been used to help identify recombinant plaques. In the simplest strategy, the general visibility of plaques is improved by insertion of the *lacZ* gene under

an appropriate promoter somewhere in the baculovirus genome, so that *all* plaques turn blue upon exposure to X-gal. More refined approaches include exploiting *lacZ* for blue–white selection: By using parental baculovirus strains in which β-galactosidase is expressed from the polyhedrin promoter, recombinants (which replace the *lacZ* gene with the foreign gene to be expressed) form clear plaques, while parental vectors form blue plaques; alternatively, by introducing *lacZ* as a marker alongside the foreign gene, the recombinant vectors form blue plaques, while the wild-type virus produces clear plaques. Due to the lack of screenable phenotype, p10 expression vectors must incorporate a reporter gene detection system to allow recombinant plaques to be identified. Recently, vectors have been designed with polyhedrin expressed from the p10 promoter, so that the original OB assay can be used.

Baculovirus genomes are large, and although strains have been constructed with unique restriction sites, allowing insertion of foreign DNA by in vitro ligation, the favored strategy is homologous recombination using plasmid targeting vectors containing a baculovirus homology region into which foreign DNA has been inserted (117,118). Generally, plasmid and wild-type baculovirus DNAs are cotransfected into the appropriate insect cells by calcium phosphate transfection, lipofection, or electroporation. This strategy generates recombinant vectors at a frequency of 0.5–5%. Linearized baculovirus genomes are noninfectious, but remain recombinogenic, and this can be used to reduce contamination from wild-type virus. The proportion of recombinants can be vastly increased through the use of nonviable deleted derivatives of the wild-type baculovirus genome, which are repaired by homologous recombination with the targeting vector. Derivatives of the wild-type AcMNPV genome, with unique restriction sites added upstream of the polyhedrin gene and within an essential gene found downstream of the polyhedrin locus, can be used to generate linear genome fragments lacking an essential function. Such nonviable linear genomes are now commercially available (e.g., BacPAK6). Compatible targeting vectors span the deletion and provide enough flanking homologous DNA to sponsor recombination between the two elements and generate a viable, recombinant genome. Such approaches result in the production of up to 90% recombinant plaques. Combinatorial approaches using deleted nonviable genomes and targeting vectors incorporating *lacZ* visible screening systems provide very powerful selection for recombinant vectors. Even the minor inconvenience of waiting one day for the blue–white screening assay to develop has been overcome with the introduction of baculovirus vectors using immediately visible markers such as green fluorescent protein (120).

Alternative systems, in which the baculovirus genome is maintained and targeted as a low-copy-number episome in bacteria (121) or yeast (122), are gaining popularity because they allow the direct isolation of recombinant vectors. Low-copy-number maintenance is important to prevent the survival of a background of nonrecombinant vectors. The baculovirus genome can be stably maintained as a low-copy-number episome in bacteria if it contains an

F-plasmid origin of replication and a bacterial selectable marker such as kanamycin resistance. This system, marketed by Gibco-BRL under the name "Bac-to-Bac," exploits the specificity of the bacterial transposon Tn7 to introduce foreign genes into the baculovirus/plasmid hybrid, which is called a *bacmid*. The foreign gene is cloned into a bacterial transfer plasmid between two Tn7 repeats. This is transformed into the appropriate strain of *E. coli*, which contains the bacmid and a helper plasmid supplying Tn7 transposase. Induction of transposase synthesis results in the site-specific transposition of the transgene into the bacmid, generating a recombinant bacmid that can be cloned and isolated from bacterial culture for transfection into insect cells. The Tn7 target site in the bacmid is inserted in-frame within the *lacZ* gene, allowing blue–white screening of recombinants, and rapid isolation of pure recombinant bacmid DNA from bacterial culture.

The baculovirus genome can also be maintained as a low-copy-number episome in yeast if it contains a suitable origin of replication, a centromere, and selectable markers: These elements are inserted as a cassette to replace the polyhedrin gene. In the original system, a pair of selectable markers was used, allowing the power of yeast genetics to be applied to vector selection. One marker was used for positive selection of transformed cells, while the other was used for counterselection against nonrecombinant vectors. The *SUP4-o* marker was initially used for counterselection. This is a nonsense suppressor that, in the particular yeast strain used, confers sensitivity to the arginine analog canavanine and the ability to grow in media lacking adenine. Removal of the marker by replacement with homologous DNA confers resistance to canavanine and a requirement for adenine. Plasmid DNA isolated from canavanine-resistant, adenine-requiring yeast cultures was used to transfect insect cells and produce pure recombinant baculovirus. In both bacteria and yeast, the maintenance sequences (origin of replication/centromere and positive selection marker) must stay in the recombinant baculovirus vector. They have been shown to have no effect on baculovirus replication or gene expression in insect cells.

Herpes Virus Vectors

Overview. Herpes viruses are large, enveloped viruses with linear, double-stranded DNA genomes varying from 100 to 200 kbp in size. Different herpes viruses differ considerably in their host range and cell tropism. Furthermore, while some cell types undergo only lytic infection, others are also permissive for latent infection, resulting in long-term episomal maintenance of the viral genome. Of the eight known types of human herpesvirus, two have been extensively developed as vectors (51,123). The first, Epstein–Barr virus, has already been discussed. EBV has a narrow host range, and its cell tropism is limited to B-lymphocytes and nasopharyngeal cells displaying the appropriate receptor. Cultured lymphocytes tend to undergo latent viral infection, but many other cell types are also permissive for latent EBV replication following the transfection of naked viral DNA. Hence, the major use of EBV has been the development of episomal plasmid

vectors for transfection (51). Conversely, the human herpes simplex viruses (HSV-I and HSV-II) have a broad host range and cellular tropism because they interact with a near-ubiquitous cell surface molecule. Many cell types therefore undergo lytic HSV infection, while neurons also undergo latent infection. HSV vectors have thus been developed both for short-term foreign gene expression in many cell types, and for long-term foreign gene expression in neurons (123–126). The vectors show great potential for gene therapy applications, especially genetic intervention in the brain (124). The major advantages of HSV vectors are their broad host range and tropism, their natural ability to cause latent infection of neurons, and their large capacity: Up to 50 kbp of foreign DNA can be incorporated, which may comprise multiple genes.

Molecular Biology of HSV-1. HSV-1 has a broad host range and cell tropism because it interacts with ubiquitous heparan sulfate molecules on the surface of target cells (127). The viral genome is linear, but after release from the nucleocapsid it gains entry to the nucleus and immediately circularizes. The capsid also contains a virion host shutoff protein (VHS) that interrupts host protein synthesis, and a transcriptional activator termed VP16. During lytic infection, VP16 forms a dimer with the host transcription factor Oct-1 and induces the expression of the five viral immediate early genes, $\alpha 0$, $\alpha 4$, $\alpha 22$, $\alpha 27$, and $\alpha 47$. The immediate early genes are all essential for lytic replication. These encode further regulators that act both on their own genes (in a self-regulatory manner) and upon a set of approximately 15 early genes controlling DNA replication. Following replication, approximately 40 late genes are activated, which encode DNA cleavage and packaging proteins and capsid proteins. Progeny genomes are then packaged into virions and transported to the cell surface, where lysis occurs (127).

Lytic infection occurs in many different cell types, but latency is restricted mostly to neurons (127). The switch to latency is thought to reflect the balance of host- and virus-encoded transcriptional regulators in the cell. The immediate early genes are not expressed, and viral activity is restricted to a 152-kbp genomic region that overlaps the $\alpha 0$ immediate early gene in the antisense orientation. This region encodes a set of latency-associated transcripts (LATs). The LATs are also synthesized during lytic infection, although no protein products have been detected (even though LATs are associated with ribosomes). During latency, the LATs remain in the nucleus. The LATs are neither required for the establishment of latency, nor its maintenance, but they are required for reactivation of the lytic cycle.

Strategies for HSV Vector Construction. HSV has a large genome, and one simple strategy for generating recombinant HSV vectors is to transfect HSV-infected cells with a targeting vector containing a foreign gene within a viral homology region (101,124). Several HSV genes are nonessential for productive infection and can be replaced with foreign DNA. The resulting viruses are replication competent and infectious. For approaches such as gene therapy, however, HSV vectors must be replication defective. Several derivatives of HSV are now available that carry deletions in one or more of the immediate early genes, and such vectors must be propagated in a complementing cell line or in the presence of a cotransfected helper plasmid. The deletion of immediate early genes is also beneficial because their products are toxic to the host cell. HSV amplicon vectors are also widely used (101,124–126). These comprise the HSV origin of replication and genome packaging site cloned in a plasmid vector along with a mammalian transcription unit. All viral genes are deleted, leaving a vector that can only be packaged in the presence of a helper virus supplying the many missing functions in *trans*. Wild-type HSV-1 can be used to supply helper functions, but the wild-type virus often causes lytic infections, resulting in rapid cell death both in vitro and in live animals. A number of HSV-1 mutants have been developed as helper viruses, as these are nonpermissive for lytic replication (but still induce latent infection when introduced into cultured neurons or injected into the brain). Initially, a temperature-sensitive mutant was used carrying a point mutation in one of the immediate early genes. This was conditionally defective, inducing latent infections in the brain and in cultured neurons at 37 °C but lytic infections at 31 °C. Unfortunately, its applicability was limited by a significant reversion frequency, resulting in the induction of lytic infections. More recently, defective helper viruses with deletions in one or more of the immediate early genes have been used, providing complementary packaging lines to produce infective recombinant particles. In some cases, the reversion frequency has been reduced to 10^{-7}.

HSV Vectors for Prolonged Transgene Expression in Neurons. Due to their ability to cause long-term latent infection of neurons, the major use of HSV-1-derived vectors has been for gene transfer to neurons either in vitro or in the central nervous system of living animals (124–126). Traditionally, neurons have been a difficult gene transfer target because they are postmitotic, and many transfection and viral transduction systems require rapidly dividing cells. The in vitro transfection of neurons often yields poor results due to limited uptake as well as the standard problems associated with position and dosage effects. HSV-1 vectors possess a number of advantages for gene transfer to neurons, including efficient DNA transfer, a large genome size permitting the transduction of large segments of foreign DNA, and long-term episomal maintenance without viral gene expression. This later property ensures that during latent infection, the host cell physiology is unaffected — in fact, it is thought that most of the human population carries latent herpes virus infections in the absence of disease symptoms. The effect of foreign gene expression can therefore be studied without considering the background effects of viral gene activity.

The original HSV-1 amplicon vector, pHSVlac, carried the *lacZ* reporter gene under the control of the constitutive HSV IE4/5 promoter (125). This vector carried plasmid backbone sequences for maintenance in *E. coli*, the latent HSV origin of replication (*oriS*) facilitating replication and maintenance as an episomal vector in mammalian cells, the HSV **a** site required for genome packaging, and

a mammalian transcription unit comprising a promoter, intron, *lacZ* gene, and SV40 polyadenylation site. No viral genes were included, and the only viral sequences present were those *cis*-acting elements required for maintenance and packaging. This vector could be established in neurons following transfection, but as discussed, neuronal transfection is inefficient. The strategy was therefore to package the amplicon vector in viral capsids and use these to infect neurons. Several packaging strategies (using wild-type HSV, conditional mutant HSV, and deletion-mutant HSV helper viruses) have been discussed previously.

Vectors based on pHSVlac have been used to transfer many genes into neurons, including reporter genes, and genes encoding growth factors and their receptors, signal transduction components, and neurotransmitters (125,126). This strategy can be used both for therapeutic intervention and for the experimental study of cell function, for example, through the introduction of novel heterologous genes, the overexpression or constitutive expression of endogenous genes, the expression of dominant negative proteins to generate loss of function effects, and the use of toxins to ablate particular cells. Generally, it has been found that in vivo transfer results in relatively long-term foreign gene expression (two weeks or more) with transformed cells restricted to those surrounding the injection site and more distant cells whose axons project into the site. The duration of transgene expression is strongly influenced by promoter choice. The number of infected cells is influenced by the extent of virion diffusion from the site of injection, and the titer of the innoculum. As discussed, HSV has a broad cell tropism and will infect glia and other nonneuronal cells as well as neurons. There have been a number of successful attempts to restrict the expression of foreign genes carried in HSV vectors using cell-type-specific promoters, such as the neurofilament L promoter, which is panneuronal, and the tyrosine hydroxylase promoter, whose activity is restricted to catecholaminergic neurons. Reporter genes driven by the IE1, IE3, and IE4/5 promoters have been shown to be active for up to 10 weeks in cultured sensory neurons.

The defective HSV-1 vectors described provide a system for therapeutic gene transfer to neurons, which could be used to treat a variety of neurophysiological disorders (124). A number of potentially therapeutic genes have been cloned in this type of vector including tyrosine hydroxylase for the treatment of Parkinson's disease, nerve growth factor for the treatment of Alzheimer's disease, and brain-derived neurotropic factor for potential repair of neuronal damage. Generally, transgene expression was detected for about two weeks following infection under the control of the IE4/5 promoter or other constitutive promoter. The rat brain glucose transporter cDNA has been introduced into the hippocampus of rats by stereotactic injection of HSV amplicon vectors, and has successfully reduced neuron loss following kainic acid–induced seizures. However, foreign gene expression was observed for only a few days. Conversely, in a rat Parkinson's disease model, the transfer of tyrosine hydroxylase cDNA in a vector derived from pHSVlac resulted in long-term (>1 year) behavioral recovery.

HSV Vectors for Transient Expression in Nonneuronal Cells. The wide cell tropism of HSV provides an opening for its development as a gene delivery and expression vector for many cell types in addition to neurons. Miyanohara and colleagues (128) carried out successful gene transfer to liver by injecting recombinant herpes virus vectors both directly into the organ and into the portal vein. Although liver cells do not support latent HSV replication, HSV-mediated gene transfer to nonneuronal cells allows short-term recombinant protein expression, which may be sufficient for short-term or repetitive gene therapy, for example, the expression of canine factor IX in liver as a potential therapeutic treatment for hemophilia B. The restriction of HSV-mediated transgene expression to short duration would be an advantage in cancer therapy, as shown by the treatment of experimental glioma by delivering HSV vectors expressing thymidine kinase, allowing infected dividing cells to be killed by treatment with gancyclovir (129).

Retrovirus Vectors

Overview. Retroviruses are RNA viruses whose unusual replication strategy includes reverse transcription of the RNA genome to generate a terminally redundant double-stranded cDNA copy, which integrates into the host genome in a semirandom manner (131). Progeny virions are produced by transcription of the provirus to yield both daughter viral genomes and subgenomic mRNAs encoding enzymes and structural proteins of the viral capsid. The host range and cell specificity of a particular retrovirus species is determined primarily by the envelope proteins, which interact with cell-surface receptors. The envelope proteins of amphotropic murine leukemia virus (MLV) are particularly promiscuous, so this virus has a broad host range and cell tropism and has been extensively developed as a vector for gene transfer to mammalian cells (132–134). Other retroviruses with more limited cellular tropism (including the human immunodeficiency virus, HIV) are also used as vectors for specific experimental purposes. Retroviruses infect a wide variety of vertebrates, and infection is usually nonlethal (HIV is an exception).

The retroviruses are an obvious choice for vector development, first, because of their natural ability to integrate DNA into the host genome, and second, because some, known as *acute transforming retroviruses*, demonstrate the inherent ability to transduce and express foreign genes. Over 100 acute transforming retroviruses have been described, leading to the discovery of many oncogenes, including those encoding growth factors and their receptors, signal transduction proteins, cell cycle regulators, and transcription factors. In many cases, the viral oncogene is fused to another viral gene so that it is expressed as a fusion protein. If this was an obligatory expression strategy, the construction of recombinant retroviral vectors could be very cumbersome. However, certain retroviruses contain oncogenes whose translation is initiated at a unique start codon (e.g., v-*src* in Rous sarcoma virus), and others carry two oncogenes (e.g., v-*erbA* and the unrelated v-*erbB* in avian erythroblastosis virus), suggesting that a number of alternative transgene integration strategies could be used. Retroviruses are attractive potential vectors for many reasons (132,133). First, their small genome is no more difficult to manipulate in vitro than a standard plasmid vector. Second, they can be propagated to high titers (10^6–10^8 pfu ml^{-1}) using appropriate packaging lines. Third, they contain a strong promoter–enhancer complex that can drive high-level transgene expression in many cell types. In all naturally occurring acute transforming retroviruses, oncogenes are driven from these LTR promoter–enhancer complexes, but transgenes can also be driven by their own promoters or by heterologous promoters from within the retroviral vector. Fourth, the efficiency of infection in vitro can approach 100%. Finally, retroviral integration produces stably transduced cell lines that can express foreign genes on a long-term basis — this makes them particularly suitable for gene therapy (135). The first successful report of human gene therapy, the correction of severe combined immunodeficiency (SCID) by transferring adenosine deaminase (*ADA*) cDNA to cultured hemopoietic stem cells or T-lymphocytes, involved the use of retroviral vectors (136). Similarly, retroviruses can be used for in vivo gene transfer simply by injecting recombinant vectors at the appropriate site. A similar concept involves the injection of retroviral vectors into embryos to generate chimeric embryos for the study of cellular interactions during development (137). One area in which this approach has been particularly useful is the study of limb development, where several discrete tissues produce signals that interact to cause limb bud growth and morphogenesis along three axes. The transfer of MLV vectors to mouse embryos in utero is possible, but many limb development experiments have been carried out in chickens by introducing concentrated recombinant Rous sarcoma virus (RSV) vectors into cultured chicken embryos, or chicken embryos in ovo. Another role for retroviral gene transfer in development is the analysis of cell lineage. In this case, recombinant vectors carrying reporter genes such as *lacZ* or *GFP* are introduced into embryos at a lower concentration so that individual cells are transduced. Since the proviral DNA is replicated along with the host chromosome, all descendants of that transduced cell express the reporter, allowing the lineage of the original transduced cell to be traced. Retroviral vectors are not used just to generate chimeric animals. Fully transgenic animals can also be produced (138) by retroviral infection of ES cells or preimplantation embryos, followed by the rearing of chimeric animals from which transgenics can be bred (the generation of transgenic animals is discussed in more detail later). Finally, the use of transposons and transfected foreign DNA as insertional mutagens and entrapment vectors was discussed earlier. Since retroviruses are also transposable elements, retroviral vectors can be used as insertional mutagens. If the appropriate vector components are included, retroviruses can also be used as entrapment vectors, and flanking sequences can be isolated by plasmid rescue (14).

Molecular Biology of the Retroviruses. Retroviral genome organization is simple and highly conserved between species (131) [Fig. 8(a)]. The integrated provirus comprises three major open reading frames (*gag*, *pol*, and *env*) bracketed by tripartite direct long terminal repeats

(LTRs). A single promoter located in the left LTR is used to transcribe genomic RNA. The *gag* region encodes viral structural proteins (*group antigen*), the *pol* region encodes reverse transcriptase (*polymerase*), integrase and protease, and the *env* region encodes viral *envelope* proteins. The full-length RNA is translated to yield two polypeptides, Gag and Gag-Pol, the latter by occasional programmed read-through of the *gag* termination codon. The full-length RNA also undergoes splicing to eliminate the *gag* and *pol* regions. The splice product is translated to generate the Env polypeptide. The protease encoded by the *pol* region (or occasionally the *gag* region, depending on the virus) cleaves the major gene products to yield approximately 10 mature polypeptides.

The retroviral infection cycle begins by uptake of virions through interaction between virus envelope proteins and the appropriate cell surface receptors (131). The capsid contains two copies of the RNA genome (i.e., it is diploid) as well as reverse transcriptase. Since the packaged RNA genome is transcribed from an integrated proviral cDNA using a promoter within the left LTR and a polyadenylation site within the right LTR, the free genome is truncated at both ends compared to the provirus, and lacks its characteristic LTR structure. Early in the replication cycle, the RNA genome is copied to generate a double-stranded cDNA replica, in a complex process involving two template jumps. It is this process that generates the LTRs. The cDNA genome, complete with redundant LTRs, is integrated into the host DNA using viral integrase in a process reminiscent of the transposition of simple "cut and paste" transposons. It is then transcribed to generate progeny genomes and mRNAs for translation. Mature viral proteins assemble with the genomic RNAs to form new virions. A specific *cis*-acting packaging site termed ψ is required for this association.

Construction of Recombinant Retroviral Vectors. Most retroviral vectors are replication defective. Several replication-competent vectors have been developed, but they have a limited insert size and most important, they allow the spread of vector DNA throughout the host genome following infection, a consequence that is usually undesirable (132–134). Most naturally occurring acute transforming retroviruses are also replication defective, because the viral oncogene replaces an essential viral function. They require superinfection with a wild-type virus to replicate successfully in the host. An exception is Rous sarcoma virus, which carries the v-*src* oncogene in addition to the entire viral genome. Replication-competent RSV vectors have been developed in which the v-*src* gene is replaced by foreign DNA. These vectors infect avian cells efficiently, but not mammalian cells, unless they have been modified to express the appropriate heterologous receptor. For mammalian cells, replication-competent vectors based on Moloney murine leukemia virus (MoMLV) have also been developed.

Replication-defective vectors are generally amplicons, with most of the viral coding region replaced by foreign DNA [Fig. 8(b)]. Such vectors can be propagated only in the presence of helper functions, either using a replication-competent helper virus or a packaging cell line (132–134).

The use of helper viruses results in the production of recombinant vector contaminated with the helper virus itself. Packaging cell lines are therefore more suitable for the production of pure, infectious viral particles capable of reverse transcription and integration, but not of further replication. A range of different packaging lines has been developed, differing in the parental virus used to create the line, and the extent to which the helper virus genome has been modified and rearranged. The former property determines the host range of the recombinant vector because it specifies the type of envelope protein inserted into the virion envelope. The most promiscuous vectors are generated using packaging lines derived from amphotropic viruses such as MLV. Many alternative packaging lines are available, which allow the tailoring of vector host range for particular experimental strategies. The latter property determines the extent to which replication-competent viruses are generated by recombination. The most efficient lines contain helper viruses with genomes modified and rearranged to (1) limit the extent of homologous sequence shared between the helper virus and the vector and (2) increase the number of independent crossover events required to form a replication-competent genome. One of the most efficient lines in this category is GP + E-86 (139), which contains split coding regions, point mutations, and deletions, and hence requires three independent recombination events to generate a replication-competent virus.

Various strategies have been used to express foreign genes in retroviral vectors (132,133,136). The simplest strategy, which is used to express single genes, is to remove all coding sequences and place the foreign gene between the LTR promoter and the viral polyadenylation site. This results in the high-level constitutive production of a single RNA encoding the foreign protein, and is useful where the aim of the experiment is to synthesize large amounts of protein. However, if a specific expression pattern is required, an internal heterologous promoter can be inserted as part of the transgene. A difficulty with vectors containing internal heterologous promoters (non-LTR promoters) is that the LTR regulatory elements can either positively or negatively affect internal transcription. This problem has been circumvented by the development of *self-inactivating* or *suicide retroviral vectors* (140), with deletions in the 3′ LTR. A mutation in the 3′ LTR is copied to the 5′ LTR during the subsequent round of vector replication, resulting in a virus with inactive LTR promoter and/or enhancer elements, but functional internal promoters. An additional advantage to these vectors is that ectopic activation of endogenous genes adjacent to the integration site is also avoided.

Selectable markers can be used to identify stably transduced cells, and it is therefore desirable to express two genes, the foreign gene and the marker, in the same vector. Many of the selectable markers listed in Table 4 have been used in retroviral vectors. The dominant markers *neo*, *hpt*, *Dhfr*, and *gpt* can be used in any cells, but *Hprt* and *Tk* require gene transfer to *hprt⁻* or *tk⁻* cell lines. The expression of two (or more) genes can be achieved in a number of ways [Fig. 8(b)]. An internal promoter can be used so that there are two independent transcription units

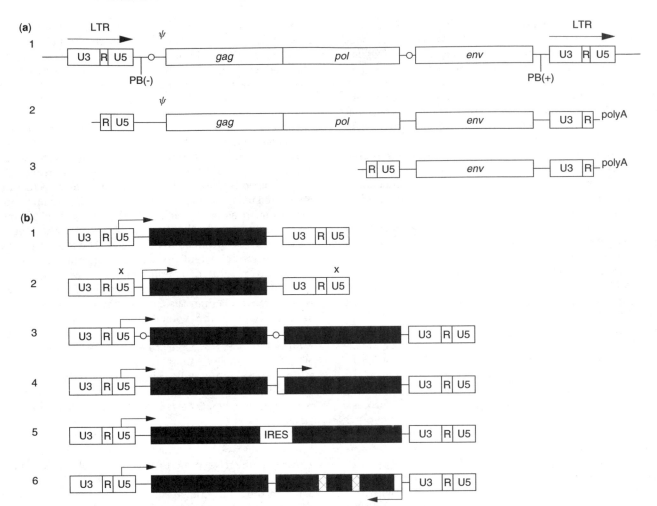

Figure 8. (a) Structure of a typical retrovirus genome and its transcripts. (*1*) The proviral genome is flanked by long terminal direct repeats and has three open reading frames, *gag*, *pol*, and *env*. The sites marked PB are primer binding sites, where genome replication is initiated. ψ is the packaging site. (*2*) The U5 region contains a promoter–enhancer complex that stimulates genomic transcription. The R region contains a polyA site. The maximum transcript thus lacks terminal U3 and U5 elements, which are regenerated during cDNA synthesis. (*3*) Splicing between acceptor and donor sites (shown as circles in *1*) generates a subgenomic transcript enabling translation of the *env* coding region. (b) Structure of recombinant retroviral vectors (black bar is foreign gene). (*1*) Simple vector with transgene driven by LTR promoter. (*2*) Vector with transgene driven by an internal heterologous promoter. Such a vector may carry a mutation in the U5 region (x) that abolishes LTR promoter activity. (*3*) Double gene vector where each gene is driven by the LTR promoter by splicing. (*4*) Double gene vector with gene 1 driven by a LTR promoter and gene 2 by its own promoter. (*5*) Double gene vector with the downstream gene under the control of an internal ribosome entry site. (*6*) Double gene vector where one transgene contains introns. The intronless transgene is controlled by the LTR promoter, and the other gene is inverted and controlled by an internal promoter.

within the virus. Alternatively, the vector can be modeled on the splicing pattern of a wild-type virus, so that full-length and spliced transcripts are produced. In both cases, it is essential to allow full-length RNAs to be produced from the recombinant genome in the packaging line; so it is important not to include a polyadenylation site at the end of the first gene, which could terminate (replicative) transcription and result in loss of the second gene. In two-promoter vectors, the lack of a polyadenylation site for the upstream gene can result in read-through transcription and occlusion of the second promoter. This

can be alleviated by placing the two genes in opposite orientations, so that the (reversed) polyadenylation site of the transgene is not recognized during full-genome transcription. For alternative splicing vectors, the possible existence of cryptic splice sites the upstream gene should be considered. Multiple gene expression with LTR-based, internal promoter-based, and alternative splicing vectors can also be achieved by using internal ribosome entry sites. Although the open reading frame downstream of the IRES is usually translated less efficiently than that using the more typical 5′ cap ribosome loading mechanism, it is certainly efficient enough for marker-based selection and reporter-based visible screening.

The interference of introns and polyadenylation signals with the virus replication cycle places certain limitations on the type of sequence that can be expressed in retroviral vectors. cDNAs are the simplest sequences to express because they can be inserted in the same orientation as the viral transcription unit (or they can be reversed with respect to the promoter, to generate antisense RNA). Genes are more difficult to express, because the introns and polyadenylation signals may interfere with viral replication and RNA processing. If full, intron-containing genes must be expressed, they need to be placed under the control of an internal promoter, and the whole expression cassette has to be reversed in orientation. This allows intron recognition and splicing (and hence normal translation) from the reversed internal promoter, but prevents the introns being spliced during forward, full genome transcription. The alternative strategy is to remove the introns artificially and insert an intronless minigene into the vector in the forward orientation. Virus titer is reduced by the inclusion of an endogenous polyadenylation site at the end of the intronless minigene, but only by 5–10-fold; so infection is still productive.

Recombinant retroviral vectors for mammalian cells are constructed using cloned retrovirus cDNA, containing the essential *cis*-acting sites for the retroviral life cycle, but lacking the *gag*, *pol*, and *env* genes whose products can be supplied in *trans*. The essential elements for high-titer virus production are the LTRs, primer binding sites, and the packaging site ψ. Importantly, it has been determined that the ψ site, originally defined as a noncoding sequence 5′ to the *gag* open reading frame, actually extends into the *gag* coding region. Contemporary retroviral vectors therefore include this entire sequence (ψ^+) to ensure high titer.

SV40 Vectors

SV40-derived transduction vectors are rarely if ever used these days; hence this section provides only a brief summary of their properties (130). As discussed earlier, SV40 is a polyomavirus that infects certain monkey cells. It has a small, icosahedral capsid, and a circular, double-stranded DNA genome approximately 5 kbp in size. SV40 was the first animal virus to be characterized in detail at the molecular/genetic level, and was hence the first to be developed as a vector.

SV40 lytic infections in monkey cells can be divided into three stages. First, there is a latent stage, where the virus genome is uncoated and transported to the nucleus. This is followed by an "early stage" where early viral genes are expressed and host cell DNA synthesis is stimulated. Finally, in the late stage, the viral genome itself is replicated and progeny genomes are packaged. The host cell is then lysed and progeny virions are released. The SV40 genome has two transcription units known as the early and late regions, which have opposite polarities. The transcriptional start sites are located close together, facing outward, and are separated by a complex regulatory region containing early and late promoters, an enhancer, and the SV40 origin of replication. Both transcription units encode single transcripts that are differentially spliced to yield multiple products. The early transcript produces two mature mRNAs encoding the large T- and small t-antigens (tumor antigens), involved in replication and transcriptional control. The T-antigen is essential for viral replication and must be supplied in *trans* to SV40-derived vectors lacking this function. Additionally, the T-antigen also plays a major role in the stimulation of host DNA synthesis by interfering with the regulation of the cell cycle. Hence, cells such as COS-7, which express T-antigen constitutively, are transformed into a continuously proliferating state. The late transcript produces three partially overlapping mRNAs that encode the major coat protein VP1, and the minor coat proteins VP2 and VP3.

In the first SV40 vectors, either the entire early region or the entire late region could be replaced by foreign DNA. Since both regions are essential for viral propagation, missing functions had to be supplied in *trans*. This initially involved coinfection with a helper virus, until the development of the complementary COS cell lines carrying a defective integrated SV40 genome. Such cell lines allowed the propagation of "early replacement" vectors by supplying T-antigen in *trans*. Many recombinant proteins have been produced in CV-1 or COS cells infected with SV40 vectors (reviewed in Ref. 130), but they suffer two serious drawbacks, which have limited their use. First, they have a restricted host range (certain permissive monkey cells, such as CV-1 and its derivatives), and most important, the maximum insert size is limited to 2.5 kbp, due to the capacity of the capsid. Such vectors have become more or less obsolete with the discovery that plasmids carrying the SV40 origin of replication can be propagated in just the same way as the virus, but without any limit to the insert size. The improvement of transfection procedures has also made transfection with SV40 replicons almost as efficient as infection by the virus itself.

Vaccinia and Other Poxvirus Vectors

Overview. The poxviruses comprise a large family of DNA viruses, with a complex architecture, a genome size ranging from 1 to 300 kbp, and a host range including vertebrates and invertebrates (141). The most unusual aspect of this DNA virus family is the cytoplasmic site of replication, which means that the virus must encode and package all the enzymes required for replication and transcription. The best-known poxvirus is undoubtedly variola virus, the agent responsible for smallpox. Edward Jenner showed that smallpox could be prevented by immunization with a related virus responsible for the milder infection known as cowpox. Later, worldwide immunization with vaccinia virus (related to variola and cowpox viruses) led to the eventual elimination of smallpox as an infectious disease. Much interest was therefore generated by the potential use of recombinant vaccinia vectors, carrying genes from other infectious microorganisms, as live vaccines. Vaccinia virus has been used to express several heterologous viral proteins in mammals, including influenza virus hemagglutinin, hepatitis B surface antigen and HIV envelope protein, and canarypox virus vectors are currently undergoing clinical trials for vaccination of humans (142). Apart from this focused area of application, poxviruses represent a generally advantageous transient expression system due to the wide host range, strong expression levels, and cytoplasmic transcription (143).

Molecular Biology of Vaccinia Virus. Vaccinia virus has a complex structure comprising a central core (containing about 100 proteins) and a lipid envelope derived from the Golgi apparatus (containing a further number of unique viral proteins). The envelope is essential for infection and (in vitro) plaque formation, and virions containing the envelope are termed *extracellular enveloped viruses* (143). The majority of infectious particles, however, exist as intracellular naked viruses in the cytoplasm. The vaccinia virus genome is double-stranded linear DNA, although the ends of the DNA strands are sealed by hairpins. The genes of the vaccinia virus genome can be divided into four temporal classes: constant, immediate, intermediate, and late. The constant and immediate genes are expressed as infection begins, using the viral RNA polymerase carried in the virion. The immediate genes encode enzymes and other proteins required for replication and exposure of the genome. Expression of most of the immediate and intermediate genes is mutually exclusive; hence when intermediate gene expression commences after replication, immediate gene expression ceases. The intermediate genes encode, among other products, late gene transcriptional regulators. The constant genes have both early and late promoters and are hence expressed throughout the infection cycle. The late genes encode packaging proteins, capsid components, and enzymes that are carried in the virion and used immediately after infection.

Construction of Recombinant Vaccinia Virus Expression Vectors. Vaccinia virus is simple to grow because of its broad host range, including both established cell lines and primary cells. However, the efficiency of plating varies according to cell type. The large genome size and unusual replication strategy represent major obstacles to the design and construction of expression vectors (143). The genome is too large to manipulate in vitro, and because the virus normally carries its own replication and transcription machinery into the cell, recombinant genomes introduced into the cell by transfection are not infectious. Although it is now possible to generate infectious recombinant genomes (142), the strategy of choice is to transfect virus-infected cells with targeting vectors carrying a vaccinia promoter/foreign gene expression unit within a vaccinia homology region, allowing the insertion of foreign DNA by homologous recombination (141,143).

Since poxviruses encode their own transcriptional apparatus to allow cytoplasmic transcription, endogenous poxvirus promoters must be used to drive the expression of foreign genes, at least in simple vectors. A number of vaccinia promoters have been used, and the gene expression parameters depend upon whether early, late, or constant promoters are chosen (141,143). Early expression may be desirable to avoid the cytopathic effects of the virus, but the highest levels of transcription are provided by late promoters. The P11 promoter is extensively used, and can generate over $1\,\mu g$ of protein per 10^6 cells. The constant promoter P7.5 is not quite as active as P11, but allows transcription throughout the replication cycle and is the most widely used of all. The vaccinia virus early transcriptional apparatus uses a specific transcriptional termination signal with the consensus sequence TTTTTNT; so it is advisable to eliminate such motifs within foreign genes to prevent possible truncation. It is also notable that, due to cytoplasmic transcription, vaccinia virus contains no introns and cannot splice introns present in foreign genes. Therefore, vaccinia vectors must be used to express cDNA sequences, or minigenes with introns artificially removed. Higher levels of foreign gene expression can be achieved using a hybrid expression system in which the transgene is driven by the bacteriophage T7 promoter, and the T7 RNA polymerase is expressed from a second vector (144). High-level transient expression can be achieved if the T7-expressing vector is a plasmid, transiently present in the cell following transfection. More prolonged expression is achieved by incorporating the T7 gene under the control of a vaccinia promoter in a second recombinant virus vector. For toxic proteins, inducible expression systems have also been designed. One example incorporates a strong vaccinia promoter, such as 4b, combined with the *lac* operator sequence from *E. coli*. The foreign gene is coexpressed with *E. coli lacI*, encoding the Lac repressor, allowing foreign gene expression to be regulated by IPTG (inducible expression systems are discussed in detail later).

Vaccinia forms large plaques on permissive cells, and these can be lifted onto nitrocellulose or nylon filters and subjected to hybridization-based screening for the foreign gene. The efficiency of screening is enhanced by various selection strategies, which depend on the site of insertion. Negative TK selection is used where the foreign gene is inserted into the viral *Tk* locus: tk^- viruses are resistant to the normally lethal effects of 5-bromodeoxyuridine and can be selected on this basis, although naturally occurring tk^- mutants are coselected and true recombinants must still be identified by hybridization. Negative HA selection is used where the foreign gene is inserted into the viral hemagglutinin locus: When chicken erythrocytes are added to the plate, HA- plaques are clear, whereas wild-type plaques are red. Selection can also be accomplished by cotransfer of a dominant selectable marker such as *neo* or *gpt*, or a visible marker such as *lacZ*. The latter is a popular screening method: recombinant plaques become blue when incubated in the presence of X-gal, while parental plaques remain clear.

Hybrid Viral Vectors

As discussed, individual viruses have certain advantages and disadvantages as vectors, and none is suitable for all applications (101). For instance, herpes virus and adenovirus each has a broad host range, and herpes virus in particular has a large capacity, but neither integrates efficiently into the host genome. Conversely, while AAV integrates with great efficiency, it has a limited capacity. Recently, there has been an effort to design customized hybrid viral vectors with selected advantageous properties from each of the component viruses. Although in its infancy, this is one direction in which the field of vector development could expand in the next few years, providing novel and superior vectors for specific applications, especially in the field of gene therapy (101). Using the example given, a herpes simplex virus vector carrying inducible AAV *rep* functions could be used to carry recombinant AAV into a broad range of cells, facilitating transfer of the AAV passenger to the genome. The advantage of this strategy is that the AAV genome does not need to be packaged, and there would therefore be no size constraints on the foreign DNA it could carry.

EXPRESSION PARAMETERS AND OPTIMIZATION — VECTOR AND INSERT SEQUENCES

We turn now to an examination of the parameters that influence foreign gene expression in animal cells. As discussed, the aims and limitations of the experiment dictate whether it is appropriate to maximize the expression of foreign DNA or to place it under some type of exogenous control. Sequences in the vector and the insert play a major role in the regulation of foreign gene expression at all levels (transcription, RNA processing, translation, and beyond), and to a large degree, the effect of such sequences is predictable. Much less predicable is the influence of the cellular environment, particularly upon integrated transgenes, which are subject to position and dosage effects, and also to variations in the level of DNA methylation.

Transcriptional Initiation: Promoters and Enhancers. Transcriptional initiation is the rate-limiting step in the expression of most higher eukaryotic genes. Control is mediated by *cis*-acting DNA elements that act as binding sites for *trans*-acting regulators termed *transcription factors*. Transcription factors can act positively or negatively and function in one of three ways: (*1*) by directly interacting with the basal transcriptional apparatus whose function is to recruit RNA polymerase, and thus either stimulating or inhibiting the recruitment of basal components, or influencing the stability of the initiation complex; (*2*) by affecting chromatin structure or DNA conformation, for example, by displacing a nucleosome or by introducing a kink in the DNA; or (*3*) indirectly, by influencing the activity of a second transcription factor.

In animals, many genes are expressed in complex spatial, temporal, and inducible patterns. The manner in which a particular gene is transcribed depends on the combination of *cis*-acting recognition sequences controlling it, and the availability of functional transcription factors in the cell (reviewed in Ref. 145). Most genes are controlled by at least two functionally distinct elements: a *promoter*, which is located at the 5' side of the gene and directly interacts with the initiation complex, and an *enhancer*, which may be located some distance away and interacts with the initiation complex by looping out of the intervening DNA. The promoter is minimally the sequence where RNA polymerase is loaded, and usually consists of an *initiator element* surrounding the transcriptional start site, and/or a motif termed the *TATA box* located about 25 bp upstream of the start site. The initiator and TATA box are not present in all promoters, but when they are present, they are found in the same orientation and on the same strand. Promoters lacking an initiator element typically have multiple start sites because RNA polymerase is not loaded at a unique position. Further motifs are located 5' to this *basal promoter*, and comprise the *upstream promoter elements*. These include (*1*) the CAAT box, GC-rich boxes, and other elements, which act as binding sites for ubiquitous transcriptional activators; (*2*) motifs that bind transcription factors synthesized or activated only in certain cell types and/or at certain developmental stages and hence control the cell type and stage specificity of gene expression; and (*3*) response elements that bind transcription factors whose activity is inducible or repressible by endogenous and exogenous signals. Similarly, enhancers are modular units made up of different motifs, some of which may act generally, and some of which may confer cell-type, temporal, or inducible specificity upon the gene. Promoters control basal transcription and are therefore orientated so that transcription proceeds in one direction only. Conversely, enhancers act to stimulate transcription from a promoter but, because they cannot load RNA polymerase, they have very little promoter activity themselves. Enhancers act in a position-, orientation-, and distance-independent manner, and may stimulate transcription up to 1000-fold from a given promoter.

Endogenous Promoters and Constitutive Viral Promoters. In the first gene transfer experiments, mammalian transgenes were expressed under the control of their own poorly characterized transcriptional control sequences. Even as mammalian regulatory elements began to be defined, the use of endogenous promoters continued to impose severe limitations on the range of cells in which foreign genes could be expressed. The rate of recombinant protein expression was wholly dependent on the ability of the cell line chosen to recognize and utilize particular promoters and enhancers (20).

The cloning of viral regulatory elements was a breakthrough in gene expression technology. The evolutionary success of viral promoters and enhancers is evident from the (in some cases) copious production of virus proteins in infected cells. Hence, foreign genes cloned in recombinant viral vectors are often expressed under the control of the most active promoters and enhancers from that viral system, especially as this often represents the most convenient cloning strategy. Examples include the baculovirus polyhedrin and p10 promoters (119), the adenoviral E1 promoter (102), and the vaccinia virus p7.5 promoter (141). The most promiscuous regulatory elements are found in viruses, because viruses have evolved to infect and propagate within a broad range of cells. Many plasmid overexpression vectors therefore employ the most generic and transcriptionally active promoter/enhancer systems, which consequently not only maximize the transcription of the cloned gene, but also allow expression in a broad range of transfected cells. The most popular systems are the SV40 early promoter and enhancer (146), the Rous sarcoma virus long terminal repeat promoter and enhancer (147), and the human cytomegalovirus immediate early promoter (148). These elements function in a broader range of cells than that defined by the productive host range of the viruses themselves, because although a virus may not be able to gain entry into all cells due to a lack of appropriate surface receptors, the transcriptional control elements have often evolved to exploit transcription factors present in many cells, generally including those outside the specified host range. Hence, while the replication of SV40 is restricted to certain simian cells, the SV40 promoter/enhancer functions in most mammalian cells. The constitutive systems are not absolutely equivalent, however, and it pays to identify the most suitable regulatory system to use in a particular cell type. Certain cells appear to repress transcription from particular viral promoters; for example, the human embryonic kidney cell line 293, which is widely exploited for propagation of adenoviral vectors, does not support transcription from the SV40 promoter (149).

Although viral promoters have been used in versatile expression vectors, the advent of transgenic technology and gene transfer to live organisms has resulted in a new requirement for cell- and stage-specific promoters to restrict transgene expression to particular cell types. Examples include the use of cell-specific promoters to ablate particular cell types, the use of milk promoters to obtain high yields of recombinant protein in the milk of transgenic mice and livestock, and the use of neuron-specific promoters to ensure that herpes virus vectors delivered to the brain express transgenes only in neurons, and not in glial or epithelial cells.

Endogenous Inducible Promoters. While high-level constitutive protein expression may be suitable for many applications, there are certain situations where the external control of transgene expression is desirable. Where protein overexpression is the aim, external control is required if the recombinant protein is potentially cytotoxic or cytostatic. Furthermore, many experiments require transgenes to be activated at a certain time or for a certain duration, for example, in studies of the cell cycle, to study the effects of transgene expression at particular stages of development, or for the conditional silencing of transgenes or endogenous genes to investigate the consequences of gene loss at particular developmental stages.

The earliest experiments involving external transgene regulation took advantage of endogenous inducible systems (reviewed in Ref. 150). The best-characterized of these include the heat shock promoter (responsive to elevated temperature; 151), the metallothionein promoter (responsive to the presence of heavy metals such as cadmium and zinc; 152), the mouse mammary tumor virus (MMTV) LTR promoter (responsive to dexamethosone; 153), and the interferon-β promoter (responsive to interferon, viral infection, and dsRNA; 154). A transgene placed under the control of one of these regulatory elements could be stably integrated, and protein expression could be induced by shifting to an elevated temperature, or by adding the appropriate inducing substance to the growth medium. While these systems provide a "complete package" for cell culture

experiments, in that control is mediated by endogenous *trans*-acting regulators, they suffer from one or more of the following major disadvantages (155): (1) substantial *leakage* (background transgene activity in the noninduced state); (2) low *induction ratio* (the ratio of induced to noninduced protein yield); (3) cytotoxic effects of the inducing agent; and (4) the concomitant activation of other, endogenous genes whose activity may be undesirable, or may interfere with the system being studied. For example, activation of the heat shock promoter can induce transgene activity up to 100-fold, but the high temperature causes extensive cell death, blocks protein synthesis, and interferes with protein secretion. Protein synthesis begins when cells are returned to 37 °C, but the rate of transcription then drops. Similarly, the metallothionien promoter has a high basal transcription level, an induction ratio of less than 10, and cadmium is cytotoxic. The glucocorticoid response element of the MMTV LTR promoter provides a more effective system because there is only minimal leakage, but the induction ratio is again less than 10, and other hormone-responsive genes are activated. These promoters have also been used in transgenic animals. In this context, even moderate leakage is unacceptable for certain experiments, such as conditional cell ablation by expressing a toxin such as ricin under inducible control. A further disadvantage is the unexpected and often undesirable tissue-specific effects of induction, reflecting the tissue-specific distribution of transcription factors, or the differential uptake of the inducing agent.

Heterologous, Recombinant, and Artificial Inducible Systems. Many of the problems attributed to the use of endogenous inducible systems can be addressed using systems that are heterologous, recombinant, or totally synthetic. A disadvantage of this approach is that the components of the system (e.g., genes encoding the appropriate *trans*-acting regulators) have to be introduced into the cell along with the target gene and its control sequences. This can be a problem when generating transgenic animals, and for this reason, specific regulator strains of mice have been (and continue to be) developed, and are commercially available. These can be used to "cross in" heterologous regulatory systems by breeding with transgenic animals carrying the regulatable transgene of interest. Despite this complication, the advantages of nonendogenous systems are manifold, benefiting from thoughtful design and modification, rather than relying on natural properties (155):

- Transgene induction is specific to exogenously supplied, nontoxic agents.
- Transgene induction does not interfere with any endogenous pathways because no endogenous genes are affected.
- There is no leaking—in the noninduced state, transgene expression is minimal.
- Undesirable cell-type-specific effects of induction can be eliminated; alternatively, transgene expression can be induced in specific cell types by design.

- The inducing agent can be chosen to penetrate cells quickly for rapid induction, and decay quickly for prompt return to the basal state.

All such systems are designed around a switch principle, where transgene expression is controlled by a heterologous, recombinant, or artificial response element. This is activated (or repressed) by a heterologous, recombinant, or artificial *trans*-acting regulator, whose activity is modulated by a small, exogenously supplied molecule

(the inducer). Four major types of system have been exploited (Fig. 9): the *E. coli lac* operon (156), the *E. coli tet* operon (157,158), the *Drosophila* molting hormone ecdysone (159), and mammalian steroid hormones (reviewed in Ref. 155). Not all inducible switches function at the transcriptional level, and switches at the protein level are discussed later.

The *E. coli lac* system (156) is based on the *lacI* gene, which encodes a transcriptional repressor protein. The *E. coli lac* operon encodes three enzymes involved

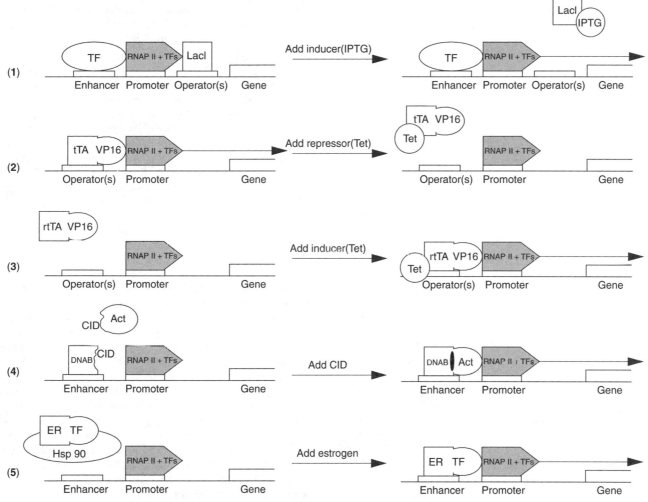

Figure 9. Mechanisms of inducible transgene controly. (**1**) Repressor-based system, e.g., the Lac switch. The transgene construct contains *lac* operator(s), which bind LacI repressor and prevent transcription. Induction is achieved with IPTG, which binds to and inactivates the repressor, causing it to release the DNA. (**2**) Activator-based system, e.g., tTA. Here, the *E. coli* Tet repressor is fused to a transcriptional activation domain, e.g., VP16. The transgene contains *tet* operators that now function as enhancers. Introducing tetracycline into the system inactivates tTA causing transgene repression. (**3**) Reverse activator-based system, utilizing a mutated Tet repressor–VP16 fusion, which binds to DNA in the presence of tetracycline and releases DNA in its absence. (**4**) Chemically induced dimerization system. A transcription factor is expressed as separate DNA-binding and activation domains, each including a binding site for a bivalent ligand such as FKBP12. Introducing the ligand into the system causes dimerization and transcription factor activity. (**5**) Steroid-based system. A transcription factor is expressed as an estrogen receptor fusion protein. In the absence of estrogen, the fusion protein is sequestered into an inactive complex by Hsp90. Introducing estrogen to the system releases, and hence activates, the transcription factor. *Abbreviations*: TF, transcription factor; RNAP, RNA polymerase; IPTG, isopropyl β-D-thiogalactopyranoside; Tet, tetracycline; Act, activator domain; DNAB, DNA-binding domain; ER, estrogen receptor.

in lactose metabolism. In the absence of lactose, the LacI repressor binds to operator sites around the transcriptional start site and prevents RNA polymerase initiating transcription. The presence of lactose in the medium results in the synthesis of a metabolic by-product, allolactose. This binds to the repressor, effecting a conformational change that causes it to release the DNA. The same result arises from treatment with a gratuitous inducer, isopropyl-1-thio-β-D-galactopyranoside (IPTG). Transcription of the genes for lactose catabolism then commences. The strategy for transgene regulation in animal cells is to place a *lac* operator sequence downstream of the transgene transcriptional start site, and introduce a second expression construct constitutively expressing the *lacI* gene. Under basal conditions, the transgene is repressed, but if IPTG is added to the medium, the repressor is released from the operator site, allowing transgene expression. This system achieves an induction ratio of about 3–500, which is up to 100-fold greater than the commonly used chemical endogenous induction systems. However, the number and position of *lac* operator sites in the target gene appears to be critical for correct regulation (157). The original *E. coli tet* system, pioneered in transgenic tobacco plants, was based on a similar principle to the *lac* system. The *tetR* gene encodes a repressor that binds to operator sequences in the *tet* operon when tetracycline is absent. Here, tetracycline itself is the inducer, and causes the release of the repressor and induction of the *tet* genes. The operational parameters of the *lac* and *tet* systems in mammalian cells were thus similar, except that the number and position of *tet* operator sequences was shown to be less important for inductive control than the equivalent *lac* operators. Although more advanced than endogenous systems, the original *lac* and *tet* systems also suffered certain disadvantages. To suppress transgene activity fully, high levels of LacI or TetR proteins were required, and were found to be cytotoxic. Furthermore, IPTG and tetracycline levels were slow to decay, resulting in a long time lag before the effects of induction could be eliminated or reversed.

Some disadvantages of the "repressor"-based systems have been addressed by converting TetR and LacI into activators, by generating fusion proteins in which the repressor is joined to the herpes simplex virus VP16 transactivator (160,161). In the case of the *tet* system, the fusion product (termed tTA) confers constitutive transgene activity in the absence of tetracycline, and is suppressible by tetracycline (or its derivative deoxycycline). These systems have a reduced basal transcription level because a eukaryotic enhancer is not required (the operator now provides the enhancer activity) and high levels of repressor protein are unnecessary. This provides an induction ratio in the order of 10^5. One disadvantage, however, is the constant requirement for tetracycline in the growth medium (for cells) or drinking water (for transgenic animals) to maintain the basal state. This has proven to be toxic in many experimental systems, and the unequal distribution of tetracycline results in significant fluctuation in the basal level of transgene activity, which is intolerable for the regulated expression of some proteins. Furthermore, since induction requires

the absence of tetracycline, it is dependent on the rate at which tetracycline can be eliminated. The tTA protein has also proven to be toxic when expressed at high levels, although autoregulatory systems have been designed to optimize tTA expression levels. These problems have been addressed by generating a mutated form of the tTA activator whose DNA-binding activity is improved rather than abolished by tetracycline (162). This protein (termed rtTA, reverse tTA) is thus an activator in the presence of tetracycline, removing the requirement for long-term exposure to the inducer. Although tetracycline-based systems have been criticized for high toxicity, low efficiency, and low stability, they are extremely versatile and have been used in many different experimental systems, perhaps explaining why weaknesses have been so readily identified. Numerous plasmid- and viral-based delivery vectors have been constructed (reviewed in Ref. 155), and it is likely that this system will continue to be exploited and improved in the future.

The *Drosophila* ecdysone system (159) exploits a steroid hormone signaling pathway endogenous to insect cells but absent from mammalian cells. The steroid hormone ecdysone is responsible for the extensive morphological changes that occur during molting in *Drosophila*. The hormone acts through a heterodimeric transcription factor of the nuclear receptor family, comprising the products of the genes *ecr* (ecdysone receptor) and *usp* (ultraspiracle). This system can be used for transgene regulation by including an ecdysone response element upstream of the transgene, and cotransfecting cells with constructs carrying the two *Drosophila* genes encoding the receptor. Transgene induction is achieved by treating cells with either ecdysone itself, or its analog muristerone A. Since both the receptor and its response element are insect specific, neither the ligand nor its receptor has any toxic or other physiological effects on mammalian cells, and thus the system is innocuous and highly specific. Ecdysone and muristerone A appear to be harmless when injected into mice and are totally eliminated within a few hours. Despite its advantages, the original ecdysone system had a poor induction ratio. This problem has been addressed by introducing mammalian components into the system to generate hybrid receptors recognizing totally artificial response elements. Saez and colleagues (155) have recently described a system in which the Ecr protein is expressed as a fusion with the HSV transactivator protein VP16 and the mammalian glucocorticoid receptor. The Usp protein is replaced by its mammalian homolog, the retinoid X receptor. The resulting hybrid recombinant receptor responds to ecdysone and muristerone A, and binds to an artificial response element recognized by no other receptor of mammalian or insect origin. This powerful system has minimal background activity and an induction ratio of up to 1000. Additionally, since the hormones are eliminated rapidly from cells and animals, this system enables rapid induction and return to the basal state. Inducible systems based on mammalian steroid hormones have also been described, although these are recent developments and remain to be optimized. Perhaps the most promising approach is the construction of a recombinant progesterone receptor carrying the yeast GAL4 DNA-binding domain and the HSV transactivator VP16 (163,164). This receptor is unable to bind progesterone, but can bind the progesterone antagonist RU486, also known as mifepristone. Transgenes driven by the yeast GAL4 recognition site are induced by RU486, apparently at levels low enough not to affect endogenous progesterone activity. However, these early systems suffer from leakage, low induction ratio, and undesirable physiological effects, and hence require further development.

Finally, a recently described system of transgene regulation exploits the principles upon which the yeast two-hybrid system (for studying protein–protein interaction) was based. This technique, known as chemically induced dimerization (CID), uses a divalent ligand simultaneously to bind and hence aggregate separate DNA-binding and transactivation domains to generate a hybrid transcription factor. This facilitates very tight transgene regulation, and shows minimal background effects. The initial system exploited the immunophilin-binding domain of the immunosuppressant drug FK-506. A divalent homodimer of this drug, FK-1012, binds to two immunophilin domains and promotes dimerization (165). A problem with this system is that homodimer transactivators and homodimer DNA-binding domains are generated at high frequency. More recent systems have used heterodimers of FK-506 and rifamycin, so that only two different proteins are able to dimerize, thus preventing such undesirable interactions (166). Unfortunately, while these CIDs penetrate and decay rapidly, they are only active at concentrations causing immunosuppressive side effects. Alternative CIDs are thus being sought and designed (reviewed in Ref. 155).

Transcriptional Termination and RNA Processing

In eukaryotic cells, the primary transcripts of protein-encoding genes are extensively processed before export from the nucleus for translation. The processing steps include the addition of an inverted 7-methylguanosine cap to the 5′ end, the removal of introns by splicing, the cleavage and polyadenylation of the 3′ end, and the methylation of certain internal bases (reviewed in Ref. 167). The function of internal methylation is not understood, but the other modification steps are essential for message stability, nuclear export, and efficient translation. These factors must therefore be taken into account when designing expression vectors.

Capping. All eukaryotic mRNAs are capped. The capping process occurs immediately following transcriptional initiation, probably because the enzyme responsible (mRNA guanyltransferase) is associated with the initiation complex. Most animal cell mRNAs have a type 1 cap, which is methylated at position G^7 of the cap itself and at position $O^{2'}$ on the ribose moiety of the next residue. The capping reaction occurs automatically, hence no special precautions are needed to ensure vector-encoded transcripts are capped. The cap serves a number of functions — it appears to be required for nuclear export, it prevents 5′ end degradation, and it serves as a recognition site for the factors that initiate translation.

Intron Splicing. Most genes in animal cells are interrupted by one or more noncoding segments of DNA, known as *introns*. These are removed from the primary transcript by a well-characterized mechanism involving the recognition of 5′ and 3′ splice sites by a large, *trans*-acting spliceosome assembly. The activities of the spliceosome result in a transesterification reaction that joins the upstream and downstream exons and eliminates the intron. Many vertebrate genes contain large and numerous introns, and the majority of mammalian genes comprise more intron material than exon material, in some cases exceeding 95% of the transcription unit. However, due to the size constraints of many expression vectors, the simplicity of in vitro manipulation, and partly due to cloning strategy, genes are often expressed as cDNAs or as artificial minigenes with all introns removed (20,6,168).

The earliest cDNA expression studies in mammalian cells provided evidence that splicing might be required for efficient mRNA synthesis, prompting the inclusion of an intron in the transcription unit of a number of expression vectors. Since then, many investigators have independently confirmed that cDNA expression is either intron dependent or significantly improved in the presence of an intron, in some cases up to 500-fold (168). However, there have also been numerous reports of cDNAs that are efficiently expressed without an intron. Furthermore, there are a number of mammalian genes that lack introns, and the vast majority of bacterial genes lack introns yet are still efficiently expressed in mammalian cells. However, the presence of an intron has rarely been shown to have adverse effects; thus many contemporary expression vectors possess a small heterologous or artificial intron in the mammalian transcription unit. Genuine introns include the SV40 small t-antigen intron (used, e.g., in vectors marketed by Invitrogen) and the human growth hormone intron. Improved expression has been documented using hybrid introns, for example, comprising a 5′ splice site from the β-globin gene and a 3′ splice site from an immunoglobulin gene. These are particularly close to the ideal splice signal consensus and are used, for example, in vectors marketed by Promega. In some cases, point mutations have been introduced so that introns match the splice consensus perfectly. As discussed later, the requirement for introns in transgenic animals is more widely accepted, and genomic constructs are generally more efficiently expressed than cDNAs (169).

Early investigations showed that the presence or absence of an intron could control gene expression by affecting the resultant levels of mRNA. The role of introns in the regulation of foreign gene expression has been investigated recently, and a post-transcriptional regulatory mechanism has been identified (170). Primary transcripts are associated with proteins during synthesis, processing, and export from the nucleus, to form heterogenous ribonucleoproteins (hnRNPs). It appears that intron-containing and intronless genes expressed in the nucleus end up associated with different sets of proteins, and that this ribonucleoprotein architecture may affect subsequent translational efficiency. Notably, these investigators found that the absence of an intron resulted in a significant amount of post-transcriptional silencing, presumably due to repression by hnRNP structure. An intron placed at the 5' end of the transcript could alleviate this silencing, but a 3' intron increased the silencing effect. Although these data were obtained using *Xenopus* oocytes rather than mammalian cells, the study provides evidence that the nature of the transcription unit can affect subsequent levels of gene expression by stimulating the recruitment of particular regulatory proteins. While the evidence from mammalian systems is in some cases contradictory, the presence of a 5' intron is also favored, and may indicate that a similar mechanism is in operation. It is possible that recruitment of alternative proteins during transcription could also affect continued transcriptional efficiency or mRNA stability, allowing the same mechanism to regulate mRNA levels. These possibilities remain to be investigated.

Another consideration involving introns is the generic nature of the splice signals, and the presence of cryptic splice sites. Generally, eukaryotic primary transcripts are spliced in a predictable fashion even though all introns carry the same consensus splice signals, which are short enough to be occur by chance both within the body of the intron and in adjacent exons. It is thought that the sequence context of the splice sites, the distance between them, and the secondary structure adopted by the nascent transcript or completed primary transcript may dictate how the splicing apparatus and RNA interact to define the introns to be removed. If a normal splice site is mutated, one or more local cryptic splice sites may become active, and these are used efficiently even if there is no "leaky" cryptic splice site usage in the wild-type transcript. This readiness to utilize alternative splice sites should be considered when designing recombinant genes with hybrid introns, as they may not be spliced in a predictable fashion, and may produce aberrant transcripts that are not translated.

Finally, the requirement for introns should be considered carefully if a viral gene delivery strategy is favored, as this may influence the choice of vector and its design. As discussed, the inclusion of sense-orientation introns in retroviral vectors can interfere with the viral replication cycle (132,133). If a cDNA or intronless minigene cannot be expressed efficiently, the intron-containing genes must be inserted in the reverse orientation so that the introns are not recognized during the transcription phase of the replication cycle. Poxviruses are unusual DNA viruses that replicate in the cytoplasm, and no viral genes contain introns because the virus does not have access to the nuclear splicing machinery. Therefore, foreign genes cloned in poxvirus vectors such as vaccinia virus must also lack introns (141). This should not affect the efficiency of gene expression, however, because the regulatory mechanisms discussed depend on nuclear history, that is, exposure of the transcript to nuclear proteins. Messenger RNAs introduced directly into the cytoplasm using poxvirus or alphavirus vectors, or by RNA transfection, are not subject to these interactions.

Transcriptional Termination and Polyadenylation. The mechanism of transcriptional termination in the protein encoding genes of animals is not fully understood (167).

Termination is thought to occur downstream of the mature 3' end of the transcript, which is generated by endonucleolytic cleavage of the nascent RNA. The cleavage reaction is followed by polyadenylation, the addition of a variable number (approximately 200) of adenylate residues to generate the so-called poly(A) tail. This occurs 10–30 nucleotides downstream of a highly conserved polyadenylation site, with the consensus sequence AAUAAA. A GU-rich sequence downstream of the polyadenylation site may influence the actual position of cleavage. Cleavage and polyadenylation are carried out by a multimeric complex comprising recognition factors that bind to the polyadenylation site, a dimeric cleavage enzyme, and the enzyme polyadenylate polymerase. Although the precise function of polyadenylation is not known, it appears to increase mRNA stability and control mRNA export. If the polyadenylation site is mutated, the level of protein synthesis can drop by as much as 90%. It is therefore essential to include an authentic polyadenylation site and terminator region in expression vectors, downstream of the foreign gene. A number of polyadenylation sites are commonly used, including those from the SV40 early transcription unit, and the mouse β-globin gene. The inclusion of a polyadenylation site within the vector removes any reliance on endogenous polyadenylation sites supplied with foreign genes and cDNAs. This is particularly advantageous for the expression of genes and cDNAs with large 3' untranslated regions, because these can be trimmed off, an operation that may also improve transgene expression by increasing mRNA stability (168).

Polyadenylation Sites in Cointegrate Vectors. Many gene transfer experiments involve the use of cointegrate vectors, that is, vectors containing multiple genes. A cointegrate vector is usually defined as one where linked genes are under separate transcriptional control, and gene transfer experiments involving two or three genes linked on the same vector are carried out routinely in many laboratories. In such vectors it is particularly important to include termination/polyadenylation sequences at the end of each transcription unit. If this is not carried out, it is possible for gene expression to be limited at three levels. First, where transcription from one gene reads through into a second downstream gene, *promoter occlusion* can occur. This involves transcription through the promoter of the downstream gene, preventing the assembly of the transcription complex and blocking gene expression (171). Promoter occlusion occurs if two adjacent genes are in the same orientation. If adjacent genes are in opposite orientation, read-through transcription from one gene generates antisense RNA that can block the expression of the second gene at the post-transcriptional level, a phenomenon termed *antisense suppression*. If both promoters are active, both sense and antisense RNA can be generated. These may associate to generate double-stranded RNA (dsRNA), activating the DAI protein kinase, which phosphorylates and inactivates eIF2, a critical translation initiation factor (69). These problems can be alleviated by preventing read-through transcription, through the inclusion of a terminator and polyadenylation site after each gene. A polyadenylation site placed upstream of a gene can block any adventitious gene activation by factors binding to backbone sequences upstream of the transcription unit. This is particularly important in vectors whose purpose is to test putative regulatory elements.

Protein Synthesis

Kozak Consensus. The requirements for high-efficiency translation of foreign genes in mammalian cells have been studied in great detail (172,173) and reflect three important properties of the foreign gene: (1) the nucleotide sequence surrounding the translational start site; (2) codon choice throughout the coding region; and (3) the structure of the 5' and 3' untranslated regions.

The optimal translational start site sequence was defined by Kozak as 5' CCRCC*AUG*G 3', with the underlined sequence representing the initiation codon (R is any purine). The adenosine residue of the initiation codon is defined as position +1 of the coding region and the residue immediately 5' to that is defined as position −1 (there is no position 0). The two most important residues appear to be the purine at position −3 and the guanosine at position +4. Most expression vectors contain the Kozak sequence as standard, although only proteins with valine, alanine, glutamine, glycine or aspartate as their second residue can be specified by a coding region with guanosine at position +4. Mutations deviating from the Kozak consensus can reduce protein expression levels by up to 90%.

Codon Choice. The genetic code is degenerate; hence most amino acids are encoded by a family of codons. Some codon families (e.g., those encoding leucine and serine) have as many as six members. The analysis of many gene sequences obtained from different organisms has revealed two important principles of codon usage. First, there is codon bias; that is, particular codons within a family are used more often than others. Second, the codon bias differs from species to species, so that a codon favored in one animal might be different to that favored in another (174). Codon bias can reflect several underlying factors. Degeneracy at first and second base positions is caused by the presence of isoaccepting tRNAs, alternative tRNAs that are charged with the same amino acid but recognize distinct codons. Third base degeneracy reflects the relaxed base pairing rules (so-called "wobble rules") applying to the third base of the codon and the first base of the anticodon, which in some cases reflects the modification of tRNA bases. A further reason for codon bias involves bulk properties of the genome. In GC-rich genomes, guanine- or cytosine-containing codons might be favored over adenine- or thymine-containing codons, while in AT-rich genomes the opposite bias might apply. Codon choice can influence transgene expression at several levels. The progress of translation can be inhibited if a particular codon is favored in the source organism, but not in the host to which the foreign gene is transferred. The translation machinery may pause at a rare codon. This may simply reduce the rate of protein synthesis, resulting in a lower yield, or it may cause more serious problems such as misincorporation, frameshifting, or truncation. This can be addressed by attempts to match codon preference in the transgene to that of the host, by introducing translationally neutral mutations into the coding region. However, this can sometimes have unpredictable effects by influencing the stability of the mRNA. It should also be borne in mind that rare codons are occasionally used in a regulatory capacity, and that under some special circumstances, they may even misread in a programmed fashion. Examples include frameshifting during the translation of retroviral *gag* and *pol* genes, and insertion of the rare amino acid selenocysteine (167).

Structure of Noncoding Regions. The structure of the 5' untranslated region influences translational efficiency by affecting ribosome assembly and scanning (172,173). Ribosomes comprise two subunits, and initial binding involves only the small subunit, which interacts with proteins assembled at the 5' 7-methylguanosine cap, and scans along the mRNA until the first AUG codon is encountered. If the 5' UTR contains a significant amount of secondary structure, assembly and scanning can be inhibited. The presence of false AUG codons upstream of the genuine start site is also deleterious, especially if they are followed by in-frame termination codons. Most expression vectors are therefore designed to incorporate minimal *processed* 5' UTR sequences (there may be an intron in the 5' UTR, but this would not be represented in the processed mRNA), or a 5' UTR known to function efficiently in concert with the appropriate promoter–enhancer system. The sensitivity of transgene expression to sequences upstream of the initiation codon means that it is important to ensure that sequences at the 5' end of the insert do not generate secondary structure or additional start codons when integrated into the vector. Particular difficulties have been caused by the homopolymer tailing method of cDNA cloning, although this is rarely used these days.

A 3' untranslated region is not usually included in expression vectors because it serves no function essential for translation. Endogenous 3' UTRs may contain regulatory elements, such as AU-rich elements conferring instability upon the message resulting in rapid turnover (175). Typically, the entire 3' UTR is removed from cloned genes or cDNAs prior to insertion, so that the termination codon of the transgene is more or less adjacent to the polyadenylation site (168).

Internal Ribosome Entry Sites and Polycistronic Vectors. As discussed, multiple genes may be expressed on the same cointegrate vector as independent transcription units, by placing each under the control of an independent promoter and polyadenylation site. Another way to express multiple genes on a single vector is to include several coding regions in the same polycistronic message. For a long time, it was thought that polycistronic protein-encoding genes were restricted to bacterial genomes, because eukaryotic translation was assumed to be universally 5' cap dependent. The discovery of internal ribosome entry sites (IRES) elements, first in the picornaviral genome, and then in endogenous animal genes, provided a useful strategy for transgene coexpression and selection for high-level foreign gene expression (176). A reporter gene such as *lacZ* can be placed downstream of an IRES in the same transcription unit as a given foreign gene. This allows cells expressing the foreign gene to be identified through coexpression of β-galactosidase. This is particularly useful in transgenic animals where expression patterns can be mapped and the effect of heterologous protein expression determined in the same animals (177). In knockout mice, the insertion of an IRES–*lacZ* construct into an endogenous gene facilitates both knockout by insertional mutagenesis and the identification of cells that now lack the targeted gene product (177). The expression of genes downstream of an IRES is much less efficient than normal 5′ cap-dependent genes. This can be exploited to isolate cells expressing foreign genes at high levels. If a selectable marker is placed in the downstream position, only cells with high levels of marker expression will survive, and this will identify cells with elevated levels of foreign gene expression (168).

Post-Translational Events

Overview. Protein synthesis is not the end of gene expression. During or following synthesis, all polypeptides undergo some form of covalent modification before folding to form functional proteins. Such modifications may involve minor chemical changes to specific amino acid side chains or the addition of major chemical adducts such as complex oligosaccharides or lipids. Other proteins are modified by endo- or exoproteolytic cleavage. In some cases, protein modification may be reversible and can be used as a means to regulate protein activity (e.g., phosphorylation of serine, threonine, and tyrosine residues). Other types of modification are permanent (e.g., glycosylation and proteolytic cleavage). Protein modification may serve several purposes. In some cases the modification is required for protein activity, while in others the protein functions equally efficiently in its modified and unmodified forms. Certain forms of modification are required for the protein to adopt its correct tertiary or quaternary structure (e.g., the formation of disulfide bonds). Certain forms of modification are characteristic of particular protein sorting pathways in the cell; for example, N-linked glycosylation occurs in the ER lumen, and O-linked glycosylation occurs in the Golgi network. In some cases, particular modifications are required for protein sorting (e.g., the addition of mannose-6-phosphate groups targets proteins to lysosomes, and the cleavage of signal peptides may be required to reveal further targeting motifs, e.g., in mitochondrial import). Finally, some forms of protein modification are involved in the regulation of protein degradation (e.g., ubiquitination of lysine residues).

The secretion of proteins from mammalian cells involves a characteristic series of modifications that take place in the ER and Golgi (reviewed in Refs. 178, 179). Such proteins generally carry an N-terminal signal peptide that causes the ribosome to associate with the ER membrane. The protein is then cotranslationally translocated into the ER lumen, a process termed *vectorial discharge*. In the lumen, the signal peptide is cleaved, and a preformed high-mannose oligosaccharide is added to asparagine residues in the "sequon" element with the consensus sequence Asn–Xaa–Ser/Thr (Xaa is any residue except proline). This initial N-linked glycosylation is followed by several modifications. Terminal glucose residues and probably a single mannose residue are removed, and fatty acylation may also occur, before the part-modified protein is transported to the Golgi network. In the Golgi, further modifications occur to the N-linked glycosyl groups, including the hydrolysis of more mannose residues, and the addition of distinct oilgosaccharide groups such as fucose, galactose, N-acetylglucosamine, and sialic acid. De novo O-linked glycosylation may also occur by the transfer of N-acetylglucosamine groups to serine and threonine residues. As well as glycosylation and acylation, other forms of modification also occur in the secretory pathway, such as the O^4-sulfation of tyrosine residues, and various forms of proteolytic processing.

Factors Affecting the Processing of Recombinant Proteins. Three major factors affect the processing of recombinant proteins: (*1*) correct targeting of the protein; (*2*) the ability of the protein to fold and undergo proper modification; and (*3*) the availability of appropriate enzymes and their positioning in the host cell. A protein that requires a particular form of post-translational modification needs to be targeted to the correct intracellular compartment for that processing to occur. Hence a normally secreted protein whose coding region is truncated so that the signal peptide is no longer translated will likely accumulate in the cytoplasm in a biologically inactive form. This problem needs to be addressed, especially if only a partial cDNA sequence is available for translation, or if a recombinant protein is to be expressed as an N-terminal fusion protein, because the endogenous signal peptide would either be missing or obscured by the fusion product. Many vectors are available with integral secretory signals to target expressed proteins to the secretory network. Other targeting motifs, such as mitochondrial entry sequences and nuclear localization signals, are also terminal, and the same precautions need to be taken when expressing proteins containing these signals.

The modification of a protein is dependent on many factors, including the presence of appropriate targeting sequences, the presence of modification consensus sequences (such as the N-linked glycosylation sequon), the sequence context surrounding this motif, and the overall tertiary conformation of the protein. It is thought that modification relies not just on the presence of particular motifs in the polypeptide primary structure, but also on the tertiary structural context in which this motif is presented to the processing enzymes, and the geometry of enzyme positioning (e.g., in the Golgi). Furthermore, where modification occurs in a series of successive steps, each modification may cause the tertiary structure of the protein to change in order to make it more accessible to the next processing enzyme. Hence any alteration to the primary structure of a polypeptide may cause a critical deviation from the optimum tertiary conformation, resulting in the failure of a particular modification reaction. This is demonstrated by the alteration of, for example, glycosylation patterns following mutations causing nonconservative amino acid changes, or following the incorporation of amino acid analogs. The dependence of late processing events on the successful completion of earlier modifications is demonstrated by the altered glycosylation patterns observed following treatment with inhibitors of the early glycosylation enzymes (180).

Finally, it has been observed that recombinant proteins may be processed differently in alternative expression hosts, probably reflecting the absence or differential abundance of processing enzymes. Some differences in glycosylation patterns have been observed between alternative mammalian hosts; for example, secreted proteins produced in CHO cells tend to have more terminal sialic acid residues than those produced in COS cells (181,182); so this may need to be taken into account when choosing a particular host–vector system. Insect cells use a distinct N-linked glycosylation pathway to that found in mammals, which is an important limitation to the utility of the baculovirus expression system (183). Proteins expressed in the popular Sf9 cell line cannot produce certain glycosylation intermediates, such as side chains ending in galactose–sialic acid residues, and this is thought to reflect the absence of a key processing enzyme synthesized in mammalian cells, N-acetyl-β-glucosidase. The baculovirus system may therefore be unsuitable for the expression of glycoproteins that function only when correctly modified. However, cell lines derived from the alternative host *Estigmene acrea* do synthesize N-acetyl-β-glucosidase, and are hence more likely to produce authentic mammalian glycoproteins. Recently, the ability of the baculovirus expression system to coexpress two or more proteins simultaneously has been exploited to alter the endogenous glycosylation pathway of Sf9 cells. Wagner and colleagues (184) have reported the coexpression of fowl plague hemagglutinin and human β-1,2-N-acetylglucosaminyltransferase, resulting in the production of recombinant protein with N-acetylglucosamine-terminated glycans. The flexibility of the glycosylation process in insect cells is likely to be widely exploited for the production of recombinant human proteins.

Many endogenous proteins are processed by cleavage. Some (e.g., the signaling protein Sonic hedgehog) are autoproteolytic, while others, including inactive proenzymes (zymogens), growth factors (e.g., pro-NGF, pro-BDNF), and a large number of hormones and neuropeptides (e.g., pro-insulin, pro-glucagon, pro-renin, proenkephalin, prodynorphin) require modification in *trans*. The overexpression of such recombinant proteins is often hampered by the low level of endogenous proteases, termed *proprotein convertases*, which are responsible for the processing reactions. Recently, a family of proprotein convertases has been extensively characterized and several members have been cloned (reviewed in Ref. 185). Several groups have successfully coexpressed the precursor and its cognate proprotein convertase in an attempt to generate high yields of mature recombinant protein, such as insulin in insect cells (186), von Willebrand factor in CHO cells (187), and coagulation factor C in transgenic pigs (188).

Inducible Protein Activity. Earlier, several inducible transcription systems were described, which allow transgene activity in cells and transgenic animals to be controlled by the application of a small molecule (an inducer) such as IPTG, tetracycline, or steroid hormones. All these transcription level regulatory systems suffer from one major disadvantage: that there is a delay between the alteration of transcriptional activity and the response at the level of recombinant protein expression. The most rapid of these inducible systems still has a lag of several hours before induction reaches its full potential. Similarly, return to the basal state is delayed by the rate of protein turnover as well as the natural rate of decay of the inducer. To address this problem, a number of post-translational approaches to the regulation of protein activity have been developed. Classical approaches, such as the isolation of temperature-sensitive alleles, and protein microinjection, are very powerful but lack versatility. Temperature-sensitive alleles suffer from the same disadvantages as heat-shock transcriptional induction (i.e., the concomitant activation of many endogenous genes with pleiotropic effects), while microinjection is not reversible.

Two more promising approaches are the use of steroid-binding fusion proteins (189) and the exploitation of chemically induced dimerization (165). The estrogen receptor exists in an inert state in the absence of estrogen because the hormone-binding domain interacts with heat shock protein 90 (Hsp90) to form an inactive complex. When estrogen is present, however, a conformational change causes the release of the receptor, which is then free to dimerize and interact with DNA. The principle of the steroid-based post-translational switch is that any protein expressed as a fusion with a hormone-binding domain will similarly interact with Hsp90 and form an inactive complex (189). A given heterologous protein can thus be expressed at high levels in an inactive state, but can be activated by feeding cells or transgenic animals with estrogen (reviewed in Ref. 190). The kinetics of the switch are rapid, on the order of seconds rather than hours, and can therefore be used to study rapid cellular events such as those occurring in signal transduction pathways. A more recently developed version of this system uses a modified estrogen receptor, which is highly specific for the ligand 4-hydroxytamoxifen, thus removing many of the pleiotropic effects of estrogen administration (191).

The chemically induced dimerization (CID) system takes advantage of the ability of ligands to facilitate the dimerization of proteins carrying ligand-binding domains (165). The CID system has already been described as a transcriptional switch, in which separate DNA-binding and transactivation domains expressed as ligand-binding fusion proteins are conditionally dimerized by supplying a divalent ligand. The same idea can be exploited to activate proteins whose normal activation requires a dimerization step (e.g., many receptors and signal transduction proteins) or the separately expressed domains of monomeric proteins (as for transcription factors in the transcriptional CID switch). CID has been successfully used to regulate the activity of a range of transmembrane receptors and intracellular signaling proteins by conditional activation. It is also possible to use inhibitory proteins to facilitate conditional inactivation, providing another potential route to conditional gene silencing.

EXPRESSION PARAMETERS AND OPTIMIZATION — CONSEQUENCES OF TRANSGENE INTEGRATION

Overview

The integration of foreign DNA into the genome of a host cell is a chaotic and typically random process (192). Certain viral vectors display various degrees of regional specificity, for example, retroviruses may preferentially integrate into actively transcribed DNA (132,133), and wild-type AAV shows definite preference for a particular region of the human genome (109). The existence of preferential integration sites for plasmid DNA transfected into animal cells has been suggested (193), but it is generally assumed that the integration mechanism exploits randomly occurring chromosome breaks. A frequent observation made in experiments dealing with the integration of foreign genes into animal genomes is that transgene expression is highly variable among cell lines or transgenic animals generated by independent transformation events. Additionally, transgene integration may cause unexpected changes in phenotype. Conversely, transgene expression within a clone of transformed cells, or within a line of transgenic animals, is more likely to be comparable, although this is not always the case. What is responsible for such interclonal variation?

Since DNA integration is both chaotic and random, several molecular parameters can vary between clones, but would be expected to remain the same within clones (192). First, the position of integration can vary, giving rise to so-called *position effects* that reflect the influence of the local molecular environment. Second, the number of integrated transgene copies can vary, giving rise to gene *dosage effects*. Third, transgene structure and organization can vary, including factors such as the internal mutation, rearrangement, or truncation of single transgenes, and the orientation and arrangement of adjacent transgenes. Finally, transgenes can become de novo methylated, a still poorly understood phenomenon that often causes transgene silencing and may represent a genomic defense mechanism. All these factors are thought to be able to contribute in some way to transgene activity, resulting in highly variable expression levels.

Timing of Integration

When DNA is introduced into cultured cells, individual cells are selected on the basis of their ability to express the foreign DNA on a long-term basis, which is prime facie evidence for stable integration. For transgenic animals, however, the organism must be considered as a whole. The timing of integration may play an important role in the behavior of transgenes in different cells and hence determine the characteristics of the resulting animal. In mice, DNA introduced into the fertilized egg by pronuclear microinjection often integrates after DNA replication, or after one or more cell divisions, and the resulting embryo may thus be mosaic for transgene insertion. As discussed

in a later section, this means that a transgene has to be transmitted through the germline before it is stably inherited as a Mendelian trait.

Mice, and mammals generally, undergo a characteristic form of development where very little material is stored in the egg, and zygotic transcription begins at the two-cell stage. Conversely, animals such as fish and amphibians have large eggs with a stockpile of proteins and RNA. The early embryo undergoes a rapid series of synchronous cleavage divisions followed by an event termed the midblastula transition, where division becomes asynchronous and zygotic transcription begins. This event is thought to reflect the titration of DNA packaging proteins such as histones. It is the initial surplus of these DNA packaging proteins that may be responsible for the unique behavior of DNA introduced into fish and amphibian eggs. Unlike mammalian systems, where the DNA is soon integrated, exogenous DNA in fish and frog eggs is rapidly concatemerized and subject to extrachromosomal replication (194). As the embryo cleaves, the distribution of transgene copies is arbitrary, resulting in mosaic and variable expression levels between equivalent cells. Although mosaic transgene expression is widely attributed to differential *distribution* of the transgene in cells of the early embryo, there may also be factors causing differential transgene *expression*: This applies to fish, frogs, and mammals (195). Eventually, exogenous DNA is degraded, but at some point integration may occur. While this is an early event in mouse development, with fish and frogs, integration occurs much later, and the resulting mosaics may contain only a low percentage of transformed cells (reflecting integration after perhaps 12 rounds of cleavage). Consequently, there are different position and dosage effects in different cells of the same animal, and it may also be more difficult to obtain fully transgenic animals.

The Fate of Foreign DNA and the Structure of the Transgenome

Exogenous DNA introduced into animal cells rapidly becomes covalently joined to form larger arrays. The size and structure of the arrays depends upon the amount, conformation, and complexity of the source DNA. In techniques such as calcium phosphate transfection, a large amount of DNA enters the cell. In many cases, at least two independent transgenes are introduced (a selectable marker and one or more nonselected genes) and carrier DNA is used to bring the DNA concentration to optimal levels for coprecipitate formation. Carrier DNA is often sheared or sonicated genomic DNA from a convenient source such as salmon sperm, and is thus linear and of high complexity. Shortly after transfection, the transgenes and carrier DNA form large, randomly arranged arrays reflecting the arbitrary ligation of DNA fragments. This structure, termed the transgenome, usually integrates at a single site. It is sometimes unstable and may be subject to full or partial excision, probably reflecting intrachromosomal recombination events (19,196).

In other transfection methods, and in microinjection, carrier DNA is not used. Less DNA therefore enters the cell and the DNA that does reach the nucleus is relatively simple (and hence repetitive) in its sequence. There are two consequences of using smaller amounts of less complex DNA. First, the transgenome is smaller; hence the number of integrated transgene copies is reduced. Single or multiple copies can integrate, but rarely more than 30 copies are present at a single site. There may be several sites of integration, and a degree of control can be exercised over transgene copy number by varying the amount of DNA introduced into the cell. Second, smaller amounts of DNA are likely to favor the generation of head-to-tail concatemers rather than randomly arranged arrays. This is because larger amounts of DNA (especially carrier DNA) increase the concentration of free DNA ends, and this can stimulate the synthesis of DNA ligase (197). Large amounts of high-complexity DNA thus favor random ligation, while small amounts of low-complexity DNA favor homologous recombination. In mammals, linear DNA is integrated five times more efficiently than supercoiled plasmid DNA because it provides a substrate for DNA ligase (76). Supercoiled plasmids presumably have to undergo homologous recombination with each other, or become randomly broken, to generate free ends. Although both linear and circular DNA is concatermerized by homologous recombination in mammals, only circular DNA tends to promote concatemerization in frogs and fish, while linear DNA is more likely to form random arrays. This is presumed to reflect the accumulation of stored DNA ligase in the precleavage embryo, which can use linear but not circular DNA as a substrate (198,199). In fish and frogs, the random ligation of linear DNA is much more rapid than the concatemerization of circular DNA, thus linear DNA is more effective for transient expression, episomal replication, and integration (200).

Position Effects

Position effect is a catch-all term used to describe variability in transgene expression conferred by the position of integration. Since the earliest transformation experiments, it has been known that the chromosomal locus of a transgene can influence its expression. For example, when a transgene isolated from an anomalously expressing transgenic mouse is microinjected back into eggs, the secondary transgenic mice may express the transgene in the normal manner (201). This suggests that the anomalous expression profile of the primary transgene was due to the site of transgene integration. Position effects are a major cause of differential transgene expression levels among independently derived transformed cell lines or transgenic animals, and they are also thought to reduce or eliminate copy-number dependence in transgene expression. The position of integration can influence transgene expression through at least three mechanisms (Fig. 10): the activity of local regulatory elements, the local chromatin structure, and the local state of DNA methylation. These factors may be interdependent.

A transgene may come under the influence of a local regulatory element, and this causes the most overt and specific position effects (16). If a transgene integrates near an endogenous enhancer, it may come under that enhancer's influence, resulting either in the elevation or depression of transcriptional activity, or in transgenic animals, an altered spatial or temporal expression pattern. The effect of local regulatory elements is succinctly demonstrated by the success of entrapment vectors, which are designed to respond to such influences (16). As discussed, an enhancer trap consists of a reporter gene linked to a minimal promoter. If this integrates near an endogenous enhancer element, the reporter gene expression pattern reveals the properties of the enhancer. In this case, the position effects are desirable and indeed useful—they can lead to the identification and cloning of a novel gene—but under most circumstances they are simply regarded as troublesome. Transgenes with weak promoters and enhancers are the most susceptible to such position effects, but local enhancers (and silencers) will affect any transgene construct, even those with strong and specific promoters and enhancers of their own. This is likely to be responsible for at least some cases of variable expression among independent cell clones, but the effects are most obvious in reporter-transgenic mice. These carry constructs with a test promoter driving a reporter gene, and their purpose is to characterize a particular gene regulatory element. In many experiments, the examination of reporter expression patterns in developing and adult mice reveals a "core" expression pattern that is found in most lines and resembles the expression pattern of the gene normally driven by the test promoter. However, there are usually some lines showing ectopic reporter expression, and some showing incomplete reporter expression, revealing the presence of local cell type-specific or stage-specific enhancers and silencers. The level of reporter activity also varies, with some lines demonstrating strong expression, some weak expression, and some transgene silencing. In these cases, it is possible that constitutive regulatory elements are also affecting transgene activity.

Transgenes can also integrate within endogenous genes, in which case they may be influenced by local promoter elements or splice signals (12). Again, there are entrapment vectors that exploit this phenomenon. As discussed, such vectors contain either a "naked" reporter gene (i.e., one driven simply by a translational start codon that can respond to adjacent promoter elements), or a splice acceptor site, which enables the vector to function as an ectopic exon when it integrates into an endogenous intron. Transgenes integrating at the 5' end of a gene may come under the control of the endogenous promoter, or the endogenous and transgene promoter elements may combine in a novel and unexpected manner. Transgenes that integrate into the body of an endogenous gene may be expressed either from their own promoter, or as an aberrant hybrid mRNA under the control of the endogenous gene promoter.

Not all position effects result from such specific influences. Gene expression is dependent not only on the availability of specific *cis*-acting sites, but also on the local chromatin structure, which may be "open" and transcriptionally active, or "closed" and transcriptionally repressed (202). Open and closed chromatin differs in several characteristic ways, including the degree of histone acetylation, the degree of DNA methylation, the

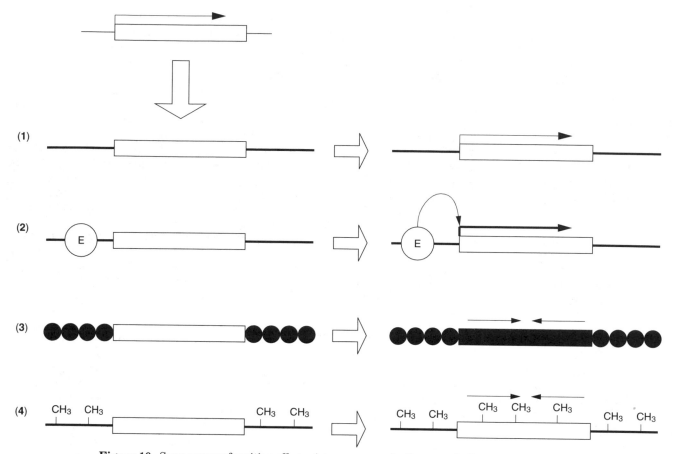

Figure 10. Some causes of position effects. A transgene under the control of its own promoter (top of figure) integrates into the host genome (left). In (**1**) there are minimal local influences and the transgene is expressed as expected. In (**2**) the transgene happens to integrate near an endogenous enhancer; so its expression may be modified by the enhancer. In (**3**) the transgene integrates into repressed chromatin, while in (**4**) it integrates into hypermethylated DNA. In either case, the epigenetic structure can spread across the transgene causing silencing.

presence of certain types of nonhistone protein, and the sensitivity of the DNA to nuclease digestion. A transgene integrating into a region of closed, inactive chromatin (heterochromatin) is often silenced by the spreading of transcriptional repression across the transgene, a form of chromatin remodeling (203). Similarly, if a transgene integrates into hypermethylated DNA, the DNA methylation may also spread across the transgene causing transcriptional silencing. Chromatin structure and DNA methylation are often linked in vertebrates, and indeed it has been shown recently that methylcytosine-binding proteins exist in a complex with histone deacetylase (204). Certain regions of the genome (e.g., centromeric DNA and the Y chromosome in mammals), consist predominantly of heterochromatin, and transgenes integrating there are likely to be subject to position-dependent silencing. Conversely, other regions of the genome, such as the subtelomeric areas, are highly transcriptionally active, and transgenes integrating there are likely to be efficiently expressed.

Position effects also occur naturally, and in humans, are often responsible for cancer. If an oncogene is transferred to a new chromosomal locus by a translocation, it may come under the influence of a novel regulatory element,

it may fuse with a different gene, or it may find itself integrated into active chromatin, all of which can increase its transcriptional activity, resulting in uncontrolled cell proliferation. In *Drosophila*, a phenomenon often associated with chromosome translocations is *position-effect variegation* (PEV) (205). This occurs when active and repressed chromatin become juxtaposed by a translocation and the transcriptional repression spreads from the heterochromatin into the active chromatin, but to a different extent in different cells. This reflects the mechanism of heterochromatinization, which is thought to involve the addition of heterochromatin proteins to pre-existing heterochromatin. Usually, this occurs until a boundary is reached (see the following section), but when such a boundary is removed by chromosome rearrangement, the spreading is limited only by the amount of free heterochromatin protein in each cell. Hence, genes near the translocation breakpoint may be inactivated in some cells but remain active in others. This epigenetic state is clonally heritable, causing a variegated pattern resulting from patches of cells with the gene either active or repressed. Similar phenomena occur in transgenic mammals through inconsistent spreading of transcriptional repression from heterochromatin into a transgene. This may cause mosaic transgene activity, and is further complicated where there are multiple transgene copies because different numbers of transgenes can be active in different cells. Position effects may therefore cause variable levels of transgene expression, either between individual transgenic animals within a given line or between transgenic lines. For example, discrete patches of transgene-expressing cells surrounded by nonexpressing cells in the mammary gland of transgenic mice expressing β-lactoglobulin transgenes have been observed. It has been proposed that patchy or variegated silencing may be a consequence of the proximity of the transgene array to centromeric heterochromatin (206) or that multicopy transgene arrays may themselves act as the focus for heterochromatin formation (207).

Integration Effects

Position effects describe the influence of the local molecular environment on transgene activity, but the effect may also be reciprocal (2). Transgene integration can generate unexpected phenotypes by influencing the expression of adjacent or even distant genes. The most overt integration effect is insertional mutagenesis, where a transgene integrates into an endogenous gene and generates a mutant phenotype. The phenotype may be apparent immediately if there is only one functional copy of the host gene, or if the locus is haploinsufficient, or if the integration event happens to generate a dominant mutant allele. Otherwise, a phenotype may only be observed if the transgene is bred to homozygosity. The effect may be due to simple insertional disruption, or through the deletion of cellular DNA surrounding the integration site. This appears to be a totally random process: In some cases the integration site remains intact, in others up to 80 kbp of DNA can be deleted. In many cases, insertional mutagenesis by transgene integration has led to the serendipitous isolation of novel interesting genes (14). For example, transgenic mice carrying a tyrosinase transgene were shown to have situs inversus (mirror-image reversal of the left–right axis). This has nothing to do with tyrosinase activity, but reveals the functional mutation of a new locus controlling left–right axis specification (208).

More subtle integration effects can also occur. A transgene may cause ectopic activation of a nearby gene that comes under the influence of transgene regulatory elements. This often occurs with retroviral vectors, which carry a strong enhancer–promoter complex in the right-hand long terminal repeat. Wild-type retroviruses also show this activity, and can occasionally activate an adjacent proto-oncogene causing it to be overexpressed. Specialized "suicide" retroviral vectors have been designed to limit this effect: They have a mutated LTR promoter–enhancer, with transgene expression driven by an internal promoter (140). Another consequence of transgene integration is the alteration of cellular methylation patterns. Surprisingly, the integration of certain sequences can cause the alteration of cellular methylation patterns at sites located a great distance from the integration locus (2). This aspect of DNA methylation is discussed in more detail in the following section.

Transgene Copy Number and Dosage Effects

Foreign DNA may integrate either as a single transgene copy or as multiple copies, and the copy number depends on the transfection method and the amount of DNA used. It might be expected that the level of recombinant protein expression would be proportional to transgene copy number. For conventional transgenes, however, there appears to be no correlation between transgene copy number and expression. Copy-number dependence may be blocked by position effects. If position effects are abolished (e.g., by using YAC transgenes or flanking a conventional transgene with boundary elements), transgene expression often becomes copy number related, if not perfectly correlated. The discrepancy may reflect interaction in *trans* between transgene copies or the unaccounted presence of nonfunctional transgenes in the cluster. The effects of transgene dosage can best be observed where a single gene causes a dose-dependent phenotype in a transgenic animal. Hence, when the *Pax-6* gene was expressed in YAC transgenic mice, a range of eye phenotypes was observed, reflecting varying dosage of this transcription factor (209). Gene amplification strategies, which produce thousands of transgene copies, eventually maximize transgene expression by saturating the protein synthesis machinery, but provide little information concerning the effect of transgene dosage on protein expression levels in a nonsaturated system.

Transgene Organization

Several aspects of transgene organization could potentially affect transgene activity, resulting in the production of mutant or aberrant proteins, or in the failure of transgene expression (2). Foreign DNA often undergoes point mutation due to damage in transit. This applies especially to transfected DNA, less so to virally transduced DNA and DNA injected directly into the nucleus. Furthermore, the integration event itself is often destructive, resulting in the deletion of terminal regions of the transgene, internal rearrangement, and transgene fusion. This can result in the production of aberrant, compound, and truncated transcripts.

Transgenes are generally integrated at a single site in pseudotandem arrays (arrays where fragments of host DNA and transgene DNA may be interposed between neighboring transgenes). In cotransfer experiments (i.e., where two or more discrete transgenes are introduced into the cell at the same time) both transgenes tend to integrate at the same site, whether the two genes were originally linked on the same, cointegrate vector or were cotransfected using separate vectors. For cointegrate vectors, the copy number of each transgene is approximately the same within individual cell clones, and the numbers covary between clones. For separate transgenes, the copy numbers of each transgene appear to vary independently between clones, although if one transgene is a selectable marker, there is often less cross-clone variability for that transgene due to selective constraints. Transgenes may integrate at more than one locus, and occasionally cotransfected transgenes may integrate separately. Adjacent transgenes may also influence each other's expression.

Tandem transgenes may cause promoter occlusion by transcriptional read-through, while inverted transgenes may cause antisense suppression. However, while adenoviral VA$_I$ RNA can improve episomal foreign gene expression following transient transfection, stable transgene expression appears not to be affected, suggesting that significant amounts of dsRNA are not synthesized. Some bacterial sequences in transgenic animals have been shown to exert specific negative transcriptional effects in *cis*. Most problems are caused by vector backbone sequences, which can be efficiently separated from the transgene prior to gene transfer (29). However, the popular selectable marker *neo* has also been shown to exert undesirable negative effects on adjacent promoters (210), and contemporary strategies for generating transgenic animals often incorporate a recombination step allowing the removal of this marker.

DNA Methylation and Homology-Dependent Gene Silencing

In vertebrate genomes, approximately 10% of cytosine residues in the dinucleotide motif 5'-CG-3' are methylated. DNA methylation is often correlated with gene silencing (reviewed in Refs. 211,212), and transgenes methylated in vitro prior to gene transfer also tend to be silent, in contrast to nonmethylated transgenes of identical sequence. It has been proposed that DNA methylation may be widely used as a form of gene regulation in mammals. However, except for the specialized cases of parental genomic imprinting and X-chromosome inactivation, it is thought more likely that DNA methylation is an effector of some other primary silencing mechanism, such as altered chromatin structure. The analysis of methylation sites in mammalian DNA suggests that the primary role of DNA methylation may be the silencing of invasive DNA, such as that of viruses and transposable elements. Most naturally occurring methylated cytosine residues in human DNA have been found to lie within *Alu* and LINE elements, two abundant classes of dispersed repetitive DNA corresponding to active and "ghost" (inactivated by mutation) transposable elements (213). Transposon methylation is used as a mechanism to prevent or limit transposition in bacteria and plants, so it is likely that a similar mechanism could be used in animals.

DNA methylation is relevant to animal cell genetic engineering experiments in several ways. First, transgenes introduced into cells and transgenic animals are frequently de novo methylated (2,214), either immediately upon integration, or within a few cell generations (in cell lines) or after passing through the germline (in transgenic animals). This type of methylation is different to the methylation spreading phenomenon discussed previously. For example, de novo methylation is position independent, and may affect transgenes integrated at known active chromosomal sites. The mechanism of de novo methylation is poorly understood, but the targeting of many unrelated transgenes suggests a specific sequence is not responsible for initiating methylation (215). The de novo methylation apparatus may scan the genome for unusual structure, such as uncharacteristic chromatin conformation following an integration event. It has also been suggested that

transgenes may be identified on the basis of their atypical base composition. Vertebrate genomes are divided into so-called isochore regions, each with a specific base composition (average %GC content). The different isochores are also characterized by differences in gene density, gene structure, chromatin conformation, replication timing, recombination frequency, and the presence of specific classes of transposable element (216). The base composition is maintained in the genes and the surrounding nontranscribed DNA, and isochore regions are separated by relatively distinct borders containing clusters of repetitive elements. In plants, it has been suggested that the tendency for some transgenes to be consistently expressed and for others to be consistently silenced in a particular host species reflects the degree of cross-species isochore similarity (217). It may therefore be possible to protect transgenes from de novo methylation by matching their base composition to that of the integration site.

A second methylation effect in gene transfer experiments was observed by Doerfler and colleagues when cells were transformed with either adenoviral or bacteriophage λ DNA (2). As discussed, integrated transgenes (in this case the viral genome) often undergo de novo methylation. A more surprising consequence of transgene integration, however, is the alteration of cellular DNA methylation patterns at loci very distant from the integration site, including endogenous genes. DNA hypermethylation generally corresponds to transcriptional repression, so it is possible that the integration of a transgene at one site in the genome can alter endogenous gene expression patterns by causing some genes to be methylated and repressed, and others to be demethylated and activated. Such global methylation effects have yet to be examined in transgenic animals or with more conventional transgenes.

In certain plants, multicopy transgene integration often leads to transgene silencing, whereas single copy insertion results in high-level transgene expression (217). This phenomenon is position independent but may be copy number related, and often involves DNA hypermethylation. Homology-dependent silencing occurs at two levels. At the transcriptional level, silencing often occurs if there is homology in the promoter region, and is thought to result from ectopic DNA pairing, which initiates de novo methylation. Cre recombinase (discussed in the following section) has been instrumental in demonstrating that this phenomenon of *repeat-induced silencing*, which has been extensively reported in both plants and *Drosophila*, also occurs in mammals (Fig. 11) (218). Silencing can also occur at the post-transcriptional level, requiring homology in the coding region, and may involve the production of aberrant or antisense RNA molecules. Alternatively, a threshold system may be in operation, where a certain mRNA dosage stimulates RNA degradation. A remarkable consequence of post-transcriptional silencing is *cosuppression*: If a transgene is homologous to an endogenous gene, multicopy integration can silence not only the transgene but also the endogenous gene, generating an apparent null phenotype (217). Until recently, this phenomenon was well documented in plants and fungi but not in animals. The first cases of cosuppression-like silencing in animals

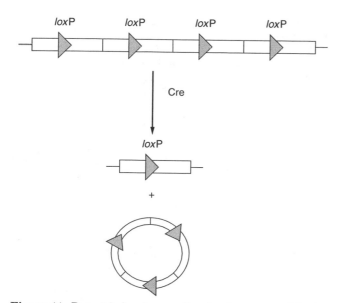

Figure 11. Repeat-induced gene silencing demonstrated by Cre recombinase. If transgenes are designed to carry a single Cre recombinase recognition site (*loxP*), the activation of Cre recombinase in a multicopy transgenic animal results in transgene copy number reduction, in this example from four to one. The excised copies are rapidly degraded, and the single copy transgene is expressed at a much higher level.

were observed in *Drosophila* (219): When two to six copies of a cassette containing an alcohol dehydrogenase (*Adh*)-reporter fusion transgene, driven by the *white* gene promoter, were introduced into the *Drosophila* genome, a reduction in endogenous *Adh* gene expression was observed both in larvae and adults. Additionally, the effect could be modified by mutations in genes such as *Polycomb*, which encode chromatin proteins involved in gene repression. Unlike that of vertebrates, *Drosophila* DNA is not methylated, so it is possible that chromatin remodeling may be the major DNA silencing mechanism.

Transgene Stability and Transmission

It is also important to consider how transgenes are maintained and transmitted through successive cell divisions following integration. In cells transfected using calcium phosphate, it is not uncommon to see complete or partial transgene excision, resulting in reversion to the nontransformed phenotype. Other forms of transformation are more stable because the transgenome is smaller, but where there are multiple transgene copies, copy number expansion or reduction can occur through unequal crossing-over or sister chromatid exchange between tandem repeats. This mechanism is thought to be responsible for generating the large transgene arrays that accompany gene amplification experiments. The maintenance of selection ensures that any cells undergoing reversion are counterselected, and increasing selection pressure selects for those cells with copy number expansions. Integrated transgene arrays and amplified units are often pseudotandemly arranged, containing fragments of host DNA between transgene copies. They also appear to contain unlinked DNA, which may originate

a great distance away from the amplification site. It is unknown how this DNA is cointegrated and coamplified, but is presumed to represent chromosomal recombination events resulting from the interaction of distant loci in *trans*.

In transgenic animals, spontaneous transgene loss is also observed. In species such as fish and frogs, the tendency for foreign DNA to be replicated and episomally expressed means that it is not always possible to confirm that integration has occurred. This can be checked by various experimental approaches, including Southern hybridization to genomic DNA, analysis of Mendelian segregation ratios, in situ hybridization to chromosomes, and sequencing across integration junctions (194). Only rarely has sustained episomal maintenance been observed in transgenic mice. Very occasionally, the loss of a transgene phenotype may be caused by transgene excision or mutation early in development, so that the resulting mouse is phenotypically and genotypically wild type. More often, the genotype of the animal is unchanged, and changes in phenotype result from transgene silencing through de novo transgene methylation. This may occur after one or more generations, and is subject to various controlling factors including the influence of different genetic backgrounds and the parental route of transgene transmission (220). Transgenes, like endogenous genes, may be subject to parental imprinting effects. Hence, the offspring of a transgenic male and wild-type female may show a different phenotype to that of a wild-type male and transgenic female, through sex-specific transgene methylation during gametogenesis (221). In mice, particular strains are associated with different forms of transgene behavior. BALB/c and C57BL/6 backgrounds are thought to promote de novo methylation, while inbred lines such as DBA/2 are thought to promote demethylation (222). Hence, crossing a founder transgenic mouse with a BALB/c wild-type mouse may cause transgene silencing in the mixed genetic background. Conversely, crossing to a DBA/2 mouse often results in continued transgene activity, and can also erase transgene parental imprinting effects. Recent studies concerning the heritability of transgene methylation patterns over many generations suggest that phenomena such as strain-specific methylation, transgene cluster mosaic methylation, cellular mosaicism for transgene methylation, and imprinting may be largely position dependent (220).

Optimal Design of Transgenes for use in Transgenic Animals

With the information presented previously concerning transgene behavior, and the time and expense required for the generation of transgenic animals, it is beneficial to give careful consideration to transgene design. The ability to modify transgene constructs in vitro means that sequences from diverse sources can be combined, and completely synthetic genes can be constructed. This is extremely useful when the intention is the ectopic expression of a protein. For example, a protein normally found in blood can be targeted to milk by linking the regulatory DNA elements from a gene normally expressed in the mammary gland to the protein coding sequences of the gene of interest (223). This type of construct is termed a *hybrid transgene*, and the strategy is being exploited to develop transgenic livestock as animal bioreactors for the commercial production of human pharmaceuticals.

Unfortunately, for the majority of genes, the exact location of the regulatory elements required for efficient expression is still unknown. Consequently, for many studies, the sequences included in the transgene and their organization have been determined on an empirical basis. Nevertheless, some general principles can be applied. First, all prokaryotic vector sequences should be removed before microinjection (192). This can be achieved by careful use of restriction enzymes, and actually improves integration since linear DNA is a fivefold more efficient integration substrate compared to supercoiled DNA. Second, transgene design should be kept as simple as possible. Where hybrid transgenes are used, the sequences from different sources are linked to generate a novel gene, and it is best to keep the number of different sequence fragments as small as possible. A third consideration is whether to use genomic or cDNA sequences. In general, genomic sequences are expressed more efficiently. Many studies have demonstrated that introns facilitate cDNA transgene expression and that intron removal reduces

genomic transgene activity (see Fig. 12), although the mechanisms involved remain to be identified (224). There is a lot of folklore within the scientific community suggesting that it is better to insert the intron in the 5′-UTR; however, there has been no definitive demonstration of this in transgenic mice (although see earlier discussion for *Xenopus*). Fourth, if precise transcriptional control elements have not been defined, it is best to use as large a promoter region as feasible. This has been facilitated by the development of methods to introduce large genomic fragments (e.g., YACs), into the mouse germline. Finally, inclusion of dominantly acting control elements, such as locus control regions (LCRs), should be considered (225). Unfortunately, this type of element has been identified for only a few genes.

Conventional transgenes have traditionally been small in size. If the desired gene covers a large genomic region, or if several genes (perhaps part of a gene cluster) are to be transferred, larger vectors are required. In this regard, transgenic animals have been produced that carry transgenes derived from bacteriophage P1 vectors and bacterial or yeast artificial chromosomes (PACs, BACs, and YACs). P1 clones carry inserts of 80–90 kbp, YACs can carry inserts over 1 Mbp, while BACs carry an

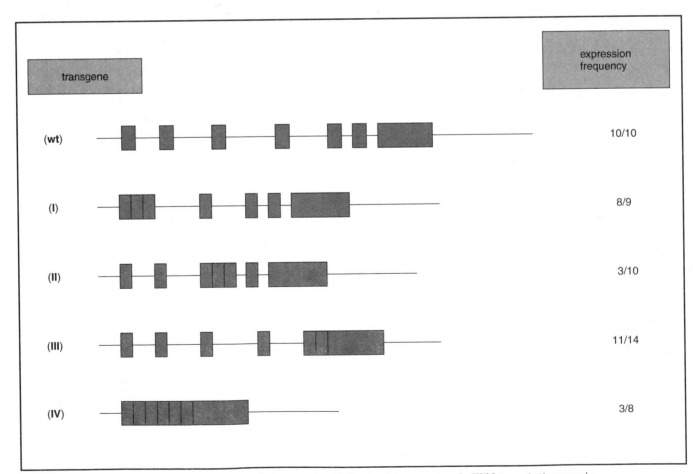

Figure 12. The reduction of transgene activity by intron removal. Wild-type (wt) genomic β-lactoglobulin transgenes are expressed in all transgenic lines generated. However, the removal of any pair of introns reduces the expression frequency (**I, II, III**), and a construct containing no introns (**IV**) was expressed in only 30% of transgenic lines.

intermediate insert size (reviewed in Ref.11). The aim now is to generate mammalian artificial chromosome (MAC) vectors, and with the recent description of a YAC-based MAC, this has come a step closer (226). Alternative approaches have been developed that rely on recombination between two injected fragments to generate a large integrated transgene. The use of these large transgenes is not limited to mice, since transgenic rabbits carrying YACs have also been produced (227). Perhaps the main use of these large clone transgenes is in positional cloning, specifically in relation to adding functional information to the genetic maps currently being generated for most livestock species. This information should, in turn, enable the definition of the genes in the human genome. Recently, the potential for introducing even larger genomic fragments has been demonstrated by the generation of transgenic mice carrying human chromosome fragments. This was accomplished by microcell-mediated chromosome transfer (MMCT) into ES cells, although further progress is required before this becomes a robust technique (91).

Overcoming Position Effects

Position effects are troublesome in gene transfer experiments because they can reduce or silence transgene expression, or generate ectopic expression patterns. There are essentially four ways to deal with position effects: (1) increase transgene copy number so that the rate of mRNA synthesis is no longer the limiting factor in recombinant protein synthesis; (2) ensure that the transgene integrates at a site that is not subject to undesirable position effects; (3) protect the transgene from position effects; and (4) import positive position effects along with the transgene.

One way to overcome position effects is simply to amplify the transgene to such a high copy number that even if each transgene copy is transcribed minimally, enough mRNA is produced to ensure that transcription is no longer the limiting step in foreign gene expression (40,41). This is achieved by cotransfecting cells with the experimental transgene and an amplifiable marker such as Dhfr, followed by subjecting the transfected cells to stepwise increments in the concentration of the selective drug, in this case methotrexate. The use of amplifiable markers to elevate transgene expression levels has been discussed in more detail earlier. It is important to note that this approach is only useful where the aim of the experiment is to maximize yields of recombinant protein, and cannot be used for the precise control of transgene expression either in cells or transgenic animals.

The alternative approaches each allow a degree of control over transgene expression and can be used in more refined experiments. The use of site-specific recombination and gene targeting systems to introduce transgenes at specific loci chosen for their favorable position effects has been proposed as one way to avoid transgene silencing and expression variability (228). Such approaches would also be advantageous because isogenic cell clones and transgenic animals could be produced on demand. Transgene targeting to a specific gene locus in transgenic mice has thus been the focus of attempts to identify permissive sites within the genome (229). The existence of position effects suggests that certain sites within the genome may prove more permissive for expression than others for a given transgene. One strategy is to identify lines of mice that efficiently express a transgene and clone the entire transgenic locus including as much chromosomal flanking sequences as possible. This assumes that sequences relatively close to the site of insertion mediate the effect. Alternatively, neutral sites within the genome, which shield the transgene, can be identified using the appropriate gene targeting construct in ES cells. Neither approach has identified a universally applicable locus, although several candidate regions have been tested.

A promising approach for overcoming position effects is to protect transgenes from surrounding chromatin in the same way that the cell is thought to isolate active and repressed chromatin domains, by using cis-dominant boundary elements. It has been observed that genes in situ reside within large chromatin domains, which extend many kilobases either side of the transcription unit. Active chromatin domains are biochemically defined by the extent of nuclease sensitivity, and transcription per se is not required for a domain to remain in the open configuration (230). There are several ways to exploit these observations. First, DNA sequences found at the domain borders can be used as artificial insulator elements. Such elements have been isolated, for example, from the chicken lysozyme A gene locus and have been shown to insulate transgenes from the activity of local enhancers and to protect transgenes from position effects in cell lines (231) and transgenic animals (232). Such elements are thought to act by attaching to the nuclear matrix and isolating the transgene as a topologically defined chromatin loop. In animals, it has generally been observed that when such boundary elements protect transgenes from position effects, transgene expression also becomes copy number dependent.

Second, susceptibility to position effects can be suppressed through the incorporation of dominantly acting transcriptional control elements in the transgene (225). The best-studied element is from the human β-globin locus and comprises of a set of DNase I hypersensitive sites normally located several kilobases upstream of the β-globin gene. This chromatin element is called the locus control region (LCR). For those β-globin transgenes that harbor the LCR, expression is seen in all transgenic lines and at a level that corresponds to the transgene copy number. Conversely, β-globin transgenes lacking the LCR are often silenced, and where expression occurs, it does so at a low level. Although a vast literature has accumulated concerning the various protein factor interactions within this region, there is no clear understanding of LCR-mediated transgene regulation. There is, however, considerable enthusiasm for the use of this type of element in gene therapy vectors (233).

Third, the use of large vectors, such as YACs and chromosome fragments, can also protect transgenes from position effects. YAC transgenes are rarely subject to position effects and tend to show dose-dependent activity, presumably reflecting the inclusion of native dominant transcriptional control elements (LCRs) and/or boundary elements within the construct.

A final strategy for overcoming position effects is termed *transgene rescue*. In this approach, which is particularly suited to cDNA transgenes, the experimental transgene is cotransfected with a second transgene renowned for its strong expression, such as the β-lactoglobulin (*BLG*) gene (234). The *BLG* transgene cointegrates with the experimental transgene, and high-level expression of both transgenes is observed. The basis of the "rescue" is thought to reflect a favorable chromatin configuration in the *BLG* transgene spreading into the surrounding chromatin and keeping it in an active state, a phenomenon that can be regarded as an "anti-position effect". Presumably, this strategy also runs the risk of reactivating repressed copies of neighboring endogenous genes.

RECOMBINATION-BASED METHODOLOGY AND GENE INHIBITION STRATEGY

Recombination and Its Use in Genetic Engineering

The term *recombination* refers to the creation of new combinations of pre-existing DNA sequences. Two major forms of recombination can be recognized: intergenic recombination (also called independent assortment), which refers to the mixing of discrete DNA elements such as complete chromosomes, and intragenic recombination, where DNA fragments are covalently joined together. There are five different classes of intragenic recombination (Table 6), all of which have been exploited in genetic

engineering strategies (235). Illegitimate recombination, which is responsible for random transgene integration, and homologous recombination, which is exploited for gene targeting, are general recombination mechanisms occurring in all cells. Conversely, site-specific recombination and transposition are controlled by enzymes encoded by particular DNA elements, such as plasmids, viruses, and transposons. Since such recombination systems are not ubiquitous, they can be exploited to carry out specific tasks in genetic engineering projects by transferring them into new host cells. The use of cloned recombination systems from heterologous sources has facilitated in vivo transgene manipulation and chromosome engineering.

Strategies for the Inhibition of Endogenous Genes

While it is fair to say, as discussed, that the major thrust of genetic engineering in animal cells has been to optimize and regulate the expression of recombinant proteins, there is now a growing precedent to use the same gene transfer technology to silence endogenous genes and alter the endogenous genome, that is, to generate functional mutants (190). Genetic analysis is founded on the study of mutants. Originally, in classical genetic analysis, experimenters obtained naturally occurring or induced mutants, and used them to map and isolate the genes involved in any given biological system of interest. With the advent of recombinant DNA technology, it became possible to address gene function from the

Table 6. Categories of Intramolecular Recombination and Their Use in Genetic Engineering

Category	Properties	Relevance to genetic engineering
Illegitimate	Ubiquitous and neither homology nor sequence dependent, although regions of microhomology may be involved. End-joining is a form of illegitimate recombination.	Random joining of multiple transgene copies. Transgene integration at random sites.
Homologous	Ubiquitous and homology dependent. Not sequence dependent. Often involves long regions of homology.	Transgene concatemerization. Gene targeting strategies. Construction of recombinant viral vectors. YAC mutation and retrofitting in yeast.
Site-specific	Encoded by specific genetic elements, e.g., plasmids and viruses. Dependent on proteins (recombinases) that recognize short consensus sequences in donor and target molecules.	Site-specific transgene integration and excision. Transgene engineering in vivo. Tissue- and stage-specific transgene (in)activation. Chromosome engineering.
Transposition	Encoded by specific genetic elements (transposons). Dependent on proteins (transposases) that recognize short consensus sequences in donor, although target site is relatively nonspecific.	Retrovirus integration. Insertional mutagenesis and cloning by tagging or plasmid rescue. Insertion of foreign DNA into viral vectors (e.g., Tn7 transposase targeting of Bac-to-Bac vectors).
Artificial	Joining DNA molecules with DNA ligase in vitro.	Preparation of recombinant vectors for gene transfer.

Note: Site-specific and homologous recombination are discussed in more detail in the current text. See earlier section on mechanisms and consequences of transgene integration for a discussion of illegitimate recombination, and earlier sections on insertional mutagenesis and entrapment vectors, and construction of recombinant baculovirus vectors for discussion of transposition. Note that Tn7 transposase is unusual in its preference for particular target sequences, allowing its use for site-specific transgene integration, while insertional mutagenesis and trap vector integration exploit the lower specificity of, e.g., P-elements and retroviruses.

opposite direction, that is by first cloning the gene, then mutating it in vitro, and reintroducing it into the source organism to study its function. Until a few years ago, the scope of this so-called *reverse genetics* approach was limited to the transfer of in vitro mutated genes into cells and later transgenic animals to study their effects. Only recently has it become possible directly to modify the genotype of a cell or animal by altering endogenous genes. Silencing is not only useful experimentally to generate mutants for functional studies, but also in applied fields to knock out undesirable traits and to correct dominant genetic disorders (a form of gene therapy known as *gene inhibition therapy*). In this section, we first review the development and use of homologous recombination and site-specific recombination in genetic engineering, with emphasis on their use for gene silencing. Other silencing strategies are then considered, such as the use of antisense RNA and dominant inhibitory proteins. Finally, we discuss the recent development of conditional gene silencing, a powerful technology that allows specific genes to be silenced either permanently or reversibly in an inducible or regulatable manner.

Homologous Recombination

Homologous recombination occurs naturally in all organisms. In mammals, homologous recombination occurs predominantly during meiosis and in some types of DNA repair. Exogenous DNA involved in homologous recombination events is probably used as a substrate by these DNA repair enzymes. Mechanistic parallels between DNA replication, recombination, and transcription are evident (236). We now know quite a lot about these events, primarily through work with yeast and other fungi. There are three possible outcomes of a homologous recombination event (Fig. 13). In most cases, the choice is between reciprocal exchange (usually termed a *crossover event*) and nonreciprocal exchange (usually termed *gene conversion*). In the former case, a recombination event occurring between two heterozygous loci will result in the exchange of markers between recombination partners (Fig. 13, panel I). In the

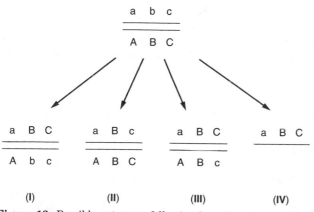

Figure 13. Possible outcomes following homologous recombination. The bars represent homologous DNA molecules, and the letters represent three genetic loci, with upper and lower cases indicating different alleles: (**I**) reciprocal recombination, (**II**) gene conversion, (**III**) gene conversion with crossover, (**IV**) nonconservative recombination.

latter case, recombination results in the unidirectional transfer of information, so that one allele appears to have been converted into the other. This can occur both in the absence (Fig. 13, panel II) and in the presence (Fig. 13, panel III) of a crossover event involving a third marker. Both crossing over and gene conversion involve the invasion of double-stranded DNA by a single strand, a process often initiated by a single- or double-strand chromosome break in the donor DNA molecule (or the free end of a linearized targeting construct). Homologous recombination then proceeds in a conservative manner with a preponderance of gene conversion over reciprocal recombination. The third possibility is extrachromosomal recombination (Fig. 13, panel IV), which occurs nonconservatively and results in the loss of the sequences at the opposite end of the two molecules.

Early Development of Homologous Recombination as a Genetic Tool

The development of engineering strategies based on homologous recombination in mammalian cells was preceded by the demonstration that exogenous DNA could participate in extrachromosomal recombination. Although such observations pointed the way, the mechanism of extrachromosomal recombination differs from that of homologous recombination between exogenous DNA and chromosomal DNA, which is loosely termed *gene targeting*. Extrachromosomal recombination involves a nonconservative recombination event where one of the substrates is lost, while gene targeting usually involves sequence conservation, unless the targeting strategy is specifically designed to remove sequences.

Homologous recombination between similar or identical DNA sequences allows the introduction of any sequence modification into a living cell. Initially, the technology was used to interrupt target genes, a gene silencing strategy popularly, if inaccurately, known as *gene knockout*. However, precise single-base-pair changes can also be generated (237). Alternatively large-scale genomic rearrangements are possible, including chromosomal translocations (238). A novel exploitation of this technique is to replace one gene with an entirely different gene, a strategy termed *gene knock in*. In each case, the desired mutation is generated in a cloned and in vitro modified DNA fragment, while the target homologous sequence representing the gene of interest resides within a chromosome of the host cell (239). The recombination event is catalyzed by the endogenous general recombination machinery of the cell, and involves mechanisms that are still incompletely understood.

Homologous recombination is a rare event in mammalian cells, with nonhomologous (illegitimate) recombination occurring three to five orders of magnitude more frequently (240). Therefore, it is necessary to incorporate a selectable marker system that will enrich for the targeted integration event. Indeed, the design of an appropriate targeting construct is a critical step for successful gene targeting. The first mammalian gene targeting experiments in the early 1980s involved the correction of artificially created mutations in somatic cell lines. Subsequently, in 1985, a mutation was generated in the human

β-globin gene using an insertion vector (241). A targeting frequency of 10^{-3} clones was achieved, but this still represented an inefficient targeting event. The procedure was refined through use of the endogenous *Hprt* marker gene, which could be selectively inactivated by homologous recombination (242). As discussed earlier (Table 4), cells *lacking* HPRT activity can be selected by culturing them in the presence of the toxic base analog 6-thioguanine (6-TG), and counterselected in the presence hypoxanthine, aminopterin, and thymidine (using HAT medium). This system allowed studies concerning the variables associated with homologous recombination to be addressed, such as the size of the homology region required and the effects of terminal homology (243).

Homologous recombination strategies in genetic engineering rely on the detection of very rare molecular events, so it is important to optimize the targeting efficiency. The targeting frequency depends on a number of factors (244). First, with current techniques, better targeting efficiencies are achieved with a larger *homology region* (the region of shared homology between the targeting vector and the target itself). Targeting efficiency increases exponentially with the size of the homology region up to about 10–14 kbp, where a plateau is reached. In addition, the degree of similarity between the sequences in the targeting construct and the endogenous locus has a major effect on the recombination efficiency. For example, the frequency of the recombination event can be increased three- to five-fold if the DNA used is from an identical (isogenic) source rather than a different strain of animal (245). Another factor with a considerable effect, restricing the choice of target genes, is the actual targeted locus. For as yet unknown reasons (but presumably due to either the specific overall sequence composition or higher-order chromosomal structure), some genomic targets are highly resistant to recombination and are thus recalcitrant to gene targeting. Finally, the design of the targeting vector also determines the outcome of the experiment, with targeting strategies reflecting the use of either insertion or replacement vectors, as discussed later. The relative efficiencies of each type of vector are still debated (246,247).

Gene Silencing—Targeting Vector Design

There are two classes of targeting vector, termed insertion vectors and replacement (or transplacement) vectors. Insertion vectors are linearized *within* the homology region, resulting in the insertion of the entire vector into the target locus (248). This type of vector disrupts the target gene but leads to a duplication of the sequences adjacent to the selectable marker [(Fig. 14(a)]. This is not always a desirable configuration (249). First, duplication of the target sequences can lead to a leaky phenotype (e.g., if the intention is to disrupt the target gene, the duplicated region can undergo variable splicing event leading to production of wild-type transcript). Second, a subsequent homologous recombination event can occur between the duplicated regions, removing the selectable marker and causing reversion to the wild-type genotype. This is the basis of the precise genetic modification strategy termed "hit-and-run," discussed in the following section [(Fig. 14(c)].

Replacement vectors are designed so that the homology region is collinear with the endogenous target. The vector is linearized *outside* the homology region prior to transfection, resulting in crossover events in which the endogenous DNA is replaced by the incoming DNA [Fig. 14(b)]. With this type of vector, plasmid backbone sequences are not inserted, only sequences within the homology region. Insertional inactivation is thus achieved by interrupting the vector homology region with extra DNA so that it is no longer functional [Fig. 14(b)]. To allow identification of targeted cell clones, the homology region is interrupted by a selectable marker such as *neo*. Insertion or replacement thus introduces the selectable marker at the target site, and growing the cells under selection (e.g., neomycin or its more widely used analog, G418) will kill all those cells that do not harbor the appropriate allele, representing the integration event. This strategy produces a disrupted target gene (250) and is termed positive selection.

The use of a single selectable marker, although allowing selection for integration events, does not discriminate between targeted events due to homologous recombination and random, nontargeted integrations. What is needed is an enrichment procedure. The most widely used system requires the inclusion of a second, counterselectable marker and is the basis of *positive–negative selection* (Fig. 15) (251). The most commonly used system involves inclusion of the HSV thymidine kinase (*tk*) gene, which will kill transfected cells in the presence of gancyclovir. The counterselectable marker is positioned at one end of the vector, outside the homology region, and will not be inserted by homologous recombination, allowing correctly targeted cells to survive. However, the marker is inserted by random integration, allowing cells carrying randomly integrated constructs to be counterselected with gancyclovir.

Variations on positive–negative selection are available, including a highly efficient system involving a promoterless construct (252). In this case the selectable marker lacks the sequences required to initiate transcription, and its expression is therefore dependent on insertion into the target gene by homologous recombination. Modifications on this approach include using an internal ribosome entry site, which generates a bicistronic messenger RNA (177). As well as providing a very efficient targeting strategy, the IRES also considerably simplifies construction of the vector, since the selectable marker does not have to be inserted in-frame.

Strategies for Introducing Subtle Mutations

While gene targeting has traditionally been used to disrupt and hence silence specific endogenous genes by introducing large insertions, more refined approaches are now being used to generate subtle mutations. The precise effects of minor deletions or point mutations cannot be assessed through simple targeting strategies, which necessarily leave the selectable marker, and in some cases the entire targeting vector, integrated at the target site. Two major strategies for introducing *clean mutations* (subtle mutations without markers or foreign sequences) have been devised, each involving two rounds

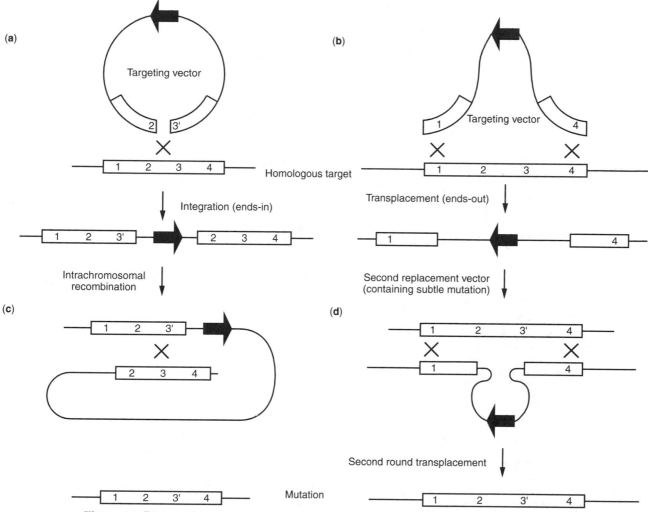

Figure 14. Design of targeting vectors and their use for gene knockout and subtle allele replacement mutations. (**a**) Insertion vector, linearized in the homology region. This undergoes "ends-in" recombination with a single crossover, and inserts the entire vector into the targeted locus. (**b**) Replacement (or transplacement) vector, linearized outside the homology region. This undergoes "ends-out" recombination with a double-crossover or gene conversion, and replaces the targeted locus with the homologous region of the vector. Gene knockout is thus achieved by interrupting the vector homology region. (**c**) Subtle mutation using an insertion vector (hit and run). The first integration generates the hit and inserts the marker(s) (black arrow), which are initially used for positive selection. The vector homology region carries the desired mutation. Subsequently, intrachromosomal recombination between the tandem homology regions replaces the endogenous gene with the mutant allele with no further intervention from the experimenter (i.e., he or she can run!). The mutation is represented by ('). Successfully targeted clones can be identified by negative selection, since the second recombination event removes the counterselectable marker. (**d**) Subtle mutation by transplacement requires two vectors. The first vector is the tag, interrupting the gene and leaving the selectable markers. The second vector carries the desired mutation and facilitates the exchange, replacing the interrupted allele with the desired mutation and removing the counterselectable marker.

of homologous recombination. These are the "hit and run" strategy [Fig. 14(c)], involving a single insertion vector, and the "tag and exchange" strategy [Fig. 14(d)] involving two replacement vectors. In each case, the first targeting event introduces a marker or markers for positive–negative selection—this event is identified by positive selection. The second targeting event introduces the mutation and removes the marker(s)—this event is identified by negative selection.

The *hit and run* or "in–out" strategy (237,253) involves the use of an insertion vector carrying two selectable markers, such as *neo* and *Tk* [Fig. 14(c)]. The insertion event is positively selected by culturing the cells in the presence of G418. Since an insertion vector is used, the entire vector is integrated and the homology region is duplicated in the targeted clone. One of these duplicated regions, the one derived from the insertion vector harbors the desired subtle mutation. The success of this

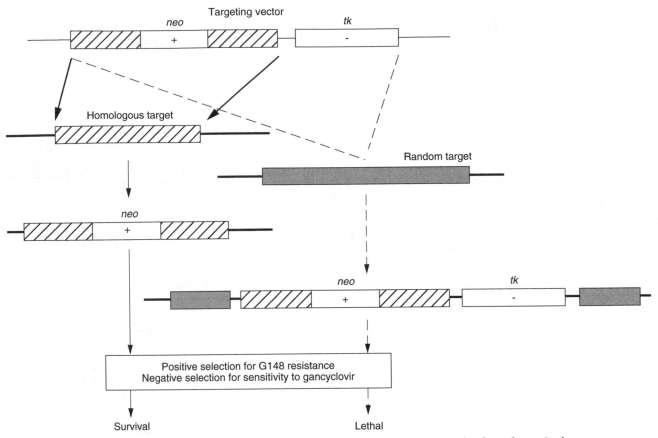

Figure 15. Positive–negative selection. Random integration occurs several orders of magnitude more frequently than homologous recombination in mammals, and a single selectable marker cannot discriminate between the two events. Positive–negative selection employs two markers, a selectable marker within the homology region, which is integrated by both recombination and random end-joining, and a counterselectable marker outside the homology region, which is only integrated by random end-joining, not by homologous recombination. Only targeted clones are therefore resistant to both G418 (conferred by *neo*) *and* gancyclovir (conferred by the *absence* of *Tk*).

approach relies on a second intrachromosomal homologous recombination event between the duplicated homology regions, which first replaces the endogenous allele with the mutant, and second deletes the markers allowing negative selection for gancyclovir resistance. Pending the resolution of this second event, the desired mutation may be left at the target locus. Although elegant in conception, this technique suffers from one disadvantage, which is that the second homologous recombination event is inefficient.

The *tag and exchange* strategy is similar in that it also requires two homologous recombination events, but differs in that it requires two replacement-type vectors (254). The first "tag" vector is designed to mutate the target gene and insert the selectable marker(s). The second vector facilitates the exchange reaction by reintroducing the desired mutation into the target gene while eliminating the selectable marker(s). Selection for the two events is analogous to that for the hit and run approach when two markers such as *neo* and *Tk* are used [Fig. 14(d)]. Variations include strategies using a single selectable marker such as *Hgprt*, which can be positively selected or counterselected as appropriate (255).

Target Cells for Homologous Recombination

In theory, any mammalian cell can provide the target for homologous recombination. However, gene targeting in the majority of cells is very inefficient, with ES cells being a notable exception (244). Indeed, the general inefficiency of homologous recombination in mammalian cells remains one of the central limiting factors in the exploitation of this powerful technique. *Embryonic stem (ES) cells* have therefore been used in most gene targeting experiments (Fig. 16) (256,257). Furthermore, when handled appropriately, ES cells are pluripotent: They can differentiate into any (all) somatic cell types (239). This means that a genetic modification introduced into ES cells can be incorporated into the germline of an animal. To date the only animals that have been genetically modified through homologous recombination are mice. This is because only mouse ES cells are currently available, although this situation is likely to change in the near future (258,259). ES cells are also a valuable cell culture-based resource for studying gene function, especially in development, since they can be

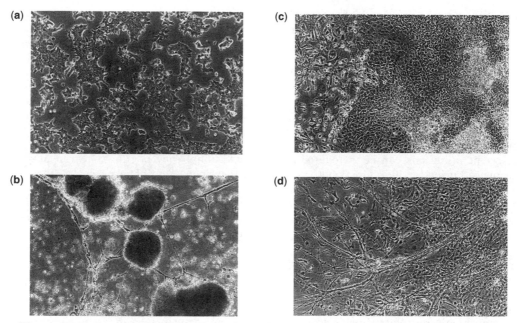

Figure 16. Embryonic stem (ES) cells. (**a**) Recently plated mouse ES cells from strain 129 (note the small cytoplasmic volume relative to nuclear size). (**b**) In culture, the cells will develop three-dimensional growth characteristics. In the absence of the growth factor LIF, embryoid bodies will be formed. Alternatively, ES cells will differentiate into a variety of cell types including (**c**) epithelial and fibroblastoid or (**d**) neuronal filament-like. Photographs courtesy of Jim McWhir and Ray Ansell (Roslin Institute).

induced to differentiate into specific cell lineages in culture (260).

DNA can be introduced in to ES cells by a variety of routes, the choice depending on the intended use of the cells. If germline transmission is the desired outcome, the effect of the protocol on the integrity of the ES cell genotype and phenotype must be considered. For example, cells that have undergone chromosomal rearrangements or cells that have differentiated will not contribute to the germline. ES cell transformation was first achieved by retroviral transduction and calcium phosphate–mediated transfection, but electroporation has now replaced these as the method of choice. Electroporation gives a higher transfection efficiency, is relatively simple and reproducible, and is compatible with germline transmission. Alternative methods to introduce DNA into ES cells include microinjection (which is technically very demanding) and lipofection, perhaps best suited for the delivery of large fragments of DNA.

Recently, there has been considerable interest in the potential of primary cells for gene targeting, at least in part due to the development of nuclear transfer techniques in mammalian species. Gene targeting is an inefficient process with individual targeting events in primary and established somatic cells occurring at low frequencies, typically less than 10^{-4}. At this efficiency, thousands of stably transfected clones must be screened to isolate a single homologous recombinant, and this requirement severely limits the use of primary somatic cells as the target for homologous recombination. Primary cells are usually isolated in only small numbers, and are capable of only a few rounds of cell division prior to senescence

or crisis. In attempts to overcome this limitation, various enrichment strategies have been developed, including the positive–negative selection system discussed, which can achieve a 30% targeting efficiency. As more experiments have been documented, however, the promoterless-type vectors have emerged as the most successful. Using these approaches for gene knockout in human primary cells, human gene function can be addressed. For example, disruption of the p21$^{CIP1/WAF1}$ gene in normal diploid human fibroblasts demonstrated its pivotal role in cell senescence (261).

There is also considerable interest in the use of somatic cells for gene targeting. For example, as the means to propagate human somatic cells in the form of lineage-specific stem cells becomes available, gene targeting could be used to correct or remedy genetic defects by interrupting dominant mutant alleles, or replacing them with the wild-type allele. The somatic cells could then be used to replace the mutant cells in vivo, a form of somatic gene therapy. Alternatively, gene targeting in somatic cells could provide a basis for the genetic modification of animals when used in conjunction with nuclear transfer technology. Gene targeting in the majority of cell lines is an inefficient process compared to ES cells, and the basis of the amenability of ES cells for homologous recombination is as yet unclear. Fortunately there are exceptions, with some obscure cell lines allowing highly efficient homologous recombination events. One example is the chicken pre-B cell line DT40. Unfortunately, no mammalian cell line with the same characteristics is known, but as research uncovers more components of the homologous recombination machinery, it may become possible to modify somatic cells to allow higher targeting frequencies. The characterization of obscure somatic cell lines such as DT40, with an intrinsic targeting capacity, may well help to achieve this goal. Although the molecular basis for the high targeting efficiency of DT40 cells is not understood, the DT40 line is of great value in experiments designed to modify genetic loci. Importantly, these cells can be used to direct genetic modification of human cells. For example, by combining gene targeting in DT40 cells and microcell fusion (which allows chromosome shuttling between cells), specific mutations can be introduced into human gene sequences prior to their functional testing in human cells. Other genetic tricks are possible in these cells, including telomerase-directed truncation, allowing gross modifications of target chromosomes (262).

Site-Specific Recombination Systems

Site-specific recombination involves the recognition of short consensus sequences by specific enzymes (recombinases) that catalyze strand exchange and resolution within small regions of DNA homology. Such systems are not ubiquitous. They are encoded by individual bacteria, plasmids, viruses, and transposons, and serve many purposes (235). Bacteriophage λ integrase, for instance, controls integration and excision of the λ prophage. Conversely, E. coli Tn3 resolvase, S. cerevisiae 2 μ plasmid FLP recombinase, and E. coli Xer recombinase control replication by resolving plasmid or genome dimers. Bacteriophage Mu Gin invertase and Salmonella typhimurium Hin invertase facilitate programmed genome rearrangements. Finally, Bacteriophage P1 Cre recombinase facilitates genome circularization following phage infection. A number of site-specific recombination systems have been studied in detail. For some, such as λ integrase, several host proteins are required in addition to the recombinase itself for efficient recombination. However, the simplest systems require only the recombinase and its target sequence, and these are the most useful for

genetic engineering because only a limited number of components need to be transferred to the new host. The most extensively used systems are Cre recombinase from bacteriophage P1 (263) and FLP recombinase (flippase) from the S. cerevisiae 2 μ plasmid (264). These have been shown to function in many heterologous eukaryotic systems, including mammalian cells and transgenic animals. Both recombinases recognize 34-bp sites (termed loxP and FRP, respectively) comprising a pair of 13-bp inverted repeats surrounding an 8-bp central element. FRP possesses an additional copy of the 13-bp repeat sequence, although this is nonessential for recombination. The introduction of these sequences into animal genomes, along with expression constructs driving expression of the recombinase protein, can therefore induce site-specific recombination events in mammals. The activity of Cre recombinase is shown in Figure 17.

Applications of Site-Specific Recombination

If two recombination sites are integrated in the same orientation, site-specific recombination between them will excise the intervening DNA. Transgenes flanked by such sites can therefore be introduced into the genome as normal, but excised by supplying the recombinase in trans. This "site-specific excision" strategy has many applications (228), including the excision of unwanted sequences from the transgene (e.g., selectable markers, plasmid backbone sequences) and deletion of blocking sequences to allow transgene activation. This last strategy, known as recombination activation of gene expression (RAGE), involves the insertion of a blocking element (such as a polyadenylation site) between the transgene and its promoter. RAGE can be used to excise the blocking element, bringing the transgene and promoter into juxtaposition, resulting in transgene activation. Site-specific recombination, in concert with gene targeting, can also be used for endogenous gene silencing. In one strategy, sometimes termed floxing, gene targeting is used to

Figure 17. Characteristics of Cre recombinase activity. (I) The loxP site recognized by Cre recombinase, comprising 13-bp palindromic sequences (arrows) surrounding an 8-bp core (boxed). (II) Cre recombinase deletes the sequence between two loxP sites in the same orientation, and such a sequence is said to be "floxed." (III) When loxP sites are inverted with respect to each other, Cre recombinase inverts the DNA sequence between them. In both cases, the reaction is reversible, but the circular excision product in (II) is quickly degraded, making the reaction effectively irreversible. Floxed linear DNA can integrate at a single loxP site in the presence of Cre, but because integration and excision occur with equal frequency, the degradation of the excision product drives the eqilibrium of the reaction towards excision. For this reason, Cre-mediated DNA integration is currently as inefficient as random integration.

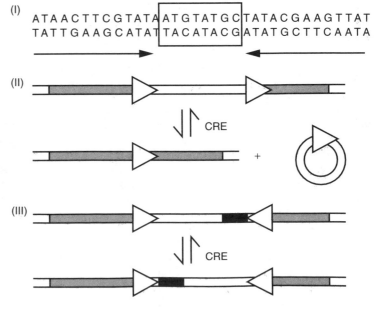

introduce recombinase sites flanking an endogenous gene. The term floxing is derived from the term "flanking *loxP*" but other recombinases are used in an analogous manner. Once the targeting strategy is complete, the introduction of recombinase into the system causes site-specific gene deletion or inversion (as appropriate), resulting in gene silencing. Similar strategies can be used to facilitate the deletion, inversion, or transposition of particular chromosome segments, an approach often used to model human diseases caused by chromosome rearrangements.

As well as catalyzing excision, site-specific recombination can be used for transgene integration. In this strategy, a single recombination site is introduced into a particular chromosomal locus by gene targeting, and if recombinase is supplied in *trans*, transgene constructs flanked by recombination sites can be transfected into the cell and persuaded to integrate by site-specific recombination. However, while the constitutive expression of recombinase is sufficient for site-specific excision strategies, a transient burst of recombinase is required for integration because the reaction is easily reversible. The availability of recombinase is difficult to control precisely; thus site-specific integration is currently only just as efficient as random transgene integration by illegitimate recombination. However, as discussed, the advantages of site-specific recombination include the ability to generate isogenic cell clones or transgenic animals, and the ability to target sites that are free from negative position effects.

Gene Silencing using Antisense RNA Constructs

Gene targeting and site-specific recombination-based strategies are now well-established technologies for gene silencing. However, the activity of an endogenous gene may also be suppressed if antisense RNA is introduced into a cell. Antisense RNA has a complementary sequence to mRNA, and can bind to the sense transcript either in the nucleus or cytoplasm to form a duplex. The mechanism of gene inhibition is unclear, and may act at several levels. Protein synthesis is a likely target, either through the prevention of productive pre-mRNA processing and export, or duplex-induced mRNA degradation, or by direct inhibition of ribosome binding, scanning, or translocation. Additionally, the presence of dsRNA induces DAI protein kinase, causing a general reduction in the rate of protein synthesis. The effects of injecting or transfecting antisense RNA into a cell are transient because the RNA cannot replicate and is rapidly degraded. However, long-term gene inhibition can be achieved simply by reversing the orientation of a transgene with respect to its promoter and introducing such a construct into cells or transgenic animals through the normal routes. If such a construct integrates and is expressed, the cell has a constant supply of antisense RNA sufficient for long-term gene inhibition. This strategy has been achieved using both transfected plasmid DNA and retroviral vectors. Antisense inhibition has been used in many cell culture experiments and in ES cells to generate transgenic animals. The results have been variable, with mRNA levels reduced by just 20% in some cases and almost 100% in others (reviewed in Ref. 265). It is not necessary to express full-length antisense RNA for "knockdown" effects to occur. The expression of an approximately 5-kb antisense RNA corresponding to the *Wnt-1* transcript resulted in 98% reduction, while just 40 b of antisense RNA corresponding to the mouse $G_{\alpha i}$ transcript resulted in 95% reduction.

Additional sequences can be added to antisense transcription units to increase the inhibitory activity of the molecule. In a few cases, targeting sequences have been used to direct antisense RNA to particular subcellular locations. A popular strategy is to exploit the ability of ribozymes linked to antisense RNA to cleave mRNA in a sequence-dependent manner. Ribozymes are catalytic RNA molecules whose complex tertiary structure allows them to adopt the molecular configurations characteristic of (protein) enzymes and hence to catalyze biochemical reactions. The self-splicing introns found in organelle genomes are autocatalytic (i.e., the RNA facilitates its own excision), whereas other ribozymes are catalytic in the strict sense, because they act in *trans* on a distinct substrate. Ribozymes have a bipartite structure including a targeting sequence and a catalytic core. The targeting sequence is an antisense RNA that forms base pairs with a specific RNA substrate and holds the catalytic core in the correct position, allowing cleavage of a phosphodiester bond. If the ribozyme catalytic core is fused in vitro to a given antisense RNA (266), the ribozyme can be targeted to the mRNA, which will be cleaved. Cleavage destroys the function of the mRNA, and the 3' fragment (lacking a cap) is rapidly degraded. Ribozyme constructs have been used to generate functional knockout mice and are currently undergoing clinical trials as a gene therapy agent to combat AIDS. However, critical comparisons of ribozyme constructs and related antisense constructs containing no catalytic core have often revealed similar levels of inhibitory activity (265). This suggests that some ribosome constructs may work simply through their antisense effects rather than by cleaving mRNA. Few such studies have involved attempts to identify the cleavage products of ribozyme activity.

Gene Silencing using Inhibitory Protein Strategies

Genetic engineering can be used to interfere with endogenous gene expression at the protein level, as well as at the RNA level. The specificity and affinity of antibodies for their complementary antigens has been widely exploited for identifying, localizing, and purifying proteins (267). Antibodies microinjected into cells have also been used to inactivate proteins (268), but such effects are only transient, and cannot readily be applied to whole organisms. A new approach is to stably transform animal cells with antibody-encoding genes. This strategy results in the long-term expression of "intracellular antibodies" known as *intrabodies*, which can be targeted to particular cellular compartments and used to abolish the activity of specific proteins. Intrabodies have been used to generate functional knockouts of important molecules such as growth factor receptors, and their potential role in gene therapy has been explored by targeting oncogenic proteins and the gp120 HIV envelope protein (reviewed in Ref. 269). The strategy for expressing intrabodies is complex. Immunoglobulin genes cannot be used for transfection due to their size and the absence of V(D)J recombinase and switch recombinase in most cells. Additionally, since *specific* antibodies are required, DNA sequences corresponding to particular mature (rearranged) immunoglobulins must be used. However, the native immunoglobulin assembly pathway occurs very inefficiently in the cytoplasm and attempts to reassemble functional immunoglobulins from distinct heavy and light chains have not succeeded. The current strategy is to synthesize single-chain antibodies carrying the antigen-binding domains of both heavy and light chains on a single polypeptide with a flexible intervening linker chain. Such molecules are capable of folding in the cytoplasm and interact with their targets, but they have shorter half-lives than secreted immunoglobulins.

An alternative strategy for gene inhibition at the protein level is to transfect cells with constructs encoding dominant inhibitory proteins. Proteins that function as oligomeric complexes possess domains for interaction with other subunits. It is often possible to identify dominant loss of function alleles (*dominant negatives*) for the genes encoding such proteins. These encode nonfunctional subunits that form stable complexes with the functional wild-type subunits, sequestering them into inactive oligomers. Dominant negative alleles may be generated by point mutations or truncations, and the overexpression of such alleles is useful for generating functional knockout phenotypes. This strategy has been used to inactivate many different types of protein, including receptor tyrosine kinases and cytokine receptors, transcription factors, and other oncoproteins. More recently, dominant negative overexpression has been combined with techniques for conditional gene expression to generate conditional silencing systems for the study of signal transduction, the cell cycle, apoptosis, and the function of telomerase (reviewed in Ref. 190). The major therapeutic application of dominant negative gene expression has been blocking the HIV replication cycle by interfering with capsid assembly (reviewed in Ref. 270).

Epigenetic Transient Gene Silencing with Oligonucleotides

Gene silencing strategies based on the integration and long-term expression of inhibitory transgenes are designed to permanently block the expression of a given endogenous gene. However, a similar but transient effect can be achieved by introducing the inhibitory gene product directly into the cell, such as antisense RNA or antibodies active against specific gene products. Another approach to transient gene silencing is the introduction of short oligonucleotides (15–30 nucleotides in length) into the cell. Depending on their design, oligonucleotides can block the expression of specific genes at the levels of transcription, RNA processing, translation, or protein function. Pyrimidine-rich oligonucleotides can interact with duplex DNA if there is pronounced pyrimidine/purine strand asymmetry. The oligonucleotide can interact with the duplex using an unusual form of base pairing called Hoogsteen pairing. The resulting triple helix is stable and blocks transcription, allowing gene-specific silencing (271). Oligonucleotides for triple-helix gene silencing can be sense or antisense with respect to the target gene, but their use is limited by the stringent

pyrimidine-rich sequence requirements. A more general approach is to use antisense oligonucleotides in the same way as antisense RNA. However, because the oligonucleotides are DNA, they are generally more stable than the RNA, and they also form DNA:RNA hybrids that act as substrates for RNaseH, and hence induce the degradation of the target mRNAs. Antisense oligonucleotides for gene therapy have been validated in animal disease models and are now undergoing clinical trials for human diseases (272). Finally, improvement in oligonucleotide synthesis technology has allowed the production of sets of degenerate oligonucleotides that can be screened for their ability to bind specific proteins. An oligonucleotide binding in such a specific manner is termed an *aptamer*, and following a number of successful experiments in which specific proteins have been inhibited, aptamer technology may well emerge as a new form of gene therapy. Current problems with oligonucleotide-mediated gene inhibition include stability and delivery. Oligonucleotides are linear and prone to exonuclease attack, but this can be alleviated by chemical modification of the terminal residues. Cellular uptake of naked oligonucleotides is poor because they are large hydrophilic molecules, and transfection may require cell permeabilization, or the use of a gene delivery system such as liposomes or lipofection.

Strategies for Conditional Gene Silencing

Constitutive and permanent gene silencing are useful techniques, but cannot address complex questions such as the effect of withholding the product of a gene for a specific duration, and the function of pleiotropic genes with embryonic lethal null phenotypes. In the latter case, it should be stressed that many genes active in early development also have roles in later development or the adult, and these roles cannot be studied with constitutive knockouts if the animal dies in early development due to loss of an early gene function. Traditional methods for studying such genes include conditional mutants, usually temperature-sensitive mutants, which can be maintained under permissive conditions and then shifted to restrictive conditions at the appropriate time. However, more sophisticated and regulatable strategies for conditional gene silencing can be devised by combining the silencing strategies discussed with the inducible gene expression systems discussed earlier in this article.

Gene targeting and site-specific recombination can be used in a number of related strategies to bring endogenous gene expression under exogenous control. In the first strategy, gene targeting is used to flox the endogenous gene, but the recombinase enzyme gene is expressed under a tissue-specific or inducible promoter, or the recombinase enzyme is expressed as, for example, a steroid receptor fusion that can be activated in a ligand-dependent manner. This allows the generation of somatic knockouts, where an endogenous gene present in all cells can be selectively deleted in particular cells or at particular stages of development. It also allows the generation of inducible knockouts, so that the timing of deletion can be controlled by the experimenter. An alternative strategy is to use gene targeting to replace the endogenous gene with a homologous copy containing a blocking element flanked by *loxP* sites. In this case, the supply of recombinase catalyzes the removal of the blocking element, leading to conditional gene activation, a strategy termed *infloxing*. In all conditionally silenced mice generated to date, either inducible or cell type-specific Cre recombinase has been used. The general strategy is to use two strains of mice, a responder carrying the floxed target and a regulator carrying a *cre* gene either under inducible or cell-type-specific control. Conditional gene silencing is observed when the two strains of mice are interbred. Although site-specific recombinases offer exciting possibilities for transgene engineering in vivo, their activity in transgenic animals is not 100% efficient. There is a low level of background recombination, leading to leaky (in)activation. There is also pronounced and undesirable tissue specificity, resulting in the production of mosaics, and unexpected cell type-preferred transgene (in)activation. Another potential problem is the presence of cryptic recombinase sites in the endogenous genome, which may result in unwanted recombination events. This may be a particular problem when engineering chromosome deletions, inversions, and translocations for disease modeling.

Strategies for conditional gene silencing that do not rely on Cre recombinase have been used most frequently in cell lines as opposed to transgenic animals (conversely, Cre-mediated silencing has not been used for conditional silencing in cell lines). Gene targeting strategies include the replacement of endogenous promoters with inducible ones. This approach has been used in DT40 cells to bring the *ASF* gene under tetracycline regulation and the *CENP-C* gene under estrogen regulation (190). Similarly, a growing number of reports demonstrate conditional silencing by the inducible transcription of antisense RNA, and the inducible expression of dominant negative proteins. So far, an inducible dominant negative strategy has not been reported in transgenic mice, although a number of inducible antisense constructs have been expressed in mice, leading to conditional inactivation of *Wnt-1*, $G_{\alpha i}$, and genes encoding angiotensin and MHC class II proteins. A final strategy is the conditional expression of a toxic transgene, such as the ricin toxin A chain gene, or the diphtheria toxin A chain gene. This strategy has been reported in mammals but has been extensively used in *Drosophila* (reviewed in Ref. 273)

THE PRODUCTION OF TRANSGENIC MAMMALS FROM MANIPULATED CELLS

Overview

A *transgenic* animal is one in which every cell carries a fragment of foreign DNA. Initially, the term *transgenic* specifically applied to animals (and plants) carrying genes from a heterologous species. In many cases, the scope of the term can be broadened to include animals carrying, for example, extra or modified copies of endogenous genes, but most researchers stop short of using the term to describe any form of genome modification, since this would include animals carrying subtle mutations (e.g., point mutations) generated by two rounds of replacement. In

the majority of cases the foreign DNA represents a gene (a *transgene*) or set of transgenes (192). The transgene integrates into one of the host chromosomes, becomes part of that animal's genetic repertoire, and is usually inherited by subsequent generations as a Mendelian trait. The transgene can be derived from any conceivable source, that is, the same species (e.g., an extra copy of an endogenous gene controlled by a heterologous promoter), a related species (e.g., human growth hormone expressed in mice), or an evolutionary distant species (such as bacterial transgenes in sheep). In addition, a hybrid gene may be generated from a variety of sources or a synthetic gene may be produced de novo. Integrated transgenes are often expressed correctly and can have profound phenotypic effects, for instance, as shown by the greatly increased size of transgenic mice carrying growth hormone transgenes. The abnormal growth resulted from the elevated levels of growth hormone in their serum (274).

A variety of methods have been developed for the production of transgenic animals. All are based on the introduction of the DNA into a single cell that contributes to the development of the animal. In most cases the cell of interest is a fertilized egg, although cell-culture-based approaches (using ES cells or nuclear transfer) are more sophisticated (these are discussed later). The advantage of transgenic animals over cell culture studies lies in their ability to show the function of a gene in its normal physiological environment, that of the whole organism (239,244). Ironically, however, this advantage can limit the utility of some studies due to the very complex nature of the interactions possible in the whole organism. Therefore, studying a gene both in vitro and in vivo is often the most beneficial approach. Nevertheless, transgenic animals permit the study of developmental and physiological events in the context of the natural processes occurring in the animal.

In mammals, the vast majority of transgenic experiments have been performed using mice, and there is now an enormous amount of literature on genetically modified mice. This has been due primarily to the economy and convenience of using a small species with a short generation interval. Nevertheless, studies have been performed in a number of other mammals (275). Transgenic rats are well suited for experiments involving multiple analyses (e.g., blood sampling) and have been successfully used in studies addressing blood pressure. Transgenic rabbits offer an intermediate between a laboratory species and a farm animal, and again have specific uses. For example, rabbits display a similar lipid metabolism to man and may provide useful models for the study of fat-related diseases (e.g., athersclerosis). However, excluding mice, it has been the generation of transgenic farm animals — pigs, sheep, goats, and cattle — which has received most attention. Certainly, transgenic livestock have provided the incentive for substantial commercial involvement in the discipline of animal genetic engineering. We now consider the methods available for generating transgenic mammals.

Pronuclear Microinjection

The most widely used method for introducing genes into the germline of mammals is the direct microinjection of DNA into the pronuclei of fertilized eggs (276). Pronuclear microinjection is conceptually simple (a fine needle is used to pierce the pronucleus and the DNA is injected; Figure 18) but requires special equipment and a considerable amount of technical expertise and dexterity from the operator. Nevertheless, the majority of research laboratories around the world now have access to such transgenic mouse facilities. By adapting the techniques employed for gene transfer to mice, pronuclear microinjection has been used to generate transgenic farm animals (277), as will be discussed in more detail.

Pronuclear microinjection, although reliable, is relatively inefficient, with only 20–30% of the mice derived from microinjected eggs carrying the transgene. This efficiency drops to 1% for domestic farm animals. It is generally accepted that the DNA integrates at or after the first round of chromosomal DNA replication. This means that the founder embryo is mosaic with regard to transgene status (278), resulting in founder animals with different integration positions and transgene copy numbers in different tissues, due to the mixing and allocation of cells during early embryogenesis. Once transmitted through the germline, however, the transgene copy number is usually stable, and the transgene is then inherited in a Mendelian fashion. There have been a few reports of transgenes undergoing rearrangement, deletion, or amplification, but these appear to be exceptions to the rule. Also, with a few obscure exceptions, the transgene does not appear to be retained extrachromosomally in mammalian species.

Variations on Pronuclear Microinjection

Although pronuclear microinjection has provided the main route for the generation of transgenic animals, a variety of other approaches are available. Integration has been observed following cytoplasmic injection or injection into the blastocoel cavity. Both routes proved to be substantially less efficient that pronuclear injection. Attempts to improve the efficiency of these approaches (e.g., using poly-L-lysine) have shown some promise,

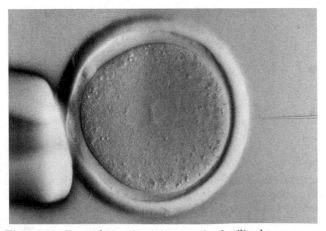

Figure 18. Pronuclear microinjection of a fertilized mouse egg. The two pronuclei are visible within the egg, which is being held by a suction pipette. The DNA is introduced through a fine glass needle. Photograph courtesy of Roberta Wallace (Roslin Institute).

but remain unreliable (279). Retroviral infection of preimplantation embryos has been successful, but this method is now used only rarely to generate transgenic animals (138). It has been proposed that adenovirus vectors may be used for germline transformation in the future (280). However, viral transduction as a method for generating transgenic animals suffers from several drawbacks, including the limited amount of foreign DNA that can be incorporated into integrating viral vectors, the effect of viral sequences both on transgene expression and the expression of endogenous genes located near to the transgene insertion site, and the susceptibility of transgenes carried in recombinant proviruses to de novo DNA methylation.

There have also been reports that transgenic animals can be produced using a simple technique in which DNA is mixed with spermatozoa prior to in vitro fertilization. Such a method would be widely applicable due to its simplicity. Unfortunately, although considerable effort has been employed in the study and development of this technique, it remains enigmatic and can be reproduced by only a few laboratories around the world. The general consensus is that a reliable sperm-mediated gene transfer technique in mammals remains to be developed (281).

Embryonic Stem Cells

Mouse embryonic stem (ES) cells have revolutionized mammalian genetics by providing a route for the directed and sequence-specific alteration of the mouse genome (239,244). ES cells possess a unique combination of useful properties: They are pluripotent (and hence compatible with germline modification), they are amenable to in vitro cell culture, and they possess an inherent capacity for homologous recombination (see earlier section). These qualities provide a very efficient and elegant method by which to generate transgenic animals (Fig. 19). First, the DNA transfected into cultured ES cells integrates into the genome (either randomly or by homologous recombination—gene targeting). Then the genetically modified cells are introduced into preimplantation stage embryos, either by blastocyst injection or by morula aggregation, to produce chimeras. In a proportion of these chimeric animals, the ES cells will have contributed to the germline, thus providing a source of fully transgenic offspring. A popular strategy is to use ES cells and preimplantation embryos from mouse strains with different coat color markers. The ES cells often carry a dominant marker such as agouti, while the recipient embryos carry a recessive black coat color. The chimeric founder mice have patchwork black/agouti coats representing cell clones derived from the two genotypes that contributed to the embryo, because the markers are cell autonomous. Chimeric males are then mated to black females, and transgenic offspring are identified by their agouti coats, showing they are entirely derived from the ES cells. This germline modification is then inherited as a Mendelian trait. This simple strategy saves performing Southern blot hybridization or PCR analysis on all offspring to determine their genotype. ES cells offer an attractive route to germline modification when compared to pronuclear injection because DNA alterations

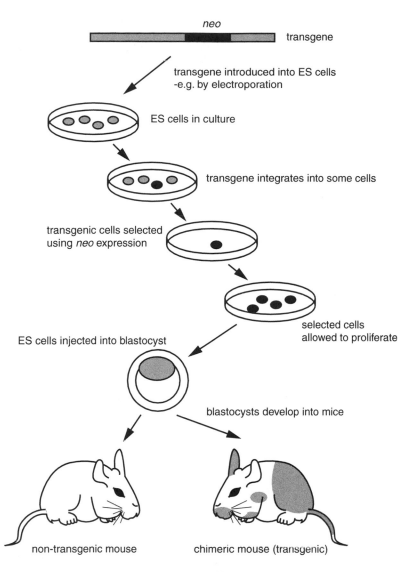

Figure 19. Generation of transgenic mice from ES cells. ES cells are modified in culture by transfection or retroviral transduction. Transformants are selected, and injected into wild-type blastocysts. A proportion of the mice developing from ES cell-injected blastocysts will be normal, and a proportion will be chimeric for donor- and ES cell-derived tissue. In some of the latter category, the germline will be ES cell derived, and any progeny of these "germline-transformed" mice will be transgenic. The identification of chimeric and transgenic mice is simplified by using donor blastocysts and ES cells carrying different coat color markers and of different sexes. Chimeric mice therefore possess a variegated coat, but transgenic mice will carry the ES coat color marker.

can be carried out in cell culture and verified before being introduced into the embryo. The limitations associated with pronuclear injection (technical requirements for working with pronuclear eggs, and the lack of preimplantation screening so that transgenic status has to be verified after birth) do not apply to ES cells. ES cells may therefore facilitate more precise genome modifications, especially by exploiting the versatility of gene targeting strategies (237,238).

The injection of ES cells into blastocysts is a delicate procedure, and there has been a considerable effort to develop improved strategies for ES cell delivery into the embryo. Morula injections are easier and give better results in terms of germline transmission but suffer from very high embryo mortality rates. Alternatively, coculturing ES cells with 8-cell stage embryos generates blastocysts with an inner cell mass containing ES cells. The in vitro derived blastocysts are then reimplanted. This is an appealing method due to its simplicity, and has proven effective. However, the resulting animals are still chimeras, and germline transmission is not always achieved. It is also possible to make aggregates between tetraploid morula cells

(obtained by electrofusion) and ES cells. Since tetraploid cells cannot support development, the postimplantation embryos developing from these aggregates give rise to mice derived entirely from ES cells (282). Under these conditions, chimeric diploid/tetraploid embryos implant and develop to midgestation at high frequency, but the efficiency drops off during later development and few embryos survive to term. Early experiments varied in their success rates. However, as more experience is gained in this *tetraploid rescue* technique, it is becoming more robust. One interesting application was to use the liver of a tetraploid rescue fetus to reconstitute the mouse hematopoietic system (283). This allowed blood cell development to be studied using genetic modification techniques in the whole animal without having to pass the mutation through the germline.

Primoridal Germ Cells

Unfortunately, although a considerable number of attempts have been made and some unconfirmed successes claimed for the development of nonmurine ES cells, such cells are currently available only for mice. In this regard, the application of the recently developed selection protocol for embryonic cells, which kills differentiated cells while leaving the undifferentiated (and pluripotent) cells to grow, may now provide a route to generate ruminant ES cells (259). The failure to derive ES cells from other species, thus limiting the extent of genetic modification possible, has been the driving force to discover alternative strategies. One alternative approach would introduce the genetic change directly into the germline by gene targeting of primordial germ cells (PGCs) (Fig. 20). Recent advances in PGC isolation and culture, and the culture of cells derived from PGCs—embryonic germ (EG) cells—have provided the impetus to develop this approach. Indeed, there have been claims that EG cells may be analogous to ES cells. Unfortunately it has proven difficult to persuade PGCs to contribute to the germline (284), and the technique is not yet routine. Perhaps EG cells will prove more efficient in this regard.

USES FOR TRANSGENIC ANIMALS

Overview

Since the first transgenic mice produced by pronuclear injection in the early 1980s (285), a vast literature has been amassed concerning genetically modified mammals (275). The majority of transgenic mammals are mice. The use of other species has been restricted by technical limitations, cost, the time involved in breeding, and welfare issues. The recent development of nuclear transfer techniques in livestock (286) provides new openings for basic research, animal breeding, and animal biotechnology (287). In this section, the various uses of gene transfer in mice are discussed. We then go on to discuss the recent success in nuclear transfer methodology, and the impact this has had on biotechnology and medicine.

Studies Addressing Gene Function

There are two basic expression strategies for studying gene function in transgenic mice. The first involves a gain-of-function by overexpression of the protein of interest. This is probably the most widely used strategy due to

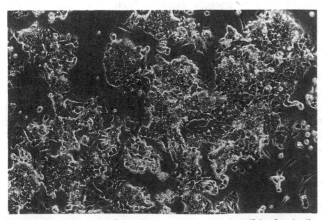

Figure 20. Mouse embryonic germ (EG) cells, strikingly similar to ES cells. Photograph courtesy of Ed Gallacher and Jim McWhir (Roslin Institute).

its simplicity. All that is required is the appropriate transcriptional control elements and the coding region of the gene of interest. The gene can be expressed according to its normal cellular parameters or deliberately expressed in an ectopic fashion. In addition, the incorporation of inducible promoters allows overexpression at a defined developmental stage. The transgene can be in the form of either a genomic fragment or a cDNA, although in general, genomic constructs are the more efficient. Examples of this approach include the overexpression of oncogenes, and the demonstration that the Y-linked *Sry* gene encodes the primary male sex-determination factor. An alternative use of this approach has been to facilitate the production of immortalized cell lines. To do this, a transgene is constructed consisting of the desired promoter linked to a gene capable of immortalizing cells, most commonly the SV40 viral T-antigen (288). Transgenes can be expressed in atypical tissues/stages of development, which can result in inappropriate but informative phenotypes (e.g., mice expressing the HSV-*Tk* gene) are sterile due to the ectopic expression of thymidine kinase gene in the testes (289). Ectopic expression can be due to influences of the adjacent cellular DNA or to unforeseen interactions between *cis*-acting sequences in hybrid transgenes.

The alternative strategy results in a loss-of-function. This can be achieved by either gene targeting approaches to generate a knockout (see the following) or directing expression of a transgenes encoding cytotoxic proteins. For example, transgenic mice, carrying a transgene comprising the diphtheria toxin under the control of the pancreatic elastase gene promoter, had no pancreas (290). More recent efforts have utilized genes encoding enzymes that convert an inactive prodrug into a cytotoxin. This approach is being developed as a strategy for cancer treatment, termed *gene-directed enzyme prodrug therapy* (GDEPT). One of the most promising examples of this approach is the *E. coli* nitroreductase gene, which offers a number of advantages over the more commonly used HSV *Tk* gene (291). As discussed, variations of this strategy include suppressing gene expression through the use of transgenes generating antisense RNA molecules, or the overexpression of a dominant-negative form of the protein (190).

Another way to use a transgene to study gene function is to use it as a tracer. This can be in the form of a physical genetic marker, since multicopy transgenes can be easily detected by chromosomal in situ techniques. Alternatively, transgene expression can be used to trace cell lineages, particularly during development (16). In particular, it is anticipated that the highly efficient promoterless targeting approach in ES cells will allow specific cell lineages to be followed in the adult animal.

Knockout (Null) Mice

The most powerful approach used to interfere with the function of a gene is to disrupt one allele by gene targeting in ES cells (239). In conjunction with the established positive−negative selection systems, precise genetic changes can be produced. However, this approach has also revealed the high degree of redundancy present in the mammalian genome. In attempts to get a round this problem, a variety of spatial and temporal expression vectors have been developed. The most recent developments in this area have come from small biotechnology companies, which have generated libraries of gene knockout clones.

Gene targeting has been used successfully to define the function of a number of genes including many proto-oncogenes (e.g., c-*Myb* and *Wnt*-1) (244). Gene targeting has also made valuable contributions to the understanding of the immune system. For example, gene targeting demonstrated that MHC class I antigens require the protein β2-microglobulin to be presented on the cell surface. Nevertheless, the greatest use of gene targeting has been to identify and characterize developmentally regulated genes. This has been most clearly demonstrated for the *Hox* genes and the transcription factors involved in muscle cell development (292).

The first step in generating a knockout mouse is to introduce the appropriately designed targeting vector into ES cells. In a few cells the vector is inserted, by homologous integration, into the target gene. As discussed, this event is identified by positive–negative selection. Subsequent clonal expansion of the target cell then generates an isogenic population of genetically modified cells. These are injected into the blastocoel cavity of a preimplantation mouse embryo. The blastocyst is surgically transferred into the uterus of a foster mother, where development is allowed to continue to term. The resulting offspring are chimeric, and these can be bred to produce transgenic knockout mice in the subsequent generation.

Studies Addressing Gene Regulation

Transgenic studies specifically designed to localize and characterize gene regulatory elements have provided important information regarding transcription regulation. The use of enhancer trap and gene trap mice falls into this category as discussed earlier. Indeed, gene regulatory elements have been identified in vivo through transgenic studies that were not apparent in cell culture studies. However, the protracted time scale and cost of producing transgenic mice limits this type of study.

Two classes of transcriptional control element have been identified by transgenic studies. Both act dominantly to facilitate transgene expression. The first is typified by the human β-globin LCR and somehow overcomes position effects. LCRs enable position-independent, copy-related expression of most genes (225). However, there are genes that even LCRs cannot drive efficiently in transgenic animals (e.g., the *lacZ* reporter gene) (293). The second element is the boundary or insulator element. These loosely characterized sequences appear to protect the transgene from *cis*-acting influences at the site of transgene integration (294). Other aspects of gene regulation have become apparent through transgenic studies. For example, several studies have clearly demonstrated that intronic sequences facilitate gene expression in vivo. Indeed, it has been argued that intron removal per se increases the sensitivity of transgenes to position effects in vivo (224).

Transgenes can also provide a valuable tool to look at the mechanisms involved in gene suppression or silencing. For example, there is evidence that specific sequences can serve as foci for gene silencing in the mammalian genome (295). These include bacterial genes, such as the routinely used *cat* reporter gene encoding chloramphenicol acetyltransferase, and the intronless versions of genomic genes, which are regularly used in expression systems. No robust route to express this type of sequence has been developed, although LCRs and transgene rescue have proved useful. Another aspect of gene silencing has also emerged as studies on transgene expression have become more detailed. There are now several examples of variegated or patchy transgene expression within a given cell type; that is, not all cells within a given population efficiently express the transgene. This phenomenon is proving to be quite complex, being subject to both position and dosage effects (206). It has also been proposed that transgenes present as a multicopy array may themselves direct the formation of heterochromatin (207).

Disease Models

Considerable effort has been directed to the development of transgenic animals as suitable models for human diseases, and there has been a number of successes that should now allow the development of novel therapies. The majority of these animals have been generated using the pronuclear injection method. Such transgenic mice have played a particularly important role in unraveling the consequence of oncogene expression in tumorigenesis. The pronuclear injection technique, however, suffers from the limitations that foreign DNA can only be added, not deleted or altered. The use of homologous recombination in ES cells overcomes this limitation (244,296).

The desire and ability to produce mouse models is clearly demonstrated by the generation of a variety of cystic fibrosis models within three years of the isolation of the cystic fibrosis transmembrane conductance regulator (CFTR) gene. This example also shows the limitation of the mouse model, as none of the cystic fibrosis mice clearly reflected the human disease phenotype (i.e., no lung pathology). Nevertheless, the mice are still of use. Although not showing the relevant disease phenotype, these mice do lack CFTR gene activity and therefore are valuable as a model to develop gene therapy strategies to restore the CFTR mRNA levels and hence protein function (297). Other models that have proved useful include mouse models for thalassemia involving modification of the globin genes and neoplasia, including retinoblastoma.

To date all genetically engineered animal disease models have been mice, although it has been suggested that alternative species might be more appropriate models for certain diseases (298). The recent development of nuclear transfer methodology may now allow the development of large animal models of human disease (e.g., sheep genetically modified to provide a model for cystic fibrosis). It is probable that a variety of animal models will become commonplace in the future, as techniques to generate them are developed.

Nonmammalian Species as Heterologous Systems

Gene transfer has been accomplished in many non-mammalian animals, including the model invertebrates

Drosophila melanogaster and the nematode *Caenorhabditis elegans* (273,275), model vertebrates such as the chicken (299), and more recently *Xenopus laevis* (300), and many species of fish (194). In all cases, DNA transfer is achieved by the microinjection of DNA into oocytes, eggs, or early embryos. As well as providing valuable information concerning gene function in these species, information relevant to mammalian genes can be generated. For instance, the use of recombinant P elements (discussed in an earlier section) has facilitated the study of vertebrate regulatory elements such as the β-globin LCR and the chicken lysozyme A boundary elements in *Drosophila* (301). Some nonmammalian species have commercial applications, such as fish, with regard to accelerating growth (302), and birds, with regard to enhanced disease resistance. The latter was brought a step closer with the development of microinjection techniques for chickens (299).

Expression Modeling

Gene regulatory elements not apparent in cell culture have been identified in vivo through transgenic studies (303). Furthermore, a comparison of the effect of various regulatory elements showed examples of high-efficiency expression in vitro and only moderately efficient expression in vivo.

These differences can relate to specific transcriptional control elements or more generic differences. For example, molecular analysis of the distal enhancer of the mouse α-fetoprotein gene has shown that mutations affecting specific transcription factor binding sites caused a 10-fold reduction in enhancer function in vitro, whereas in transgenic mice, the same mutation resulted in sporadic tissue-specific expression of the transgene, dependent on the site of integration. In contrast, mutations in the glucocorticoid receptor element of the ovine β-lactoglobulin promoter all but abolished expression in transfected cells but had no effect on expression in transgenic mice, as compared to wild-type constructs. The same contrast between in vitro and in vivo experiments is also observed for the basal transcription machinery. Mutagenesis of the αB-crystallin TATA-box sequence had no effect on promoter activity in transfected lens cells but preferentially reduced promoter activity in the lenses of transgenic mice. Therefore, when comparing cell transfection and transgenic mice, it would seem that regulation of transcription differs in vitro from in vivo at the levels of both the basal transcription machinery and upstream regulatory elements. There is also considerable evidence to support the hypothesis that a more stringent requirement for introns exists in transgenic mice than in cell culture. For example, while introns increase transcriptional efficiency of metallothionein-I promoter-driven rat growth hormone gene constructs in transgenic mice, expression in cultured cells seems to be insensitive to the presence of introns (304). This observation led to the proposal that introns facilitate gene expression, but only once the target genes have passed through the germline.

Transcriptional control mechanisms observed in vivo are often not consistent with those acting in vitro. However, pre-mRNA processing mechanisms observed in cell culture have been shown to correlate with the post-transcriptional modifications observed in transgenic mice. For example, β-lactoglobulin minigene constructs were inefficiently spliced, with the frequency of intron retention similar in vitro and in vivo (305). This similarity may prove distinctly useful by allowing transgene constructs to be tested for efficient post-transcriptional processing in vitro prior to their use in transgenic livestock. As more effort is diverted to addressing post-transcriptional processing events in transgenic animals, the validity of cell culture models is gaining strength.

Transgenic Livestock

Classical animal breeding regimes rely on gene import by cross-breeding, and are therefore limited to the improvement of those traits already present in a given species. Transgenic animal technology can overcome these limitations since the exogenous DNA can be derived from a heterologous species and it can be modified in vitro prior to being introduced into the germline.

Working with domestic animals poses a number of technical problems (275). The recovery of adequate numbers of pronuclear eggs, and their successful transfer following microinjection, requires a large number of donor and recipient animals. In addition, the pronuclear eggs of livestock species are delicate and relatively opaque. In pigs and cattle, centrifugation is often necessary prior to injection, in order to visualize the pronuclei. In sheep, eggs must be observed using a differential interference optics (DIC) microscope to see the pronuclei clearly. These technical hurdles add to the physical and financial constraints of dealing with large animals with generation intervals of several years.

It has been proposed that transgenesis may allow the generation of farm animals with improved traits, animal models for research, and animal bioreactors. This includes the production of animals with modified growth characteristics and carcass compositions, novel properties of the digestive system, enhanced wool yields, and the production of novel proteins. It is this last opportunity that has seen the most progress over the past decade, with the expression of a variety of proteins targeted to the milk of sheep, cattle, pigs, goats, and rabbits (223). Indeed, this application of gene transfer in livestock is fast approaching commercial success, with the first products currently undergoing clinical trials. This is likely to be the first widely exploited property of genetically modified livestock.

Modulation of Production Traits

The ability to transfer genes into the germline of livestock may well be instrumental in providing an alternative route to satisfying the ever-increasing demand for animal food and products. For centuries, domestic animals have been used as food, as well as providing a variety of additional products such as wool and leather. Productivity traits that may be amenable to modification by transgenesis include growth rate, nutrient composition of food products, quality of wool, and resistance to disease. Initial experiments concentrated on the transfer of growth related genes (306). These studies were on the whole unsuccessful due to undesirable side effects. The problem was identified as a lack of stringent control over the expression of the transgene. Perhaps the recent developments involving temporal and spatial transcriptional control elements will enable more appropriate transgene expression to be obtained. In another project, encouraging results have been obtained with attempts to improve wool production (307). Perhaps the greatest progress has been made in projects aiming to modulate milk composition through the generation of transgenic animal bioreactors (223). In the near future, most progress will perhaps be seen in the area of engineering disease resistance. However, while several strategies addressing disease management have potential, additional research is still required before these approaches can be applied in the field (308).

Animal Bioreactors

To date, the most successful application of gene transfer technology in livestock has been to target the expression of commercially and medically valuable proteins to milk. In the early 1980s, it was speculated that transgenic animals could be used to produce important human proteins for medical use. It was perceived that transgenic animal bioreactors would overcome the limitations of the other recombinant protein production systems and provide proteins with appropriate post-translational modifications in large amounts. In addition, after an initial investment in development, the maintenance cost associated with animal bioreactors should be relatively small. These assumptions are now proving to be correct (223,309). The first step involves the generation of a hybrid transgene, comprising DNA control elements from a gene normally expressed in the mammary gland linked to the coding region of a valuable gene that is normally expressed in a different tissue, such as the liver.

Clark and colleagues provided the first demonstration of the feasibility of this approach in large animals (310). In this study, transgenic sheep were generated that expressed a transgene encoding human clotting factor IX. Unfortunately, in this early experiment, the level of product detected in the milk was very low (25 mg l^{-1}). The problem of low yield has now been solved for many proteins, and this general approach has been applied to several animal species, including rabbits, goats, sheep, pigs, and cattle (223). In some cases, the observed expression levels were deemed to be economically viable. Many different proteins have now been produced in the milk of transgenic animals, although these predominantly reflect model studies in the mouse. These range from relatively simple proteins, such as albumin, to highly complex proteins such as monoclonal IgA antibodies and hexameric fibrinogen (311). The successes in large animals include tissue plasminogen activator in rabbits and goats, antithrombin III in goats, α-1-antitrypsin and clotting factor IX in sheep, and protein C in pigs. In one of these studies, very high-level production was obtained, earning Tracy the transgenic ewe considerable fame (Fig. 21). Tracy produced human α-1-antitrypsin in her milk at 30 g l^{-1}, which approaches half that of the total protein content (312).

It may be that certain species are more appropriate bioreactors for the synthesis of specific proteins. For example, rabbits have been proposed to be appropriate for those products required in small quantities, while the generation of transgenic birds using a DNA microinjection approach opens up the possibility of producing pharmaceuticals in chicken eggs (299). Different tissues may also have particular advantages, for example, because they carry out a specific form of post-translational modification. Whatever the direction, it is very likely that in the near future many more proteins will be produced in a variety of species, as reflected in the growing number of patents associated with this technology.

NUCLEAR TRANSFER TECHNOLOGY

Overview

Although to date all gene transfer experiments in livestock have involved the *addition* of genetic material, there is an understandable desire to develop gene targeting strategies. This would open up a vast range of applications in livestock. For example, gene targeting techniques could allow disruption of the prion-related protein gene (*Prp-1*) in cattle and sheep, which could facilitate the production of bovine spongiform encephalopathy (BSE)- and scrapie-resistant animals. Additionally, the removal of certain histocompatibility genes would allow the production of animals (probably pigs) as a source of xenograft organs for transplantation surgery. Furthermore, the ability to derive live animals from cultured cells would provide a more efficient way to produce superior farm animals. Before such strategies become feasible, however, cell lines that can contribute to the germline must be derived from livestock. Only recently have such goals become feasible (258,287).

Nuclear transfer was the first cell culture-based procedure used to produce livestock, and was achieved by Campbell and colleagues at the Roslin Institute in 1995 with the generation of the cloned sheep Megan and Morag (286) (Fig. 22). Two years later, the same group announced the generation of Dolly (Fig. 23), who was derived from an adult cell by nuclear transfer (287). Variations on this procedure, including the generation of ruminant ES or EG cells, are being actively explored. Notably, this area of research is likely to accelerate with the recent demonstration of live births following nuclear transfer in mice (313). Whatever the route to gene targeting in livestock, the inevitable experimental time scale and the unavoidable financial costs will mean that only those projects likely to yield profitable biotechnological or agricultural applications will be undertaken. At present there would be little public support for the production of genetically modified livestock for the food chain, though this might well change if it could be shown the animals would benefit (e.g., by having improved resistance to disease). Therefore, the first applications of this second-generation transgenic technology will almost certainly concern biotechnology and medicine (e.g., xenotransplantation or the production of therapeutic proteins in milk). The following section describes the

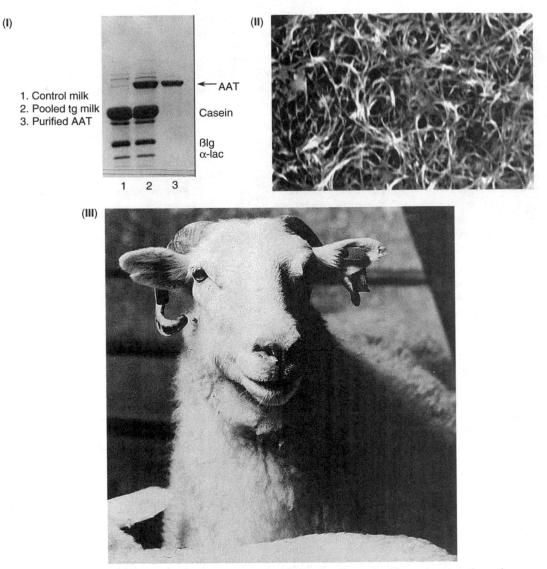

Figure 21. Animal bioreactors. (**I**) Western blot showing production of human α-1-antitrypsin (AAT) and (**II**) Structure of fibrinogen, both products of animal bioreactors. (**III**) Tracy the transgenic ewe, expressing AAT in her milk. Photographs courtesy of Ian Garner and April D'Arcy (PPL Therapeutics plc).

enormous potential gene targeting in livestock holds for agriculture, biotechnology, and medicine.

Advantages of Cell-Based Gene Transfer Procedures

There are two driving forces behind the development of cell-based gene transfer procedures in livestock. First, the desire to overcome position and dosage effects (314), and second, the desire to overcome the laborious techniques involved in the production of transgenic livestock by pronuclear microinjection (primarily reflecting the large number of animals required). In addition, microinjection can only add genes. A cell-based method to produce transgenic livestock allows single-copy transgene integrants to be generated at predetermined sites, which should limit problems such as variegated transgene expression. Future transgenic livestock will probably have the transgene integrated into a permissive site, and although such

Figure 22. Megan and Morag, the first sheep to be produced by nuclear transfer from cultured cells.

Figure 23. Dolly, the first mammal produced by nuclear transfer from an adult cell, and her lamb Bonnie.

an appropriate genomic site remains to be determined, this approach has been evaluated in the mouse model. The outcome is likely to be more predictable in terms of generating the anticipated transgene expression profile. Expression levels from these single-copy transgenes may need to be enhanced, since multiple-copy transgene loci can generate very high levels of expression. It is likely that many of these issues can be evaluated in cells prior to generating a transgenic animal.

For many years targeted integration has been possible in the mouse model through ES cell technology (239). Although there has been considerable effort to generate ruminant ES cells, to date all attempts have been unsuccessful. An alternative approach involves the transfer of nuclear genetic material from cells grown in culture into an unfertilized egg (315). Now, rather than merely evaluating a transgene construct in cell culture, the actual cell is the genetic material from which the transgenic animal is generated. The gateway has been opened for the production of a variety of livestock for both agricultural and biomedical applications. There are many advantages to this technology; for example, all founder animals are transgenic, mosaic founders are not produced, the sex of the founder can be selected, and a flock/herd of clonal animals can be produced within one generation. More important, many aspects of the transgene can be analyzed in vitro prior to the generation of an animal. The integrity of the transgene locus can be evaluated, which may be particularly important when large transgenes such as YACs are used. Furthermore, with some ingenuity, it will be possible to check the expression potential of a transgene before going through the cost of producing the animal. Expression strategies could, for example, involve the transient production of an appropriate transcriptional activator, which could mediate *trans*-induction of transgene expression. The

most important point, however, is that it is possible to select for site-specific integration events generated by gene targeting, thus allowing strategies involving gene knockout or replacement to be performed. The ES cell and nuclear transfer routes are compared in Figure. 24.

Ruminant Embryonic Cells

As discussed, no ruminant ES or EG cells are currently available. In this regard, there is an ongoing debate about which in vitro, environmental, and genetic factors could be responsible for the differences between mice and other mammalian species. We need more information regarding differentiation markers in the various species and novel culturing methods, although one recently developed isolation procedure does show some promise (259). The rationale behind this approach is that ES cells can be isolated from some mouse strains more efficiently than others. It was proposed that this may reflect the differences in the control of ES progenitor cells by other lineages within the embryo (316). Thus, if these other lineages were removed, the ES cell progenitors might survive. This is indeed the case, at least for some mouse strains nonpermissive for ES cells (Fig. 25). This approach is currently being tried in pigs and rabbits. Although encouraging, the selection method is limited by the initial requirement of the appropriate transgenic line. In an attempt to overcome this limitation, transient expression strategies are being developed.

An alternative cell type is the EG cell derived from primordial germ cells. There is some considerable progress in the development of this cell type, and recent advances in PGC isolation and culture, and hence the culture of EG cells, have provided the impetus to develop this approach.

Nuclear Transfer

Xenopus nuclear transfer was first reported in 1952. Since then, it has been widely used in amphibians, primarily for experiments addressing early development (317). Although adult frogs could be generated from the nuclei of early embryonic cells, the nuclei of adult cells failed to produce adult animals (the embryos never developed beyond the tadpole stage). Then in 1977, a mouse was generated by nuclear transfer using a cell from a very early embryo. The procedure in mice proved to be very difficult. Since then, most research has concentrated on farm animals, driven by the prospect of large financial benefits derived from cloning elite and/or transgenic embryos. In the 1980s, there were several exciting developments: Cloned sheep and cattle were generated using early embryo cells as donors. Furthermore, some experiments in the United States showed that live calves could be derived by nuclear transfer using cells from the late blastocyst stage. At this stage of mammalian development, primitive cells types are distinguishable; therefore, this was the first suggestion that nuclear transfer in mammals was possible from at least partially differentiated cells. The major breakthrough came in 1995, when Ian Wilmut and Keith Campbell produced two live lambs—Megan and Morag—by nuclear transfer of embryonic cells grown in culture (286). Within a year, a lamb had been produced

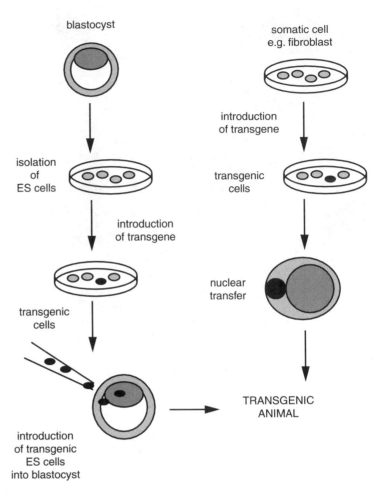

Figure 24. A comparison of the ES cell and nuclear transfer routes to generate transgenic livestock. Either procedure is amenable to gene targeting strategies, following introduction of DNA by microinjection, electroporation, or other forms of transfection.

from an adult cell (287). This lamb was called Dolly, and her arrival had a major impact on scientific and public thinking. Since then, a number of lambs and calves have been generated using this technology, some of which are transgenic (258,315). The objective is now to expand the number of species where nuclear transfer can be applied. In this regard, the recent demonstration of nuclear transfer in mice should dramatically accelerate the development of this technology (313).

Embryo reconstruction by nuclear transfer involves the transfer of a single nucleus to an unfertilized oocyte or one-cell zygote from which the genetic material has been removed. For livestock, the recipient cell of choice is usually an unfertilized oocyte that has been arrested at metaphase of the second meiotic division. The first step is to enucleate the recipient oocyte. The genetic material is removed using a small glass pipette, a highly skilled procedure. The genetic material from the donor cell is then introduced into the enucleated oocyte, usually by cell fusion using a short electrical pulse, although treatment with polyethylene glycol or Sendai virus is also possible. The next phase involves the activation of the reconstructed embryo. In nature, this is achieved by fertilization and involves calcium mobilization. Activation can be mimicked by a variety of chemical agents, such as phorbol esters or calcium ionophores. In practice, this step is often simplified, since the electric pulse used to fuse

Figure 25. Selective ablation of differentiated cells permits isolation of ES cell lines from nonpermissive strains. The photograph shows a germline chimera derived from line 39/1, its albino MF1 mate, together with germline (agouti) and nongermline (albino) littermates, courtesy of Jim McWhir and Helen Wallace (Roslin Institute).

the cells can also activate the embryo. Finally, the embryo is cultured to a stage at which it can be transferred to a synchronized recipient animal for development to term. Some livestock generated by nuclear transfer are shown in Figure 26.

(a)

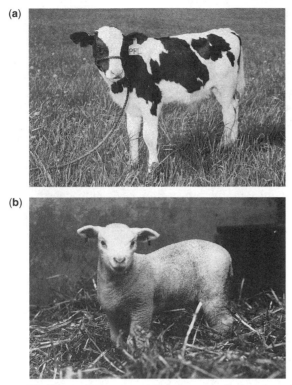

(b)

Figure 26. Livestock generated by nuclear transfer. (**a**) Mr. Jefferson, a Holstein calf produced by nuclear transfer from a fetal fibroblast cell line in 1998. (**b**) Polly, the first transgenic lamb produced by nuclear transfer, born in 1997. Photographs courtesy of Ian Garner and April D'Arcy (PPL Therapeutics plc).

Source of Donor Nuclei

The highly publicized generation of Dolly demonstrated that the donor cell for nuclear transfer could be derived from a differentiated cell. In this case the source was a cultured mammary cell line, the cells being derived originally from a six-year-old ewe. However, this experiment was very inefficient with only one animal being produced from about 250 cultured cells (287). The donor cell must be neither aneuploid nor contain any other chromosomal damage. In addition, for technical reasons, it must be easy to handle and manipulate in culture. The most commonly used cell type is the fetal fibroblast (315). Obviously, if ruminant ES or EG cells become available, they would provide ideal donor cells (258).

One of the main requirements for successful nuclear transfer using ruminant cells is the synchronization of the cell cycle between donor and recipient cells. The outcome of these studies demonstrated that cell cycle arrest in G_0 phase was crucial for the procedure to work. This can be accomplished simply by reducing serum levels in the culture medium, although whether this is the best strategy remains to be investigated. The suitability of the quiescent donor nuclei may reflect a number of factors, such as reduced transcription and translation, low metabolic activity, and condensed chromatin. Presumably these changes render the nucleus and cytoplasm more compatible with the mechanisms of reprogramming.

Reprogramming

Reprogramming refers to the change in differentiation state associated with nuclear transfer. The donor cell is differentiated, to varying degrees, while the egg is not. Prior to transfer, a variety of cell-type-specific genes would be active in the donor nucleus. These must be repressed, and the appropriate genes required for early embryonic development must be activated; that is, the nucleus has to "forget" its history (whether it was taken from a fibroblast, mammary cell, etc.) and take instructions from the cytoplasm of the recipient cell. Reprogramming is anticipated to depend on a large number of factors, the majority of which are undefined and not understood at present. As well as differences in the levels of various transcription factors, the nucleus itself also changes during development, through chromatin remodeling and DNA methylation, resulting in the silencing of many genes. Such changes also need to be erased before development can be recapitulated by nucleus transferred to a reconstituted embryo. Another important factor is the age of the donor nucleus. The cell used to generate Dolly was derived from a six-year-old ewe, raising the question of whether Dolly would show signs of premature aging. One anticipated effect is that the telomeres, which protect the chromosome ends, become progressively shorter. A recent study (318) showed that Dolly's telomeres were indeed shorter than expected for a sheep her age. However this does not appear to have affected the health or reproductive ability of Dolly or any other cloned animal—indeed Dolly has already had two successful pregnancies. This finding does have important implications for some nuclear transfer strategies, such as sequential cloning, although there is no obvious commercial reason for adopting this approach. There is now a considerable interest in defining the changes that occur at the nuclear level during differentiation and aging, and elucidating the underlying mechanisms.

Xenotransplantation

Over the past few decades, transplantation has become the preferred treatment for human organ failure. However, there is a chronic shortage of donor organs, so that only half of the potential operations are actually performed. If animal organs could be used instead of human organs (xenotransplantation), this shortage would be overcome (319). The major limitation to the use of nonprimate organs in human patients is tissue rejection. Since the immune system plays such a critical role in the host defense, there is considerable interest in engineering tissue compatibility into the xenograft donor as opposed to suppressing the patients' immune response. Transgenic animals offer a route to overcome this limitation.

The hyperacute rejection of organs reflects the activity of the host's complement system. One proposed strategy involves the generation of animals that carry transgenes allowing evasion of the complement system. For example, transgenic pigs have been produced carrying a transgene encoding a complement inhibitory factor that coats the cells (320). At present, further developments are required including modulation of the antibody response induced by xenotransplantation (321). Here, the ability to remove genes could have a major impact on the success of xenotransplants. Surprisingly, most of the antibodies in our blood that would react against a pig organ recognize a single carbohydrate linkage present on pig cells (322). This disaccharide, Gal-α1-3-Gal, is synthesized by α1,3-galactosyltransferase. Primates do not have a functional α1,3-galactosyltransferase gene, and therefore do not recognize this carbohydrate. Elimination of this enzyme in pigs by gene knockout could therefore reduce hyperacute rejection of transplanted organs. This strategy requires the ability to perform germline gene targeting experiments in pigs. This may now be possible with the development of nuclear transfer technology (258,287).

The first experimental transfer of a genetically modified pigs heart was into cynomolgus monkeys (323). None of the 10 hearts was rejected, and the monkeys survived for an average of 40 days. Conversely, hearts from control pigs were rejected within hours. This is encouraging, but the routine use of xenotransplantation by the surgeon will require equally challenging approaches to overcome delayed rejection, such as cellular rejection. Currently this type of rejection is controlled by immunosuppressive drugs, but here again gene transfer technology may hold the answer. Notwithstanding the technical hurdles required to generate transgenic pigs with the appropriate genetic modifications, there are many ethical issues that need to be debated. In addition, xenotransplantation may well bring novel disease problems, and the potential severity of these issues remains to be examined. For example, the transplantation of a pig heart into a human patient may expose that individual to infection from endogenous retroviruses present in the pig cells (319).

Nuclear Transfer and Somatic Cell Therapy

An alternative approach to in vivo gene therapy is to modify cells genetically ex vivo and then reintroduce them into the patient. This route overcomes many of the serious problems associated with efficient gene delivery, but has been restricted by the ability isolate the appropriate cells. The development of nuclear transfer using somatic cells grown in culture has provided an new impetus to these studies (287). These pioneering nuclear transfer experiments have demonstrated that a differentiated cell can be programmed to restart development. Once the mechanisms behind this process are understood, it may be possible to reprogram animal cells without resorting to the use of an egg. In the future, this may well allow a patient's own cells to be used for personal gene therapy. This would avoid the expense and uncertainty of tissue matching. In this treatment scenario, cells would be removed from the patient, converted into the desired cell type in the laboratory by nuclear reprogramming, and then reintroduced into the same patient. In conjunction with gene transfer technology this may represent a powerful form of surgery for the future. Before this exciting prospect becomes reality, major advances are required in our understanding of reprogramming and cellular differentiation.

Animal Cloning

The cloning of animals provides immediate advantages for both animal breeding and basic research. The main advantage in breeding would not be in the selection programs but in the rapid dissemination of the genetic progress from elite herds to the commercial farmer. There is a risk attached, that of loss of genetic diversity, but this could be avoided, for example, by systems to ensure that breeding companies produce a limited number of clones of each type. Alternatively, nuclear transfer from cultured cells could be of use for species where repeated breeding is impractical or prohibitively expensive. It may also prove useful in providing new approaches for genetic conservation. In the context of research, genetic variation between individuals tends to confound the often subtle responses to test diets or drugs. The advantages of genetic uniformity has been demonstrated in studies with inbred lines of mice and exploited to some extent with the numerous back crosses that provide the basis for many animal genome mapping schemes.

BIBLIOGRAPHY

1. E.H. Szybalska and W. Szybalski, *Proc. Natl. Acad. Sci. U.S.A.* **48**, 2026–2034 (1962).

2. W. Doerfler et al., *Trends Biotechnol.* **15**, 297–301 (1997).

3. M. Dawson and M. Butler, in M. Butler and M. Dawson, eds., *Cell Culture Labfax*, BIOS Scientific Publishers/Blackwell, Oxford, U.K., 1992, pp. 177–189.

4. L. McCarroll and L.A. King, *Curr. Opin. Biotechnol.* **8**, 590–594 (1997).

5. A. Colman, in B.D. Hames and S.J. Higgins, eds., *Transcription and Translation: A Practical Approach*, IRL Press, Oxford, U.K., 1984, pp. 271–302.

6. V. Chisholm, in D.M. Glover and B.D. Hames, eds., *DNA Cloning 4, Mammalian Systems: A Practical Approach*, 2 ed., IRL Press, Oxford, U.K., 1995, pp. 1–42.

7. S.R. Kain and S. Ganguly, in *Current Protocols in Molecular Biology*, Suppl. 29, Wiley, New York, 1995, pp. 9.6.1–9.6.12

8. J. Messing and J. Vieira, *Gene* **19**, 269–276, (1982).

9. M. Lusky and M. Botchan, *Nature (London)* **293**, 79–81, (1981).

10. R. Grisshammer and K. Nagai, in D.M. Glover and B.D. Hames, eds., *DNA Cloning 2, Expression Systems: A Practical Approach*, 2nd ed., IRL Press, Oxford, U.K., 1995, pp 71–87.

11. K.R. Peterson, C.H. Clegg, Q. Li, and G. Stamatoyannopoulos, *Trends Genet.* **13**, 61–66 (1997).

12. A.L. Joyner, ed., *Gene Targeting: A Practical Approach*, IRL Press, Oxford, U.K., 1993.

13. L. Cooley, C. Berg, and A. Spralding, *Trends Genet.* **4**, 254–258 (1988).

14. T. Rijkers, A. Peetz, and U. Ruther, *Transgenic Res.* **3**, 203–215 (1994).

15. C.J. O'Kane and W.J. Gehring, *Proc. Natl. Acad. Sci. U.S.A.* **84**, 9123–9127 (1987).

16. N.D. Allen et al., *Nature (London)* **333**, 852–855 (1988).

17. M.J. Evans, M.B.L. Carlton, and A.P. Russ, *Trends Genet.* **13**, 370–375 (1997).

18. I. Lowry et al., *Cell* **22**, 817–823, (1980).

19. M. Perucho, D. Hanahan, L. Lipsich, and M. Wigler, *Nature (London)* **285**, 207–210 (1980).

20. J. Sambrook, E.F. Fritsch, and T. Maniatis, *Molecular Cloning: A Laboratory Manual*, Cold Spring Harbor Laboratory Press, Cold Spring Harbor, N.Y., 1989, pp. 16.1–16.81.

21. C.M. Gorman, D.R. Gies, and G. McCray, *DNA Protein Eng. Tech.* **2**, 3 (1990).

22. P. Mellon, V. Parker, Y. Gluzman, and T. Maniatis, *Cell* **27**, 279–288 (1981).

23. W.J. Muller, M.A. Naujokas, and J.A. Hassel, *Mol. Cell. Biol.* **4**, 2046–2412 (1984).

24. R.D. Gerard and Y. Gluzman, *Mol. Cell Biol.* **5**, 3231–3240 (1985).

25. D.C. Rio, S.G. Clark, and R. Tjian, *Science* **227**, 23–28 (1985).

26. R.M. Twyman and E.A. Jones, *J. Mol. Neurosci.* **8**, 63–73 (1997).

27. J. Alam and J.L. Cook, *Anal. Biochem.* **188**, 245–254 (1990).

28. I. Bronstein et al., *Anal. Biochem.* **219**, 169–181 (1994).

29. C.M. Gorman, L.F. Moffat, and B.H. Howard, *Mol. Cell Biol.* **2**, 1044–1051 (1982).

30. J. Berger et al., *Gene* **66**, 1–10 (1988).

31. B.R. Cullen and M.H. Malim, *Methods Enzymol.* **216**, 362–368 (1992).

32. J.F. Thompson, L.S. Hayes, and D.B. Lloyd, *Gene* **103**, 171–177 (1993).

33. S. Welsh and S.A. Kay, *Curr. Opin. Biotechnol.* **8**, 617–622 (1997).

34. M. Chalfie et al., *Science* **263**, 802–805 (1994).

35. A.B. Cubitt et al., *Trends Biochem. Sci.* **20**, 448–455 (1995).

36. R. Heim and R.Y. Tsein, *Curr. Biol.* **6**, 178–182 (1996).

37. R.E. Kingston, in *Current Protocols in Molecular Biology*, suppl. 14, Wiley, New York, 1996, pp 9.5.1–9.5.6

38. M. Wigler et al., *Cell* **16**, 777–785 (1979).

39. J.W. Littlefied, *Science* **145**, 709–710 (1964).

40. R.J. Kaufman, *Methods Enzymol.* **185**, 537–566, (1990).

41. C. Bebbington, in D.M. Glover and B.D. Hames, eds., *DNA Cloning 4, Mammalian Systems: A Practical Approach*, 2nd ed., IRL Press, Oxford, U.K., 1995, pp. 85–112.

42. G. Stark, *Cancer Surv.* **5**, 1 (1986).

43. G. Urlaub and L.A. Chasin, *Proc. Natl. Acad. Sci. U.S.A.* **77**, 4216–4223 (1980).

44. G. Urlaub, E. Kas, A.M. Carothers, and L.A. Chasin, *Cell* **33**, 405–412 (1983).

45. A. Debenedetti and R.E. Rhoads, *Nucleic Acids Res.* **19**, 1925–1931 (1991).

46. M. Sabbioni et al., *Arch. Virol.* **140**, 335–339 (1995).

47. N. Sarver et al., *Mol. Cell Biol.* **1**, 486–496 (1981).

48. M.S. Campo, in D.M. Glover, ed., *DNA Cloning: A Practical Approach*, 1st ed., Vol. 2, IRL Press, Oxford, U.K., 1985, pp. 213-244.

49. D. DiMaio, in N.P. Salzman and P.M. Howley, eds., *The Papovaviridae: The Papillomaviruses*, Vol. 2, Plenum, New York, 1987.

50. J. Mecsas and B. Sugden, *Annu. Rev. Cell Biol.* **3**, 87–108 (1987).

51. R.F. Margolskee, *Curr. Top. Microbiol. Immunol.* **185**, 67–95 (1992).

52. R.F. Margolskee, P. Kavathas, and P. Berg, *Mol. Cell. Biol.* **8**, 2837–2847 (1988).

53. D. Kioussis et al., *EMBO J.* **6**, 355–361 (1987).

54. Z. Larin, in N.R. Lemoine and D.N. Cooper, eds., *Gene Therapy*, Bios Scientific Publishers, Oxford, U.K., 1996, pp. 113–126.

55. W.A. Keown, C.R. Campbell, and R.S. Kucherlapati, *Methods Enzymol.* **185**, 527–537 (1990).

56. K. Kawabata, Y. Takakura, and M. Hashida, *Pharm. Res.* **12**, 825–830 (1995).

57. J.A. Wolff et al., *Science* **247**, 1465–1468 (1990).

58. C.R. Middaugh, M. Chastain, and C.T. Caskey, in N.R. Lemoine, and D.N. Cooper, eds., *Gene Therapy*, BIOS Scientific Publishers, Oxford, U.K., 1996, pp. 11–32.

59. E.G. Nabel, V.J. Pompilli, G.E. Plautz, and G.J. Nabel, *Cardiovasc. Res.* **28**, 445–455 (1994).

60. F.L. Graham and A.J. van der Erb, *Virology* **52**, 456–467 (1973).

61. M. Wigler, A. Pellicer, S. Silverstien, and R. Axel, *Cell* **14**, 725–729 (1977).

61a. C. Chen and H. Okayama, *Mol. Cell. Biol.* **7**, 2745–2752 (1987).

61b. C. Chen and H. Okayama, *Bio/Techniques* **6**, 632–638 (1988).

62. R.E. Kingston, C.A. Chen, and H. Okayama, in *Current Protocols in Molecular Biology*, Suppl. 17, Wiley, New York, 1996, pp. 9.1.7–9.1.9.

63. E. Orrantia and P.L. Chang, *Exp. Cell Res.* **190**, 170–174 (1990).

64. J.H. McCutchann and J.S. Pango, *J. Natl. Cancer Inst. (U.S.)* **41**, 351–354 (1968).

65. G. Milman and M. Hertzberg, *Somatic Cell Genet.* **7**, 161–168 (1981).

66. M.A. Lopata, D.W. Cleveland, and B. Sollner-Webb, *Nucleic Acids Res.* **12**, 5707–5717 (1984).

67. D.J. Sussman and G. Milman, *Mol. Cell. Biol.* **4**, 1641–1643 (1984).

68. R. Reeves, C. Gorman, and B. Howard, *Nucleic Acids Res.* **13**, 3599–3615 (1985).

69. R. Kaufman, *Proc. Natl. Acad. Sci. U.S.A.* **82**, 689–693 (1985).

70. H. Luthman and G. Magnusson, *Nucleic Acids Res.* **11**, 1295–1308 (1983).

71. C.M. Gorman and B.H. Howard, *Nucleic Acids Res.* **11**, 7631–7648 (1983).

72. S.S. Boggs, R.G. Gregg, N. Bornstein, and O. Smithies, *Exp. Hematol.* **14**, 988–994 (1986).

73. W. Bertling, K. Hunger-Bertling, and M.J. Cline, *J. Biochem. Biophys. Methods* **14**, 233–232 (1987).

74. N.R. Drinkwater and D.K. Klinedinst, *Proc. Natl. Acad. Sci. U.S.A.* **83**, 3402–3406 (1986).

75. T.K. Wong and E. Neumann, *Biochem. Biophys. Res. Commun.* **107**, 584–587 (1982).

76. H. Potter, L. Weir, and P. Leder, *Proc. Natl. Acad. Sci. U.S.A.* **81**, 7161–7165 (1984).

77. H. Potter, *Anal. Biochem.* **174**, 361–373 (1988).

78. X. Zaho, *Adv. Drug Delivery Rev.* **17**, 257–262, (1995).

79. S. Kurata, M. Tsukakoshi, T. Kasuya, and Y. Ikawa, *Exp. Cell Res.* **162**, 372–378 (1986).

80. M. Schaefer-Ridder, Y. Wang, and P.H. Hofschneider, *Science* **215**, 166–168 (1982).

81. T. Itani et al., *Gene* **56**, 267–276 (1987).

82. R.K. Scheule and S.H. Cheng, in N.R. Lemoine and D.N. Cooper, eds., *Gene Therapy*, BIOS Scientific Publishers, Oxford, U.K., 1996, pp. 93–112.

83. C.M. de Fiebre et al., *Neurochem. Res.* **18**, 1089–1094, (1993).

84. P.L. Felgner et al., *Proc. Natl. Acad. Sci. U.S.A.* **84**, 7413–7417 (1987).

85. J.H. Felgner et al., *J. Biol. Chem.* **269**, 2550–2561 (1994).

86. I. van der Woude et al., *Biochim. Biophys. Acta* **1240**, 34–40 (1995).

87. P. Hawley-Nelson et al., *Gibo-BRL Focus* **15**, 3–6 (1994).

88. W.G. Charney et al., *Somatic Cell Mol. Genet.* **12**, 237–244 (1986).

89. W. Schaffner, *Proc. Natl. Acad. Sci. U.S.A.* **77**, 2163–2169 (1980).

90. F.C. Wiberg, P. Sunnerhagen, and G. Bjursell, *Exp. Cell Res.* **173**, 218–231 (1987).

91. K. Tomizyka et al., *Nat. Genet.* **16**, 133–143 (1997).

92. M.R. Capecchi, *Cell* **22**, 479–485 (1980).

93. T.M. Klein et al., *Proc. Natl. Acad. Sci. U.S.A.* **85**, 2305–2309 (1988).

94. D.C. Lo, A.K. McAllister, and L.C. Katz, *Neuron* **13**, 1263–1268 (1994).

95. D. Arnold, L. Feng, J. Kim, and N. Heintz, *Proc. Natl. Acad. Sci. U.S.A.* **91**, 9970–9974 (1994).

96. J.R. Haynes et al., *J. Biotechnol.* **44**, 37–42 (1996).

97. H.L. Vahlsing et al., *J. Immunol. Methods* **175**, 11–22 (1994).

98. G.Y. Wu and C.H. Wu, *J. Biol. Chem.* **262**, 4429–4432 (1987).

99. D.T. Curiel, S. Agarwal, E. Wagner, and M. Cotten, *Proc. Natl. Acad. Sci. U.S.A.* **88**, 8850–8854 (1991).

100. M.G. Stebestyen et al., *Nat. Biotechnol.* **16**, 80–85 (1998).

101. P.D. Robbins, H. Tahara, and S.C. Ghivizzani, *Trends Biotechnol.* **16**, 35–40 (1998).

102. K.L. Berkner, *Curr. Top. Microbiol. Immunol.* **158**, 39–67 (1992).

103. R.D. Gerard and R.S. Meidell, in D.M. Glover and B.D. Hames, eds., *DNA Cloning 4, Mammalian Systems: A Practical Approach*, 2nd ed., IRL Press, Oxford, U.K., 1995, pp. 285–306.

104. C.J.A. Ring, in N.R. Lemoine and D.N. Cooper, eds., *Gene Therapy*, BIOS Scientific Publishers, Oxford, U.K., 1996, pp. 61–76.

105. I. Kovesdi, D.E. Brough, J.T. Bruder, and T.J. Wickham, *Curr. Opin. Biotechnol.* **8**, 583–589 (1997).

106. A.J. Bett, L. Prevec, and F.L. Graham, *J. Virol.* **67**, 5911–5921 (1993).

107. K.J. Fischer et al., *Virology* **217**, 11–22 (1996).

108. S. Kochaneck et al., *Proc. Natl. Acad. Sci. U.S.A.* **93**, 5731–5736 (1996).

109. N. Muzyczka, *Curr. Top. Microbiol. Immunol.* **158**, 97–129 (1992).

110. J.S. Bartlett and R.J. Samulski, in N.R. Lemoine and D.N. Cooper, eds., *Gene Therapy*, BIOS Scientific Publishers, Oxford, U.K., 1996, pp. 77–92.

111. P. Berglung, I. Tubulekas, and O. Liljestrom, *Trends Biotechnol.* **14**, 130–134 (1996).

112. K. Lundstrom, *Curr. Opin. Biotechnol.* **8**, 578–582 (1997).

113. A. Garcia-Sastre, *Trends Biotechnol.* **16**, 230–235 (1998).

114. G.W. Blissard and G.F. Rohrmann, *Annu. Rev. Entomol.* **35**, 127–155 (1990).

115. F.M. Boyce and N.L. Butcher, *Proc. Natl. Acad. Sci. U.S.A.* **93**, 2348–2352 (1996).

116. G. Patel and N.C. Jones, in D.M. Glover and B.D. Hames, eds., *DNA Cloning 2, Expression Systems: A Practical Approach*, 2nd ed., IRL Press, Oxford, U.K., 1995, pp. 205–244.

117. D.R. O'Reilley, L.K. Miller, and V.A. Luckow, *Baculovirus Expression Vectors: A Laboratory Manual*, Freeman, San Francisco, (1992).

118. L.A. King and R.D. Possee, *The Baculovirus Expression System: A Laboratory Guide*, Chapman & Hall, London, 1992.

119. M.J. Fraser, *Curr. Top. Microbiol. Immunol.* **158**, 131–172 (1992).

120. R.D. Possee, *Curr. Opin. Biotechnol.* **8**, 569–572 (1997).

121. V.A. Luckow, S.C. Lee, G.F. Barry, and P.O. Ollins, *J. Virol.* **67**, 4566–4579, (1993).

122. G. Patel, K. Nasmyth, and N. Jones, *Nucleic Acids Res.* **20**, 97–104 (1992).

123. J.-M.H. Vos, in J.-M.H. Vos, ed., *Viruses in Human Gene Therapy*, Carolina Academic Press/Chapman & Hall, Durham, N.C./London, U.K., 1995, pp. 109–140.

124. J.-M.H. Vos, E.-M. Westphal, and S. Banerjee, in N.R. Lemoine, and D.N. Cooper, eds., *Gene Therapy*, BIOS Scientific Publishers, Oxford, U.K., 1996, pp. 127–153.

125. A.I. Geller, M.J. During, and R.L. Neve, *Trends Neurosci.* **14**, 428–432 (1991).

126. F. Lim et al., in D.M. Glover and B.D. Hames, eds., *DNA Cloning 4, Mammalian Systems: A Practical Approach*, 2nd ed., IRL Press, Oxford, U.K., 1995, pp. 263–283.

127. B. Roizman, in B.N. Fields and D.K. Knipe, eds., *Virology*, 2nd ed., Raven Press, New York, 1990, pp 1787–1793.

128. A. Miyanohara et al., *New Biol.* **4**, 238–246 (1992).

129. E.J. Boviatsis et al., *Cancer Res.* **54**, 5745–5751 (1994).

130. C.C. Hentschel, in R.E. Spier, J.B. Griffiths, and B. Meignier, eds., *Production of Biologicals from Animal Cells in Culture*, Butterworth-Heinemann, Oxford, U.K., 1991, pp. 287–321.

131. J.M. Coffin, in B.N. Fields and D.N. Knipe, eds., *Virology*, 2nd ed., Raven Press, New York, 1990, pp. 1437–1500.

132. A.C. Brown and J.P. Dougherty, in D.M. Glover and B.D. Hames, eds., *DNA Cloning 4, Mammalian Systems: A Practical Approach*, 2nd ed., IRL Press, Oxford, U.K., 1995, pp. 113–142.

133. A.D. Miller, *Curr. Top. Microbiol. Immunol.* **185**, 1–24 (1992).

134. C. Cepko, in *Current Protocols in Molecular Biology*, Suppl. 17, Wiley, New York, 1996, pp. 9.10.1–9.10.7.

135. W.H. Gunzburg and B. Salmons, in N.R. Lemoine and D.N. Cooper, eds., *Gene Therapy*, BIOS Scientific Publishers, Oxford, U.K., 1996, pp. 33–60.

136. H.B. Gaspar and C. Kinnon, in N.R. Lemoine and D.N. Cooper, eds., *Gene Therapy*, BIOS Scientific Publishers, Oxford, U.K., 1996, pp. 225–239.

137. C.L. Cepko et al., *Methods Enzymol.* **225**, 933–960 (1993).

138. E. Robertson, A. Bradley, M. Kuehn, and M. Evans, *Nature (London)* **323**, 445–448 (1986).

139. D. Markowitz, S. Goff, and A. Bank, *J. Virol.* **62**, 1120–1124 (1988).

140. R.G. Hawley, L. Covarrubias, T. Hawley, and B. Mintz, *Proc. Natl. Acad. Sci. U.S.A.* **84**, 2406–2410 (1987).

141. B. Moss, *Curr. Top. Microbiol. Immunol.* **185**, 25–39 (1992).

142. M.W. Carroll and B. Moss, *Curr. Opin. Biotechnol.* **8**, 573–577 (1997).

143. M. Mackett, in D.M. Glover and B.D. Hames, eds., *DNA Cloning 4, Mammalian Systems: A Practical Approach*, 2nd ed., IRL Press, Oxford, U.K., 1995, pp. 43–83.

144. B. Moss, *Proc. Natl. Acad. Sci. U.S.A.* **93**, 11341–11348 (1996).

145. R.M. Twyman, *Advanced Molecular Biology, A Concise Reference*, BIOS Scientific Publishers, Oxford, U.K., 1998, pp. 443–465.

146. R.C. Mulligan and P. Berg, *Proc. Natl. Acad. Sci. U.S.A.* **78**, 2072–2076 (1981).

147. C.M. Gorman, G.T. Merlino, and M.C. Willingham, *Proc. Natl. Acad. Sci. U.S.A.* **79**, 6777–6781 (1982).

148. M. Boshart et al., *Cell* **41**, 521–530 (1985).

149. C.M. Gorman, D. Gies, G. McCray, and M. Huang, *Virology* **171**, 377–385 (1989).

150. G.T. Yarrington, *Curr. Opin. Biotechnol.* **3**, 506–511 (1993).

151. M.M. Bendig, P.E. Stephens, M.I. Crocket, and C.C. Hentschel, *DNA* **6**, 343–352, (1987).

152. G.N. Pavlakis and D.H. Hamer, *Proc. Natl. Acad. Sci. U.S.A.* **80**, 397–401 (1983).

153. F. Lee, R. Mulligan, P. Berg, and G. Ringold, *Nature (London)* **294**, 228–232 (1981).

154. F. McCormick et al., *Mol. Cell Biol.* **4**, 166–172 (1984).

155. E. Saez, D. No, A. West, and R.M. Evans, *Curr. Opin. Biotechnol.* **8**, 608–616 (1997).

156. M.C. Hu and N. Davidson, *Cell* **48**, 555–566 (1987).

157. M. Gossen, A.L. Bonin, and H. Bujard, *Trends Biochem. Sci.* **18**, 471–475 (1993).

158. P.E. Shockett and D.G. Schatz, *Proc. Natl. Acad. Sci. U.S.A.* **93**, 5173–5176 (1996).

159. D. No, T.P. Yo, and R.M. Evans, *Proc. Natl. Acad. Sci. U.S.A.* **93**, 3346–3351 (1996).

160. M.A. Labow, S.B. Baim, T. Shenk, and A.J. Levine, *Mol. Cell Biol.* **10**, 3343–3356 (1990).

161. M. Gossen and H. Bujard, *Proc. Natl. Acad. Sci. U.S.A.* **89**, 5547–5551 (1992).

162. M. Gossen et al., *Science* **268**, 1766–1769 (1995).

163. Y. Wang, B.W. O'Malley, S.Y. Tsai, and B.W. O'Malley, *Proc. Natl. Acad. Sci. U.S.A.* **91**, 8180–8184 (1994).

164. J.P. Delort and M.R. Capecchi, *Hum. Gene Ther.* **7**, 809–820 (1996).

165. D.M. Spencer, *Trends Genet.* **12**, 181–187 (1996).

166. P.J. Belshaw, S.N. Ho, G.R. Crabtree, and S.L. Schreiber, *Proc. Natl. Acad. Sci. U.S.A.* **93**, 4604–4607, (1996).

167. R.M. Twyman, *Advanced Molecular Biology, A Concise Reference*, BIOS Scientific Publishers, Oxford, U.K., 1998, pp. 411–424.

168. R.J. Kaufman, *Methods Enzymol.* **185**, 487–511, (1990).

169. R.D. Palmiter et al., *Proc. Natl. Acad. Sci. U.S.A.* **88**, 478–482 (1991).

170. K. Matsumoto, K. Montzka Wassarman, and A.P. Wolffe, *EMBO J.* **17**, 2107–2121 (1998).

171. B.R. Cullen, P.T. Lomedico, and G. Ju, *Nature (London)* **307**, 214–245 (1984).

172. M. Kozak, *Cell* **44**, 283–292 (1986).

173. M. Kozak, *Nucleic Acids Res.* **12**, 3873–3893 (1984).

174. T.A. Brown, ed., *Molecular Biology Labfax*, BIOS Scientific Publishers/Blackwell, Oxford, U.K., 1991.

175. G. Shaw and R. Kamen, *Cell* **46**, 659–667 (1986).

176. D.S. Peabody and P. Berg, *Mol. Cell Biol.* **6**, 2695–2703 (1986).

177. P.S. Mountford and A.G. Smith, *Trends Genet.* **11**, 179–184 (1995).

178. R. Kornfield and S. Kornfield, In W. Lennarz, ed., *The Biochemistry of Glycoproteins and Proteoglycans*, Plenum, New York, 1985, pp. 34–87

179. M. Sakaguchi, *Curr. Opin. Biotechnol.* **8**, 595–601 (1997).

180. A.J. Dorner, D.G. Bole, and R.J. Kaufman, *J. Cell Biol.* **105**, 2665–2674 (1987).

181. P. Hsieh, M.R. Rosner, and P.W. Robbins, *J. Biol. Chem.* **257**, 2548–2554 (1983).

182. D.B. Williams and W.J. Lennarz, *J. Biol. Chem.* **259**, 5105–5114 (1984).

183. A.H. Davies, *Curr. Opin. Biotechnol.* **6**, 543–547 (1995).

184. R. Wagner et al., *Glycobiology* **6**, 165–175 (1996).

185. N.G. Seidah and M. Chrétien, *Curr. Opin. Biotechnol.* **8**, 602–607 (1997).

186. D.A. Bravo et al., *J. Biol. Chem.* **269**, 25830–25837 (1994).

187. T.A.Y. Ayoubi, S.M.P. Meulemans, A.J.M. Roebroek, and W.J.M. van de Ven, *Mol. Biol. Rep.* **23**, 87–95 (1996).

188. A. Subramanian et al., *Ann. NY Acad. Sci.* **782**, 249–255 (1996).

189. D. Picard, *Curr. Opin. Biotechnol.* **5**, 511–515 (1994).

190. A. Porter, *Trends Genet.* **14**, 73–79 (1998).

191. T.D. Littlewood et al., *Nucleic Acids Res.* **23**, 1686–1690 (1995).

192. R.D. Palmiter and R.L. Brinster, *Annu. Rev. Genet.* **20**, 465–499 (1986).

193. H.F. Sutherland, R.H. Lovell-Badge, and I.J. Jackson, *Gene* **131**, 265–268 (1993).

194. A. Iyengar, F. Muller, and N. Maclean, *Transgenic Res.* **5**, 147–166 (1996).

195. R.K. Kothary et al., *Biochem. Cell. Biol.* **70**, 1097–1104 (1992).

196. O.K. Miller and H.M. Temin, *Science* **200**, 606–609 (1983).

197. J.O. Bishop and P. Smith, *Mol. Biol. Med.* **6**, 283–298 (1989).

198. G.W. Stuart, J.R. Vielkind, J.V. McMurray, and M. Westerfied, *Development* **109**, 577–584 (1990).

199. D. Endean and O. Smithies, *Chromosoma* **97**, 307–314 (1989).

200. S.S.C. Chong and J.R. Vielkind, *Theor. Appl. Genet.* **78**, 369–380 (1989).

201. R. Al-Shawi, J. Kinnaird, J. Burke, and J.O. Bishop, *Mol. Cell. Biol.* **10**, 1192–1198 (1990).

202. S.C.R. Elgin, ed., *Chromatin Structure and Gene Expression*, IRL Press, Oxford, U.K., 1995.

203. T. Tsukiyama and C. Wu, *Curr. Opin. Genet. Dev.* **7**, 242–248 (1997).

204. T.H. Bestor, *Nature (London)* **393**, 311–312 (1998).

205. J.C. Eissenberg, S.C.R. Elgin, and R. Paro, in S.C.R. Elgin, ed., *Chromatin Structure and Gene Expresion*, IRL Press, Oxford, U.K., 1995, pp. 147–171.

206. K. Dobie, M. Mehtali, M. McClenaghan, and R. Lathe, *Trends Genet.* **13**, 127–130, (1997).

207. D.R. Dorer, *Transgenic Res.* **6**, 3–10 (1997).

208. T. Yokoyama et al., *Science* **260**, 679–682 (1993).

209. A. Schedl et al., *Cell* **86**, 71–82 (1996).

210. P. Artelt et al., *Gene* **99**, 249–254 (1991).

211. S. Eden and H. Cedar, *Curr. Opin. Genet. Dev.* **4**, 255–259 (1994).

212. Z. Siegfried and H. Cedar, *Curr. Biol.* **7**, R305–R307 (1997).

213. J.A. Yoder, C.P. Walsh, and T.H. Bestor, *Trends Genet.* **13**, 335–340 (1997).

214. D. Jahner et al., *Nature (London)* **298**, 623–628 (1982).

215. W. Doerfler, *Microb. Pathog.* **12**, 1–8 (1992).

216. K. Gardiner, *Trends Genet.* **12**, 519–534 (1996).

217. P. Meyer, *Trends Biotechnol.* **13**, 332–337 (1995).

218. D. Garrick, S. Fiering, D.I.K. Martin, and E. Whitelaw, *Nat. Genet.* **18**, 56–59 (1998).

219. P.M. Bingham, *Cell* **90**, 385–387 (1997).

220. P.A. Koetsier, L. Mangel, B. Schmitz, and W. Doerfler, *Transgenic Res.* **5**, 235–244 (1996).

221. W. Reik, S.K. Howlett, and M.A. Surani, *Development, Suppl.*, pp. 99–106 (1990).

222. H. Sasaki et al., *Development* **111**, 573–581 (1991).

223. I. Wilmut and C.B.A. Whitelaw, *Reprod. Fertil. Dev.* **6**, 625–630 (1994).

224. J. Webster et al., *Gene* **193**, 239–243 (1997).

225. R.T. Kamakaka, *Trends Biochem. Sci.* **22**, 124–128 (1997).

226. J.M.H. Vos, *Curr. Opin. Genet. Dev.* **8**, 351–359 (1998).

227. G. Brem et al., *Mol. Reprod. Dev.* **44**, 56–62 (1996).

228. B. Sauer, *Curr. Opin. Biotechnol.* **5**, 521–527 (1995).

229. A.J. Stacey et al., *Mol. Cell. Biol.* **4**, 1009–1016 (1994).

230. P.K. Geyer, *Curr. Opin. Genet. Dev.* **7**, 242–248 (1997).

231. A. Steif, D.M. Winter, W.H. Stratling, and A.E. Sippel, *Nature (London)* **341**, 343–345 (1989).

232. R.A. McKnight et al., *Proc. Natl. Acad. Sci. U.S.A.* **89**, 6943–6947 (1992).

233. J. Ellis et al., *Nucleic Acids Res.* **25**, 1296–1302 (1997).

234. A.J. Clark et al., *Philos. Trans. R. Soc. London, Ser. B* **339**, 225–232 (1993).

235. D.R.F. Leach, *Genetic Recombination*, Blackwell, Oxford, U.K., 1996.

236. T. Kodadek, *Trends Biochem. Sci.* **23**, 79–83 (1998).

237. P. Hasty, R. Ramirez-Solis, R. Krumlauf, and A. Bradley, *Nature (London)* **350**, 243–246 (1991).

238. R. Ramirez-Solis, P. Liu, and A. Bradley, *Nature (London)* **378**, 720–724 (1995).

239. M.R. Capecchi, *Sci. Am.* **270**, 34–41 (1994).

240. J. Zhang and H.M. Temin, *Science* **259**, 234–248 (1993).

241. O. Smithies et al., *Nature (London)* **317**, 230–234 (1985).

242. S. Thompson et al., *Cell* **56**, 313–321, (1989).

243. S. Kumar and J.P. Simons, *Nucleic Acids Res.* **21**, 1541–1548 (1993).

244. M.L. Hooper, *Embryonal Stem Cells: Introducing Planned Changes into the Animal Germline*, Harwood Academic Publishers, Chur, Switzerland, 1992.

245. H. Te Riele, E.R. Maandag, and A. Berns, *Proc. Natl. Acad. Sci. U.S.A.* **89**, 5128–5132 (1992).

246. P. Hasty, J. Rivera-Perez, C. Chang, and A. Bradley, *Mol. Cell. Biol.* **11**, 4509–4517 (1991).

247. K.R. Thomas and M.R. Capecchi, *Cell* **51**, 503–512 (1987).

248. A.J.H. Smith and P. Berg, *Cold Spring Harbor Symp. Quant. Biol.* **49**, 171–181 (1984).

249. S. Fiering et al., *Genes Dev.* **9**, 2203–2213 (1995).

250. C.B. Moens et al., *Genes Dev.* **6**, 691–704 (1992).

251. S.L. Mansour, K.R. Thomas, and M.R. Capecchi, *Nature (London)* **336**, 348–353 (1988).

252. M. Jasin and P. Berg, *Genes Dev.* **2**, 1353–1363 (1988).

253. V. Valencius and O. Smithies, *Mol. Cell. Biol.* **11**, 1402–1408 (1991).

254. R.C. Moore et al., *Bio/Technology* **12**, 999–1004 (1995).

255. S.G. Hormuzdi, R. Pentinen, R. Jaenisch, and P. Bornstein, *Mol. Cell. Biol.* **18**, 2268–3375 (1998).

256. M.J. Evans and M.H. Kaufman, *Nature (London)* **292**, 154–156 (1981).

257. G.R. Martin, *Proc. Natl. Acad. Sci. U.S.A.* **78**, 7634–7638 (1981).

258. J.B. Cibelli et al., *Nat. Biotechnol.* **16**, 642–646 (1998).

259. J. McWhir et al., *Nat. Genet.* **14**, 223–226 (1996).

260. C. Dani et al., *J. Cell Sci.* **110**, 1279–1285 (1997).

261. J.P. Brown, W. Wei, and J.M. Sedivy, *Science* **277**, 831–834 (1997).

262. Y. Kuroiwa et al., *Nucleic Acids Res.* **26**, 2447–2448 (1998).

263. M. Lewandoski and G.R. Martin, *Nat. Genet.* **17**, 223–225 (1997).

264. F. Buchholz, P.O. Angrand, and A.F. Stewart, *Nat. Biotechnol.* **16**, 657–662 (1998).

265. D.L. Sokol and J.D. Murray, *Transgenic Res.* **5**, 363–371 (1996).

266. L.A. Coutre and D.T. Stinchcomb, *Trends Genet.* **12**, 510–515 (1996).

267. E. Harlow and D. Lane. *Antibodies: A Laboratory Manual*, Cold Spring Harbor Press, Cold Spring Harbor, N.Y., 1988.

268. D.O. Morgan and R.A. Roth, *Immunol. Today* **9**, 84–88 (1988).

269. J.H. Richardson and W.A. Marasco, *Trends Biotechnol.* **13**, 306–310 (1995).

270. E. Gibola and C. Smith, *Trends Genet.* **10**, 139–144 (1994).

271. J.M. Chubb and M.E. Hogan, *Trends Biotechnol.* **10**, 132–136 (1992).

272. S. Agrawal, *Trends Biotechnol.* **14**, 376–387 (1996).

273. J.W. Sentry and K. Kaiser, *Transgenic Res.* **3**, 155–162 (1994).

274. R.D. Palmiter et al., *Nature (London)* **200**, 611–615 (1982).

275. L.M. Houdebine, *Transgenic Animals: Generation and Use*, Harwood Academic Publishers, Chur, Switzerland, 1997.

276. B. Hogan, F. Constantini, and E. Lacey, *Manipulating the Mouse Embryo: A Laboratory Manual*, Cold Spring Harbor Press, Cold Spring Harbor, N.Y., 1986.

277. R.E. Hammer et al., *Nature (London)* **315**, 680–683 (1985).

278. C.B.A. Whitelaw, A.J. Springbett, J. Webster, and A.J. Clark, *Transgenic Res.* **2**, 29–32 (1993).

279. R.L. Page et al., *Transgenic Res.* **4**, 353–360 (1995).

280. A.R. Clarke, *Nat. Biotechnol.* **14**, 942, (1996).

281. B. Maione, B. Lavitrano, C. Spadafora, and A.A. Kiessling, *Mol. Reprod. Dev.* **50**, 406–409 (1998).

282. A. Nagy et al., *Development* **110**, 815–821, (1990).

283. L.M. Forrester, A. Bernstein, J. Rossant, and A. Nagy, *Proc. Natl. Acad. Sci. U.S.A.* **88**, 7514–7517 (1991).

284. P.A. Labosky, D.P. Barlow, and B.L.M. Hogan, *Development* **120**, 3197–3204 (1994).

285. J.W. Gordon et al., *Proc. Natl. Acad. Sci. U.S.A.* **77**, 7380–7384 (1980).

286. K.H.S. Campbell, J. McWhir, W. Ritchie, and I. Wilmut, *Nature (London)* **380**, 64–66 (1996).

287. I. Wilmut et al., *Nature (London)* **385**, 810–813 (1997).

288. M. Noble et al., *Transgenic Res.* **4**, 215–225 (1995).

289. R. Al-Shawi et al., *Mol. Cell. Biol.* **11**, 4207–4216 (1991).

290. A. Bernstein and M. Breitman, *Mol. Biol. Med.* **6**, 523–530 (1989).

291. A.J. Clark et al., *Gene Ther.* **4**, 101–110 (1997).

292. M. Kessel, R. Balling, and P. Grus, *Cell* **61**, 301–308 (1990).

293. l.G. Guy et al., *EMBO J.* **15**, 3713–3721 (1996).

294. R. Kellum and S.C.R. Elgin, *Curr. Biol.* **8**, R521–R524 (1998).

295. A.J. Clark, G. Harold, and F. Yull, *Nucleic Acids Res.* **25**, 1009–1014 (1997).

296. G.L. Evans and R.A. Morgan, *Proc. Natl. Acad. Sci. U.S.A.* **95**, 5734–5739 (1998).

297. G. McLachlan and D.J. Porteous, *Transgenic Animals: Generation and Use*, Harwood Academic Publishers, Chur, Switzerland, 1997, pp. 435–444.

298. A. Harris, *Hum. Mol. Genet.* **6**, 2191–2193 (1997).

299. J. Love, C. Gribben, C. Mather, and H. Sang, *Bio/Technology* **12**, 60–63 (1994).

300. S.G. Gong and L.D. Etkin, *Transgenic Animals: Generation and Use*, Harwood Academic Publishers, Chur, Switzerland, 1977, pp. 123–127.

301. J.H. Chung, M. Whiteley, and G. Falsenfeld, *Cell* **74**, 505–514 (1993).

302. R.H. Devlin, T.Y. Yesaki, E.M. Donaldson, and C.L. Hew, *Nature (London)* **371**, 209–210 (1994).

303. R.M. Twyman and E.A. Jones, *J. Neurogenet.* **10**, 67–101 (1995).

304. R.L. Brinster et al., *Proc. Natl. Acad. Sci. U.S.A.* **85**, 863–840 (1988).

305. G. Donofrio, E. Bignetti, A.J. Clark, and C.B.A. Whitelaw, *Mol. Gen. Genet.* **252**, 465–469 (1996).

306. V.G. Pursel and C.E. Rexroad, *Mol. Reprod. Dev.* **36**, 615–623 (1993).

307. S. Damak, H.Y. Su, N.P. Jay, and D.W. Bullock, *Bio/Technology* **14**, 185–188 (1996).

308. M. Muller and G. Brem, *Reprod. Fertil. Dev.* **6**, 605–613 (1994).

309. B.O. Hughes, G.S. Huges, D. Waddington, and M.C. Appleby, *Anim. Sci.* **63**, 91–101 (1996).

310. A.J. Clark et al., *Bio/Technology* **7**, 487–492 (1989).

311. I. Sola et al., *J.Virol.* **72**, 3762–3772 (1998).

312. G. Wright et al., *Bio/Technology* **9**, 830–834 (1991).

313. T. Wakayama et al., *Nature (London)* **394**, 369–374 (1998).

314. C. Wilson, H.J. Bellen, and W.J. Gehring, *Annu. Rev. Cell Biol.* **6**, 679–714 (1990).

315. A.E. Sschnieke et al., *Science* **278**, 2130–2133 (1997).

316. F.A. Brook and R.L. Gardner, *Proc. Natl. Acad. Sci. U.S.A.* **94**, 5709–5712 (1997).

317. R.G. McKinnell, *Cloning: Of Frogs, Mice and Other Animals*, University of Minnesota Press, Minneapolis, 1985.

318. P.G. Shiels et al., *Nature (London)* **399**, 316–317 (1999).

319. R.P. Lanza, D.K.C. Cooper, and W.L. Crick, *Sci. Am.* 40–45 (1997).

320. D.J.G. White, G.A. Langford, E. Cozzi, and V.K. Young, *Xenopus* **2**, 213–217 (1995).

321. J.L. Greenstein and D.H. Sachs, *Nat. Biotechnol.* **15**, 235–238 (1997).

322. J.L. Platt and J.S. Logan, *Transgenic Animals: Generation and Use*, Harwood Academic Publishers, Chur, Switzerland, 1997, pp. 455–460.

323. D.J.G. White and G.A. Langford, *Animal Breeding: Technology for the 21st Century*, Harwood Academic Publishers, Amsterdam, 1998, pp. 229–242.

See also CELLULAR TRANSFORMATION, CHARACTERISTICS; ETHICAL ISSUES IN ANIMAL AND PLANT CELL TECHNOLOGY; TRANSFORMATION OF PLANTS; TRANSCRIPTION, TRANSLATION AND THE CONTROL OF GENE EXPRESSION.

GERMPLASM PRESERVATION OF IN VITRO PLANT CULTURES

LEIGH E. TOWILL
USDA-ARS National Seed Storage Laboratory
Fort Collins, Colorado

OUTLINE

Introduction

Germplasm Banks

Types of In Vitro Cultures

    Callus and Suspension Cultures

    In Vitro Plants

    Somatic Embryos

    Root Cultures

    Recalcitrant Seed/Embryonic Axes

Acquisition

Maintenance

    Normal Growth Conditions

    Reduced Growth Conditions

    Cryopreservation

Distribution

Characterization and Evaluation

Information Management

Banking Issues

    Costs

    Safety

Bibliography

INTRODUCTION

The preservation of lines for plant cell, tissue, organ, and plant culture is important in providing a sample to the user that is identical to the initial stock. This concern is the same whether dealing with suspension cultures that produce a secondary product, callus that has the ability to regenerate, or in vitro plants that are maintained vegetatively for some unique characteristic. Acquisition, maintenance, distribution, characterization, and information management are crucial functions of a bank, and many of the practical aspects are the same whether dealing with maintenance of cells or in vitro plants. Maintenance procedures for plants are similar to procedures for other organisms that are asexually multiplied and consists either of continued multiplication under normal or restrictive growth conditions or of cryogenic storage whereby propagation is unnecessary until distribution is needed. Maintenance of a line in an unchanged form is conceptually simple, but it is often difficult to determine whether any alterations are introduced during propagation procedures. This article defines some aspects of the banking of cell, tissue, organ, and plant cultures.

GERMPLASM BANKS

The importance of plants in today's society cannot be overstated. In a world with a vastly increasing population, we depend upon plants for nutritious food, clothes, shelter, extracted chemicals, medicinals, and a quality environment. Many of these dependencies require active intervention, for example, in developing plant improvement programs for the quality and quantity of produce, or in reintroducing plants from populations that have been reduced in nature. Improvement depends upon a source of diversity, and this has come mainly from landraces, native populations, and wild relatives. It is all too apparent that novel methods of single and multiple gene transfer among and across either species, genera, or even families will become more important as "improved" or altered plants are developed to enhance quality, yield, disease tolerance, etc. Although we depend upon relatively few plant species for feeding our population, the species diversity used for other aspects in our society is large. But diversity for some important groups, in the form of different species or populations within a species, are decreasing due to the pressures of expanding human populations. It is within this context that the need for genebanks of higher plants has become critical. The value of both in situ and ex situ genebanks has been stated and are complementary (1). In vitro collections of plants and cells are becoming common for aspects of ex situ germplasm preservation.

There is no general term for a collection of plant lines. In crop germplasm conservation studies, the collection of genotypes is often termed a germplasm bank or genebank. The main purpose for preserving these crop and related species, usually in the form of botanical seed, is to ensure their availability for breeding programs that utilize conventional crossing and/or biotechnological methodologies. There are other reasons for establishing banks of cell lines. The present ability to culture nearly any plant species creates the capability to examine aspects of growth and development, metabolism, and gene structure, function, and expression. The establishment of unique cell lines possessing alterations in biochemical paths or specific gene functions are valuable for many reasons. The function of the bank, therefore, is to preserve these lines and distribute them to the user community. In addition, the ability to patent certain life forms often requires, as part of the process, deposition of a sample at a designated location recognized by the Budapest Treaty of 1977 (2). Although the number of plant lines currently patented is relatively small, this will greatly expand in a relatively short time. Thus any bank is concerned with the preservation of important genotypes in a manner that minimizes change and risk of loss (3). Maintenance includes holding of the line and also its multiplication for distribution. Procedures need to be easy to apply, give reproducible results, and ensure that the line distributed is identical to the original deposited line. In practice this latter point may be difficult to ascertain since characterization may be incomplete and only qualitative. Efficient and effective procedures are important for successful operation and for cost considerations. A key issue is safety of the preservation system.

The concept has evolved, particularly for crop species, that two types of genebanks are necessary for successful germplasm conservation, and has been applied mainly for botanical seed storage (4,5). The active genebank (also sometimes termed the active collection) is charged with acquiring, maintaining, distributing, and characterizing germplasm. The base genebank (also termed the base collection) serves as the long-term conservation site, the major function of which is storage of the germplasm under the best conditions possible to avoid loss of diversity. The active and base genebanks preferably should be at different geographic locations such that the potential of loss of any given line is minimized. Of course, only organizations that have substantial resources can set up such a detailed system, and where resources are limited various modifications may exist. Use of two banks for cultures may not be feasible or cost effective. A decision has to be made about what the function of the individual bank is and what can be accomplished. Often either slow growth or cryopreservation (see below) are desired options. For lines that are seldom distributed, a cryogenic storage system may be chosen as the sole maintenance system; safety still can be addressed by having storage at different sites with independent sources of liquid nitrogen.

The overall functions used in crop seed genebanks are directly applicable to in vitro systems. Any bank or collection of cells, etc., is concerned with topics of acquisition, maintenance, distribution, and characterization. Any information about origin, growth, multiplication, and characterization of the culture is advantageous and should be compiled for distribution to the user. There have been several reviews on germplasm preservation and on maintenance of lines (6–9), and the reader is referred to these for a detailed discussion of the concepts and concerns. Information from banks for animal and microbial cultures also contain useful insights for management (10–13). Many issues are very similar for any type of organism, and differences often exist only in the details.

TYPES OF IN VITRO CULTURES

The in vitro systems that are usually maintained in a genebank are callus, cell suspensions, root cultures, somatic embryos, or in vitro plants. Occasionally interest in the preservation of other higher plant systems (for example, pollen, isolated sperm cells, tissue fragments) arises from the research community, but these materials are not maintained for proliferation, that is, as cultures. An example here is the isolation of sperm cells from maize pollen and their cryopreservation, where they can be used for either transformation and/or in vitro fertilization (14). Cultured embryonic axes are not usually a proliferative system and are held as a way to store germplasm where whole seed storage is difficult (see below).

It is reiterated that germplasm for most crop plants is maintained as botanical seed and that guidelines for viability testing (usually germination), storage, and regeneration are well described. Actual conditions for seed storage at a bank depend upon available facilities and monetary support. Pollen preservation is well described for some species, very similar to seed storage, and very simply accomplished for many crops (15). Procedures for maintenance of vegetatively propagated species in field or greenhouse collections, likewise, are often well defined and supported by a wealth of practical experience. But the maintenance of in vitro forms is a recent technology, and procedures are still being developed (16). Thus there are not as many useful generalizations and little consensus on the most desirable procedures for practical maintenance. Methods often are species specific, and sometimes even genotype specific, but some aspects of this problem for crop species have been overcome in many instances. For example, the substantial in vitro plant collections of potato and sweet potato genotypes held at several locations are usually initiated by a single method and cultured on a single medium.

Callus and Suspension Cultures

Callus cultures can be initiated from virtually any species. Efficiencies of induction from different plant organs vary, and the selection of choice depends upon what characteristics are being sought. Once callus is proliferating, it can be maintained as callus or inoculated to obtain a suspension culture. There is extensive information available on callus and suspension culture induction, multiplication, nutritional requirements, and plant regeneration capacity (17,18).

In Vitro Plants

Plants have been introduced into culture from preexisting meristems and micropropagated for a multitude of species. Some difficulties still exist such as introduction from mature-phase woody plants (19) and the elimination of associated endophytic contaminants (20). Once established, in vitro maintained plants form an important part of germplasm maintenance systems for crop plants and have several benefits, including reduced space for storage, easier retention of the disease-tested state, potential of freeing the plant from viruses, bacteria, etc., ease of shipping, and more rapid and efficient propagation (21). Some of these benefits are more important for herbaceous crops such as sweet potato and potato, and may be less so for woody perennial trees or shrubs. For example, in apple breeding the timely induction of flowering may be required by the user. Grafting of a bud from scion wood produces a flower in about 12–18 months, whereas flowering from an in vitro plant might take several years after removal

from the in vitro condition. But supplying the user with in vitro apple line would be beneficial for genetic alterations, using, for example, particle bombardment of meristem tips, whereby culture and selection would be needed to isolate the desired genotype. This example further illustrates that the bank must determine what form the species can be supplied to the user. Does the user convert the species to the in vitro plant, or does the genebank?

Somatic Embryos

Somatic embryos and embryogenic callus or cell suspensions are a means used to micropropagate a selected genotype and may have advantages with regard to reduced frequency of offtypes during propagation, asexual embryo possessing the desiccation characteristics of the sexual embryo, and potential for packaging for synthetic seed production. Somatic embryos may be produced from cell suspensions or may be produced on other embryos, and may be used for rapid multiplication, artificial seed production, or biotechnological studies. The storage of somatic embryos may be beneficial for holding lines until characteristics of a given genotype can be determined. Elite genotypes of forest trees are only identified after several years of growth, but with current understanding, the ability to induce somatic embryogenesis only exists while the plant is in the juvenile state. Somatic embryos are induced for each line of segregants of a cross and are cryogenically stored until the appropriate, useful individuals are identified for rapid, clonal multiplication. This strategy, of course, would be beneficial for any species where maturity characteristics take several months or years to be distinguished.

Root Cultures

Historically, excised roots were one of the first plant systems to be examined in vitro, and a considerable amount of information on growth and physiology was generated. Root cultures are important for secondary metabolite production and analyses of the pertinent catabolic and anabolic paths. Renewed interest in root culture growth and storage has occurred due to the potential of transforming plants with *Agrobacterium rhizogenes* and subsequent plant regeneration from the root explant.

Recalcitrant Seed/Embryonic Axes

Many plant species produce seed that are not entirely desiccation tolerant (22). Such seed has been termed recalcitrant. The critical moisture value, below which viability is lost, is usually quite high relative to usual storage moisture conditions. These seeds also are quite short-lived under higher moisture contents and usual temperature conditions, such as at $+4\,°C$, $-5\,°C$, or $-20\,°C$. For these species, plants themselves are maintained either as ex vitro or in vitro lines. But storage of such seed would be valuable, for example, for collecting species when seed is the only propagule available, or where quarantine only allows import of seed and not plants. As will be described, cryogenic storage of the embryonic axis may be feasible, given appropriate treatment. Culture of the axis to regenerate a plant would be used for recovery.

ACQUISITION

The policy of a genebank determines what materials are to be stored and how they can accommodate new materials that are either obtained from other locations or are generated from research activities. Criteria are established for acquisition into the collection, and these criteria obviously relate to the mission of the specific bank. It is difficult to generalize, but the bank function may be either for a specific crop or for lines that possess specific attributes. A bank also may exist for patented lines, since there are requirements for storage at a designated site. The ability now to transform and genetically engineer many species potentially could lead to the generation of a multitude of lines. Although cell lines could be held, the production of true seed could also maintain the engineered state for some species. The manner in which the line is held will relate to the reason it was derived. Was it generated for production of a product via a bioreactor system or for ultimate inclusion of gene(s) for a field-grown crop system? In concept you could store a given line in several different forms, but the practical issue of what is best will have to be addressed since bank costs could be quite high. The tendency of many researchers is to save as many lines as possible. But costs of doing this are great. Thus it becomes imperative to evaluate what is being saved and why. It is impossible to know what the future may require, but some evaluations or decisions are needed to avoid the extensive buildup of lines that might never be used. The efficient ability to generate and select mutant lines of desired types, such as by site-directed mutagenesis, ultimately may reduce the need to store some genotypes.

MAINTENANCE

Once stocks are obtained, a suitable protocol for maintaining the culture in a viable state is implemented. This is generally by growing the culture under normal growth conditions, growing the culture under restrictive conditions, or cryopreservation. The culture medium and conditions of growth are described by the supplier of the culture, but it should not be assumed that the protocol is necessarily optimum nor that extensive tests have been done to describe growth responses. For most cultures, studies have not been done to develop either a reduced growth or a cryopreservation system. What works in one laboratory sometimes is not exactly duplicated in another laboratory. Amongst laboratories minor variations in the manner in which chemical stocks and growth media are made and procedures followed can affect growth characteristics and rate. Detailed, standardized methods need to be developed and accurately described for all operations of the genebank. Trained personnel are required for operations. Computerized systems with bar codes and labels for cultures and media are helpful for quality control.

An axenic in vitro culture is desired, but the presence of bacterial contaminants is often difficult to assess, especially when it may be contained within the vascular tissue of in vitro plants. Contaminants on plant culture media often show either no signs of extensive growth or visually occur only sporadically in individuals. Certification of cultures as free from microbial contamination or viral infections is often necessary for international shipment. Use of enriched culture media for microbes can identify some problems, but some contaminants are still elusive.

Normal Growth Conditions

Cell lines are maintained as either callus or suspension cultures under specified environmental conditions and are propagated by periodic subculturing. Subculture may occur every few days for suspension cultures or days to a few weeks for callus cultures, depending upon growth characteristics. There is ample evidence to suggest that some characteristics are altered over time, although the time frame for such change may be quite variable among species (23). Numerous reports have shown ploidy changes and other alternations of the genetic material with continuous culture of cells, but some lines have proved remarkably stable over many subcultures. Maintenance costs, which would include labor, supplies, and growth space for such frequent propagation, are quite high. Thus in a practical sense many lines cannot be maintained in this way unless they are extensively used. It should also be noted that change in a culture may not be easily discernible. Change may occur with regard to growth rate and morphological form, but may also relate to metabolic alterations that are not directly or immediately observable. In concept, a culture should be periodically tested to be sure that it at least has the characteristic for which is was preserved.

In vitro plants under normal growth conditions are held at about 20–30 °C with light photoperiods ranging from 8 to 16 h and intensities usually supplied by fluorescent or fluorescent/incandescent fixtures. Although high carbon dioxide/high-intensity light systems (with sugarless media) give very good growth for in vitro plants (24), such systems are not reported to be routinely used in banks. Some optima of the physical environment have been described for selected materials, but a bank usually has minimal capacity to provide wide-ranging conditions. Depending upon the species, type of vessel, and growth conditions, typical durations between subculture may vary from 1 month to about a year. Visual inspection usually is sufficient to determine when a culture needs to be replenished. In contrast to unorganized tissues such as callus or suspensions, there is little evidence to suggest that frequent subcultures lead to variants, providing care is taken to ensure that the plants regenerated came from pre-existing apical meristems, such as from terminal or axillary buds. Some banks, however, routinely obtain a fresh culture periodically from the original ex vitro plant to minimize the potential for selection.

Somatic embryos, once initiated into culture, are often proliferated by subculturing a portion to fresh medium. In some cases, somatic embryos form directly on the older embryos, whereas in other cases, embryos initiate from embryogenic callus and it is this form of callus that is transferred. The incidence of change with continuous culture is argued to be less with somatic embryos than with callus or suspension cultures, but there is not a clear answer. As with all other culture systems, the duration of storage is quite short, being a matter of a few days to a few weeks. Continued multiplication is again labor intensive and costly, and is not useful to a bank maintaining many lines. Delays in transfer affect potential for somatic embryogenesis, frequency of somatic embryos, and increase offtypes. Some systems have a range of callus types within the embryogenic mass, and technicians must be trained correctly to manipulate the culture.

The growth and subculturing of root cultures is straightforward. Apical portions of roots are excised and reinoculated into fresh medium. This is necessary each month or two.

Embryonic axes are not maintained as proliferative systems. Culture of an axis at room temperature leads to "germination" of the axis and results in a seedling. Subculture of the line would then be done as with in vitro plants. Cryogenic storage of the axis itself is the only manner of holding the system without growth and development.

In addition to high costs and the potential for genetic change in any of the above systems, frequent culture may lead to potential problems with mislabeling, introduction of contamination, culture mixups, and culture loss.

Reduced Growth Conditions

Conceptually, problems associated with normal growth conditions may be reduced by holding cell cultures under some sort of growth restriction (25,26). Growth reduction may occur through use of temperature reduction, reduced oxygen tension, nutritional restrictions, exposure to inhibitors, or exposure to osmotic stress. The approach has been largely empirical in determining what restrictive conditions are useful. Temperature reduction is the favored approach, but from literature reports, lower temperatures have not been as useful for retaining viable callus or suspensions as they have been for in vitro plants. Callus or suspension cultures derived from tropical or subtropical species may exhibit a chilling injury if held at temperatures below about 15 °C, although this critical temperature is highly variable among species. It can be argued that inhibitors or osmotic stress may exert a strong selective pressure, or even be mutagenic, and can induce an altered culture or plant that may not easily regain typical growth when transferred back to normal growth conditions. There, however, are very few data that directly address these questions. It is anticipated that answers would be very species specific. If a suitable condition can be identified, maintenance costs from labor and supplies can be reduced.

Costs of maintenance of in vitro plants can be reduced by restricting growth and subculture frequency. Although growth inhibitors have been tested in a few systems, most research has centered on temperature reduction. In general, a reduction in temperature is beneficial, but it has been difficult to predict any enhanced longevity. Reports exist for holding in vitro plants from temperate zone species over 8 years at temperatures in the range of 4–10 °C. Cultures may periodically need to have an addition of fresh liquid medium. If one is dealing with tropical or subtropical species, chilling injury is often a concern, and thus in vitro plants cannot be stored below about 15 °C. The type of container used for storage and its manner of closure affect frequency of contamination and of culture desiccation. Various options exist, but the use of heat sealable, autoclavable plastic seem to offer distinct advantages (27).

The use of lower temperatures for enhancing duration of storage has not been extensively reported for somatic embryos multiplied directly on other embryos. Some information is available with regard to enhanced longevity of embryogenic suspensions. While these treatments may enhance longevity, maintenance of the embryogenic potential and offtype production must also be critically assessed. There is little information with regard to using inhibitors or osmotic stress for reducing the subculture frequency. Caution is advised, since the embryogenic process itself is often very sensitive to these stresses. There are few reports that supply useful information on preservation of either roots or embryonic axes under restrictive growth conditions. As with other culture types, costs of development and application of growth conditions must be assessed in developing the overall preservation strategy.

Cryopreservation

The concept behind the use of cryogenic storage (cryopreservation) has been that the low temperatures of storage (ca. −150° to −196 °C) reduce molecular motion such that normal molecular reactions have a low probability of occurring. At low temperatures remaining liquid within cells probably exists as a glass in which diffusion is very slow as a consequence of the high viscosity. Thus some events that may lead to deterioration and viability loss are much reduced. In most cases, cryopreservation utilizes liquid nitrogen as a cryogen because of its inert behavior and relatively cheap cost. Storage is accomplished within the liquid (−196 °C) or in vapour phase over the liquid (ca. −150° to −180 °C). A reliable source of liquid nitrogen and a supply tank have to be available to refill the storage vat. From a practical viewpoint, the ability to cryopreserve a sample is an advantage because labor costs involved in the holding of the sample are very low. The cost of the storage containers and of liquid nitrogen vary considerably among countries, but probably are comparatively cheaper than growth culture requirements. The cost of storage containers must be considered, but they are inexpensive relative to growth facilities and are much cheaper to operate.

Models of dewars or liquid nitrogen refrigerators are available that have variable sample capacities. Expected durations of storage before refilling are published. Storage systems for samples within the vats also vary. Although samples can be held in small straws, such as semen straws, most samples are placed within plastic cryoampoules, which are available from several suppliers. The 1.2-mL volume ampoule is often used. If the cryoampoule is stored within liquid nitrogen, the potential exists for seepage of the nitrogen into the vial, and upon warming, the liquid nitrogen is rapidly converted to vapor, building considerable pressure, which may cause the cryoampoule to explode. To avoid this potentially injurious condition, some banks store materials within the vapor phase. There is some concern whether the somewhat elevated storage temperatures in the vapor phase may shorten longevity, but no data are published on this issue. This is indeed a difficult issue to test directly, but pragmatically one could argue that even if longevity were somewhat reduced using storage at ca $-160\,°C$, the duration would be sufficient for banking purposes. Some mechanical refrigeration systems exist that can achieve about $-135\,°C$, but a power backup system must be present in the event of an electrical power loss. There is no information in the literature to conclude whether this temperature is adequate for true long-term storage.

The common storage system for vials within a cryogenic container is by their attachment to an aluminum cane. Labeled canes, often in cardboard or plastic sleeves to avoid vials falling off in storage, are placed vertically within a suitable box or canister, as supplied with some dewars. These boxes are stored within either the liquid or vapor phase of liquid nitrogen. The National Seed Storage Laboratory uses aluminum cans ($2'' \times 2'' \times 11''$) for holding samples vertically. Placing vials within plastic boxes is also suitable, but this is more useful for vapor-phase storage and only within certain types of storage dewars. Some sort of inventory system is essential. Retrieval needs to be quick and simple such that other samples are not warmed in the sorting process. Damage to stored samples may occur with only a moderate amount of warming, such as to $-100\,°C$. Conceptually this damage may be due to devitrification of the glass within the cell, and the temperature of occurrence would depend upon the composition of the cell contents.

The use of liquid nitrogen presents some hazards. Large amounts of nitrogen in confined spaces may lead to oxygen deprivation, disorienting workers and possibly even leading to asphyxiation; adequate air circulation and replacement are obviously necessary. In large-scale systems, it is beneficial to have automated cutoffs with low-oxygen alarms. The use of safety glasses or face shields is very important as a precaution from cryoampoules that might explode during warming and splashes of liquid nitrogen that may cause eye damage. Frostbite can also occur in handling samples that are very cold, and suitable gloves are necessary when handling canisters at low temperatures. Be sure not to inadvertently warm any sample by inappropriate handling.

Cryopreservation for plant systems largely has been a research topic and, to date, has not been widely implemented. A recent book contains many chapters with information on the cryopreservation of cultures from diverse species (28). Basic aspects of cryopreservation in a range of systems have been described in other publications (29–32). From studies with plant, animal, and microbial systems, there has emerged an understanding of the important stages in obtaining viability from a culture system. There is often enough information to initiate studies aimed at developing practical cryopreservation systems, although answers to many important questions are unknown or incomplete. The details and concepts for cryopreservation are described in another chapter (see Benson). Here it suffices to mention that slow-cooling, vitrification, and alginate-encapsulation/vitrification methods have been reported for protoplasts, callus, suspension cultures, somatic embryos, shoot tips, and embryonic axes. Methods for cryopreservation of hairy root cultures have been reported using both slow-cooling (33) and vitrification systems (34).

Cryopreservation has been practicable for botanical seed storage at the U.S. National Seed Storage Laboratory, Fort Collins, Colorado, where currently 33,500 accessions are held in vapor-phase storage. Cryogenic storage of clonal materials is also being expanded. About 1,400 clones of apple are held as dormant, cold-acclimated vegetative twigs, which upon warming are grown by excising the bud and grafting it to rootstocks. Buds from in vitro plants of several pear species have been cryopreserved at the National Clonal Germplasm Repository in Corvallis, Oregon, and shipped to NSSL for storage. Other repositories are expanding their cryopreservation programs. At the German Collection of Microorganisms and Cell Cultures, Braunschweig, Germany, over 200 lines of the clonal potato collection are currently cryopreserved as shoot tips, and the International Potato Center, Lima, Peru has a major program to cryopreserve clonal lines of *Solanum* sp. Clearly, cryopreservation will be utilized to a greater extent in the future.

The longevity expected at cryogenic temperatures is unknown. Research results generally have shown samples from several animal and microbial systems to remain viable after 30+ years of cryogenic storage, but this time frame is short relative to the long storage times projected. Most studies have shown no loss in viability with storage, but some suggest problems. For example, two isolates of *Phytophthora clandestina* treated with DMSO lost viability during 4 months of storage in liquid nitrogen (LN) (35). The ultrastructural appearance of four *Trypanosoma* spp. was altered after 30 years of cryogenic storage; samples differed from those observed after 13 years of storage (36). In these types of studies questions remain about whether temperatures were always kept in the cryogenic range and whether samples were warmed/diluted and assayed similarly. There is a further problem of comparing quantitative data obtained 30–40 years apart because of changes in methods, reagents (quality), personnel, etc.

Under cryogenic storage the genetic material of the organism is still subject to damage from background irradiation, and upon warming the accumulation of damage may eventually swamp the genetic repair mechanisms, resulting in lethality (or mutations). Limited studies in animal systems using high irradiation levels with short-term storage have suggested that this would not be a problem for at least two thousand years (37). Similar studies have not been done with plant systems.

An operational question is whether samples should be warmed periodically to assess viability, such as is done with true botanical seed samples that are stored at $-20\,°C$. The latter is performed to determine when viability begins to decrease such that the sample then can be grown out and pollinated to obtain fresh seed for storage. Timely seed regeneration preserves the diversity of gene frequencies within heterozygous, heterogeneous populations. Periodic testing of cryogenically stored clonal lines probably is of little value and would only serve to waste most materials. One strategy might be to have one accession within each group of preserved accessions represented by more aliquots. A sample of this accession then can be tested over time and used as a gauge, albeit qualitative, for viability decline of the group as a whole.

DISTRIBUTION

Distribution is a key component of a culture bank. Depending upon how the culture is held, once a request is made the culture may need to be propagated before a sample can be sent to the user. Samples of callus may be sent in tubes with an increased agar content in the growth medium or portioned on moist cotton or a similar substrata. The use of gas-permeable bags for shipment has benefits for shipment to avoid breakage and minimize contamination. Cryogenically stored samples are usually warmed and placed under growing conditions before being sent to the user. Direct shipment of cryopreserved samples is feasible with suitable insulated shipping containers, but it is usually simpler, and perhaps more effective in retaining survival, if the bank does the warming and regrowth of the culture. Overnight express services facilitate delivery of the culture to the user before deterioration becomes significant. In all cases adequate packaging is needed to minimize breakage or damage of culture containers, and to avoid extraneous sources of contamination.

CHARACTERIZATION AND EVALUATION

In vitro lines can be initiated from virtually any plant species. Two events can lead to a change of the line. One is biological and relates to selection during the growth process. The other event is the inadvertent mixup that may occur through mislabeling or other events in dealing with propagation where many lines are held. A number of different tools exist to determine the proper characterization of the line. Metabolite analysis can be used where the culture possesses some distinct attribute. Isozymes have been examined in a number of species, but are not reported to be widely used for plant culture characterization. The great expansion of techniques used to examine the genome can be used to characterize the line. Thus microsatellites, RAPDs, RFLPs, AFLPs, and other analyses can characterize the line and be used for comparisons of identity over storage time (38,39). This can be very important to a culture bank, but development and application of these techniques can be quite costly. Thus these are not routine at most banks, but probably will be incorporated as methods become simpler and costs decline.

INFORMATION MANAGEMENT

Within germplasm banks, information is critical in decisions about what accession(s) can fulfill needs of the user. Large-scale computer programs have been developed,

such as the Germplasm Resources Information Network (GRIN) for the U.S. National Plant Germplasm System (5). This compiles passport, descriptive, and availability data for crop germplasm important to U.S. agriculture and is accessible through the Internet (http://www.arsgrin.gov). Many smaller commercial programs for data management exist and can be modified to fit the needs of the individual bank. The data system is useful not only to the user but also for management of the system itself. Development and expansion of database capabilities, use, and linkages certainly facilitate culture use.

BANKING ISSUES

The discussion herein has described many issues that are pertinent to genebanks. Two crucial items need to be summarized since they are crucial for bank operation. These relate to the cost of the overall culture system and the safety of materials within the bank.

Costs

The costs needed to operate banks differ considerably among the types of storage used. Likewise, costs for labor, supplies, and electricity vary among countries. Hence, it is of little value to try to assign actual costs for processes. It is, however, valuable to list what might be major cost considerations in operating a genebank.

With normal growth condition storage, costs occur due to labor, expendable supplies, equipment, and electrical power to operate the growth facility. Purchase or construction of suitable growth rooms or incubators and the periodic repair of them must be factored in. From a safety viewpoint, any growth facility must have some mechanism to avoid temperature extremes. This requires some type of automatic shutoff of all systems (refrigeration, heating, lights, fans, etc.) such that cultures are not lost due to temperature extremes. Alarm and personnel notification systems are now readily available. These are most valuable during off hours when personnel are not present manually to turn off the system. Virtually the same equipment costs exist for reduced growth storage. Cost reductions from restrictive growth conditions usually are due to decreased needs for supplies and labor for subculturing; however, some of this reduction may be offset by increased power consumption and repair needs.

Cryopreservation using liquid nitrogen systems has an initial labor and supply cost associated with processing the samples. Initial costs of the storage tanks may be high, but long-term maintenance, compared to growth rooms, is considerably less. Automatic low-level detection and filling options also are available. The cost, availability, and reliability of liquid nitrogen supply to the facility is also a major factor in determining what is the best strategy for efficient management.

Safety

The most critical issue affecting the conservation is the safety of the maintenance or storage system such that lines are not lost. It is obvious that many can never be replaced and others may be, but often at an extreme cost. A solution for safe storage is holding samples in two, preferably distinctly different, locations. Cryogenic storage in one site may serve as the backup to materials held in growth conditions at another site. Again the cryogenic condition is used because it is cheaper in the long run than a duplicate held in growth conditions. If only cryogenic storage is used, samples could be held in two different containers, preferably at two sites. Whatever the mode of preservation, some sort of replication is needed. Safety of storage is only part of the overall process, however, and safety of preservation also requires extreme attention to avoid problems of mislabeling, culture mixups, and contamination, all of which ultimately affect the integrity of the system. The importance of adequate training and dedication cannot be overemphasized, since, in large part, human activities account for all stages of the preservation process.

BIBLIOGRAPHY

1. T.F. Stuessy and S.H. Sohmer, eds., *Sampling the Green World: Innovative Concepts of Collection, Preservation and Storage of Plant Diversity*, Columbia University Press, New York, 1996.

2. A.P. Halluin, in J.C. Hunter-Cevera and A. Belt, eds., *Maintaining Cultures for Biotechnology and Industry*, Academic Press, San Diego, Calif., 1996, pp. 1–13.

3. E.E. Benson and L.A. Withers, in M.S.S. Pais, F. Mavituna, and J.M. Novais, eds., *Plant Cell Biotechnology*, Springer-Verlag, Berlin, 1988, pp. 431–443.

4. J.T. Williams, in J.H.W. Holden and J.T. Williams, eds., *Crop Genetic Resources: Conservation and Evaluation*, Allen & Unwin, London, 1984, pp. 1–17.

5. J. Janick, ed., *Plant Breeding Reviews*, Vol. 7, Timber Press, Portland, Oreg., 1989.

6. L. Knutson and A.K. Stoner, eds., *Biotic Diversity and Germplasm Preservation: Global Imperatives*, Kluwer Academic Publishers, Dordrecht, The Netherlands, 1988.

7. J.A. Callow, B.V. Ford-Lloyd, and H.J. Newbury, eds., *Biotechnology and Plant Genetic Resources*, CAB International, New York, 1997.

8. P.K. Bretting and D.N. Duvick, *Adv. Agron.* **61**, 1–51 (1997).

9. R.H. Ellis, T.D. Hong, and E.H. Roberts, *Handbook of Seed Technology for Genebanks*, Vol. 1, International Board for Plant Genetic Resources, Rome, 1985.

10. R.J. Hay, in R.I. Freshney, ed., *Animal Cell Culture: A Practical Approach*, IRL Press, Oxford, 1986, pp. 71–112.

11. A. Doyle, C.B. Morris, and W.J. Armitage, in A. Mizrahi, ed., *Upstream Processes: Equipment and Techniques*, Alan R. Liss, San Diego, Calif, 1988, pp. 1–17.

12. J.C. Hunter-Cevera and A. Belt, eds., *Maintaining Cultures for Biotechnology and Industry*, Academic Press, San Diego, Calif., 1996.

13. D. Smith and A.H.S. Onions, *The Preservation and Maintenance of Living Fungi*, IMI Tech. Handb. No. 1, CAB International, Wallingford, U.K. 1994.

14. P. Roeckel and C. Dumas, *Sex. Plant Reprod.* **6**, 212–216 (1993).

15. W.W. Hanna and L.E. Towill, in J. Janick, ed., *Plant Breeding Reviews*, Vol. 13, Wiley, New York, 1995, pp. 179–207.

16. S.E. Ashmore, *Status Report on the Development and Application of In Vitro Techniques for the Conservation and Use of Plant Genetic Resources*, International Plant Genetic Resources Institute, Rome, 1997.

17. E.F. George, *Plant Propagation by Tissue Culture*, Part 1, Exegetics Ltd., London, 1993.

18. E.F. George, *Plant Propagation by Tissue Culture*, Part 2, Exegetics Ltd., London, 1993.

19. W.P. Hackett, in J. Bonga and D.J. Durzan, eds., *Cell and Tissue Culture in Forestry*, Vol. 1, Martinus Nijhoff, Dordrecht, The Netherlands, 1987, pp. 216–231.

20. E.B. Herman, *Recent Advances in Plant Tissue Culture IV: Microbial Contamination of Plant Tissue Cultures*, Agritech Consultants, Shrub Oak, N.Y., 1996.

21. L.E. Towill, *HortScience* **23**, 91–95 (1988).

22. H.F. Chin and E.H. Roberts, *Recalcitrant Crop Seeds*, Tropical Press, Kuala Lumpur, Malaysia, 1980.

23. V. Peschke and R.L. Phillips, *Adv. Genet.* **30**, 41–75 (1992).

24. K. Fujiwara and T. Kozai, in J. Aitken-Christie, T. Kozai, and M.A.L. Smith, eds., *Automation and Environmental Control in Plant Tissue Culture*, Kluwer Academic Publishers, Dordrecht, The Netherlands, 1995, pp. 319–370.

25. S.Y.C. Ng and N.Q. Ng, in J.H. Dodds, ed., *In Vitro Methods for Conservation of Plant Genetic Resources*, Chapman & Hall, London, 1991, pp. 11–39.

26. A. Krikorian, *Bot. Rev.* **62**, 41–108 (1996).

27. B.M. Reed, *Plant Cell Rep.* **10**, 431–434 (1991).

28. Y.P.S. Bajaj, ed., *Biotechnology in Agriculture and Forestry*, Vol. 32, Part I, Springer-Verlag, Berlin, 1995.

29. L.A. Withers, *Methods Mol. Biol.* **6**, 39–48 (1990).

30. K.K. Kartha, ed., *Cryopreservation of Plant Cells and Organs*, CRC Press, Boca Raton, Fla., 1985.

31. B.W.W. Grout and G.J. Morris, eds., *The Effects of Low Temperatures on Biological Systems*, Edward Arnold, London, 1987.

32. R.E. Lee, Jr., G.J. Warren, and L.V. Gusta, eds., *Biological Ice Nucleation and Its Application*, APS Press, St. Paul, Minn., 1995.

33. K.H. Teoh, P.J. Weathers, R.D. Cheetham, and D.B. Walcerz, *Cryobiology* **33**, 106–117 (1996).

34. K. Yoshimatsu, H. Yamaguchi, and K. Shimomura, *Plant Cell Rep.* **15**, 559–564 (1996).

35. S. Simpfendorfer, T.J. Harden, and G.M. Murray, *Aust. Plant Pathol.* **25**, 234–239 (1996).

36. J.P. Schuster, H. Mehlhorn, and W. Raether, *Parasitol. Res.* **82**, 720–726 (1996).

37. P.H. Glenister, D.G. Whittingham, and M.F. Lyon, *J. Reprod. Fert.* **70**, 229–234 (1984).

38. W.G. Ayad, T. Hodgkin, A. Jaradat, and V.R. Rao, eds., *Molecular Genetic Techniques for Plant Genetic Resources*, International Plant Genetic Resources Institute, Rome, 1997.

39. A. Karp et al., *Molecular Tools in Plant Genetic Resources Conservation: A Guide to the Technologies*, International Plant Genetic Resources Institute, Rome, 1997.

See also CRYOPRESERVATION OF PLANT CELLS, TISSUES AND ORGANS; MICROPROPAGATION OF PLANTS, PRINCIPLES AND PRACTICES; PLANT CELL CULTURE, LABORATORY TECHNIQUES.

H

HAIRY ROOTS, BIOREACTOR GROWTH

WAYNE R. CURTIS
The Pennsylvania State University
University Park, Pennsylvania

OUTLINE

INTRODUCTION

A wide variety of bioreactor configurations have been used to cultivate plant roots. Bioreactors range from traditional stirred tanks to unusual configurations such as a rotating drum (1–3). From these reviews, it is apparent that plant roots in culture can be grown at a small scale in virtually any reactor configuration. While any given study may present the "best" performance of several configurations tested, few studies critically discuss scaleup to industrial scale production. If the product is sufficiently expensive, and volume is sufficiently small, then virtually any bioreactor could be used. However, the major interest in root cultures is for products with a large market. An example calculation of production and market scale based on "typical" plant root culture growth and productivity provides a useful starting point to emphasize the importance of scale (and scaleup) when considering alternative bioreactor designs. The rate at which root cultures grow, coupled with a specified yield of desired product, is sufficient information to calculate the culture volumes that will be required to produce a specified mass of product. Assuming an average specific growth rate of 0.25 day^{-1} (doubling time of 2.8 days), growth to a final tissue density of 250 g FW/L, and a 2-day reactor "turn-around," the biomass productivity would provide roughly 1 gram of cell biomass produced per liter of culture volume per day. A moderate market volume of 1000 kg product per year that is produced as 10% of the biomass dry weight, would require a daily operational volume of 35,000 L. Using a working culture volume that is roughly 75% of the nominal reactor volume, this hypothetical process would require a reactor volume of roughly 50,000 L, operating 280 days a year. Figure 1 shows the sensitivity of the required reactor volume to cellular productivity. Although it is possible to fabricate different production scenarios, this analysis should make it clear that the production volumes of interest are exceptionally large, and scaleup is a dominant consideration for feasibility of root-culture-based processes.

While the scales of production indicated in Figure 1 are not inconceivable for a bioprocess, utilizing roots as the biocatalyst at such a scale is a formidable challenge. The technical objective of this work can be thought of as fitting the roots of a full-grown tree into a reactor. From an engineering perspective, the real challenge is achieving growth of a several ton mass of roots at tissue concentrations that approach 50% of the physical volume available within the reactor. A consideration of equal importance is the recovery of biomass or product from such a reactor configuration. Based on these observations, scaleup and product recovery will be central themes in this discussion of bioreactor growth of root cultures. After discussing the influence of product recovery on reactor design, the sections that follow examine in more detail the influence of root culture growth kinetics, morphology, and reactor transport properties. The discussion will emphasize those reactor configurations for which scaleup appears promising based on experience at the pilot scale and logic. Since no commercial process yet exists, many of these assertions are speculative, and these hypothetical "best practices" remain to be demonstrated at an industrial scale.

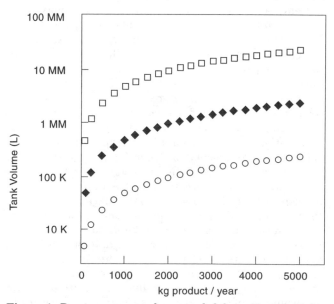

Figure 1. Reactor process volume needed for a 40-week (7-day per week) production schedule when product is formed at a rate corresponding to 0.1% ($\square$), 1% ($\blacklozenge$), and 10% ($\bigcirc$) of the root biomass volumetric productivity.

INFLUENCE OF PRODUCT RECOVERY ON BIOREACTOR DESIGN AND OPERATION

If a metabolite can be continuously produced and released to the surrounding media, then the tissue biomass is effectively reused many times. Under these circumstances, the root tissue is acting as a catalyst. In contrast, if the product is retained intracellularly, the roots must be periodically and destructively harvested. Therefore, although the tissue provides the biocatalytic activity for an intracellular product, the root biomass is handled as a product, and is not a true catalyst in the sense that it is effectively consumed in the production process. The two production scenarios depicted in Figure 2 therefore represent contrasting extremes in production strategy where extracellular products are produced in an essentially continuous manner, and intracellular products are produced in a batch process.

Bioreactors for Recovery of Intracellular Metabolites

Many root metabolites are retained inside the cells — particularly in the vacuolar compartment (4). Such a sequestration of product might require destructive harvest of the tissue. Under some circumstances it might be desirable to market root tissue where the consumer associates the product with a root (such as ginseng, for example) or as plant tissue (such as for herbal tea). Simplicity of design is critical for tissue recovery. Even at moderate root tissue concentrations, the biomass becomes interlocked and essentially a solid mass of tissue. The specific gravity of most root tissues in culture is very close to 1.0 g FW/mL (5); therefore, a root tissue concentration of 250 g FW/L corresponds to tissue occupying 25% of the bioreactor working volume. The typical use of a scaffold for root attachment within the reactor is not desirable if tissue must be harvested. Although the presence or absence of a support matrix may seem to be a minor design change, this difference directly impacts the operational strategies in Figure 2, because a matrix severely impairs the ability to recover the tissue. Support elements have been designed with the intent of permitting tissue recovery (6); however, given the production scales of interest, this approach does not seem practical. The advantage of a support matrix is that it improves performance due to more uniform tissue distribution, as discussed in more detail in the subsection below on reactor inoculation. Therefore, a requirement for tissue harvest conflicts with the need to provide for tissue distribution to avoid localized root clumps that become nutrient limited. The organization of this article around a theme of intracellular versus extracellular products serves to emphasize this difference related to ease of tissue recovery. The simple bubble column and the traditional stirred tank are reactor designs that facilitate tissue recovery (Fig. 3). It is important to note that most of the literature descriptions of these bioreactors are presented as examples of problems. Less well recognized is the observation that essentially all "improvements" to these simple reactors effectively eliminate the ability to recover biomass easily.

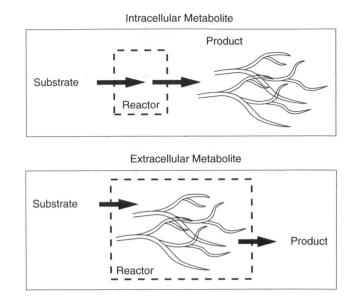

Figure 2. Influence of product recovery on root culture reactor design and operation. For extracellularly recovered products, the tissue acts as a catalyst; roots are effectively the product for intracellularly retained metabolites.

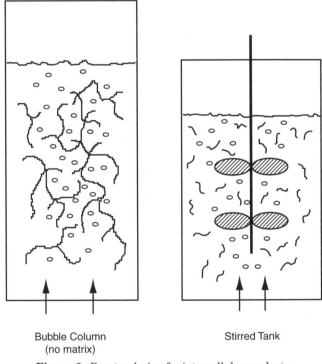

Figure 3. Reactor design for intracellular products.

Bubble Column. A simple bubble column is not much more than an aseptic process tank fitted to facilitate gas sparging. To be consistent with the objective of tissue recovery, air-lift reactors that employ draft tubes or other vessel internals will be discussed in the section on bioreactors for recovery of extracellular metabolites. Bubble columns have been used for extremely large-scale fermentation (>500,000 L) for which mechanical agitation is no longer practical. Descriptions of bubble column performance can also be found for use in nonbiological gas–liquid contacting (7). Reports on the performance of root cultures in simple bubble columns are limited (Table 1) (8–20).

The vessels used often appear to reflect adaptations of available vessels rather than typical bubble column design. The largest bubble columns reported to date were fabricated from an inverted 20-L carboy (11) and an inverted water bottle (D.-C. Yang, personal communication, 1999, see Table 1). Earlier work by Rhodes et al. (21) utilized a 1-L stirred fermentor vessel without the impellers. Smaller-scale sparged vessels include a wide variety of geometries such as sparged Erlenmeyer or pear-shaped flasks (22). Much of the descriptions of this

work are qualitative, and provide little if any information on the effects of geometry or operational conditions; however, it is very clear that the distribution of the tissue and tendency of roots to accumulate in localized clumps is the biggest problem with this design. Although simple bubble columns usually display poorer growth than other small-scale reactors (1,23), the ease of recovery of tissue from a simple unbaffled bubble column may outweigh the advantages of more complex designs. This approach would likely rely on tissue harvest at relatively low root tissue concentrations. Since productivity of simple reactors is likely to be lower than more sophisticated reactor designs, we have proposed the use of a low-cost reactor technology that will greatly reduce capital investment and production

Table 1. Tabulation of Performance of Root Cultures in Pilot-Scale Reactors. Bioreactors that Permit Tissue Recovery are Listed in Order of Volumetric Biomass Productivity. Bioreactors that Permit Recovery of Extracellular Metabolites from Roots Attached to a Matrix are Listed in Order of Tissue Density

Volume (w.v.)	Total mass (g DW)	Reactor type	Root culture	X_i (g DW/L)	X_f (g DW/L)	Δt (day)	Doubling time[a] (day)	Productivity (g DW/L/day)	Ref.
		Biomass recovery							
5	44.5	Stirred tank	*Hyoscymus muticus*	0.2	8.9	11.9	2.17	**0.731**	(8)
100	881	Bubble column	*H. muticus*	0.2[b]	881	31	5.67	**0.28**	c
2.5	15	Bubble column	*A. belladona*	0.2	6.0	21	4.28	**0.276**	(9)
20	200	Bubble column	*Panax ginseng*	0.25	10	45	8.46	**0.217**	d
10	67.5	Stirred tank (intermittent)	*Atropa belladona*	(0.415)	6.75	60	14.9	**0.106**	(10)
300	1755	Stirred tank (intermittent)	*A. belladona*	0.415[b]	5.85[b]	60	15.8	**0.091**	(10)
20	200	Bubble column	*Tagetes patula*	–	10	–	–	–	(11)
		Media recovery							
14	507	Bubble column / trickle bed (+O_2)	*H. muticus* (T)	0.2	**36.2**	25	3.3	1.44	(12)
12	248	Isolated impeller	*Datura stramonium*	0.178	**20.7**	37	5.4	0.555	(13)
14	243	Bubble column / trickle bed	*H. muticus* (R)	0.2	**17.4**	34	5.33	0.506	(12)
14	210	Bubble column / trickle bed	*H. muticus* (T)	0.2	**15**	38	6.3	0.389	(14)
15	180	Bubble column (+ matrix)	*Solanum tuberosum*	0.14	**12**	28	4.3	0.42	(15)
15	179	Bubble column / trickle bed	*H. muticus* (R)	0.22	**11.9**	28	4.95	0.417	(14)
15	151	Bubble column / trickle bed	*H. muticus* (T)	0.17	**10.8**	16	2.67	0.664	(12)
3	21	Bubble column (+ matrix)	*Duboisia leichhardtii*	0.5[b]	**7.0**	77	20.4	0.084	(16)
20	126	Isolated impeller	*Calystegia sepium*	0.03	**6.3**	15	1.94	0.418	(17)
500	1990	Bubble column / trickle bed	*D. stramonium*	(0.2)	**3.98**	64	13.86	0.059	(6)
8	27[b]	Trickle bed	*D. stramonium*	–	**3.4[b]**	–	2.9	–	(18)
(26.3)	6.3[b]	Nutrient mist	*Nicotiana tabacum*	7×10^{-5b}	**0.24[b]**	28	2.39	0.0086	(19)

Quantities in parentheses are assumed based on other information in the article, but not explicitly given in the reference.

[a]Effective doubling time calculated as $\ln(2) - \Delta t / \ln(X_f/X_i)$, not indicative of maximum doubling time (Δt is the total culture interval).

[b]Calculated based on assumed fresh / dry weight ratio of 20.

[c]Unpublished data carried out in pilot-scale reactor of design described in Ref. (20).

[d]Deok-Chun Yang, Principal Research Scientist, Ginseng & Tobacco Research Institute, Korea, personal communication, 1999.

costs (24). The successful application of this technology to plant cell suspensions has been demonstrated (20) and an application to root culture at 100 L (w.v.) successfully generated 24 kg fresh weight of root tissue in 31 days.

Stirred Tanks without Attachment Matrix. The problems of tissue clumping can be avoided by dispersing the tissue in a traditional stirred tank bioreactor. Growth of root cultures in traditional stirred tank fermentors has been attempted with various degrees of success. The productivity of an intracellular metabolite will be proportional to the biomass productivity calculated as the grams dry weight per liter per day. The tabulation of performance of root cultures in pilot-scale reactors (Table 1) reveals that stirred vessels have displayed some of the highest reported biomass productivities. Under conditions developed for cell suspension culture growth, we observed the biomass accumulation rate for *Hyoscyamus muticus* root cultures was comparable to shake flask cultured tissue (8). Our observations were similar to Hilton et al. (25), where the root tissue did not maintain its typical morphology. Instead, the interaction with the impeller resulted in a slurry of tissue fragments that were roughly 1 cm in length. Growth of *Tagates patula* in a 2-L stirred tank was more than a 6.5-L bubble column (26); however, it is important to recognize that for small vessels, the tissue can become immobilized on the probes and baffles (see photograph in Refs. 17,27). As a result, the small-scale vessels perform as if they contained an immobilization matrix and are subject to issues described in the next section. It is likely that some cultures will perform poorly under conditions of mechanical stress; however, reports of an inability to grow cultures (28) are often based on limited testing of growth conditions. Even in situations where the performance of a stirred tank is less than other lab-scale reactors (1), the ability to scale up, combined with the potential use of established technology, could favor this approach. The potential of this approach is ultimately dependent on the effect of mechanical stress and altered morphology on metabolite productivity. Therefore, when considering alternative reactor designs that have the potential for scaleup, the use of traditional stirred tanks should not be entirely discounted. This approach would clearly be attractive to companies that have bioreactor capacity available.

Intermittent operation of an impeller is a potential compromise between mechanical stress and periodic dispersion of the tissue. This technique was used by Kawamura et al. (10) to grow root cultures of *Atropa belladona* in 10- and 500-L stirred tank fermentors. These cultures were quite slow growing and were apparently not transformed by *Agrobacterium rhizogenes*; therefore, it is difficult to assess whether the observed slow growth was an intrinsic characteristic of the culture or imparted by the culture environment. Intrinsic culture growth rate is an important aspect of bioreactor performance characterizations that is often overlooked. This will be discussed in more detail in the next section under principles of bioreactor operation. Another possible means of achieving tissue dispersion in a stirred tank might be the partial dedifferentiation of roots using phytohormones. Such a dedifferentiation might be accomplished with low levels of phytohormones. It should be warned, however, that phytohormone-induced "callusing" would have detrimental influence on many root-derived metabolites that are closely linked to the developmental state of the root. In those cases where dedifferentiation is possible, the root culture might be useful as a means to stabilize against the typical decline in productivity observed in cell suspensions.

In Situ Destructive Harvest. An alternative operational strategy for intracellular products is to facilitate destructive extraction and recovery within the bioreactor vessel. Although this could increase the time for reactor "turnaround," it does eliminate the need for tissue handling and separate extraction vessels. The ability to separate spent media from root tissue by simple drainage could provide a distinct advantage to this approach. The extent of media drainage is highly dependent on physical characteristics of the root culture, as will be discussed in more detail in the section on root morphology. In terms of reactor design, an in situ destructive harvest would alleviate the requirement for intact tissue removal. Therefore, the reactor designs discussed for extracellular product recovery could be utilized for this application. The disadvantage of in situ destructive extraction is potential problems of vessel cleaning and validation for subsequent growth.

Bioreactors for Recovery of Extracellular Metabolites

The "ideal" root culture production system would involve the recovery of an extracellular metabolite where the culture is initially grown to a high biomass loading, and production is facilitated by long-term continuous perfusion of the catalytic bed of roots. For this production scenario, the slow rate of growth of plant tissue culture has minimal impact on overall process economics. Since the potential for volumetric productivity is proportional to biomass, reactor designs should facilitate high biomass loadings. The ability to achieve and sustain high-density root culture at an industrial scale is a unique challenge. The presence of an attachment matrix provides for distribution of growing tissue, and provides mechanical support for liquid dispersed reactors. The presence of a matrix does, however, make it exceedingly difficult to harvest the biomass, as discussed in the previous section. The use of an immobilization matrix is therefore a logical choice for metabolites that will be recovered from the media. Such a matrix can be employed in a bubble column or stirred tank of the types described above, or a spray-type reactor where media is dispersed over the root bed (Fig. 4).

The maximum root tissue concentration that can be achieved in these systems is dependent on the delivery of oxygen and other nutrients into the dense matrix. The mechanisms of nutrient delivery are quite different for the reactors shown. A bubble column relies on the dispersion of gas, an isolated impeller provides enhanced convection, while the spray or trickle-bed reactor enjoys greater gas contacting at the expense of media contacting.

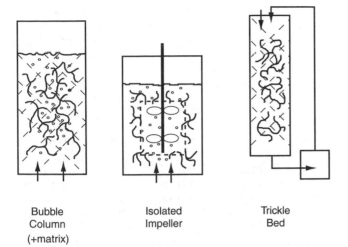

Bubble
Column
(+matrix)

Isolated
Impeller

Trickle
Bed

Figure 4. Reactor designs for recovery of extracellular metabolites from roots attached to a support matrix.

Airlift/Immobilized Bubble Column. Gas sparging in the draft tube "riser" of an airlift bioreactor provides both gas contacting and liquid circulation. Designs can usually be classified as either internal or external loop, both of which have been studied quite intensively for industrial application (29). The internal loop is typically a concentric cylinder with sparging in either the inside or outside annulus. The external loop is two vertical standpipes that are connected to permit circulation. Root clumps quickly entangle on bioreactor internals; therefore, culture roots become immobilized. This type of localized entanglement was also observed in a liquid-impelled loop, where the circulation is similar to an airlift, only the fluid circulation is driven by an immiscible extraction phase (26). The problems of blockage of the circulation flow path result in an uneven immobilization of the tissue at a relatively low reactor tissue loading. As a result, this type of reactor lacks the simplicity to permit harvest of the simple bubble column, and does not have the advantage of more uniform distribution that can be achieved in a more dispersed attachment matrix. Bubble columns that contain an attachment matrix such as a wire mesh or process packing elements have been very widely utilized (1,30,31). These matrices contain a uniform distribution of "pinch points" that entrap the inoculum root fragments early in the culture period. Uniform distribution of the root tissue delays the onset of mass transfer limitations that would be encountered if the roots clustered in certain regions of the reactor. The mixing in a bubble column root reactor rapidly declines as the biomass increases, which limits the availability of oxygen for respiration (32,33). The energy provided by the rising and expansion of the sparged gas is simply not adequate to overcome the flow resistance in the roots. In a recent 15-L bubble column study, we observed mixing times of nearly 5 h when the reactor reached 200 g FW/L. The immobilized bubble column bioreactor should be scalable for low to moderate tissue concentrations. Therefore, although it is unlikely that this reactor configuration can provide tissue concentrations greater than 15 g DW/L, the simplicity might justify use at lower tissue concentrations.

Isolated Impeller/Convective Flow. Contact of the roots and impellers can be avoided if the roots attach to a matrix outside the impeller zone in a stirred tank bioreactor. The typical implementation involves a "cage" that surrounds the impeller (13,17,34). Impeller-induced convection provides growth to high tissue concentrations (Table 1). The local root concentrations are higher than indicated by concentrations based on working volume because the impeller zone remains free of tissue. The extent to which performance will scale is not clear, since larger vessels will have proportionately thicker root zones that require convective nutrient delivery. The typical scaleup criterion for mechanically agitated bioreactors based on constant power per volume would suggest that the energy available to provide convection will not increase upon scaleup. A recent quantitative assessment of power dissipation in root beds suggests that it may not be possible to realize such convective performance enhancements at a large scale (35). Growth of root cultures in tubular convective flow reactors provides necessary kinetic information under non-mass-transfer-limited conditions (36), but these are not reactors that have significant application as production systems (35).

Trickle-Bed Bioreactors. Liquid dispersed bioreactors permit removal of the majority of the medium that is the source of the mixing and oxygen mass-transfer limitations of submerged root culture systems. Medium is drained into a reservoir, and recirculated by spraying at the top. Virtually all reports of performance for small-scale liquid-sprayed vessels display encouraging results (37–39), and our laboratory has recently used this configuration to achieve root tissue concentrations that are more than double the highest previously reported tissue concentrations reported for other bioreactor configurations (Table 1). Trickle operation is typically initiated after a submerged bubble column phase to provide for tissue distribution on the support matrix. A downward co-current flow of gas and liquid is preferred to counter-current gas flow because it facilitates drainage and provides more uniform availability of oxygen. An upward flow of gas in a trickle bed can result in column flooding, which is the situation where the media accumulates within the column by bridging the small gaps between adjacent roots. Co-current down-flow of gas prevents "flooding" by providing a gas-phase pressure gradient to assist gravity drainage and displace accumulating liquid down through the column. The sustained availability of oxygen is reflected in high growth rates and sustained oxygen uptake rates (OUR) to high reactor tissue concentrations (12). Once high tissue concentration has been attained, the packed bed of roots can be treated as a catalytic reactor, where productivity will be dependent on the continued long-term release of product to the media. The challenge that remains for these reactors is the development of principles for scaleup, which is addressed in the final section of this article.

Nutrient Mist Reactors. Nutrient mist bioreactors provide a potential means of delivering the liquid phase as an aerosol rather than a trickling liquid film. The ability to scale these systems will be dependent on the penetration of the aerosol into the bed. It has been argued that media will be depleted of nutrients on a scale of 1–3 L (34); however, recent experimental measurements have suggested that a greater depth of penetration should be possible for aerosol-based nutrient delivery (40). Details of aerosol technology applied to plant tissue culture will be discussed elsewhere in this encyclopedia, and will not be repeated here. A qualitative comparison of the nutrient mist and the trickle bed may help clarify the difference between these superficially similar reactor types. In the trickle bed, the medium is sprayed as relatively large droplets onto the top of the root column. The liquid is delivered to the bed by gravity and the momentum imparted by the pressure drop of the spray nozzle. The gas phase is typically operated at comparatively low superficial velocity and has minimal influence on media delivery. As a result, the spray of the trickle bed is deposited onto a relatively narrow zone of the upper part of the root bed. In contrast, the nutrient mist aerosol particles are so fine that their delivery to the root bed is primarily dependent on convective gas flow. These small aerosol particles tend to follow gas flow streamlines, which results in deposition throughout the root culture bed. In principle, it is possible to deliver aerosolized media in proportion to metabolic requirements. However, this approach would be counterproductive if the metabolite is to be recovered from the recirculating media. Aerosol capture (or cumulative aerosol capture along the root bed) could eventually result in a trickle-film environment within the root bed. The extent to which current reports of nutrient mist bioreactors behave as aerosol-based trickle-film bioreactors to provide distributed liquid delivery along the axis of the reactor is not clear.

Cyclic Gas–Liquid Dispersed Reactors.

Reactors such as a rotating drum (39) or ebb-and-flow (1,41) type vessel expose the root tissue to cyclic submerged and exposed tissue environments. Although these have been used with considerable success, they will not be discussed at length here because these reactors have limited potential for scaleup. The rotating drum provides excellent gas–solid liquid contacting, and rotating biological contactors have been used for wastewater treatment. For smaller-scale root culture (<5000 L), this might prove useful, particularly for an application such as biotransformation, where large processing volumes could be achieved with a relatively small reactor volume. However, even in this capacity, the performance enhancement would have to be substantial to justify the increased mechanical complexity over a liquid-dispersed reactor. At a small scale, the ebb-and-flow or fill-and-drain reactor can provide reasonably high superficial liquid velocities that approach rates needed to overcome boundary-layer mass-transfer limitations. In this manner, such a reactor is similar to the convective flow reactor mentioned above. Unfortunately, the ability to achieve rapid cycle times and reasonable superficial velocities is quickly lost upon scaleup; therefore, it seems unlikely that performance would be any greater than other bioreactor configurations at a large scale.

Facilitated Release.

Metabolites can be recovered from the media if secreted, or if the release can be facilitated from intracellular stores. The nature of sequestration of intracellular metabolites has important implications on the ability to facilitate release without loss of viability (42). The ability to facilitate release of molecules partitioned based on pH will be dependent on the pK_a of the metabolite of interest (43). In cases where extracellular accumulation is limited by aqueous solubility, providing an extracelluar sink can be an effective means of facilitating extracellular accumulation of a root metabolite (18,44). Release facilitated by nonspecific membrane permeabilization is usually accompanied by substantial cell death. Review of integrated product recovery can be found elsewhere (45). Many of the studies of metabolite release have been conducted with plant cell suspension cultures. An interesting aspect of root cultures is the localization of growth in the meristem and typical accumulation of metabolites in the maturing root tissue. This spatial separation of developmentally controlled metabolite formation can provide the opportunity to recover product selectively without affecting biomass growth. In principle, 90% of the biomass could be destroyed without affecting continued growth. We recently employed this logic with beet root cultures for the release of betalains (46). Growth was sustained even for 50% release; however, localization of viability using tetrazolium dyes clearly indicated that the retained growth potential was due to survival of the nascent lateral meristems — much of the mature tissue was killed by the procedure.

A general design consideration for extracellular metabolite recovery is minimizing the volume of the aqueous phase. This reduces media volume if changes in media properties are required (such as pH or temperature), as well as minimizing dilution and liquid process volume. An advantage of liquid-dispersed reactor designs is the ability to minimize the liquid volume needed to support root culture growth. It is possible to achieve a biomass to liquid volume ratio greatly in excess of 1000 grams of tissue per liter of media, since the liquid volume is a small fraction of the reactor volume (47).

PRINCIPLES OF BIOREACTOR OPERATION

The preceding summary of reactor design considerations that are affected by metabolite storage and transport is not by any means a comprehensive review of reactor design principles applied to the growth of roots in reactor systems. We have published more detailed accounts of design principles in a series of book chapters, including fluid dynamics (5), inoculation and liquid mixing (48), root morphology effects (8), and oxygen transfer and scaleup (49). Some of this information is summarized below with a continued emphasis on effects on scaleup and choice between intracellular versus extracellular product recovery.

Growth Kinetics

Biomass Accumulation. Root cultures vary considerably in the intrinsic rate of growth. For organisms such as bacteria, growth is truly exponential, since each cell after deviation is (in general) capable of continued growth. The specific growth rate, or logarithmic growth rate, is a measure of the growth potential per unit biomass:

$$\mu = (1/\Delta t)\ln(X_f/X_i) \tag{1}$$

The fundamental nature of root biomass accumulation is not so clear. Growth results from cell division at the meristem and subsequent cell expansion in the zone adjacent to the meristem. The vast majority of the cells in the root culture are not undergoing either division or cell expansion. Descriptions of growth based on branching patterns have been developed (50). Despite the complex morphology, there are numerous descriptions of root cultures that display logarithmic growth. Often the precise nature of growth kinetics is less important than a comparison of biomass accumulation in different reactor systems. For these comparisons, the calculational basis such as doubling time or effective specific growth rates is not critical. It is important to recognize that cultures that display higher growth rates provide a more sensitive reactor comparison. Rapid nutrient consumption — particularly oxygen — will emphasize the influence of differences in environment provided by different reactors. Slower-growing roots will be less sensitive to environment and will underestimate reactor differences. Biomass accumulation can be affected by virtually any nutrient or environmental condition, including temperature, pH, organic, and inorganic nutrients. For many of these parameters, achieving growth is a matter of having adequate bioreactor monitoring and control. Optimal conditions have not been explored for most root cultures, and observed growth rates reflect typical media and culture conditions.

Media sterilization is an example where scaleup can influence biomass indirectly. Figure 5 shows the differential growth rate observed for beet root cultures grown on autoclaved versus filter-sterilized B5 (51) medium that contains fructose as the sugar source. The poor growth observed on autoclaved fructose medium can be attributed to the formation of toxic compounds from thermal degradation (52). Media stability is relevant to scaleup because steam sterilization time usually increases from the bench to pilot scale, and can be reduced at large scale through the use of a continuous sterilizer. This is an example where poor performance at the pilot scale could reflect media deterioration rather than bioreactor design problems.

If the metabolite can be recovered from the media, as depicted in the scenario in Figure 1, then the rate of culture growth only needs to be reasonably rapid to establish the catalytic bed of roots. In contrast, growth rate is critically important for the recovery of intracellularly accumulated metabolites. As presented in Table 1, volumetric productivity is a primary concern for metabolites that will be recovered from tissue biomass. Because volumetric productivity is proportional to tissue concentration, the operational tissue concentration during growth has a substantial impact. For example, a root culture with the same specific growth rate that is sustained from 100 to 200 g FW/L will have less than 60% of the volumetric productivity of the same culture grown from 200 to 300 g FW/L. This provides motivation to sustain growth rates at high tissue concentration.

Inoculation. Plant cell suspension cultures display reduced growth rates or extended lag phase if inoculated at low cell concentrations (53). This phenomenon is referred to as a "minimum inoculation density." Root cultures do not appear to display a critical minimum inoculation. In fact, we have observed improved growth rates for tissue inoculated as low as 0.02 g FW/L. The significance of this

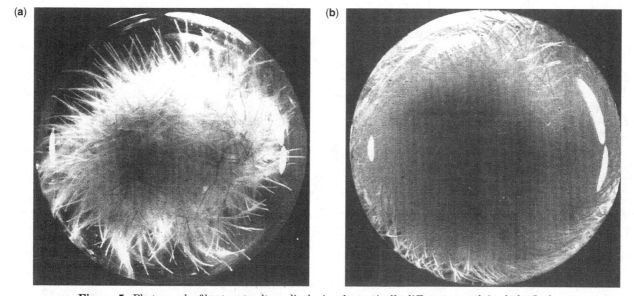

(a)   **(b)**

Figure 5. Photograph of beet root culture displaying dramatically different growth in shake flask culture when grown on: (**a**) autoclaved and (**b**) filter-sterilized media. Presented as an example of a parameter that can complicate interpretation of reactor performance if sterilization procedures are changed for different reactor scales or designs.

observation is that the tissue inoculation level does not place limitations on the density at which a bioreactor can be inoculated. This is particularly important for root tissue because tissue handling is problematic. The inoculation of a large-scale system can be accomplished with a relatively small amount of inoculum as long as there is sufficient tissue to provide for distribution throughout the reactor (14).

Oxygen Utilization Kinetics. As with virtually all aerobic culture systems, providing adequate oxygen is the major performance constraint for roots cultured in bioreactor systems. Of particular interest are the intrinsic kinetics of oxygen utilization. We have shown the consumption of oxygen to be limited by the diffusion inside the tissue, where oxygen uptake from the media is shown to be proportional to the concentration of the dissolved oxygen in the surrounding medium (15). In addition, the linear extension rates of root cultures of H. muticus increased with oxygen partial pressure (49). An important kinetic parameter for oxygen utilization is the critical oxygen pressure (COP), which is the oxygen tension at which growth will become impaired due to inadequate oxygen supply. The COP of A. belladona root cultures has been reported to be as low as 50% of saturation of air in media (54). Interpretation of the physiological meaning of COP for roots is complicated by intratissue transport; however, the engineering significance is straightforward. Such a high apparent COP indicates that growth rates will be reduced under conditions of relatively high oxygen availability. It is important to recognize that the biological oxygen demand (BOD) of a culture will be proportional to the growth rate; therefore, different root cultures will display different kinetics, and the likelihood of oxygen limitation will be greater for faster-growing root cultures. This dependence of oxygen demand on relative growth rate is reflected in different tissues of the same root. The localization of cell division in the meristems presents another important constraint for oxygen utilization. We have shown that the oxygen demand of root meristems can be ten times greater than the bulk tissue. The implications of high local oxygen demand at the meristem is that the local mass transfer coefficient must be much higher than would be predicted by the average oxygen demand measured from overall reactor oxygen consumption (55). The influence of oxygen demand and availability will be discussed in more detail in the section on principles for bioreactor design and scaleup.

The preceding observations indicate the difficulty in obtaining and interpreting information on intrinsic kinetic parameters for root culture growth and oxygen demand. Relatively sophisticated bioreactor geometries have been implemented to measure these kinetics under defined flow conditions (56,57). The tubular convective flow reactors are particularly useful for BOD measurements under non-mass-transfer-limited conditions (36,54,58,59). It should be kept in mind that these bioreactors are designed for experimental measurements and not intended to be used as production-scale reactors. Most of these studies have come to similar conclusions where linear velocities of roughly 1 cm/s past the surface of the root are required to overcome nutrient mass-transfer limitations. For the purpose of design, our laboratory utilizes measurements obtained from a rapidly growing clone of H. muticus to provide an upper bound for oxygen transport requirements. These correspond to bulk tissue oxygen demand of 0.01 mmol O_2/g FW/h and meristematic BOD of 0.10 mmol O_2/g FW/h. For circumstances where direct measurements of BOD are not available, it is possible to obtain estimates of oxygen utilization based on growth rate and typical culture yield and stoichiometry (60). It should also be noted that oxygen demand can increase substantially during stress- or elicitor-induced metabolite formation.

Inorganic Growth Kinetics. Growth kinetics are often expressed in a saturation form with respect to the inorganic substrate (S),

$$\mu = \mu_{max}S/(k_s + S) \qquad (2)$$

where μ_{max} is the maximal rate that is observed at high substrate levels, and k_s is the saturation constant. The parameter k_s is often referred to as an affinity because it reflects the concentration of substrate at which growth rate would be attenuated. Most inorganics are assumed to be in adequate supply and sufficiently above their apparent k_s so that they do not influence growth rate. Phosphate limitation has been studied rather extensively because it can be utilized to manipulate growth kinetics and associated secondary metabolite pathways (61). While the focus of most studies is on increasing growth, the ability to stop growth is equally important for extracellular metabolites. For metabolites that are released from the tissue, it is desirable to maintain a constant viable biomass so that oxygen transfer requirements can be met to retain long-term productivity. The ability of plant tissues to accumulate inorganics and utilize them from intracellular stores complicates the kinetics; however, models are available (62).

The saturation constant, k_s, has another important influence on bioreactor performance. The magnitude of k_s indicates the concentrations that should be maintained to avoid nutrient limitations. The collective influence of inorganics has been assessed by examining growth in diluted media. Hilton maintained logarithmic growth on half-strength media (13), and we have not observed significant reduction in short-term growth rate for media containing only 20% of standard inorganic salts levels (35). It is not too surprising that root cultures can effectively utilize low nutrient levels, since inorganic uptake from dilute environments is a fundamental physiological role for intact plant roots. This is particularly relevant for the production of intracellular metabolites. As discussed in the initial sections of this article, it is anticipated that reactors such as the stirred tank and simple bubble column would have to be operated at low tissue concentrations. The ability to utilize low inorganic nutrient levels (small k_s) suggests that growth rates of cultured roots can be sustained with the same mass of inorganics supplied—diluted in a larger reactor volume.

Biomass Yield — Reactor Monitoring and Control

Whereas reaction rates determine how fast a product can be made, yield provides an indication of how efficiently the substrates are utilized. Biomass yield can be generally defined as the amount of biomass produced for a unit of substrate consumed. The inverse of yield is the amount of substrate consumed for a unit of biomass. For inorganics, the amount consumed is equal to the amount within the tissue; therefore, the apparent yield is simply the inverse of the biomass content (e.g., yield = g cell mass produced/g of phosphate consumed; cell content = g phosphate/g cell mass). Although the composition of biomass can change to some extent, the general consistency of biomass composition results in relatively constant biomass yield. Similarly, the amount of energy that is needed to construct cells is relatively constant. For example, one can anticipate yields of cell mass on carbohydrate of roughly 50%, which gives 10 to 15 g DW/L for the typical 2 to 3 w% sugar used in plant cell culture media.

The relative constancy of yield permits the use of measurements of nutrient consumption from the media as a means of inferring growth. The ability to estimate growth is extremely important for root culture, since it is not possible to obtain a representative volumetric sample of media and root tissue. The most common means of estimating root tissue biomass growth is based on changes in media conductivity, where a proportionality is established between root mass and changes in electrical conductivity. The progress of a reactor can be roughly estimated based on the percentage depletion in inorganics (as measured by electrical conductivity) or sugar (as measured by refractive index). A more rigorous approach is complicated by the fact that the tissue concentrates the extracellular nutrients by removing water from the reactor. This water removal is not insignificant. Utilizing nutrient replenishment and supplemental oxygen, we recently achieved a reactor tissue loading of 752 g FW/L (12). This would correspond to a removal of more than three-quarters of the media for a conventional submerged reactor. The water content of the tissue can be used to account for liquid uptake into tissue and develop correlations based on mass of nutrients rather than the empirical concentration changes. For a high level of precision, the variations in water content can be related to medium osmoticum (60). The ability to monitor biomass growth permits implementation of control strategies such as nutrient feed, oxygen supplementation, or elicitation of secondary metabolism in a systematic manner for process validation.

Influence of Root Morphology on Reactor Design

The physical structure of roots in culture represents a unique geometry as compared to typical biocatalytic systems. These morphological features give rise to unique reactor design considerations. Although it is tempting to consider design of reactors for a "generic" model root system, the physical characteristics of root culture such as thickness, branching, root hair proliferation, and mechanical properties vary tremendously for different root types. The importance of these differences in root morphology on reactor design is the theme of a recent publication from our laboratory (8); therefore, only a brief summary will be presented here.

Influence of Physical/Mechanical Properties on Reactor Design. The rate of sedimentation of root fragments is important for distribution of inoculum and subsequent growth in a reactor (14). The sedimentation rates are dependent on root diameter and specific gravity. Fifteen different root cultures were found to vary from neutrally buoyant to sedimentation rates of 2 cm/s, resulting in calculated specific gravities ranging from 1.0 to 1.05. Since the specific gravity of root tissue is not that much different from unity, the volume occupied by roots, and in overall water mass balance, can be calculated from fresh weight. The fifteen cultures examined above displayed species-dependent differences in root diameter that ranged nearly an order of magnitude (0.17 to 1.5 mm), with most root cultures falling between 0.7 to 1 mm. Given the indications of intratissue oxygen transport limitations within roots, the thickness of a root will invariably influence the availability of oxygen throughout the root cross-section. Differences in tissue structure within the root will presumably play a significant role in oxygen transport as well (32).

Root cultures displayed an equally impressive variation in mechanical properties. The bending modulus calculated from the force required for a 0.5-cm displacement of a 2-cm length of tissue varied from 6×10^7 to 82×10^7 dyn/cm^2. This modulus is an indicator of the deflection that would be experienced in a flow field as well as the ability to support weight (such as a trickle bed). This large variation should be expected, since different root culture types vary from being rather rigid to being unable to support their own weight. An even greater range was observed in the forces required to break root segments. Clearly these large variations in physical and mechanical properties would alter the performance in the different reactor systems proposed, such as the stirred tank (where mechanical disruption and sedimentation are important) as compared to a trickle bed (which lacks the buoyant support of the surrounding fluid).

Geometric Properties that Influence Reactor Design. The branched morphology of roots is inherently self-limited because growth radiates from a central point. On one hand, a high degree of branching benefits biomass accumulation by generation of more root meristems. On the other hand, profuse branching will concentrate root meristems in a small volume and hasten the inevitable competition for available space and nutrients. Differences in root culture branching patterns are evident from photographs, and can be captured as quantitative differences in fractal dimension (8). From an overall reactor performance perspective, a more apically dominant root culture is likely more effectively to explore and utilize the available reactor volume. This situation exemplifies the complex logic of considering the ultimate objective of either rapid biomass proliferation for intracellular metabolites or efficient long-term reactor operation for recovery of extracellular metabolites. One of the most important morphological characteristics that influences reactor performance is the extent of root hair formation. The influence of root hairs appears to be almost entirely detrimental. This is somewhat ironic because initial observations of the "hairy root" phenotype presumed the root hairs to be contributing to the rapid growth by facilitating nutrient uptake. A simple flux analysis of tissue water uptake combined with the relatively high levels of inorganic nutrients quickly reveals that the increased surface area provided by root hairs is not needed for nutrient uptake (8). We have recently confirmed this experimentally by eliminating root hair formation with a putative auxin transport inhibitor, observing essentially identical growth rates of the same root culture with and without root hairs (32). In a submerged reactor environment, the root hairs represent the dominant flow resistance and therefore contribute extensively to mixing problems. This issue of mixing has significant impact on approach to scaleup, as will be addressed in the final section of this article. In a mist reactor system, root hairs have been observed greatly to increase aerosol capture (63). This is particularly important for a mist configuration reactor, since root cultures tend to have very pronounced root hair formation when the roots are not submerged. Most cultures display greatly increased root hair proliferation when grown on agar media (personal observation), which has also been observed when grown in a nutrient mist environment (40). Due to the delicate nature of root hairs, assessing the impact requires that studies be done with minimally disturbed tissues. Otherwise, the potentially large influence of these structures on the root surface will be lost for studies carried out with cultures manipulated into an experimental apparatus. This seemingly small difference has a tremendous impact on the quantity and effort required to obtain data. For example, experiments on pressure drop using manipulated tissue took only a few months (5), while aseptic in situ reactor work to obtain the same quantity of data required several years (35). It is important to recognize the influence of tissue handling to avoid obtaining misleading data or wasting an exorbitant amount of time in setting up unnecessary bioreactor studies.

PRINCIPLES FOR BIOREACTOR DESIGN AND SCALEUP

The primary focus of bioreactor design principles for root cultures is on oxygen transport (49). Several aspects of oxygen transport have already been discussed. Diffusion of oxygen in tissue is related to absolute culture growth rate and root diameter. Transport of oxygen at the surface of the root is dependent upon the higher rates of oxygen utilization at the root meristem. These aspects of oxygen transport are somewhat unique to root cultures. The final issues of oxygen transport described in this section are more typical of bioreactor engineering: (1) transport of oxygen from the gas phase into the media, and (2) the subsequent distribution of that oxygenated medium to the tissue through liquid mixing and flow. The issues of oxygen transport are clearly different for gas-dispersed or liquid-dispersed environments; therefore, these issues will

be discussed separately for submerged and spray reactor systems.

Submerged Reactor Environment

Most organic and inorganic nutrients can be supplied in the media at initial levels that are sufficient for a several week growth period. In contrast, there is only sufficient oxygen dissolved in the medium for a few minutes of growth. As a result, oxygen must be continuously replenished to the media of a submerged culture system. Gas contact is improved in spray reactor systems; however, the need to distribute inoculum will invariably require that any reactor initially start as a submerged culture environment. The interlocked matrix of root cultures presents a substantial resistance to fluid flow. This should be apparent from the photographs of root culture and is shown schematically in Figure 6.

The principles for describing mass-transfer limitations within a reactive matrix are well established and can be found in terms of a Theile modulus or effectiveness factor in virtually any reactor design text. Weisz provides excellent discussions of this concept as it applies to biological systems for describing the balance of oxygen transport and consumption (64). Intraclump mass-transfer limitations were experimentally demonstrated as a flow-rate-dependent rate of oxygen consumption for flow past a spherical "tea ball" containing root tissue (56). Further refinement of this observation was conducted in which oxygen gradients were measured to verify limitations in oxygen availability within such a clump of root tissue (57). Although this idealized geometry permits characterization, it does not provide a measure of flow resistance or a means of quantifying mixing that ultimately affects reactor performance upon scaleup. This approach also requires manipulation, which

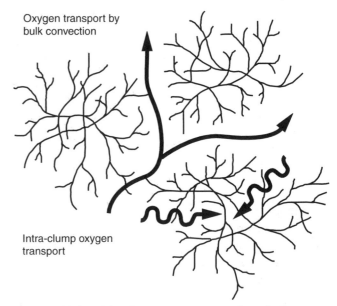

Oxygen transport by bulk convection

Intra-clump oxygen transport

Figure 6. Schematic of oxygen transport throughout a root culture bioreactor by convection and into a root clump. Regions of high root tissue concentration have greater oxygen need but greater resistance to oxygen transport.

can alter root morphology, as described previously in this article. Flow resistance in root beds was recently quantified by direct measurements of pressure drop in a 2-L tubular reactor (35). A picture of the reactor system used to accomplish these measurements is shown in Figure 7, where medium was recirculated through an aerated–agitated reservoir.

Predictions of pressure drop can be made for a packed bed (chromatography column, for example) based on the geometry of the packing, where the bed is described by a characteristic dimension (such as diameter for beads or fibers). It was found that the experimental flow resistance in a root culture bed was an order of magnitude higher than would be predicted based on root diameter (65). The experimentally observed pressure drop was closer to what would be expected based on the diameter of the root hairs. These results implicate the root hairs as the dominant contributor to flow resistance. Within a submerged culture reactor, flow resistance manifests itself as poor liquid media mixing. A fluorescent tracer system has recently been developed for measurement of mixing in root cultures (48). Riboflavin is an excellent tracer because it is

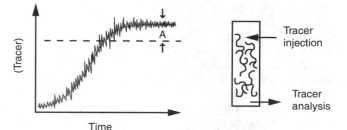

Figure 8. Measurement of mixing based on dispersion of a tracer dye into the media within a root culture reactor. The dashed line represents the calculated final dilution based on tracer mass and liquid volume, and the quantity indicated by "A" is indicative of the unmixed "dead volume" within the reactor.

nontoxic and quantifiable over several orders magnitude of dilution due to its fluorescence characteristics. Absolute quantification permits an assessment of the nonmixed volume in the reactor. This is accomplished as shown schematically in Figure 8.

Applying these techniques to a 15-L bubble column, we have shown mixing time to increase from less than 2 to over 40 min at a tissue density of 180 g FW/L *Solanum tuberosum* (15). Rigorous application of the mixing time analysis is quite involved and requires accounting for injection volume, sampling, and biomass volume (as indicated in the previous section discussing reactor monitoring). Much can be learned from less precise qualitative changes in mixing time. We recently observed mixing times longer than 5 h at a tissue concentration of 204 g FW/L for *H. muticus* in a 15-L bubble column. From a bioreactor design perspective, this clearly indicates that the typical assumption of complete mixing in the liquid phase is not applicable to submerged root culture reactors at any appreciable tissue concentration. The typical design equation based on the interfacial oxygen balance for a well-mixed gas and liquid phase is a familiar relationship for the oxygen transfer rate (OTR) in a bioreactor.

$$\text{OTR} = k_{\text{L}}a(C^* - C_{\text{L}})V_{\text{L}} \qquad (3)$$

The well-mixed case permits evaluation of the equilibrium dissolved oxygen (C^*) using the Henry's law constant (H) at the uniform outlet oxygen mole fraction (Y_{out}), and the dissolved oxygen level (C_{L}) is uniform throughout the reactor volume (V_{L}). In the case of a root reactor, the driving force for mass transfer will vary with reactor depth (z), and the composition of both the gas and liquid phase will vary throughout the reactor. We have recently presented preliminary design calculations based on the more reasonable assumption of complete stratification of the liquid phase (49). To contrast the simple design approach of equation (3), if the liquid does not mix, and gas flows as a plug flow rate (G) up through the reactor, the analogous design equation becomes:

$$\text{OTR} = GY_{\text{in}}\left\{1 - \exp\left[-\left(\frac{k_{\text{L}}aV_{\text{L}}\varepsilon_{\text{L}}}{G}\right)\left(\frac{\beta}{\beta + 1}\right)\right.\right.$$
$$\left.\left.\times \left(\frac{1}{H}\right)\left(P_{\text{s}} + \rho g\frac{L}{2}\right)\right]\right\} \qquad (4)$$

Figure 7. A recirculating tubular reactor used to measure flow resistance of a root bed. Medium was oxygenated in a 14-L stirred tank fermentor, and bubble-free medium was passed through the tubular reactor at flow rates that ranged from 0.3 to 2.4 L/min (35).

Here it becomes necessary to introduce oxygen use kinetics, and the parameter β is analogous to the dimensionless Damkohler number that is familiar in the reaction engineering literature. The details of this analysis can be found in the preceding reference; the important point is that the analysis for root reactor design must take mixing into account. Qualitatively, the effect of inhibited mixing in Eq. (4) is to increase oxygen mass transfer at the bottom of the reactor ($z = L$) due to the hydrostatic "head" (ρgz). The significance of this effect is directly proportional to the depth of the tank. Since one atmosphere (1.01 bar) is equal to the pressure at a depth of 33 ft (10.3 m), this effect should become significant at liquid depths of 4 ft (1.2 m). Design relationships that couple quantitative measurements of flow resistance with mixing and ultimately reactor performance are currently under development.

We have recently observed that mixing time in a 15-L bubble column reactor is very insensitive to the gas sparging rate at tissue densities above 100 g FW/L (Lia Tescione, unpublished observation, 1998). This is consistent with our previous report that specific respiration did not improve with aeration rate (15). Our current explanation for this observation is shown schematically in Figure 9. The schematic shows the severe gas-phase channeling that occurs in liquid-submerged reactors because of the presence of the root tissue. The implication of this observation is that oxygen availability cannot be altered substantially using gas flow rate. Increasing aeration rate will only affect bulk liquid mixing in the local regions of the gas channels. At higher tissue

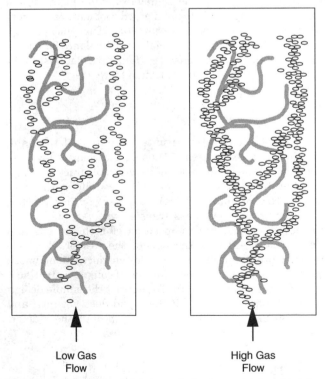

Figure 9. Schematic explaining relative insensitivity of mixing to gas flow. Channeling of the gas phase through the root matrix keeps gas–liquid interaction relatively constant.

Low Gas Flow

High Gas Flow

densities, this localized mixing becomes insignificant to the overall mixing of the bulk liquid phase. Doran recently confirmed the importance of gas distribution by demonstrating improved growth performance in a reactor system with multiple sparger locations (33). The observation that performance improved when the sparger placement is only 0.13 m apart suggests that such an approach to improving gas distribution will have limited applicability on a large scale. The reason for these gas-phase effects can be observed through a glass bubble column (15). The root matrix quickly coalesces the gas in the sparger region. Bubble coalescence leads to slug gas flow at high tissue densities. The sparger can be submerged in a gas envelope with gas periodically leaving by surging through the gas channels within the root bed. Gas-phase coalescence, and flow through gas channels, tends to keep gas–liquid interfacial area constant and diminishes dependence on aeration rate.

The resistance to fluid flow can also be assessed in terms of power requirements for the reactors. At a typical gas sparging rate of 0.2 VVM, the gassed power would be 0.02 W/L. In contrast, the convective flow experiments permitted calculation of the power required for overcoming flow resistance as 2 W/L at a tissue density of 550 g fresh weight per liter. These results indicate that it is impractical to attempt to induce mixing in high-tissue-concentration root cultures. This does not imply that large-scale submerged culture is not possible; it simply indicates that the ability to achieve high tissue concentrations will be severely limited. Therefore, submerged root culture reactors can be expected to be most productive when operated at low tissue loadings. It should be kept in mind that "low" tissue concentrations for root culture would be on the order of 20% of the reactor volume. By comparison, *E. coli* would have an optical density of at least 50 for the same cell volume fraction. The key issue of achieving growth to 200 g FW/L will be maintaining a reasonable distribution of the tissue. If the tissue aggregates in a small fraction of the vessel, then the overall biomass productivity could be very low due to zones of tissue-free media.

Liquid-Dispersed Reactor Environment

A liquid-dispersed reactor is a system in which the media is sprayed as droplets over the top of the reactor. By replacing the continuous liquid phase with low-viscosity air, the issues of flow resistance and mixing of the contentious phase can be eliminated. A fundamental difference of using gas as the continuous phase is the loss of buoyant support of the roots. The weight of roots in a given reactor volume produces a pressure that can be as great as the hydrostatic "head" of a column of water to the top of the bed (note that tissue cross-sectional area is the same as tissue volume fraction). The hydrostatic head is the product of density, the gravitational constant and tank depth (ρgz), which corresponds to nearly 1×10^5 dyn/cm^2 for a tank depth of 1 m (0.43 psi/ft). By comparison, the yield stresses required to break cultured roots range from 10 to 100 dyn/cm^2. Although it is difficult to develop a direct relationship between these mechanical forces, clearly there is a mismatch in the physical properties of root tissue and the forces they would experience. For this reason, liquid-dispersed reactors of significant dimension always employ some means of mechanical support for the roots. The need for such a mechanical support greatly reduces flexibility with regard to product recovery. The logic presented at the beginning of this article suggests that liquid-dispersed reactor systems would be limited to recovery of metabolites from the media.

The advantage of these reactor configurations is improved performance and scaleability at high tissue loadings. This is reflected in the tabulated performance of root cultures in reactors (Table 1), where the trickle bed achieved final biomass and volumetric productivities that are nearly twice other reactor configurations. Industrial applications of trickle-bed reactors include wastewater treatment and petroleum processing (66). The study of these applications provides a basis for design and performance correlations. The flow regime of primary interest for root culture bioreactors is "trickle flow," where the liquid trickles over the packing as continuous film that has a low degree of interaction with the gas. This behavior is observed for superficial (empty column) liquid velocities from 0.01 to 2 cm/s depending on reactor scale (67). The amount of liquid that is retained inside the reactor bed at a given flow rate is referred to as the total liquid holdup. This holdup is typically divided into two components. The dynamic holdup is the volume of liquid that will drain from the bed after cessation of flow. The static holdup is the liquid that is retained after draining, and is therefore the difference between total and dynamic liquid holdup. The study of a trickle-bed bioreactor for root cultures is far more complicated than a traditional chemical reactor. Besides maintaining asepsis during operation and measurements, the tissue void fraction and media volumes will change during culture growth. A bioreactor designed to carry out these measurements is shown in Figure 10. This reactor provided for measurement of respiration from differential oxygen and carbon dioxide as well as monitoring of media components as described in the preceding section on reactor monitoring. Liquid retained in the bed at different liquid flow rates could be determined by careful monitoring of all water within the system and reservoir weight (carboy in Fig. 10).

This system provides for monitoring of root culture growth from the transition of bubble column growth and attachment to the support matrix, to trickle-bed operation at high root tissue loadings. The vastly improved oxygen transport characteristics of the trickle bed are confirmed experimentally by increases in respiration and growth when the media is drained and trickle flow is commenced. Information on liquid holdup and gas-phase pressure drop have been obtained to provide a basis for preliminary calculations on feasibility of large-scale (10,000-L) root culture systems (12). The details of this work are still under development and beyond the scope of what can be presented here, but some of the highlights are provided for those interested in the details of reactor design. Correlations for liquid holdup are complicated by the changing root tissue concentration. We have found, however, that

Figure 10. Photograph of a 15-L pilot-scale trickle-bed root culture bioreactor constructed to provide detailed performance measurements of liquid holdup, respiration, and on-line biomass estimation.

by expressing liquid retention as a specific holdup (mL media/g FW), the data can be correlated as a function of superficial liquid velocity per root culture void fraction (V_{sup}/ε_r). The flow exponent of 0.64 obtained for the relationship between specific liquid holdup and flow rate for several root reactors is comparable to the value of 0.55 obtained for conventional trickle-bed systems (67). Respiratory activity displays a behavior that is consistent with theory (68) and suggests a transition from laminar regime (where respiration declines with increasing liquid flow due to a thicker liquid film) to a well-mixed regime (where flow is sufficiently high to provide increasing respiration with increased flow). Finally, the largest deviation from traditional trickle-bed reactor theory is static liquid holdup. The root culture beds were observed to retain an order of magnitude higher media levels than would be predicted for traditional trickle-bed packings. This observation is consistent with previous reports that root tissue could retain 20 to 60% of their biomass fresh weight (5) and indicates the potential problems of using reactor drained weight as a measure of biomass content. The important aspect of these initial efforts is that the preliminary calculations for scaleup indicate that gas compression and liquid pumping costs can be kept to reasonable levels (about 2 W/L or 10 hp/1000 gal) for scaleup to 10,000 L. Therefore, although more analysis is needed, the preliminary indications are that such a trickle-bed reactor should be able to provide the large-scale capacity indicated by Figure 1 for industrial production of chemicals.

ACKNOWLEDGMENTS

The majority of the material presented from research in our laboratory is based on work supported by the National Science Foundation under Grant Nos. BCS-9110288 and BES-9522033 that dealt with design of reactor systems for root culture. We would also like to acknowledge auxiliary support from an NSF Young Investigator Award (BCS-9358452) and associated industrial matching funds and equipment: Perkin-Elmer, Merck & Co., BASF Corporation, Rohm & Haas Co., Mobil Foundation Inc., Exxon Company USA, Philip Morris Europe, Bayer Corporation, and Smith Kline Beecham. The numerous contributions of individual laboratory researchers can be found on the laboratory web page: http://www.personal.psu.edu/~wrc2.

LIST OF VARIABLES

Symbol	Definition (with typical units)
C^*	Equilibrium (saturation) dissolved oxygen concentration (mass of oxygen per volume of liquid medium, $mol \cdot m^{-3}$)
C_L	Dissolved oxygen concentration (mass of oxygen per volume of liquid medium, $mol \cdot m^{-3}$)
g	Acceleration of gravity ($m \cdot sec^{-2}$)
G	Molar flow rate of the gas phase ($mol \cdot sec^{-1}$)
H	Henry's law coefficient ($N \cdot m^{-5} \cdot mol^{-1}$)
$k_L a$	Volumetric interfacial mass-transfer coefficient for the liquid-side film (sec^{-1}); Composite mass-transfer parameter made up of the liquid mass transfer coefficient (k_L, $cm \cdot sec^{-1}$) and the interfacial area per unit volume of the tank (a, cm^{-1}).
k_s	Saturation constant, kinetic parameter that defines affinity for substrate ($g \cdot L^{-1}$)
L	Depth of the liquid within the reactor (cm)
OTR	Total oxygen transfer rate in the reactor ($mol \cdot sec^{-1}$)
P_s	Pressure in the headspace at the top of the reactor ($N \cdot m^{-2}$)
S	Substrate concentration (mass of substrate per volume of liquid medium, $g \cdot L^{-1}$)
V_L	Volume of liquid medium in the reactor (m^3)
X_i	Inoculum biomass concentration (tissue mass per unit volume of reactor; $g \cdot L^{-1}$)
X_f	Final biomass concentration (tissue mass per unit volume of reactor; $g \cdot L^{-1}$)
Y_{in}	Oxygen mole fraction in the inlet gas stream (dimensionless)
β	Dimensionless group, ratio of rate of oxygen consumption to rate of oxygen mass transfer
Δt	Culture time interval (day)
ε_L	Liquid void fraction (volume of liquid per reactor volume, dimensionless)
ρ	Liquid medium density ($g \cdot mL^{-1}$)
μ	Specific growth rate (weight of cells produced per unit weight per day, day^{-1})
μ_{max}	Maximum specific growth rate, growth under non-nutrient-limited conditions (day^{-1})

BIBLIOGRAPHY

1. M. Taya et al., *J. Chem. Eng. Jpn.* **22**(1), 84–89 (1989).
2. W.R. Curtis, *Curr. Opin. Biotechnol.* **4**(2), 205–210 (1993).
3. L. Toivonen, *Biotechnol. Prog.* **9**, 12–20 (1993).
4. M. Wink. in R.A. Leigh and D. Sanders, eds., *The Plant Vacuole*, Academic Press, San Diego, CA., 1997, pp. 141–169.
5. D. Ramakrishnan and W.R. Curtis, in S. Furusaki and D.D.Y. Ryu, eds., *Studies in Plant Science, 4: Advances in Plant Biotechnology*, Elsevier, Amsterdam, pp. 281–305.
6. P.D.G. Wilson, in P. Doran, ed., *Hairy Roots*, Gordon & Breach/Harwood Academic, U.K., pp. 179–190.
7. W.-D. Deckwer, *Adv. Biotechnol.* **1**, 465–476 (1981).
8. E.B. Carvalho, S. Holihan, B. Pearsall, and W.R. Curtis, in P. Doran, ed., *Hairy Roots*, Gordon & Breach/Harwood Academic, U.K., 1997, pp. 151–167.
9. J.M. Sharp and P. Doran, *J. Biotechnol.* **16**, 171–186 (1990).
10. M. Kawamura, T. Shigeoka, M. Akita, and Y. Kobayashi, *J. Ferment. Bioeng.* **82**(6), 618–619 (1996).
11. G.F. Payne, V. Bringi, C. Prince, and M.L. Shuler, *Plant Cell Culture in Liquid Systems*, Hanser Publishers, New York, 1991.
12. D. Ramakrishnan, Ph.D. Thesis, The Pennsylvania State University, Dept. of Chemical Engineering, University Park, 1997.
13. M.G. Hilton and M.J.C. Rhodes, *Appl. Microbiol. Biotechnol.* **33**, 132–138 (1990).
14. D. Ramakrishnan, J. Salim, and W.R. Curtis, *Biotechnol. Tech.* **8**(9), 639–644 (1994).
15. L. Tescione, D. Ramakrishnan, and W.R. Curtis, *Enzyme Microb. Technol.* **20**, 207–213 (1997).
16. T. Muranaka, H. Ohkawa, and Y. Yamada, *Appl. Microbiol. Biotechnol.* **40**, 219–223 (1993).
17. G. Jung and D. Tepfer, *Plant Sci.* **50**, 145–151 (1987).
18. P. Holmes et al., in P. Doran, ed., *Hairy Roots*, Gordon & Breach/Harwood Academic, U.K., 1997, pp. 201–208.
19. P.J. Whitney, *Enzyme Microb. Technol.* **14**, 13–17 (1992).
20. T.Y. Hsiao, F.T. Bacani, E.B. Carvalho, and W.R. Curtis, *Biotechnol. Prog.* **15**(1), 114–122, (1999).
21. M.J.C. Rhodes et al., *Biotechnol. Lett.* **8**(6), 415–420 (1986).
22. S.A. McKelvey, J.A. Gehrig, K.A. Hollar, and W.R. Curtis, *Biotechnol. Prog.* **9**, 317–322 (1993).
23. A.M. Nuutila, M. Vestberg, and V. Kauppinen, *Plant Cell Rep.* **14**, 505–509 (1995).
24. W.R. Curtis, in T.-J. Fu, G. Singh, and W.R. Curtis, eds., *Plant Cell Culture for the Production of Food Ingredients*, Kluwer Academic/Plenum, New York, 1999, pp. 225–236.
25. M.G. Hilton, P.D.G. Wilson, R.J. Robins, and M.J.C. Rhodes, in R.J. Robins and M.J.C. Rhodes, eds., *Manipulating Secondary Metabolism in Culture*, Cambridge University Press, Cambridge, U.K., 1988, pp. 239–245.

26. R.M. Buitelaar, A.A.M. Langenhoff, R. Heidstra, and J. Tramper, *Enzyme Microb. Technol.* **13**, 487–494 (1991).

27. J. Mugnier, in P. Doran, ed., *Hairy Roots*, Gordon & Breach/Harwood Academic, U.K., 1997, pp. 123–131.

28. P.D.G. Wilson, M.G. Hilton, R.J. Robins, and M.J.C. Rhodes, in G.W. Moody and P.B. Baker, eds., *International Conference on Bioreactors and Biotransformations*, Elsevier, London, 1987, pp. 38–51.

29. Y. Chisti and M. Moo-Young, *Chem. Eng. Commun.* **60**, 195–242 (1987).

30. M.A. Rodriguez-Mendiola, A. Stafford, R. Cresswell, and C. Arias-Castro, *Enzyme Microb. Technol.* **13**, 697–702 (1991).

31. S.J. Sim and H.N. Chang, *Biotechnol. Lett.* **15**, 145–150 (1993).

32. J. Bordonaro, M.S. Thesis, The Pennsylvania State University, Dep. of Chemical Engineering, University Park, 1997.

33. K.H. Kwok and P.M. Doran, *Biotechnol. Prog.* **11**, 429–435 (1995).

34. S.H. Woo, J.M. Park, and J.-W. Yang, *J. Chem. Tech. Biotechnol.* **66**, 355–362 (1996).

35. E. Carvalho and W.R. Curtis, *Biotechnol. Bioeng.* **60**(3), 375–384 (1998).

36. S.N. Vani, Ph.D. Thesis, Rice University, Dept. of Chemical Engineering, Houston, TX., 1996.

37. H.E. Flores and W.R. Curtis, *Proc. N.Y. Acad. Sci.* **665**, 188–209 (1992).

38. A.A. DiIorio, R.D. Cheetham, and P.J. Weathers, *Appl. Microbiol. Biotechnol.* **37**, 463–467 (1992).

39. O. Kondo, H. Honda, M. Taya, and T. Kobayashi, *Appl. Microbiol. Biotechnol.* **32**, 291–294 (1989).

40. B.E. Wyslouzil et al., *Biotechnol. Prog.* **13**, 185–194 (1997).

41. J.L. Cuello, Ph.D. Thesis, The Pennsylvania State University, Dept. of Agricultural and Biological Engineering, University Park, 1994.

42. A.A. Di Iorio, P.J. Weathers, and R.D. Cheetham, *Appl. Microbiol. Biotechnol.* **39**, 174–180 (1993).

43. W.A. Larsen, J.T. Hsu, H.E. Flores, and A.E. Humphrey, *Biotechnol. Tech.* **7**(8), 557–562 (1993).

44. J.P. Corry, W.L. Reed, and W.R. Curtis, *Biotechnol. Bioeng.* **42**, 503–508 (1993).

45. P. Brodelius and H. Pedersen, *Trends Biotechnol.* **11**, 30–36 (1993).

46. U. Mukundan, V. Bhide, G. Singh, and W.R. Curtis, *Appl. Microbiol. Biotechnol.* **50**, 241–245 (1998).

47. G. Singh, G.R. Reddy, and W.R. Curtis, *Biotechnol. Prog.* **10**(4), 365–371 (1994).

48. J. Bordonaro, E. Carvalho, and W.R. Curtis, in *Proceedings of the '97 Agricultural Biotechnology Symposium on Plant Biotechnology on New Biomaterials*, Seoul National University, Research Center for New Bio-Materials in Agriculture, Suwan, Korea, 1997, pp. 91–106.

49. L. Tescione, P. Asplund, and W.R. Curtis, in T.-J. Fu, G. Singh, and W.R. Curtis, eds., *Plant Cell Culture for the Production of Food Ingredients*, Kluwer Academic/Plenum, New York, 1999, pp. 139–156.

50. J. Flint-Wandel and M. Hjortso, *Biotechnol. Tech.* **7**(6), 447–452 (1993).

51. O.L. Gamborg, R.A. Miller, and J. Ojima, *Exp. Cell Res.* **50**, 151–158 (1968).

52. G. Singh and W.R. Curtis, *Life Sci. Adv.—Plant Physio. (India)* **13**, 163–168 (1994).

53. K. Syono and T. Furuya, *Plant Cell Physiol.* **9**, 103–114 (1968).

54. G.R.C. Williams and P.M. Doran, *Aust. Biotechnol.* **5**, 92–94 (1995).

55. D. Ramakrishnan and W.R. Curtis, *J. Chem. Eng. Jpn.* **28**(4), 491–493 (1995).

56. C.L. Prince, V. Bringi, and M.L. Shuler, *Biotechnol. Prog.* **7**, 195–199 (1991).

57. S. Yu and P.M. Doran, *Biotechnol. Bioeng.* **44**, 880–887 (1994).

58. T. Yukimune, H. Yamagata, Y. Hara, and Y. Yamada, *Biosci. Biotechnol. Biochem.* **58**(10), 1824–1827 (1994).

59. M. Kino-Oka, M. Taya, and S. Tone, in W.K. Teo, M.G.S. Yap, and S.K.W. Oh, eds., *Proceedings of the Third Asia-Pacific Biochemical Engineering Conference*, National University of Singapore, Department of Chemical Engineering and Bioprocessing Technology Unit, Singapore, 1994, pp. 95–97.

60. D. Ramakrishnan, D. Luyk, and W.R. Curtis, *Biotechnol. Bioeng.* **62**(6), 711–721 1999.

61. D.S. Dunlop and W.R. Curtis, *Biotechnol. Prog.* **7**, 434–438 (1991).

62. W.R. Curtis, Ph.D. Thesis, Purdue University, Dept. of Chemical Engineering, West Lafayette, IN., (1998).

63. C. Chatterjee et al., *Biotechnol. Tech.* **11**(3), 155–158 (1997).

64. P.B. Weisz, *Science* **170**, 433–440 (1973).

65. S. Ergun, *Chem. Eng. Prog.* **48**, 89–94 (1952).

66. A. Lister, *Chem. React. Eng. Proc. 3rd Eur. Symp.*, 1965, pp. 225–234.

67. P.A. Ramachandran and R.V. Chaudhari, *Three-Phase Catalytic Reactors*, Gordon & Breach, New York, 1983, pp. 200–255.

68. C.N. Satterfield, A.A. Pelossof, and T.K. Sherwood, *AIChE J.* **15**(2), 226–234 (1969).

See also BIOREACTOR CULTURE OF PLANT ORGANS BIOREACTORS, CONTINUOUS CULTURE OF PLANT CELLS; BIOREACTORS, MIST; BIOREACTORS, RECIRCULATION BIOREACTOR IN PLANT CELL CULTURE; CONTAMINATION DETECTION AND ELIMINATION IN PLANT CELL CULTURE; OFF-LINE ANALYSIS IN ANIMAL CELL CULTURE, METHODS; OFF-LINE IMMUNOASSAYS IN BIOPROCESS CONTROL; ON-LINE ANALYSIS IN ANIMAL CELL CULTURE; PHYSIOLOGY OF PLANT CELLS IN CULTURE; STERILIZATION AND DECONTAMINATION.

HAPLOID PLANT PRODUCTION: POLLEN/ANTHER/OVULE CULTURE

RICHARD E. VEILLEUX
Virginia Polytechnic Institute and State University
Blacksburg, Virginia

OUTLINE

Anther Culture

Microspore (Pollen) Culture

Ovule Culture

Conclusion

Bibliography

Haploid plants bear the gametic chromosome number of a species and are generally derived from gametophytic tissue that develops during the short-lived reproductive phase of higher plants. Gametophytes develop after meiosis both in anthers (microsporogenesis) and in ovules (megasporogenesis). Haploid microspores ordinarily develop into pollen grains (mature male gametophytes), whereas one of four haploid megaspores generates an eight-celled embryo sac (mature female gametophyte) bearing the egg cell, synergids, polar nuclei, and antipodals. Union of a haploid sperm cell from the male gametophyte with a haploid egg cell from the female gametophyte upon fertilization produces a zygote that develops into an embryo, restoring the somatic chromosome number of a species. An interruption of normal meiotic development, either natural or induced, causes the microspore or megaspore to undergo mitotic divisions without fertilization, eventually resulting in a haploid plant. Such extraordinary development of these gametophytic tissues can be induced in plant tissue culture, resulting in androgenesis or gynogenesis of higher plants.

Haploid plants have numerous applications in plant genetic research. These include: rapid development of homozygous lines, cell selection, simplified segregation of complex genetic traits, chromosomal reduction of polyploids to facilitate breeding with germplasm that differs by ploidy, and generation of somatic hybrids with reduced ploidy level. Homozygous lines are important in both self-pollinated and cross-pollinated crops. For self-pollinated crops such as wheat (Triticum aestivum L.), cultivars represent homozygous lines that have been selected for various traits of economic importance. New cultivars are developed by crossing two inbred lines to create a heterozygous F_1 hybrid followed by many (6–12) cycles of self-pollination to develop homozygous lines bearing desirable traits from both parents. The process can take many years depending on the life cycle of the plant. Derivation of haploids from the F_1 hybrid followed by chromosome doubling of promising haploids can generate homozygous lines, thereby shortening the breeding cycle to a single generation. With cross-pollinated crops such as maize, inbred lines that differ genetically for many traits are crossed to generate F_1 hybrid cultivars that exhibit considerable hybrid vigor, or heterosis, over the parents for traits of agronomic significance. Hence, haploids can again facilitate cultivar production by generating inbred lines efficiently. Haploid cell cultures offer the advantages of microbial selection in plant systems. Cell selection has been used extensively in microbial research to recover mutant lines that can efficiently produce some secondary product, for example, a medicinal or aromatic substance, in a bioreactor. Microbes are haploid organisms; therefore, selection of recessive mutations is efficient. Pharmaceutical firms have shown considerable interest in developing production systems for certain rare or difficult-to-obtain plant secondary products in plant cell cultures. However, the diploid or polyploid nature of plants hinders the selection of cells that may be high producers of the compound of interest because recessive mutations may never be observed due to expression of the corresponding dominant allele. Haploid cells have only a single allele per locus, therefore, mutant cell lines for traits of interest could be identified easily and isolated. For traits that are controlled by three or more recessive genes, the number of F_2 individuals that must be examined in order to observe all possible genotypes increases dramatically, thereby obscuring segregation ratios when the population size is too small. However, if haploids can be derived from the F_1, only the homozygous genotypes will be observed in the next generation, so that genotypes can be more easily assigned to phenotypes. Determination of the inheritance of seed color in Brassica napus L. has been facilitated in this manner (11). In many polyploid crops, such as the tetraploid cultivated potato (Solanum tuberosum L.), there is a wealth of germplasm at the diploid level that can be used for introgression of valuable traits such as disease or insect resistance, processing characteristics, etc. However, the difference in ploidy is a hindrance to accessing this germplasm. Haploidization of cultivated potato from the tetraploid ($2n = 4x = 48$) to the dihaploid level ($2n = 2x = 24$) has been used to transfer exotic germplasm into diploid hybrids. Finally, somatic hybrids derived by protoplast fusion between species or genotypes of interest generally carry the entire chromosome complement of both parents and are necessarily polyploid. If the ploidy of parents selected for somatic hybridization has been reduced to the haploid level, then it may be possible to derive somatic hybrids with chromosome number similar to that expected of sexual hybrids between the same parents. Given all these applications of haploid plant production and the relative ease with which haploids can be obtained through tissue culture, attempts to derive haploid plants through culture of gametophytic tissues have received considerable attention in plant science research since Guha and Maheshwari (2) first demonstrated the possibility of androgenesis by anther culture of Datura innoxia Mill. Although anther culture has been the most successful means to obtain haploid plants, microspore (pollen) culture and ovule culture have also been successful, especially for plants where anther culture has failed.

ANTHER CULTURE

Technically, anther culture is a simple procedure. Buds containing anthers at the appropriate stage of development are picked from plant material that has been grown in a greenhouse or growth chamber. Field-grown material is rarely acceptable because of the high bacterial and fungal contamination that frequently occurs in subsequent tissue culture. The stage of bud development is critical. After meiosis, four haploid microspores are released from each pollen mother cell. The microspores are thin walled, generally transparent, and perfectly spherical during the early uninucleate stage. The cell walls start to thicken as the nucleus undergoes a single mitotic division and the microspores become binucleate with two haploid nuclei. The mature pollen grain, the final product of microsporogenesis, is either bi- or trinucleate with a thick, opaque cell wall. The late uninucleate stage of microspore development, just before the microspore mitosis, generally responds best to anther culture. It is believed that the in vitro culture environment redirects this mitosis such that an embryogenic (direct androgenesis) or callus induction (indirect androgenesis) pathway results. Occasionally, morphological features of the sporophytic tissue can be used to predict the stage of microspore development within the anthers, as in tobacco, where the equal length of corolla and calyx tubes corresponds well with the microspore uninucleate stage. However, in most species, size of the buds as an indicator of microspore developmental stage generally yields variable results, because of environmental and positional effects on bud size.

Surface sterilization of buds before dissection of anthers is required to prevent microbial contamination of cultures. Because the anthers are well protected within the buds of most species, the sterilization routine can be reasonably severe without inflicting damage to the anthers. For potato, we often use 30 sec in 80% ethanol followed by 5 min in full-strength commercial bleach (5.25% sodium hypochlorite), with three rinses in sterile distilled water. On the other hand, anthers of some species are not well protected by the buds, allowing entry of more potential microbial contaminants as well as increased exposure of the anthers to the caustic effects of disinfecting agents. Mercuric chloride (0.1–1% for 2–10 min) or longer disinfection with weaker bleach solution can be used in these cases. Once the disinfectant has been sufficiently rinsed from the buds, they are transferred to a sterile surface, such as sterilized paper towels or Petri plates in a laminar flow bench where the anthers are dissected and placed on a sterilized tissue culture medium. The medium can be either autoclaved (20 min at 110 kPa) or filter sterilized (0.2 μm pore size).

There is usually considerable difference among anthers and even more among buds for androgenic response. This likely reflects the variable frequency of microspores that are amenable to androgenesis within a given anther. Hence many anthers must be cultured in order to determine the proper medium and culture conditions for a given species. Anther culture response among anthers bearing different stages of microspore development in potato anther culture is demonstrated in Table 1. In addition, because of bud-to-bud variability, treatment effects can often be confounded with bud variation. Because anther-to-anther variability within a bud is usually less than bud-to-bud variability, it is advisable to distribute anthers from a single bud across treatments when evaluating the effects of several treatments for their influence on anther culture (3). Anther culture medium has been developed specifically for tobacco (4). Plant tissue culture medium developed for other purposes, such as by Murashige and Skoog (5), Gamborg et al. (6) B5, or

Table 1. Mean Embryo Yield in Anther Culture of Potato Cultured at Four Stages of Anther Development

Stage of microsporogenesis	Anther length (mm)	Embryos per cultured anther
Meiosis	2.1 ± 0.1	0.01
Early uninucleate	2.5 ± 0.2	0.93
Late uninucleate	3.0 ± 0.4	1.18
Binucleate	3.7 ± 0.5	0.28

Linsmaier and Skoog (7), has also been modified for anther culture. Some of the most common modifications are: increased sucrose concentration; substitution of another sugar, such as maltose, for sucrose; use of activated charcoal to remove impurities from the medium on autoclaving; or addition of plant growth regulators. The state of the medium may be critical: for potato, liquid medium has been most efficacious. However, media solidified with agar, agarose, potato starch, gelrite, or other gelling agents have been frequently employed; alternatively, a bilayer medium consisting of a gelled medium on which a small amount of liquid medium has been placed has been effective for some species. A high-temperature treatment (e.g., 35 °C for 24 h) may be necessary before or at the initiation of anther culture of some species. Alternatively, for many species, a cold treatment (e.g., 3 days at 4 °C) may be a beneficial pretreatment to flower buds before anthers are cultured.

There are several measures of anther culture response that can be quantified: the number of responding anthers per total anthers cultured, the number of embryos or calluses per responding anther, the number of plantlets obtained per anthers cultured, or the number of haploids obtained per cultured anther. The frequency of haploids among the regenerants is often genotype dependent, as is the response to anther culture. Within a species, some cultivars may respond readily to anther culture, whereas others are recalcitrant. The androgenic ability of a plant has been studied in several crops and found to be genetically inherited. The response has been primarily dominant and controlled by a few genomic regions (8,9). In tobacco, plantlets emerge directly from cultured anthers. However, this one-phase response is an exception. The anther culture response of most species is two-phased. Usually embryos or calluses emerge from the anthers, and a separate regeneration phase, where the anther-derived structures must be transferred to a new medium or even a series of media before plantlets can be obtained, is required. In this case, the responses to anther culture and regeneration are often independent, such that a particular genotype may generate many embryos but few regenerate, or vice versa. The medium used for regeneration is often different in composition from the anther culture medium, especially with regard to growth regulator content. Cytokinin or gibberellic acid may be required to stimulate anther-derived embryos to regenerate. Often a combination of auxin and cytokinin is required for microspore-derived callus to regenerate. Multiple transfers of quiescent embryos to fresh regeneration medium may be required before regeneration actually occurs.

Plantlets that emerge from anther culture often exhibit a range of ploidy other than the expected haploid level. Somatic tissue of the anther itself can give rise to regenerative callus, yielding anther-derived plants genetically identical to the anther donor plant, except for possible somaclonal variation. Alternatively, androgenesis can occur from unreduced, heterozygous microspores (10). Finally, chromosome doubling by endopolyploidization may occur during cell culture, resulting in doubled haploid, homozygous plants. In order to distinguish haploid from diploid or greater derivatives of anther culture, some method of ploidy determination or molecular marker analysis may be required (10). For ploidy determination, root tip squashes of mitotic cells at metaphase (11), chloroplasts counts per pair of guard cells in leaf stomata (12), or flow cytometry of nuclei stained with a DNA stain (13) may be employed.

MICROSPORE (POLLEN) CULTURE

An alternative method of obtaining haploid plants has been found in pollen culture or, more appropriately, microspore culture. Although the process was first described as pollen culture (14), mature pollen is never used; instead, microspores at the same stage of development required for anther culture (late uninucleate) are released from the anthers and cultured in a liquid medium. Advantages of microspore culture are that the development can be viewed directly under a microscope, regeneration from microspores rather than somatic tissues of the anthers is more likely, and amendments to the medium exert their influence more directly on the target cells. In addition, transformation of microspores with exogenous DNA by microprojectile bombardment can be accomplished more readily in microspore culture compared to anther culture, with the subsequent regeneration of homozygous transformants (15). Given all these advantages, microspore culture would appear to be a preferable technique to anther culture. A major disadvantage, however, is that microspore culture has been far less successful than anther culture and the range of species on which it can be practiced is limited (16). Most success has been obtained in *Nicotiana tabacum* L. (17) and *B. napus* (18).

As with anther culture, pretreatment to the microspores is required to induce cell division. This generally requires some kind of metabolic shock. For *B. napus*, this consists of a heat shock (35 °C for 24 h at the onset of culture). For *N. tabacum*, a nutritional shock has been most successful where the microspores are first cultured in a "starvation" medium without a source of nitrogen and subsequently transferred to an enriched medium to induce cell division and embryonic development (19). Again, disruption of the normal course of development of microspores into pollen grains is prerequisite to androgenic development.

Removal of the microspores from the anthers can be accomplished in a variety of ways. Gentle crushing of anthers in a sterilized mortar and pestle containing 1–2 ml of liquid medium has been successful. The microspores are then purified by filtering through a 63-μm mesh and centrifuging to pellet them. The supernatant can then be removed and replaced with fresh medium. The centrifugation step may be repeated until the medium is clear. An alternative to crushing the anthers has been blending them using an Omni mixer or alternative miniblender. The density of microspores is critical in order for cell division to occur. The density can be estimated by using a haemacytometer and then adjusted to 10^4 to 10^5 per ml. Once cell division has occurred, dilution of the cultures is often required in order to reduce competition for nutrients at the initial high density. Small Petri plates (35 × 10 mm) serve best for microspore culture. The media used for microspore culture have been similar to those for anther culture. It is frequently filter-sterilized, especially if it contains amino acids or reduced nitrogen sources that may break down on autoclaving. Carbohydrate source is critical, and sucrose levels as high as 17% have been used to initiate microspore cultures. Embryos derived from microspore culture can be regenerated as for anther culture. Desiccation of embryos may be beneficial prior to their placement on regeneration medium (20). For *B. napus*, thousands of embryos can be recovered from the microspores isolated from the anthers of a single flower bud.

OVULE CULTURE

The relative scarcity of haploid cells within an ovule compared to the many thousands generally found within anthers has made ovule culture, or gynogenesis, a less attractive alternative to anther or microspore culture for researchers intent on developing haploid plants. However, for a few species including onion (*Allium sativum* L.), ovule culture has been successful when anther culture has failed. San Noeum (21) first reported successful ovule culture of barley (*Hordeum vulgare* L.) in 1976. As with anther and microspore culture, the ability of a genotype to regenerate haploid plants from ovule culture (gynogenesis) is genetically determined.

For ovule culture, ovules are usually dissected from unpollinated flowers. In some cases, irradiated pollen, where the pollen has been inactivated but not destroyed, has been used to stimulate gynogenesis. The critical stage for success in culture is difficult to determine directly because the embryo sac containing haploid nuclei is embedded deep within the ovule. Hence, an indirect method of determining the proper stage has been employed, that is, examination of the more readily accessible microspore stages within anthers of the same bud. For most species, the late uninucleate stage of microspore development corresponds to mature embryo sac development. Mature embryo sacs have been most responsive to ovule culture. It is generally the egg cell, the haploid synergids adjacent to the egg, or occasionally the haploid antipodal cells that give rise to haploid plants in ovule culture. Division of one or more of these haploid cells occurs within a few days of culture. Development may occur along a direct embryogenic pathway or, as with indirect androgenesis, through a callus stage. Several different basal media, especially those of Murashige and Skoog (5) and Gamborg et al. (6), have been used for ovule culture. Growth regulators, particularly auxin, are often added to the media along with cytokinin and gibberellin. High sucrose may be beneficial, but this is species specific. Overall, the gynogenic response of most species has been low, with only a small percentage of cultured ovules regenerating plants, although the percentage of haploid regenerants has ranged from 37 to 91 in *Beta vulgaris* L. (22). Only onion and sugar beet have been the objects of large-scale haploidization studies using ovule culture.

CONCLUSION

The promise of haploid plants for cultivar development has only recently come to fruition. A microspore-derived cultivar of *B. napus* has just recently been released (23), an anther-derived cultivar of wheat (24), and a hybrid asparagus (*Asparagus officinalus* L.) cultivar (25) derived from crosses of inbred lines derived by anther culture are now available, among others (26,27). It remains to be seen if these cultivars will be commercially successful. Considerable research has been required to adapt the haploid-inducing cell culture techniques first observed in nonagronomic plants to crop plants. However, the application of these techniques (with appropriate modifications) has been expanded to include a large array of commercially important species. Plant breeding is a slow process with a long history of success. The twenty-first century will see many new cultivars of existing crops and likely many new crops as well. As transgenic researchers search primarily for single genes to deliver various traits to existing cultivars, it is crucially important to continue haploid research for the production of new and untested combinations of genes for crop development.

BIBLIOGRAPHY

1. K.P. Pauls, in S.M. Jain, S.K. Sopory, and R.E. Veilleux, eds., *In Vitro Haploid Production in Higher Plants*, Vol. 1, Kluwer Academic Publishers, Dordrecht, The Netherlands, 1996, pp. 125–144.

2. S. Guha and S.C. Maheshwari, *Nature (London)* **204**, 497 (1964).

3. K.T. Snider and R.E. Veilleux, *Plant Cell, Tissue Organ Cult.* **36**, 345–354 (1994).

4. J. Nitsch and C. Nitsch, *Science* **163**, 85–87 (1969).

5. T. Murashige and F. Skoog, *Physiol. Plant.* **15**, 473–497 (1962).

6. O. Gamborg, R. Miller, and K. Ojima, *Exp. Cell Res.* **50**, 151–158 (1968).

7. E. Linsmaier and F. Skoog, *Physiol. Plant.* **18**, 100–127 (1965).

8. R. Bernardo et al., *Theor. Appl. Genet.* **94**, 652–656 (1997).

9. C. Singsit and R.E. Veilleux, *Euphytica* **43**, 105–112 (1988).

10. R.E. Veilleux, L.Y. Shen, and M.M. Paz, *Genome* **38**, 1153–1162 (1995).

11. K. Fukui and S. Nakayama, eds., *Plant Chromosomes: Laboratory Methods*, CRC Press, Boca Raton, Fla., 1996.

12. C. Singsit and R.E. Veilleux, *HortScience* **26**, 592–594 (1991).

13. H.R. Owen, R.E. Veilleux, D. Levy, and D.L. Ochs, *Genome* **113**, 755–759 (1988).

14. C. Nitsch and B. Norreel, *C.R. He bd. Seances Acad. Sci., Ser. D* **278D**, 1031–1034 (1974).

15. E. Stöger, C. Fink, M. Pfosser, and E. Heberle-Bors, *Plant Cell Rep.* **14**, 273–278 (1995).

16. J.M. Dunwell, in S.M. Jain, S.K. Sopory, and R.E. Veilleux, eds., In Vitro *Haploid Production in Higher Plants*, Vol. 1, Kluwer Academic Publishers, Dordrecht, The Netherlands, 1996, pp. 205–216.

17. E. Heberle-Bors, *Sex. Plant Reprod.* **2**, 1–10 (1989).

18. Y. Takahata, D.C.W. Brown, and W.A. Keller, *Euphytica* **58**, 51–55 (1991).

19. A. Touraev, O. Vicente, and E. Heberle-Bors, *Trends Plant Sci.* **2**, 297–302 (1997).

20. T. Senaratna, L. Kott, W.D. Beversdorf, and B.D. McKersie, *Plant Cell Rep.* **10**, 342–344 (1991).

21. L.H. San Noeum, *Ann. Amélior. Plant.* **26**, 751–754 (1976).

22. E.R.J. Keller and L. Korzun, in S.M. Jain, S.K. Sopory, and R.E. Veilleux, eds., In Vitro *Haploid Production in Higher Plants*, Vol. 1, Kluwer Academic Publishers, Dordrecht, The Netherlands, 1996, pp. 217–235.

23. G.R. Stringam, M.R. Thiagarajah, V.K. Bansal, and D.F. Degenhardt, *Plant Biotechnol. In Vitro Biol. 21st Century, 9th Int. Cong. Plant Tissue Cell Cult.*, Jerusalem, 1998, Abstr., p. 111.

24. J. de Buyser, et al., *Plant Breed.* **98**, 53–56 (1987).

25. L. Corriols, C. Doré, and C. Rameau, *Acta Hortic.* **271**, 249–252 (1990).

26. G.S. Khush and S.S. Virmani, in S.M. Jain, S.K. Sopory, and R.E. Veilleux, eds., *In Vitro Haploid Production in Higher Plants*, Vol. 1, Kluwer Academic Publishers, Dordrecht, The Netherlands, 1996, pp. 11–33.

27. R.E. Veilleux, *HortScience* **29**, 1238–1241 (1994).

See also ADVENTITIOUS ORGANOGENESIS; BIOREACTOR CULTURE OF PLANT ORGANS; CRYOPRESERVATION OF PLANT CELLS, TISSUES AND ORGANS.

HERBICIDE RESISTANT PLANTS, PRODUCTION OF

D.D. SONGSTAD
Monsanto Company
St. Louis, Missouri

OUTLINE

Introduction

Resistance to Imidazolinone, Sulfonyl Urea, and Related Herbicides

Resistance to Glutamine Synthetase Inhibitor Herbicides

Resistance to Acetyl Coenzyme a Carboxylase Inhibiting Herbicides

Resistance to Photosystem II Inhibiting Herbicides

Resistance to 2,4-D and Related Herbicides

Glyphosate-Resistant Plants

Utilization of Herbicide Tolerance

Acknowledgments

Bibliography

INTRODUCTION

The use of chemicals to regulate plant growth has been instrumental in the ability of agriculturists to provide food to an expanding global population. Weeds compete with crop plants for all factors necessary for plant growth including soil nutrients, water, and exposure to light. Aside from robbing field plants of nutrients, weeds can reduce crop yields by attracting undesirable crop pathogens and insects. If left uncontrolled, weeds that are allowed to produce seeds will result in a substantial increase of overgrowth the following growing season. Because of the reasons described, it is estimated that close to 100% of the United States' corn and soybean acres are treated with herbicides.

There are a wide range of herbicides available today. Some are specific for broadleaf weeds, such as 2,4-dichlorophenoxyacetic acid, abbreviated 2,4-D (1). Others, such as the acetyl coenzyme A carboxylase inhibiting herbicides, are specific for the elimination of grass weeds (2). There are other herbicides that are nonspecific because they are used to eliminate both monocot and dicot weeds (3). The most widely used of these is glyphosate (trade name Roundup®), which is the world's most popular herbicide. With the advent of herbicide-resistant crops, the agriculturist now has the ability to use these plants to regulate the spectrum of efficacy of these chemicals.

The ability to produce transgenic crop plants has provided agriculturists not only herbicide resistance, but also new uses for commercial herbicides. For example, Roundup® is a popular herbicide that traditionally has been used in pre-emergence weed control. With the introduction of Roundup®-resistant crops, this herbicide can now be used pre- and post-emergence for superior weed control. This is especially true with glyphosate-resistant crop plants, such as Roundup Ready® soybeans (4).

Herbicide resistance does not necessarily require genetic transformation to result in a commercial product. Imidazolinone-resistant (IR) corn were produced by selection of maize callus cultures that were resistant to this class of herbicide (5). Plants regenerated from these IR callus cultures were also resistant to imidazolinone herbicides, and this trait was introduced into elite inbred lines via conventional backcrossing (5). In other cases IR plants have been obtained by selection of mutagenized microspores, which was demonstrated to produce IR canola (6). Similar approaches using gametophytic selection show promise in developing herbicide tolerant plants (7) that do not involve genetic transformation, although this may be limited to specific classes of herbicides.

There are numerous plant species that have been either genetically transformed or selected as somaclonal variants that display resistance to various herbicides. This section will be represented by the most well-characterized examples of herbicide-resistant plants that are available — primarily those that have been, or are being, developed into commercial products.

RESISTANCE TO IMIDAZOLINONE, SULFONYL UREA, AND RELATED HERBICIDES

Imidazolinone and sulfonyl urea herbicides have the same mode of action that consists of inhibiting the enzyme acetolactate synthase, abbreviated as ALS or AHAS (8–10). This enzyme is critical in the production of the amino acids valine, lysine, and isoleucine. These classes of herbicides kill by starving the plants for these three amino acids (8). The ALS-inhibiting herbicides are able to kill plant cells by binding with the regulatory site of this enzyme (11).

One well-studied sulfonylurea herbicide is chlorsulfuron, which has been used in various physiological studies ranging from plant transformation (12,13) to assessing the effect of this herbicide on polyamine titers (14). Knowledge of herbicide function can also assist in understanding physiological aspects of amino acid biosynthesis (15).

Aside from chlorsulfuron, there are approximately two dozen additional ALS-inhibiting herbicides that are either commercially available or in development (10). These herbicides are predominately of the sulfonylurea and imidazolinone classifications, although there are other chemicals that can inhibit ALS, such as hiamine analogs (16), triazolopyrimidine, and pyrimidinylthiobenzoate compounds (10). Since production of ALS inhibitors is relatively commonplace, it is not surprising that there are about ten companies that offer commercial formulations of these herbicides for use on a variety of crop plants.

In the past, the development of selective herbicides involved determining which agronomically important crop plants would tolerate a level of application that was lethal to the nontarget plants. Examples of several major crops that are naturally resistant to specific ALS-inhibitor herbicides are described by Saari et al. (10). One specific example is primisulfuron, an ALS-specific herbicide that can be used to eliminate weeds in corn fields (17).

In vitro selection has been utilized to produce herbicide-resistant crop plants. The first instance of this was from tobacco (*Nicotiana tabacum* L.) callus cultures grown on medium containing 2.0 ppb chlorsulfuron or sulfometuron methyl (18). Plants regenerated from these cell lines were tolerant to a concentration of chlorsulfuron that was 100 times higher than the control plants. Anderson and Georgeson (5) described tissue culture selection for imidazolinone-resistant maize mutants that simply relied upon the natural variability that exists within a population of maize cells grown in an in vitro environment. Plants regenerated from these cultures also showed field efficacy for imidazolinone resistance due to several alleles, one of which was XA17. These resistance alleles were further characterized after crossing into the susceptible inbred B73 (19). The XA17 allele conferred resistance to imazethapyr, imazaquin, and sulfometuron methyl. On the other hand, alleles XI12 and QJ22 gave resistance to imazethapyr and little or no resistance to the other two herbicides. Products from this work have been marketed by a major maize seed company as IR corn.

Aside from tobacco and maize, in vitro selection has been used for improved chlorsulfuron tolerance in barley (20) and carrot (21). The in vitro selected barley plants were assessed for chlorsulfuron tolerance in the greenhouse. Increased dry weight of root and plant tissues was observed in the in vitro selected plants. Chlorsulfuron-resistant carrot cell lines and plants produced via in vitro selection were the result of ALS gene amplification. A stepwise increase in chlorsulfuron selection strategy was used to produce cell lines capable of tolerating 1 μM of this herbicide. One chlorsulfuron-resistant cell line was shown to contain at least ten copies of the ALS gene.

Gametophytic selection is a promising area for development of herbicide tolerance. Combining mutagenesis along with gametophytic selection has also been used as a means to increase variability in attempts to select for herbicide resistance. In one example, canola microspores were mutagenized and selected for resistance to imidazolinone herbicides (6). In this approach, the induced variability was not necessarily known at the molecular level but gives the desired efficacy upon herbicide spraying in the field. In other reports, natural variation within the microspore can result in chlorsulfuron resistance in maize (7).

Gametophytic selection for chlorsulfuron resistance in maize has been used to alter the expected 1:1 segregation ratio for this trait (22). In this study, maize plants containing the XA17 allele (5) were treated with chlorsulfuron in planta. Pollen was collected from treated and untreated (control) plants and used to fertilize wild-type females. In approximately 50% of the crosses, treated pollen produced progeny that were 99–100% chlorsulfuron resistant based on foliar application of this herbicide. The control pollinations resulted in the expected 1:1 segregation for chlorsulfuron resistance. Similar results were obtained when in vitro gametophytic selection was applied to transgenic tobacco plants (23).

The advent of genetic engineering and crop transformation has allowed another approach for the development of transgenic plants that are resistant to various ALS-inhibiting herbicides. One of the first reports of genetic transformation of maize used a mutant maize ALS gene driven by the cauliflower mosaic virus 35S promoter (12). This gene rather than an antibiotic resistance gene was used as a selectable marker for the production of transgenic maize plants via microprojectile bombardment of suspension and callus cultures. Subsequent research has shown that bombardment of cultured maize immature embryo explants with microprojectiles carrying this same construct also leads to production of transgenic maize plants resistant to chlorsulfuron (13). A mutant ALS gene from *Arabidopsis thaliana*, referred to as csr1-1, was used to generate transgenic rice (*Oryza sativa* L.) plants via protoplast transformation (24). This gene, when driven by the cauliflower mosaic virus 35S promoter, conferred at least a 200-fold increase in chlorsulfuron resistance in comparison with the nontransformed rice callus control. The csr1-1 gene was also used to produce transgenic tobacco plants tolerant to chlorsulfuron (25). Tolerance was noted in plants in the hemizygous state, whereas those homozygous for this trait showed up to 59% damage when sprayed with this herbicide. It was reported that the csr1-1 transgene was able to co-suppress the surA and surB genes encoding acetolactate synthase (ALS or AHAS).

RESISTANCE TO GLUTAMINE SYNTHETASE INHIBITOR HERBICIDES

Basta™ and bialaphos are two herbicides that kill plants by inhibiting glutamine synthetase (GS). Bayer et al. (26) first described the herbicidal effects of the active ingredient in Basta™, phosphinothricin. The mechanism of action involves ammonium toxicity resulting from the failure of the plant to store ammonium as glutamine (by inhibiting GS). Both Basta™ and bialaphos are contact herbicides, meaning that Basta™ and bialaphos do not translocate through the plant. One technical advantage is localized

"leaf painting" of this herbicide, allowing one to determine if an individual plant will be sensitive to this herbicide without killing the entire plant.

The primary method for generation of Basta™ and bialaphos-resistant plants is via genetic transformation. The **bar** or **pat** genes, which confer resistance to these herbicides via phosphinothricin-N-acetyl-transferase, have been used extensively in plant transformation research as selectable markers (12,27–33). The resistance is conferred by acetylation of Basta™ and bialaphos herbicides. The **bar** gene was isolated from *S. hygroscopicus* (34), while the **pat** gene was isolated from *S. viridochromogenes* (35). The first reports of production of bialaphos-resistant transgenic maize plants and progeny were by Fromm et al. (12) and Gordon-Kamm et al. (27). The expression of the 35S::**Bar** transgene confers resistance in these plants. Extensive evaluation of the 35S::**Bar** transgene inheritance has been reported (36). In addition to biolistics, Omirulleh et al. (37) also produced Basta™-resistant transgenic plants by free DNA uptake into maize protoplasts through use of silicon carbide fibers (38,39), and Ishida et al. (32) produced transgenic maize plants via *Agrobacterium tumefaciens*–mediated infection of immature embryos. Aside from the transgenic approach, there are no known methods of producing plants that are resistant to GS-inhibiting herbicides. However, Basta™ has been used for in vitro selection of tolerant tobacco (40) and alfalfa (41) cell lines due to increased activity of GS within these cells.

There are various known inhibitors of glutamine synthetase that could potentially become herbicides. However, Basta™ and bialaphos have been used in production of transgenic plants since they have the greatest affinity (K_m) for the *bar* enzyme (42). Basta™ is a glutamic acid analog, and bialaphos is identical in structure with Basta™, except it also contains two alanine residues. One other inhibitor of GS that is often used in the laboratory is methionine sulfoximine (MSO). However, MSO will probably not be routinely used with the *Bar* or *Pat* genes, since its K_m is greater than that of Basta™ or bialaphos (42).

MSO along with Basta™ and bialaphos have been used as GS inhibitors in various plant tissue culture and whole plant applications. For example, bialaphos has been demonstrated to promote shoot regeneration from hairy root cultures of snapdragon, *Antirrhinum majus* L. (43). Furthermore, Basta™ has been used to determine the effects of higher ammonium levels on photosynthesis (44) and GS and glutamate dehydrogenase activities in alfalfa (45), and MSO has been used to study changes in amino acid profiles in maize (46). Bialaphos has been used to induce male sterility in rice (47). In addition, physiological result of Basta™ detoxification by transgenic tobacco and carrot plants (*Pat* gene via acetylation) and nontransgenic controls were performed (48). As expected, transgenic plants containing the *Pat* gene inactivated Basta™ via N-acetylation. However, nonlethal application of this herbicide was converted into 4-methylphosphinico-2-oxo-butanoic acid (PPO) via deamination of Basta™ in wild-type plants. Subsequently, PPO was decarboxylated to form 3-methylphosphinico-propanoic acid (MPP), which was stable in the plants. Results such as these suggest that a gene exists that is capable of phosphinothricin deamination. Using molecular approaches for ectopic expression of such a gene may lead to an alternative method for Basta™ and bialaphos resistance.

RESISTANCE TO ACETYL COENZYME A CARBOXYLASE INHIBITING HERBICIDES

There are various herbicides that are inhibitors of acetyl coenzyme A carboxylase (49). These are grouped into two classes, the aryloxyphenoxypropanoate and cyclohexanedione herbicides (2). The mechanism by which these chemicals control plant growth is by disrupting fatty acid biosynthesis in the plastids. Specific areas of the cell affected by these herbicides are those composed of membranes, such as the plasma membrane, tonoplast, plastids, and mitochondria.

There are a variety of herbicides that inhibit acetyl coenzyme A carboxylase (ACCase). These include sethoxydim, clethodim, and diclofop-methyl; readers are encouraged to peruse the review by Devine and Shimabukuro (2) for a more extensive list of these herbicides. Before the implementation of biotechnology, development of selective herbicides involved determining which agronomically important crop plants would tolerate a level of application that was lethal to weeds. These herbicides are especially effective in control of annual grass weeds and have little effect on perennial grasses (2).

Sethoxydim-resistant maize callus cultures were described by Parker et al. (50). In this study, maize callus cultures were exposed to a stepwise increase in sethoxydim. Callus cultures were 40-fold more tolerant to sethoxydim and 20-fold more tolerant to haloxyfop (an aryloxyphenoxypropionate herbicide) than the wild-type control. Plants regenerated from these cultures that were heterozygous for the resistance allele exhibited high-level, but not complete, tolerance to foliar application of both herbicides. Selfing these plants and selecting for those that were homozygous for this allele gave plants that were fully tolerant to 0.8 kg sethoxydim per ha, which had 16-fold greater tolerance than the wild-type control. Further characterization of the sethoxydim-tolerant maize callus cultures revealed an overproduction of ACCase (51).

ACCase has been isolated and characterized from plant species such as maize (52,53) and pea (54). Furthermore, there are now several reports describing successful cloning of the ACCase gene from species such as alfalfa (*Medicago sativa*) (55), *Arabidopsis thaliana* (56), canola (*Brassica napus*) (57), and maize (53,58). This now allows researchers to use molecular techniques for overexpression of ACCase in transgenic plant tissues.

RESISTANCE TO PHOTOSYSTEM II INHIBITING HERBICIDES

There are a series of chemical herbicides that control plant growth by inhibiting photosynthetic electron transport, which leads to destruction of the photosystem II reaction center, leading to photooxidation of critical chloroplast components, such as lipids and chlorophyll (59). The herbicides that inhibit PS II are the triazines, phenylureas,

pyridazinones, and biscarbamates (60). Perhaps the best-known PS II inhibiting herbicide is atrazine.

The reason for the selectivity of PS II inhibiting herbicides is due to the presence or lack of detoxification enzymes within resistant or susceptible species, respectively. Glutathione S-transferase is one enzyme that has been associated with detoxification of these herbicides (61). Safeners have been used to induce glutathione S-transferase activity to promote herbicide tolerance in crop plants (62). These herbicides are inactivated by conjugation with glutathione.

Cytochrome P450-dependent enzyme activity has also been shown to be involved in herbicide detoxification. Fonne-Pfister and Kreuz (63) reported that this enzyme system was responsible for ring-methyl hydroxylation of chlortoluron that was applied to maize. This enzyme system is also capable of detoxification of chlortoluron herbicides via N-dealkylation (59). Since resistance to these herbicides is acquired by enzymes that are relatively common in plants, this may explain why various weed species are no longer susceptible to some of these PS II inhibiting herbicides.

The first atrazine-resistant crop plants were the result of conventional breeding. Atrazine resistance, which was found in *Brassica campestris*, was backcrossed into canola (*B. napus*) (64). These triazine-resistant canola varieties did not develop wide acceptance since there was a 10–20% yield penalty when compared with the wild-type controls (59).

The gene conferring atrazine resistance has been obtained from either resistant species or by site-directed mutagenesis of the *psbA* gene (59). This gene has been engineered so it is driven by a nuclear encoded promoter with a chloroplast transit peptide and transformed into tobacco (65). These transgenic plants were not resistant to a high level of atrazine since the chloroplasts still contained the wild-type *psbA* allele.

Transgenic tobacco plants have also been produced that are resistant to another photosystem II inhibitor, bromoxynil (66; Fig. 1). The bromoxynil resistance gene (**bxn**) is a nitrilase that originated from *Klebsiella ozaenae* (67). **Bxn** is able to convert bromoxynil into its

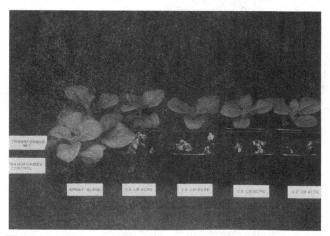

Figure 1. Production of bromoxynil-resistant transgenic tobacco (*Source*: Photo courtesy of D. Stalker and K. McBride, Calgene).

primary metabolite 3,5-dibromo-4-hydroxybenzoic acid. More important, this gene has been transformed into cotton varieties of agronomic importance, and these have been marketed by Calgene.

RESISTANCE TO 2,4-D AND RELATED HERBICIDES

2,4-Dichlorophenoxyacetic acid (2,4-D) is one of the most commonly used herbicides. This herbicide is in a class of chemicals that have auxin (indole-3-acetic acid) activity in plants (68). The effects of 2,4-D on plants include enhanced cell growth and an increase in ethylene emanation. If 2,4-D is applied to a susceptible plant according to herbicide label directions, death is the result of the increase in cell growth and physiological effects of ethylene. However, if the 2,4-D level is reduced, it can be used as a growth stimulant for initiation of callus from various monocot and dicot plants cultured in vitro (69,70). Ethylene emanation, attributed to the effect of as little as 1.0 mg/L 2,4-D, has also been detected from maize callus cultures (71). Auxin and 2,4-D physiology and biochemistry have been extensively reviewed (72–74).

Auxin-like herbicides have had a profound effect on agriculture. 2,4-D was the first selective herbicide based on its ability to eliminate dicot weeds without destroying monocot crop plants. However, it should be noted that this selective nature is dosage dependent. Coupland (1) has described the various means by which plants can metabolize or inactivate 2,4-D and related herbicides.

The development of plants that are resistant to 2,4-D and related herbicides has been correlated with repeated use of these herbicides over several seasons. This has primarily occurred within various weed species, and the exact mechanism of resistance is not known. However, various crop plants have been manipulated so that they are resistant to 2,4-D. Conventional breeding has resulted in *Lotus corniculatus* (birdsfoot trefoil) and *Trifolium pratense* (red clover) resistance to 2,4-D (75,76).

Transgenic plants have also been produced that are resistant to 2,4-D. *Agrobacterium*-mediated delivery of the 2,4-D monooxygenase gene (*tfdA*), isolated from *Alcaligenes eutrophus*, was utilized to produce tobacco (77,78) and cotton (79) plants resistant to 2,4-D. And again, 2,4-D resistance was used in the transformation–selection process. Aside from molecular techniques, transformants were characterized by the level of monooxygenase-catalyzed 2,4-dichlorophenol product accumulation. There may be stringent substrate specificity for this gene, since it did not appear to be effective in conferring resistance to 2,4,5-trichlorophenoxyacetic acid (2,4,5-T).

GLYPHOSATE-RESISTANT PLANTS

Glyphosate, also known as N-[phosphonomethyl]glycine or by its trade name of Roundup®, is a nonselective, broad-spectrum, postemergence, systemic herbicide with positive environmental attributes. Unlike other herbicides where development of analogs are commonplace, no other herbicides are currently marketed with the same mode of action (80).

Rapid degradation of glyphosate by soil microbes is one reason for its positive environmental attribute (81). The bacteria that catabolize glyphosate are considered ubiquitous and primarily consist of various *Pseudomonas* and *Arthrobacter* species. Two mechanisms by which bacteria degrade glyphosate involve lyase and oxidoreductase activities (4). The first mechanism consists of a C-P lyase gene that converts glyphosate into sarcosine and phosphate. The second involves the GOX gene (glyphosate oxidoreductase) that converts glyphosate into aminomethylphosphonate (AMPA) and glyoxylate. It is the GOX mechanism that appears to be more prevalent in nature (4).

The mechanism by which glyphosate kills plant cells is by aromatic amino acid starvation. This is achieved by glyphosate's ability to inhibit the key regulatory enzyme in the shikimate acid pathway, 5-enolpyruvylshikimate-3-phosphate synthase (EPSPS). This enzyme catalyzes the reaction of shikimate-3-phosphate and phophoenolpyruvate to form 5-enolpyruvylshikimate-3-phosphate (4). Glyphosate does not inhibit any other PEP-dependent enzyme systems (3). The result of this is cessation of biosynthesis of tryptophan, tyrosine, and phenylalanine.

Various whole plant studies have been conducted to screen for genetic variability associated with glyphosate resistance (3). A slight variation in glyphosate tolerance has been observed, which seems to be limited by extreme genotype by environment interactions. The overall results from these whole plant selection programs have been described as "disappointing" (3). The one exception is with rigid ryegrass (*Lolium rigidum*) grown in Australia (82). In this report, following 15 years of successful use of Roundup®, a biotype of this grass weed exhibited resistance 7- to 11-fold that of the susceptible control. However, it is important to keep this in perspective, since Roundup®, is still the most efficacious herbicide currently used in agriculture.

Use of plant tissue culture techniques have been employed to select for glyphosate-resistant cell lines. Examples of this are from callus or suspension cultures of alfalfa (83), carrot (84), maize (85), and tobacco (86,87). Most of these reports described a stepwise increase in the cultured cells' ability to tolerate glyphosate. The mechanism of this tolerance was due to EPSPS gene amplification and has been documented in carrot (88) and tobacco (87) cell cultures. In vitro glyphosate tolerant cells appear to be most resistant when selection pressure is present. Removal of glyphosate from in vitro selected tobacco cell lines resulted in decreased tolerance in both the cultured cells and regenerated plants (87). A more reliable method of producing glyphosate-resistant cell lines and plants was required.

Genetic engineering techniques have been extensively utilized to isolate and characterize genes associated with glyphosate degradation. This has been an iterative process where the early research was the impetus for later advances. For example, Padgette et al. (4) described three fundamental mechanisms for tolerance to glyphosate in transgenic plants. The first and second mechanisms involve alteration of EPSPS either by its overproduction or by having a decreased affinity for glyphosate. The genes responsible for altered EPSPS are either of plant or bacterial origin. The third mechanism is by the introduction of a glyphosate degradation gene into transgenic plants. The primary gene for glyphosate degradation in transgenic plants is GOX.

One of the first instances of transgenic plants produced with glyphosate tolerance was in 1985 (89). Transgenic tobacco plants were produced containing the **aroA** gene driven by the octopine or mannopine synthase promoters. The **aroA** gene was isolated and conferred a mutant EPSPS enzyme from *Salmonella typhimurium* that was identified as a glyphosate-tolerant mutant (90). The nature of this mutation was a single amino acid change at position 101 from proline to serine. The **aroA** gene was also used to produce transgenic tomato plants tolerant to glyphosate (91). In both instances, transgenic plants were approximately three times more resistant to glyphosate in comparison with the nontransgenic control plants. These results were somewhat unexpected, since the native EPSPS is found in the chloroplast and the **aroA** enzyme was expressed in the cytoplasm.

Glyphosate tolerance by overexpression of EPSPS was first demonstrated in petunia by Shah et al. (92). This was achieved by expression of the chloroplast-targeted wild-type petunia EPSPS driven by the cauliflower mosaic virus 35S promoter. These transgenic plants were approximately four times more tolerant to glyphosate than the controls.

Aside from overproducing the wild-type EPSPS or expressing a mutant of this enzyme, naturally occurring glyphosate-tolerant EPSPS genes have been sought for improved Roundup® tolerance. An EPSPS referred to as CP4 gave increased tolerance to glyphosate, which was attributed to an increased catalytic efficiency in the presence of this herbicide (4). The source of the CP4 EPSPS was *Agrobacterium* sp. strain CP4. Characterization of this protein revealed that it was 47.6 kDa and a single polypeptide of 455 amino acids (4). The CP4 EPSPS was bombarded into soybean meristems, which resulted in transgenic plants that were tolerant to up to 64 ounces of Roundup® per acre (4; Fig. 2). Since EPSPS is located in the chloroplast, this level of tolerance was achieved only when the CP4 protein was directed via the chloroplast transit peptide (CTP) to this organelle. In these bombardments, selection was achieved by visual detection of GUS expression in transgenic tissues. However, use of glyphosate for selection pressure has been used to produce transgenic maize callus and plants expressing CP4.

Glyphosate tolerance by degradation has been achieved by the action of the GOX gene. The oxidation of glyphosate by transgenic plants expressing GOX results in detectable levels of AMPA. The chloroplast transit peptide (CTP) was also used to direct GOX to plastids in transgenic plants. In the case of transgenic tobacco plants containing GOX directed by CTP, glyphosate tolerance was observed in some of the plants sprayed with high levels of this herbicide (4).

Glyphosate-tolerant crops have had a profound influence on agricultural practice. The traditional use of glyphosate as a pre-emergence herbicide has changed so that it is now used both pre- and postemergence when applied to crops that are resistant to Roundup®. This was obvious by the clear acceptance of Roundup Ready® soybeans by farmers since its introduction in 1996. Demand for this product has increased annually.

The recommended use of Roundup® on Roundup Ready® soybeans first involves an application for preplant burndown. Following planting, a second application of Roundup® (32 fl. oz. per acre) is applied to the field when the weeds are 4 to 8 inches tall. This can be applied to the soybean field either pre- or postemergence. Based on farmer discretion, a second application of Roundup® may be applied (24 fl. oz. per acre) if additional weeds appear.

One of the recommended weed control systems for Roundup Ready® corn (Fig. 3) involves an application of Roundup® to the field prior to planting for early weed control (burndown). After planting, Roundup®, at 24–32 fl. oz. per acre, is applied to the field when the weeds are 1 to 4 inches. This can be applied to a corn field either pre- or

Figure 3. Improved weed control by postemergence application of Roundup® to Roundup Ready® corn plants. The rows on the right show an unsprayed control corn plants separated by a solid canopy of weeds. The rows on the left show corn plants that tolerated application of 64 ounces per acre of Roundup®. Note the dead weeds adjacent to these plants (*Source*: Photo courtesy Monsanto Ag Sector Public Affairs).

Figure 2. Roundup Ready® soybeans tolerant of 64 ounces of glyphosate per acre (*Source*: Photo courtesy of Monsanto Ag Sector Public Affairs).

postemergence. A second application of Roundup® may be necessary if additional weeds appear (at a rate of 24 to 32 ounces per acre; note—consult label for the most current application rates and directions).

One advantage of using Roundup Ready® products involves the practice of no-till planting. The advantage to the farmer is that reduced overhead costs are the result of not tilling the soil prior to planting. Instead, a preplant application of Roundup® is used for weed burndown followed by planting of the Roundup Ready® seed. Aside from the overhead savings, no-till farming is an environmental savings due to reduced soil erosion and reduced risk of soil compaction.

UTILIZATION OF HERBICIDE TOLERANCE

Production of transgenic or tissue culture variant plants that are herbicide resistant have the clear utility for improved weed control. However, there are other uses that will also have a positive impact on agriculture. In a patent application by Songstad et al. (93), a novel herbicide seed treatment was used to maintain a male sterile phenotype maize seed segregating 1:1 for resistance to GS-inhibiting herbicides, such as Basta™ (also known as Liberty) and bialaphos. Maintaining transgenic male sterile and herbicide-resistant maize is typically achieved by spraying a 1:1 segregating population with the herbicide so that the 50% of the progeny that is wild type (male fertile) will die and the transgenics (male sterile) will live. However, wind drift can result in misapplication of herbicide to nontransgenic plants, leading to reduced stand and decreased seed production. The wind drift problem is eliminated by application of the herbicide to the seed of the segregating population. This was achieved by mixing captan with Basta™ so the herbicide would stick to the maize kernels. Out of several thousand kernels evaluated, the only plants that survived this seed treatment were herbicide tolerant; there were no escapes reported in this patent.

Another use of herbicide resistance is to generate transgenic plants capable of producing an active herbicide in specific tissues. In the first instance, this was achieved by producing transgenic tobacco plants expressing a tapetum-specific deacetylase gene (94). These plants were sprayed with the inactive herbicide N-acetyl-L-phosphinothricin, which was translocated throughout the plant. However, anthers of these plants could deacetylate N-acetyl-L-phosphinothricin, rendering them male sterile through the production of phosphinothricin—the active ingredient in Liberty.

This same strategy has been used with the herbicide glyphosate. Dotson et al. (95,96) reported a phosphonate monoester hydrolase (PEH) gene from *Burkholeria caryophilli* was capable of hydrolyzing the nontoxic chemical glycerol glyphosate into the potent herbicide glyphosate. PEH can be utilized as a conditional lethal gene. For example, expression of PEH in anther tissues can be used to obliterate cells for the purpose of male sterility (96). PEH has also been proposed as a negative selection tool in homologous recombination efforts (96).

ACKNOWLEDGMENTS

I wish to thank Steve Padgette, Fritz Behr, Ken Barton, Charles Armstrong, and Jean-Noel Mutz for critical review of this article.

BIBLIOGRAPHY

1. D. Coupland, in S.B. Powles and J.A.M. Holtum, eds., *Herbicide Resistance in Plants. Biology and Biochemistry*, Lewis Publishers, Boca Raton, Fla., 1994, pp. 171–214.
2. M.D. Devine and R.H. Shimabukuro, in S.B. Powles and J.A.M. Holtum, eds., *Herbicide Resistance in Plants. Biology and Biochemistry*, Lewis Publishers, Boca Raton, Fla., 1994, pp. 141–169.
3. W.E. Dyer, in S.B. Powles and J.A.M. Holtum, eds., *Herbicide Resistance in Plants. Biology and Biochemistry*, Lewis Publishers, Boca Raton, Fla., 1994, pp. 229–241.
4. S.R. Padgette et al., in S.O. Duke, ed., *Herbicide-resistant Crops. Agricultural, Environmental, Economic, Regulatory, and Technical Aspects*, Lewis Publishers, Boca Raton, Fla., 1996, pp. 53–84.
5. P.C. Anderson and M. Georgeson, *Genome* **31**, 994–999 (1989).
6. E.B. Swanson et al., *Theor. Appl. Genet.* **78**, 525–530 (1989).
7. M. Sari Gorla, E. Ottaviano, E. Frascaroli, and P. Landi, *Sex. Plant Reprod.* **2**, 65–69 (1989).
8. T.B. Ray *Plant Physiol.* **75**, 827–831 (1984).
9. H.M. Brown and P.C. Kearney, *ACS Symp. Ser.* **443**, 32–49 (1991).
10. L.L. Saari, J.C. Cotterman, and D.C. Thill, in S.B. Powles and J.A.M. Holtum, eds., *Herbicide Resistance in Plants. Biology and Biochemistry*, Lewis Publishers, Boca Raton, Fla., 1994, p. 83–139.
11. M.V. Subramanian, V. Loney-Gallant, J.M. Dias, and L.C. Mireles, *Plant Physiol.* **96**, 310–313 (1991).
12. M.E. Fromm et al., *Bio Technology* **8**, 833–839 (1990).
13. D.D. Songstad et al., *In Vitro Cell Dev. Biol.—Plant* **32**, 179–183 (1996).
14. M.C. Giardina and S. Carosi, *Pestici. Biochem. Physiol.* **36**, 229–236 (1990).
15. G.M. Coruzzi *Plant Sci.* **74**, 145–155 (1991).
16. C. Roux, E. Delfourne, and J. Bastide, *Plant Physiol. Biochem.* **34**, 293–299 (1996).
17. C.T. Harms, A.L. Montoya, L.S. Privalle, and R.W. Briggs, *Theor. Appl. Genet.* **80**, 353–358 (1990).
18. R.S. Chaleff and T.B. Ray, *Science* **223**, 1148–1151 (1984).
19. K. Newhouse, B. Singh, D. Shaner, and M. Stidham, *Theor. Appl. Genet.* **83**, 65–70 (1991).
20. A.M.R. Baillie, B.G. Rossnagel, and K.K. Kartha, *Euphytica* **67**, 151–154 (1993).
21. S. Caretto, M.C. Giardina, C. Nicolodi, and D. Mariotti, *Theor. Appl. Genet.* **88**, 520–524 (1994).
22. E. Frascaroli and D. Songstad, "41 Convegno SIGA (Italian Society of Agricoltural Genetics)," Abbadia di Fiastra, Tolentino, 1997, p. 129.
23. A. Touraev, C.S. Fink, E. Stoger, and E. Heberle-Bors, *Proc. Natl. Acad. Sci. U.S.A.* **92**, 12165–12169 (1995).
24. Z. Li, A. Hayashimoto, and N. Murai, *Plant Physiol.* **100**, 662–668 (1992).
25. J.E. Brandle et al., *BioTechnology* **13**, 994–998 (1995).
26. E. Bayer et al., *Helv. Chim. Acta* **55**, 224–239 (1972).
27. W.J. Gordon-Kamm et al., *Plant Cell* **2**, 603–618 (1990).

28. D.A. Somers et al., *Bio Technology* **10**, 1589–1594 (1992).

29. V. Vasil, A.M. Castillo, M.E. Fromm, and I.K. Vasil, *Bio Technology* **10**, 667–675 (1992).

30. Y. Wan and P.G. Lemaux, *Plant Physiol.* **104**, 37–48 (1994).

31. F. Altpeter et al., *Plant Cell Rep.* **16**, 12–17 (1996).

32. Y. Ishida et al., *Nat. Biotechnol.* **14**, 745–750 (1996).

33. Q.A. Yao et al., *Genome* **40**, 570–581 (1997).

34. M.J. DeBlock et al., *EMBO J.* **6**, 2513–2518 (1987).

35. W. Wohlleben et al., *Gene* **70**, 25–37 (1988).

36. T.M. Spencer et al., *Plant Mol. Biol.* **18**, 201–210 (1992).

37. S. Omirulleh et al., *Plant Mol. Biol.* **21**, 415–428 (1993).

38. H.F. Kaeppler, D.A. Somers, H.W. Rines, and A.F. Cockburn, *Theor. Appl. Genet.* **84**, 560–566 (1992).

39. B.R. Frame et al., *Plant J.* **6**, 941–948 (1994).

40. Y. Ishida, T. Hiyoshi, M. Sano, and T. Kumashiro, *Plant Sci.* **63**, 227–235 (1989).

41. G. Donn, E. Tischer, J.A. Smith, and H.M. Goodman, *J. Mol. Appl. Genet.* **2**, 621–635 (1984).

42. C.J. Thompson et al., *EMBO J.* **6**, 2519–2523 (1987).

43. Y. Hoshino and M. Mii, *Plant Cell Rep.* **17**, 256–261 (1998).

44. M.B. Gonzalez-Moro et al., *J. Plant Physiol.* **142**, 161–166 (1993).

45. M.B. Lacuesta et al., *J. Plant Physiol.* **134**, 304–307 (1989).

46. J.R. Magalhaes and D.M. Huber, *J. Plant Nutr.* **14**, 883–895 (1991).

47. A. Shimada, T. Nagal, H. Seto, and Y. Kimbura, *Phytochemistry* **32**, 813–816 (1993).

48. W. Droge, I. Broer and A. Puhler, *Planta* **187**, 142–151 (1992).

49. A.R. Rendina and J.M. Felts, *Plant Physiol.* **86**, 983–986 (1988).

50. W.B. Parker et al., *Proc. Natl. Acad. Sci. U.S.A.* **87**, 7175–7179 (1990).

51. W.B. Parker et al., *Plant Physiol.* **92**, 1220–1225 (1990).

52. M.A. Egli et al., *Plant Physiol.* **101**, 499–506 (1993).

53. A.R. Ashton, C.L.D. Jenkins, and P.R. Whitfeld, *Plant Mol. Biol.* **24**, 35–49 (1994).

54. M. Bettey, R.J. Ireland, and A.M. Smith, *J. Plant Physiol.* **140**, 513–520 (1992).

55. B.S. Shorrosh, R.A. Dixon, and J.B. Ohlrogge, *Proc. Natl. Acad. Sci. U.S.A.* **91**, 4323–4327 (1994).

56. K.R. Roesler, B.S. Shorrosh, and J.B. Ohlrogge, *Plant Physiol.* **105**, 611–617 (1994).

57. W. Schulte, J. Schell, and R. Topfer, *Plant Physiol.* **106**, 793–794 (1994).

58. M.A. Egli, S.M. Lutz, D.A. Somers, and B.G. Gengenbach, *Plant Physiol.* **108**, 1299–1300 (1994).

59. J.W. Gronwald, in S.B. Powles and J.A.M. Holtum, eds., *Herbicide Resistance in Plants. Biology and Biochemistry*, Lewis Publishers, Boca Raton, Fla., 1994, pp. 27–60.

60. W. Tischer and H. Strotmann, *Biochim. Biophys. Acta* **460**, 113–125 (1977).

61. M. Sari-Gorla et al., *Euphytica* **67**, 221–230 (1993).

62. D.C. Holt et al., *Planta* **196**, 295–302 (1995).

63. R. Fonne-Pfister and K. Kreuz, *Phytochemistry* **29**, 2793–2796 (1990).

64. W.D. Beversdorf et al., *Can. J. Genet. Cytol.* **22**, 167–172 (1980).

65. A.Y. Cheung, L. Bogorad, M. Van Montagu, and J. Schell, *Proc. Natl. Acad. Sci. U.S.A.* **85**, 391–395 (1988).

66. D.M. Stalker, K.E. McBride, and L.D. Malyj, *Science* **242**, 419–423 (1988).

67. D.M. Stalker and K.E. McBride, *J. Bacteriol.* **169**, 955–960 (1987).

68. F.B. Salisbury and C.W. Ross, in F.B. Salisbury and C.W. Ross, eds., *Plant Physiology*, Wadsworth, Belmont, C.a.f., 1978, pp. 240–257.

69. K.L. Giles, J.P. Ranch, and D.D. Songstad, in J. Prakash and R.L.M. Pierik, eds., *Plant Biotechnology. Commercial Prospects and Problems*, Oxford & IBH Publishing, New Delhi, 1993, pp. 169–195.

70. B.V. Conger, L.L. Hilenski, K.W. Lowe, and J.V. Carabia, *Exp. Bot.* **22**, 39–48 (1982).

71. D.D. Songstad, C.L. Armstrong, and W.L. Petersen, *Plant Cell Rep.* **9**, 699–702 (1991).

72. H. Kende and J.A.D. Zeevaart, *Plant Cell* **9**, 1197–1210 (1997).

73. J. Normanly *Physiol. Plant.* **100**, 431–442 (1997).

74. S. Abel and A. Theologis, *Plant Physiol.* **111**, 9–17 (1996).

75. T.E. Devine et al., *Crop Sci.* **15**, 721–724 (1975).

76. S.G. Taylor, D.D. Baltensperger, and K.H. Quesenberry, *Crop Sci.* **29**, 1109–1114 (1989).

77. W.R. Streber and L. Willmitzer, *Bio Technology* **7**, 811–816 (1989).

78. B.R. Lyon et al., *Plant Mol. Biol.* **13**, 533–540 (1989).

79. C. Bayley et al., *Theor. Appl. Genet.* **83**, 645–649 (1992).

80. J.E. Franz, in E. Grossbard and D. Atkinson, eds., *The Herbicide Glyphosate*, Butterworth, London, 1985, pp. 3–17.

81. L. Torstensson, in E. Grossbard and D. Atkinson, eds., *The Herbicide Glyphosate*, Butterworth, London, 1985, pp. 137–150.

82. S.B. Powles, D.F. Lorraine-Colwill, J.J. Dellow, and C. Preston, *Weed Sci.* **46**, 604–607 (1998).

83. P. Binarova et al., *Biol. Plant.* **36**, 65–73 (1994).

84. E.D. Nafziger, J.M. Widholm, H.C. Steinrucken, and J.L. Killmer, *Plant Physiol.* **76**, 571–574 (1984).

85. G. Forlani, E. Nielsen, and M.L. Racchi, *Plant Sci.* **85**, 9–15 (1992).

86. W.E. Dyer, S.C. Weller, R.A. Bressan, and K.M. Herrmann, *Plant Physiol.* **88**, 661–666 (1988).

87. J.D. Jones, P.B. Goldsbrough, and S.C. Weller, *Plant Cell Rep.* **15**, 431–436 (1996).

88. Y.Y.J. Shyr, S. Caretto, and J.M. Widholm, *Plant Sci.* **88**, 219–228 (1993).

89. L. Comai et al., *Nature (London)* **317**, 741–744 (1985).

90. L. Comai, L. Sen, and D.M. Stalker, *Science* **221**, 370–371 (1983).

91. J.J. Fillatti, J. Kiser, R. Rose, and L. Comai, *Bio Technology* **5**, 726–730 (1987).

92. D.M. Shah et al., *Science* **233**, 478–481 (1986).

93. U.S. Pat. 5,717,129 (February 10, 1998), D.D. Songstad, S.J. Corak, D.A. Pierce, and M. Albertsen (to Pioneer Hi-Bred Intl. Inc.).

94. G. Kriete et al., *Plant J.* **9**, 809–818 (1996).

95. S. Dotson et al., *J. Biol. Chem.* **271**, 25754–25761 (1996).

96. S. Dotson, M.B. Lanahan, A.G. Smith, and G.M. Kishore, *Plant J.* **10**, 383–392 (1996).

See also Disease resistance in transgenic plants; Toxin resistant plants from plant cell culture and transformation; Transformation of plants; Virus removal from plants.

HISTORY OF ANIMAL CELL TECHNOLOGY

R.E. Spier
University of Surrey
Guildford, Surrey
United Kingdom

OUTLINE

Buried in the history of a subject are the messages and lessons of our predecessors. From the questions they asked, the information or evidence they amassed, and the critical and creative imagination they brought to bear, we can discern the thrusts of their endeavors and the factors that motivated their strivings. In this section of the Encyclopedia, I will seek to expose these efforts in the area of animal cell technology and to distill, from them ideas and concepts that may yet be of value to workers in the contemporary world. Such understandings will also provide an appreciation of the intellectual and practical platforms on which we are presently building for our future well-being.

A variety of themes provide a plexus for this story. Most living organisms directly or indirectly exploit the cellular mode of being; how did this happen and what are the connections between cellularity and life? In coming to an appreciation of the nature of the cellularity of living organisms, how did developments in the knowledge base (science) interact with parallel advances in technical capabilities (engineering)? In this we can discern both the way advances in instrumentation have led to increases in knowledge and how developments in the application of animal cells to useful ends have also extended our appreciation of cellular biochemistry and physiology. Or, how did the incomplete concepts of both animal and plant cells come together to provide a more comprehensive appreciation of both cell types? In this latter event, we have a strong justification for treating animal and plant cell technology as a single subject to be covered in a single encyclopedic work.

There is also a human story which cannot be severed from these writings. In the history of the way came to our contemporary ideas about the cell and its origins, some individuals rose to considerable fame and fortune, and others, perhaps even more deserving of recognition and plaudits, have been consigned to the backwaters or even ignored. Then, as now, bitter rivalries prevailed. Nationalistic pride and linguistic ignorance distorted the reporting of discoveries, and those in charge of the media (books, scientific journals, archives, reviews etc.) were able to both promote themselves and their allies. A quotation from Lucretius (98–55 B.C.E., Rome: *De Rerum Natura*; Book V) illustrates this point:

> So it would be a better thing by far
> To serve than rule; let others sweat themselves
> Into exhaustion, jamming that defile
> They call ambition, since their wisdom comes
> Always from other's mouths, and all their trust
> Is put in hearsay; when do they believe
> Their own good sense and feelings? Never, never.

Indeed this history raises serious issues that we have not yet satisfactorily resolved. How do we assign credit to the discoverers of a particular long-lived and highly valued concept of the way nature is constructed and works? We often neglect to mention the people who worked on perfecting the instruments and techniques without which it would have been physically impossible to see and infer the structure of the cell and the way it divides. How do we appraise the individuals who "have the idea first," "who communicate the idea first," "who write down the idea first," "who, through observation and experiment, provide evidence that the idea can withstand practical testing," "who report such tests and make firm (if not categorical) statements about the nature of the world outside?" Although some of the studies were effected by scientists who were independently wealthy, most were done by people struggling in the quagmire of university structures that were primarily set up to deliver people educated for the church, medicine, and law. Their ambition contained visions of a high position in a university hierarchy, the respect of a society of peers recognition in the writings of others working in the same field and of making that discovery that would stand out as a change or shift in the conventional paradigm (1) thus giving rise to new ways of thinking and conceptualizing the world. How these studies were to influence thinking about deeper or religious issues was not necessarily at the forefront minds of the investigators of yesteryears. Before the twentieth century, the universities of Europe required members of their staffs to swear oaths of allegiance and profession to the religious system prevailing at their institutions. But an intellectual tradition of enquiry, experiment, and rational empiricism was able to develop and provide the basis on which we are erecting our future world.

In the following subdivisions of this section, I examine how the concept or theory of the cellular nature of living organisms emerged which then enables, the story of how cells could have come into being some 4 billion years ago. This is followed by an account of how cells came to be grown in culture and eventually used to generate valued products.

THE EMERGENCE OF THE CONCEPT OF A CELL

The divisibility of natural objects has ever occupied the minds of the most profound thinkers. Today's philosophers grapple with issues related to hypothetical entities called "strings" and attempt to relate them to the subdivisions of matter that can be made in the atom-smashers built at great public expense (2). Living objects have been subject to an equivalent scrutiny, the outcome of which established the concept of a "cell."

PREPARING THE MIND

Humans, uniquely, have asked question about the nature of their being and the composition and workings of the world around them. They have used the answer to enunciate statements, codes, or laws intended to modulate their behavior. Two issues were prominent in early discussions. The first concerned questions as to whether all observable objects were made from a continuum or were composed of discrete, separable elements? And the second asked whether life could emerge spontaneously from inanimate entities or was, of necessity, a product of other living beings? If the latter were to be the case, then it would only be necessary to explain the origin of the first living being. The former question will be dealt with first and the latter will be treated later.

Aristotle (384–322 B.C.E., Stagira Thessaloniki; Physics Book VI) stated that time, lines, motions, and magnitudes are continuous; their elements are not divisible, and there is nothing between the elements other than the elements themselves. This is in contrast to the atomic theory of Leucippus (circa. 440 B.C.E. of Miletus, a Greek city-port which used to be on the southern bank of the estuary of the Menderes River in Turkey) who conjectured that a void exists between indivisible elements (the atoms). These ideas were further promulgated and extended by Democritus (460–370 B.C.E. of Abdera near Kavalla, Greece) who regarded atoms as innumerable tiny particles, homogeneous in substance, infinitely various in shape and size, compact, unmodifiable operating in infinitely empty space (3), (4). The atomic theme was taken up by Lucretius in his De Rerum Natura. His fully and well-reasoned position on this issue, expressed in poetic hexameters, has a contemporary feel; it also echoes and amplifies the concepts of Leucippus and Democritus. As Aristotelian thinking dominated thought well into the Middle Ages, ideas that living beings could be composed of discrete indivisible elements were not encouraged. But

in the seventeenth century both Descartes (1596–1650, born in France, lived in Holland) and Newton (1642–1727, Cambridge and London) adopted the atomic model to explain the workings of nature. Such ideas developed into an entirely mechanistic vision of the way both animate and inanimate objects worked, except that for humans the possession of a "soul" provided an additional feature that linked them to choice, free will, and a God. Nevertheless, in the mid seventeenth century these views prevailed, and because they gave rise to a sense that much more about the world could be discovered if we had the investigative means, they set the scene for the emergence of the cellular theory of life.

DEVELOPMENTS IN MICROSCOPY

The first recorded use of a lens in 424 B.C.E., turns up in Aristophanes' (445–388 B.C.E., Athens) play, The Clouds, where Strepsiades asks Socrates, "You must have seen at the druggist's the stone, pretty, transparent, to kindle fire with?" Subsequently, both Artistotle and Euclid discovered the properties of reflective mirrors of different shapes, but the most extensive and ancient work on reflection and refraction was effected by Ptolemy (70–circa. 141 A.D., Alexandria) although his work in this area was not taken up till the nineteenth century (5). Other observations of classical authors such as Seneca (5–65 A.D.) provided evidence that the magnifying capability of rounded, water-filled transparent objects could be most useful as a reading aid. Roger Bacon (1214–1292, Oxford) is held to have constructed spectacles based on plano-convex lenses. So, by the close of the sixteenth century and the beginning of the seventeenth, many individuals in Holland, Italy, and England were engaged in using lenses to look at small objects, mainly insects. The word "microscopio" was coined by Giovani Fabri, a member of the Academi of the Lincei in 1625 (6), but it was in 1656 that the word. "microscope" first appeared in English (7).

Looking backward, it is clear that the Jansen family of Middleburg, Holland, made microscopes before the year 1590 (8). And Galileo (1564–1642, Florence and Padua) was using lenses for telescopes and microscopes from the year 1609, a year after Johannes Lippershey, an optictian also of Middleburg, petitioned the states-general of the Low Countries to manufacture a lens-based instrument for increasing the apparent size of remote objects (9). In 1646, M. Fontana of Naples wrote that he had invented the compound microscope in 1618 using two convex lenses mounted in a copper tube 18 inches long. Yet we have the claims of Cornelius Brebell, a Dutchman resident in the English court that he made the first compound microscope in 1621. While these contestants for the honor of being the first to invent the gateway into the heretofore invisible world of the minuscle were making their several claims, it is of note to realize that in the medieval world, communications were problematic in terms of the time and reliability of delivery services. Working independently, each individual thought they had an edge. But in terms of the advances in the competence of humans to engage in examining a new facet of their unfolding world, both the lens makers and the users of the lenses (sometimes one and the same, as in the case of Galileo) were the people who were responsible for the advances; the individuation of the events is just as much a product of the circumstances of the person, as well as their dexterity and brilliance of mind.

The causal chain that led Antoni van Leeuwenhoek (1632–1723, Delft) to discover the *animalcules* we now include in the bacteria and protista illustrates how situation plus personal attributes combine to make the breakthroughs we need to advance. Trained to be a linendraper in Amsterdam, Leeuwenhoek set up a draper/haberdashery business in Delft in 1654 (10). For such a business, the use of magnifying lenses would have provided commercially sensitive information about the quality of the fabrics which he was engaged in buying and selling. (This author's father was similarly engaged and was never without a 10× mounted lens secreted in a waistcoat pocket.) Clearly, the more powerful the lens, the greater the value of the information that could be obtained. This may explain how Leeuwenhoek came to learn how to make lenses of high magnification from M. Hartsoeker (according to R. Hooke as published in his *Micrographia Illustrata* of 1656 (see Ref. 8, p. 4) or from J. Hudde (as per Harris, Ref. 6), p. 15). He developed the techniques of shaping and polishing glass drops to a fine art whose details he never disclosed. Nevertheless, with one such lens held in a device that enabled the mounting of a specimen on the tip of a needle held millimeters from the extremities of the lens, he was able to obtain magnifications of 100× to 300× (although he would have had to use some clever illumination technique to see bacteria at this magnification). From his observations (communicated in Dutch by letter to the Royal Society of London), he concluded that all animal matter was composed of globules. This was supported by a comment in a letter written in 1675 by C. Huygens (1629–1695, The Hague) "...our Mr Leeuwenhoek turns everything into little balls."

Hooke, working at the Royal Society in the 1650s as curator of experiments, directed his newly designed compound microscope to the examination of thin sections of cork. Here, in 1655, he saw cells. (The word 'cell' comes from the Latin *cella* which denotes a small underground chamber used by the Romans for the storage of the wine or foods they wished to keep cool.) During the same period, M. Malpighi (1628–1694, Rome) and N. Grew (1641–1712, London) were working with microscopes on the structures of living tissues, the former on plants and animals, whereas the latter concentrated on plants. As a result of work with both sorts of tissues, Malphigi referred to the xylem in plants as trachea because it resembled that tissue in animals. During such studies, the round objects viewed by these early microscopists were called by a wide variety of terms which included utriculi (small bottles of skin), sacculi (small bottles for straining liquids), globules, vesicles, bubbles, corpuscles, granules (Körnen), Kugle (spheroid), Kugelchen (vesicle), Körnchen (small grain or granule), Körperchen, Zellen, balls, etc.

For the next 150 or so years (1670–1820), there were few, if any, conceptual advances of note with regard to the basic elemental structure of living organisms. K. Wolff (1733–1794), drawing on the diagrams of Grew and

Malphigi, as well as his own work, concluded that all tissues were made up of globules which he sometimes called cells. In 1823, H. Milne-Edwards (1800–1885, Bruge, Paris) wrote that all animal tissues are composed of a concatenation of small uniform globules of 1/300-mm diameter (3.3 μ), and to see them he used one of the first achromatic compound microscopes made by Adams (10). Others were developing achromatic lenses at the same time, and much of the credit for such devices may be attributed to J.J. Lister (1786–1869, Upton) who not only constructed such lenses and used them in microscopes, but in 1830, he developed and published the theory on which they might be based. In this he showed that both chromatic and spherical aberration could be corrected by using a compound lens. This departure gave renewed energy to a surge of studies on the structure and function of animal and plant tissues, as evidenced by the construction of an achromatic lens microscope by Simon Plossl (Vienna) in 1832 which in the hands of J.E. Purkyně (1787–1869, Libochowitz and Wroclaw) and his group led to many further discoveries. Among these were the development of the microtome by G.G. Valentin (1810–1883), as well as methods for fixation, embedding, staining, and mounting preparations; Purkyně also used daguerreotypes for the first time. The new microscopes of Pistor and Schiek of Berlin made in 1836 (6, p.26), in the hands of T. Schwann (1812–1822, Berlin) and M. Schleiden (1804–1881, Hamburg) also enabled those protagonists to offer both considered and contentious views as to the nature of cells and the way they divide.

Yet further developments of the microscope were in hand when E. Abbé (1840–1905, Jena) invented the condenser to provide strong illumination to the specimen (1870) and the oil immersion lens to achieve higher magnifications as a consequence of the higher refractive index of oil vis-à-vis air although the prior development of such a lens in 1840 by G.B. Amici (1786–1863, Modena) is to be noted (6, p.85). Furthermore, Abbé produced the first distortion free lenses (apochromatic) that permitted achieving the maximum theoretical resolving power (0.2 μ) of the optical microscope. In 1896, he reorganized the Zeiss optical works as a cooperative where the workers, managers, and the university shared in the profits.

The need to "see" specimens at higher levels of magnification, that were as "native" as possible prompted yet further developments. With the development of the built-in light source (complete with filter and diaphragm) in 1934, phase-contrast microscopy made its first appearance. Also in the early 1930s both scanning and transmission electron microscopes, were invented and developed. They provided a theoretical resolution of some 10,000 times greater than the light microscope, but in practice only a 100-fold increase in magnification (to 0.002 μm) is routinely obtained (11). Dark-field, fluorescent, confocal, cine, and video (with image enhancement) microscopy were also developed, culminating in the awesome ability of the atomic force microscope (invented in 1986 by G. Binnig, C.F. Quate, and C. Gerber) to examine the anatomy and physiology of a single unstained molecule of a biopolymer (12,13)

It is clear that as each advance in the tools used to examine the details of living material becomes available, there are *subsequent* discoveries of the way cells and their components work. This, in turn, inspires the instrument makers and inventors to further develop their arts and theories as to how it might be possible to achieve further progress. From iterative oscillations between the tool users and the toolmakers, we build the physical and intellectual structures of the modern and future worlds.

CELLS AS THE BASIC UNITS OF LIVING BEINGS

Knowing what we are, is a basis on which we can build our ideas as to how we should behave. Developments in microscopy, as recounted above, provided an avenue to such discoveries. The issues that occupied the microscopists of the middle to late nineteenth century revolved about the universality of the cell as the basic unit of animal and plant tissue, the nature of the cell nucleus and nucleolus, how cells divided, and what was at the boundary between cells. The schematic outline of some of these discoveries presented below is not intended to be fully comprehensive or to include all those who made contributions (see Ref. 6 for a fuller rendition). Rather, the main messages of the way discoveries are made and credit assigned are portrayed. The lessons that can be learned from this history will also be discussed.

Following the 1704 use of the word "nucleus" (Latin; *nucleus*, nut, kernel, innerpart) to describe the center of a comet, R. Brown (1773–1858, London) availed himself of the same word to describe a common feature of all of the plant cells that he studied. He reported this at a meeting of the Linnean Society in 1831. Some four years later, R. Wagner described a nucleus within a nucleus or nucleolus in Graffian follicle of sheep. Although binary fission of polyp cells had been described in 1747 by A. Trembley (1710–1784, Geneva), O.F. Muller in his 1756 book on infusoria noted the binary fission of microscopic green algae and fresh water flagellates. This was followed up (1832) by B. Dumortier (1797–1878, Belgium) who discovered and published work showing that the apical cells of the alga *Conferva aurea* (silkweeds) divide by binary fission. However, the priority for this latter discovery was claimed by H. von Mohl (1805–1872, Stuttgart, Tubingen) who examined *Conferva glomerata*, but this work was published in 1835. Again, in 1846, von Mohl may have overstepped the mark in seeming to have been the first to use the word "protoplasma" to describe the contents of the cell, because Purkyně had already coined that term in 1840 (6, p. 64 *et seq.*).

It is widely held, that the theory of the cellularity of living organisms, both animal and plant, was first proposed in a substantive manner by Schleiden and Schwann. Having been advised about 1835 of the similarity between the cells of the notochord of a developing frog and plant cells by J. Muller (1801–1858, Berlin) and stimulated by conversations with Schleiden, Schwann published a major work in 1839 entitled "*Mikroskpische Untersuchungen uber dei Uebereinstimmung in der Struktur und dem Wachsthum der Thiere und Pflanzen.*" In this work he emphasizes the commonality of the cell as the structural unit of both animals and plants and asserts that this is based, not so much on the microscopic resemblance of animal and plant cells, as on the similar way in which these cells divide. In this he was much influenced by Schleiden who had the notion that cells were built about nuclei (cytoblasts) and the latter were formed *de novo* by a process akin to crystallization around a precrystallized nucleolus (6, p. 97 *et seq.*) formed in the granular material that exists in the space between existing cells. Now we believe that neither of these notions is representative of the way cells divide, so the attribution of the cellular theory of living organisms to the above investigators may be a serious misjudgment.

That cells are the common and basic units of animal and plant life was enunciated by many researchers before the publication of Schwann's book. In 1805 L. Oken (Okenfuss, 1779–1851, Jena and Zurich) had the idea that all large animal and plants are made of aggregates of cooperating "infusoria" or free living cellular creatures. F.V. Raspail (1794–1878, Paris), using a microscope made by Deleuil of Paris, made many observations on animal cells and in 1825 concluded that "*Omnis cellula e cellula*" (every cell is derived from another cell). This expression was also used in 1858 by R. Virchow (1821–1902, Swidwin, Berlin), to whom this assertion is usually attributed. He also used chemical reagents to stain the components of frozen tissues. Some nine years later, Purkyně's student Valentin submitted a prize essay to the Institut de France in 1834 in which he spelled out in detail the parallelism between animal and plant cells. This work (1,000 pages) was not published nor was a 300 page revision, although the former work was cited by von Humboldt in 1836. So, it is clear that both Purkyně and Valentin were teaching that animals and plants were both made up of cellular entities, and this was several years before Schwann's famous publication. Also, in 1837 H. DuTrochet (1776-1847, Paris) wrote that "Life is one." "... everything is ultimately derived from the cell"; there are cells of different sizes and these constitute the basic units for metabolic exchange. He described and named the process of osmosis and noticed that cells exchanged materials with the external world via the processes of endosmosis and exosmosis across a semipermeable membrane.

Opposition to Schleiden's concept of cell division was not long in developing. In 1844, F. Unger (1800–1870, Vienna) disposed of the idea that cytoblasts (nuclei) are the source of new cells. This work, further developed by R. Remak (1815–1865, Posen and Berlin), repudiated the formation of cytoblasts in the extracellular fluids, denied the existence of naked nuclei (1852), and noted that in some animal tissues, nucleated mother cells partitioned into two nucleated daughter cells (1845). In 1848, W. Hofmeister (1824–1877, Lindenau, Tubingen) described how the plant nucleus divided and recognized the presence of certain "Klumpen" (discrete bodies) that separated into two massess; in this discovery he defined all but one (telophase) of the phases of mitosis. He also noted that in the germinal cells, each of the daughter gametes received half the number of Klumpen. A follow-up to this was the discovery in 1869/74 that the nucleus is the unique residence for nucleic acids (J.F. Miescher (1844–1895, Basel, Tubingen). The process of ordinary cell division was called "mitosis" by W.Flemming (1843–1905, Keil) who also noted the longitudinal splitting of the "threads." Later in 1888, H..W.G. Waldeyer-Harz (Berlin) proposed the word "chromosome" to replace the panoply of terms then in use. And it was left to W. Roux (1850–1924, Wroclow) to propose in 1883 that, on a theoretical basis, each of the chromosomes carries a panoply of hereditary determinants. That these determinants could be transferred between bacteria was discovered by the English microbiologist, F. Griffith, in 1928 when he showed that nonvirulent strains of bacteria become genetically changed to virulence when exposed to heat-killed virulent strains (14). But it was left to the Americans, O.T. Avery, C.M. MacLeod, and M. McCarty, to show, in 1944, that the material that carries the hereditary determinants is the nucleic acid, DNA (15).

Readers will notice that although German researchers have been credited with many of the new discoveries about the nature of cells and the way they divide, workers in many other European countries discovered much of this new information, often before their German counterparts. Harris (6) examines this issue in some detail and concludes that it is the manner of presentation of the material, as well as omissions in crediting the prior discoverers that has led to this situation. National chauvinism may be held responsible in the development of such practices. Whether we, as humans, are better served by such outright competitiveness or whether progress would be faster and more advantageous were more cooperative practices that entail appropriate recognition adopted, is a debate which is yet ongoing. Indeed, the outcome of this discussion may have components of both practices conjoined in an overarching structure that controls the areas and degrees of competitiveness and recognition to achieve the most beneficial results.

THE FIRST CELLS

Having recognized the almost universal association between living beings and cells, it is heuristic to consider how cells came into being, how they relate life to and how such understanding might inform our current need to work with living cells to generate goods and services for the benefit of humans and animals.

ON VARIOUS BEGININGS

Paleontological evidence of cellular structures in rocks some 3.5 billion years old means that cellularity followed relatively closely on the consolidation of the early earth about 4.6 billion years ago (16). It is generally held that for the first 0.6 billion years of the earth's existence, conditions that might have provided the cradle for life and living cells were precluded. During this period of intense volcanic activity, violent climate perturbations due to comet collisions and high levels of radioactivity, the temperatures at the surface of this nascent planet were in excess of those that would enable the formation of seas and oceans of water. However, following a cooling off period, it is clear that in the 500-million-year period between 4 to 3.5 billion years ago, life and cells arose

then from the otherwise inanimate materials that made up the surface materials of this planet. Indeed the first evidence of the activity of living organisms may be dated to 3.85 billion years ago (17). This requires that life did form spontaneously and that the adage *omnium vivum ex viva* (all life comes from life) is not a trustworthy reflection of events (*pace* Pasteur). (Were cellular life forms, borne on a comet or meteor, to have infected earth from another part of the universe, we would still be left with the need to explain how that cellular life arose from the inanimate material of its parent body.)

As our burgeoning knowledge of the conditions of early earth unfolds, the prospects of constructing a plausible and testable story that accounts for the origin of life and cells becomes more feasible. So, although attempts to achieve such a synthesis were discouraged by Pasteur's famous (1864) experiment (he invented an open swan-necked flask that maintained a rich culture medium in a sterile condition indefinitely and so demonstrated that life could come only from another living form), it was not until the 1920s that this position was seriously challenged by Oparin (1924) and Haldane (1929). And we had to wait till 1952 for the Miller–Urey experiment that showed that organic materials could be formed from simple inorganic precursors under appropriate conditions. (Many of the original papers of these and other seminal thinkers on the origin of life can be found in Deamer and Fleischaker (18).) This latter experiment became a turning point in origin-of-life studies because it led to a plethora of further discoveries and inventions that in turn have fueled speculation and critical examination of the concepts that may be adduced to bear upon the way life and cells began. These have given rise to a voluminous literature on the origin of life well summarized in the recent editions of the Encyclopaedia Britannica. However, my purpose in this Encyclopedia is to examine the origin of life in the context of the cell. This departure from most other renditions of this subject leads me to contend that *were it not for cells, life may not have started*. What follows is a compilation of the evidence and ideas (some of which are guesses) that gives me confidence in presenting a somewhat different approach to cells, life, and their origins.

LIFE THEN CELLS OR CELLS THEN LIFE?

One may consider a definition of a cell (in a biological context) as a small entity, normally between 0.1 to 100 μ in diameter, that provides an enclosed space. Life is more difficult to define because some individuals seek to associate immaterial properties (spirits, souls, life forces) to living organisms (vitalism). If we do *not* do this, then a starting definition of life could take the form of—"*a living organism is an entity which "seeks" (happens) to reproduce itself such that deviations in the reproductive process may be carried through into subsequent generations.*" (In this expression the word "seeks" has the meaning "*has the particular physical and chemical properties that, in the presence of the appropriate materials, spontaneously results in a reaction.*") This allows for the inclusion of viruses, seeds and other dormant or nondividing forms, because they may be thought of as entities that while yet seeking to reproduce themselves, have used a technique to permit them to survive inclement conditions or to enable them to move to a more propitious environment. It also moves such entities into the realms where the "Natural Selection of the Fittest" can occur (Darwin and Wallace, 1858; Spencer 1864); this provides the driving force that has transformed the living systems of 4 billion years ago into those that inhabit planet earth at this time, including humans.

Since the discoveries of Griffiths, Avery et al., and Crick and Watson (see above), we have come to believe that properties of self-replication with the faithful copying of mistakes can be most convincingly demonstrated only in the class of molecules called nucleic acids. Because it has also been shown that the ribose nucleic acids (RNAs) have enzymatic properties (19), much attention has been focused on them as the molecules that may have been the first to express the properties of life; hence their establishment of an RNA world. Incorporation of the more stable genetic material of the deoxyribose nucleic acids (DNAs) is generally thought to have arrived later. Because the origin of life may be envisaged as a molecular event its origin does not, in principle, require the presence of cells. However, it is also clear that for simple and dilute solution chemistry with molecules that are less than stable, rapidly oscillating physical conditions and circumstances where hydrolysis is favored over condensation is a less than salubrious environment in which to postulate the presence of the first molecules that expressed the property of life. So, were cells a necessary component of the system whereby living molecules came into being?

MESSAGES FROM CONTEMPORARY CELLS

Before we can consider the properties of a putative primordial cell, it is useful to survey some of the relevant parameters that could affect such thinking. Cells in the contemporary world are surrounded by a double layer of phospholipids, in which a wide variety of glyco- and lipo proteins are embedded. Eukaryotic cells have cholesterol as part of the lipid bilayer, but prokaryotes do not. In the absence of constraints, cells are spherical because this is the minimum energy structure whereby the smallest surface area surrounds contains the maximum volume.

Phospholipids are amphipathic structures that can react with ionized molecules and atoms through ionized phosphate groups, and at the same time, the lipid portion of the molecule can dissolve in other lipids. In this way the phospholipid can bridge between the world of the hydrophilic (lipophobic) ionized and charged molecules and atoms and the uncharged and water-insoluble lipid world (hydrophobic or lipophilic). The phospholipids of the cells we observe today are based on glycerol. Two fatty acids with 10–20 carbon atoms and a variable number of double bonds replace the first and second hydroxyls of the glycerol, and on the third arm of the glycerol is an adduct such as phosphoryl choline or phosphoryl ethanolamine or simply phosphoric acid. The ions commonly found in association with negatively charged phosphate groups are bivalent calcium^{2+} and magnesium^{2+}, as well as univalent sodium^{1+} and potassium^{1+} ions. Chloride^{1-} is the main univalent ion associated with positively charged groups such as choline.

The proteins that are associated with such bilipid membranes are located on the outside or inside of the membrane, or they traverse across the membrane and link the external to the internal worlds. Those parts of the protein that make contact with the lipid part of the membrane are mainly the lipophilic aminoacids, valine, alanine, leucine, isoleucine, and phenylalanine. Those proteins that traverse the membrane may do so via multiple loops of primarily lipophilic aminoacids (10 such traverses are not uncommon) and groups of five or so such molecules may gang together to form a "pore" in the membrane whose internal composition determines the ions/molecules for which that pore is selectively permeable. The carbohydrate residues attached to the protein are located either on the outside or inside parts of the protein and are not involved in the lipid bilayer. Proteins and their derivatives may move in the plane of the membrane, and higher temperatures enhance that motion.

Vesicles made of such lipid bilayers fuse readily with other such vesicles, in which case the membranes amalgamate and merge. Additional lipidic material may be added into the membrane at any time and place. When the surface has expanded and the dynamics of the movement of internal and external fluids creates conditions where the enlarged cell becomes unstable, the cell may split into two or more subcells and begin the accretion and growth process again. It is possible to make such vesicles in the modern laboratory from lipids such as lecithin and surfactant molecules such as Triton X; they are called liposomes. When they are made in the presence of other molecules such as viral antigens or nucleic acids, the vesicles that form contain the adventitious molecules within the lipid bilayer (or multiples thereof). Consequently, they find uses in preparing vaccine adjuvants and in transportation systems that seek to implant molecules of DNA into cells for the purpose of genetically engineering those cells.

WHAT CAN CELLS (AS SUCH) BRING TO THE TABLE?

The cell provides an enclosed space. Movement of materials between the external world and the internal space is restricted and/or controlled. The boundary layer creates a phase shift in that it is a solid (an ordered array of molecules), whereas the external world is liquid and disordered. The following are a result of this separation of an enclosed space.

- It is possible to create a concentration gradient for one or other molecular species across the membrane. This can lead to the increased or decreased (by specific exclusions or excretions) concentrations of particular molecular or ionic species within the cell.

- An osmotic pressure is a consequence of this concentration gradient.

- A membrane is also capable of generating an electrical charge difference between the internal and external worlds. This charge may migrate as adjacent regions of the membrane polarize and depolarize.

- A concentration gradient across a membrane is a way in which energy can be stored. Typically, a hydrogen ion gradient across a lipid bilayer membrane is the basis of the generation, storage and use of energy in all biology systems.

- Small molecules and ions will traverse a lipid bilayer when there are some 10 or so carbon atoms in the lipid components, but polymers of such molecules will not pass this bilayer. This means that polymers are more likely to be stable within a cell because the relative effective concentration of water for hydrolysis is lower than in the external world. (Some of the internal water would be bound into the electrostatic double layer which surrounds charged ions and molecules.)

- The surfaces created by the lipid bilayer enable the concentration of particular molecular species as a result of the charge disproportionation which is found at the surface. It could lead to the activation and reaction of such concentrated molecules as if it were a nonspecific catalyst. It could also aid in the removal of the elements of water in reactions where the condensation of two molecular species requires that elimination.

- The lipid bilayer can act as an anchor for the lipophilic portions of proteins and proteinoids in which case it may act as the support for a system of immobilized and diverse catalysts.

- By regulating the passage of materials across the membrane, it is possible to **control** the composition of the internal environment vis-à-vis the external surroundings. This means that fluctuations in the external world can be prevented from causing corresponding perturbations in the internal world of the cell. This in turn provides stability and protection to the molecular species so sequestered.

- The lipid bilayer membrane can provide an environment in which lipophilic molecules such as the porphyrins may dissolve and create electron or charge gradients under the influence of the capture of light energy.

- By synchronizing the flow of membrane material in relation to external objects, it is possible to engender cell motility.

- In the event that contiguous vesicles do not fuse on contact, it is possible to develop molecule selective pores or junctions to act a gates between the two compartments.

- Membranes around cells allow for cell growth by accretion and the division of such cells via a budding process or binary fission.

This welter of properties could provide a basis that enabled a subset of molecules to acquire the necessary attributes to live.

WHAT CAN A PRIMORDIAL ENVIRONMENT OFFER?

There is much speculation as to the nature of the primordial environment that existed 4 billion years ago. The recent (1979) discovery of deep sea volcanoes (hydrothermal vents) that provide aqueous and sulfurous environments at temperatures in excess of 300 °C in which living organisms thrive, has supported evidence for emergence of life on earth that was neither cool nor free of poisonous materials such as hydrogen sulfide. Yet such temperatures lead to the rapid breakdown of unprotected organic molecules (20). Additionally, analysis of meteors has revealed that organic molecules may be formed in all regions of the universe. It is also alleged that much of the carbon of the earth is as a result of its transportation by meteors and comets. Nevertheless, the discharge from contemporary volcanoes contains much carbon dioxide, carbon monoxide, nitrogen, water, sulfur, and hydrogen sulfide, so that the presence of such molecules on the primitive earth is likely to have been plentiful. The amount of oxygen in the atmosphere was virtually zero at this time. What is also likely is that climatic conditions fluctuated widely and that water was a crucial component of the earth's surface when life began. Such water may have been boiled off and recondensed many times over, in addition, there may have been locations where masses of water existed in relative stability. Under conditions of rapidly varying temperatures and water activities, unprotected organic polymers such as the nucleic acids are not stable.

Since the Miller–Urey (1953) experiment, the subject of prebiotic or abiotic chemistry has proceeded apace. Beginning with mixtures of the inorganic molecules delineated above and adding catalysts (montmorillonite clay or such), energy (electrical sparks, heat, pressure, impact), and water, it has been possible to produce a wide range of organic molecules. The amino acids glycine, alanine, glutamic, and aspartic acids tend to predominate in the amino acid class whereas formaldehyde, hydrogen cyanide, cyanamide, and carbodiimide are important monomers for the formation of carbohydrates and purines. Such abiotic syntheses have also produced such complex molecules as porphyrins (21,22).

In 1924 Oparin published his first book on the origin of life. In later works (1936, etc.) he quotes the work of Bungenberg de Jong (23) who coined the term "coacervates" to describe the globular materials of the colloid-rich region which forms when a colloid suspension spontaneously separates out into colloid-rich and colloid-poor regions. Such globules could be formed from hydrophilic, hydrophobic, organic, or inorganic materials. Solutions of 0.001% gelatin may form such coacervates and effectively concentrate the gelatin in the colloid-rich layer. Gelatin will also form coacervates with carbohydrate polymers such as gum arabic, gum acacia, araban, and agar, as well as various starches (24). Having shown that mixtures of amino acids will polymerize to produce proteinoids when heated to 170 °C (25,26). Fox, in 1958, went on to convert molten mixtures of amino acids to hollow proteinaceous spheres by placing the hot melt in boiling water (27). Many researchers have worked with such proteinoid spheres and have shown that they embody many of the properties of modern biotic cells listed above. Furthermore, parallel investigations have sought to show that such materials could well have been components of the prebiotic environment on the early earth. The one reservation I would note in placing such proteinoid spheres on the pathway to living organisms is that all modern cells boast a bilayer membrane of phospholipid and not protein.

If the molecules associated with life in our modern world are to serve as guidelines for postulates as to how life began, then we have to look in more detail at how the primordial world could have provided these needed substrates. And as all modern cells are based on a phospholipid bilayer semipermeable membrane, then this is one of the molecules whose origin is of crucial significance. The demonstration of the abiotic synthesis of glycerol, glycerol phosphate, fatty acids, and phospholipids has been achieved.

Glycerol is formed from the condensation of formaldehyde and acetaldehyde, a reaction that is common to the formation of sugars and is catalyzed by divalent metal oxides (28,29). Fatty acids and fatty aldehydes derive from the reductive (hydrogen-based) polymerization of carbon monoxide in the presence of cobalt or iron catalysts via a Fischer-Tropsch synthesis. It may be conjectured that an admixture of steam and burning carbon (initially derived from the extraterrestrial objects which condensed to form the early earth (30)) under conditions similar to those of a hydrothermal vent could have produced carbon monoxide and hydrogen in the presence of range of divalent metal ions (echoed by the late nineteenth century process for producing water gas), that could be polymerized to the fatty acids and aldehydes that subsequently rose to the surface of the prevailing waters. The phosphate component of the phospholipid could have been derived from inorganic phosphate deposits. Most of the earth's phosphate rock is in the form of calcium hydroxyapaptite ($Ca_5(PO_4)_3OH$) which is also a major component of animal bones. Such rocks are found in localized deposits on the seabed off the north coast of Africa and adjacent to the southern coasts of North America. The reaction of such rocks with acidic materials results in a variety of soluble phosphates and superphosphates. In 1997 Hargreaves et al. showed that, under conditions which might have prevailed on prebiotic earth, it is possible to produce phospholipids from glycerol, fatty acids, or aldehydes and phosphate and that such materials could form membrane-bound vesicles (31). Thus we have a plausible abiotic route to phospholipid bound cells or vesicles, that is independent of the preexistence of living entities.

Recognizing that primitive earth may have produced proteinoids by mechanisms and processes that were reconstituted in the modern laboratory by Fox and his colleagues, it is not inconceivable that some such proteinoids interacted with the phospholipid vesicles formed, as postulated above, to produce the proteinoid/phospholipid bimembrane similar to that which graces our modern cells. Such proteinoids, in association with the phospholipid membrane would have provided channels for incorporating charged ions or small organic molecules and they would have increased the repertoire of activities of the primitive, lifeless cells, many fold. It also would not be intemperate to imagine that because sequence-specific proteins would eventually be formed through the modern-day mechanisms, such proteins would replace the nonspecific proteinoids at the cell surface, as dictated by natural selection processes.

INTRODUCING LIFE

Life as a self replicating molecule of RNA, which is capable of making inheritable mistakes (this is but one way of satisfying the definition presented above), may occur in free solution or within the confines of an otherwise abiotic cell. In both such circumstances, it is necessary to have adequate concentrations of the monomers of the nucleic acid, available as well as the precursor materials for the monomers. These latter materials, phosphate, ribose sugar, purine, and pyrimidine bases, could have either been present or were formed by abiotic syntheses. Considerations of how such precursors might combine to form the monomers for the RNA would include

- the preeminence of ribose as the sugar for the nucleic acids when the polymerization of formaldehyde into sugars produces a rich mixture that contains trioses, tetroses, pentoses, and hexoses;
- the addition of the base material to the C-1 of the ribose;
- the addition of phosphate (polyphosphate) to the C-5 of the ribose;
- the linking of the C-5 of one ribose with the C-3 of the next ribose in the chain;
- the nonuse of C-2 for concatenating the monomers;
- the catalysts for such reactions;
- the conditions which favored reaction and condensation with the elimination of the elements of water rather than hydrolysis.

But what is clear is the improbability of the formation of the formation of the ribose nucleoside phosphates (nucleotides) with the appropriate linkages by the use of simple solution chemistry in the absence of some sort of catalyst. What might such catalysts be?

Much in the way of accelerated reactions occurs at the interfaces between different states of matter. In particular, the solid phase affords an opportunity for reactive molecules to condense on its surface (attracted by a charge disproportionation due to the concentration of atoms or molecules below the surface via-à-vis the absence of those molecules in the region beyond the surface). There was not a lack of possible surfaces for the adsorption or absorption with reaction that could facilitate the condensation of the precursors of the nucleic acid monomers. Clays, silicates, phosphate minerals, and even the proteinoid-coated vesicles of phospholipids, made as envisaged above, could suffice. Such surfaces not only provided opportunities for adsorption but they also enabled the concentration of reactants, the activation of those species by the charged groups available on the solid surface, and they protected the nascent condensation product against hydrolysis because the water activity at the surface of the solid is not nearly as large as it is in the bulk fluid.

A second spur to reaction could be the continual oscillation of the external conditions. Were the precursors of the nucleotides mopped up into the lumen of the coacervate vesicles under mild conditions and then were temperatures to rise, the materials in the vesicle would be concentrated by the consequent dehydration. Reactions would occur, and on subsequent rehydration the condensation products may have changed the environment within the vesicle to the point where hydrolysis was impeded.

Although the catalytic activity of RNA has been extensively investigated in recent years, researchers into the origin of life are not wholly convinced that the ability of RNA to catalyze its own replication (to make a mirror image molecule which can leave the mother molecule and can serve as the template for the production of a new mother molecule) has been demonstrated in the absence of proteins that have been selected over hundreds of millions of years to effect that process; see Ref. 26 for a comprehensive review of prebiotic nucleic acid chemistry (32). However, were the concept of the emergence of a self-replicating RNA molecule to be associated with the interior of an abiotic cellular environment where there is some separation of the internal environment from the external and where there is an abundance of both nucleic acid precursor materials, as well as proteinoid materials attached or associated with the phospholipid bilayer of the vesicle envelope, then some sort of nonspecific catalytic activity may have been sufficient to set the system in motion. The first self-replicator that could copy replication mistakes could have emerged in this way. Thus life may be said to have begun.

Although the speculations of the above paragraph may seem astonishing, they do provide some guidelines for further experimental investigations that could result in the *de novo* production of living entities in the laboratory within a reasonable time frame.

An RNA molecule that does not code for the sequence of amino acids in a protein can express its phenotypic properties only in terms of its ability to self-replicate. Thus, the process of natural selection may occur in promoting the dominance of the most rapid replicator. The sequence of bases for this replicator is the gene or genotype; the property of rapid self-replication is the phenotype.

Having produced a molecule that is capable of living within the environment of an abiotically produced cell (33,34), much yet remains to be done to transform this progenitor life form into the cellular entities that populate our present biosphere. Some such tasks would include

- controlling the sequence of amino acids in the erstwhile proteinoids, so that a consistent material is produced by a process on which natural selection can operate to refine the sequence of bases in the RNA that controls the sequence of amino acids in the protein;
- transfering the depository of information on base sequences from the relatively unstable RNA to the more stable DNA;
- gradually substituting the almost random amino acid sequences of the proteinoids that inhabit the lipid bilayer around the vesicles for the more controlled sequences of amino acids in the proteins;
- establishing methods for energy transformation such that external supplies of energy may be used to

further the reactions that the cell can use to promote its own survivability; (it should be noted that: (i) abiotically produced porphyrins (21,22) may have been sequestered into the lipid bilayer as a result of their preferential solubility in a hydrophobic environment; it is not too much to envisage that this tetrapyrrole, after complexing with a divalent metal ion, can become a useful electron pump under the influence of incident illumination; this may cause hydrogen ion disproportionations across the lipid bilayer (which polarization?) that may have been converted to chemical energy by some activable proteinaceous system of molecules; (ii) it is possible that phosphate to phosphate bonds may not have been the first chemistry to have been involved in energy transfer reactions; rather sulfides and other thioesters may have been implicated, which system was superseded by the phosphate-based operation (33); (iii) it may have been possible to scavenge energy by catabolizing already polymerized materials such as the proteinoids or lipids which resemble the heterotrophic metabolism that most modern cells possess; (iv) the oxidation and reduction of sulfur or sulfides may also form a source of oxido-reductive energy that could be channeled into polymer synthesis);

- developing a light-dependent physical chemistry which not only pumped electrons across bilayer lipid membranes but which also liberated oxygen from water; two billion years later, cells emerged that could use the oxygen to recapture a much higher proportion of the energy locked up in a wide diversity of complex organic molecules; and
- generating a protective mechanism that would prevent active species of oxygen from degrading essential biochemicals.

Having acquired an armamentarium of facilities and materials, the cell that would have resulted would resemble a modern prokaryote. A subset of such beings still inhabit waters close to the hydrothermal vents or the hot springs as exemplified by waters in Yellowstone Park in the United States, where temperatures approaching 100 °C provide an environment for a maximum growth rate. Such organisms are also "at home" in environments rich in sulfur and the products of its chemistry. They also are comfortable in the presence of methane and hydrogen and can use these materials as energy source. These are the Archea. Another subset of prokaryotes, the blue-green algae or cyanophytes, developed photosynthesis to a high order of efficiency. This latter group are held to be responsible for transforming the atmosphere of the earth from one in which there was relatively diminutive amounts of oxygen to the present *circa* 20% level. This would probably have caused the death of over 99% of the organisms then living that were not protected against the damaging effects of superoxides. Some such organisms did survive to form the group that was capable of using the molecular oxygen to "burn" organic substrates and to capture the resulting liberated energy in the form of chemical energy and an increase in the disproportionation of the distribution of hydrogen ions across a lipid bilayer membrane. From unique combinations of this battery of diverse cell types came the modern animal and plant cells.

CONGLOMERATES OF PROKARYOTES

There is convincing evidence now that mitochondria, chloroplasts (including the colorless bodies that develop into chloroplasts in the light; protoplasts), and cilia/flagellae were once free-living entities. As prokaryotes they would have had a genome whose genes coded for all the proteins necessary for their survival. When they became components of a larger cell, many of those genes were subsumed into the nucleus of the host cell to the point where human mitochondria endure with about 37 genes. Human cells might contain up to a thousand mitochondria, whereas plant cells, in addition to the mitochondria, can be furnished with from one to several 100s of chloroplasts, each of which might contain up to 120 genes. Other self-replicating entities associated with nucleated (eukaryotic) cells are the basal bodies at the cellular extremity of cilia and flagella. Such concepts were extant in the first decade of the twentieth century in Russia, and the phenomenon was called "symbiogenesis" (35). It was largely discounted until the early 1960s when Margulis took it up and developed it further because it was then becoming likely that both the mitochondria and the chloroplasts contain DNA (36,37).

What may have begun as a symbiosis could well have ended as an amalgamation of genomes (38). Also, many such processes probably occurred in the past as evidenced by the multitude of symbioses that presently occur between diverse representatives of the biosphere (39). Indeed, the way in which the genome is reassembled following the incorporation of the symbiont into the body of the host cell resembles the way information is transferred between commercial companies that are engaged in "take over" operations. This leads to a further consideration in that the genetic development of cells is as much via the acquisition of whole genes and genomes as it is via the well-known sources of variation, mutation (including all forms of chromosome replication, breakage and, reassembly) and reassortment. Such genes may be obtained by a "virus" infection of the cell (40). Because the word "virus" means "noxious or evil fluid" (*virus;* Latin, slime, poison, strong smell, saltiness) the meritorious function of viruses in the "beneficial" transport of genes has been generally overlooked. (It is also noteworthy that of the many different viruses that are acquired by a living being in a lifetime, a relatively small number cause noticeable (pathogenesis.) Natural selection would then favor the survival of the fittest genome.

Viruses have had an important role in the emergence of the modern cell, and hence, of organisms, which may be supported by examining the gene sequences of mammalian genomes. In the mouse, for example, some 70% of the genome consists of "long terminal repeats". Such repeats are present in retroviruses and herpesviruses and they facilitate the incorporation of those viruses into the genomes of modern cells. The sequencing of the human genome is expected to show a similar picture because

only some 3% of that genome codes for proteins that are expressed during the life of the animal whereas the rest of the genome or "junk DNA" may come to be recognized as the carcasses of viruses which have imparted their useful genes and whose remaining genes, or noncoding DNAs, have been sidelined as redundant information.

In this respect, viruses (including bacteriophage) may be regarded as prototypical agents for the genetic engineering of contemporary prokaryotic and eukaryotic cells. Although the system present in nature is ostensibly random, the same device, as used by genetic engineers has a more directed character. The further development of these efforts to generate benefits for humans and other biota is recounted in the pages of this Encyclopedia and elsewhere.

PHILOSOPHICAL ISSUES

The origin of life, and cellular life at that, is a subject which has received much attention lately. The previous outline description of the origin of life does not call for any supernatural phenomena. Yet other writers on this subject introduce words and concepts that would predispose the reader to necessarily invoke the supernatural (41). Such words are complexity, randomness/chance and purpose. The questions posed are

- Does an increase in complexity (or size) denote progress?
- Can laws be enunciated to describe the random processes that result in evolution?
- Is "mind" the inevitable product of evolving life forms?
- How can such complex entities as, say, humans or their minds, be prodcts, of a random process of mutation and natural selection?
- Is there "directionality (or evidence of purposefulness)" in the process of evolution?

It is not my purpose here to examine each of these issues in detail. Rather, I seek to provide one or two pointers showing the way answers to such questions may be formulated.

In a world in which each effect is the result of a preceding cause, all events are determined only by the state of the system, even if we cannot know what those system states are, nor can we write equations or laws that encompass them. This means that processes that occur in nature are not random nor do they occur by chance. That we cannot predict the outcome which will result from a particular set of circumstances does not mean that such an outcome is not predetermined; it is just that we cannot, at present, perform that task.

Were commentators on the evolutionary process to be aware of the way in which genomes can evolve by the capture and exploitation of the whole genomes of other organisms containing 100s to 1,000s of genes, then much of the difficulty in appreciating how a complex genome may come to exist would evaporate. In this regard, organisms may be thought of as DNA scavengers that seek to acquire preformed and pretested DNA molecules and then to determine whether they can make a useful (contributing to an increase in their survivability) contribution to that organism in exchange for the reliable replication of that molecule of DNA. In this case, the process of operations mutation and reassortment might be considered "fine-tuning" processes.

The notions of directionality, purpose, and goal are words that humans use to promote their survival. (Indeed all words are entities or tools that humans have devised to promote their survival. But like other tools, words can also be used to impugn survivial. This latter word usage may be categorized as bad, wrong, or evil.) Whether or not increases in complexity, size or intelligence are the direction in which evolution is moving is a debatable point; suffice it to note that we are a part of an evolving system, and we may but watch with interest the direction(s) that it takes.

Finally, the question of mind (or the property of consciousness based on sense data [qualia] which result in sensation) as an entity that may ask questions of its own being and function needs examination. Animal experimenters generally hold that only humans and some of the higher primates are self-aware and hence self-conscious. Other animals reason, plan, live socially, hunt cooperatively, train offspring, fashion tools and habitations but without being self-aware; they are automatons. It has also been observed recently that human brains give instructions for muscles to move before there is a conscious awareness that an instruction for the muscles to move has been issued. That means that under some circumstances at least, humans behave as animals behave, as automatons (the reflex arc is an example of this). This could well leave the function of the consciousness of humans as a supervisory control system that is capable of examining instructions for actions, *but after the event*, so that some reprogramming of the autonomic system may occur to improve performance on future occasions.

USING ANIMAL CELLS IN CULTURE

This section will focus on issues and events that have led to the use of animal cells in the *in vitro* environment for the beneficial use of humans and animals. It is a story that begins by seeking solutions to what might seem academic problems, but they represented the passionate concerns of the investigators of the day. The techniques that were developed to answer these questions were rapidly redeployed, and through further developments and many innovations they were applied to solve more practical questions, mainly in the health care area.

A MULTIPHASIC PROCESS

Merely raising the issue of "culture" ensures a vigorous debate as to its meaning in any one particular context. The word itself derives from the cultivation (L. *colere*; to cultivate) of land. It clearly involves an activity of humans that is over and above the effects on land and crops that nature provides. Also implicit is the notion of growth and reproduction of some nonhuman

living entity. From this we can see that the original cultivation of animal cells was probably in the area of the protista where amoebae, euglenae, and various rotifers and turbellaria were raised in laboratory cultures. This may be regarded as phase one which may have begun with von Leeuwenhoek's seventeenth-century observations of the existence of animalcules and which continued at a low level until the twentieth century when it expanded considerably.

In the middle of the nineteenth century, additional efforts were made to keep alive cellular materials and tissues from higher animals. F.D. von Recklinhausen (1833–1910) attempted to keep blood cells alive in tubes of serum and plasma in 1866, and C. Ljunggren (1898) showed that he could keep a human skin tissue alive in ascitic fluid so that it might be successfully reimplanted. Arnold placed chunks of alder pith under the skin of frogs, and after recovering them and placing them in a dish containing supportive fluids, cells were seen to migrate out of the pith into the dish. The work of Roux, Loeb, and Harrison (see below) and many others on embryos and embryonic cells cultivated *in vitro* are considered typical of this second phase. The culmination of this phase may be taken as the regular and more less reliable cultivation of chick explants by Carrel (see below) and his colleagues in the period 1911 to 1925 and beyond.

A third phase may be recognized as the period, from 1925 to 1941 at the culmination of which antibiotics were first used in cell cultures. Here, Willmer and others examined the conditions that promoted cell growth and replication. They devised more complex media and attempted to determine the active components of the complex mixtures of embryo extract or serum which seemed to be necessary for healthy thriving cultures. During this period, the main thrust of tissue culture work, according to Willmer (42) was "... a method, in helping to elucidate some of the problems of normal growth and differentiation, and in furthering the knowledge of the processes involved in the normal development of the animal organism."

A variety of different culture systems were also investigated that included such substratum materials as silk, spider's web, and cotton wool (42 p.15). Lowenstadt was the first to use rotating tubes in 1925 (43) which were developed by Gey in 1933 into the roller bottle system in common use today (44).

Following the introduction of antibiotics, animal cell culture began in earnest. The HeLa cell line from the cervical cancer of Henrietta Lacks, derived in 1953 by technician Mary Kubicek in the laboratory of George Gey (45), provided investigators with an axenic culture of animal cells that grew reliably and on which a diverse suite of experiments could effectively be performed. At the end of the 1940s, Enders and colleagues discovered that they could grow polio virus *in vitro* in human embryonic tissues (46). This led to both killed (Salk) and live (Koprowski, Cox, and Sabin) polio vaccines grown in the cells of green monkey kidneys in culture. The fourth phase may be taken as starting in 1941 and ending when monoclonal antibody producing systems were instigated by Kohler and Millstein in 1975. It includes the 'golden age" of virus vaccine development which brought about effective cell-culture-based vaccines for human diseases such as mumps, measles, and rubella, as well as veterinary vaccines for foot-and-mouth disease, rinderpest and Marek's disease. The development of human diploid cell cultures with limited life spans (in terms of the numbers of cell doublings) by Hayflick and Moorhead in 1961 (47) provided yet another option for the production of viral vaccines from a cell culture substrate of known and exhaustively tested provenance in apposition to the primary cell cultures that dominated the field of human virus vaccines.

A fifth phase, which exists presently, began in the mid-1970s with the development and use of cell culture systems for producing monoclonal antibodies from hybridoma cells. This was rapidly followed by genetically engineering animals cells to produce specific biopharmaceuticals or growth factors. Two further developments are of note, animal cell cultures are being considered with greater earnestness as surrogates for humans and animals in the safety testing of vaccines, drugs, cosmetics, soaps, detergents, and other agents that are potentially toxic to cells. The second development, which is largely unexploited at this time (the middle of 1999) is the use of animal cells in culture to make genetically engineered viruses with which to correct genetic defects or achieve other modifications to whole animals following their integration into host cell's nuclear material.

IDEAS AND EXPERIMENTS: ANIMAL CELLS IN THE SOLUTION OF CONTROVERSIES

Most of the core intellectual issues that excited investigators in the latter half of the nineteenth century and that, to some extent, remain as issues today may be found in the history of the use of animal cells in culture. For example, the "vitalists" (*vide supra*) held that it was impossible to effect meaningful experiments on humans or animals because, for these beings, causes could not be meaningfully related to effects as animals were, in part, governed by "vital" forces that were outside the reach of physics and chemistry. "Determinists" held the counter view that the phenomena associated with all beings, animal or otherwise, were explicable in physical and chemical terms. Of the determinists, it may be opined that Claude Bernard (1813–1878, Villefranche and Paris) was a leading proponent of the contention that all biological phenomena were explicable in terms of physics and chemistry and that the experimental method could be the basis of acquiring a full understanding of the workings of humans in their normal and pathogenic conditions. He fully expounded these views in his *Introduction to the Study of Experimental Medicine* of 1865 where in the H.C Greene English translation published by Henry Schuman in 1949 at page 60 he states, "... *the science of vital phenomena must have the same foundations as the science of the phenomena of inorganic bodies, and that is no difference in this respect between the principles of biological science and those of physico-chemical science.*"

In this work he also set up a debate that flourishes yet. This deals with the relevance of the external to internal worlds in determining the nature and activities of living beings: clearly reflected in the ongoing nature versus nurture controversy. His writings on this dichotomy have had a considerable influence on the development of whole-animal and cellular physiology. In his (translated) words (48),

> The conditions of our cosmic environment generally govern the mineral phenomena occurring on the surface of the earth; but organised beings include within themselves the condition peculiar to their vital manifestations, and in proportion as the organism, i.e., the living machine, perfects itself, and its organised units grow more delicate, it creates conditions peculiar to an organic environment which becomes more and more isolated from the cosmic environment.

Jacques Loeb (born Isaak Loeb in Mayen 1859–1924 America), working independently from Bernard, had a different approach. For the major portion of his working life he was driven by the urge to control biological phenomena through the imposition of particular and defined external forces. In this way he aspired to change the way evolution proceeded, from the selection of chance variations to the directional control of humans. He also bitterly resented the wasted efforts of the "schoolmen" who sought only to analyze nature and report on its structural aspects. This difference in approach was also mirrored in the German education system where the *Gymnasien* provided the classical education that led to university and the analytic approach, areas the *Realschulen* led to training in technical subjects and agricultural colleges. Loeb held that it was more important to achieve the ability to modulate nature for the benefit of humans without knowing in detailed analytical terms how that modulation was actually effected. Nevertheless, it maybe that some preknowledge was necessary, but this should be the absolute minimum (49). This overtly "engineering" approach to biology was unique, although it was supported by the positivist approach to physics of Ernst Mach (1838–1916, Austria and Germany) and the engineer Joseph Popper-Lynkeus who in the 1860s glorified engineering as a higher art that should be appreciated for its aesthetic qualities. It might also be maintained that this provided a paradigm for developing the effective virus vaccines of the 1950s and 1960s where it is clear that the mechanism whereby the cell-culture-derived vaccine worked was and, to a great extent, is yet largely unknown.

Both Bernard and Loeb appreciated the heuristic value of studies on plants compared to those on animals. Whereas Bernard was wont to focus on the influence of temperature and humidity on plants as instructive, Loeb, under the tutelage of Julius von Sachs (1832–1897 Breslau and Wurzburg), was impressed by the factors that caused plant tropisms, light, gravity, galvanic field, and ion concentrations, to the point where in 1887 he wrote when requesting research space "to continue investigations that have demonstrated a far-reaching correspondence between animals and plants."

Such thoughts led to Loeb's famous studies on the effect of different ion concentrations in making unfertilized sea urchin eggs develop parthenogenetically into the pluteal stage. This work on the *in vitro* manipulation of the growth and development of animal cells that occurred at the University of Chicago in 1892 is considered one of the pioneering works in animals cell culture. It led to a fruitful controversy between Loeb and Thomas Hunt Morgan (Bryn Mayr, Philadelphia) who thought that the changes in the sea urchin eggs were due to a poisoning effect, whereas Loeb thought that they were an irritant or stimulus for development. Both of these workers did many experiments looking at the effects of different salts and their relative concentrations on the development of sea urchin eggs. They watched the cells divide and differentiate into the components of the sea urchin larvae. Later refinements of the stimulated parthenogenetic process led to the production of frogs from unfertilized eggs and led Loeb to write about the prospects for human parthenogenesis, a process that was immediately seen to have serious implications for the cornerstone contentions of one of the world's major religions.

Embryology was also the subject that brought Wilhelm Roux (1850–1924, Jena and Halle) into the field. He was interested in showing that cells were internally programmed and did not depend on external factors for their normal development, a view contrary to that of Loeb and the environmentalists. So, in 1885 in seeking to add to this debate, Roux discovered that on transferring the neural tube of a developing chick embryo to warm saline, the closure of the tube occurred naturally, not as a result of any external pressure. Therefore, such a development was driven by internal and not by environmental mechanisms. This constituted one of the first growing cultures of organized animal tissues *in vitro*.

German investigators working in areas allied to medicine fueled another controversy that revolved around the notion of whether it was useful to consider animals holistically or as reduced to their parts (reductionism). In considering the development of humans and the ways in which their brains worked, it was clear from the 1880 work of Hermann Munk that different parts of the human brain had different functions. This was disputed by Loeb whose experiments on dog brains indicated to him that if you washed away half of the brain, the rest of the brain would take over and eventually perform a complete service for the dog, in which case it was not useful to think about specialized areas of the brain. Roux contributed to this dispute through his experiments with frog embryos. Having destroyed one cell of a two cell embryo, the resulting development of an abnormal embryo was the result of the preprogramming of the remaining cell to produce just half an embryo. It was later noted that were he to have removed the damaged cell, the remaining cell was totipotent and would have produce a half-sized frog, a result which was more consonant with Loeb's thinking about the malleability of living matter and its control by exogenous forces.

TIME FOR A RECONSIDERATION?

Many authors of histories of animal cell or tissue culture regard the hanging drop experiments of Ross G. Harrison (1870–1959, Germantown and Yale), first reported in 1907 and more fully in 1910, as the take-off point for animal cell culture (50). This experiment was effected to determine the way the nerve fiber originated. There were three guesses; (1) it formed *in situ* from the cells of the nerve sheath, (2) it is made from preformed protoplasmic bridges, and (3) it is an outgrowth of the nerve cell itself. To settle this debate, Harrison set up a hanging drop culture made from the lymph removed from the frog lymph heart in which he instilled a portion of a nerve tube derived from a frog embryo before the nerve fibers had been formed. In the resulting clotted lymph, he was able to observe microscopically, over a few days, the emergence and growth of the nerve fiber. This established the third guess as the most reliable contention. It also gave credence to the hypothesis that the cell is the primary developmental unit of the multicellular organism. Other investigators (Loeb, Arnold, Born, and Haberlandt) had been attempting such experiments during the previous decade with a conspicuous lack of success. So, when Harrison's work was reported, they redoubled their efforts to achieve similar successes. Indeed, following his move to Yale, he attracted many people to his laboratory to learn the new technique. One such individual was Montrose Burrows who was working with Alexis Carrel in the Rockefeller Institute in New York City and who made the trip to Yale in 1910.

Alexis Carrel (1873–1944, Lyons, New York, and Paris) was a medical practitioner who was not averse to innovation. In 1902 in Lyons, he developed new techniques and skills in joining severed blood vessels, using fine instruments coated with paraffin jelly to prevent blood clotting at the site of the junction. Using these techniques when resident at the University of Chicago, he effected kidney transplants in animals. In 1906, he moved to the Rockefeller Institute. There, in an environment that sought to provide the greatest possible freedom from interference with the work of the many gifted individuals who were employed, Carrel and his associates flourished. First, he chose to approach the problem of growing cells in culture with a view to replacing pathogenic tissues or organs with normal equivalents grown in culture, an objective that is close to realization some 95 years later even if it may involve the use of human embryonic stem cells (see article on Ethics). Noting Harrison's success and building on what Burrows had learned on his trip to Yale, the Rockefeller team set to work.

From the onset, it was clear that Harrison's experiment did not provide the wherewithal for the successful growth and production of animal cells in culture. It was based on frog cells that are adapted to growth at temperatures lower than cells of warm-blooded animals, and the cultures lasted only a relatively short time. Burrows found that lymph clots were not suitable for long-term cultures and discovered that plasma clots were a more effective substitute. Carrel and Burrows were the first to prolong the life of the hanging drop cultures by transplanting fragments of the original culture to new slides using a fresh supply of plasma, and in 1913 Carrel reported on his discovery that the most potent stimulator of the growth of chick embryo explants was an extract made from centrifuged minced chick embryo homogenates. For the next 13 years, Carrel, Burrows, and Ebeling persevered with transplanting hanging drop cultures. So diligent was this work that a culture of cells from a heart fragment of a chicken embryo established in January 1912 survived this process for a period of more than 23 years. In 1923, Carrel introduced his eponymous flask culture. This increased the ease of handling tissues, and sequential cultures were thereby facilitated. It sustained decreasing levels of bacterial contamination and enabled the scale-up of the culture size and numbers. Additionally, experiments on the composition of the culture media were initiated, and Ebeling began to quantitate cell growth based on measuring the extent of the outgrowth the original tissue mass. Thus the case can be made to consider the combination of these developments as the epochal take-off point for animal tissue and cell culture.

In describing his work on tissue culture, Carrel drew attention to the details of the precautions and manipulations that he held were absolutely necessary to prevent contamination. No doubt he was influenced by his surgical experiences, where aseptic techniques were heavy-handed and ponderous. Specially prepared rooms, impermeable rubber garments that could be swabbed with antiseptics covered workers from head to toe, high temperatures, and highly defined manipulations effected rapidly and precisely were some of the elements he would have insisted upon. Some commentators have surmised that the mandatory requirement for such elaborate precautions, seeming to be a set of mystical activities, held back the development of the subject. However, readers of this Encyclopedia will be familiar with the myriad of techniques and specialized equipment that is presently used to achieve the same effect of freedom from exogenous contamination. Familiarity and clear and simple protocols may have expunged the mystique while leaving us with a suite of reliable procedures that enables us to progress.

Carrel was awarded the Nobel prize in 1912 for his surgical and cell-culture experiments. In his popular philosophic writings (51), he was much impressed with the "survival of the fittest" and "natural selection" mechanisms propounded by Darwin. He, like many others, projected these ideas into eugenic formulas for the betterment (he thought) of the human conditions (51, p. 198). He was also a publicist who used the media to project extravagant claims such as the immortality of the chick heart cells whose culture he and Ebeling began in 1912. He also held that "Christian mysticism constitutes the highest form of religious activity." (51. p. 131). It is possible that these extraneous facets of his character and writings prevented the historians of these events from providing Carrel with the credit to which he may be due in cell and tissue culture. For example, John Paul in his General Introduction to *Growth, Nutrition, and Metabolism of Cells in Culture* (1972) (52) fails to mention Carrel at all while maintaining that Harrison was "This founder of modern tissue culture... (52, p. 1), and both Willmer and Abercrombie also credit Harrison with the pioneer role (see Ref. 50). However, I assess Carrel's contribution otherwise.

Harrison's experiment may well have been an inspiration for researchers to examine living cells in culture to answer questions about the anatomy and physiology of cellular materials. But there is a major difference between the solution to analytical and structural questions and the synthetic abilities needed to achieve technical breakthroughs. The thrust of Harrison's work was analytical; that of Carrel (rather like that of Loeb) was synthetic. Insofar as we have an animal cell culture technology at this time will have been largely due to the more synthetic type of researcher such as Carrel, although it would be inappropriate to discount the value of the many analytical investigations that led to further synthetic advances. For these reasons, it may be timely to reconsider the relative roles of Harrison and Carrel as the fonts of cell culture and more aptly conclude that it was Alexis Carrrel who sent the subject on its way ahead.

A HOME FROM HOME

To achieve successful cell culture, researchers might be guided by the common sense notion that were a physical and chemical environment to be provided for the cells, equivalent to that which the cells experience *in vivo*, then there is a high probability that the cells will grow, reproduce, and generally thrive. However, there may be differences in the *in vivo* situation which are difficult to mimic in the *in vitro* condition. The following are some of the difference:

- Cultures tend to be zero- or two-dimensional, whereas tissues are three- dimensional. A homogeneous cell suspension of monodisperse cells may be considered zero-dimensional. Some more recent culture conditions create the three-dimensional tissue type of environment.

- In tissues, cells are under stress/tension/compression unlike that in culture.

- The supply of oxygen is tailored to the cell type in tissues but not in culture (generally).

- In tissues, a mixture of chemokines and lymphokines exists whose nature and relative concentrations vary, a situation not normally achieved in cell culture.

- Tissue cells come under the physical and chemical surveillance of the immune system cells for which there is not a counterpart in culture.

- The mechanism for the control of differentiation in tissues is not the same as that in culture.

- Cells in tissues have a different life history from those in cell culture.

- Cells in the body experience short-term (heart beats), medium-term (diurnal), and long-term (life-cycle) fluctuations in nutritional, hormonal, and environmental parameters (nutrient concentrations, waste material concentrations, oxygen), whereas in cell culture, efforts are made to keep parameters invariant.

- Tissue cells are supported on a secreted extracellular matrix which would be different in cell culture.

Nevertheless, cell culturists have expressed much genius in coming to terms with these difficulties and have, largely, by a process of "*rational empiricism*," arrived at a level of capability that has contributed to many of the outstanding advances of the present century. (Rational empiricism is a process in which the observation of the effect of one's actions determines what the next action is to be, coupled with the application of the relevant knowledge base to design the initiating action, and also, any general rules that can be derived from these activities are recycled for further testing and examination. This differs from the purely rational approach, "*rationalism*," that relies more on the existing knowledge base and the theories derived from that base as the determinants for action, while it plays down the value of effecting experiments and responding to the observed results.)

An environment has physical and chemical components. The former may be divided into material and energetic aspects. Further consideration of the energy-related parameters include the environmental variables such as temperature, pressure (including ionic concentrations such as that of the proton [pH]), magnetism, gravity, light (color), electrical charge, shear, stress, density, viscosity, phase/interface, and gel strength. On the material side we have to consider the way in which a material is presented to the cells, as well as its general shape and size. For the chemical components of the environment, we have to be aware of the materials that comprise any supporting or containing structures, as well as the fluid media that bathe the cells when so contained. Although we can find a mixture of defined (save for impurities, inevitably present at levels below those at which they are detectable or measurable) chemicals that will sustain many cell lines and types, this is not always possible for unadapted primary cultures nor for specific and fastidious cell types. For the latter, complex undefinable extracts, hydrolyzates, mincates, or homogenates of biologically derived materials might be required. These chemical environments contain many components which could include sugars, tricarboxylic acid cycle intermediates, oxygen, carbon dioxide, amino acids, lipids, salts, trace elements, shear protectants (Pluronic F68), pH indicators, nucleotides, vitamins, hormones, cytokines, antifoams, transferrin or ferric citrate, fibronectin (attachment factors), and a host of viscosity modifiers such as Methocel or polyvinylpyrolidone. However, there are many components we manage to incorporate into the chemical media to provide the cells with energy and the building materials for growth and reproduction, and we cannot provide the equivalent environment that occurs *in vivo*. Here, the fluids bathing the cells may contain thousands of components that are in a state of flux in terms of both their absolute and relative composition and concentration. In cell cultures, components either decrease in concentration or increase in concentration in a fairly regular manner, whereas in living systems the component concentrations tend to cycle with short, medium-, and long-term variations. In animal tissues, cells are held together by a matrix of glycoproteins and are subjected to stretching and squeezing forces on both an irregular and cyclical basis. Culture environments, where cells adhere to a substratum or are part of a three-dimensional clump or proto-tissue, are altogether more static and less physically demanding. Cells in suspension cultures, on the other hand, experience a rapidly fluctuating physical environment as they move between areas of differing shear and compressive forces with a relatively constant or slowly changing chemical environment.

The history of the development of the complex mixtures that constitute cell culture media is largely based on the application of rational empiricism (*vide supra*). From a knowledge of the components of cells, it is sensible to provide those self-same components in the culture medium. Charity Waymouth has written many such histories summarized in reference 53. Further amplification of this aspect of animal cell technology history as well as other facets of the subject may be obtained from a collection of the references complied by Margaret Murray and Gertrude Kopech in 1953 (54). For each cell type and product, there is likely to be a medium or several media that provide maximum productivity. Other criteria obtrude on the selection of the medium that are more dependent on the circumstances in the local laboratory or factory rather than on providing the medium with the most outstanding biological properties. Cost, ease of formulation, ease and efficacy of sterilization, reliability, reproducibility and quality control validation, and certification of external source materials are but a subset of the factors that need to be taken into account when selecting a medium.

Although Lewis and Lewis (55) experimented with serum-free and defined media for the production of animals cells in culture in 1911, it was not until the 1980s that both serum-free and protein-free media of a defined nature were successfully formulated for the large-scale production of monoclonal antibodies and genetically engineered proteins (56). The need for such media became more acute when the potential for unscreened or partially tested serum to be contaminated with human pathogens (bovine spongiform encephalitis, BSE, or bovine viral diarrhoea virus) became increasingly apparent.

In providing a physical home for the cells to grow and replicate, animal cell technologists have been outstandingly inventive. Whether the cells are to grow attached to a surface as monodispersed individual cells in suspension culture or as cell masses held or trapped within the interstices of artificial matrices, the many and varied culture containers devised for such purposes have all been used with some degree of success. Summaries of such a plethora of culture systems may be found in the articles in this Encyclopedia and in Ref. 57 and 58.

The physical containers for the animal cell cultures which required a surface for attachment and which were effected up to mid-1960s were based on flasks (Carrel, Roux) or static and rolled tubes (Strangeways, Gey, Enders, Salk) (59) which matured into roller bottles where a standard size would be a 1-liter bottle expressing 600 cm^2 area for cell growth and a 6-cm diameter, and an extraordinary bottle might have the same diameter as the 1-liter bottle but have a length of 1–2 meters. To scale up such systems requires an increase in the number of units deployed. After 1965, much effort was expended on combining multiples of these unit cultures into one containing structure so as to decrease handling operations and improve controllability. A series of reviews on the progress of this transformation have been published (60–64). Current developments in the production of animal cells in the form of tissue cultures where the cells colonize a preformed matrix of a dissolvable polymer such as polylactide-polyglycolide are also offering exciting new opportunities to achieve what Carrel set out to do; the replacement of pathogenic human tissues with normal tissues grown in culture (65–67). The progression of such work via the emerging use of embryonic stem cells (made from human cloned embryos or otherwise) is likely to become a major area for technical, medical, and commerical activities in the near future (68).

Cultures that do not need a substratum (suspension cultures) to thrive have also been grown on a large scale. Whereas most suspension cultures up to the mid-1960s tended to be at the 0.1–100-liter scale, modern suspension cell cultures may operate at the 2,000 to 10,000-liter scale. Although the details of the mixing system, aeration equipment, and control facilities may vary considerably, they do hover about the paradigm for the standard microbial stirred tank reactor (STR) technology. In addition to the articles describing such systems in this Encyclopedia, other reviews have been published (69–71). Up to the advent of the use of antibiotics in 1941 and the development of the process for the production of virus vaccines (polio) in the mid-1950s, animal cell culture, was a difficult technology to master. Results were variable and susceptibility to contamination was rife. Techniques for measuring cell growth were rudimentary and not well used, and the estimation of virus production was also difficult. Nevertheless, the field progressed, and the ability of the cell culturists to provide physical and chemical environments that were more conducive to cell growth, replication, and the generation of cell-derived products improved by leaps and bounds. Some such developments were not technical, they were social.

ENVIRONMENTS FOR CELL CULTURISTS

Until the mid-1970s, cell culture had two main functions: the first was for the scientific investigation of the anatomy and physiology (developmental, embryological) of cells to increase the understanding the way they worked, the second was for the production of the virus vaccines, which by that time had moved from the initial vaccine of polio to those of mumps, measles, and rubella vaccines for humans and foot-and-mouth disease, rinderpest, and Marek's vaccines for animals. Newcomers to the field of cell culture and virus vaccine production relied on the literature published as research papers in a wide variety of journals. These journals were allied to the medical literature or to journals in physiology and biochemistry. The biological aspects of cells and tissues in culture were also catered to by various scientific societies such as the British Society for Cell biology and the American Tissue Culture Society. However, the clear objectives of these societies were more analytic than synthetic, and they did not deal with issues which sought to use animal cells in culture at large commercially attractive scales to generate beneficial products.

In 1963 a group of people interested in cell culture and the development of cell lines for the production of virus vaccines began to meet annually as the Cell Culture Committee (72). This group was primarily concerned with the development and characterization of new cell lines and media for the production of virus vaccines and in the rigorous quality control of that process. In 1971 this group translated into the newly designated International Association for Biological Standardization (IABS) that itself was derived from the The Permanent Section of Microbiological Standardization of the International Association of Microbiological Societies which began its life in 1955. The aims of the new International Association were "... *to inform the members of the Association of all matters concerned with the standardization of biological substances and to publish papers concerned with this subject.*" It may be surmised that the objects for the establishment of the society were to make sure that biologically derived vaccines, antibiotics, nutraceuticals, and pharmaceuticals were both produced to high standards of safety and efficacy and also that the methods which could be applied to the determination of safety and efficacy were well developed, reliable, readily applicable and standardizable.

The IABS also runs symposia and publishes a series of successful meeting procedures under the heading of "Developments in Biological Standardization," as well as a quarterly journal called the '*Journal of Biological Standardization*' which became the journal '*Biologicals*' in 1990. There is much of interest and value for the cell culturist in the publications of this Association. However, it was clearly not strictly focused on animal cell culture as a topic in and for itself, nor was it necessarily the appropriate organization to promote the wide ranging suite of activities which led from the appreciation of a need for a vaccine to the effects and issues generated when using vaccines in the field. This left openings for further developments.

Having returned to the United Kingdom in 1973 after leaving the virus vaccine development group of Dr. Maurice Hilleman at Merck Sharpe & Dohme in West Point, Pennsylvania, U.S.A., I noted the paucity of opportunities to share cell culture information dealing with large-scale production issues with colleagues in the United Kingdom. So, when I met with Dr. Simon Barteling in the latter's laboratory in Lelystadt in The Netherlands, in the summer of that year, I was excited to learn that Dr. Barteling was also mindful of the difficulties of exchanging information on product-generating cell cultures and that if a forum for such an exchange were to be established it should be European. After this conversation and following my return to the United Kingdom, I commissioned the printing of headed note paper for the putative "European Society for the Large-Scale Production of Animal Cells and Viruses," and, so armed, I approached a number of the leading workers in the field to determine whether it would be possible to form an *ad hoc* committee to bring about such a society. This grouping came together, and under the urging of Dr. Toon van Wezel (1935–1986, Utrecht), a change of name was accepted so that the European Society for Animal Cell Technology (ESACT) was duly established at the time of its first symposium held in the Krasnapolsky Hotel in Amsterdam in November, 1976. The proceedings of this symposium and the subsequent 15 sesquiennial meetings of ESACT were published and form part of an ongoing series. The novel and applied aspect of the thrust of ESACT is clear from extracts of its 1999 mission statement:

> ... The aim of ESACT is to promote the communication between European investigators working with human and animal cells to increase their scientific and economic application and to achieve the acceptance of the tools and products derived from them.
> ESACT is committed to furthering the use of animal cell technology from the current product areas such as vaccines, monoclonal antibodies and recombinant proteins into new and emerging fields. These will include gene therapy, cell therapy, tissue engineering, drug and safety testing and the replacement of animal tests by *in vitro* systems.

The sequelae of the formation of ESACT included recognition of the economic value of animal cell technology to the European Union (EU) and the formation of an industrial association which had the specific purpose of working with the officials of the EU for the advancement of this area (73). National offshoots of the society were also formed in Belgium, Germany, the United Kingdom, and the Netherlands. ESACT was the first European society to become a member of the European Federation of Biotechnology (EFB) and was well represented from 1983 to 1996 on its Working Party for Animal and Plant Cell Technology.

The Americans and the Japanese also felt the need for more opportunities to exchange information on applied cell culture, and the Americans established a biennial series of Cell Culture Engineering meetings under the aegis of the American Engineering Foundation beginning in 1989. In 1988, the Japanese began an annual series of meetings under the guidance of Hiroki Murakami (1941–1993, Inoshima and Kyushu) and colleagues of the Japanese Association for Animal Cell Technology (JAACT). The proceedings of these latter meetings are published separately, and the Cell Culture Engineering meetings have been published as special issues in the journal established in 1985 (first issue, 1987) by Dr. Bryan Griffiths and me called *Cytotechnology*. We also initiated the six volume edited book series *Animal Cell Biotechnology* (74) to provide practitioners with understanding and methods whereby they could effectively and reliably acquire the beneficial use of scaled-up animal cell cultures. These works provided a more industrially oriented and large-scale complement to the cell culture manuals of Ian Freshney (first published in 1983) (75) and Michael Butler (1987) (76). In their turn, these works were followed by a welter of other edited books and monographs that have provided depth and variety to what has become a rapidly expanding area of human endeavor.

The second development contingent on the restricted profile of interests of the IABS was the instigation of the journal *Vaccine* (first issue, 1983) by this author. This provided animal cell technologists with a vehicle for the publication of their work on the methods whereby virus vaccines might be produced and improved.

CHOOSING APPROPRIATE TOOLS

During the twentieth century, the beneficial use of animal cells in culture has developed from a "black art," available only to a few, to a reliable and robust technology on which several hundred companies depend for their product streams. The mysterious arts of the past have been transformed into the codified protocols of today, many of which appear in this Encyclopedia. This transformation had depended on the development of potent and readily available tools. One such facility may be found in the cellular substrate which can be used for virus vaccine production.

The world was declared free of smallpox on December, 9, 1979. This momentous milestone in human history was the result of a World Health Organisation (WHO) inspired smallpox eradication campaign that began in 1966 and was based on the universal dissemination of a live virus vaccine. At this time of (1999), WHO is in the throes of a campaign to eradicate the disease poliomyelitis (polio, infantile paralysis) by the application of virus vaccines produced from animal cell cultures. The production of such vaccines was the first use of animal cell cultures to generate a product of material (rather than intellectual or scientific) benefit to humans and animals.

The take-off point for the animal cell culture vaccine that would protect humans against the disease of poliomyelitis was demonstration by Enders, Weller, and Robbins that the polio virus would grow in various human embryonic tissues and especially in tissues other than those of the nervous system (46). Tissue fragments from arms, legs, intestine, and brain were used and were refed with fresh medium every 4–7 days with subculturing every 8–20 days. Both penicillin and streptomycin (100 u/mL) were used to prevent contamination. Such tissue cultures were then used to subdivide the polio viruses into various types. Additionally, they showed that the cells of infected tissues did not stain, whereas those of the control uninfected tissues did take up the stain. The infected cells could also be detected by microscopic examination, and the changes thus wrought were termed the "cytopathogenic effect" (CPE) by Enders. These changes were then used to follow successful infections and were a marker for screening cells and tissues that could be used to produce the virus in large amounts.

But it was Jerome Syverton and his colleagues at the University of Minnesota who showed in 1951 that all three types of polio virus would grow in monkey testes cell cultures (77). This work opened the way to the use of primary monkey kidney cells grown in roller tube cultures for the routine production of polio virus; the method which was used by Jonas Salk (1914–1997, New York and La Jolla) in his University of Pittsburgh laboratory to produce a formaldehyde-inactivated polio vaccine and deployed in preliminary studies on humans in 1953 (78). In parallel with Salk's work, Raymond Parker and Andrew Rhodes at the Connaught Laboratory in Toronto were able to scale up the production of the vaccine for the epochal 1954/5 field trial of the killed (Salk) polio vaccine (KPV) on some 1,800,000 children in all parts of the United States (79). The success of the trial was announced triumphally by

Thomas Francis, Jr. in Ann Arbor, Michigan, on April 12, 1955: On the same day the Licensing Committee of the Public Health Service agreed to license the Salk type of polio vaccine.

While the killed virus approach to a polio vaccine was progressing apace, those who thought that a live attentuated virus vaccine would be a more effective vaccine were working assiduously to produce a licensable vaccine. Hilary Koprowski, then at the Lederle Laboratories, reported the safe and oral delivery of a cotton rat attenuated polio vaccine to 20 volunteers in 1951. By the mid-1950s, Herald Cox took over this group after Koprowski moved to the Wistar Institute in Philadelphia where he continued to make attenuated strains of polio virus in cell culture and to test those strains in clinical trials. Albert Sabin (1906–1997, Poland and New York) had experienced the use of killed and live virus vaccines when he served as a medical officer in the U.S. Army (1941–1945) (as had Jonas Salk). Before the war, Sabin had a developed interest in the disease poliomyelitis and in producing attenuated strains of the virus which might be used in a vaccine. In 1955, Koprowski claimed to have orally vaccinated 150 subjects successfully, while Sabin reported to the same meeting that he had vaccinated 80 volunteers with each of the three attentuated strains he was testing. It is clear that Koprowski believed that he was ahead of Sabin in arriving at an attenuated vaccine. Indeed, by 1957, he had tested his vaccine on nearly 250,000 people in Ruanda-Urundi, while Sabin had sent his strains for testing in the Soviet Union. Some 20 trials in 15 countries were under way by 1960, and the three-strain live attenuated polio vaccine was licensed in 1962. Although, ultimately, it was Sabin who was recognized for developing the successfully licensed live polio vaccine, he did not relinquish the bitterness and animosity he had acquired during the highly competitive struggle with Koprowski and Cox to achieve the dominant position in live polio vaccines; an attitude which was certain to have been reciprocated by the two men who were not so recognized.

During the height of this conflict for supremacy in the vaccine race, work at the Wistar Institute on the development of a new cell substrate for virus vaccines was conquering new peaks. In 1961, Hayflick and Moorhead (47) of that Institute demonstrated that they could produce a cell line from human embryonic lung tissue whose cells would replicate a maximum number of times (circa 50) before they became senescent; the WI38 cell line. These cells were diploid and did not express the chromosomal number abnormalities that other cell lines possessed. They also could be frozen and revived efficiently and on exhaustive examination were shown to be free from the kind of contaminating viruses that infected primary monkey kidney cells. (In 1960 Maurice Hilleman at the Merck Institute for Therapeutic Research showed that there was a contaminating virus, "a vacuolating agent," in primary monkey kidney cells. This was shown by Bernice Eddy at the Division of Biologic Standards (DBS) of the National Institutes of Health (NIH) to be the Simian Virus 40 [SV40] a cancer-causing virus when deposited in the cheek pouch of a hamster). Therefore, the WI38 cells were an ideal substrate (tool) for producing newly licensed polio vaccines and other vaccines intended for human prophylaxis and in testing a variety of vaccines made from W138 cells in several million people, abreactions to the vaccine were not observed.

Therefore, Stanley Plotkin's rubella vaccine was developed using the WI38 cell substrate. In 1967 overtures were made to the DBS for licensure of this vaccine. Their response was to ask the applicants to reconsider the nature of the cell substrate and to use duck embryo or dog or rabbit kidney cells. In 1969, Sabin also entered the fray and joined the opposition to the use of the WI38 cell line for rubella, alleging, without evidence, that it may have unknown contaminants one of which could be a human leukemia virus (72). However, in the late 1960s, polio vaccines made on WI38 cells were licensed in Yugoslavia, the United Kingdom, France, and the USSR, and in 1972, Pfizer Laboratories succeeded in obtaining a license to make polio vaccine in the United States from the WI38 cells. It took 10 years to supplant a clearly potentially hazardous cell substrate with a well-tested and almost risk-free alternative. Clearly some vested interests may have been at work in the DBS, as shown by their relocation of the Food and Drug Administration (FDA), coupled with the ardent opposition of Sabin whose antipathy to Koprowski and hence the work of the Wistar Institute carried through to irrational criticism of a major technical advance. It is fortunate that, despite strenuous opposition, the technology that could be most relied upon eventually prevailed.

The spirit of rationality (as opposed to unlimited multiplication of conjectural hazards), once engaged, was able to be applied to licensing of products made from cell lines whose chromosomal counts could vary widely and whose number of cell replications was not bounded. Thus, under the untiring and inspired direction of Norman Finter of the Wellcome Foundation, Namalwa interferon was licensed to be made from a transformed human cell line in 1986 in the United Kingdom (80) and rabies vaccines and KPV were made in VERO (a transformed monkey cell line) cells in France. Hybridoma cells were found acceptable substrates for the production of monoclonal antibodies, and genetically transformed CHO cells were licensed to make tissue plasminogen activator by Genentech in 1989.

Leonard Hayflick's work on the WI38 cells had many social repercussions. It led to the transfer of the DBS from the NIH to the FDA. Following a lengthy lawsuit that was settled out of court in Hayflick's favor, the principle, that the inventors (or possessors of intellectual property on the basis of having achieved a novel process or product via an inventive step or act) of a product, although funded by federal monies may obtain some beneficial reward for that invention for themselves or their institutes (81), was accepted nationally.

REFLECTIONS

The recounting of history is, of necessity, a recitation of the author's biases. What is written above is not an exception to this generalization. However, the justification of taking the reader's time to engage with something which cannot be other than the "truth" has to be found in stimulating that individual to examine for him or herself the issues and events that have been recounted. What I have sought to reveal in this article is an interaction between powerful personalities, prevailing philosophies, and pertinent phenomenologies. What emerges are the generalization that define the way in which we gain confidence in our concepts of the world outside ourselves, the way that world functions and how we might intervene in that world to make it more propitious for our personal and social survival.

We will never become omniscient. But during the last 100 years, we have witnessed sensational progress in all areas where we have striven to become knowledgeable and capable. As Eric Sevareid, a commentator on American television at the time of the first moon landings in 1969, remarked, "It is not that we have landed on the moon which is of importance. It is that, having set ourselves a seemingly impossible goal we have demonstrated that if we are determined enough we can achieve it. How then do we face the needy of the world?" (author's paraphrasing).

The story, told above, about how we came to the realization of the cellular nature of living beings and a possible route as to how such living cells may have come into existence, beginning with the inanimate materials present on earth some 4 billion years ago, becomes more and more realistic as we refine our chemical and biological understandings. The transformation of such knowledge to the practical ends that support our well-being is the task that is ever before us. For we have not only to cater to our material being but, equally importantly, we have to recognize that the way we think and what we think are just as important to our overall health as is the regular supply of nutrients and the removal of wastes. We are beginning to come to terms with such thinking in that we can recognize the development of a new subject area in "psychoneuroimmunology." But we have a long path to tread before we come to grips with those properties of cells that enable them to communicate and to set up the neural networks that become capable of thought and consciousness.

Such challenges may be faced boldly if, and, probably, only if, we can eschew any and all notions of vitalism. Developments in computing and in the silicon world may come into a closer and more interactive engagement with the carbon-based computers littered about our bodies. We are limited only by our imaginations and the laws of thermodynamics: therefore it behooves us to look to the area of our visions and see if we can find the guidelines whereby we and our descendants can continue the traditions set out in these pages by seeking to improve the quantity and reliability of our informational base and, by using that resource, to continue to enhance the quality of life on planet earth and beyond.

BIBLIOGRAPHY

1. T.S. Kuhn, *The Structure of Scientific Revolutions*, University of Chicago Press, Chicago, 1962.
2. G. Taubes, *Science* **285**, 512–517 (1999).
3. Aristotle, *On Generation and Corruption*, p. 325a.
4. B. Russell, *History of Western Philosophy*, Allen & Unwin, London, 1946, pp. 84–93.
5. See *Encyclopaedia Britannica*, 7th ed., 1842, for a History of Optics in the premodern world and *Encyclopaedia Britannica*, 11th ed., 1911, for a history of the Microscope.
6. H. Harris, *The Birth of the Cell*, Yale University Press, New Haven, conn., 1999, p. 5.
7. *Oxford English Dictionary*.
8. J. Hogg, *The Microscope*, 6th ed., 1867, p. 3.
9. *Encyclopaedia Britannica*, 11th ed., Vol. 11, pp. 406–411.
10. C. Dobell, *Antony van Leeuwenhoek and his "Little Animals"*, Swets & Zeitlinger, Amsterdam, 1932.
11. *Encyclopaedia Britannica*, 15th ed., 1983.
12. B. Alberts et al., *The Molecular Biology of the Cell*, 3rd ed., Garland Publishing, London, 1994, pp. 139–191.
13. M. Rief, H. Clausen-Schaumann, and H. Gaub, *Nat. Struct. Biol.* **6**, 346–349 (1999).
14. F. Griffith, *J. Hyg.* **27**, 113–159 (1928).
15. O.T. Avery, C.M. MacLeod, and M. McCarty, *J. Exp. Med.* **79**, 137–158 (1944).
16. J.W. Schopf, *Science* **260**, 640–646 (1993).
17. S.J. Mojzsis et al., *Nature (London)* **384**, 55–59 (1996).
18. D.W. Deamer and G.R. Fleischaker, eds., *Origins of Life: The Central Concepts*, Jones Bartlett, Borton 1994.
19. T.R. Cech, *Proc. Natl. Acad. Sci. U.S.A.* **83**, 4360–4363 (1986).
20. S.L. Miller and J.L. Bada, *Nature (London)* **334**, 609–611 (1988).
21. G.W. Hodgson and C. Ponnamperuma, *Proc. Natl. Acad. Sci. U.S.A.* 22–28 (1968).
22. M. Calvin, *Chemical Evolution*, Oxford University Press, Oxford, U.K. 1969.
23. H.G. Bungenberg de Jong, *Protoplasma* **15**, 110 (1932).
24. A.I. Oparin, *The Origin of Life on the Earth*, 3rd ed., Oliver & Boyd, London, 1957, pp. 303 *et seq.*
25. S.W. Fox and K. Harada, *Science* **128**, 189 (1958).
26. D.L. Rohlfing, in K. Matsuno, K. Dose, K. Harada, and D.L. Rohlfing, *Molecular Evolution and Protobiology*, Plenum, London, 1984 pp. 29–43.
27. A. Cherkin, in K. Matsuno, K. Dose, K. Harada, and D.L. Rohlfing, *Molecular Evolution and Protobiology*, Plenum, London, 1984 pp. 49–61.
28. J. Oro, in S. Bengston, ed., *Early Life on Earth*, Columbia University Press, New York, 1994, pp. 48–59.
29. A.S.U. Choughuley, in ed., K. Matsuno, K. Dose, K. Harada, and D.L. Rohlfing, eds., *Molecular Evolution and Protobiology*, Plenum, London, 1984 pp. 63–81.
30. M.P. Bernstein, S.A. Sandford, and L.J. Allamandola, *Sci. Amer.* **281**, 26–33 (1999).
31. W.R. Hargreaves, S.J. Mulvihill, and D.W. Deamer, *Nature (London)* **266**, 78–80 (1977).
32. A. Eschenmoser, *Science* **284**, 2118–2124 (1999).
33. C. DeDuve, *Blueprint for a Cell: The Nature of the Origin of Life*, Neil Patterson Publishers, Burlington, N.C., 1991.
34. W. Day, *Genesis on Planet Earth: The Search for Life's beginning*, 2nd ed. Yale University Press, London, 1984.
35. L. Margulis and J. Cohen, in S. Bengtson, ed., *Earth Life on Earth*, Columbia University Press, New York, 1994, pp. 327–333.
36. L. Margulis, *Symbiosis in Cell Evolution: Life and Its Environment on the Early Earth*, Freeman San Francisco, 1981.

37. A. Tomitani et al., *Nature (London)* **400**, 159–162 (1999).

38. Z. Zhang, B.R. Green, and T. Cavalier-Smith, *Nature (London)* **400**, 155–159 (1999).

39. P.S. Nutman and B. Mosse, eds., *Symbiotic Associations, 13th Symp. Soc. Gen. Microbiol.*, Cambridge University Press, Cambridge, U.K., 1963.

40. John Martin, quoted by A. Coghlan, *New Sci.* **163**, 11 (1999).

41. P. Davies, *The Fifth Miracle: The Search for the Origin of Life*, Penguin Group, London, 1999.

42. E.N. Willmer, *Tissue Culture: The Growth and Differentiation of Normal Tissues in Artificial Media*, Methuen, London, 1935.

43. H.L. Lowenstadt, *Arch. Exp Zellforsch. Besonders Gewebezuech.* **1**, 251–256 (1925).

44. G.O. Gey, *Am. J. Cancer* **17**, 752–756 (1933).

45. M. Gold, *A Conspiracy of Cells: One Woman's Immoral Legacy and the Medical Scandal it Caused*, State University of New York Press, New York, 1986.

46. J.F. Enders, T.H. Weller, and F.C. Robbins, *Science* **109**, 85–87 (1949).

47. L. Hayflick and P.S. Moorhead, *Exp. Cell Res.* **25**, 585–621 (1961).

48. Bernard Claude, *Introduction to the Study of Experimental Medicine* (1865). H.C. Greene translation published by Henry Schuman, New York, in 1949, p. 97.

49. P.J. Pauly, *Controlling Life; Jacques Loeb and the Engineering Ideal in Biology*, Oxford University Press, U.K., 1987.

50. J.A. Witkowski, *Med. Hist.* **23**, 279–296 (1979).

51. A. Carrel, *Man the Unknown*, Penguin Books, New York, 1948, 1935.

52. J. Paul, in G.H. Rothblat and V.D. Cristofalo, eds., *Growth, Nutrition, and Metabolism of Cells in Culture*, Academic Press, London, 1972 pp. 1–9.

53. C. Waymouth, G.H. Rothblat, and V.D. Cristofalo, eds., *Growth, Nutrition, and Metabolism of Cells in Culture*, Academic Press, London, 1972 pp. 11–47.

54. M. Murray and G. Kopech, *A Bibliography of the Research in Tissue Culture 1884–1950*, Academic Press, New York, 1953.

55. A.S. Lewis and W.H. Lewis, *Anat. Rec.* **5**, 277–293 (1911).

56. K.J. Lambert and J.R. Birch, in R.E. Spier and J.B. Griffiths, eds., *Animal Cell Biotechnology*, Vol. 1, Academic Press, London, 1985 pp. 86–122.

57. R.E. Spier, in K.C. McCullough and R.E. Spier, eds., *Monoclonal Antibodies in Biology and Biotechnology: Theoretical and Practical Aspects.* 1990, pp. 265–315.

58. J.B. Griffiths, in R.E. Spier, and J.B. Griffiths, eds., *Animal Cell Biotechnology*, Vol. 3, Academic Press, London, 1988 pp. 279–221.

59. E.N. Willmer, *Cells and Tissues in Culture: Methods, Biology and Physiology*, Vols. 1–3, Academic Press, London, 1965.

60. R.E. Spier, *Adv. Biochemi. Eng.* **14**, 119–162 (1980).

61. R.E. Spier, in R.E. Spier and J.B. Griffiths, eds., *Animal Cell Biotechnology*, Vol. 1, Academic Press, London 1985 pp. 243–265.

62. M.A. Tyo and R.E. Spier, *Enzyme Micro. Technol.* **9**, 514–520 (1987).

63. R.E. Spier and N. Maroudas, in C. Ho and D. Wang, eds., *Animal Cell Bioreactors*, Butterworth-Heinemann, Stoneham, Mass., 1990 pp. 191–212.

64. R.E. Spier and A. Kadouri, *Enzyme Microb. Technol.*, **21**, 2–8 (1997).

65. B.-S. Kim and D.J. Mooney, **16**, 224–230 (1998).

66. F. Oberpenning, J. Meng, J.J. Yoo, and A. Atala, *Nat. Biotech.* **17**, 149–155 (1999).

67. H.D. Humes et al., *Nat. Biotech.* **17**, 451–455 (1999).

68. J.D. Flax et al., *Nat. Biotech.* **16**, 1033–1039 (1998).

69. R.E. Spier, in A. Mizrahi and A.L. van Wezel, eds., *Advances in Biotechnological Processes*, Vol. 2, 1983 pp. 23–59.

70. R.E. Spier, in A. Moreira and K.K. Wallace, eds., *Information Science Applications in Bioprocess Engineering*, Kluwer Academic Publishers, Dordrecht, The Netherlands, 1996, pp. 325–47.

71. R.E. Spier and M.W. Flowler, in *Compr. Biotechnol.* **1**, 301–330 (1985).

72. L. Hayflick, *Dev. Biol. Stand.* **70**, 11–26 (1989).

73. *Animal Cell Technology Industrial Platform (ACTIP), Beneficial Effects of Animal Cell Technology*, Drukkerij Humanitas, Rotterdam, The Netherlands, 1994.

74. R.E. Spier and J.B. Griffiths, eds., *Animal Cell Biotechnology*, Vols. 1–6, Academic Press, London, 1985–1994.

75. R.I. Freshney, *Culture of Animal Cells: A Manual of Basic Technique*, 2nd ed., Alan R. Liss, New York, 1988.

76. M. Butler, *Animal Cell Technology: Principles and Products*, Open University Press, Milton Keynes, 1987.

77. J.T. Syverton, W.F. Sherer, and G. Butorac, *Proc. Soc. Med.* **77**, 23–27 (1951).

78. F.C. Robbins, in S.A. Plotkin, and E.A. Mortimer, eds., *Vaccines*, Saunders, Philadelphia, 1988, pp. 98–114.

79. J.R. Paul, *A History of Poliomyelitis*, Yale University Press, New Haven, Conn., 1971, pp. 369–470.

80. N.B. Finter, in R.E. Spier, J.B. Griffiths, and B. Meignier, eds., *Production of Biological from Animal Cells in Culture*, Butterworth-Heinemann, Oxford, U.K., 1991 pp. 3–12.

81. L. Hayflick, *Exp. Gerontol.* **33**, 191–207 (1998).

I

ICH GCP GUIDELINES: PREPARATION, CONDUCT AND REPORTING OF CLINICAL TRIALS

Jean-Luc De Bouver
Smithkline Beecham Biologicals
Rixensart, Belgium

OUTLINE

INTRODUCTION

This article will take you through the procedures used when initiating and conducting clinical trials. After setting the scene and describing the main players of this essential part of the medical research, the different steps of the preparation, conduct, and closing of a clinical trial will be described. Frequent references will be made to the International Conference for Harmonisation Good Clinical Practice (GCP) Guidelines (1) described in another article of this book.

All of these steps will be described from the point of view of a monitor, a person who is placed in charge on behalf of the sponsor, to follow the study conducted on site by the investigator from the first to the last day of a clinical trial (Fig. 1). The article will begin, when the decision is taken to move (a new candidate drug) into the clinical development stage.

THE PREPARATION

After much laboratory research, animal testing, and many regulatory approvals, the drug is now ready for clinical trials. Usually, the first approvals are given by the Ministry of Health of the country where the clinical trial will take place. Having carefully examined the preclinical file containing all the data collected so far on the new drug, they deliver the authorization to use it in clinical trials. In the United States, the United Kingdom, and countries with similar regulatory systems, this authorization is called (Investigational New Drug IND) or (Clinical Trial Exemption CTX) (2–4).

Clinical Development Plan

Any project to develop a new drug in an important pharmaceutical company will be carefully prepared and decided on the basis of a "Clinical Development Plan." At this stage, the project leader with the help of the regulatory affairs department will describe the clinical work required by the regulatory authorities. It will be structured in a plan with different phases, each phase usually including several clinical trials.

Phases of Clinical Development

Classically the development plan is divided into 4 sequential phases:

Phase I studies focus mainly on the safety and pharmacokinetics of the drug used for the first time in humans. These studies are generally conducted in a small number of healthy volunteers (maximum around 50) and will be the basis of a go no go decision to enter into a more extensive phase of clinical research.

Phase II studies consist of larger trials (20–50 subjects per group and 2–6 groups or more) including comparisons between different dosages (e.g., dose range studies), different administration modes, routes, or schedules, different presentations, etc. Phase II and later phases studies are conducted in patients or subjects for whom the drug will be used, progressively moving from the strongest (healthy adult volunteers) to the weakest (e.g., babies presenting with the specific disease condition for which the drug is being developed). These studies will be statistically analyzed to draw conclusions on the mode of administration, the dosage, the regimen, the schedule, the ideal presentation of the drug, and to give an idea how the drug compares with other developmental and commercialized products and with a placebo. From Phase II studies, the ideal profile of the future drug should be decided. This product, as close as possible to the future production drug presentation, is then moved to Phase III.

Phase III includes large studies (from several hundreds up to several thousand subjects or more, often patients).

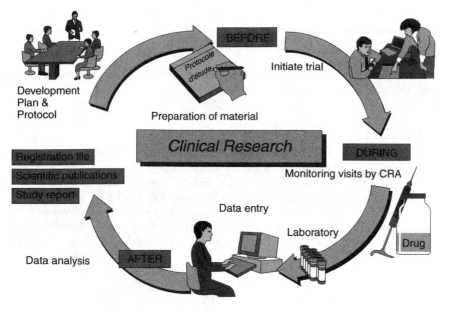

Figure 1. A clinical trial from preparation to report.

These studies should confirm that the proposed drug formula is the most effective for treating or preventing the disease, that it compares positively with other available or potential drugs (and of course with a placebo), does not have medium, or long-term unacceptable side effects, and can be produced consistently in industrial conditions.

Phase IV studies, (which will not be described here,) include all studies conducted after the drug has been approved by the regulatory authorities for specific indications. The ICH Guidelines are now introducing a new classification into phases based more on the objectives of clinical trials than on their timing (5).

From Development Plan to Study Protocol

A clinical development plan including studies for the different development phases has been written. Now each study will need to be described, prepared, initiated, conducted, and reported. The first step is to prepare a protocol that describes the future study in detail. For this purpose, a study protocol written according to the strict structure of the ICH guidelines[1] is prepared in the Clinical Research department of the sponsor, normally an international pharmaceutical company. According to the "Declaration of Helsinki" principles, now integrated into the ICH GCP guidelines, the study must be built on sound scientific principles. Its benefits for subjects or patients should always outweigh risks at any time of the study. The protocol is the basis on which the Ethics Committee decides on the acceptability of the study.

The document starts by describing the background and rationale for conducting the study. Clear objectives are defined: the primary objective (usually one) and secondary objectives (two or three) are each linked with clear and measurable end points. The key part of the document is

the description of the study procedures and the people who are responsible.

Other parts include a description of the statistical methods and analyses, standard sections on ethics, adverse events reporting, confidentiality, audits, and ancillary documents. After having been approved by the Ethics Committee or Institutional Review Board, the protocol should be strictly adhered to by all parties involved. If procedures need to be modified at any time, an amended version of the protocol should be submitted and approved by the Ethics Committee before any practical change is implemented.

Investigator Brochure

All available clinical and preclinical data have to be described in a document called the *Investigator Brochure*. The ICH guidelines define its structure and content. This brochure is provided to the investigator early in the contacts with the agency to prepare the study. It is also an important document for the Ethics Committee to help them decide on the acceptability of the proposed study. This document, written by the sponsor, must be updated annually with new study data or other safety information about the product gathered from any available source included in the amended document.

The Case Report Form

To collect individual patient data during the study, the investigator is provided with individual booklets for each patient. These documents called *Case Report Forms* or *Case Record Forms* (CRF) are usually standard across the studies of a particular project. They are structured to follow the different study procedures in sequential order and contain fields aimed at collecting all data and observations required by the study protocol for each study patient (6).

The CRFs should be user-friend and easy to fill in by the investigator while avoiding mistakes or unclear data.

---

[1] ICH guidelines stands for "International Conference on Harmonization"—Guidelines on Good Clinical Practice, Chapter E6 (May 96, revised Sept 97) (1).

They should also be easy for the monitor to review and easy to understand by the people who will be in charge of the data management and analyses.

The CRFs are often presented as bound booklets printed on *no carbon required* (NCR) paper with two, three, or more color copies per page for the different users, for example, one for the sponsor and official archives, one for data management, and one for the investigator. These documents, filled in by the investigator or his staff, constitute the official set of data that is reviewed by the site monitor during monitoring visits and controlled by the auditors or authorities during inspection.

Investigator Selection

In any study, the investigators are key people. They agree on the protocol, recruit the patients and follows the drug administration procedures described in the protocol. They are responsible for obtaining the ethical approval for the study, taking care of the patients, collecting the study data, acquiring adverse event information, and reporting them to the sponsor and the Ethics Committee, as required by the applicable regulations. They are closely involved in writing the study report and presenting or publishing the data. Effective collaboration between the sponsor, the monitor, and the investigator's staff is essential for the success of any trial (7).

Responsibilities

Most Good Clinical Practice guidelines include a clear definition of the responsibilities of the different parties involved in clinical trials. Table 1 gives a summary of them.

The Critical Path of a Clinical Trial

As in any managing other project, many different actions have to be taken at the same time to minimize the preparatory time for a clinical trial. It is important to identify these "critical (that is, the key steps which, when delayed, will delay the whole clinical trial) path" steps, early. For instance, logistic aspects and regulatory approvals could be prepared at the same time. If a protocol summary or schematic is used to describe the details of the study procedures, the CRF and protocol could be finalized at the same time as the packaging of the study drug is taking place. During the study, data can be entered on an ongoing basis, and questions can be generated as soon as the data have been checked. This would save time at the end when the last questions or *Data Resolution Queries* (DRQs) are sent to the site. Indeed, those last DRQs are on the critical path because delaying them would delay the closing of the database and, consequently, the analysis of the study.

Ethics Committee Approval

Before any study can start, written approval from an Independent Ethics Committee (IEC) should have been obtained in writing by the investigator. This committee, which should work according to the GCP and agree to cover the region where the study would take place; should work according to Standard Operating Procedures (SOPs); meet at regular intervals, and have a minimum composition defined by the ICH guidelines or the local regulations.

These requirements are among the most difficult to comply with. Indeed, many IECs do not follow or are even not aware of these requirements. Often, the IEC approval takes several months. The approval document often misses standard elements like details of the protocol identification or the list of other approved documents, for example, Informed Consent, advertisements, or protocol amendments.

The quality of the IECs is improving in many regions of the world, but the standards of these committees are still behind most other aspects of the clinical trial process. Regulatory authorities are key in these improvements. No doubt an increase in the training and inspections by these committees would contribute to increased awareness by the IECs to the international standards and requirements (8).

The Informed Consent Process

As mentioned earlier, the Informed Consent (IC) document and Subject Information Sheet (SIS) should also be submitted to the IEC. Their content, detailed in the ICH under the description of the investigators' responsibilities, contains a list of about 20 mandatory elements. Regional directives and regulations often add elements to this list, like the European Directive on data privacy protection

Table 1. GCP Responsibilities in the Conduct of a Clinical Trial

The sponsor	The monitor	The investigator
• SOPs (Standard Operating Procedures)	• Appointed by Sponsor	• Agrees to the protocol
• Protocol design	• Works according to SOP's	• Selects patients
• Investigator selection	• Regularly oversees conduct of study	• Provides facilities and staff
• Product knowledge	• Reviews CRFs against source documents	• Independent Ethics Committee approval
• Medication	• Adheres to protocol	• Informed consent
• Appoints trained monitors	• Conduct of study to Good Clinical Practice	• Confidentiality
• Safety reporting	• Interface between sponsor and investigator	• Medication
• Data and analysis		• Collects data
• Report		• Reports adverse events
• Quality assurance and internal audit program		• Archives data
• Compensation		

that requires a specific consent to keep patients[1] private data and to transfer these data to countries with less stringent regulations.

Informed consent should be obtained under the investigator's authority in the language of the subject. The process for obtaining this consent is as important as the text of the information (9). Subjects should indeed be free to enter or withdraw from the study without any impact on the way they are cared for by their medical doctors. The signed individual informed consent could sometimes be obtained by a legal representative or in presence of a witness for example, for minors or illiterate patients. The consent should always obtained before any specific study procedures are undertaken.

Ready to Start

The protocol and the contract have been signed. The material, for example, CRFs, Informed consents medications, and other ancillary study documents are ready. The regulatory authorities and ethical approvals have been obtained, and the study staff has been adequately briefed or trained. The study site has been evaluated and prepared, and the patient recruitment strategy has been agreed upon.

The study can start, and patients can be enrolled, but not before an initiation visit or visits by the monitor or a representative of the sponsor has taken place on-site. This mandatory visit must be conducted at each study center, in the presence of all key investigator staff members. It is one of the longest and most important site study visits. Its quality often decides on the quality of the data collected. It is also key and marks the start of the active collaboration between the site monitor and the investigator's team. The medications are brought on site at that particular visit. After this last step, patient recruitment starts.

THE INITIATION OF THE STUDY

Initiation Visit

Initiation could take place in one or several visits. A first visit could cover all the administrative aspects, like the review of the protocol, the study documents and the responsibilities of the investigator. It could also be organized in the form of an investigator meeting for all study site personnel. The second part of the initiation visit could include a review of the study medication which should be organized at each study site with the appropriate people present.

Review of Study Documents. The CRF is the key document at this stage (6). The protocol has usually already been reviewed earlier with the principal investigator. The CRF review could be a more practical way to go through all aspects of the study procedures with all the people involved in the conduct of the study at the site. Other important documents to be reviewed at this stage would include subjects' informed consents, identification logs and other recruitment documentation, Serious Adverse Event forms and the way to report all adverse events, study medication

documentation, DRQs or questions on collected data, and the way to correct data in the CRF.

The Study Drug. Although at the first stage of study initiation, dummy medications could be a useful tool for explaining how to handle and administer the study drug, the second part of the initiation visit must include a review and an inventory of the actual medications delivered on site. The way to store and distribute those medications should be discussed with the pharmacist or the person in charge of the study medication at the study site. Other important aspects include the final inventory and the return or disposal of all study medications after the study is completed.

STUDY MONITORING AND FOLLOW-UP

During the study, regular monitoring visits to the site by the study monitor will take place. They usually will be organized every six to eight weeks, but their frequency will vary according to the stage, the quality, and the complexity of the study. The main objectives of the visits is to assess the progress of the study, to check compliance with GCP, the regulations, and adherence to the study protocol and to maintain the quality of the data.

Source Data Verification

Source data are defined as the original recording of the data to be transcribed in the CRF or to be used in the study (10). The direct access to the documents containing these original data has become an absolute requirement for the ICH GCP guidelines: a study should not be conducted any longer at a site that does not allow the monitor or the auditors to consult patient files and other source documents related to the study.

At each monitoring visit, the monitor will confirm the existence and maintenance of these source documents and systematically review the correct transcription of the data into the CRFs. The level of review should be adapted to the importance and the quality of the data. All of the primary efficacy variables should be checked, as well as the receipt of each individual informed consent. Other information could be sampled for verification: The percentage checked could be decreased if the quality of the data is high, but an immediate increase in the percentage verified should take place if more mistakes are spotted or when the study procedures become more complex. The detail of the source documents and CRF review should be documented in the report at the end of each monitoring visit.

Collaboration between Monitor and Investigator's Staff. Collaboration between the investigator, the study nurse, the staff, and the monitor will be required at every step of the study (7). During the monitor's visits, some time will be devoted by the monitor to the individual review of the CRFs, at which stage the investigator is not required to attend. Later on, the investigator should be available to spend some time with the monitor to review all of the main issues about the progress of the study. The correction of the CRFs must be signed and dated by an authorized member of the investigator's staff, and medical procedures should be discussed with medically qualified personnel (6). Although the study nurse, the administrative coordinator, or the pharmacist do an important part of the job, the investigator must retain full responsibility for the conduct and quality of the study.

After each monitoring visit, the monitor has to document in a visit report the information collected and the actions discussed at the visit. This report will remain in the sponsor's documentation. Written communication should also be maintained between the study staff and the sponsor to summarize the elements discussed during the site visits, confirm the actions decided, and provide additional information and decisions for the future of the study. Study documentation, the progress of the project, the financial aspects of the study and the conclusions of audits and inspections should also be reviewed regularly.

ADVERSE EVENTS REPORTING

Sponsors are legally required to report adverse events regularly to their regulatory authorities. The continuous collection of this information will maintain the safety profile of the product up-to-date ensuring appropriate information about and protection of the subjects enrolled in the clinical studies.

Responsibilities Linked with the Conduct of Clinical Studies

The Sponsor. Sponsors are responsible for maintaining databases with all safety information about the drugs under development. They should report any changes in the safety profile of these products to the authorities within strict time lines.

Via the monitor, they will be in regular contact with investigators who should be provided with all safety information relevant to the conduct of the study and the protection of the subjects. The monitor will have to check that the investigator's staff is adequately trained and understands the safety reporting mechanisms and will often take an active part in this educational process at the study site.

The Investigator. Investigators should be familiar with the product safety profile, the protocol, and the time lines for reporting serious and nonserious adverse events to the sponsor. Late reporting of serious adverse events (SAEs) is one of the most common alert findings in study site audit reports.

The investigator should establish a mechanism for immediate (i.e., within 24 hours) reporting of SAEs to the sponsor. Adequate follow-up of the subjects until complete recovery or stabilization of their health conditions is required for all adverse events.

Another issue in adverse events reporting by investigators is their responsibility for reporting unexpected serious adverse drug reactions to the Ethics Committee and to the regulatory authorities, if required by the local regulations. SAEs will be considered unexpected if they have not yet been described in the relevant safety documentation, that is during the study, in the investigator's brochure.

STUDY CLOSING AND LAST VISIT ON SITE

At the end of each study, a site closing or completion visit is mandatory. It ensures that (1) all necessary information has been collected (CRFs, Adverse Events), (2) all medications have been accounted for and disposed of appropriately, (3) the administrative aspects of the documentation meet regulatory requirements, and (4) the remaining financial aspects have been appropriately addressed. Together with the investigator's staff, the monitor ensures that all site activities and responsibilities are completed before closure of the study site.

In order not to delay this last step, the visit should be planned as soon as the date of the last visit of the last subject enrolled is known. The visit should then take place immediately after all remaining material and documents have been prepared by the investigator. The monitor checks with the investigator on all outstanding Case Report Forms and data queries. Excess medications are returned to the sponsor or disposed of as appropriate. With the help of the monitor, the investigator makes sure that all study documents are adequately filed in the study file and are ready for later inspection by regulatory authorities.

Archiving Study Documentation. The current ICH GCP guidelines do not provide any fixed duration for archiving study documentation. They are very detailed about the list of essential study documents to be maintained, but archiving requirements are linked to the last marketing application within the ICH region, which is difficult to plan at the time of study closing. A more practical archiving period definition would be welcome. In the meantime, the sponsor has the responsibility for informing the investigators when they are allowed to discard the study documents.

The sponsor can help the investigator in this archiving process. Often there is not any space at the study site. Because of the changes in institution's personnel, it not may be easy to ensure long-term protection of the study documents. One easier way to ensure these obligations may be for the sponsor to archive all investigator study documents in sealed containers for the period required by the authorities. Those boxes should not be opened without the presence of the investigator or an authorized staff member.

STUDY ANALYSIS, REPORT, AND PUBLICATIONS

The analysis and reporting of clinical studies have been extensively detailed in recent ICH guidelines (11,12). Before any report is written, a report analysis plan (RAP) should be approved by the sponsor. Any study analyses should then be done according to the analysis plan detailed in that document. As required for a protocol, when changes in the analysis are decided, the RAP should be amended and reapproved.

Statistical analyses of Phase I to III studies are conducted more and more by specialized sponsor personnel. Their statistical report will then be the basis of the study report. Again, this document should follow the strict table of contents provided by the ICH guidelines if it is intended to be submitted to regulatory authorities as part of a registration file. The investigators could also do the analysis and write the study report. More often, they review the report written by the sponsor and approve its final version.

Publications are an important aspect of investigative medical research. They can take place at any time of the study. Usually, the sponsor and the investigator have established a contract before the study starts, including publication plans and agreement as to authorship. Additional unplanned presentations or publications should be submitted for agreement between the sponsor and the investigator.

Although the sponsor could not prevent an investigator from publishing study data, contracts are often executed to protect the confidentiality of research data. They usually include provisions for mutual agreement and a review period to allow each of the parties to adequately secure discoveries and protect new manufacturing processes or medical procedures and devices through patents or registration applications. Presentations at congresses and scientific meetings and publications in peer-reviewed journals ensure that all important scientific data collected during any clinical trials are made available in an unbiased way to the entire scientific and medical community.

BIBLIOGRAPHY

1. *Int. Conf. Harmonization*, 1996, Chapter E6.

2. J. Winslade and D. Hutchinson, *Dictionary of Clinical Research*, Brookwood Medical Publications, U.K., 1992.

3. G. Neher and D. Hutchinson, *A Practical Guide to FDA GCP for Investigators*, Brookwood Medical Publications, U.K., 1993.

4. D. Hutchinson, *MRECs, LRECs and GCP Ethics Requirements*, Brookwood Medical Publications, U.K., 1998.

5. *Int. Conf. Harmonization*, 1997, Chapter E8.

6. EFGCP Audit Working Party, *Appl. Clin. Trials* **4**(10), 67–69 (1995).

7. A. Raven, *Clinical Trials, An Introduction*, Radcliffe Medical Press, Oxford, U.K., 1993.

8. J. Williams, *Appl. Clin. Trials* **6**(5), 78–80 (1997).

9. M. Hochhauser, *Appl. Clin. Trials* **6**(5), 66–73 (1997).

10. V. Zepp and D. Mackintosh, *Appl. Clin. Trials* **5**(3), 42–46 (1996).

11. *Int. Conf. Harmonization*, 1995, Chapter 3, CPMP/ICH/-137/95.

12. *Int. Conf. Harmonization*, 1998, Chapter 9, CPMP/ICH/-363/96.

ADDITIONAL READING

Council for International Organizations of Medical Sciences (CIOMS), *International Ethical Guidelines for Biomedical Research Involving Human Subjects*, CIOMS, 1993.

Raven A., *Consider it Pure Joy . . .*, 3rd ed. Cambridge Healthcare Research, U.K., 1997.

Raven A., *Beyond What is Written*, Cambridge Healthcare Research, U.K., 1998.

World Health Organization, Division of Drug Management and Policies, *Guidelines for Good Clinical Practice (GCP) for Trials on Pharmaceutical Products*, WHO, Geneva, 1992.

See also cGMP COMPLIANCE FOR PRODUCTION ROOMS IN BIOTECHNOLOGY: A CASE STUDY; ETHICAL ISSUES IN ANIMAL AND PLANT CELL TECHNOLOGY; PRODUCT DEVELOPMENT, QUALITY AND REGULATORY ISSUES; STERILIZATION AND DECONTAMINATION; VIRAL INACTIVATION, EMERGING TECHNOLOGIES FOR HUMAN BLOOD PRODUCTS.

IMMUNO FLOW INJECTION ANALYSIS IN BIOPROCESS CONTROL

KATJA KLOCKEWITZ
Institut für Technische Chemie
Hannover, Germany

OUTLINE

Introduction
Fundamental Considerations
    Flow-Injection Analysis
    Immunoanalysis
Applications
    Turbidimetric Immuno-FIA
    Heterogeneous Elution Assay
    Flow ELISA
    Capacitance Immunoassay
    Grating Coupler
Conclusion
Bibliography

INTRODUCTION

For the determination of biotechnologically produced proteins, fast and automated analytical methods are essential to monitor and control the bioprocess during the cultivation of mammalian and bacterial cells (1). Using antibodies as highly specific binding partners for the analyte of interest, a selective and sensitive determination in complex protein mixtures and cultivation media without further purification steps is possible. Due to an expanded production of polyclonal and monoclonal antibodies, obtained from infected animals and hybridoma cells, their application in immunoassays in clinical and biological analysis, drug and environmental applications, and bioprocess monitoring has become increasingly common. A combination of flow-injection analysis (FIA) with different kinds of immunoassay (homogeneous and heterogeneous) see Plasier has been found to be a powerful tool for an automated system for precise online monitoring of bioprocesses and process control. These assays provide an enormous improvement in accuracy, precision, and sensitivity. Compared to batch methods, a dramatic reduction of analysis time (close to real-time performance), online coupling to industrial processes, easy calibration, and the possibility of integrating many types of reactions, separations, and detection processes with different assay formats become possible.

FUNDAMENTAL CONSIDERATIONS

Flow-Injection Analysis

The principle of flow-injection analysis was developed by Ruzicka and Hansen in 1974 (2,3). It is based on the controlled and reproducible dispersion of a sample zone when it is injected in a continuous carrier flow. This transports the segment through a reaction coil (manifold, to a detector), where a detectable reaction of the analyte is performed. A schematic setup is shown in Figure 1.

The pump used can be simple, as, unlike HPLC, high pressure does not develop in the flowing stream. A syringe or piston pump is superior to a peristaltic pump to reduce pulsation and maintain continuous flow rates. Injection of samples and standards in the analysis stream is normally performed by a sample loop in combination with a rotary valve or a combination of valves if further reagents have to be added. The overall precision of the method may depend on the precision of the sample injection, especially if small volumes are used. A minimal washing volume of about 2–3 sample-loop volumes is recommended (4). The manifold consists of one or several reaction coils or of a membrane or a carrier material, placed in a cartridge or column as in chromatography, on which either the antibody or antigen is covalently attached. In some cases magnetic particles held by an electric field have also been used. Finally, a detector with a flow-through cell is required. Here all kinds of detectors for spectroscopic, electrochemical, chemilumenescence, or fluorimetric measurement are suitable, depending on the assay performed. As all these components are available for HPLC systems, they can be used with minimal modifications. The size and form of the resulting signal depend significantly on the dispersion of the sample on its way through the flow channel and detector. System control and data processing should be automated and performed by a computer to ensure the reproducibility of the assays (5).

Immunoanalysis

Immunoassays. Immunoassay procedures (see article by Plasier) have two parts: the actual immunoreaction and the subsequent detection of the immunocomplex formed. These detection methods can be divided into two major classes: immunoreactions with or without chemical labeling of the immunocomplex. Tables 1 and 2 give a detailed overview of known techniques. Some of them are, of course, not suitable for on-line use, but are mentioned here to complete the picture.

When labeling is not used, the formation of the immunocomplexes must be monitored directly. Five classes of methods are known, as shown in Table 1 (6–10). The measurement of the light scattering behavior of the immunocomplex suspension by turbidimetry is one of the simplest methods used for bioprocess monitoring.

In order to improve the sensibility of immunoassays, labeling techniques have been developed. In Table 2 different assays involving labels are listed. The use of radioactive labeling is well known and used a lot in medical applications. Assays using enzyme labels are often based on competition between free and labeled immunopartners (11–13). The best-known type of enzyme immunoassay (EIA) is the ELISA (enzyme-linked immunoabsorbent assay), normally combined with a photometric detection system. ELISA tests are widely used in many areas of biotechnology and medicine, due to their high sensitivity; typical concentration measurements are in the attomolar (aM) to picomolar (pM) range. This means that time-consuming sample diluting is necessary, leading to a problem with accuracy. Furthermore, the assay involves several time-consuming washing and incubation steps, which is why this method is unsuitable for (quasi) on-line process monitoring.

As shown, many different immunoassay types have been developed; however, only RIA, ELISA, and some nephelometric assay are widely used for off-line assays. The use of RIA is decreasing due to health and environmental problems.

Selection of Antibodies. All immunochemical methods are based on the specific reaction between the antigen (Ag) and its antibody (Ab). Today, polyclonal antibodies, obtained from infected animals, and monoclonal antibodies, produced by hybridoma cells, are used in immunoreactions. In traditional immunoassays, the most efficient and strongest binding antibodies are used. In repeated binding assays, like the immuno-FIA, other criteria become more important. A critical point in this context is the dissociation step in heterogeneous assays, when the Ab–Ag complex is broken and the system is equilibrated for the next assay. It is important to achieve complete dissociation; otherwise the capacity of the system will be reduced at each analysis cycle. Remaining labeled antigen may also interfere with the subsequent assay. As the dissociation step is time dependent, a compromise must be reached between the time consumed and the remaining material. The antibodies must be efficient in binding, but they must also be efficient in releasing the bound material under reasonable conditions, where the antibody remains active. This means that antibodies that are less efficient in binding and with appropriate properties with respect to dissociation are the most suitable (14).

Reactant Immobilization. Although homogeneous and heterogeneous assays have been developed in immuno

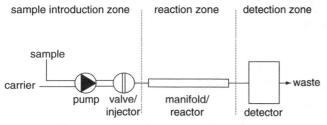

sample introduction zone | reaction zone | detection zone

Figure 1. Scematic setup of a FIA system.

Table 1.

Immunoanalytical methods without labeling

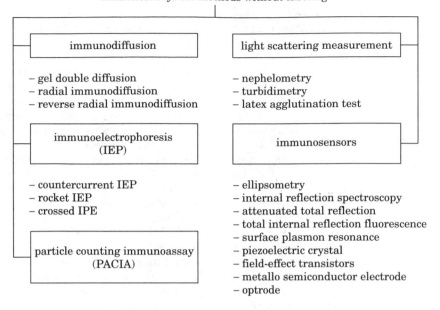

Table 2.

Immunoanalytical methods with labeling

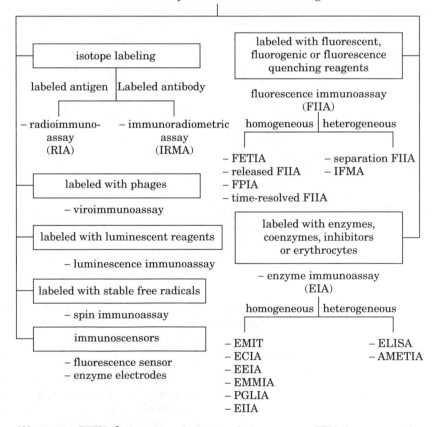

Abbreviations: FETIA, fluorescence excitation transfer immunoassay; FPIA, fluorescence polarization immunoassay; IFMA, immunofluorimetric assay; ELISA, enzyme-linked immunosorbent assay; AMETIA, antibody masking enzyme tag immunoassay; EMIT, enzyme multiplied immunoassay technique; ECIA, enzyme channeling immunoassay; EEIA, enzyme enhancement immunoassay; EMMIA, enzyme modulator immunoassay; PGLIA, prosthetic-group-label immunoassay; EIIA, enzyme inhibition immunoassay.

flow-injection analysis, heterogeneous assays comprise the majority of the currently performed immunoassays (15). The use of a solid phase enables easy separation of the bound and the unbound portion of the analyte, normally by means of an immobilized antibody, binding the analyte, while the remaining components of the sample can be washed out. Automated heterogeneous immunoassays offer many advantages (16). They are more sensitive and extremely flexible as to the choice of solid phase and detection principle. Furthermore, they offer accelerated binding kinetics, as the surface-area-to-volume ratio is high, leading to an effective concentration of captured antibodies.

A variety of supports are available: soft gels (agarose), cellulose, resins, polymers, bonded-phase silica, and glass beads in different presentations, which can be easily washed and retained in the test tube. Additional applications with immunomagnetic beads, held in place by a magnetic field, facilitating the deposition of the beads, activated membranes, capillaries, or other high-surface-area matrices are used (17–19). The choice of support and immobilization method is of central importance. but no one system works effectively for all applications. More detailed discussion on this topic can be found in several monographs (20,21). In any case, covalent binding of the antibody to the substrate in the reaction zone is preferable, especially if an elution/regeneration step is part of the assay. The covalent binding of the antibodies via protein primary amine functionalities results in specific activities of about 5–25%. Loss of activity can be explained by (1) steric blockage of the binding side due to inappropriate orientation of the antibody on the substrate, (2) crowding and (3) excessive multiple attachment of antibodies on the substrate, and (4) insufficient room for antigen binding, particularly if the antigen is large. Higher activities can be obtained by controlling the immobilized antibody density, using the Fab' fragments or by coupling through a thiol group created by the reduction of an inter-heavy-chain disulfide bond (22).

Nonspecific adsorption of sample components must be kept to a minimum, as any irrelevant binding to the support will influence the background value and the sensitivity of the assay. Following antibody coupling, the excessive groups are often blocked with either small amine-containing species (e.g., ethanolamine) or nonspecific protein. A further important aspect of the preparation is the removal of noncovalently bound material by exposing the coupled matrix to wash cycles of alternating high and low pH or chaotropic conditions such as high salt concentrations (14).

APPLICATIONS

On-line protein monitoring has been developed with turbidimetric as well as with homogeneous and heterogeneous immunoassays. Despite numerous publications concerning the on-line application of immunoassays on model systems, the number of on-line immunochemical systems applied to real samples, especially to bioprocess monitoring, is relatively low.

Turbidimetric Immuno-FIA

The turbidimetric assay is based on the optical density determination of the precepitation curve of immunocomplexes (23). In a solution with an excess of antibodies, a linear correlation between the concentration of an added antigen and the turbidity can be observed.

In the turbidimetric assay system, an antigen-containing sample or standard is injected into the FIA system at the same time as an aliquot of antibody solution. They are mixed and flow to the thermostated reaction coil, where the flow is stopped to extend the incubation time. The formation of the immunocomplex leads to precipitation. The particles stay in solution for a while, scattering the light. The solution is then pumped into a flow-through spectrophotometer, where the turbidity is measured at 340 nm. The medium blank absorbance is monitored on a second channel as a reference. The level of turbidity is then related to the difference of both channels. The schematic setup of the turbidimetric immuno-FIA (TIA) system is shown in Figure 2 (24).

Antigen concentration can be correlated to peak area or peak height. An analysis cycle consists of the following steps: injection of the sample, incubation for immunocomplex formation [depending on the system; e.g., 20 sec for anti-A-Mab, 90 sec for rt-PA (25)], and the reequilibration of the system. Several analysis variables such as reaction temperature, injection and reaction time, ratio of antigen to antibody concentrations, and the influence of media components have to be studied and optimized for every assay. The assay time can range from 1 to 6 min depending on the optimized incubation time. As a cell-free sample stream is necessary, a sampling system is recommended. With this automated system it was possible to quantify pullulanase isoenzymes produced in bacteria in a range of 1–100 mg L^{-1} (26,27), AT III in a range of 0–30 mg L^{-1} (26), and mouse IgG in the range of 10–900 mg L^{-1} (24). Figure 3 shows a comparison between the on-line turbidimetric immunoassay detected

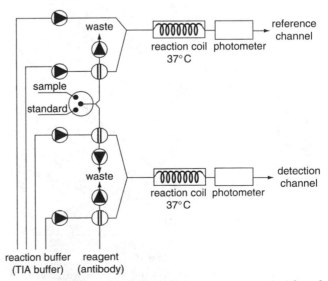

Figure 2. Automated turbidimetric immunoassay system based on the principle of a FIA system. *Source*: Ref. 24.

rt-PA concentration to an off-line ELISA in a cultivation of CHO cells (28).

Heterogeneous Elution Assay

These assays are based on the direct binding between antibodies and unlabeled antigen, while an excess of one of the binding partners is immobilized to a solid support (comparable to affinity chromatography). This technique enables an easy separation of the unbound components and the analyte. After the application of an elution step, the target protein can be detected by protein fluorescence without any further labeling.

The elution conditions should be chosen carefully, as exremes of pH or high concentrations of chaotropic salts may cause permanent or temporary damage, like denaturation (see previous discussion on the selection of antibodies).

Monitoring of Antigen Production. An excess of antibodies is immobilized to a solid support [e.g., CNBr-activated Sepharose; VA-Epoxy Biosyth (29)] and placed in the flow system in a small cartridge (e.g., 1 mL MoBiTec) behind an injection valve with a sample loop (Fig. 4) (29). The principle of the heterogeneous elution assay is shown in Figure 5 (29). After injection of the sample and the binding of the antigen to the immobilized antibody in the cartridge, the whole system is rinsed with carrier buffer to wash out byproducts. In the following procedure the antigen–antibody bond is broken by the application of an elution step (e.g., high pH), and the washed-out target protein is detected by a spectrofluorometer; λ_{exc} is fixed at 280 nm and λ_{em} at 340 nm (29). The integral of the peak area is correlated to the antigen concentration. After a short equilibration step the system can be reused for the next sample. The total cycle time including elution and equilibration is 6–8 min, depending on the complexity of the media used. The ability of this system is demonstrated in Figure 6 for the rt-PA concentration in culture supernatant over several days (29).

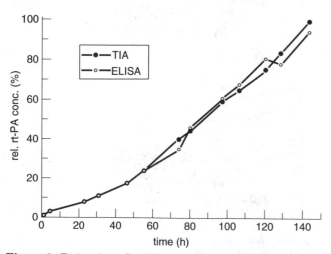

Figure 3. Estimation of rt-PA concentration with the turbidimetric immunoassy (TIA) and an off-line ELISA in a culture of CHO cells (28).

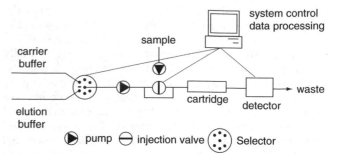

Figure 4. Setup of a heterogeneous elution assay (29).

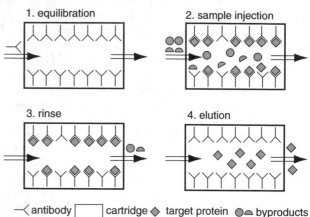

Figure 5. Principle of the heterogeneous elution assay (29).

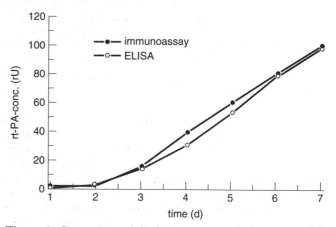

Figure 6. Comparison of the heterogeneous elution assay with an off-line ELISA for rt-PA determination (29).

At very low concentrations it might be more suitable to perform a competitive immunoassay with labeled antigens to increase the sensitivity. The antigen from the samples competes with labeled antigen (e.g., FITC labeled) for a defined number of binding sites in the reaction zone. The more antigen is in the sample, the less the labeled antigens can bind to the immobilized antibodies. After an elution step, the fluorescence of the labeling compound can be measured (Fig. 7). With an increasing content of antigen in the sample, less fluorescence can be detected. The same setup and principle as mentioned before can be

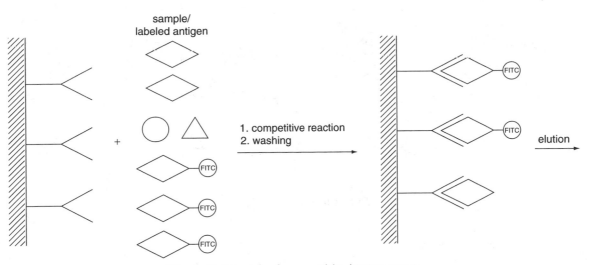

Figure 7. Principle of a competitive immunoassay.

used, except that the sample with the analyte has to be mixed with a reagent containing labeled antigen (28).

Monitoring of Antibody Production. Comparable heterogeneous immuno systems as mentioned above can also be used to monitor the production of different immunoglobins during mammalian cell cultivation. To catch the immunoglobins, immobilized anti-mouse IgG antibodies, Protein A or Protein G can be used (30,31). New approaches have also been made to use thiophilic gels binding antibodies from a wide variety of animal species (22,32). To elute the antibodies from the antigen matrix, a shift to low pH (down to 3.0–2.5) is widely used in these applications (33). Figure 8 indicates the ability of this system by comparing the IgG titer from a mammalian cell cultivation process analyzed with ELISA and the heterogeneous elution immunoassay over the range 0–400 μg mL^{-1} (31).

Flow ELISA

ELISA assays are well established as an off-line technique but are commonly regarded as being too slow for process

monitoring and control. This non competitive assay is based on the formation of a sandwich of an excess of immobilized antibodies, the antigen, and an excess of enzyme-labeled antibodies. Normally, the reaction of an substrate with the enzymes leads to a colored product, which can be detected spectrophotometically (34). By adapting the ELISA principle (Fig. 9) to flow-injection conditions, a lot of its advantages like high sensitivity can be kept and most of the disadvantages can be overcome. Furthermore, this system can be fully computerized and made capable of registering dynamic changes in concentration.

The technique was subject to several investigations concerning stability, reproducibility, and capacity, where it was found to be suitable for determining the concentration of macromolecules (35,36), but it has not been used for monitoring a fermentation process.

Another application was found in the process monitoring of several different downstream processes (37). Here a sample stream was withdrawn into the FIA system before the UV detector, which continuously measured the absorbance of the effluent from the column (Fig. 10). The system was found to be suitable to achieve precise information about the elution time of the target protein, which enables the user to determine the fractions to be collected. Furthermore, the use of this highly sensitive technique reduces the volume of sample to be analyzed.

Capacitance Immunoassay

This technique is based on the principle that for electrolytic capacitors the capacitance depends on the thickness and dielectric behavior of a dielectric layer on a surface of a metal plate. As the capacitance and the sensitivity of the device are inversely related to the thickness of the dielectric, thin layers have to be formed to get highly sensitive sensors. Tantalum strips with an electrochemically grown 25 nm tantalum oxide layer were found to be efficient in this type of assay (Fig. 11) (38). Antibodies or antigens were immobilized onto the tantalum oxide surface by silanization of the surface and coupling to it

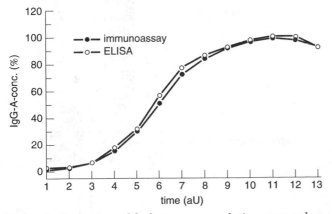

Figure 8. Comparison of the heterogeneous elution assay and an off-line ELISA during an IgG production run (31).

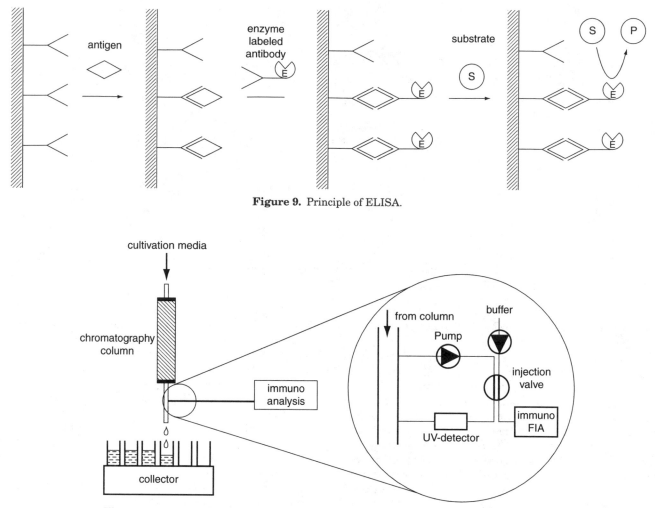

Figure 9. Principle of ELISA.

Figure 10. Schematic setup of the immunoassay combined with a downstreaming process.

with carbodiimide. Binding of the corresponding analyte to the immobilized protein resulted in modification of the electrical capacitance of the system, which can be measured with an impedance meter. Each measuring cycle consisted of the following steps: rinsing the sensor, incubation of the sample, and rinsing again (39). Changes in capacitance were observed continuously. The difference between the initial (before incubating the sample) and the final capacitance (after the second rinsing) are taken as the analytical signal indicating the amount of analyte.

With this assay it was possible to monitor the production of IgG during a cultivation process with an error of about 8–15%, which is in the range of the standard deviation of an ELISA test used as reference (39). The detectable concentration range was about 2–200 μg mL^{-1} IgG.

Grating Coupler

This technique is based on the physical principle of the evanescent wave, which is sensitive to changes in the refractive index at the sensor surface. The change in refractive index at the sensor surface due to antibody binding is observed by measuring the

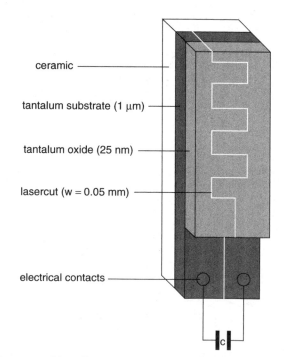

Figure 11. Thin-film tantalum oxide flowthrough sensor (38).

uncoupling angle. From the measured change of the uncoupling angle the effective refractive index is calculated (40). The system does not require reagents or labels and is based on the principle of a biosensor (conjugation of transducer with biological component).

Immobilization of the antibodies on the grating coupler was performed after silanization and activation with glutaraldehyde. Remaining free groups were blocked by bovine serum albumin (BSA) solution. With a sensor chip placed in a flow system a production run of IgG by a hybridoma cell line was monitored (40). After rinsing the sensor, the sample is injected. Using the stop-flow technique, the sample segment is incubated in the flow cell, followed by rinsing and regeneration. As indicated in Figure 12, the data obtained by the on-line measurement with the grating coupler coincide with the off-line reference ELISA. A detection range of about $10-150$ μg mL^{-1} was found to be obtainable with this technique.

CONCLUSION

To summarize: immuno flow-injection analysis is a useful analytical tool for bioprocess monitoring. Rapid results, heightened sensitivity, and great specificity are the powerful properties of this analysis technique. Characterization of the immunoassays themselves is complex as any assay with a biological receptor, but they can be highly specific. Throughput and loss of sensitivity due to regeneration are the issues needing the most attention in further research. But as an alternative to robotic systems, FIA systems offer a simplified system of automation with a high potential as to the new miniaturization (microfabricated) systems. The ability to increase the number of manifolds or channels offers a throughput advantage, especially compared with traditional, time-consuming off-line methods like ELISA.

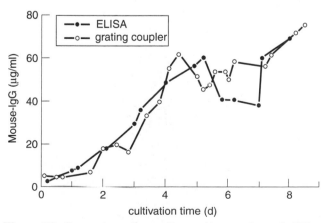

Figure 12. Comparison of an on-line grating coupler and off-line ELISA for the determination of mouse IgG during a cell culture (40).

BIBLIOGRAPHY

1. T. Scheper and F. Lammers, *Curr. Opin. Biotechnol.* **5**, 187–191 (1994).
2. J. Ruzicka and E.H. Hansen, *Anal. Chim. Acta* **78**, 145–157 (1975).
3. J. Ruzicka and E.H. Hansen, *Anal. Chim. Acta* **99**, 37–76 (1978).
4. J.W. Dolan and L.R. Snyder, *Troubleshooting LC Systems*, Humana Press, Clifton, N.J., 1989, p. 244.
5. B. Hitzmann et al., *Anal. Chim. Acta* **313**, 55–62 (1995).
6. J.T. Whicher and D.E. Perry, in W.R. Butt, ed., *Practical Immunoassay: The State of the Art*, Decker, New York, 1984, pp. 117–177.
7. J.F. Place, R.M. Sutherland, and C. Dähne, *Biosensors* **1**, 321–353 (1985).
8. C.L. Cambiaso et al., *J. Immunol. Methods* **18**, 33–44 (1994).
9. J. Clausen, *Immunochemical Techniques for the Identification and Estimation of Macromolecules*, Elsevier, Amsterdam, 1984.
10. D. Collet-Cassart, N.J. Limet, L. Van Krieken, and R. De Hertog, *Clin. Chem. (Winston-Salem, N.C.)* **35**, 141–143 (1989).
11. M. Oellrich, in J. Bergmeyer and M. Grassl, eds., *Methods of Enzymatic Analysis*, Verlag Chemie, Weinheim, pp. 233–260, 1983.
12. C. Blake and B.J. Gould, *Analyst (London)* **109**, 533–547 (1984).
13. R.C. Boguslaski and T.M. Li, *Appl. Biochem. Biotechnol.* **7**, 401–414 (1982).
14. E. Liddell and I. Weeks, *Antibody Technology*, Bios Scientific, Oxford, U.K., 1995, pp. 121–124.
15. G. Gübitz and C. Shellum, *Anal. Chim. Acta* **283**, 421–428 (1993).
16. D.W. Chan, *Immunoassay Automation: A Practical Guide*, Academic Press, San Diego, Calif., 1992.
17. C.H. Pollema, J. Ruzicka, and G.D. Christian, *Anal. Chem.* **64**, 1356–1361 (1992).
18. S. Solé, S. Alegret, F. Céspedes, and E. Fàbregas, *Anal. Chem.* **70**, 1462–1467 (1998).
19. P.M. Krämer and R.D. Schmid, *Pestic. Sci.* **32**, 451–462 (1991).
20. K. Mosbach, ed., *Immobilized Enzymes*, Vol. 44, Academic Press, New York, 1976.
21. M. Wilchek, T. Miron, and J. Kohn, *Methods Enzymol.* **104**, 3–55 (1984).
22. D.A. Palmer, M. Evans, and J.N. Miller, *Anal. Proc. Anal. Commun.* **31**, 123–135 (1994).
23. J.T. Whicher, C.P. Price, and K. Spencer, *Crit. Rev. Clin. Lab. Sci.* **18**, 213–260 (1983).
24. A. Degelau et al., *J. Biotechnol.* **25**, 115–144 (1992).
25. B. Schulze et al., *Cytotechnology* **15**, 259–269 (1994).
26. R. Freitag, T. Scheper, and K. Schügerl, *Enzyme Microb. Technol.* **13**, 969–975 (1991).
27. R. Freitag et al., *Anal. Chim. Acta* **249**, 13–122 (1991).
28. C. Middendorf et al., *J. Biotechnol.* **31**, 395–403 (1993).
29. K. Beyer, M. Reinecke, W. Noe, and T. Scheper, *Anal. Chim. Acta* **309**, 301–305 (1995).
30. W. Stöcklein, V. Jäger, and R.D. Schmidt, *Anal. Chim. Acta* **245**, 1–6 (1991).

31. M. Reinecke and T. Scheper, *J. Biotechnol.* **59**, 145–153 (1997).

32. T.W. Hutchens and J. Porath, *Anal. Biochem.* **159**, 217–226 (1986).

33. A. Junbauer et al., *J. Chromatogr.* **476**, 257–268 (1989).

34. K. Schügerl, *Analytische Methoden in der Biotechnologie*, Vieweg, Braunschweig, 1991, p. 120.

35. M. Nilsson, H. Haakanson, and B. Matthiasson, *Anal. Chim. Acta* **249**, 163–168 (1991).

36. M. Nilsson, G. Matthiasson, and B. Matthiasson, *J. Biotechnol.* **31**, 381–394 (1993).

37. M. Nilsson, H. Haakanson, and B. Matthiasson, *J. Chromatogr.* **579**, 383–389 (1992).

38. A. Gebbert, M. Alvares-Icaza, W. Stöcklein, and R. Schmid, *Anal. Chem.* **64**, 997–1003 (1992).

39. A. Gebbert et al., *J. Biotechnol.* **32**, 213–220 (1994).

40. R. Polzius et al., *Biotechnol. Bioeng.* **42**, 1287–1292 (1993).

See also FLUX ANALYSIS OF MAMMALIAN CELL CULTURE: METHODS AND APPLICATIONS; OFF-LINE ANALYSIS IN ANIMAL CELL CULTURE, METHODS; OFF-LINE IMMUNOASSAYS IN BIOPROCESS CONTROL; ON-LINE ANALYSIS IN ANIMAL CELL CULTURE.

MEASUREMENT OF CELL VIABILITY

M. BUTLER
University of Manitoba
Winnipeg, Manitoba
Canada

OUTLINE

INTRODUCTION

Viability is a measure of the metabolic state of a cell population which is indicative of the potential of the cells for growth. One of the simplest assays is dye exclusion, which is an indication of the ability of the cell membrane to exclude a dye. This may be included in a protocol for microscopic cell counting in which the relative proportion of stained and nonstained cells is determined. More sophisticated measures involve the assessments of the cell's capability to make DNA or proteins. A further metabolic assay measures the intracellular adenylate nucleotide concentrations. This allows the determination of the energy charge, which is an index of the metabolic state of the cells.

Viability, assayed using one of these protocols, may be monitored during the course of the culture of a cell line in order to follow changes during the phases of growth. Alternatively, many of these techniques have been developed as cytotoxicity assays to determine the potential toxicity of a test compound on a specific cell line. Such cytotoxicity tests in cell culture have become viable alternatives to live animal tests such as the Draize rabbit eye irritancy test (1).

The viability index is a measure of the proportion of live, metabolically active cells in a culture, as indicated by the ability of cells to divide or to perform normal metabolism. The index is determined by a measure of the metabolic state of the cells (such as energy charge) or by a functional assay based on the capacity of cells to perform a specific metabolic function.

The viability index may be expressed as a percent of viable cells in a population; that is, viability index equals 100 times the number of viable cells/total number of cells.

DYE EXCLUSION

Cell viability may be observed microscopically following a staining technique such as dye exclusion. This is based on the ability of viable cells to exclude large molecules. Dead or damaged cells are unable to prevent passage of the dye through the cell membrane and are therefore stained with a characteristic color. The most commonly used exclusion dye is trypan blue, which stains nonviable cells blue, and these can be observed using a light microscope. Trypan blue is often added to a cell suspension before counting by a hemocytometer-based method (2). The dye should be at a low concentration in a physiological buffer to minimize cell damage during the assay. The dye penetrates the membrane of nonviable cells, which are stained blue and can therefore be distinguished from viable cells.

In this method, an equal volume of trypan blue (0.2% w/v in phosphate-buffered saline) is added to a cell suspension and the mixture is incubated for 5 min at room temperature. The sample is then aspirated repeatedly by a Pasteur pipette to ensure a homogeneous cell suspension. An aliquot can be introduced into the hemocytometer for counting. The procedure should be performed rapidly, not longer than 1 h before examination. The percentage of cells that are not stained is a measure of the viability of the cell population.

Other exclusion dyes that can be used include eosin Y (0.15%), erythrosin B (0.02%), and nigrosin (0.05%) (3). The concentrations given are the recommended optimal concentrations in the cell suspension. Normally stock solutions ($\times$10) may be prepared in phosphate buffered saline pH 7.3. The dye solution may then be diluted 1:10 with the cell suspension. All these dyes are taken up preferentially by dead cells, which then can be identified under a light microscope. However, at high dye concentrations viable cells may exhibit a slow uptake.

VITAL STAINS

Viable cells exhibit specific uptake or passive infiltration of certain vital dyes or stains. The dyes cause a coloration of viable cells but not dead or damaged cells. Procedures used with the vital dyes should be rapid—typically no longer than 1 h before microscopic examination. Suitable dye solutions are dilute (0.01%) and in a physiological buffer. This will minimize damage to the cells during the assay. Stable stock solutions at $\times$100 of the working concentration are commonly prepared as indicated (Table 1).

Table 1. Vital Dyes that can be used to Monitor Cell Viability

Stain	Action	Stock concentration
Methylene blue	stains viable cells	45 mg/mL methylene blue in 15 : 1 v/v ethanol/100 mM KOH ($\times$100)
Toluidine blue	stains viable cells	5 mg/mL toluidine blue in 1 : 4 v/v ethanol/water ($\times$100)
Janus green	stains mitochondria	2.5 mg/mL in water ($\times$100)
Neutral red	stains lysosomes	4 mg/mL in water ($\times$100)
Diacetyl fluorescein/propidium bromide	differential fluorescent stain: dead cells red; live cells green	10 μg/mL diacetyl fluorescein/500 μg/mL propidium iodide in PBS ($\times$10)
Ethidium bromide/acridine orange double stain	differential fluorescent stain: dead cells red; live cells green	1 mg/mL ethidium bromide/1 mg/mL acridine orange in PBS ($\times$100)

An assay using neutral red is a good example of the type of technique that can be used (4). Neutral red is 3-amino-7-dimethyl 2-methylphenazine hydrochloride, which is soluble in water, resulting in a slightly basic solution. The cellular uptake of this dye is based on passive transport across the plasma membrane. Within the cell, neutral red accumulates in the lysosomes, probably because of binding to fixed acidic groups within the lysosomal matrix. The acidic environment of the lysosome of viable cells is essential for trapping the dye. Dead or damaged cells do not retain neutral red because of the loss of the integrity of the lysosomes.

A suitable protocol for a neutral red assay is as described below. Although the assay can be adapted to any cell type, it is easiest with anchorage-dependent cells contained in multiwell plates, as this allows rapid changes of medium and solutions.

> Remove the cells from the normal growth medium and resuspend in medium containing 40 μg/mL neutral red. This is a $\times$100 dilution of the stock solutions (Table 1).
> Incubate for 3 h.
> Wash the cells with phosphate-buffered saline and a solution of 1% $CaCl_2$/0.5% formaldehyde. The latter will remove extraneous dye crystals
> Extract the dye into 1% acetic acid/50% ethanol by rapid agitation for 10 min.
> The absorbance of the extracted dye can be determined at 540 nm. This can be performed directly with a multiwell plate using a plate reader.

If this protocol is designed to measure the relative viability of cell populations that may have been exposed to potentially toxic compounds, then a comparison is typically made to control cells as follows:

loss of viability = absorbance from treated
cells/absorbance from control cells

In Table 1 alternative vital stains are listed. Each of these could be adapted to a similar protocol for viability monitoring using the suggested stock solutions. The exact times and concentrations of exposure to each dye will vary depending upon the cell type.

DUAL FLUORESCENT STAINING

Differential staining of viable and nonviable cells may be achieved by the use of two dyes, a technique useful in fluorescence microscopy or in a flow cytometer. A commonly used fluorescent agent is diacetyl fluorescein (1 μg/mL), which is taken up and hydrolyzed to fluorescein only by viable cells, which emit a green fluorescence. Nonviable cells may be stained with ethidium bromide or propidium iodide (50 μg/mL), both of which emit a red fluorescence. In both cases the recommended dye concentration in the cell suspension is given. Ideally $\times$10 stock solutions would be prepared and diluted with a cell suspension (Table 1).

RELEASE OF RADIOACTIVE CHROMIUM (^{51}Cr)

The method is based on the initial rapid uptake of ^{51}Cr–sodium chromate into cells. Viable cells will oxidize the Cr^{3+} to Cr^{2+}, which does not cross the membranes of viable cells (5). By counting the gamma radiation of the supernatants and cell pellets of aliquots of a cell suspension over a period of time, the rate of loss of radioactive chromium can be determined. It has been shown that the rate of loss of ^{51}Cr correlates with the loss of cell viability. Thus the release of radioactivity represents an efflux from damaged or dead cells. The advantage of this method compared to dye exclusion or vital staining is that it has the potential for a high degree of sensitivity. It can also be a rapid method if multiple samples are analyzed using automated equipment.

TETRAZOLIUM ASSAY

Cell viability can be determined by a functional assay such as the tetrazolium assay, which is a measure of cellular oxidative metabolism (6). The tetrazolium dye, MTT [3-(4,5-dimethylthiazol-2-yl)-2,5-diphenyltetrazolium bromide] is reduced to a colored formazan product by the activity of dehydrogenase enzymes and indicates a high rate of cellular oxidative metabolism (7). The color development (yellow to blue) is proportional to the number of metabolically active cells. The dark blue formazan product is insoluble in water and must be extracted by an organic solvent prior to absorbance determination. The response obtained in this assay varies considerably between cell types.

The cellular reduction of MTT is dependent on the oxidative metabolism and the cellular content of NADH or NADPH. Cells having a significant glycolytic rate and high NADH production produce a good response in the MTT assay. The reduction of MTT occurs intracellularly and may be facilitated by NAD(P)H-dependent enzymes of the endoplasmic reticulum as well as succinate dehydrogenase in the mitochondria.

The method is particularly convenient for the rapid assay of replicate cell cultures in multiwell plates. Plate readers are capable of measuring simultaneously the kinetics of reactions in each well of a standard 96-well plate.

A suitable protocol is as follows:

Add 0.1 mL MTT reagent (5 mg/mL in PBS) to 1 mL culture.

Incubate for 2 h at 37 °C.

Extract the formazan product, which is insoluble, with 600 μL of SDS reagent (20% w/v sodium dodecyl sulfate in N,N-dimethyl formamide/water (1 : 1 v/v).

Measure the absorbance at 570 nm.

The volumes may be reduced proportionally for determinations in a multiwell plate. A linear relationship has been shown between the absorbance and cell number up to 10^5 cells per well. For higher cell numbers it may be necessary to construct a standard curve based upon serial cell dilutions.

Alternative tetrazolium dyes are XTT (2,3-bis(2-methoxy-4-nitro-5-sulfophenyl)-5-[(phenylamino)carbonyl]-2H-tetrazolium hydroxide) (8) and WST-1 (Boehringer). These can be incorporated into similar assays but with the advantage that the formazan products are water soluble. Therefore, there is not a need for solubilizing samples prior to measurement of absorbance. Both XTT and WST-1 are available from Boehringer. Care must be taken with the use of these reagents in interpreting cell viability, as they may be reduced in the absence of cell extracts. Unlike MTT the reduction of XTT and WST-1 may be brought about by NADH or NADPH even in the absence of cells. Also other reducing agents including dithiothreitol, mercaptoethanol, reduced glutathione, cystine, or ascorbic acid may reduce XTT and WST-1. The reduction of WST-1 may also occur on the cell surface.

COLONY-FORMING ASSAY

The most precise of all the methods of viability measurement is the colony-forming assay. Here the ability of cells to grow is measured directly (9). A known number of cells at low concentration is allowed to attach and grow on the surface of a Petri dish. If the cell concentration is kept low, each viable cell will divide and give rise to a colony or cluster of cells. From this the "plating efficiency" is determined as the number of colonies scored per 100 cells plated times 100. Although the colony-forming assay is time consuming, it has been widely used in cytotoxicity studies.

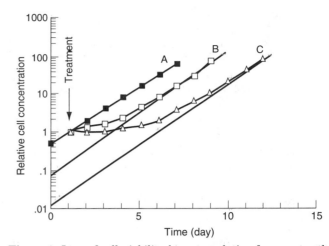

Figure 1. Loss of cell viability by extrapolation from a growth curve (from 9). The culture is grown for one day from an inoculum of 0.8×10^4 cells/mL. At day 1 the culture is split into 3 (A, B, and C). Culture A is an untreated control, whereas cultures B and C are treated with different toxic compounds at the point marked by an arrow. The effect of the treatments can be determined from the relative surviving fraction by back-extrapolation of each growth curve. In B loss of cell viability = 0.1/0.8 = 0.125; in C loss of cell viability = 0.01/0.8 = 0.0125.

A less precise method of determining the viability by the cellular reproductive potential is from the lag phase of a growth curve. Figure 1 shows that by extrapolation from the linear portion of a growth curve to time zero, the derived cell number can be compared with the original cell count. This method can be easily adapted to determine how a particular treatment (such as addition of a toxic compound) affects cell viability.

LACTATE DEHYDROGENASE DETERMINATION

A decrease in viability of cells is usually associated with a damaged cell membrane, which causes the release of large molecules such as enzymes from the cell into the medium.

Thus the loss of cell viability may be followed by an increase in enzyme activity in the culture medium (10–12). Lactate dehydrogenase (LDH) activity is the enzyme most commonly measured in this technique. The enzyme activity can be measured easily by a simple spectrophotometric assay involving the oxidation of NADH in the presence of pyruvate. The reaction is monitored by a decrease in UV absorbance at 340 nm.

$$\text{pyruvate} + \text{NADH} + \text{H}^+ \xrightarrow[\substack{\text{NADH absorbs at} \\ \lambda = 340 \text{ nm}}]{\text{LDH}} \text{lactate} + \text{NAD}^+$$

The method is well suited for the determination of multiple samples, particularly if a multiwell plate reader is available. However, care must be taken when interpreting the results by this method because the LDH content per cell can change considerably during the course of batch culture. The loss of cell viability can be expressed as the activity of LDH in the medium as a proportion of total LDH in the culture.

A suitable protocol is as follows:

Mix 2.8 mL Tris HCl (0.2 M), pH 7.3, 0.1 mL NADH (6.6 mM), and 0.1 mL sodium pyruvate (30 mM) in a cuvette.

Preincubate for 5 min at the desired reaction temperature (25 or 37 °C).

Start the reaction by adding 50 μL of sample or standard LDH enzyme.

Determine the enzyme activity as an absorbance decrease at 340 nm.

INTRACELLULAR ENERGY CHARGE

The energy charge (EC) is an index based on the measurement of the intracellular levels of the nucleotides AMP, ADP, and ATP.

$$EC = ([ATP] + 0.5[ADP])/([ATP] + [ADP] + [AMP])$$

This is based on the metabolic interconversion of the three adenylate nucleotides in the cell:

$$AMP \longleftrightarrow ADP \longleftrightarrow ATP$$

The index (EC) varies between the theoretical limits of 0 and 1. For normal cells values of 0.7 to 0.9 would be expected, but a gradual decrease in the value gives an early indication of loss of viability by a cell population.

These nucleotide concentrations can be measured by chromatography (HPLC) or by luminescence using the luciferin–luciferase enzyme system. Such measurements are not as easy to perform as the routine counting procedures discussed earlier but can allow a means of monitoring the decline in the energy metabolism of a cell culture that occurs during the loss of viability (13,14).

The luminescence assay is dependent upon the emission of light resulting from the enzymatic oxidation of luciferin, a reaction requiring ATP.

$$ATP + LH_2 + O_2 \longrightarrow AMP + PPi + CO_2 + L + light$$

ADP and AMP can also be measured by the luciferase assay after conversion to ATP by coupled enzymatic reactions.

$$ADP + PEP \xrightarrow{\text{pyruvate kinase}} ATP + pyruvate$$

$$AMP + CTP \xrightarrow{\text{myokinase}} ADP + CDP$$

A suitable protocol is as follows:

Extract soluble nucleotides by addition of 0.1 mL perchloric acid (20% v/v) to 1 mL of a cell culture sample (10^6 cells/ml).

Place on ice for 15 min and centrifuge for 5 min at 10,000 g.

Remove supernatant and neutralize with 5 M KOH.

For ATP determination: Mix 860 μL 0.1 M Tris acetate, pH 7.75, 10 μL sample and 100 μL ATP monitoring reagent (MR). The latter is obtained from LKB and contains a lyophilized mixture of firefly luciferase, D-luciferin, bovine serum albumin, magnesium acetate, and inorganic pyrophosphate. This is reconstituted from each vial with 4 mL buffer plus 1 mL potassium acetate (1 M).

For ADP determination: Add a further 10 μL PK-PEP [55 μL tricyclohexylammonium salt of phosphoenolpyruvate (0.2 M) + 50 μL pyruvate kinase (500 U/mg) in Tris buffer].

For AMP determination: Add a further 10 μl MK-CTP [95 μL myokinase (2500 U/mg) + 10 μL CTP (110 mM) in Tris buffer].

For standardization: Add a further 10 μL ATP (0.1 μmol) standard.

Measure the light emission at each stage in a luminometer (LKB 1250) after 1 min.

RATE OF PROTEIN SYNTHESIS

The rate of protein synthesis of intact cells can be measured by incubation in standard culture medium to which is added a radioactively labeled amino acid. Any radioactive amino acid is suitable, but those most commonly used are ^{3}H-leucine or ^{35}S-methionine. The cells should be incubated in the medium for sufficient time to measure radioactivity in the extracted cell pellet, normally up to 4–6 h (15). It is important to allow enough time during incubation for sufficient radioactivity to be incorporated into the cells.

A suitable protocol is as follows:

Add ^{3}H-leucine or ^{35}S-methionine at a final specific activity of 20–40 μCi/mL to a cell suspension at $(5-10) \times 10^6$ cells/mL.

Remove $(5-10) \times 10^5$ cells at each time point up to 4–6 h.

Isolate the cell pellet by centrifugation in a microcentrifuge tube and wash in PBS.

Precipitate protein by addition of 500 μL trichloroacetic acid (TCA) (5%) containing unlabeled amino acids.

Wash the protein precipitate three times in the TCA solution.

Add 30 μL NCS tissue solubilizer to the pellet and leave for 60 min.

Cut tip of tube and place in scintillation fluid for radioactive counting.

RATE OF DNA SYNTHESIS

The rate of DNA synthesis of a cell population can be determined in a similar radioactive incorporation assay to that described for protein synthesis. The commonly used radioactively labeled nucleotide precursor is tritiated thymidine (^{3}H-TdR) or deoxycytidine (^{3}H-CdR). The exposure period may be short (30–60 min) for DNA synthesis rate determinations and a specific activity of 1 µCi/mL of culture is sufficient. However, higher specific activities may be required if using culture media containing thymidine (such as Ham's F12). The radioactivity incorporated into DNA can be determined from the TCA insoluble fraction, which can be trapped on a filter disc following vacuum filtration. The incorporated radioactivity is determined by liquid scintillation counting of the filter. This is a similar method to that described for the determination of protein synthesis. Although only cells in the S-phase of the cell cycle will be able to utilize ^{3}H-TdR, the incorporation may still allow a comparison between the DNA synthesizing activity of two or more cell populations. This technique of incorporation of ^{3}H-TdR can also be used to determine a labeling index as a measure of the relative proportion of cells in the S-phase (16).

BIBLIOGRAPHY

1. E. Borenfreund and B. Borrero, *Cell Biol. Toxicol.* **1**, 55–65 (1984).

2. M.K. Patterson, *Methods Enzymol.* **58**, 141–152 (1979).

3. J.P. Kaltenbach, M.H. Kaltenbach, and W.B. Lyons, *Exp. Cell Res.* **15**, 112–117 (1958).

4. A. Doyle and J.B. Griffiths, eds., *Cell and Tissue Culture: Laboratory Procedures in Biotechnology*, Wiley, New York, 1998, pp. 65–70.

5. R. Zawydiwski and G.R. Duncan, *In Vitro* **14**, 707–714 (1978).

6. A. Doyle and J.B. Griffiths, eds., *Cell and Tissue Culture: Laboratory Procedures in Biotechnology*, Wiley, New York, 1998, pp. 62–64.

7. T. Mosmann, *J. Immunol. Methods* **65**, 55–63 (1983).

8. N.W. Roehm, G.H. Rodgers, S.M. Hatfield, and A.L. Glasebrook, *J. Immunol. Methods* **142**, 257–265 (1991).

9. J.A. Cook and J.B. Mitchell, *Anal. Biochem.* **179**, 1–7 (1989).

10. R.E. Spier, *Biotechnol. Bioeng.* **19**, 929–932 (1977).

11. A. Doyle and J.B. Griffiths, eds., *Cell and Tissue Culture: Laboratory Procedures in Biotechnology*, Wiley, New York, 1998, pp. 71–75.

12. A. Wagner, A. Marc, and J.M. Engasser, *Biotechnol. Bioeng.* **39**, 320–326 (1992).

13. O. Holm-Hansen and D.M. Karl, *Methods Enzymol.* **57**, 73–85 (1978).

14. A. Lundin, M. Hasenson, J. Persson, and A. Pousette, *Methods Enzymol.* **133**, 27–42 (1986).

15. A.J. Dickson, in M. Butler, ed., *Mammalian Cell Biotechnology: A Practical Approach*, Oxford University Press, Oxford, U.K., 1991, pp. 85–108.

16. R. Baserga, ed., *Cell Growth and Division: A Practical Approach*, Oxford University Press, Oxford, U.K., 1989, pp. 1–6.

See also BIOREACTOR OPERATIONS—PREPARATION, STERILIZATION, CHARGING, CULTURE INITIATION AND HARVESTING; CHARACTERIZATION OF CELLS, MICROSCOPIC; OFF-LINE ANALYSIS IN ANIMAL CELL CULTURE, METHODS.

MEMBRANE STRUCTURE AND THE TRANSPORT OF SMALL MOLECULES AND IONS

ANDRÁS KAPUS
Toronto Hospital
Toronto, Ontario
Canada

OUTLINE

INTRODUCTION: THE CELL MEMBRANE: BARRIER AND BRIDGE

Every cell is an independent living unit surrounded by a well-defined boundary, the plasma membrane. This structure separates the cell from its environment and allows the maintenance of an intracellular milieu that markedly differs from the extracellular space (Fig. 1). Moreover, each cell contains intracellular membranes that enclose specific subcompartments or organelles such as the mitochondria, the endoplasmic reticulum, the lysosomes, or the Golgi network. The uneven distribution of ions and other solutes (i.e., the existence of *transmembrane electrochemical gradients*) is the thermodynamic basis of

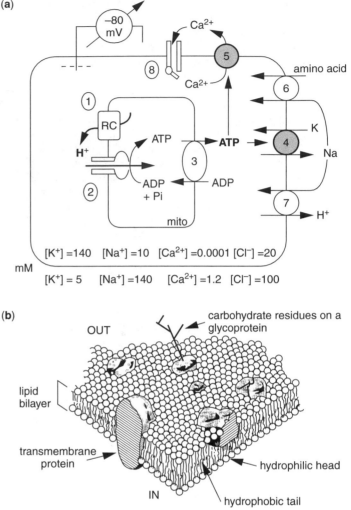

Figure 1. The role of membrane transport processes in biological energy production and conversion. (**a**) Substrate oxidation by the respiratory chain (RC, 1) of the mitochondrion (mito) results in the extrusion of protons from the intramitochondrial space. H^+ backflux into the mitochondrion energizes the F_0F_1-ATPase (2) to catalyze ATP synthesis. The generated ATP is transported into the cytoplasm by the ATP/ADP exchanger (3), where it drives primary active transport systems of the plasma membrane such as the Na^+/K^+ pump (4) and the Ca^{2+} pump (5). These transporters build up transmembrane ion gradients that can be used to drive secondary active transport processes or channel-mediated diffusion of ions. For example, the Na^+ gradient is utilized to drive amino acid uptake through the Na^+–amino acid cotransporter (6) or H^+ release through the Na^+/H^+ exchanger (7). The electrochemical gradient of Ca^{2+} is the driving force for the regulated influx via the voltage-gated Ca^{2+} channels (8). The uneven ion distribution and the selective permeability of the membrane for the various ions results in the formation of an inside-negative membrane potential. Typical intra- and extracellular concentrations of some important ions are shown at the bottom of the model cell. (**b**) The basic structure of the cell membrane. The text explains how this architecture provides both separating and connecting functions.

a multitude of vital physiological phenomena [Fig. 1(a)]. A breakthrough in the understanding of the essential role of biological membranes in energy conservation was achieved in the early 1960s, when Peter Mitchell, in his *chemiosmotic hypothesis* (1), postulated that substrate oxidation through the respiratory chain induces *vectorial translocation* (i.e., extrusion) of protons from the intramitochondrial space, leading to the formation of an H^+ electrochemical gradient ($\Delta\mu H^+$) across the mitochondrial membrane. This $\Delta\mu H^+$ is then the driving force for H^+ backflow, which occurs through an H^+-translocating enzyme complex, the F_0/F_1 ATPase. The H^+ current flowing through the enzyme enables it to catalyze the formation of ATP from ADP and inorganic phosphate. The ATP generated during oxidative phosphorylation can be used to build up other electrochemical gradients (e.g., for K^+, Na^+, and Ca^{2+}) across the plasma membrane, which can be further utilized for many purposes, including the formation of action potentials, the accumulation of nutrients, the release of waste products, the regulation of contraction and exocytosis, and the control of cell volume or intracellular pH. The chemiosmotic theory, which has been repeatedly validated by experimental observation (2), points to two crucial features of biological membranes:

(1) the presence of "active components," which generate uneven distribution of certain materials across the membrane, and (2) the selective permeability, which helps to maintain and allows the regulated dissipation of the existing gradients. Both the formation of these gradients and their useful dissipation (conversion) require a plethora of subtly controlled transport processes. It is therefore not surprising that pro- and eukaryotic cells contain a large number of transport proteins (which serve to provide passageways for ions, nutrients and waste products), the genes for which amount to 5–15% of their genome (3).

The aim of this article is to give a concise summary of the major transport processes of the plasma membrane for small molecules. Since both the separating and the connecting functions of the membrane are intimately related to its structure, this will be discussed first, followed by the classification of various transport entities according to their *energetics* and *mechanism*. Subsequently, I will describe the major characteristics of *channels, carriers*, and *pumps*, using representative examples in each category. Finally, I will show how the interplay between several transport systems can result in the fine control of complex physiological functions such as pH and volume homeostasis.

BASIC ARCHITECTURE OF THE CELL MEMBRANE: A TRANSPORT-MINDED VIEW

Cell membranes are composed of lipids, proteins, and carbohydrates. The ratio of these constituents can vary greatly depending on cell type and subcellular localization of the membranes. For example, the lipid/protein ratio by weight is $4:1$ in the myelin of nerve cells, whereas it is $1:4$ in the mitochondrial inner membrane. The plasma membrane of an "average" mammalian cell, like a hepatocyte, contains approximately 50–55% lipid, 40–45% protein, and 5% carbohydrate, the latter being covalently bound to proteins and lipids forming glycoproteins and glycolipids (4). These components are organized into a well-defined architecture [Fig. 1(b)]. The basic structural unit of the cell membrane is a *phospholipid bilayer*. This bilayer is composed of two *leaflets* of amphipatic phosholipid molecules whose polar head groups are in contact with the intra- or extracellular water phase, whereas their apolar tails face each other, constituting the hydrophobic interior of the membrane. This structure, held together mostly by hydrophobic interactions between the fatty acyl chains, forms a "two-dimensional" lipid continuum around the cell. This is the structural basis of the separating function of the membrane because the bilayer can be penetrated only by small and lipid soluble molecules (see the following).

The connecting function is related to the proteins. Membrane proteins are either attached to the external or internal layer of the polar head groups of the phospholipids or are embedded into the lipid bilayer. The first group is called *extrinsic* or *peripheral* membrane proteins, while the other group is termed as *integral* or *intrinsic* membrane proteins. Many representatives of this latter group, the so-called *transmembrane proteins*, span the whole lipid bilayer one or more times and are therefore available both from the outer and inner (cytoplasmic) side. Practically all proteins catalyzing membrane transport (or certain subunits of these, in the case of multicomponent transporters) belong to this category. To traverse the lipid core of the membrane, proteins should contain a long enough (>3 nm) sequence composed of 19 or more hydrophobic amino acids forming an α-helical structure. If the whole amino acid sequence of a protein is known, the presence of such potentially membrane-spanning α-helical rods can be predicted by various algorithms. Of these, the most widely used is the *Kyte–Doolittle hydropathy plot* (5), in which a hydropathy index is assigned to each amino acid reflecting the hydrophobicity of its side chain. Then, using a moving window approach, a running average is generated for 10–20 neighboring amino acids and the values are plotted against the amino acid sequence number [Fig. 2(a)] (6). Although the validity of the predicted results were completely authenticated only in those few transport proteins [e.g., bacteriorhodopsin (7,8)] that had been crystallized and directly analyzed, the hydropathy plots are generally in good agreement with less direct experimental approaches and have revealed previously unsuspected similarities in the *topology* of various membrane proteins. For example, many hormone and neurotransmitter receptors possess 7 transmembrane domains (7-TM receptors), while 12-TM segments can be found in a large number of apparently nonrelated, and mechanistically distinct transporters, including the mammalian Na^+/H^+ exchangers (9,10) [Fig. 2(a) and (b)], a "famous" Cl^- channel, the so-called cystic fibrosis transmembrane regulator (CFTR) (11), and the bacterial galactose-H^+ cotransporter (3). The significance of this fact is not clear at present, but it may indicate a common steric mechanism underlying solute translocation.

The intramembrane domains of proteins are connected to each other by alternating extra- and intracellular sequences that often form longer exo- or cytoplasmic loops. The free N- and C-terminal tails of the proteins are generally hydrophylic and in the case of many transport proteins are localized in the cytoplasm. The chemical analysis of the water-soluble sequences helps the determination of the correct topology, since glycosylated amino acids can exclusively be found in the extracellular domains. While the membrane-spanning regions of most transporters are probably involved in the actual tarnslocation of the transported species across the membrane, the connecting sequences play a major role both in the binding of the carried molecule and in the *regulation* of the transporter itself. The intracellular sequences are targets for chemical modification (e.g., phosphorylation) or interaction with intracellular regulatory molecules (e.g., with the Ca-binding protein, calmodulin), which can dramatically change the kinetic properties of the transporters. Moreover, the loops connecting the intramembrane domains can be binding sites for various toxins and other specific inhibitors. The application of these pharmacological agents has played a quintessential role in the physiological and biochemical characterization and purification of many transporters.

So far, we have considered the components of the membrane from a static point of view. In fact the membrane is a very dynamic structure that can be envisaged as an ever-changing two-dimensional fluid in which proteins are floating. Biophysical measurements have demonstrated that both the lipids and the proteins perform fast *rotational movements*. The *flip-flop* of phospholipids from one leaflet to the other is thermodynamically unfavorable and is therefore a rare event. In contrast, the *lateral diffusion* of lipids within a single leaflet is permitted and is quite fast (≈ 50 µm/sec), except in the vicinity of membrane proteins, which tend to slow down ("immobilize") the lipid molecules. Proteins themselves move more slowly and show as much as a 1000-fold difference in their individual mobility depending on their size and their relationship to the *cytoskeleton*, an array of intracellular fibrous proteins. The *fluidity* of the membrane, the optimal value of which is a prerequisite for normal cell growth and function, depends on lipid composition and temperature. In general, the incorporation of short and unsaturated fatty acids, as well as an increase in the temperature, tends to elevate membrane fluidity. This is particularly relevant to cell culture applications, since a few degree drop in the temperature may result in a *phase transition* from a freely flowing, low-viscosity, fluidlike membrane structure to a more rigid, gel-like organization. This "frozen state" obviously interferes with the operation of those transporters that, while performing their transport function, undergo

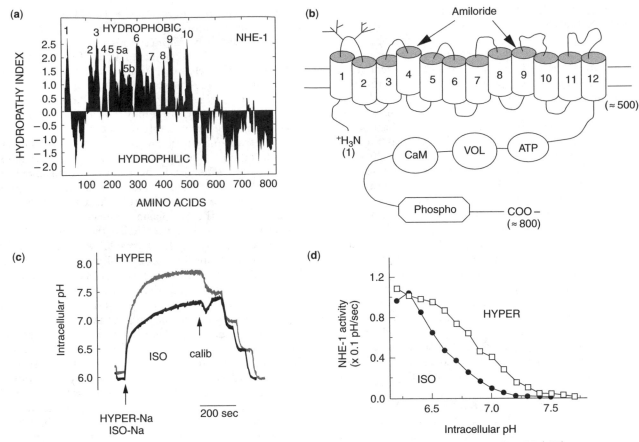

Figure 2. Structure and function of a membrane transport protein, the mammalian Na$^+$/H$^+$ exchanger (NHE-1). (**a**) Hydropathy plot showing the typical 12-TM (transmembrane) organization of the membrane domain of the antiporter (6). (Note that on this representation 3 neighboring TM segments are labeled 5, 5a, 5b). (**b**) The predicted topology of NHE-1. Different segments of the C-terminal tail are involved in the ATP sensitivity (ATP), volume responsiveness (VOL), calmodulin binding (CaM), and phosphorylation (Phospho). (**c**) Original recordings showing the function of the exchanger. Chinese hamster ovary cells expressing NHE-1 were loaded with a fluorescent pH indicator and acidified using the ammonium prepulse technique (see the section on lipid-phase diffusion). Recovery of intracellular pH (pH$_i$) was initiated by the addition of isotonic (300 mOsM) or hypertonic (500 mOsM) NaCl. At the end of the measurement the fluorescence response was calibrated in terms of pH$_i$. (**d**) NHE-1 activity is plotted against pH$_i$. Note that hypertonicity (cell shrinkage) induces a rightward shift in the pH$_i$-dependence of the exchanger without influencing its maximal velocity.

conformational changes *within* the membrane. Interestingly, in the long run most cells are capable of adapting to an altered temperature by changing the lipid composition of their membrane, thereby maintaining optimal membrane fluidity.

The relatively free lateral mobility of the membrane constituents would suggest that the distribution of lipids and proteins within a single leaflet is more or less homogenous. This is the case in a variety of cells, such as in many of the free-floating blood cells. In contrast to these *nonpolarized cells*, the membrane of many cells shows significant asymmetry. The reason for this phenomenon may be either functional or structural. To explain the former case, suppose that an otherwise nonpolarized cell, such as a fibroblast (connective tissue cell), is first kept in suspension and then it is allowed to sediment to the bottom of a tissue culture dish. The contact of the cell

surface with the substratum induces the assembly of a cell attachment machinery, leading to the appearance of so-called *focal adhesion sites* (12). These sites contain integral membrane proteins (e.g., members of the *integrin* family) that physically interconnect the extracellular matrix with the intracellular cytoskeleton (13,14). In addition, these interactions attract a large number of signal tranducing molecules that can influence the activity of membrane transporters in their vicinity (12–16). Moreover, these attachment sites can recruit certain transport molecules. For example, the Na$^+$/H$^+$ exchanger has been shown to cluster at focal adhesion plaques (17). Taken together, the structure and the function of the membrane near the contact sites are different from those of other areas.

In contrast to these induced changes, many cell types exhibit a high level of membrane asymmetry as a constant and intrinsic feature, which is intimately related to their physiological function. These *polarized cells* are mostly epithelial cells, which line the external layer of mucus membranes of hollow organs or tissues such as the gastrointestinal, respiratory, or urinary tract. Functionally, these cells are engaged with absorption and secretion of solutes and fluids. The membrane area that faces the lumen (i.e., the external world) is called the *apical* or *luminal* membrane, whereas the opposite side oriented toward the interstitial space is called the *basolateral* membrane. The protein composition of these compartments is strikingly different. The localization of various transport molecules is so characteristic that these proteins can be used as biochemical markers for one or the other membrane. For example, the Na^+/K^+ pump is a hallmark of the basolateral membrane (18), whereas a certain isoform of the Na^+/H^+ exchanger (NHE-3) is present exclusively in the apical membrane (19). Such organization of the transporters enables a kidney cell to perform Na^+ reabsorption from the lumen to the interstitium: Na^+ can enter the cell through the apical Na^+/H^+ exchanger; it diffuses through the cytoplasm and reaches the basolateral membrane, where it is extruded by the Na^+/K^+ pump.

The exact transport mechanisms of these ion translocators will be discussed later. Here it is enough to emphasize that cell polarity is the structural basis of *transcellular* vectorial transport, a vital physiological process in almost every multicellular organism. It is self-evident that meaningful transcellular transport can only take place if the cells separating the external and internal compartments are coupled to each other tightly enough to prevent the immediate *paracellular back-flux* of the transported material. A large number of proteins are involved in the formation of tight cell–cell contacts. These proteins are organized into morphologically distinguishable connecting elements such as *tight junctions*, *adherent junctions*, *desmosomes*, etc. These and other structures also form physical barriers between the basolateral and apical membranes (20,21) that completely inhibit the mixing of proteins of these compartments. Interestingly, the movement of lipids of the inner leaflet is also restricted, whereas those localized in the external leaflet can intermingle relatively freely. The discussion of the mechanisms responsible for the correct *targeting* and *sorting* of the newly synthesized transporters to their destination, as well as the description of the mechanism that keeps them there, is beyond the scope of this article. The interested reader is referred to excellent recent reviews on this topic (18,22,23). Instead, some aspects of cell polarity are considered that are relevant to tissue culture application and should be considered when one investigates epithelial transport in vitro.

Under appropriate conditions many types of epithelial cells can be grown in tissue culture, and they *may* preserve their original polarity. However, the expression and the correct localization of the transporters, as well as the tightness of the epithelial monolayer, depends on many factors, such as on the presence of growth factors and other serum components, cell density, the age of the culture (passage number), etc. (24–26). Another caveat is that actively transporting epithelial cells grown on an impermeable surface may secrete fluids under themselves, which eventually lifts off certain parts of the monolayer, leading to so-called *dome formation* (appearance of small fluid-filled spheres lined with cells) (27). To circumvent this problem, cells can be grown on a *permeable support* (such as collagen filters), which enables the experimenter to gain access to both sides of the monolayer and to measure transepithelial fluxes under near-physiological conditions (28–30). The *heterologous expression* of transporter genes (i.e., the expression of genes whose products are originally not present in the transfected cell) has become a routine practice in everyday transport research. For example, the already mentioned NHE-3 or CFTR, which are apically localized in natural expressors, can be expressed in nonpolarized fibroblasts (31,32). This approach provides an excellent opportunity to study the function of normal and mutated proteins without the confounding effect of an endogenous transporter. On the other hand, while the kinetic properties and the regulation might be similar, the sorting and the processing of these transport proteins is bound to be different in this setting compared to the physiological situation.

TRANSPORT ACROSS THE PLASMA MEMBRANE: GENERAL PROPERTIES

The structure of the membrane dictates that transport across it can occur either through the lipid bilayer or through the proteins. The characteristics of *lipid-phase permeation* and *protein-mediated transport* are basically different. The former can be described with the laws of diffusion, while the latter involves much more complex mechanisms. First we provide a brief overview on some quantitative aspects of diffusional movements across cell membranes. This will be followed by a summary of water transport, which takes place both through the bilayer and via proteinaceous pores, and therefore represents a transition between the two fundamental modes. The rest of this section will be devoted to the major mechanisms of protein-mediated solute transport.

Diffusion through the Lipid Phase

The flux (J) of a substance is defined as the number of its molecules (dn) that pass across a given area (A) in a unit time (dt).

$$J = \frac{dn}{dt}/A \qquad (1)$$

This flux is proportional to the concentration of the molecules (C) and the driving force (F_d) acting on them. The proportionality constant is called the mobility (μ):

$$J = \text{mobility} \times \text{concentration} \times \text{driving force} = \mu C F_d \quad (2)$$

The components of the driving force are the concentration gradient (dC/dx), the electric gradient (dV/dx), and the pressure gradient (dP/dx). These combined forces constitute the electrochemical potential gradient ($d\mu/dx$), which can be expressed as

$$\frac{d\mu}{dx} = -\left(\frac{RT}{C}\frac{dC}{dx} + \bar{v}\frac{dP}{dx} + z\frac{dV}{dx}\right) \quad (3)$$

where R is the gas constant, T is the absolute temperature, $\bar{v}$ is partial molar volume, and z is the valency of the diffusing molecule. The negative sign simply indicates that flow takes place down the negative electrochemical gradient.

Substituting the total driving force (3) into (2) we get the so called Nernst–Planck equation:

$$J = -\mu C\left(\frac{RT}{C}\frac{dC}{dx} + \bar{v}\frac{dP}{dx} + z\frac{dV}{dx}\right) \quad (4)$$

The pressure gradient is generally negligible; so for an *uncharged* molecule (4) reduces to

$$J = -\mu RT\frac{dC}{dx} \quad (5)$$

μRT is defined as the *diffusion coefficient D*; thus

$$J = -D\frac{dC}{dx} \quad (6)$$

This relationship is called Fick's first law, and it states that under these conditions the rate of diffusion is linearly proportional to the concentration gradient. The diffusion coefficient depends on the size of the diffusing molecule and the viscosity of the solution in which it moves. Since the viscosity of the membrane is 100–1000 times higher than that of water, the rate-limiting step in the diffusion across the membrane is the diffusion within the membrane.

We can now use Fick's law to describe diffusion across the cell membrane assuming that the transport is perpendicular to the plane of the membrane and that its rate is constant within the bilayer. Then the transport rate (dn/dt) across the A area of the membrane is

$$\frac{dn}{dt} = -(D_m/x)A(C_e^m - C_i^m)$$

or expressed as flux

$$J = -(D_m/x)(C_e^m - C_i^m) \quad (7)$$

where x is the thickness of the membrane and C_e^m and C_i^m are the concentrations of the molecule just inside the hydrophobic region of the external and internal leaflets, respectively. How does the concentration of a molecule in the lipid phase of the membrane (C^m) relate to its concentration in the surrounding aqueous phase (C^{aq})? The relationship is given by the so-called *partition coefficient K*, which is the relative distribution of the compound between water and lipid in equilibrium, and simply speaking reflects the affinity of the substance for lipid versus water

$$K = C^m/C^{aq} \quad (8)$$

Since K is the same for the external and internal leaflet, we can rewrite equation (7) as:

$$J = -K(D_m/x)(C_e^{aq} - C_i^{aq}) \quad (9)$$

This simple relationship states that flux across the membrane is directly proportional to the concentration difference between the extra- and intracellular space. The diffusion is linearly related to the lipid/water partition coefficient; that is, the higher the lipid solubility, the faster the transport is. This classical observation led Earnest Overton at the turn of this century to conclude that biological membranes are of lipoid nature. The proportionality coefficient $-K(D_m/x)$ is usually expressed as P, the *permeability coefficient*. Thus

$$J = P(C_e^{aq} - C_i^{aq}) \quad (10)$$

See the Appendix for an example of this equation. P is expressed in cm/sec, and its value can vary over several orders of magnitude. For example, in red blood cells P is 10^{-2} cm/sec for water (for which the membrane is very permeable) and 10^{-10} for sucrose (for which the membrane is practically impermeable). Net simple diffusion always occurs down the concentration gradient; therefore it is always a *passive transport* process. This is the way that the vital gases (e.g., O_2 and CO_2) enter or leave the cell, and the way by which many uncharged molecules such as NH_3, urea, alcohols, steroid hormones, lipid-soluble vitamins, and drugs cross the membrane.

Regarding tissue culture conditions, the free diffusion of ammonia (NH_3) may induce toxic effects. NH_3 can be generated from glutamine and may reach quite a high concentration in the culture medium. One reason for its toxicity is that, similar to the effect of many other weak bases, it dissipates transorganellar (e.g., lysosomal) pH gradients. The underlying mechanism is that it permeates the vesicular membranes, and it picks up a H^+ and converts to NH_4^+. This conversion regenerates the original NH_3 gradient, leading to further accumulation. To keep the NH_3 concentration of the medium at a low level, several methods have been used, including the replacement of glutamine with glutamic acid and the application of ion-exchange resins (33). While a nuisance under certain circumstances, the same phenomenon can be exploited in experiments when acidification of the cytoplasm is required. The basis of the method lies in the significantly different permeability of the membrane for the apolar NH_3 and the charged NH_4^+ (34). Cells are first incubated in the presence of NH_4Cl solution, which at physiological pH values always contains a sufficient amount of NH_3. The entry and subsequent protonation of this NH_3 leads to an abrupt alkalinization of the cytoplasm. This is followed by a gradual reacidification toward the original pH, due to the slower permeation of NH_4^+. At this point the external medium is removed and quickly replaced with an NH_4^+- (and thus NH_3-) free solution. This maneuver results in an immediate strong acidification (much below the starting level) because the NH_3 generated from the intracellular NH_4^+ instantaneously diffuses out, leaving the very poorly permeant H^+ ion behind. This so-called NH_4^+-prepulse technique is widely applied for studying various H^+-eliminating transport systems (e.g., H^+ channels or H^+ exchangers), which can catalyze the pH recovery of the cytoplasm under appropriate conditions. Furthermore, the very same principle of selective diffusibility can be used to follow the operation of the above-mentioned transporters. A straightforward way to measure membrane transport is to monitor the intracellular changes of the transported species. This can be accomplished by introducing appropriate indicators (e.g., fluorescent ion-sensitive dyes) into the cells. This approach, however, is burdened by an inherent contradiction: If the indicator is highly membrane permeable, the cells can be easily loaded with it, but it is quickly released as soon as the cells are washed free of the extracellular dye. Conversely, membrane-impermeant indicators cannot be efficiently introduced. A brilliant solution to this riddle was provided by Roger Tsien and his colleagues (35), who developed esterified indicators, such as the acetoxymethylester forms of the Ca-sensitive FURA-2 or the pH-sensitive carboxyfluorescein. The parent dye molecules are highly charged and would not penetrate the cells. However, they can be made hydrophobic by esterifying their carboxyl residues. The ester forms are readily taken up by the cells, and are quickly hydrolyzed by various cytoplasmic esterases. This has three important consequences: The dye regains its ion-sensitive fluorescence, it becomes water soluble, and thus it remains entrapped in the cytoplasm, and the concentration gradient which drives the uptake of new ester molecules is continuously regenerated. The application of this technique has proved to be one of the most fruitful means of studying transport and signal transduction.

In summary, diffusion through the membrane is essential for both life and research. On the other hand, due to its passive nature, low velocity, and nonselectivity, this transport mode alone is clearly insufficient to meet the homeostatic needs of the living cell.

Water Transport

Water is the most important solvent, and constitutes 60–70% of a mammalian cell. The rate of water transport (J_w) across the cell membrane is linearly proportional to the driving force. The components of the driving force include the hydrostatic pressure difference (ΔP) and the osmotic difference ($\Delta\Pi$) across the membrane

$$J_w = L_p(\Delta P \pm \Delta\Pi) \qquad (11)$$

where L_p is the permeability coefficient for water. The cell membrane can support only very small pressure gradients (≤ 2 kPa); thus in animal cells — which are not surrounded by a rigid wall — water movements are dictated almost exclusively by osmotic differences (36). Water, just like any other substance, moves from the higher to the lower concentration. However the "water concentration" is high where the solute concentration is low, and vice versa. Therefore, the osmotic pressure difference (i.e., the pressure that is necessary to stop net water movement through a membrane that separates two compartments

with different solute concentration) will depend on the difference in the total solute concentration ($\sum \Delta C_i$) at the two sides:.

$$\Delta\Pi = RT \sum \sigma_i \Delta C_i \qquad (12)$$

See the Appendix for an example of this equation. σ_i is the so-called reflection coefficient, which is a relative measure of "how impermeable" the membrane is to a given solute as compared to water. (If the solute is almost as permeable as water, it can exert very little osmotic effect). These equations describe the direction and driving force for the movement of water across the membrane, but do not tell us how it moves.

It has long been known that osmotic changes affect the size of liposomes, spherical phospholipid bilayers with an entrapped volume. When a liposome filled with 100 mM NaCl is placed into a 50 mM NaCl solution, it swells. The reason is that the liposomal membrane is practically impermeable to Na^+ and Cl^-, but quite permeable to water. Therefore, the more concentrated (less water-containing) inner solution sucks water from the outer space. That water can penetrate through the bilayer relatively freely is somewhat surprising because it is a substantially polar molecule. Nevertheless, it can go through certain gaps created by the kinks of the acyl chains. However, at least three experimental observations suggest that cellular water transport cannot be completely explained by this lipid-phase diffusion. First, the water permeability of some cells, such as the red blood cell, is 10–20-fold greater than that of pure phospholipid bilayers. Second, mercurials, such as $HgCl_2$, can strongly inhibit water permeation across these cell membranes. And third, the water permeability of certain tissues (e.g., the collecting duct of the mammalian kidney or the amphibian bladder) can be dramatically increased by the addition of antidiuretic hormone (ADH). Intensive research in recent years led to the identification of the water pathway (37–40). It turned out that the route is not a single molecule, but a whole new family of related proteins that function as water-conducting pores or water channels. The two most important representatives are CHIP28 (for channel-forming integral protein of 28 kDa) or aquaporin-1 and WCH-CD (for water channel of the collecting duct) or aquaporin-2. These molecules have been cloned, sequenced, purified, and reconstituted into low-water-permeability membranes (e.g., into frog oocytes) where they induce high water permeability. The aquaporins contain 6 transmembrane segments and a characteristic tandem repeat structure with two asparagine–proline–alanine (NPA) sequences that have been proposed to participate in the formation of the pore. Aquaporin-1 is constitutively present in the plasma membrane of many cells. Aquaporin-2 resides in the membrane of intracellular vesicles, which, upon stimulation by ADH, fuse with the apical membrane. This event confers high water permeability to the collecting duct cells and enables the reabsorption of water driven by the high osmotic concentration of the kidney medulla. This process is vitally important for maintenance of normal salt and water balance, and its disturbance manifests in a severe human disease, diabetes insipidus.

Protein-Mediated Solute Transport: General Properties, Classification, and Useful Concepts

Protein-mediated transport processes are very diverse but they have a few important *common characteristics* that distinguish them from simple diffusion.

1. Since the number of transporters in the membrane is finite, the transport velocity has a limit that cannot be surpassed even if the driving force keeps increasing. In other words: the transport exhibits *saturation*. This phenomenon is less pronounced in channels, which can be conceptualized as protein pores through which diffusion occurs, and is very characteristic in carriers, which can be conceived as enzymes whose substrate is the transported species at one side of the membrane and whose product is the same molecule on the other side. Nevertheless, channels do show signs of saturation, but generally only above the physiological concentration of the transported material (41)

2. The vast majority of transport systems show *specificity* or at least *selectivity*; that is, they transport exclusively or preferably certain compounds or ions. This feature is so predominant in many systems that they are named after it: That is why we can speak about K^+ *channels* (which will not conduct Na^+ or Ca^{2+}), the *glucose carrier* (which does not take xylose) or Na^+/H^+ *exchanger* (which will not move K^+), etc. Specificity is a consequence of the interaction of transporters with their "substrates." The mode and level of this interaction, however, is very different in the various systems. In general, channels tend to show lower, while carriers higher, levels of specificity. Nevertheless, specificity is not absolute, and this explains a related general feature: *competition*. Similar compounds may use the same pathway for permeation, and thereby they slow down each other's movement. For example, the glucose carrier can transport mannose (although a much higher concentration is required for the same transport rate), and in the presence of high mannose levels, the rate of glucose uptake is slower.

3. Transport physiology and biochemistry have capitalized a great deal on the use of specific inhibitors. *Pharmacological inhibition* of a transport process is not only a strong indication of its protein-mediated nature but also a major tool in the assessment of its physiological function. Many natural toxins have evolved to serve as lethal and very specific weapons against vital transport processes. For example tetradotoxin (TTX), a poisonous guanidinium compound from the Japanese puffer fish, binds with high affinity ($K_d \approx 10$ nM) to the voltage-dependent Na^+ channels. This agent proved to be extremely conducive for the determination of the role of Na^+ channels in the formation of action potentials and was also used to quantify the number of channels in nerve cells (41). Moreover, toxins can help to gain insight into fine details of the transport mechanisms: With their aid one can define different *conformational states* of a transporter. For example, in contrast to TTX, which inhibits the opening of the Na^+ channel, batrachotoxin (BTX), a deadly poison of a South American frog, binds preferentially to the already open Na^+ channel and keeps it constantly in the open

state (42). The application of yet another Na^+ channel poison, α-scorpion neurotoxin, was indispensable for the labeling, purification, and subsequent cloning of the channel molecule (43). Differential pharmacological sensitivity is often the basis to distinguish independent transport entities (or isoforms) that catalyze the same transport. For example, the diuretic compound amiloride is a potent inhibitor of the ubiquitous and basolaterally localized isoform of the Na^+/H^+ exchanger (NHE-1), whereas it is much less effective against the apical (NHE-3) (44) or the mitochondrial (NHE-6) isoforms of this transporter (45). Similarly, two major classes of Ca^{2+} channels (L- and T-type) were initially distinguished by their differential drug sensitivity (46), since the L- but not the T-type channels can be blocked by dihydropyridine compounds, or so-called Ca^{2+} antagonists, a widely used family of antihypertensive agents.

4. Finally, we can mention *asymmetry* as a unique property of protein-mediated transport. This does not mean that the transporter carries or conducts its ligand only in one direction. In fact, most transporters are capable of catalyzing either the uptake or the release of their ligands as dictated by the net driving force. Using the examples given, K^+ channels can permit the movement of K^+ into or out of the cell; the Na^+/H^+ exchanger, which physiologically mediates Na^+ influx and H^+ efflux, can work in the reversed mode under experimental conditions; and the glucose carrier may import or export glucose depending solely on the transmembrane sugar gradient. However, the *kinetic properties may be* quite different when a transporter is engaged in mediating net entry or egress. In case of channels this phenomenon is called *rectification*, which means that the inward-out and the outward-in resistance of the channel is different. For example, in an *outwardly rectifying* K^+ channel the outward current at a given driving force is greater than the inward current at the same, but oppositely directed, driving force. This property is the consequence of the fact that channels are proteins, and the driving force (e.g., voltage) acts on them as well as on the transported particles. In a somewhat analogous manner, the dependence of the rate of Na^+/H^+ exchange on the external and internal pH is strikingly different. The underlying reason is that H^+-ions are not only substrates but also internal *regulators*, which can bind to so-called modifier site(s) on the cytosolic tail of NHE and induce an *allosteric conformation change* that activates the transporter (47). The operation of the glucose carrier is also asymmetric: It has been shown that the maximal velocities of glucose influx and efflux may differ by a factor of 10 (48). (The underlying mechanism for this phenomenon is described in the section on uniporters. In essence, the asymmetry of the transport processes reflects the asymmetry of the transporters themselves. Importantly, the same structural and functional asymmetry is the basis of a vital characteristic of membrane transporters, namely, that they can be *regulated* by a variety of specific extra- and intracellular signals including physical parameters, ligands, and biochemical processes.

The huge number of transport processes necessitates some didactic classification. While the categories are always somewhat arbitrary, they facilitate the understanding of the basic principles.

We can classify transport phenomena according to their *energetics*. *Active transport* denotes the situation when a solute is transported against its electrochemical gradient, or in other words, uphill. We speak about *primary active transport* when the energy necessary to drive an unfavorable solute movement is derived from metabolic energy; that is, the transport is *directly coupled* to the hydrolysis of ATP. The transporters that can catalyze this kind of coupling are called *pumps*. These are therefore both transporters and real enzymes (ATPases). Major representatives include the Na^+/K^+ pump (or ATPase), the H^+/K^+ pump, the Ca^{2+} pumps of the plasma membrane or the sarcoplasmic reticulum, active drug transporters (P-glycoprotein), vacuolar H^+-ATPases, and the mitochondrial F_1F_0-ATPase. The latter, as mentioned in the introduction, normally catalyzes the reverse reaction; that is, it synthesizes ATP using the energy of the respiratory chain-generated H^+ electrochemical gradient. *Secondary active transport* takes place when a gradient (usually an ion gradient, built up by primary active transport) is used to fuel the release or uptake of other ions or molecules. Therefore, transporters catalyzing secondary active transport always couple the movement of two (or more) substrates in such a way that the downhill movement of one species can be used for the uphill movement of the other. As an illustration, we mention the Na^+/H^+ exchanger and the Na^+-K^+-Cl^- and Na^+-amino acid cotransporters, all of which (under physiological conditions) are driven by the Na^+-gradient generated by the Na^+/K^+ pump. Besides the most often used Na^+-gradient (the "favorite" transplasmalemmal ion gradient of the animal kingdom), H^+ gradients formed by H^+ pumps are also put to work, for example, to drive the accumulation of neurotransmitters into synaptic vesicles through the H^+/neurotransmitter exchangers. The energy source of *passive* protein-mediated transport processes is the electrochemical potential of the transported substrate, that is, the same as for passive diffusion. However, the relationship between the driving force and the transport velocity (i.e., the kinetics of the transport) is markedly different. To emphasize this difference, these carrier-mediated passive transports are referred to as *facilitated diffusion*. A classic example is the movement of glucose catalyzed by the glucose translocator.

From a mechanistic point of view, we can classify transporters according to the nature of solute coupling that may occur during the transport. Single, noncoupled fluxes are called *uniports*. When the movement of a substrate is strictly coupled to the movement of other substrate(s) in the same direction, we speak about *cotransport* or *symport*, and proteins mediating such reactions are called *cotransporters* or *symporters*. Conversely, when the transmembrane movement of one molecule is linked to the opposite movement of its partner, the transport is called *exchange* or *antiport*, and the transporter is therefore an *exchanger* or *antiporter*.

Another useful concept to characterize transports and transporters regards whether their operation results in *net charge translocation* across the membrane. The transport is electroneutral if no net charge movement occurs

(e.g., the flux of the uncharged glucose through the glucose carrier, or the exchange of 1 Na^+ for 1 H^+ by the Na^+/H^+ antiporter). If the transport leads to net charge translocation, it is *electrogenic*, or *rheogenic*. Electrogenic transport affects and can be affected by the membrane potential. For example, the Na^+/K^+ pump imports 2 K^+ and simultaneously exports 3 Na^+; that is, it moves 1 positive charge out of the cell. Its electrogenic operation directly contributes to the negative inside membrane potential, which is evidenced by the fact that stopping the pump using an alkaloid inhibitor, oubain, causes an immediate, slight depolarization of the cell membrane. (The much greater *indirect* contribution of the pump to the maintenance of the membrane potential is discussed in the section on ion transport through channels). Another example highlights a mechanism where the regulation of a rheogenic exchanger by the membrane potential has major physiological significance. The plasma membrane Na^+/Ca^{2+} antiporter in the heart muscle catalyzes the transport of 3 Na^+ against 1 Ca^{2+}. The resting membrane potential of heart muscle cells is highly negative inside (−80 mV), which promotes the entry of positive charges; therefore, the exchanger works in the 3 Na^+ in → 1 Ca^{2+} out direction, and helps the Ca^{2+} pump to maintain a low intracellular Ca^{2+} level. However, during activation when the muscle cell depolarizes, the net driving force for the Na^+/Ca^{2+} exchange may reverse, and now the system may catalyze the uptake of Ca^{2+}, which is important for muscle contraction (49).

In the description of the general characteristic of protein-mediated transport, such concepts as transporter, channel, and carrier were used rather intuitively, without giving their exact definition. In this article by *transporter* is meant any protein that — regardless of the underlying mechanism — is directly involved in transport. [There is no consensus in the literature on the definition of this concept. For example, a recently published excellent textbook entitled *The Transporter Factsbook* (50) describes the amino acid sequence of over 800 transporters, but these are all pumps and other carriers. In this definition, therefore the channels are not included.] Here we essentially follow Bertil Hille's classification (41), which divides transporters into two major functional groups: channels and carriers. Pumps can be easily defined as carriers that possess ATP-ase activity and can catalyze primary active transport. However, due to their characteristic structure and real enzymatic nature, they are handled separately, following the didactic view of Wilfred D. Stein, who classifies transporters as *channels*, *carriers*, and *pumps* (48). What remains therefore is to draw the line between channels and carriers. To do this meaningfully we have to take a short historical look at the development of the "carrier" concept.

The name "carrier" comes from the view that this type of transporter *carries* its substrate across the membrane: First the substrate binds to the transporter at the external surface, then the complex diffuses through the membrane, and this is followed by the debinding of the substrate at the internal surface, from where the unloaded carrier shuttles back to repeat the cycle. Models based on this concept (e.g., assigning a rate constant to each step) were very successful in describing the kinetics of many transport processes and were able to interpret or predict many experimental findings, such as transport asymmetry or the phenomenon of trans-stimulation (see the section on uniporters). What made this approach even more attractive was that it offered a clear parallelism between transport and enzyme kinetics, a well-worked-out classical discipline. However, the picturesque image of this ferry-boat carrier was seriously challenged by the newer results of membrane biochemistry and molecular biology. Based on the primary sequences and topology analyses, it became evident that carriers are huge integral proteins that are firmly fixed in the bilayer and cannot flip over or shuttle. Instead, the binding of the substrate induces intramolecular conformational changes that expose the binding sites alternately to the intra- and extracellular compartments. This implies that the old kinetic models are still quantitatively valid, but the physical meaning of the various transport steps (and the related rate constants) should be reconsidered. The ultimate goal is to understand the nature of the intramolecular movements (conformational states) of the transporters. The specific binding of the transported molecule to the carrier resembles the binding of a substrate to an enzyme. However, carriers probably also contain channel-like structures (e.g., a tunnel with one open end) that may "conduct" the transported material. The truth is that currently we have no experimental data that would satisfactorily describe what happens when a carrier transports its substrates. Nevertheless, the exploration has begun, and important structural information has been gained using X-ray diffraction analysis of two-dimensional crystals (51) and site-directed mutagenesis. For example, in their pioneering studies, Ronald Kaback and his colleagues have clarified which amino acids are important in the various transport modes of the electrogenic lactose-H^+ cotransporters of *E. coli* (52).

While the exact carrier image awaits elucidation, molecular biology has unambiguously proved that channels are what they were thought to be: gated transmembrane pores. Nevertheless, it should be pointed out that they interact with the transported ions and contain selectivity filters. It seems that nature applied channels when a transport process of lower selectivity but high capacity was required, and developed carriers when meticulous specificity was more important than velocity. In fact, the transport rate is perhaps the best experimentally apparent difference between these transporters: A single channel can conduct as many as $10^6 - 10^8$ particles/sec, which approximates the rate of free diffusion of an ion in water; in contrast, a single carrier moves $10^2 - 10^4$ molecules/sec (or, more properly, this is the number of transport cycles/sec, the so-called *turnover number*).

Evolutionary biology, however, suggests that the difference between channels and carriers should be viewed rather as a continuous transition than as an antagonism. This is best exemplified by members of the so-called ABC (ATP-binding cassette) superfamily. These include CFTR, a vitally important Cl^- channel, as well as the structurally similar multidrug resistance protein (MDR), which is an ATP-driven pump that removes foreign organic compounds (e.g., cytostatics) from the cell (see the section on multidrug transporters).

Having discussed some general features of biological transport, the rest of this article will deal with more specific aspects of transport mediated by channels, carriers, and pumps. The overwhelming amount of literature on this topic compelled the author to select only a few representative examples in each category. The guideline in the selection was to concentrate on those plasma membrane transporters that best illustrate the characteristics of their group and have general relevance to animal cell physiology.

CHANNELS

Ion Transport through Channels: Some basic Principles and Crucial Methods

Ion channels are present in every animal cell. Their physiologic importance was first recognized in excitable tissues (nerve, muscle), where their primary role is to elicit and orchestrate ion movements responsible for the generation and propagation of *action potentials*. Later, it became clear that channels are involved in many other cell functions, including secretion, resorption, intracellular signal transduction, and pH and volume regulation. Channels are protein pores that can exist in open (conductive) or closed (nonconductive) states. The process that determines the transition between these states is called *gating*. From a physiologic standpoint we can classify channels according to the type of stimulus that governs their gating. Thus we distinguish *voltage-gated, ligand-gated,* and *mechanically gated* channels. (These categories are not mutually exclusive.) The *membrane potential* (i.e., the voltage difference across the plasma membrane) has a double significance in channel function: It is the gating signal for voltage-operated channels, and it is a major component of the net driving force (the electrochemical potential difference) acting on each ion that flows through any type of channel.

To understand the operation and regulation of channels, first we have to discuss the ionic basis of the *membrane potential*. There are two conditions in every living cell that have a major contribution to the maintenance of an electrical potential difference across the membrane: (*1*) a *concentration difference* exists between the intra- and the extracellular space for many ions; (*2*) the membrane is *selectively permeable* to the different ions. To illustrate how this scenario leads to the generation of an electrical potential difference, let us consider first the situation when an artificial membrane separates two compartments containing different concentrations of the same salt solution, such as 100 mM KCl (in) and 10 mM KCl (out). (For the sake of simplicity we assume that the osmotic difference is compensated by the addition of a nonelectrolyte, e.g., sugar to the outer compartment.) What happens if we make this membrane selectively (and exclusively) permeable to K^+ ions? The K^+ ions, driven by their concentration gradient, would tend to migrate from the inner to the outer compartment. However their net egress will cease before any measurable change in the K^+ concentration could develop because a membrane polarization builds up that prevents the further K^+ efflux. The reason for this is that the negatively charged Cl^- ions (which are not permitted to go) line up along the inner surface of the membrane and tend to attract the K^+ ions back. Therefore, very soon an *equilibrium* is reached at which the chemical driving force acting on K^+ is exactly counterbalanced by the electrical driving force. The magnitude of the electrical potential at which this equilibrium is achieved (the *equilibrium potential for the ion*, E_{ion}) is given by the *Nernst equation*:

$$E_{ion} = -(RT/zF)\ln([ion]_{in}/[ion]_{out}) \quad (13)$$

where F is the Faraday constant. In our example, at ambient temperature this is: $E_K = -60\log([100\ mM]/[10\ mM]) = -60\ mV$. We should note that under these conditions the system is in equilibrium; therefore, it cannot be used to do work. Another reason why one suspects that the Nernst equation could not be an adequate description of the cell membrane potential is that the cell is permeable not only to one but to several ions. What happens in our model system if we allow Cl^- to move across the membrane, but with a lower permeability than K^+? In this case net *diffusion* will occur. However, due to the difference in the diffusibility (permeability) of the moving ions, there still will be a potential difference across the membrane. Referring to its origin, this potential difference is called the *diffusion potential*. What are the characteristics of this potential type? First, the bigger the mobility difference, the bigger the initial diffusion potential will be; second, this potential difference is transient (depends on time), since sooner or later both the cation and the anion will distribute evenly in the solution.

However, a real biological membrane contains transport systems (active pumps) that can maintain (or restore) the "original" concentration differences, thereby assuring a *steady state* (as opposed to a thermodynamic equilibrium). We may say that the presence of the active components "free" the diffusion potentials from the time dependence. Of course, in a physiological setting there are not only two but many kinds of ions. Each of these can contribute to the overall diffusion potential across the membrane, and the level of their contribution will be proportional to their individual transmembrane concentration difference and their permeability. Thus the membrane potential (E_m) can be regarded as a compound diffusion potential, or as a "weighted average" of several diffusion potentials. The exact quantitative expression is given by the famous *Goldman–Hodgkin–Katz equation*, which relates the membrane potential (E_m) to the intra- and extracellular concentrations and the permeability coefficients (P_{ion}) of the three most important contributing ions, K^+, Na^+, and Cl^-:

$$E_m = -60\log\frac{P_K[K]_{in} + P_{Na}[Na]_{in} + P_{Cl}[Cl]_{out}}{P_K[K]_{out} + P_{Na}[Na]_{out} + P_{Cl}[Cl]_{in}} \quad (14)$$

See the Appendix for an example of this equation. In most cells the resting membrane potential is dictated predominantly by the K^+ gradient, and its value is not far from the K^+ equilibrium potential. The reason for this is that at rest K^+ is the most permeable ion across the cell membrane. In contrast, Na^+ and Ca^{2+} ions are very far from their equilibrium, and they are attracted inward both by the negative membrane potential and by their concentration gradient. However, their contribution to the resting potential is very modest (in the case of Ca^{2+} it is negligible) because at rest the Na^+ and Ca^{2+} channels are closed, and therefore the membrane permeability is very small for these ions.

The force that drives any ion through an open channel is the difference between the actual membrane potential and the equilibrium potential for the ion, $E_m - E_{ion}$. Ohm's law—the best known force–flux relationship—states that the current (ion flux) is linearly proportional to the voltage (driving force). The proportionality constant is the conductance (the reciprocal of the resistance). This simple relationship is the basis of channel-mediated transport.

$$I_{ion} = g_{ion}(E_m - E_{ion}) \quad (15)$$

See the Appendix for an example of this equation. I is the current and g_{ion} is the conductance for a given ion (the electrical equivalent of its permeability). The total current carried by various kinds of ions will be the sum of the individual ion currents.

In spite of the simplicity of this relationship, there is a major complication when we want to study ionic currents across the membrane at a given voltage. Suppose that we induce a small depolarization of the membrane in a nerve cell. This will lead to the opening of some voltage-dependent Na^+ channels, through which some Na^+ will enter the cell. This Na^+ influx then will further depolarize the membrane, which will lead to the opening of more voltage-dependent channels, which will change the membrane potential again, and so on. Thus, in order to measure the current at a fixed voltage, we need a method that keeps the membrane potential constant in spite of the voltage-dependent changes in the ion conductances. This method was developed by Hodgkin, Huxley, and Katz and is known as the *voltage clamp* (53). They performed their experiments on the squid giant axon, a huge cell in which more than one intracellular electrode could be inserted. They used two electrode pairs, one that measured the membrane potential and another one that passed current through the cell membrane until a given potential value was reached. Using this feedback method, the membrane potential can be stabilized or "clamped" at any desired value, and the corresponding ion currents can be measured. These classic studies not only clarified the ionic movements and conductance changes during the nerve action potential (see any physiology textbook) but also established the basic biophysical parameters and properties of ion channels. These experiments led to the determination of *voltage thresholds* for various channels, and to the discovery of a phenomenon called *channel inactivation*. This means that a channel stops conducting in spite of the continuous presence of the opening condition (e.g., depolarization). The time and voltage dependence of the inactivation are very characteristic features of a given channel, and they generally have major importance in the physiologic function, because they are essential for the timely termination of the ion flux. The inactive state is a distinct conformation of the channel protein that is not identical with the closed state. The inactive channel should return to the closed state before it can be opened again. Another observation that permitted insight into the mechanism of channel function was the presence of *gating currents*. These currents do not reflect ion fluxes through the channel, but are due to voltage-induced movements of charged residues of the channel protein itself. Their existence indicated the presence of *voltage-sensor* domains within the channel proteins.

While these methods were indispensable for the understanding of many aspects of channel biophysics, they measured currents flowing through many channels, and often many kinds of channels simultaneously. The breakthrough that enabled scientists to investigate channel function on the molecular level came in the mid-1970s, when Erwin Neher and Bert Sackmann developed a revolutionary technique, the *patch clamp* method (54,55). The basis of this technique is the use of a very clean glass micropipette (with a tip diameter of ≈ 1 µm) that is attached to the cell membrane very firmly by gentle suction [Fig. 3(a)]. The seal between the cell and the pipette should be very tight: Its electrical resistance must be in the giga (10^9) ohm range. Under these conditions, the tip is in close physical contact with a little patch of the membrane, and currents flowing through this isolated area can be detected. Because the pipette aperture is small, there might be only a single channel molecule (or a few channels) in the patch. Using voltage clamping and very low-noise amplifiers, single channel currents of less than one pico = 10^{-12} amp can be recorded and analyzed. A variety of patch clamp configurations can be used: Beside this so-called *cell-attached* mode, the patch can be removed from the cell in an *inside-out* or an *outside-out* orientation, or the membrane can be broken through without losing the cell–pipette contact, and thereby a *whole-cell* configuration can be established [Fig. 3(b) and (c)]. The latter application permitted voltage clamp experiments on a large variety of small animal cells in which microelectrodes cannot be used. The application of various configurations provides access to either side of the channels, and therefore the effect of external or internal regulatory ligands or enzymes can be readily tested. The single-channel recordings show square impulses indicating that the transitions between the different states occur practically instantaneously [Fig. 3(c)]. Voltage or other relevant stimuli influence the *probability of the channel being open* and the time that the channel spends in the open state (mean open time). In most cases, the single-channel conductance is fairly constant and characteristic for the given channel.

In summary, the patch clamp enabled a detailed classification of channels and led to the discovery of many distinct entities based on their single-channel conductance, ion selectivity, voltage- dependence, gating and inactivation kinetics, rectification properties, etc. This was the first method in the history of science that made us capable of monitoring the function of a single protein molecule. The combination of this technique with molecular biology has resulted in a previously unimaginable progress in our understanding of the relationship between channel structure and function.

Voltage-Gated Cation Channels

Voltage-operated Na^+, K^+, and Ca^{2+} channels are essential for the generation of action potentials in excitable tissues, which is a prerequisite for a wide range of physiological functions from cardiac rythmogenesis to neurotransmission. The action potential is composed of a depolarizing phase (usually due to Na^+ and/or Ca^{2+} entry) and a repolarizing phase (usually due to K^+ efflux and inactivation of the other channels). The individual kinetic properties and the interplay between the various channels determine the shape and duration of the action potential, which may vary from 3 ms to several seconds in different tissues. The coordinated entry of Ca^{2+} is the basis of contraction and exocytosis. Voltage-gated cation channels play a vital role in the physiology of nonexcitable cells as well, since they are involved in such general functions as transepithelial transport, degranulation, and signal transduction.

The structures of the various cation channels show striking similarity, suggesting that they belong to a huge superfamily and that the individual members (there are many different gene products in each cation-selective category) can be regarded as variations on the same molecular theme (56–58). Many channels are built up from *different subunits*; for example, the Na^+ channel is composed of three polypeptides: $\alpha 1$, $\beta 1$, $\beta 2$. However, the α subunit is responsible for most of the functional characteristics of the whole channel, and this is the part that shows high structural homology among the different cation channels (Fig. 4).

The α-chain of the Na^+ channel is a huge protein (≈ 2000 amino acids) composed of four homologous *internal domains* (I–IV). Each of these domains contains six *transmembrane segments* (S_1–S_6). A loop between S_5 and S_6, called the short (S) or H segment, partially penetrates the membrane, but it does not form an α-helix. The four domains together constitute the transmembrane pore, and the various segments within each domain are associated with certain functional characteristics. For example, S4 is the voltage sensor: It contains several highly charged amino acids (lysine, arginine), and site-directed mutagenesis studies show that replacement of these to neutral ones induces a dramatic decrease in the voltage sensitivity. The "strange" H segment lines the mouth of the pore and is responsible for the ionic selectivity. Exchanging only two amino acids in this region can turn a Na^+ channel into a Ca^{2+} channel. This part is also important in the determination of the conductance. The regions involved in inactivation have also been identified. In Na^+ channels a short loop between domain III and IV acts as a "hinged lid": When a certain time has elapsed after activation, it moves and obliterates the inner aperture of the channel. This fine detail was also demonstrated by the application of molecular biology: the α subunit of the Na^+ channel was expressed in two pieces, so that a cut was made between domain III and IV. These peptides assembled to form a channel that could be normally activated but failed to show inactivation.

The *epithelial Na^+ channels* (59), localized specifically in the apical membrane of Na^+-reabsorbing cells, belong to

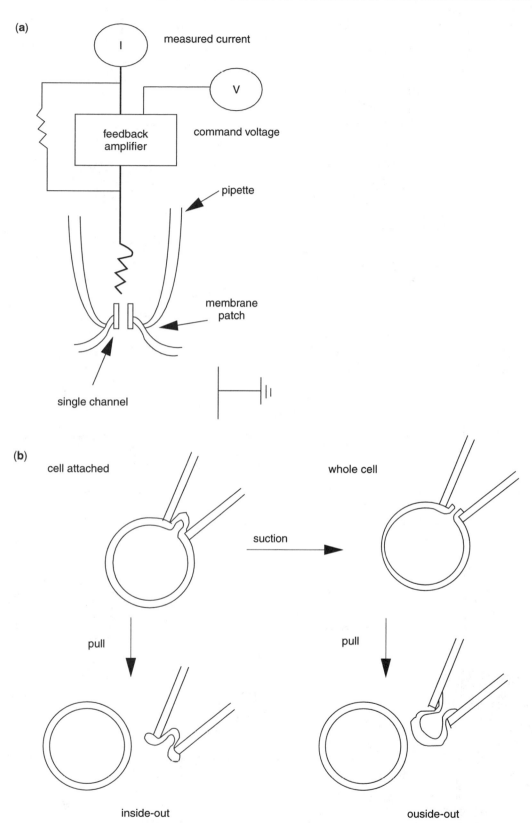

Figure 3. The patch clamp technique. (**a**) The scheme of the patch pipette and the patch clamp apparatus. The electronics provide both voltage clamping and the measurement of the transmembrane currents. (**b**) Different patch clamp configurations; modified from (54). (**c**) Typical single-channel and whole-cell recordings. The whole-cell currents are voltage-dependent H^+ fluxes from an activated macrophage. The voltage protocol (2.8-sec pulses from -90 to $+75$ mV in 15-mV increments) is shown below the current traces.

(c)   single channel currents

whole cell currents

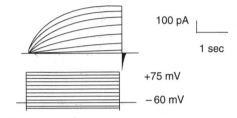

Figure 3. *Continued.*

Na$^+$ Ca^{2+} channels

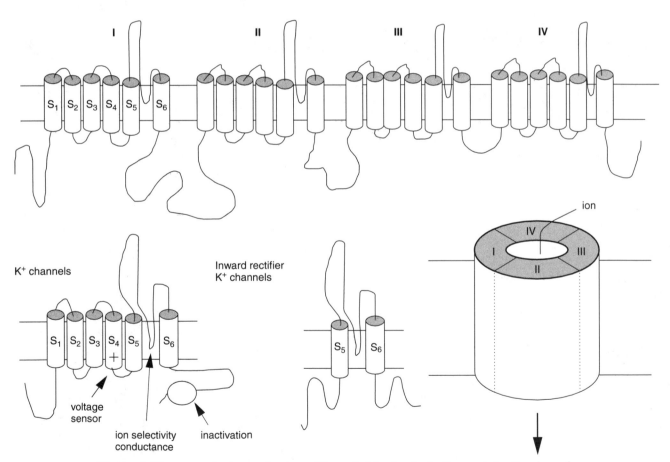

Figure 4. The proposed primary structure of the main (α) subunit of voltage-gated cation channels (see explanation in the text). The circular structure at the C-terminal end of the K$^+$ channel represents the "ball-and-chain" model explaining the inactivation of these channels. The ball-like domain, connected to the last membrane segment with a flexible tail, moves into the inner aperture of the pore in a time- and voltage-dependent manner and obliterates K$^+$ transport. The last panel shows how the four internal domains (for Na$^+$ and Ca^{2+} channels) or the four separate polypeptides (for K$^+$ channels) form a functional pore.

a recently described and completely different superfamily. They contain a large extracellular domain between two alpha helices. These channels are essential for transepithelial Na^+ transport, their transcription is regulated by steroid hormones, and errors in the channel molecule are thought to be associated with severe disease states such as hypertension or cystic fibrosis.

The structure of Ca^{2+} channels follows the basic design described for the voltage-gated Na^+ channels. Three major types can be distinguished: the *L-type* channels, which have large conductance and long-lasting activity; the *T-type* channels, which conduct tiny currents in a transient manner; and *N-type* channels, which are so called because they were identified in neurons. L- and T-type channels exhibit very different activation thresholds: The former require a much bigger depolarization to open (46,60). The major role of these channels is to coordinate the duration of action potentials with the time course of Ca^{2+}-dependent cellular responses, such as contraction and exocytosis. As Bertil Hille writes: "without these channels, our nervous system would not have outputs" (41). We briefly mention here that, in addition to the plasma membrane pathways, cells contain very important intracellular Ca^{2+} channels as well. These are localized in the membranes of Ca^{2+}-containing vesicles, and their opening results in the rapid release of Ca^{2+} into the cytosol. The Ca^{2+} channel of the endoplasmic reticulum is a ligand-gated pore, opened by the intracellular messenger *inositol trisphosphate* (61), while the Ca^{2+} efflux route of the sarcoplasmic reticulum, the so-called *ryanodine receptor* (62), is a voltage-gated system.

Plasmalemmal K^+ channels show more diversity than Na^+ or Ca^{2+} channels (56–58). They lack internal repeats, and many of them are composed of a single six-helix-containing peptide; so they look like 1/4 of a Na^+ channel (Fig. 4). However, these units assemble to form a tetramer; that is, the functional channel has the same 4×6 transmembrane segment organization, except that the parts are not contained within a single peptide chain. It is likely that these channels are the most ancient ion conductors from which the other families evolved with multiple gene duplications. The four major classes of the voltage-sensitive K^+ channels include the *delayed rectifier*, the so-called *shaker* (from a shaking *Drosophila* mutant that contained a defective version), the Ca^{2+}-*activated*, and the *inward rectifier* types. Most of these channels are involved in some way in the re- or hyperpolarization of the cells, because their opening leads to K^+ egress, which brings or keeps the membrane close to the K^+ equilibrium potential and thereby counteracts depolarizing stimuli and helps repolarization. This "calming" function is particularly apparent in the case of the Ca^{2+}-activated K^+ channels: Their conductance is strongly stimulated by two major attributes of cell activation: depolarization and the increase in intracellular Ca^{2+}. The inward rectifiers represent a new and particularly interesting group within the family: They contain only two transmembrane segments, which correspond to the S_5 and S_6 helices (63) (Fig. 4). These channels are closed at depolarizing potentials; therefore, they do not help repolarization but rather let depolarization persist for a longer time, which is important in such tissues as the heart, where the duration of the action potential should be lengthened so that the relatively slow muscle contraction can "catch up" before a new action potential is generated. The *ATP-dependent K^+ (K_{ATP}) channels* (64), another subclass of this group are targets of intensive research because of their prominent role in insulin secretion and in diabetes. Let us discuss this point in a little more detail. These channels are inhibited by high intracellular ATP levels. Under fasting conditions, the ATP concentration in the insulin-secreting cells of the pancreas is low, so that the K_{ATP} channels are open and keep the membrane potential at a high negative value. After eating, the plasma glucose rises, which leads to increased ATP synthesis, inducing the closure of the channel. The decreased K^+ efflux results in depolarization, which opens up the voltage-gated Ca^{2+} channels. The subsequent Ca^{2+} influx triggers the exocytosis of insulin-containing vesicles. In short, the metabolic state of the cell regulates hormone secretion through the coordinated operation of two cation channels. The antidiabetic drug sulfonylurea was known to stimulate insulin release by inhibiting the K_{ATP} channels. The recent cloning of the sulfonylurea receptor (SUR) has provided surprising results showing that the SUR is not identical with the K_{ATP} channel. Instead, it is a member of the ABC superfamily. It seems that the SUR and the K_{ATP} channel form a complex, in which the ATP and drug sensitivity are brought about by the SUR, whereas the transport is mediated by the channel. Evidence has been accumulating that other members of the ABC family may also play critical roles in the regulation or modulation of ion channels (see the following).

Anion Channels

In this section we discuss only two major groups of Cl^- channels: the so-called *background Cl^- channels* and *CFTR*. The ligand-operated Cl^- conductances will be mentioned in the next section. The functions of the Cl^- channels include stabilization of the resting membrane potential, participation in fluid secretion or resorption, and involvement in cell volume regulation.

In many cells (e.g., in muscle) the membrane is quite permeable to Cl^- at rest, and therefore Cl^- is close to its equilibrium. The name "background channel" indicates that a significant fraction of these channels is open at the resting membrane potential. This implies that a depolarization will induce a Cl^- flux that tends to move the potential back toward the resting level. If this buffer function is lost, the cells become hyperexcitable, and, especially after exercise, long-lasting muscle cramps (myotonia) will develop. In the past few years some channels were cloned that seem to participate in the background Cl^- permeability. These belong to the so-called *CIC (Cl^- channel) family* (65,66) and contain 12–13 putative TM domains. They show variable voltage dependence, and are permeable for halides and some smaller organic ions. Importantly, their mutations are associated with myotonia.

Another Cl^- conducting protein is CFTR (11,65–67). The crucial importance of this transporter is underscored by its involvement in cystic fibrosis (CF), the most common genetic disorder in the Caucasian population, afflicting 1 newborn in every 2000. CF is characterized by abnormally viscous bronchial and pancreatic secretions. The underlying reason is a defective epithelial ion transport due to a mutation in the CF gene. The most common error is a single alanine deletion at position 508 (Δ508), which results in improper folding and subsequent degradation of the protein. CFTR contains 12 TM segments clustered into two symmetric groups, which are separated by a long cytoplasmic loop that includes a so-called nucleotide binding domain (NBD) and a regulatory (R) domain. A second NBD can be found between the last TM segment and the C-terminal end. The gating of CFTR requires phosphorylation of the R domain by the cAMP-activated protein kinase (PKA). In addition, binding and hydrolysis of ATP by the NBDs also seem to be necessary for proper transport. Thus, although Cl^- flux through the CFTR is passive, the regulation of the channel requires substantial metabolic energy. Once open, the channel can conduct Cl^- and probably also ATP, which may act on the same cell from the extracellular surface via ATP receptors (autocrine effect) (68). In addition to being a transporter itself, CFTR affects other transport proteins: It appears to regulate apical Cl^- and Na^+ channels (66,69). Thus CFTR is not only an important but a very complex and puzzling molecule: It is a real channel, but also an ATPase and a regulator.

Ligand-Gated Ion Channels

The electrical signals conducted by nerves are converted to chemical signals at the synapse. The ligand-gated channels (LGCs) are devices that convert the message back to electrical signals in the postsynaptic neuron or muscle cell. These structures therefore have a dual nature: They are receptors *and* channels. The strong coupling between these two functions is the guarantee for highly specific and very efficient transmission of the information.

The various LGCs also constitute a superfamily (41,56), which includes three major classes: the nicotinic acetylcholine receptor (nAChR), the glutamate receptors (GluR), and the γ-amino butyric acid, plus the closely related glycine receptors (GABAR, GlyR). The former two are nonselective cation channels; so their opening induces postsynaptic depolarization, whereas the latter two are Cl^- channels; so their opening causes hyperpolarization. Thus the postsynaptic membrane can "interpret" the presynaptic action potential, which, depending on the released neurotransmitter, can result in an excitatory or an inhibitory postsynaptic response.

The nAChR of the neuromuscular junction, the prototype of LGCs, is a huge molecule ($\approx$10 nm long) composed of five subunits ($\alpha_2\beta\gamma\delta$), which assemble to form a large pore. Similarly to the voltage-operated channels, each subunit contains repetitive transmembrane segments (4 helices/subunit in this case). The natural ligand ACh, as well as nicotine, a pharmacological agonist, and the inhibitor bungarotoxin, bind to the α-subunit. Two ligand molecules must bind to cause channel opening. Since the pore has a large nonselective cation conductance, the nAChR density is high, and the amount of ACh released

is in excess, the firing of the nerve is bound to depolarize the muscle cell membrane sufficiently to elicit an action potential. This executive type of relationship is restricted to the nerve–muscle junction. In the central nervous system (CNS) many de- and hyperpolarizing influences can reach the postsynaptic membrane where an integrative information processing will determine whether a propagating signal (AP) will be generated. The GABARs and the GlyRs have essentially similar pore structures, but because their selectivity filter is different, they mediate anion permeation. The fact that inhibition is as important as activation in the CNS is underlined by the well-known effects of various pharmacological agonists (e.g., barbiturates) and antagonists (e.g., strychnine) of these receptors.

Without going into details, we mention that GluRs are the predominant excitatory LGCs in the CNS. They can be classified further into three major categories, and their structure is the least homologous to those of the other members of the LGC family. They play an essential role in such complex neuronal functions as learning and memory.

The combined application of cell culture and the patch clamp method has been indispensable for the characterization of these transport pathways. With these techniques, cells could be separated from the overwhelming complexity of neuronal circuits and their channels could be investigated on the molecular level.

Mechanically Gated Channels

Translating mechanical forces into electrical signals is the central topic of sensory physiology and it is also an important mechanism for regulation of smooth muscle function and cell volume. Considering only the latter two (more general) areas, most often *membrane stretch* is the gating signal. In smooth muscle it leads to the opening of *nonselective cation channels* and the consequent depolarization triggers muscle constriction (Bayliss effect). Regarding volume control, the cell-swelling-induced opening of K^+ and Cl^- channels is the predominant process by which swollen cells restore their normal size: The combined, electroneutral KCl release drives osmotically obliged water out of the cell (regulatory volume decrease). Various cation and anion channels, including voltage- and Ca^{2+}-sensitive K^+ channels and ClC2 (Cl^- channel 2), have been reported to mediate this ubiquitous phenomenon. The mechanism of coupling between stretch and gating is not yet well understood. Mechanical forces may influence the conformation of the channels directly or through the cytoskeleton (36,70). Alternatively, swelling can activate kinases, which in turn phosphorylate and thereby open up channels (71).

CARRIERS

Uniporters

The best-understood uniport mechanism is the facilitated diffusion of glucose mediated by various isoforms of the glucose transporter family (GLUT-1–5). These carriers are composed of ~500 amino acids and possess 12 TM segments. Individual members differ in their kinetic properties, tissue distribution, and regulation (72,73). The

GLUT-1 (erythrocyte), GLUT-2 (liver), GLUT-3 (brain), and GLUT-5 (small intestine) isoforms are constitutively expressed on the cell surface, whereas GLUT-4, the predominant isoform of skeletal muscle and adipose tissue, is stored in intracellular vesicles, which upon insulin stimulation fuse with the plasma membrane, thereby increasing several-fold the rate of sugar uptake. In addition to this essential mechanism, other factors such as direct phosphorylation and the control of GLUT gene transcription are also involved in the regulation. The general kinetic principles of carrier-mediated transport were partially derived from the investigation of glucose permeation. The rate of transport (v) can be well described with the following equation:

$$v = V_{max}/(1 + K_m/C) \tag{16}$$

where V_{max} is the maximal transport velocity, K_m is the substrate (glucose) concentration at which the half-maximal transport rate is attained, and C is the concentration of the substrate. This relationship is formally equivalent with the Michaelis–Menten equation, which relates the velocity of enzyme reactions to the substrate concentration. The K_m values, which can be viewed as the *affinity* of the isoforms to glucose, vary between 1.8 mM (for GLUT-3) and 13.2 mM (for GLUT-2), and this feature is very important physiologically. The plasma glucose level in a healthy individual can change between 3.5 and 10 mM. Thus the brain transporter can always work close to or at its maximal velocity, whereas the activity of the liver isoform will be sharply controlled by the actual glucose level, enabling the organ adequately to regulate the sugar metabolism of the body. Regarding tissue culture applications, it is important to note that the glucose (and insulin) requirement of various cell lines differs greatly, and therefore attention must be paid to selection of the appropriate media.

The transporter can catalyze the net movement of glucose across the membrane (uptake or release), and under equilibrium conditions it can function as a glucose/glucose exchanger. The maximal velocity of these transport modes is different, the exchange being much faster than the uptake. This allows some insight into the possible transport mechanism. The simplest model is the following: There is a single substrate binding site facing the extracellular space. Upon glucose binding a conformational change occurs, causing the exposure of the same site to the intracellular space. Now glucose can dissociate from the carrier, and this event induces another conformation change, transforming the transporter from an inward-facing, glucose-free carrier to an outward-facing glucose-free carrier. Alternatively, the inward-facing and still (or again) glucose-loaded carrier can transform back into an outward-facing glucose-loaded carrier. Kinetic studies show that the conformational change of the glucose-free carrier is much slower (rate limiting) than the transitions of the glucose-loaded carrier or the dissociation and association of the substrate. This accounts for the interesting phenomenon of trans-activation: The uptake of labeled glucose into a completely glucose-free red cell is slower than into a cell that contains some glucose. In other words, the presence of glucose at the other (trans) side of the membrane facilitates entry. The reason is that in the presence of internal sugar the carrier can reorient itself much faster from the inward-facing to the outward-facing mode, where it can exchange the unlabeled glucose for a labeled one and then transport it inward. Moreover, it was found that even in the case of a glucose-loaded carrier, the rate of the inward-out transition is not the same as that of the outward-in transition. The structural and functional asymmetry of the carrier can also be demonstrated by using cytochalasin B, an inhibitor of GLUTs whose mechanism of action will depend on the sidedness of its application.

Although much less characterized as yet, other uniport systems have been reported in kidney, liver, and nerve cells. Probably, electrogenic uniports mediate the transport of some organic cations (e.g., choline, putrescine, spermidine, and many xenobiotics). Beside uniporters, the growing family of *organic cation transporters* (OCTs) include Na^+- and H^+-coupled exchangers (74).

Antiporters

Exchangers (antiporters, or so-called exchange-only systems) can be used for two functional purposes. First, such transporters can be exploited as secondary active transport systems that help remove solutes against their gradient using the downhill gradient of the partner (e.g., Na^+/H^+ and Na^+/Ca^{2+} exchangers). Second, they can rapidly exchange the products of enzyme reactions for the substrates, thereby assuring the appearance of the product in the right compartment and the continuity of the reaction (due to low product and high substrate concentration). Examples for this function include the Cl^-/HCO_3^- exchange (see the following) or the mitochondrial ATP/ADP antiport. When the transport of two molecules, say S and P, is coupled in this manner, the rate of exchange will be proportional to the concentration of S at one side (e.g., out) *and* to the concentration of P at the other (e.g., in). Thus, after reaching a steady state, where no *net movement* of S or P occurs any further:

$$[S]_{out}[P]_{in} = [S]_{in}[P]_{out}, \text{ or } [S]_{out}/[S]_{in} = [P]_{out}/[P]_{in} \tag{17}$$

that is, in the steady state the concentration ratio of one substrate is exactly the same as that of the other. The homoexchange (i.e., exchange of S_{out} to S_{in} or P_{in} to P_{out}), which is also catalyzed by antiports, will not affect this distribution. However, this relationship is true only if the transport is electroneutral, so that the membrane potential (E_m) cannot act as an additional driving force. With electrogenic systems, such as the already-mentioned Na^+/Ca^{2+} exchanger, the relationship is more complex and will depend on the difference in the valence of the substrates ($z_s - z_p$) and E_m:

$$\ln(S_{out}/S_{in}) = \ln(P_{out}/P_{in}) + (z_s - z_p)(FE_m/RT) \tag{18}$$

In this section we will concentrate on two well-characterized families of electroneutral plasma membrane antiporters, the Na^+/H^+ (NHEs) and the Cl^-/HCO_3^- or anion exchangers (AEs).

The 1:1 exchange of Na^+ for H^+ is an essential process for a variety of vital physiological functions, including the regulation of intracellular pH (pH_i) and cell volume, as well as the mediation of transepithelial Na^+ transport (9,10,75,76). pH_i regulation has both a protective (housekeeping) and a regulatory aspect. Every cell produces a substantial amount of metabolic acid that should be removed since a drop in pH_i affects practically every enzyme function and structural protein. Moreover, pH_i should be kept normal in view of the large negative membrane potential which would cause a tenfold excess of protons in the cytoplasm if H^+ ions were to be distributed passively. The regulatory function stems from the observation that certain processes (such as cell proliferation, migration) seem to require a net alkalinization of the cytoplasm, so that H^+ (or OH^-) can be regarded as a second messenger (77). It is therefore understandable that a large selection of hormones, growth factors, and other ligands modify NHE activity through a variety of intracellular signaling mechanisms.

The diverse tasks mentioned are brought about by several recently cloned isoforms of the NHE family (from NHE-1 to 6) (9,10). These transporters are composed of $\approx$800 amino acids (AA) organized into two functional clusters: the N-terminal $\approx$500 AAs form 10–12 TM α-helices that are embedded in the membrane, while the remaining 300 AAs constitute a C-terminal cytosolic tail [Fig. 2(b)]. The membrane domain shows a high level of homology among the different isoforms (especially segments 5 and 6), indicating that this part mediates the exchange. Segments 4 and 9 contain the amiloride binding site. The inhibitor sensitivity is isoform dependent, NHE-1 being the most and NHE-3 the least amiloride inhibitable. The C-terminal tail is the regulatory domain of the antiporters, and accordingly it is characteristic to each individual isoform. NHE-1 is expressed in every cell, and this isoform is the main pH_i and volume regulator. NHE-2, 3, and 4 are localized in epithelial cells of the gastrointestinal tract and the kidney, suggesting that they play an important role in Na^+ reabsorption and H^+ secretion. NHE-6 has recently been identified as the mitochondrial exchanger (78).

The regulation of NHEs is very complex and diverse. H^+ ions themselves are important regulators, as evidenced by the sigmoidal dependence of the transport rate on intracellular H^+ concentration: Above a certain pH_i (approx 7.3 for NHE-1) the antiporter is practically inactive, whereas a small decrease in pH_i below this so-called "set point" induces a sharp activation (47). Protons are believed to act at a cytoplasmic modifier site, and most stimuli affect the transport by changing the H^+ affinity of this locus, thereby shifting the pH_i dependence of the exchange [Fig. 2(c) and (d)]. Although ATP is not hydrolyzed during the transport, the presence of this nucleotide is necessary for the normal operation of each isoform. NHE-1 is a phosphoprotein in the resting state, and a variety of agonists induce its further phosphorylation via the activation of certain protein kinases, including protein kinase C (PKC) and mitogen-activated protein kinase. However, many stimulatory effects are not mediated by direct phosphorylation. For example, growth factors can still partially activate NHE-1 after the deletion of all phosphorylatable sites, and interestingly, a part of ATP's effect is also preserved under these conditions. Furthermore, hypertonicity (cell shrinkage) activates NHE-1 without inducing phosphorylation of the antiporter (79). The emerging picture is that phosphorylation-independent regulation of the transporters might be due to interaction with regulatory proteins. For example, calmodulin was shown to associate with and activate NHE-1 (80). Recent studies indicate a cross-talk between the antiporters and heterotrimeric and small G proteins (81). Interestingly, a number of stimuli affect NHE-1 and NHE-3 in a diametrically opposed manner. For example, PKC and hypertonicity inhibit NHE-3 (31,76). The mechanism of osmotic regulation is currently unknown, but it might be related to altered cytoskeletal interactions. NHE-3 is inhibited by PKA as well. This effect seems to be mediated by NH-REF, an NHE-3 binding protein (82). Obviously, many details of the complex regulation of these vitally important transporters warrant further investigation.

The anion exchanger (AE) family has three members: AE-1,2,3 (83,84). The first isoform, also known as *band 3* protein of red blood cells, is one of the fastest, most abundant, and most "famous" carriers. It plays an essential role in CO_2 transport by the blood: When CO_2 generated by the tissues enters the red cell, it is immediately hydrated to HCO_3^- and H^+. The H^+ is picked up by hemoglobin, whereas HCO_3^- is removed from the cells (it is exchanged for a Cl^-) through AE-1. This sequence of events ensures the continuous generation and transport of HCO_3^- into the plasma, which carries it to the lungs where, due to the high oxygen pressure, hemoglobin deprotonates and the opposite transport takes place. These reactions must proceed very fast. This requirement is satisfied since a single red cell contains one million AE-1 molecules (1000-fold more than the Na^+/K^+ ATPase) and since the turnover number of the carrier (30,000/sec) is the highest known value. In addition to its transport role, AE-1 is also a key structural protein: It connects the membrane to the submembranous cytoskeleton. An alternatively spliced version of AE-1 is localized in the apical membrane of kidney cells, where it participates in HCO_3^- reabsorption. The various AE isoforms show differences in their tissue distribution and their sensitivity toward stilbene inhibitors (e.g., DIDS). AE-2 is widely expressed, whereas AE-3 is present in the brain and heart. Both isoforms are involved in pH_i regulation. They are activated by an increase in pH_i, thereby protecting the cells from alkalinization. Thus NHE-1 and AE-2 work together to maintain the basal pH_i within a narrow range. Moreover, the coordinated action of these exchangers is necessary for normal volume regulation as well. Cell shrinkage activates NHE-1, which results in cytosolic alkalinization. This activates HCO_3^-/Cl^- exchange. The net result is the entry of NaCl together with osmotically obliged water, a process that leads to the normalization of cell volume (regulatory volume increase). Finally, we note that normal pH_i is a critical requirement for normal cell growth in tissue culture. Dividing cells are more alkaline than resting ones (by 0.2 pH units). If the culture conditions jeopardize this alkalinization (e.g., too much

CO_2 is present or the medium is inadequately buffered) the cell growth will slow down or stop.

Cotransporters

The transmembrane Na^+ electrochemical gradient ($\Delta\mu Na^+$) is a huge source of energy used by a large number of cotransporters (or symporters) that couple the uptake of inorganic ions (e.g., Cl^-, SO_4^-), nutrients (e.g., glucose, amino acids, nucleosides), neurotransmitters (e.g., GABA), organic osmolytes (e.g., myoinositol), and many other molecules to the movement of Na^+. Using similar considerations as for the antiport, the distribution of the transported molecules at the steady state can be formulated as:

$$[S]_{out}[P]_{out} = [S]_{in}[P]_{in} \text{ or } [S]_{out}/[S]_{in} = [P]_{in}/[P]_{out} \quad (19)$$

This means that the ratios are reciprocals of each other. The situation is more complicated if more than one substrate molecule of the same kind is transported and if the overall process is electrogenic. Mathematical analyses of these cases can be found in textbooks (48,85). The sodium cotransport proteins represent a very diverse group of transporters that includes the products of many different gene families. The basic structure of most cotransporters follows the 12-TM design; however, several exceptions have been reported. Here we restrict our discussion to a few important members.

The *Na$^+$-glucose cotransporters* (SGLTs) catalyze the Na^+-driven apical entry of glucose into the epithelial cells of the kidney tubules and the small intestine (86,87). This transporter is electrogenic so that its operation can be followed by voltage clamping (88). Such measurements have provided insight into the transport mechanism: In the absence of sugar, a rapid depolarization of the membrane resulted in the appearance of large transient currents, which were due to the reorientation (conformational change) of the carrier within the membrane. This suggests that the rate-limiting step in the transport is the reorientation of the unloaded carrier, and this is probably a general property of many transporters. Molecular relatives of SGLTs are the *Na$^+$-myoinostol* (SMIT) and *Na$^+$-nucleoside* (SNST) translocators. The former is important for volume regulation (its mRNA transcription is upregulated by hypertonicity, (89,90)), whereas the latter is a major pathway for uptake or reabsorption of adenosine, uridine, guanosine, and citidine (91,92). These constituents can also be taken up by uniports.

The *transport of amino acids* is mediated by several independent entities, with overlapping substrate specificities. Some of these transporters are Na^+-carrying cotransporters, while others are Na^+-independent uniporters. Based on transport specificity, these carriers were classically categorized into 13 different groups (93). Some of the corresponding genes have been cloned, giving a basis for a new (albeit incomplete) molecular biological classification (94,95). The Na^+-dependent transporters include (1) members of the *glutamate carriers* [glutamate/aspartate transporter (GLAST), glutamate-transporter-1 (GLT-1), the excitatory amino acid carrier (EAAC), the excitatory amino acid transporter (EAAT)]; (2) members of the so-called *ASC* (for alanine–serine–cysteine) *transporters,* which carry neutral amino acids; and (3) the highly specific *glycine transporters* (GLYTs), which are Na^+ and Cl^- dependent. The positively charged amino acids (arginine, lysine, ornithine, and hystidine) are transported in a Na^+-independent way by members of the *cationic amino acid transporter* (CAT) *family* (94). The molecular identity of several other amino acid transport systems remains to be defined. Since amino acids serve both as vitally important building blocks and as neurotransmitters, their transporters play a central role in the regulation of metabolism and neuronal functions. The mechanisms by which these carriers are regulated warrant further intensive research.

The *Na$^+$–K$^+$–2Cl$^-$ cotransporter* (NKCC) is an electroneutral, 12-TM type carrier that has a prominent role in transepithelial Cl^- transport (96,97). In certain tissues, such as in mammalian airways, fluid secretion is driven by the apical Cl^- efflux through anion channels. In these cells Cl^- entry, a prerequisite for continuous secretion, is mediated by the basolateral NKCC-1. Conversely, in absorptive epithelia, such as the thick ascending limb of the kidney, Cl^- uptake is catalyzed by the apical NKCC-2, and the ion leaves the cell through basolateral anion channels. Obviously, Cl^- flux through the Cl^- channels and the NKCCs should be somehow coordinated. This is brought about by several mechanisms. Many agonists stimulate Cl^- channels via activation of protein kinase A. The same kinase phosphorylates and stimulates NKCC as well (98). Furthermore, when Cl^- channels open and fluid efflux takes place, the cell shrinks and the intracellular Cl^- level decreases. Both of these events were shown to stimulate NKCC. The loop diuretic bumetanide is a specific inhibitor of the cotransporter. Interestingly, bumetanide binding increases several-fold upon NKCC stimulation, and this does not seem to be due to the insertion of new transporters into membrane (99). This finding therefore implies that the NKCC has a distinct conformation in its activated (presumably phosphorylated) state. Other studies show that the level of actin polymerization is also an important regulator of the transporter. Further work is needed to identify the exact sites and mechanisms of action of the various effectors.

PUMPS

Active ion pumps generate transmembrane gradients that are necessary to drive a large variety of carrier- and channel-mediated transport processes. Based on functional and structural criteria, ion-motive ATPases can be grouped into three major classes: P-, V-, and F-type. With the recent discovery of ATP-powered drug transporters, such as the P-glycoprotein, it became clear that pumps can catalyze not only ion movements but also the uphill transport of hydrophobic compounds. These enzymes are members of the ABC superfamily, and represent a new category of active transporters. Here, we will focus predominantly on the P-type enzymes, since most of these are localized in the plasma membrane. V-type ATPases are found mainly in the membranes of intracellular vesicles ("V" denotes vesicular), such as lysosomes or endosomes, where they generate a highly acidic internal environment. However, in certain cells they may also be present in the plasma membrane, where they promote acid extrusion. The F-type ATPases are mitrochondrial enzymes responsible for oxidative ATP synthesis. Their operation is not covered in this article, but the interested reader is recommended to consult a recent outstanding review by Paul Boyer (100) in which the author summarizes the structure and the reaction mechanism (the so-called *rotational catalysis*) of these fascinating molecular machines.

P-Type ATPases

The pioneering work of György Gárdos, Jens Skou Robert Post, and Hans Schatzmann led to the recognition that (*1*) ATP is necessary to maintain high intracellular K^+ and low intracellular Na^+ concentrations, (*2*) the plasma membrane contains an *ATPase activity* that can be stimulated by the *combined presence of Na^+ plus K^+*, and (*3*) the glycoside alkaloid *oubain* inhibits both Na^+ and K^+ pumping *and* the K^+-plus-Na^+-stimulated ATPase activity. Taken together, the picture emerged that the Na^+ and K^+ pump(s), as well as the Na^+-plus-K^+-dependent ATPase, represent one and the same molecular entity (101). A large body of experimental evidence has accumulated proving that the Na^+/K^+ ATPase is a membrane-embedded enzyme that, while splitting ATP, catalyzes the coupled and opposite movement of Na^+ and K^+ across the cell membrane (102,103). The reaction mechanism of the Na^+/K^+ pump can be written as follows:

$$E_1 \longleftrightarrow E_1ATPNa \longleftrightarrow E_1PNa \longleftrightarrow E_2PNa$$
$$E_1K \longleftrightarrow E_2K \longleftrightarrow E_2PK \longleftrightarrow E_2P$$

The enzyme first stays in the E_1 conformation in which the cation binding sites face the cytosol. Na^+ ions (in fact, three of them) and ATP bind to the pump, and this results in the phosphorylation of the enzyme (E_1PNa). This step is followed by a conformational change (E_2 state) that reorients the cation binding sites toward the extracellular space. At this point, the Na^+ ions dissociate from the pump, and extracellular K^+ ions (two of them) bind to it. These events trigger the dephosphorylation of the enzyme followed by its interconversion to the E_1 conformation. K^+ ions are then released into the cytosol and the pump is ready for the next cycle. The two most important features of this greatly simplified model are the formation of *phosphorylated intermediates* and the *existence of two (E_1 and E_2) conformational states*. The ion-dependent phosphorylation of the enzyme was convincingly demonstrated in membrane preps, to which radioactive ATP was added in the presence of Na^+ but in the absence of K^+. Under these conditions, the membrane became highly labeled because the reaction stopped before the K^+-requiring dephosphorylation step could occur. Addition of K^+ resulted in quick dephosphorylation. A number of observations indicated the existence of the two states as well. Sulfhydryl reagents froze the enzyme in

one conformation (E_1), thereby preventing the K^+-induced ATP hydrolysis. Moreover, the proteolytic digestion of the enzyme differed in the presence or absence of K^+ and/or Na^+ because the two conformational sates are differentially sensitive to chymotrypsin.

The formation of phospho intermediates is a common characteristic of the Na^+/K^+ pump and related ATPases such as the K^+/H^+ ATPase and the Ca^{2+} ATPases of the plasma membrane and the sarcoplasmic reticulum. Therefore, these enzymes were named P (phospho) ATPases. (They are often referred to as E_1-E_2 ATPases as well, although the phosphorylation-independent presence of these two states is not certain in Ca^{2+}-ATPases). Another common feature of the P-type pumps is that they can be inhibited by the ATP analog vanadate.

Under physiologic conditions, 3 Na^+ are pumped against 2 K^+ for every ATP hydrolyzed. This stoichiometry suggests that the system is electrogenic, and pump-related currents have in fact been measured. Normally, the ion movements are strongly coupled to each other; that is, very little *slippage* occurs. The operation of the pump may consume as much as 25% (in erythrocytes 50%) of the total ATP produced. The enzyme has been cloned and investigated at the molecular level. It is a heterodimer composed of a ca. 100-kDa α subunit and a ca. 50-kDa glycoprotein β subunit. Several isoforms have been defined for both subunits. The α-subunit is responsible for ATP hydrolysis and ion pumping while the β subunit is important for the correct assembly of the ATPase in the endoplasmic reticulum and the subsequent maturation of the protein (18,104,105). The α-subunit contains 10 TM segments and a 500-amino-acid-long cytosolic loop between segments 4 and 5. This domain contains the ATP-binding site and the critical phosphorylated residue which has been identified as aspartate 369. The first TM segment is believed to be involved in the E_1-E_2 transition. The activity of the Na^+/K^+ pump is regulated at multiple levels (106–108). An increase in intracellular Na^+ is a major acute stimulus that can elevate pump activity over 20-fold in working muscle. Also, several hormones such as insulin, catecholamines, angiotensin etc. have been shown to upregulate the ATPase through different mechanisms, including covalent modification and changes in gene and protein expression. Many details of the exact transport mechanism of this vitally important protein await further elucidation.

The closest relative of the Na^+/K^+ pump is the H^+/K^+ ATPase. This is also an $\alpha\beta$ heterodimer, and is expressed in the H^+-secreting parietal cells of the stomach and in certain cells of the kidney (109,110). In the resting state the enzyme molecules of the parietal cells reside in the membrane of the so-called tubulovesicular elements. Upon stimulation, these structures fuse with the apical membrane conferring a huge acid-secreting capacity to it. The rapid electroneutral exchange of $2H^+$ for $2K^+$ during the hydrolysis of 1 ATP can build up a transmembrane H^+ gradient of six orders of magnitude ($pH_{in} \approx 7.0$, $pH_{out} \approx 1$). K^+ ions are recycled through apical K^+ channels, while the replenishment of cytosolic H^+ is provided by the hydration of CO_2 ($H^+ + HCO_3^-$). The formed HCO_3^- is released through the basolateral HCO_3^-/Cl^- exchanger, and the imported Cl^- is removed to the gastric juice through apical Cl^- channels. The net result, HCl secretion is a process based on a finely tuned interplay among pumps, channels, and carriers. The β subunit seems to be involved in the retrieval of the ATPase, which is necessary for the termination of acid secretion.

The Ca^{2+} pumps can be classified into two major groups, the plasma membrane enzyme (PMCA) and the one localized in the sarco- or endoplasmic reticulum (SERCA) (111–113). These pumps have a major role in keeping the intracellular free Ca^{2+} concentration around 100 nM, which is 10,000-fold lower than the extracellular concentration, in spite of the negative membrane potential. Here we deal only with the PMCA. In contrast to the pumps discussed previously, this ATPase is a single polypeptide chain with a molecular mass of $\approx$140 kD. Various isoforms are coded by four different genes, and further variability originates from alternative mRNA splicing. The membrane-spanning part is composed of 10 TM segments. Three sizable units protrude into the cytoplasm. The first one is responsible for the coupling of ATP hydrolysis and Ca^{2+} transport, the second harbors the ATP-binding site and the characteristic aspartyl-phosphate residue, and the third one contains two bindings sites for calmodulin, the most important regulator of pump activity. The calmodulin binding site and its continuation, the C-terminal end of the molecule, are thought to act as an autoinhibitory domain. Proteolytic cleavage or the binding of Ca^{2+}-calmodulin relieves this hindrance and thereby strongly activates the pump. This unique feature allows the ATPase to adjust its transport rate to the demand: A moderate increase in cytosolic Ca^{2+} concentration induces greatly elevated Ca^{2+} extrusion, which continues until the Ca^{2+} concentration returns to the basal level. In addition to this mechanism, the pump is controlled by acidic phospholipids and direct phosphorylation as well. The PMCA is a high-affinity but low-capacity system, so that the quick removal of a stimulus-induced rise in cytosolic Ca^{2+}, especially in muscle cells, necessitates concomitant operation of the SERCA and the Na^+/Ca^{2+} exchanger.

V-Type ATPases

The vacuolar ATPases are multisubunit enzymes composed of a membrane-embedded part (V_0) responsible for H^+ translocation, and a peripherial domain (V_1) catalyzing ATP hydrolysis (114,115). These parts are assembled together in a "stalk and ball" structure. The V_1 domain contains 5–8 different polypeptides (labeled from A to G) organized into a 500–600-kDa complex (e.g., $A_3B_3C_1D_1E_1$), while the V_0 domain contains 3–5 polypeptides (labeled a, b, c, c', c") constituting an integral 250–300-kDa complex. The vacuolar H^+-ATPases do not undergo phosphorylation during ATP hydrolysis and are insensitive to vanadate but can be blocked with the alkylating agent dicocyclohexylcarbodiimide (DCCD) and more specifically with the antibiotic bafilomycin. The complex can transport 2 H^+ ions per ATP split. However this stoichiometry can change due to slippage of the ATPase, a process that is likely to be under regulatory control. Operation of the enzyme is electrogenic so that it can build up a lumen-positive membrane potential. The various subunits are involved in nucleotide binding, hydrolysis, H^+ flux, and the correct assembly and targeting of the various isoforms to the appropriate vesicles. The physiological functions of vacuolar H^+-ATPases are multifaceted. For example, vesicular acidification is a prerequisite for the recycling of endocytosed receptors and for the targeting of many newly synthesized proteins. The H^+ gradient generated by the pump is the driving force for the H^+/neurotransmitter (e.g., noradrenaline) exchange present in the membrane of synaptic vesicles. H^+ extrusion mediated by *plasma membrane H^+-ATPases* is involved in H^+ secretion by kidney cells, bone resorption by osteoclasts, the acidification of forming phagosomes and the regulation of pH_i in phagocytes.

Multidrug Transporter

Proof for the existence of a separate group of ATP-powered transporters came from studies directed to understand the mechanisms by which a great variety of tumor cells can acquire resistance against a multitude of chemostatic agents. The appearance of multidrug resistance, a phenomenon of obvious medical and cell biological importance, was associated with the overexpression of a 170-kDa glycoprotein called P170, P-glycoprotein, or MDR1 protein. By now it has become the prototype of several related drug transporters that all belong to the ABC transporter superfamily (116–119). The structure of P-glycoprotein is similar to that of CFTR: It contains 12 TM segments organized in two roughly symmetrical domains, and two nucleotide binding folds, one between TM 6 and 7, and one C-terminal to TM 12. The protein, energized by ATP hydrolysis can export a variety of drugs against their concentration gradient, *and* in addition, it also seems to inhibit their influx. This dual function was puzzling, as was the fact that the transport, although very effective, exhibits very little substrate specificity. The transporter can handle structurally very different drugs and toxins, including protein and nucleic acid synthesis inhibitors, antibacterial compounds, Ca^{2+} channel antagonists, etc. The only common characteristic of the accepted substrates appears to be their high hydrophobicity and its direct consequence, namely, that these compounds are taken up by free lipid-phase diffusion. This feature might give us a clue as to the mechanism by which P-glycoprotein liberates the cells of these compounds. It is believed that the transporter "keeps clean" the lipid phase of the membrane. Its substrates first intercalate with the bilayer, and only then can they interact with the protein.

A model has been proposed that suggests that the compound to be transported is dissolved in the membrane from whence it penetrates *into* the P-glycoprotein molecule, which contains an internal barrel that is open to the extracellular space. The protein then expels its contents to the exterior. In other words, it would work as a "hydrophobic vacuum cleaner." Such a mechanism can explain inhibition of drug uptake by the transporter, since drugs can be removed from the cell membrane before they have a chance to reach the cytosol. The likely physiological role of MDR1 is to provide a cellular antitoxic mechanism. In addition, it also seems to be a major contributor to the blood–brain and blood–testis barriers for hydrophobic compounds. On the other hand, its operation provides a serious obstacle for effective anticancer drug therapy. Substantial efforts have been directed to develop safe inhibitor strategies, since these may dramatically improve the efficacy of chemotherapy. Members of a related enzyme family, the multidrug resistance-associated proteins (MRP) export large organic anions such as bile salts and glutathione conjugates. Further work is required to evaluate the intriguing model and to explain the various transport capabilities of these interesting ATPases.

TRANSPORTERS IN ACTION: AN INTEGRATED VIEW

Channels, carriers, and pumps do not work in isolation. While describing the operation of specific systems, it was our aim throughout this article to hint at the integrative aspects of membrane transport. Now, as a short summary, we will take a physiologist's viewpoint and show how the various transporters collaborate to realize a complex function. This example, which is one of thousands of highly integrated responses, regards the pH_i and volume regulation of activated phagocytes.

The primary role of phagocytes is to eliminate invading microorganisms. One of their important antimicrobial weapons is the NADPH oxidase, an enzyme that upon cell stimulation is assembled from cytosolic and membrane components into a functioning complex that catalyzes the one-electron reduction of molecular oxygen to superoxide, a precursor of bacteriotoxic radicals. The electrons originating from NADPH are translocated across the membrane while the remaining protons are released into the cytoplasm. These events have two major consequences: an immediate depolarization (due to the efflux of negative charges), and a tremendous increase in metabolic acid production. It has been calculated that if H^+ equivalents were to remain in the cytosol, the pH_i would drop more than 5 units within minutes (120). Both the extreme depolarization and the acidification would jeopardize the continuous superoxide production. Moreover, in order to fight effectively phagocytes (e.g., neutrophils) have to migrate through blood vessel walls to the site of bacterial invasion. In the resting state neutrophils are among the "driest" cells in the body, and they have to take up fluid in order to become more deformable, a requirement for transmigration. Once they reach their target, they have to phagocytose it. However, for effective killing, the phagocytic vacuole has to be acidic. So, the complex requirements are: to eliminate H^+ from the cytosol, to prevent extreme depolarization, to swell, and to acidify the phagosome. How are these complex tasks brought about? The short answer is: by transporters. First a transient acidification occurs due to activation of the oxidase. This rise in intracellular H^+ concentration activates the NHE since H^+ ions are both substrates for and allosteric regulators of the transporter. Interestingly, in a short time net cytosolic alkalinization develops in spite of the large increase in H^+ production (121). This cannot be accounted for by the simple H^+-dependent activation of NHE, since this could

only normalize pH_i but would not induce an overshoot. The main underlying reason for the alkalinization is that the same stimuli (e.g., bacterial peptides) that provoke superoxide production act on various signaling pathways (e.g., PKC) that directly stimulate NHE by increasing its affinity for H^+. Furthermore, the ensuing alkalinization can activate the Cl^-/HCO_3^- exchanger. The net result is the accumulation of osmotically active solutes and accompanying water: In other words, swelling takes place (122). The volume increase of activated neutrophils may be as much as 20–25%. This change in size is essential for normal function as evidenced by the fact that the prevention of swelling by hyperosmotic solutions seriously interferes with migration and other neutrophil functions (123). However, all these pathways are electroneutral; so that they cannot counteract the oxidase-mediated depolarization. This task is fulfilled by a voltage- and pH-dependent H^+ channel localized in the plasma membrane (124–126). This pathway is activated by depolarization, and its conductance is further increased by the submembraneous drop in pH_i in the vicinity of the oxidase, as well as by arachidonic acid, an important inflammatory mediator liberated in the activated cell (127). Besides mitigating depolarization, the H^+ conductance helps the NHE eliminate deleterious acid. Finally, a third system joins the already-mentioned H^+-eliminating transporters: a V-type ATPase. This enzyme is translocated to the membrane and starts pumping H^+ ions into the extracellular space or into the forming phagosome (128). Inhibition of any of the three H^+ transporters (NHE, channel, ATPase) has been reported to alter the normal pH_i and voltage changes in stimulated cells. Taken together, the coordinated action of these different transport proteins culminates in the effective fulfillment of a complex biological function.

APPENDIX

To illustrate some quantitative aspects of important transport-related phenomena, we will provide here a few examples using some of the equations discussed in the text.

Equation 10

The permeability coefficient of ethanol (in case of an "average membrane") is approximately 1.1×10^{-3} cm/sec. This means that if the concentration difference across the membrane is 1 M, 1.1 mmol ethanol would flow across 1 cm² membrane area in 1 sec. If we put cells in medium containing 2 mM ethanol (i.e., the concentration gradient between the extracellular space and the initially alcohol-free intracellular equals 2 mM), the initial rate of transport is:

$$J = 1.1 \times 10^{-3} \text{ cm/sec} \times 2 \times 10^{-3} \text{ M}$$
$$= 2.2 \times 10^{-6} \text{ mol/sec/cm}^2$$

Equation 12

At physiological temperatures ($37\,°C = 310$ K), and if the solute is completely impermeable across the membrane

$(\sigma = 1)$, Eq. 12 can be written as $\Delta\pi = 25.4\,\Delta C$ in atm, or $2573\,\Delta C$ in kPa, where ΔC is expressed in mol/liter. This means that if the difference in solute concentration is 1 mol/liter, the osmotic water flow through the semipermeable membrane can be prevented by applying 25.4 atm at the more concentrated compartment.

It is important to note that in order to calculate the osmotic concentration (e.g., in osmole/liter or osM), the concentration of *all osmotically active particles* should be added together. For example, if a solute is composed of 150 mM NaCl, 50 K_2SO_4, and 130 mM sucrose, each of which is practically impermeant through the membrane compared to water, then the total active osmotic concentration of this fluid would be:

NaCl:

$$150 \times 2 \text{ (for Na}^+ \text{ and Cl}^-) = 300 \text{ mosM}$$

K_2SO_4:

$$50 \times 3 \text{ (for K}^+ \text{ plus K}^+ \text{ and SO}_4{}^{2-}) = 150 \text{ mosM}$$

Sucrose:

$$130 \times 1 = 130 \text{ mosM}$$

that is:

$$300 + 150 + 130 = 580 \text{ mosM}$$

When animal cells are placed in such a solution, they will shrink because the external osmolarity is higher than the physiologic internal osmolarity (approx. 290 mosM). Since in this case the extracellular osmotic concentration is twice as much as the internal one, cells will shrink by 50% (they behave as perfect "osmometers"). The *rate* of this shrinkage will be determined by the osmotic permeability coefficient (L_p) of the membrane. L_p can be expressed as $cm^3/(cm^2 \times sec \times osM) = cm/(sec \times osM)$. The numeric value of L_p shows how many cm^3 water can flow across a 1-cm^2 membrane area if the difference in the osmotic concentration is 1 osM. If we multiply the value with the molal volume of water (= 55 mol/liter), we get the water permeability units in cm/sec.

The water permeability of the red cell membrane is 0.02 cm/sec, or expressed in osmotically more explicit terms:

$$0.02/55 = 3.6 \times 10^{-4} \text{ cm}^3/(\text{cm}^2 \times \text{sec} \times \text{osM})$$

Let us calculate how fast the water movement will occur if we place the cells in the above solution:

$$J_{\text{water}} = 3.6 \times 10^{-4} \text{ cm}^3/(\text{cm}^2 \times \text{sec} \times \text{osM})$$

$$\times\, 0.29 \text{ osM} = 1.04 \times 10^{-4} \text{ cm}^3/(\text{cm}^2 \times \text{sec})$$

$$\text{or } 104 \text{ nL/(cm}^2 \times \text{sec}) \text{ or } 1.04 \times 10^{-7} \text{ L/(cm}^2 \times \text{sec})$$

The surface area of a single red cell is approximately 1.5×10^{-6} cm^2; thus the initial rate of water flow out of a single cell would be:

$$1.04 \times 10^{-7} \text{ L/(cm}^2 \times \text{sec}) \times 1.5 \times 10^{-6} \text{ cm}^2$$

$$= 1.56 \times 10^{-13} \text{ L/sec}$$

The volume of the red cell is approximately 0.9×10^{-13} L; so to lose half of this with the above rate would last $0.45/1.56 = 0.29$ sec. (In reality a little more time will be required since as water moves out, the osmotic gradient decreases.)

Equations 14 and 15

To calculate the *resting plasma membrane potential* in an "average" animal cell, let us assume the following intra- and extracellular ion concentrations and permeabilities:

$$[K]_{\text{in}} = 140 \text{ mM}, \qquad [K]_{\text{out}} = 4.5 \text{ mM},$$

$$P_K = 5 \times 10^{-7} \text{ cm/sec}$$

$$[Na]_{\text{in}} = 20 \text{ mM}, \qquad [Na]_{\text{out}} = 145 \text{ mM},$$

$$P_{Na} = 5 \times 10^{-9} \text{ cm/sec}$$

$$[Cl]_{\text{in}} = 10 \text{ mM}, \qquad [Cl]_{\text{out}} = 110 \text{ mM},$$

$$P_{Cl} = 1 \times 10^{-8} \text{ cm/sec}$$

Substituting these values into Eq. 14, we get:

$$E_m = -60 \log \frac{\left(\begin{array}{c}(5 \times 10^{-7} \times 140) + (5 \times 10^{-9} \times 20) \\ + (1 \times 10^{-8} \times 110)\end{array}\right)}{\left(\begin{array}{c}(5 \times 10^{-7} \times 4.5) + (5 \times 10^{-9} \times 145) \\ + (1 \times 10^{-8} \times 10)\end{array}\right)}$$

$$= -81.9 \text{ mV}$$

Note that a 5000-fold increase in P_{Na}, with all other values remaining the same, would depolarize the membrane to +48.2 mV.

Using Eq. 15, we can calculate the *magnitude of the current* carried by a certain ion at a given membrane potential.

Suppose that the membrane is depolarized to (and held at) -55 mV. In this case, the net driving force acting on Na$^+$ will be the difference between $E_m = -55$ mV and the Na$^+$ equilibrium potential. The latter is:

$$E_{Na} = -60 \log(Na_i/Na_o)$$

$$= -60 \log(20/145) = -60 \log 0.138$$

$$= +51.6 \text{ mV}$$

The difference is therefore

$$-55 \text{ mV} - (+51.6 \text{ mV}) = -106.6 \text{ mV}.$$

This will drive Na$^+$ into the cell. If the conductance of Na$^+$ (g_{Na}, the electrical equivalent of permeability) at this voltage is 0.3 mS/cm^2 (S stands for siemens, the reciprocal of ohm), the Na^+ current (i_{Na}) will be:

$$i_{Na} = g_{Na}(E_m - E_{Na}) = 0.3 \text{ mS/cm}^2 \times (-106.6) \text{ mV}$$
$$= -31.98 \text{ } \mu amp/cm^2$$

Similarly, we can calculate the initial K^+ current under the same conditions, assuming that g_k is 0.9 mS/cm^2 at -55 mV.

$$E_k = -60 \log(K_i/K_o) = -60 \log(140/4.5)$$
$$= -60 \log 31.1 = -89.6 \text{ mV}$$

Thus,

$$(E_m - E_K) = -55 - (-89.6) = +34.6 \text{ mV}$$

From this:

$$i_K = 0.9 \text{ mS/cm}^2 \times 34.6 \text{ mV} = +31.14 \text{ } \mu amp/cm^2$$

Taken together:

$$i_{Na} + i_K = -31.98 \text{ } \mu amp/cm^2 + 31.14 \text{ } \mu amp/cm^2$$
$$= -0.84 \text{ } \mu amp/cm^2$$

Thus a small net flux of positive charges would occur into the cell (and this should be counterbalanced by voltage clamping).

Note that at near-threshold levels (when the difference between the rate of positive charges moving into and out of the cell is little), Cl^- fluxes may have a significant modifying ("buffering") role. If, however, g_{Na} becomes overwhelming, Cl contribution becomes negligible.

BIBLIOGRAPHY

1. P. Mitchell *Nature (London)* **191**, 144–148 (1961).
2. V.P. Skulachev *Membrane Bioenergetics*, Springer-Verlag, Berlin, 1983, pp. 338–353.
3. P.J.F. Henderson, in J.K. Griffith and C.E. Sansom, eds., *The Transporter FactsBook*, Academic Press, San Diego, Calif., 1997, pp. 3–29.
4. G. Guidotti *Annu. Rev. Biochem.* **41**, 731–752 (1972).
5. J. Kayt and R.F. Doolittle, *J. Mol. Biol.* **157**, 105–132 (1982).
6. C.M. Tse et al., *J. Biol. Chem.* **267**, 9340–9346 (1992).
7. R. Henderson et al., *J. Mol. Biol.* **213**, 899–929 (1990).
8. N. Grigorieff et al., *J. Mol. Biol.* **259**, 393–421 (1996).
9. S. Wakabayashi, M. Shigekawa, and J. Pouyssegur, *Physiol. Rev.* **77**, 51–74 (1997).
10. J. Orlowski and S. Grinstein, *J. Biol. Chem.* **272**, 22373–22376 (1997).
11. J.R. Riordan et al., *Science* **245**, 1066–1073 (1989).
12. M.D. Schaller *Soc. Gen. Physiol. Ser.* **52**, 241–255 (1997).
13. S. Dedhar and G.E. Hannigan, *Curr. Opin. Cell Biol.* **8**, 657–669 (1996).
14. R.O. Hynes and H. Hughes, *Cell* **69**, 11–25 (1992).
15. D.E. Ingber *Annu. Rev. Physiol.* **59**, 575–599 (1997).
16. M.A. Schwartz, C. Lechene, and D.E. Ingber, *Proc. Natl. Acad. Sci. U.S.A.* **88**, 7849–7853 (1991).
17. S. Grinstein et al., *EMBO J.* **15**, 5209–5218 (1993).
18. M.J. Caplan *Am. J. Physiol.* **272**, G1304–G1313 (1997).
19. J. Noël, D. Roux, and J. Pouysségur, *J. Cell Sci.* **109**, 929–939 (1996).
20. L.L. Mitic and J.M. Anderson, *Annu. Rev. Physiol.* **60**, 121–142 (1998).
21. M. Cercijado, J. Valdis, L. Shoshan, and R.G. Contreras, *Annu. Rev. Physiol.* **60**, 161–197 (1998).
22. I. Mellman *Annu. Rev. Cell Dev. Biol.* **12**, 575–626 (1996).
23. T. Weimbs, S.H. Low, S.J. Chapin, and K.E. Mostov, *Trends Cell Biol.* **7**, 393–398 (1997).
24. M.J. Briske-Anderson, J.W. Finley, and S.M. Newman, *Proc. Soc. Exp. Biol.* **214**, 248–257 (1997).
25. K. Hashimoto and M. Shimizu, *Cytotechnology* **3**, 175–184 (1993).
26. A. Hakvoort et al., *J. Neurochem.* **71**, 1141–1150 (1998).
27. C. Tanner, A. Donald, F. Misfeldt, and D.S. Misfeldt, *Biophys. J.* **43**, 183–190 (1983).
28. D.S. Misfeldt, S.T. Hamamoto, and D.R. Pitelka, *Proc. Natl. Acad. Sci. U.S.A.* **73**, 1212–1216 (1976).
29. M. Cereijido et al., *J. Cell Biol.* **77**, 853–880 (1978).
30. J.P. Lavelle et al., *Am. J. Physiol.* **273**, F67–F75 (1997).
31. A. Kapus et al., *J. Biol. Chem.* **269**, 23544–23552 (1994).
32. G.L. Lukacs et al., *J. Biol. Chem.* **268**, 21592–21598 (1993).
33. M. Schneider, I.W. Marison, and U. von Stockar, *J. Biotechnol.* **46**, 161–185 (1996).
34. W.F. Boron *Annu. Rev. Physiol.* **48**, 377–388 (1986).
35. R.Y. Tsien, T. Pozzan, and T.J. Rink, *J. Cell Biol.* **94**, 325–334 (1982).
36. F. Lang et al., *Physiol. Rev.* **78**, 247–306 (1998).
37. G.N. Preston T.P. Carroll, W.B. Guggino, and P. Agre, *Science* **256**, 385–387 (1992).
38. A.S. Verkman *Water Channels*, R.G. Landes, Austin, tex., 1993.
39. M.A. Knepper and T. Inoue, *Curr. Opin. Cell Biol.* **9**, 560–564 (1997).
40. S. Sasaki, K. Ishibashi, and F. Marumo, *Annu. Rev. Physiol.* **60**, 199–220 (1998).
41. B. Hille *Ionic Channels of Excitable Membranes*, Sinauer Assoc., Sunderland. Mass., 1992.
42. E. Moczydlowski and L. Schild, in C. Peracchia, ed., *Handbook of Membrane Channels*, Academic Press, San Diego, Calif., 1994, pp. 137–160.
43. M. Noda et al., *Nature (London)* **322**, 826–828 (1986).
44. J. Orlowski *J. Biol. Chem.* **268**, 16369–16377 (1993).
45. A. Kapus et al., *Biochim. Biophys. Acta* **944**, 383–390 (1988).
46. B.P. Bean and I.M. Mintz, in C. Peracchia, ed., *Handbook of Membrane Channels*, Academic Press, San Diego, Calif., 1994, pp. 199–210.
47. P.S. Aronson, J. Nee, and M.A. Suhm, *Nature (London)* **299**, 161–163 (1982).
48. W.D. Stein *Channels, Carriers are Pumps*, Academic Press, San Diego, Calif., 1990.
49. K.D. Philipson and D.A. Nicholl, *Curr. Opin. Cell Biol.* **4**, 678–683 (1992).
50. J.K. Griffith and C.E. Sansom, eds., *The Transporter FactsBook*, Academic Press, San Diego, Calif., 1998.
51. L. Dux, K.A. Taylor, H.P. Ting-Beall, and A. Martonosi, *J. Biol. Chem.* **260**, 11730–11743 (1985).

52. S. Frillingos, M. Sahin-Toth, J. Wu, and H.R. Kaback, *FASEB J.* **12**, 1281–1299 (1998).

53. A.L. Hodgkin, A.F. Huxley, and B. Katz, *J. Physiol. (London)* **116**, 424–448 (1952).

54. O.P. Hamill et al., *Pflügers Arch.* **391**, 85–100 (1981).

55. E. Neher and B. Sakmann, *Nature (London)* **260**, 799–802 (1976).

56. D. Gordon *Curr. Opin. Cell Biol.* **2**, 695–707 (1990).

57. W.A. Catterall *Curr. Opin. Cell Biol.* **6**, 607–615 (1994).

58. W.A. Catterall *Annu. Rev. Biochem.* 493–531 (1995).

59. N. Voilley et al., *Comp. Biochem. Physiol. A* **118**, 193–200 (1997).

60. Y. Mori, in C. Peracchia, ed., *Handbook of Membrane Channels*, Academic Press, San Diego, Calif., 1994, pp. 199–210.

61. C.D. Ferris and S.H. Snyder, *Annu. Rev. Physiol.* **54**, 469–488 (1992).

62. G. Meissner, *Annu. Rev. Physiol.* **56**, 485–508 (1994).

63. C.G. Nichols and A.N. Lopatin, *Annu. Rev. Physiol.* **59**, 171–191 (1997).

64. J. Bryan and L. Aguilar-Bryan, *Curr. Opin. Cell Biol.* **9**, 533–555 (1997).

65. T.J. Jentsch *Curr. Opin. Cell Biol.* **6**, 600–606 (1994).

66. J.K. Foskett *Annu. Rev. Physiol.* **60**, 689–717 (1998).

67. A. Petris, C. Trequattrini, and F. Franciolini, in C. Peracchia, ed., *Handbook of Membrane Channels*, Academic Press, San Diego, Calif., 1994, pp. 245–254.

68. S. Devidas and W.B. Guggino, *Curr. Opin. Cell Biol.* **9**, 547–552 (1997).

69. M.J. Stutts et al., *Science* **269**, 847–850 (1995).

70. F. Sacs, in ed., *Cytoskeletal Regulation of Membrane Function*, Rockefeller University Press, Buffalo, N.Y., 1997, pp. 209–218.

71. A. Leple-Wienhues et al., *J. Cell Biol.* **141**, 281–286 (1998).

72. S.A. Baldwin *Curr. Opin. Cell Biol.* **2**, 714–721 (1990).

73. J.E. Pessin and G.I. Bell, *Annu. Rev. Physiol.* **54**, 911–930 (1997).

74. K. Kirk and K. Strange, *Annu. Rev. Physiol.* **60**, 719–739 (1998).

75. J. Noël and H. Pouysségur, *Am. J. Physiol.* **268**, C283–296 (1995).

76. C.H.C. Yun et al., *Am. J. Physiol.* **269**, G1-G11 (1995).

77. S. Wakabayashi et al., *Rev. Physiol. Biochem. Pharmacol.* **19**, 158–186 (1992).

78. N. Numata, K. Pertecca, N. Lake, and J. Orlowski, *J. Biol. Chem.* **273**, 6951–6959 (1998).

79. S. Grinstein et al., *J. Biol. Chem.* **267**, 23823–23828 (1992).

80. B. Bertrand et al., *J. Biol. Chem.* **269**, 13703–13709 (1994).

81. T. Tomiga and D.L. Barber, *Mol. Biol. Cell* **9**, 2287–2303 (1998).

82. E.J. Weinman, D. Steplock, J. Wang, and S. Shenolikar, *J. Clin. Invest.* **95**, 2143–2149 (1995).

83. S.L. Alper *Annu. Rev. Physiol.* **53**, 549–564 (1991).

84. R.A.F. Reitheimer *Curr. Opin. Cell Biol.* **6**, 583–594 (1994).

85. S.G. Schultz *Basic Principles of Membrane Transport* Binghamton, N.Y., 1980.

86. E.M. Wright, K.M. Hager, and E. Turk, *Curr. Opin. Cell. Biol.* **4**, 696–702 (1992).

87. E.M. Wright *Annu. Rev. Physiol.* **55**, 575–589 (1993).

88. L. Parent, S. Supplisson, D.A.F. Loo, and E.M. Wright, *J. Membr. Biol.* **125**, 49–62 (1992).

89. H.M. Kwon and J.S. Handler, *Curr. Opin. Cell Biol.* **7**, 465–471 (1995).

90. J.S. Handler and H.M. Kwon, *Am. J. Physiol.* **265**, C1449–C1455 (1993).

91. A.M. Pajor and E.M. Wright, *J. Biol. Chem.* **267**, 3557–3560 (1992).

92. J. Wang and K.M. Giacomini, *J. Biol. Chem.* **272**, 28845–28848 (1997).

93. H.N. Christensen, *Physiol. Rev.* **70**, 43–46 (1990).

94. M.S. Malandro and M.S. Kilberg, *Annu. Rev. Biochem.* **65**, 305–36 (1996).

95. Y. Kanai *Curr. Opin. Cell Biol.* **9**, 565–572 (1997).

96. M. Haas *Am. J. Physiol.* **267**, C283–C296 (1995).

97. M. Haas and B. Forbush, 3rd, *J. Bioenerg. Biomembr.* **30**, 161–172 (1998).

98. C. Lyttle and B. Forbush, 3rd, *J. Biol. Chem.* **267**, 25438–25443 (1992).

99. M. Haas, L.G. Johnson, and R.C. Bousher, *Am. J. Physiol.* **259**, C557–C569 (1990).

100. P.D. Boyer *Annu. Rev. Biochem.* **66**, 717–749 (1997).

101. J.D. Robinson *Moving Questions: A History of Membrane Transport and Bioenergetics*, Oxford University Press, New York, 1997, pp. 103–204.

102. P.L. Jorgensen, in J.A. Shafer, H.H. Ussing, P. Kristensen, and G.H. Giebisch, eds., *Membrane Transport in Biology*, Vol. 5, Springer-Verlag, Berlin, 1992, pp. 1–55.

103. J.P. Andersen and B. Vilsen, *Curr. Opin. Cell Biol.* **2**, 722–730 (1990).

104. D.C. Chow and J.G. Forte, *J. Exp. Biol.* **198**, 1–17 (1995).

105. P. Beguin, U. Hasler, A. Begah, and K. Geering, *Acta Physiol. Scand., Suppl.* **643**, 283–287 (1998).

106. J.P. Middleton *Miner. Electrolyte Metab.* **22**, 293–302 (1996).

107. O.B. Nielsen and A.P. Harrison, *Acta Physiol. Scand.* **162**, 191–200 (1998).

108. G. Sweeney and A. Klip, *Mol. Cell. Biochem.* **182**, 121–133 (1998).

109. E.C. Rabon and M.A. Reuben, *Annu. Rev. Physiol.* **52**, 321–344 (1990).

110. C.S. Wingo and B.D. Cain, *Annu. Rev. Physiol.* **55**, 323–347 (1993).

111. H.J. Schatzmann *Annu. Rev. Physiol.* **51**, 473–485 (1989).

112. D.H. MacLennan and T. Toyofuku, *Biochem. Soc. Trans.* **20**, 559–562 (1962).

113. E. Carafoli *Basic Res Cardiol.* **92**, (Suppl. 1), 59–61 (1997).

114. N. Nelson *Curr. Opin. Cell Biol.* **4**, 654–650 (1992).

115. T.H. Stevens and M. Forgac, *Annu. Rev. Cell Dev. Biol.* **13**, 779–808 (1997).

116. B. Sarkadi et al., *J. Biol. Chem.* **267**, 4854–4858 (1992).

117. C.F. Higgins *Curr. Opin. Cell Biol.* **5**, 684–687 (1993).

118. M.M. Gottesman and I. Pastan, *Annu. Rev. Biochem.* **62**, 385–427 (1993).

119. B. Sarkadi, M. Muller, and Z. Hollo, *Immunol. Lett.* **54**, 215–219 (1996).

120. A. Nanda and S. Grinstein, *Proc. Natl. Acad. Sci. U.S.A.* **88**, 10816–10820 (1991).

121. S. Grinstein and W. Furuya, *Am. J. Physiol.* **251**, C55–C65 (1986).

122. S. Grinstein, W. Furuya, and E.J. Cragoe, Jr., *J. Cell. Physiol.* **128**, 33–40 (1986).

123. S. Rosengren, P.M. Henson, and G.S. Worthen, *Am. J. Physiol.* **267**, C1623–C1632 (1994).

124. N. Demaurex et al., *J. Physiol. (London)* **466**, 329–344 (1993).

125. A. Kapus et al., *J. Gen. Physiol.* **102**, 729–760 (1993).

126. G.L. Lukacs et al., *Am. J. Physiol.* **265**, C3–C14 (1993).

127. A. Kapus, R. Romanek, and S. Grinstein, *J. Biol. Chem.* **269**, 4736–4745 (1994).

128. A. Nanda et al., *J. Biol. Chem.* **271**, 15963–15970 (1996).

See also ANATOMY OF PLANT CELLS; CELL STRUCTURE AND MOTION, EXTRACELLULAR MATRIX AND CELL ADHESION; CELL-SURFACE RECEPTORS: STRUCTURE, ACTIVATION, AND SIGNALING; TRANSCRIPTION, TRANSLATION AND THE CONTROL OF GENE EXPRESSION.

MICROPROPAGATION OF PLANTS, PRINCIPLES AND PRACTICES

ARIE ALTMAN
The Hebrew University of Jerusalem
Rehovot, Israel

BETH LOBERANT
StePac L.A., Ltd.
Tefen Industrial Park
Tefen, Israel

OUTLINE

INTRODUCTION

Micropropagation, and *in vitro* propagation are the most common terms used now for clonal, true-to-type propagation of plants by a variety of tissue and cell culture methods. This implies the culture of aseptic small sections (i.e., explants) of tissues and organs, in vessels with defined culture media and under controlled environmental conditions. Micropropagation is at present the most commercially efficient and practically oriented plant biotechnology, resulting in rapid generation of a large number of clonal plants, which are in many cases also virus- or other pathogen-free. Moreover, micropropagation is now the technical link in the commercialization of transgenic and otherwise genetically modified plants. Efficient production of transgenic plants relies heavily, if not exclusively, on the ability to regenerate whole plants from those cells, tissues, or organs in which "foreign" DNA has been inserted and expressed. Additionally, micropropagation and other tissue culture techniques, as well as new modalities in molecular biology, allow for faster testing of new genotypes or field selections of plants, as compared with the lengthy traditional breeding and selection of commercial plants.

Plant cloning through *in vitro* methods, by regeneration of whole plants from cells and cell clusters, tissue, and organ explants, has been known since the 1940s (1–4), mainly under experimental, small-scale laboratory conditions. *In vitro* mass production of clonal propagules of a small number of agriculturally important plants, primarily ornamentals, became practical in the early 1970s (5–7). Since then, the diversity of plant species that can be propagated *in vitro* has dramatically increased, and it is now practiced on a commercial scale worldwide, resulting in over 600 million plants annually, 60–75% of them flowers and ornamental plants (8–12). Micropropagation is now an integral part of the plant propagation industry, complementing or replacing other methods of clonal vegetative propagation (cuttings, grafting, division, and separation), or in some cases also propagation by seeds. The history, science, and practice of plant micropropagation have been dealt with extensively in several books and reviews (4,6,11,13–24). In the following, the basic principles of plant regeneration *in vitro* and various micropropagation procedures will first be outlined and reviewed, followed by laboratory operation. World distribution of the micropropagation industry and trends, along with the applied, economic, and commercial considerations, will be presented and evaluated.

PLANT REGENERATION IN CELL, TISSUE, AND ORGAN CULTURES

Generative (Sexual) and Vegetative Propagation (Cloning)

Plant reproduction by seeds (sexual propagation) is routinely used, is usually inexpensive, and is easy for most field crops and vegetables. This is possible in homozygous plants and in annual plants for which pure seeds can be produced by back crossing, in a relatively short period of time. However, most perennial heterozygous cultivated plants, including many ornamental plants, plantation crops, and fruit trees, are propagated vegetatively by a variety of techniques (i.e., cuttings, layering, separation, division, grafting, and budding), resulting in true-to-type clonal plant material (13). In this respect, *in vitro* propagation is synonymous with vegetative propagation, the main differences between cuttings and micropropagation being:

1. A very small plant part (explant), usually in the range of a few millimeters or less, is being used as starting material for *in vitro* propagation.
2. The explant is maintained in vials, in a defined and balanced culture medium, and under controlled environmental conditions.
3. Micropropagation is carried out under aseptic conditions.
4. Micropropagation usually results in numerous clonal propagules per unit of initial (stock) plant material, many times over that by other means of vegetative propagation, and in a much shorter time. Therefore, a dramatic increase of the "propagation coefficient" is obtained.

Totipotency and Regeneration

The general basic aspects of plant regeneration *in vitro* are common to all micropropagation procedures. They rely on the unique totipotency of plant cells, that is, the regeneration of whole plants from individual cells, or groups of cells from within a tissue or an organ, expressing the full plant genome (25,26). This potential for regeneration is usually realized after the tissue or the organ, or in some cases isolated callus, have been excised from the source ("mother") plant and the resulting explant is placed on a defined culture medium *in vitro*. Exceptions include young seedlings that can be cultured intact without prior excision. Regeneration involves the following consecutive events (2,3,26):

1. Dedifferentiation of the source tissue or organ that results in the activation of physiological and molecular mechanisms that lead, under the appropriate endogenous and exogenous conditions, to cell division.
2. Active cell division in the entire cut surface, or localized meristematic activity in specific regions of the explant, or both. This often, but not always, results in proliferation of a callus tissue.
3. Organization of defined promeristems and meristems, which occurs within the zones of active cell division and results in formation of shoot or root meristems, or both. In several cases clusters of meristems may form, leading to regeneration of groups of shoot meristems.
4. Regeneration and differentiation of new organized structures from those meristems, resulting in *organogenesis* (formation of new shoot buds or new roots) or in *somatic embryogenesis* (the bipolar differentiation of somatic embryos).

The different pathways of regeneration in tissue culture are presented schematically in Figure 1. Organogenesis and somatic embryogenesis may be *direct*, originating from the explant and not involving callus formation, or *indirect*, from a callus tissue that is formed first. The difference between direct and indirect regeneration, and between the different types of regeneration (see below) is important mainly where it relates to genetic stability of the resulting plantlets and to the propagation rate (coefficient). A callus stage, and meristem organization from callus cells, usually lead to more genetic aberrations than direct regeneration (20,22,27). The entire micropropagation process must be carefully controlled and monitored, otherwise it may result in generation of plantlets that are not true to type. Regeneration (both organogenesis and somatic embryogenesis), in contrast with proliferation of axillary buds, may also be a disadvantage for clonal propagation of chimeric varieties. The problem of tissue stability and trueness to type is discussed separately. Some micropropagation stages do not necessarily involve a regeneration process. Culture of shoot tips, for example, may lead to proliferation of already-existing axillary buds, but their further development into plantlets involves a regeneration process (i.e., root formation).

Major basic Types of Micropropagation

Axillary Bud Proliferation. Axillary bud proliferation *in vitro* is usually considered a convenient route for micropropagation, although the final number of newly regenerated plantlets can sometimes be lower than in other methods. Because axillary bud proliferation does not include a callus stage, it is considered "safer" for the preservation of clonal characteristics. In fact, this pathway does not involve regeneration of new buds, since bud meristems already exist in the axils of leaves (16,19,20,27). However, because of apical control, they normally do not develop *in planta* until the stem elongates and grows. Thus the short stem tip that is used as an explant already contains many axillary buds, at different stages of development, condensed in a small explant. A very large number of otherwise quiescent axillary shoot buds grow extensively when the shoot tips, or even small apical meristems, are excised and cultured in an appropriate medium, usually containing high concentrations of cytokinins. Both the excision of the explant and the cytokinin-rich medium "activate" the buds, leading to massive proliferation of many side shoots. After induction, these shoots are separated for further culture and rooting.

Organogenesis: Formation of Shoots, Roots, and Specialized Structures. Organogenesis from explants, or from callus and cell cultures, results in *de novo* formation of shoots and/or roots. These two events may take place simultaneously during culture, but frequently either shoots or, less frequently, roots are formed first. Regeneration of the complementary organ occurs only later, either in the same medium or after subculture to another medium and under environmental conditions that favor the formation

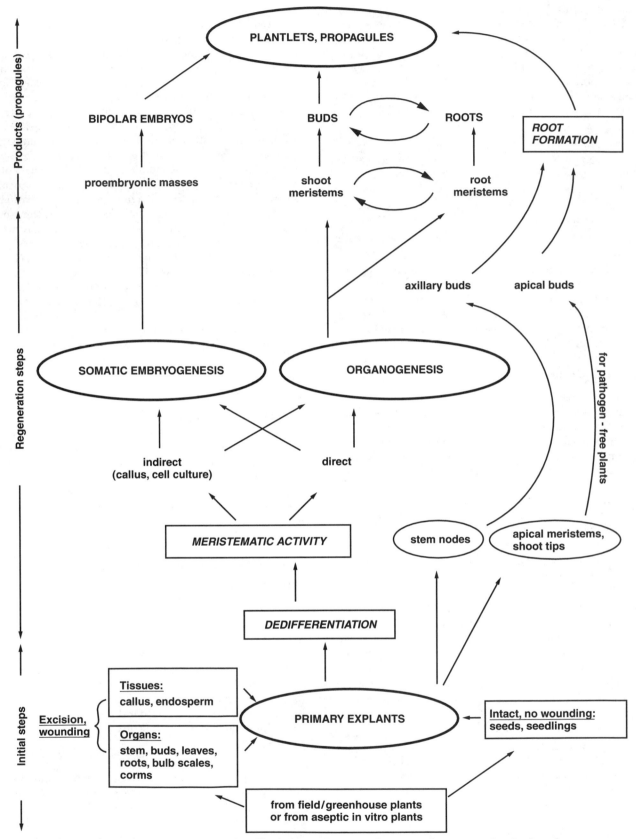

Figure 1. Plant regeneration in cell, tissue, and organ cultures: explants, steps involved, and regeneration processes that lead to micropropagation. The sources of explants are shown in rectangles (regular letters); the primary, intermediate, and final "products" of micropropagation are in ovals (capital letters), the major regeneration processes are in rectangles (bold, italics).

of the specific organ. Organogenesis starts with a distinct organization of a group of a few meristematic cells (meristemoids), directly within the explant or from the callus, that later turn into a shoot or a root meristem (3,20,22,27). The type of explant, composition of the culture medium (especially the balance of growth regulators), and the environmental conditions during culture affect the formation of either a shoot or a root meristem.

Once shoot or root meristems have been organized, they start developing, forming small shoots and roots. Further stages of organization, differentiation, and growth include the formation of functional vascular connections between the developing shoots and roots, finally giving rise to plantlets *in vitro*. This sequence of events and operations result in new plantlets that are removed from the vials and subjected to *ex vitro* conditions that include acclimatization and cultivation under greenhouse or field conditions. In some cases organogenesis brings about the formation of modified shoots and roots, usually storage organs such as bulbs and tubers. Here, the shoot or the root meristem forms as described previously, but instead of further growth and elongation, minibulbs, minitubers, or minicorms (depending on the specific genotype) soon develop. These can grow further or become dormant, depending on the culture conditions. These storage organs can also develop from axillary buds without true regeneration, especially when basal plates of bulbs or certain corm and tuber tissues are used as primary explants.

Somatic Embryogenesis. Somatic embryogenesis is different from organogenesis in that regeneration and organization is bipolar: The shoot and the root meristems are formed simultaneously from progenitor cells that give rise to a group of cells known as proembryonic masses (22,26,28). As with organogenesis, differentiation and organization of a somatic embryo take place directly in the explant or from the callus, depending on the type of explant, composition of the culture medium, and the subculture regime. Usually, a two-stage culture is involved: first, induction of proembryonic masses, which is frequently favored by an initial exposure of the tissue to 2,4-D or other auxin-type growth regulators; second, by transfer of the proembryonic cultures to a medium with a modified composition from which the auxin has been removed, in which the somatic embryos fully differentiate. Somatic embryogenesis is often favored by culture in agitated liquid medium. The patterns of differentiation are very conserved (26,28). First, globular embryonic structures are formed. This is followed by the "heart" stage, in which the shoot and root meristems can be clearly distinguished at the two poles, and continues to the "torpedo" stage, at which elongation of the shoot, and especially the root, takes place, and vascular connections between the two are established. This coordinated development results, after some time, in the formation of a well-organized somatic embryo or plantlet. Careful control of medium composition and subculture regimes is required in many cases to obtain synchronized development of the somatic embryos. The possibility for large-scale formation of somatic embryos has set the stage for developing the concept and practice

of "artificial seeds," also referred to as "synthetic seeds" (29). Commercial micropropagation has proved itself useful when true seeds either are unavailable or inadequate, and production of clonal artificial seeds may become an alternative to traditional seeds, offering a unique combination of traits to the market (17,30). Since somatic embryos are functionally similar to regular embryos that are contained, partially or fully dormant, within the seed coats, a procedure has been developed to handle them as seeds. This procedure involves large-scale production of somatic embryos, synchronization of somatic embryo development and encapsulation in a seed coat-like "envelope" with or without simultaneous partial dehydration of the embryos (30,31). This is followed by storage under appropriate conditions that permit further development of the plantlet at a later stage. Synthetic seed production was aimed initially to provide sufficient survival and germination rates, but for commercial mass production these goals have yet to be reached.

Some examples of the organogenesis and somatic embryogenesis patterns are shown in Figure 2.

THE PRACTICE OF MICROPROPAGATION

Micropropagation is a technique used commercially for producing propagules for the agricultural and horticultural industries. Consequently, it should be used only when it confers a competitive advantage over the available alternative methods of vegetative plant propagation. This means that micropropagation should enable a significant performance or cost advantage over the traditional methods for propagating the particular crop (32).

Advantages and Disadvantages of Micropropagation

Micropropagation offers significant advantages in quality, quantity, and economics over conventional vegetative propagation for many species (11,16). Moreover, these advantages support the relatively early arrival, in commercial quantities, of newly bred and selected plants to the marketplace. There are, however, several inherent disadvantages (16). The advantages are:

1. A very large number of clonal propagules may be produced within a relatively short time span, reaching an exponential increase of the propagation coefficient. Depending on the multiplication rate (i.e., the average number of new propagules produced from one explant within a unit of time), thousands and millions of plants can be rapidly produced *in vitro* from relatively few selected source plants.

2. Production of disease-free plant material with the possibility of eliminating viral, bacterial, and fungal contamination. Diseases that are carried over from source plant material are a significant limiting factor in conventional plant propagation (33). Specific *in vitro* techniques that are designed to control and limit this phenomenon (see other entries in this volume) address the issues of contamination and its negative ramifications.

(a)

1

2

3a

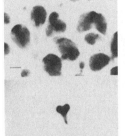

3b

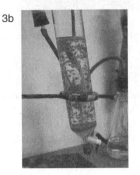

3c

3d

4

5

6

7

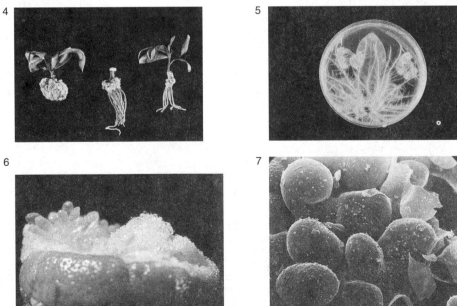

Figure 2a. Major types of regeneration and micropropagation. 1. *Scilla* scale culture: callus production (high auxin); 2. *Scilla* scale culture: organogenesis resulting in bulblet and plantlet formation (high cytokinin); 3. stages of celery somatic embryogenesis, from test tubes to plants: a. free-floating embryos with single, heart-shaped embryo, b. embryo clusters in liquid medium in bioreactor, c. *in vitro* rooting of plantlet on paper bridge, d. transplants after acclimatization; 4. Jaffa orange stem explants: left, shoot formation with callus at base (medium auxin); center, callus with root formation (high auxin); right, simultaneous shoot and root formation (balanced growth regulators); 5. tobacco regeneration *in vitro*: leaf, root, and callus formation; 6. callus, right and juice vesicles, left, from a lemon fruit explant; 7. scanning electron micrograph of callus cells cultured from peel of a young lemon fruit.

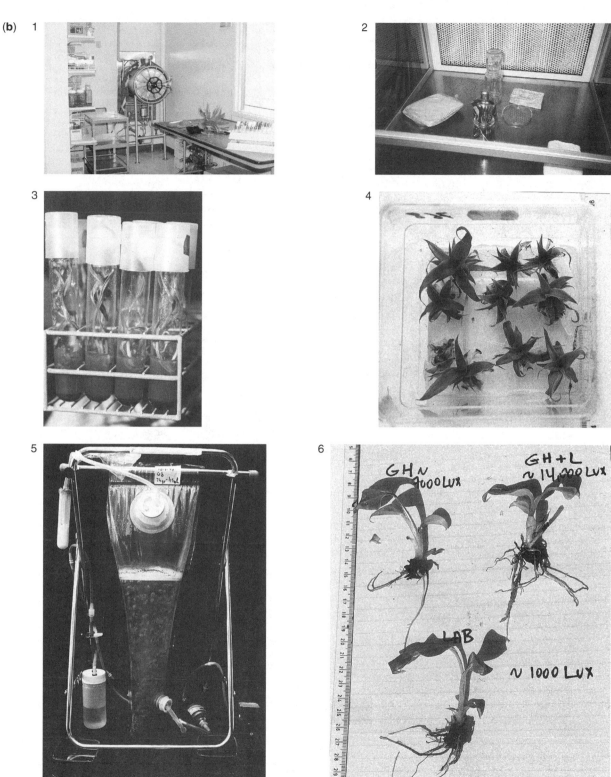

Figure 2b. Operations, steps, and modalities in micropropagation. 1. Preparation room: *Platycerium* fern mother plant on bench, prior to explant excision and culture; autoclave and storage shelves in background; 2. aseptic laminar flow work table with tools for micropropagation; 3. test tube rack with date palm cultures (courtesy of Rahan Meristem, Propagation Nurseries); 4. Stage III, *in vitro* pineapple plants in agar-based medium in plastic growing vessel (courtesy of Rahan Meristem); 5. meristematic clusters of *Lilium* cultured in a pre sterilized, disposable bioreactor (courtesy of Prof. M. Ziv); 6. rooted, Stage III banana plantlets grown at different light intensities (courtesy of Rahan Meristem).

3. The ability to produce and maintain a large stock of true-to-type propagation material. Species and cultivar-specific methods have been developed to provide the maximum number of true-to-type plantlets from a minimal number of selected source (mother) plants. This guarantees a consistently high degree of likeness between the source plant and the product. This issue is of primary importance for commercial propagation (34).

4. The ability to air-ship large quantities of micropropagated propagules quickly, efficiently, and relatively inexpensively. As many as 30,000–50,000 *in vitro* (in closed vials or small containers), or 3,000–10,000 *ex vitro* (acclimatized) plants can be packed into a cubic meter of shipping space.

The disadvantages are:

1. Contamination (endogenous and/or exogenous): The greatest economic losses, direct and indirect, in commercial micropropagation, are caused by endogenous and/or environmentally induced contamination of plant cultures.

2. Higher than acceptable levels of somatic variation, plant variants, genetic, or epigenetic, can be the result of poor source plant selection or incomplete monitoring of production methods, processes, and plant material during micropropagation.

3. Losses incurred during transfer of micropropagated plants to the *ex vitro*, acclimatization stage: *in vitro* plants that are not in optimal condition, combined with inadequate acclimatization methods, can account for significant waste and economic loss in a commercial facility.

4. High production costs: The combination of expensive laboratory technology and facilities, and the labor-intensive nature of tissue culture, often render micropropagation economically unfeasible and engender costs that are untenable for certain plants, varieties, or markets.

Stages of Micropropagation

Plant micropropagation is an integrated process in which cells, tissues, or organs of selected plants are isolated, surface sterilized, and incubated in a growth-promoting sterile environment to produce many clonal plantlets. At least five critical and ordered operational stages are involved (6,7), as schematically presented in Figure 3 (and see also Figure 2):

1. *Stage 0 — selection and preparation of explant source and mother plants*. The success of micropropagation is largely dependent on the quality of the source plant. Selection and adequate maintenance of source plants is designed to provide assurance that the plant is: (a) a certified, horticultural, true-to-type representative of the desired species and cultivar, (b) free from contamination and disease, or can become pathogen-free using specific *in vitro* procedures, (c) viable and vigorous, thus potentially able to respond to the culture conditions by

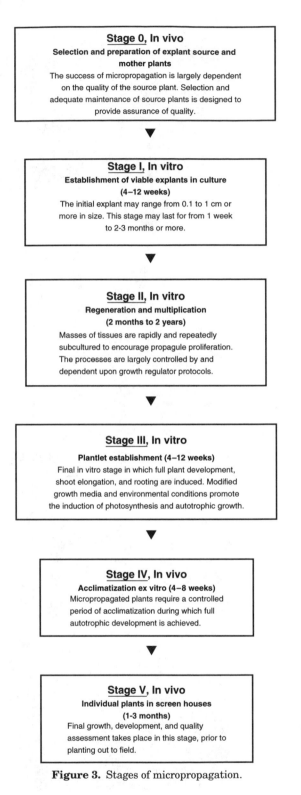

Figure 3. Stages of micropropagation.

active regeneration processes. To comply with these requirements, adequate mother plants are selected and often "preconditioned" by a variety of growth regimens and horticultural procedures. These may include nutrition and irrigation; optimization of day length, light quality, and temperature; treatments with growth regulators; pruning and pest control.

2. *Stage I—Establishment of viable explants in culture.* The initial explant may range in size from 0.1 mm (e.g., meristems used for establishing virus-free plants) to about 1 cm or more (e.g., bulb scales, stems, corms). During this stage, lasting from 1 week to 2–3 months, or even longer, the explant is established in culture, resulting in tissue activation and rapid cell division. This stage is usually carried out on agar-based media, but liquid media can also be employed. The choice of basal media and growth regulators at this stage is of special importance, and may vary according to plant and tissue type and to the desired multiplication method (6,24). This stage is also used to screen for microbial contamination and agricultural fitness, by continual visual monitoring. The relatively few primary explants thus established, and their small size, render this the most cost-effective and efficient stage for evaluation and treatment of *in vitro* plant material.

3. *Stage II—Rapid regeneration and multiplication of numerous propagules.* Primary explants that have successfully passed through the former stage are used for generation of numerous clonal propagules. Masses of tissues are repeatedly subcultured aseptically onto new culture media that encourage propagule proliferation. The types of regeneration and proliferation are largely dependent on growth regulator combinations. A high proportion of cytokinins usually stimulates continued multiplication of axillary or adventitious shoots, and a higher proportion of specific auxins is required for callus proliferation or for somatic embryogenesis. The combined and balanced adjustment of growth regulators and vitamins, macro- and micronutrients and environmental conditions are optimized to achieve maximal generation of quality, new, plant propagules (24,35,36). Although basic media formulations tend to remain constant, extensive experimentation may be necessary to reach commercially efficient multiplication with specific cultivars or varieties. The duration of this stage is potentially unlimited, but usually lasts from several months to 1 to 2 years. At the chosen end point, the stock culture is renewed to prevent possible accumulation of mutations and the loss of vigor and regeneration potential.

4. *Stage III—Plantlet elongation, rooting, and establishment of complete plants.* After repeated subcultures and screening in Stage II, the resulting plantlets are transferred to the final *in vitro* stage, which is designed to arrest rapid multiplication and to induce the establishment of fully developed plantlets. This includes shoot elongation, root formation, and, in specific plants and where required, formation of storage organs that serve as independent propagation units (bulbs, corms, and tubers). During this stage, conditions for stimulation of photosynthesis and other physiological changes are provided, allowing for autotrophic, *ex vitro* growth in the acclimatization stage (6,24). This is achieved by culture media modifications (e.g., reduction of cytokinin concentrations or their total elimination, sometimes increased auxin levels to induce root formation, and reduced sugar levels), and by modifying environmental conditions (e.g., increased light intensity).

5. *Stage IV—Acclimatization ex vitro.* The healthy *in vitro* grown plantlets are usually incapable of existence under field or greenhouse conditions, and they require 4–8 weeks of acclimatization under specifically controlled conditions. The first few days in the greenhouse are spent under low light, high temperatures, and high humidity, often provided by fogging or an incubator for *ex vitro* plants (37). As cuticular waxes, stomatal function, and new, functional roots develop, photosynthetic activity is increased and plants become more self-sufficient. Light intensity is raised, and ambient temperature and humidity are regulated to natural-growing conditions. Rooting hormones may be used additionally to stimulate root development. In some cases, especially when hyperhydric plantlets develop *in vitro*, specific acclimatization procedures are required (38).

6. *Stage V—Growing out to accomplish complete development of functioning plants.* After acclimatization, plants destined for open fields usually require additional growth and development. This is often accomplished in individual pots in screen/shade houses where plants reach a level of maturity allowing them to be safely transplanted to field conditions. Additional monitoring of trueness to type and freedom from disease is usually carried out during this stage.

Establishing and Operating a Micropropagation Laboratory

All forms of *in vitro* plant micropropagation, at all production levels, require adherence to certain basic principles and practices.

1. *Facilities.* The basic structure of a tissue culture laboratory requires areas for explant preparation, media preparation, an aseptic plant production center, plant growing rooms, quality control laboratory, packing and shipping area, and space for ancillary services such as offices, storage, and personnel support.

2. *Systems and departments.* Quality assurance program (TQM, ISO 900X, etc.) (39), computer-based information systems, a marketing and sales program, a technical backup system for clients, and a framework for research and development.

3. *Asepsis. In vitro* micropropagation and storage of plant material requires axenic cultures and an aseptic environment. This is achieved by combining surface sterilization of the plant material from which primary explants are removed, followed by planting and subculture under aseptic conditions. Presterilized culture media and vials, and continuous culture and storage of plant material in a clean, controlled environment are employed. Aseptic work spaces must be buffered and isolated from other areas of the laboratory. This usually involves

a gradient of spaces, which are progressively cleaner and require more stringent operations as the relatively aseptic plant production and transfer room is approached. The range of techniques for achieving asepsis in plant micropropagation is large. All facilities, however, will require a plan that defines and separates distinct work areas according to function and degree of asepsis. Most commercial companies employ rigid regimes, which include the use of: clean room technology, widespread disinfection and sterilization, surface sterilization of plant material, continual monitoring of the environment, and regular monitoring and education of workers.

4. *Environmental conditions.* Maintenance of optimal environmental conditions for the handling and development of *in vitro* plant cultures is a key factor in all operational steps. A constant balance between complex and expensive electrical, air conditioning, and air filtration systems is required. The most critical environmental balance should be maintained in plant growing rooms. Different plant species, micropropagation technologies, and stages of growth often demand different environmental conditions. Laboratories may be equipped with multiple growing rooms and options for altering standard parameters. In recent years, a great deal of research has dealt with environmental factors in the growth and development of *in vitro* plants, and there are experimental data showing that many of the standard methods described here are not optimal (40). *Temperature: in vitro* growth conditions for most plants require ambient temperatures between 22 and 27 °C. Some species, growth stages, or storage conditions may require different or variable temperature regimes. *Relative humidity (RH):* Humidity within the plant growth container is the most significant humidity factor. It is generally accepted that the RH in the container is approximately 98–100%. However, recent studies indicate that for some plants, it might be more effective to maintain RH at 88–94% (18). Growth room ambient humidity is much lower, usually 50–80%. Room RH lower than 40% can result in culture media desiccation, increased salt concentration, and drying out of plant material. Room RH higher than 85% may contribute to the incidence of microbial contamination. In extreme climates or areas with significant variation in weather conditions, a humidity control system may be necessary. *Light:* Conventional *in vitro* growth media provide cultures with a carbon source. Although there is some photosynthetic activity *in vitro*, the plantlets do not rely on photosynthetic carbon fixation for growth. However, light may have a photomorphogenetic effect on culture development, and low light intensities are usually used for *in vitro* culture. Fluorescent lamps have been the primary light source, with a photon density between 20 and 200 $\mu mol/m^2/s$ and a standard photoperiod of 16 h (24,35).

5. *Culture media.* A sterile nutrient source in appropriate growth containers must be provided in order to initiate and sustain *in vitro* plant growth.

An appreciation and knowledge of the nutritional requirements and metabolic needs of cultured cells and tissues is invaluable (20,24,41). Today, synthetic growth medium is the primary source of nutrition for plants and plant tissues *in vitro*. Basal media components are water, sugar(s) as a primary carbon source, inorganic salts providing macro and microelements, vitamins (some essential, others beneficial), and various hormones and growth regulators. The discovery, isolation, and synthesis of the plant growth hormones (auxins, cytokinins, gibberellins, ABA, and ethylene) has provided the ability to achieve hormonal control of plant growth, development, and regeneration. Additional factors, including complex, undefined materials such as coconut milk, yeast extract, or protein hydrolysates may be beneficial for certain plants. The most widely used standard medium formulation is that of Murashige and Skoog, (MS) (36). Gelling of media solutions is usually achieved with agar or agar substitutes, but liquid media may also be used.

6. *Vials, containers, and closures.* The growth and development of a plantlet *in vitro* is affected by light transference, relative humidity, temperature, and gas exchange. The microenvironment may in turn be influenced not only by the generation and absorption of gases by the plantlet and the culture medium, but also by the gas exchange between the room and the vessel (8,18,24). Therefore, a multitude of configurations and materials for growth containers and stoppers is available for micropropagation. Additional specifications universally sought are availability, low unit cost, uniformity, nonphytotoxicity, and ease in sterilization and handling. Standard growing vessels have been glass test tubes, flasks, and jars, but in recent years the material of choice has been a variety of plastics, polypropylene, polycarbonate, often disposable, which are used for Petri dishes, tubs, boxes, and even flexible wall disposable bioreactors (42). Limitations in production methods still require that most containers be small, usually holding from 1 to 100 plantlets. Storage space for containers at various stages of use is a significant issue in commercial laboratories. New techniques in liquid culture often use bioreactors, which may hold from 1 to 2000 L of culture media and plant material, and save a significant amount of space. Traditionally, much of the equipment and materials used in micropropagation was adapted from other industries.

7. *Packing and shipping.* As a high-value, perishable aseptic product, micropropagated plants require packing, shipping, and handling protocols that meet the needs of producers and customers. The packaging area should be environmentally controlled, clean, and a physical part of the laboratory. Containers being shipped must be examined carefully for contamination and vigor. This process must be carried out in a timely fashion, and the shipment executed promptly, in order to avoid excess time in transit and the resulting damage to the plants.

Crop-Oriented Micropropagation

A short summary of the status of micropropagation in the various categories of plants is given in the following. A detailed account of the application of micropropagation to economically important crop plants is discussed in subsequent articles of this encyclopedia and elsewhere (11,16,19).

1. *Field crops and vegetables.* Most field and vegetable crops (e.g., cereals, corn, legumes, and tomato) are grown in large number of plants and on large areas, and are generally propagated by seeds, since pure, true-to-type seeds are relatively easy to produce and are relatively cheap. Exceptions include several vegetables and field crops that have been specially bred or genetically altered, and/or for which micropropagation methods are required for production of virus- or bacteria-free propagation material (e.g., potato, asparagus, artichoke, strawberry).

2. *Flowers and ornamental species.* Initial ventures in commercial micropropagation concentrated on flowers and ornamental plants. As traditional consumer products with great horticultural and commercial value, and in which the price of the individual plant is relatively expensive, they lent themselves to the new technology. Small laboratories, associated with established nurseries, began experimenting with and producing standard cut flower species, ornamental house plants, and foliage crops. Eventually, these plants and others have been the production models for micropropagation methods and problem-solving techniques. Micropropagation has affected significant changes in the industry in the past 25 years, because of the following advantages: (a) the ability to control or limit the frequency of off-types for many species, resulting in a higher level of uniformity than with conventional methods, (b) the possibility of bringing plant material to market year round, (c) the ability to eliminate or significantly reduce disease, and (d) the ability to bring new varieties and cultivars to market quickly. Most of the commercial micropropagation laboratories worldwide are primarily involved in the production of flowers and ornamental plants, including roses, carnation, gerbera, orchids, lilies, gladiolus, chrysanthemums, ferns, ficuses, and many others.

3. *Fruit trees and plantation crops.* Fruit trees have not been recognized as yet as a high-volume product of commercial micropropagation. However, the use of micropropagation for fruit trees is being practiced commercially in several laboratories that specialize in woody plants and fruit trees. Fruit tree micropropagation is especially realistic for three major purposes: (a) rapid propagation of rootstock microcuttings (e.g., apple, apricot, peach), (b) shoot tip grafting of virus-free varieties from selected, disease-free mother plants (e.g., citrus, grape), (c) rapid, large-scale propagation of micrografts for dense orchards. Micropropagation has also become a commercial practice for some plantation crops, both herbaceous and woody, that require large quantities of clonal planting material on a regular basis (e.g., pineapples, sugarcane, oil and date palms, and bananas).

4. *Forest trees.* Although feasible, micropropagation methods are not as yet economically viable for most forest trees. A major constraint on the use of *in vitro* procedures in forestry is the common belief that, from the ecological perspective, the genetic diversity of forests should be conserved, hence, the traditional use of mixed populations of seedlings for forestation. Three major exceptions, for which the application of micropropagation has become most relevant for forest trees (43), do exist; (a) breeding, both to accelerate the process of provenance selection and to establish selected mother trees for further breeding; (b) clonal propagation, where uniformity of the trees is desired in industrial forests for pulp or specialized timber production (e.g., certain poplar and eucalyptus genotypes); (c) whenever a need exists for rapid, large-scale production of selected trees for forestation. In some of these cases micropropagation can compete with traditional methods of vegetative propagation, and large-scale micropropagation procedures have been developed, for example, for some poplars, eucalyptus, and pines, and for somatic embryogenesis of spruce (44).

COMMERCIALIZATION AND ECONOMIC CONSIDERATIONS

Economic Considerations

The economic potential for *in vitro* propagation of plants was recognized in the 1970s, when it became clear that conventional propagation methods and equipment were often inadequate because of the increasing incidence of plant disease and abiotic stress and the decreasing quality of soil and water. It was soon realized that benefits could be gained from crop improvement and mass production programs utilizing *in vitro* plant technologies. However, the potential of rapid *in vitro* clonal propagation of a given plant genotype does not necessarily mean that this technique is also practical or economically feasible. Moreover, the number of plant species that can be regenerated in tissue cultures in the laboratory far exceeds the number of plants that are actually being micropropagated on a commercial scale. The practical application of micropropagation relative to alternative methods of propagation is dependent on:

1. A very high propagation rate of true-to-type plants
2. The current market value of the plant and its potential in horticulture or agriculture
3. The cost effectiveness of micropropagation relative to alternative, conventional methods of multiplication for the same plant.
4. The level of plant quality that can be consistently offered to the market.

Before embarking on the commercial production of a particular cultivar, the following questions must be addressed: Does there exist a practical micropropagation technology for this species or cultivar, and is micropropagation expected to provide solutions to problems that have arisen in conventional propagation? The latter two issues are manifested in the application of micropropagation to specific groups of plants (11,16,34). Generally, the potential of micropropagation has been realized in plants that are normally vegetatively propagated, and where the market price of the individual plant is relatively high. The defining characteristics of industrialized plant micropropagation are size, self-sufficiency in a broad range of activities and disciplines (e.g., production, plant nursery maintenance, research and development, and sales and marketing), and engagement in vertically integrated agritechnology projects. A successful industrialized plant technology company will have achieved expertise in most aspects of developing and growing a particular product. When this is coupled with a business like approach to marketing, management, and customer service, there is a greater likelihood of economic success.

Financial Aspects of Commercial Micropropagation

Costs. Establishing a commercial micropropagation facility, and the accompanying agricultural, research, marketing, and management systems that are necessary to support it, may cost more than $1 million. Currently, the major production cost for most laboratories is labor, which may reach 40–60% of total costs. Size, location, and necessary level of sophistication will determine the initial investment. However, even the most primitive home- or village-based laboratory must be backed up by a source of quality stock plant material, technical expertise, and appropriate research and development. This is an expensive technology, and most companies, of all sizes, have had limited financial success. This has led to a constant search for less expensive technology and labor, resulting — among other things — in a shift of many micropropagation companies to countries where labor is relatively cheap. Alternatively, more automated systems can be introduced.

Prices. Reducing production costs and, therefore, prices becomes the goal of a commercial micropropagation company. The tissue-cultured product must also demonstrate a quantifiable advantage over traditionally produced plant material. The agricultural community is slow to accept change, and demands significant justification for the cost, time, and effort involved.

Quality. Micropropagation has become an established technology and a complex business venture commanding high prices. In recent years the quality issues, common in traditional manufacturing, have also arisen in commercial plant technology. Farmers and nursery managers are unwilling to accept the inconsistencies that plagued micropropagation in its earlier development stages. Agricultural companies and more sophisticated growers demand products, education, and services in line with the standards of the ISO 9000 system, which are being employed worldwide. Economic survival will be awarded only to those micropropagation companies and laboratories that are able and willing to comply.

Table 1. Commercial Production of Micropropagated Plantlets (production in millions of plantlets)

Country/region	Domestic use	For export	Total
United States	120	Small pct.	120
Europe[a,b]	100	Small pct	100
India	150–200		150
Asian Pacific Rim	150+		150
Middle East[c]	3	20	23
Other regions[d]	50–100		50–100
Approximate worldwide total			600

Source: Refs. 8,9,45,46,47.
[a] Including U.K. and Ireland; mostly domestic use and internal European export.
[b] Many plantlets exported to be reimported as finished plants.
[c] Israel produces 20 million plantlets annually, 90% of them for export.
[d] South/Central America, Former Soviet Union, Sub-Saharan Africa, China.

A Survey of World Production and Distribution

Plant tissue culture is carried out in most countries of the world (Table 1). Commercial foci are found in the United States, Europe, India, and in the Asian Pacific Rim (Japan, Taiwan, Thailand, and Australia/New Zealand). Additionally, commercial tissue culture is an important element in commercial plant biotechnology activities in South Africa, Eastern Europe (where cheaper labor and overhead has created direct competition against companies in central and Western Europe), and Israel. China has significant research in and production of micropropagated plant material, but it appears that most plant tissue culture is subsidized or state-run commercial production. Although most tissue-cultured plant material remains in its country or region of production, 10–20% of *in vitro* or acclimatized plantlets is exported. The current trend is for *in vitro* production of plant material in more developed countries and facilities, which is then shipped to less developed, agriculturally based regions of the world for downstream production, or more often for acclimatization and field production. Much of the European production is shipped *in vitro* to centers of cheaper labor and warmer climate for acclimatization and planting out, and a large quantity of the finished plants is subsequently shipped back to Europe for distribution and sale. The high turnover in the business makes it difficult to amass figures that are reliable in real time. The numbers presented here (Table 1) are the best available estimates as of 1998 (45–47).

CURRENT ISSUES AND PROGRESSION OF MICROPROPAGATION

There are critical issues that micropropagation, whether research or commercial, must deal with constantly. While each is a separate issue and often a specific problem, the issues are often integrated; for example, recalcitrance or trueness to type may be controlled by undetected contamination.

Recalcitrance

Recalcitrance in plant tissue culture refers to those plant types of specific varieties or genotypes that, when produced *in vitro*, continually fail to grow or develop into healthy acclimated plants. Contrary to laboratory experience, routine and commercially-viable micropropagation methods have traditionally been less successful with many different types of plants. Recalcitrant plants remain the subjects of research and development, or are abandoned for more amenable cultivars or species and do not rise to the level of commercial production. The causes for recalcitrance appear to be many and varied, and endogenous contamination, often undetected, seems to be a major one (48). Additionally, the commercial value of many ornamental plants is due to visual characteristics such as variegation and coloration, which often result from chimeras. Micropropagation may cause disorganization of chimeras, especially sectorial and mericlinal (49), and it is often impossible to produce a sufficient quantity of horticulturally attractive chimeric plants. In both research and marketing terms, recalcitrance is the worst case, and the opportunity to reach a solution or a product remains elusive.

Somatic Variation and Trueness-to-Type

Trueness to type refers to the degree of genetic and/or epigenetic likeness that the micropropagated plants bear to the source plant from which the initial explants were taken. However, variations in micropropagated plants can occur, under certain conditions, due to genetic and/or epigenetic changes, thus interfering with the reliability of micropropagation. When these changes occur in explants that are composed of somatic cells, they are termed somaclonal variation, but under specific conditions changes can occur also in gametes (pollen, ovules) that serve as explants — termed gametoclonal variation (20,50). These changes should, and to a large extent can be avoided, and they should be monitored. The resulting variation in the micropropagated plants can result from existing variations in the source plants, or can be induced by the culture medium and/or culture processes and conditions (50–52). Some plants exhibit relatively frequent variation (e.g., mutations, chromosomal aberrations) *in vivo*, and these plants also tend to exhibit higher levels of somaclonal variation *in vitro*. Additionally, it has been shown that the composition of the culture media, especially quantities and proportions of certain plant growth regulators and other medium components, and/or length of time in culture, may contribute to an increase in the rate of somaclonal variation (15,50,52). New understanding of the phenomenon and new technologies will allow for early detection of variability (34), which is highly desirable. Trueness to type is the most important issue for both the micropropagation laboratory and the client, since a plant which is not true to type is not a saleable product.

Contamination

Contamination-free culture schemes and disease-free planting material are primary goals of micropropagation. Endogenous and exogenous contamination of cultures from virus, bacterial, bacteria like, fungal, and insect pests cause the most damaging and consistent economic losses and logistical problems in the micropropagation process.

When present, contamination can destroy the culture or significantly weaken or change the micropropagated plants. Contaminated cultures must usually be destroyed, and the source of the contamination is often impossible to discern or eliminate. The plant biotechnology industry is going to great efforts to understand, minimize, and treat the sources and consequences of contamination in and associated with micropropagated plant material (48). One solution to this problem that may be applicable in certain cases is *in vitro* production of semiautotrophic plants under non fully axenic conditions (53).

Large-Scale Production and Automation

As discussed previously, widespread use of micropropagation for major crops in agriculture and forestry is still restricted because of relatively high production costs. Therefore, in recent years, much effort has been devoted to developing automated, robotized, and more efficient transplant production methods. The dynamics of scaling up must be harnessed to stringently engineered inventory control and quality assurance programs. Expanded inventories with short shelf life are especially difficult to manage in export-based companies. Additionally, because most crops are not planted or harvested on a year-round basis, there are peaks in the production schedule. Thus commercially viable, year-round employment of staff and facilities and maintenance of large stocks of start up cultures are necessary. Developing low-cost, automated mass-propagation systems for producing *in vitro* plantlets will become more and more important in the twenty-first century (54,55). The following issues seem most relevant:

Liquid culture. Despite its many advantages, the use of liquid culture systems is still a subject of considerable research, and there are several physiological limitations to propagation of many plant species in immersed culture. Among these are hyperhydration (vitrification) (24,38), deformation, and somaclonal variation because of sometimes uncontrolled multiplication (56). Although these conditions may appear also in agar-based, semisolid micropropagation schemes, the relatively small number of plants usually minimizes the damage. In the event of contamination, the entire liquid culture system may be destroyed or damaged, and the technical problems and economic losses are potentially severe.

Plantlet complexity. Systems using semiautomated, automated, robotized, or computer-aided excision tools and procedures for subculturing are hampered by the complex and unique nature of the plant material. Tools or systems are often appropriate only for one plant type or culture protocol, and for many commercial laboratories the combination of these two issues makes the systems undesirable.

Costs. In addition to the basic costs of establishing and operating a plant micropropagation laboratory, the high costs associated with the research, development, and purchase of automated systems limit their use. Established companies usually consider it as an option only for a high-volume, single product. Additionally, when robots or machines become unnecessary, they remain in house and continue to utilize space and resources.

Practical applications. Many pitfalls and unsolved problems remain in the scaling up and full automation of plant micropropagation. As a result, many commercial laboratories have successfully implemented partial or semiautomation, for example, development of a prototype for the automated manipulation of growth containers with *in vitro* plants. This robotic system carries out the sterile exchange of liquid medium at an accelerated rate with minimal worker participation. There are processing systems where media components are measured, mixed, processed, and poured into containers using computer programming and minimal human support. Based on need and experience, each laboratory creates many original, in-house solutions to the problems of time, space, and costs (57–60).

ADDITIONAL IMPLICATIONS OF MICRPROPAGATION

In addition to the internationally accepted use of *in vitro* culture and plant regeneration for commercial rapid clonal propagation, this technique is highly important for several other purposes, as discussed earlier (61) and in other articles of this encyclopedia:

1. Production and maintenance of pathogen-free stock plants
2. Long-term *in vitro* conservation of germplasm
3. Selection and generation of transgenic plants

BIBLIOGRAPHY

1. P.R. White, *The Cultivation of Animal and Plant Cells*, 2nd ed., Ronald Press, New York, 1963.
2. J. Reinert and Y.P.S. Bajaj, eds., *Plant Cell, Tissue, and Organ Culture*, Springer-Verlag, Berlin, 1977.
3. H.E. Street, ed., *Plant Tissue and Cell Culture*, Blackwell, Oxford, 1977.
4. E. Thomas and M.R. Davey, *From Single Cells to Plants*, Wykham Publications, London, 1975.
5. R.A. De Fossard, *Tissue Culture for Plant Propagators*, University of New England, Armidale, Australia, 1976.
6. T. Murashige and F. Skoog, *Annu. Rev. Plant Physiol.* **25**, 135–197 (1973).
7. T. Murashige, M. Serpa, and J.B. Jones, *HortScience* **9**, 175–180 (1974).
8. R.H. Zimmerman, in A.C. Cassells, ed., *Pathogen and Microbial Contamination Management in Micropropagation*, Kluwer Academic, publishers, Dordrecht, The Netherlands, 1997, pp. 39–44.
9. F. O'Riordain, Compiler, *Cost '87 Directory of European Plant Tissue Culture Laboratories 1993*, Commission of the European Communities, Brussels, 1994.
10. Sasson, ed., *Biotechnologies in Developing Countries: Present and Future*, Vol. 1, UNESCO, Paris, 1993.
11. P. Debergh and R. Zimmerman, eds., *Micropropagation: Technology and Application*, Kluwer Academic Publishers, Dordrecht, The Netherlands, 1990.
12. Sasson, ed., *Biotechnologies in Developing Countries: Present and Future*, Vol. 2, UNESCO, Paris, 1998.
13. H. Hartmann, D. Kester, and F.T. Davies Jr., eds., *Plant Propagation Principles and Practices*, 5th ed., Prentice-Hall, Englewood cliffs, N.J., 1990.
14. R.L.M. Pierik, *In Vitro Culture of Higher Plants*, Martinus Nijhoff, Dordrecht, The Netherlands, 1987.
15. R.H. Zimmerman, R.J. Griesbach, F.A. Hammerschlag, and R.H. Lawson, eds., *Tissue Culture as a Plant Production System for Horticultural Crops*, Martinus Nijhoff, Dordrecht, The Netherlands, 1986.
16. A. Altman and B. Loberant, in A. Altman, ed., *Agricultural Biotechnology*, Dekker, New York, 1998, pp. 19–48.
17. K. Redenbaugh, in P. Debergh and R. Zimmerman, eds., *Micropropagation: Technology and Application*, Kluwer Academic Publishers, Dordrecht, The Netherlands, 1990, pp. 285–310.
18. T. Watanabe, T. Kozai, M. Hayashi, and K. Fujiwara, *Collected Papers: Studies on the Effects of Physical Environment in the Tissue Culture Vessels on the Growth of Plantlets in vitro 1986–1989*, Japan, 1989.
19. I.K. Vasil and T. Thorpe, eds., *Plant Cell and Tissue Culture*, Kluwer Academic Publishers, Dordrecht, The Netherlands, 1994.
20. S.S. Bhojwani and M.K. Razdan, *Plant Tissue Culture: Theory and Practice*, Elsevier, Amsterdam, 1996.
21. R.A. Dixon, *Plant Cell Culture: A Practical Approach*, IRL Press, Oxford, U.K., and Washington, D.C., 1985.
22. D.A. Evans, W.R. Sharp, P.V. Ammirato, and Y. Yamada, *Handbook of Plant Cell Culture*, Vol. 1, Macmillan, New York, 1983.
23. I.K. Vasil, ed., *Cell Culture and Somatic Cell Genetics of Plants*, Vol. 1, Academic Press, Orlando, Fa., 1984.
24. E.F. George and P.D. Sherrington, *Plant Propagation by Tissue Culture*, Exegetics Ltd., Eversley, England, 1984.
25. P.F. Wareing and I.D.J. Phillips, *The Control of Growth and Differentiation in Plants*, Pergamon, Oxford, 1970.
26. F.C. Steward, *Growth and Organization in Plants*, Addison-Wesley, Reading, Mass., 1968.
27. T.A. Thorpe, in I.K. Vasil and T. Thorpe, eds., *Plant Cell and Tissue Culture*, Kluwer Academic Publishers, Dordrecht, The Netherlands, 1994, pp. 17–36.
28. P.V. Ammirato, *Bio Technology* **1**, 68–74 (1983).
29. Y. Sakamoto et al., in *Transplant Production Systems: Proceedings of the International Symposium on Transplant Production Systems*, Yokohama, 1992.
30. J.A.A. Fujii et al., *Trends Biotechnol.* **5**, 335–339 (1987).
31. S.L. Kitto and J. Janick, *J. Amer. Soc. Hortic. Sci.* **110**, 277–282 (1985).
32. R. Long and T. Roche, *Proc. 9th Int. Congr. Plant Tissue Cell Cult.* Jerusalem, 1998, abstract.
33. A.C. Cassells, ed., *Pathogen and Microbial Contamination Management in Micropropagation, Kluwer Academic Publishers*, Dordrecht, The Netherlands, 1997.
34. A.C. Cassells, in A. Altman, M. Ziv, and S. Izhar, eds., *Plant Biotechnology and In vitro Biology in the 21st Century*, Kluwer Academic Publishers, Dordrecht, The Netherlands, 1999, pp. 241–244.
35. K. Lindsey, ed., *Plant Tissue Culture Manual*, Kluwer Academic Publishers, Dordrecht, The Netherlands, 1991, 1993.
36. T. Murashige and R. Skoog, *Physiol. Plant.* **15**, 473–497 (1962).
37. B. Loberant, *1st Int. Conf. Biotechnol.* Jerusalem, 1994.
38. M. Ziv, in P. Debergh and R. Zimmerman, eds., *Micropropagation: Technology and Application*, Kluwer Academic Publishers, Dordrecht, The Netherlands, 1990, pp. 45–69.
39. C. Shore, *Total Quality Management (TQM), Quality Control and Design for Quality*, Tel Aviv, 1992.

40. T. Kozai, *Ifac Math. Control Appl. Agricul. Horti.* Matsuyama, Japan, 1991, pp. 99–102.

41. O.L. Gamborg, in K. Lindsey, ed., *Plant Tissue Culture Manual*, Kluwer Academic Publisher, Dordrecht, The Netherlands, 1991, pp. 1–24.

42. M. Ziv, G. Ronen, and M. Raviv, *In Vitro Cell Dev. Biol—Plant* **34**, 152–158 (1998).

43. D.R. Smith, *Plant Tissue Cult. Plant Biotechnol.* pp. 63–73 (1997).

44. M.R. Becwar et al., in M.R. Ahuja, ed., *Somatic Cell Genetics of Woody Plants.* Kluwer Academic Publishers, Dordrecht, The Netherlands, 1988, pp. 1–18.

45. M. Abo El Nil and A. Ilan, in A. Altman, M. Ziv, and S. Izhar, eds., *Plant Biotechnology and In Vitro Biology in the 21 st Century*, Kluwer Academic Publishers, Dordrecht, The Netherlands, 1999, pp. 677–680.

46. A.F. Mascarenus, in A. Altman, M. Ziv, and S. Izhar, eds., *Plant Biotechnology and In Vitro Biology in the 21st Century*, Kluwer Academic Publishers, Dordrecht, The Netherlands, 1999, pp. 713–720.

47. A. Atanassov, L. Antonov, and T. Twardowski, in A. Altman, M. Ziv, and S. Izhar, eds., *Plant Biotechnology and In Vitro Biology in the 21st Century*, Kluwer Academic Publishers, Dordrecht, The Netherlands, 1999, pp. 685–688.

48. A.C. Cassells, in A. Altman, ed., *Agricultural Biotechnology*, Dekker, New York, 1998, pp. 43–56.

49. H.J. Swartz, in P. Debergh and R. Zimmerman, eds., *Micropropagation: Technology and Application*, Kluwer Academic Publishers, Dordrecht, The Netherlands, 1990, pp. 95–121.

50. A. Karp, in I.K. Vasil and T. Thorpe, eds., *Plant Cell and Tissue Culture*, Kluwer Academic Publishers, Dordrecht, The Netherlands, 1994, pp. 139–151.

51. P.J. Larkin and W.R. Scowcroft, *Theor. Appl. Genet.* **60**, 197–214 (1981).

52. S. Mohan Jain and G.J. De Klerk, *Plant Tissue Cult. Plant Biotechnol.* **4**, 63–75 (1998).

53. T. Kozai, C. Kubota, and B.R. Jeong, *Plant Cell, Tissue Organ Cult.* **51**, 49–56 (1997).

54. J. Aitken-Christie, in M. Terzi, ed., *Current Issues in Plant Molecular and Cellular Biology: Proceedings of the 8th International Congress on Plant, Tissue and Cell Culture*, Florence, 1995.

55. I.K. Vasil, ed., *Scale-Up and Automation in Plant Propagation*, Academic Press, Inc., Orlando, Fa., 1991.

56. M. Ziv, in *Transplant Production Systems: Proceedings of the International Symposium on Transplant Production Systems*, Yokohama, 1992.

57. J. Aitken-Christie and H.E. Davies, *Acta Hortic.* **230**, 81–87 (1988).

58. K. Kurata, in *Transplant Production Systems: Proceedings of the International Symposium on Transplant Production Systems*, Yokohama, 1992.

59. D.P. Holdgate and E.A. Zandvoort, in *Transplant Production Systems: Proceedings of the International Symposium on Transplant Production Systems*, Yokohama, 1992.

60. L.D. Gautz and C.K. Wong, in *Transplant Production Systems: Proceedings of the International Symposium on Transplant Production Systems*, Yokohama, 1992.

61. A. Altman, in A. Altman, M. Ziv, and S. Izhar, eds., *Plant Biotechnology and In Vitro Biology in the 21st Century*, Kluwer Academic Publishers, Dordrecht, The Netherlands, 1999, pp. 1–7.

See also CULTURE ESTABLISHMENT, PLANT CELL CULTURE; CULTURE OF CONIFERS; EMBRYOGENESIS IN ANGIOSPERMS, SOMATIC; EQUIPMENT AND LABORATORY DESIGN FOR CELL CULTURE; HAPLOID PLANT PRODUCTION: POLLEN/ANTHER/OVULE CULTURE; MICROPROPAGATION, HYPERHYDRICITY; MONOCOT CELL CULTURE; PLANT CELL CULTURE, LABORATORY TECHNIQUES; SOMACLONAL VARIATION.

MICROPROPAGATION, HYPERHYDRICITY

PIERRE C.A. DEBERGH
University Gent
Gent, Belgium

OUTLINE

Introduction
Terminology
Symptoms
Causes
    Plant Genera
    Gelling Agent
    Type of Culture Vessel and Closure Device
    Culture Room
    Cytokinins
    Enzymes
    Mineral Elements
Remedies
Positive Aspects of Hyperhydricity
Bibliography

INTRODUCTION

Hyperhydricity is a physiological anomaly observed by many people working in various fields of plant tissue culture (in vitro culture). The symptoms are not clear cut, and in many cases they are poorly recognized or not recognized at all. In this article symptoms, causes, and possible remedies are reviewed.

TERMINOLOGY

The first research workers who clearly recognized the phenomenon, which is now routinely named *hyperhydricity*, were Grout and Crisp (1). In their work with cauliflower micropropagated the survival rate was less than 50%, and they stated "the main problem is to develop controlled water relations. ..." Debergh et al. (2) were the first to introduce the term *vitrification*. However, the term vitrification was already used to describe two types of processes related to tissue cultured plant material. The first is used to describe organs and tissues having an abnormal morphological appearance and physiological function. The second meaning of vitrification refers to the transition from liquid to solid state, that is, the formation of ice during low-temperature storage of in vitro cultured cells, tissues, and organs (3). The second meaning is more correct based on long-term usage in cryobiology. Therefore, the use of the term hyperhydricity is now favored, as it refers to the major factor involved: the hydric status of the plant material and of the environment.

SYMPTOMS

Hyperhydricity refers to anatomical, morphological, physiological, and biochemical anomalies in tissue cultured plants (Table 1). Most papers dealing with the problem only make reference to morphological symptoms, which are easily recognized by the naked eye. However, the symptoms are not the same for all plants; therefore, it is not possible to give general features describing hyperhydricity, a detailed description is required for each plant species under investigation. A consequence of the fact that attention is only paid to the clearly visible symptoms is that different problems encountered in a tissue culture procedure are not recognized as hyperhydricity. Indeed, the phenomenon can occur in any stage of a tissue culture scheme. Especially in the weaning of so-called "normal plants" failures are most often not associated with hyperhydricity problems, notwithstanding there is a lot of similarity between the symptoms and problems encountered in both cases (4,5). Too often it is not considered that hyperhydricity is a gradually evolving process, whereby visual symptoms occur only after a certain period of time has elapsed under certain culture and explant conditions (3). The evaluation of hyperhydricity is frequently approached from the perspective hide and seek; when no visible symptoms are detected, the plant is called nonhyperhydric and the treatment is called "a procedure overcoming hyperhydricity." It is claimed that so-called "normal plants" have been produced. This is an oversimplification leading to erroneous conclusions.

The only acceptable demonstration that hyperhydricity is not a problem is the rate of success during acclimation. In other words, hyperhydricity cannot just be evaluated by appreciation of the plant material while still in culture, and certainly not by a visual appreciation of plant quality.

The most obvious morphological symptoms of hyperhydricity are visualized in the leaves, especially the glassy, water-soaked outlook (Fig. 1). There are no compelling reports on easily recognizable symptoms in stems and roots, and therefore they are most often not easily recognized.

It is obvious that most features listed in Table 1 (5–7) are symptomatic for plants grown under conditions of (too) high relative humidity, comparable to symptoms that have also been described for plants growing in vivo under such adverse circumstances (e.g., wet rot of lettuce grown in greenhouses under winter conditions, cutting production under a double cover).

CAUSES

Different authors have identified or pinpointed diverse causes for the hyperhydricity syndrome. However, most often the published information does not allow us to formulate clear statements, because the work lacks the scientific rigor to associate the factor under investigation with the causes of the problem. Indeed, changing one parameter can have tremendous consequences on many other characteristics of the system. For example, changing one mineral element (such as nitrogen) can have far-reaching consequences on the pH of the medium; for most

Table 1. Different Symptoms of Hyperhydricity Reported in the Literature

Morphological	Anatomical	Physiological	Biochemical
glassy (water-soaked) leaves	more aerenchyma or intercellular space	high ethylene production	hypolignification
higher propagation ratio	reduced cuticular wax or different crystalline shape	increased transpiration	higher phenolics content
shorter internodes, rosette shape	more or less stomata, which are raised and with more callose	changes in chlorophyll content (higher and lower)	reduced cellulose
wrinkled, brittle leaves	reduced number of palisade cell layers	higher water content	low PAL (phenylalanine ammonia lyase)
needles stick together (conifers)	defective epidermal tissue: smaller cells with few sinuous undulations		increased ACC (alpha-amino cyclopropane-1-carboxylic acid)
weaning problems	reduced or abnormal vascular system	nonfunctional stomata	increased activity of basic isozymes
often glaucous green	thin cuticle		increased protein content
stem and leaves can be thicker	more hydathodes		high activity of glutamate dehydrogenase
	abnormal organization of chloroplasts		
	thin cell walls		
	vascular deformations occurring at the junction between root and stem		

Note: See 5–7.

Figure 1. Hyperhydric (right) and "normal looking" (left) shootlets of *Oreopanax nymphaeifolius* (Decne and Planch).

gelling agents, a drop in pH lowers the gel strength or liquifies the medium; this engenders changes in the physicochemical characteristics of the system and thus the water status. In general, when research is carried out with respect to hyperhydricity, not enough attention has been paid to the physicochemical and ecophysiological parameters of a tissue culture system. Therefore, it is difficult or impossible to formulate clear conclusions, and caution is advised in interpreting the data.

The different causes mentioned in literature have been grouped, and are discussed in the following.

Plant Genera

The plant genus or even the species, is held to have considerable impact on the appearance of the phenomena. In some genera or species, hyperhydricity problems have never been reported, while others are often referred to in the literature: among others, carnation (*Dianthus caryophyllus L.*) (8,9), globe artichoke (*Cynara scolymus L.*) (2,10), and brassica species (11,12). It is striking that the most vulnerable species, mentioned previously, are all characterized by the presence of a prominent wax layer on top of the leaves. Grout and Crisp (1) reported that hyperhydricity in cauliflower was paralleled by a decrease of wax weight.

Gelling Agent

Generally speaking hyperhydricity effects occur more often with plants grown in a liquid than on a gellified medium. The type and the concentration of the gelling agent have a considerable influence on the development of the phenomenon. Hyperhydricity occurs more often on Gelrite™ than on agar-gelled media. Increasing the agar concentration and choosing an agar with a higher gel strength usually improves the quality of the plantlets (2,10,13). However, increasing the agar concentration or choosing a gel with a higher strength usually lowers the propagation ratio drastically, and as a consequence the efficiency of a micropropagation scheme.

Fundamental studies with gelling agents have been undertaken, and have led to different hypothesis:

- The matric potential, a component of the water potential of tissue culture media, is a major factor associated with the induction of hyperhydricity (2,14)
- Specific agars contain toxic substances inducing hyperhydricity (15)
- Specific agars contain an antihyperhydric agent (15,16)

Type of Culture Vessel and Closure Device

In most reports on hyperhydricity not enough attention is paid to the type of container and the closure device, although they have a major impact on the gas composition of the head space (17,18). The more air-tight a container, the more accumulation of different components in the head space will take place. A few considerations are formulated hereafter:

- On different occasions accumulation of ethylene has been associated with the occurrence of hyperhydricity. However, there are no reports clearly stating that ethylene induces hyperhydricity. It can therefore be questioned if ethylene is the cause or a consequence of hyperhydricity.
- The ventilation of a container influences the ambient relative humidity in the container. Improving ventilation can dramatically reduce problems associated with hyperhydricity (19, see also remedies).

Culture Room

Different features of a culture room influence the environmental conditions (the ecophysiology) of a tissue culture container, and as a consequence the anatomy, physiology, morphology, and biochemistry of the plant material in culture. Hereafter a few illustrative examples are presented.

Although published information is not available, most people involved in tissue culture know that the location of a culture container on a shelf and the location of a shelf, in a rack can, to a large extent, influence the quality of the produced plant material. Rather often the weaning quality of plants is better when they have been placed on the lower shelf of a rack (without bottom heating provided by the lamps of the lower level).

The presence or absence of condensation on the closing device is a good indicator for a water vapor saturated head space. Placing containers in two layers on a same shelf can be responsible for a different ecological situation in the containers in the two layers (Fig. 2). The velocity of the air in a culture room, which is controlled by the air conditioning, influences the ventilation of the container, and this, in turn, is a function of the closure device.

Most often the different factors mentioned are not considered when interpreting data on hyperhydricity studies. This can be the reason why successful approaches in one laboratory are not efficient in another.

Cytokinins

In many reports it is argued that cytokinins are the factor responsible for the induction of hyperhydricity. Most often these reports only show that higher cytokinin concentrations increase the percentage of hyperhydric plants or emphasize the symptoms. However, there is clear experimental proof that cytokinins are evocators of hyperhydricity (they increase the symptomatology) (10,13), and are not inductive in se.

Enzymes

Many enzymes have been associated with hyperhydricity, especially those related to the phenolic metabolism. A scheme proposed by Gaspar et al. (6) shows its involvement in lignification. It is evident that changes in enzymes are not causative in se, but that they are the consequences of changes in other parameters involved. Therefore, changes in enzymes are a consequence because they have been triggered by other parameters.

Mineral Elements

By using specific conductivity measurements and electrophoretical studies, it can be proven that the mineral elements are not equally available in comparable media gelled with different agars; the availability can

Figure 2. Placing containers in two layers on the same shelf can be responsible for a different ecological situation in the two layers. The bottom layer is heated by the lamps from the lower shelf, and condensation water can be observed on the lid of the container; the top layer is not heated, and no condensation is observed on the lid.

Table 2. Remedies

Physical	Changes to standard TC media	Not conventional additives
bottom cooling	lower ammonium concentration	agar hydrolysate
more ventilated containers	lower the cytokinin concentration or use a weaker cytokinin	charcoal
lower the matric potential (higher agar concentration)	increase K$^+$	potato juice
solid instead of liquid media	increase Ca^{2+}	polysaccharide producing rhizosphere bacteria
increase light intensity	increase Co^{2+}	sulfated polysaccharides
lower temperatures	lower salt concentration	pectin
	lower Mg^{2+}	fractions of bacto pepton
	increase agar concentration or use an agar with a higher gel strength (see also physical)	growth inhibitors
		polyethylene glycol

Note: See 5–7.

range between 60 and 84% (M. Beruto and P. Debergh, unpublished). The availability of minerals is also influenced by the agar concentration. Changing one mineral element can evoke or repress symptoms of hyperhydricity (20). This is not surprising, since some ions promote (K^+, SO_4^{2-}, and Cl^-) or retard (NO_3^-) the rate of gelification (21).

REMEDIES

Table 2 lists most of the remedies proposed in the literature to overcome hyperhydricity. All the approaches, except one, can be categorized either under physical approaches or as additives to the culture medium. The exception is that specific agars contain a "toxic substance," inducing hyperhydricity or a nongelling, cold-water-soluble constituent avoiding the problem (15).

From most of the remedies listed in Table 2 it is obvious that they change the physicochemical and/or ecophysiological characteristics of the culture environment in the container. The agar concentration and label, as well as most of the nonconventional additives to the culture medium, change the water availability from the medium, because they alter the water potential. Bottom cooling (22), ventilated containers (19), increasing the light intensity, and lowering the culture temperature all interfere in the water housekeeping of the plants in culture. Generally speaking, they promote long-distance transport in the plants by creating a gradient in water retention capacity between the surrounding headspace and the stomatal cavity.

POSITIVE ASPECTS OF HYPERHYDRICITY

One of the symptoms of hyperhydricity (Table 1) is a higher propagation ratio. When kept under control, hyperhydricity can indeed be exploited as a tool to increase the efficiency in a propagation scheme. This means that the symptoms should be allowed to evolve to such an extent that they do not become detrimental. It is impossible to give a more precise description, as it is dependent on the plant and the laboratory conditions.

An interesting observation is that hyperhydric meristems are more readily transformed (23).

BIBLIOGRAPHY

1. B.W.W. Grout and P.C. Crisp, *Acta Hortic.* **78**, 289–296 (1978).
2. P. Debergh, Y. Harbaoui, and R. Lemeur, *Physiol. Plant.* **53**, 181–187 (1981).
3. P. Debergh et al., *Plant Cell, Tiss. Org. Cult.* **30**, 135–140 (1992).
4. J.E. Preece and E.G. Sutter, in P.C. Debergh and R.H. Zimmerman, eds., *Micropropagation: Technology and Application*, Kluwer Academic Publishers, Dordrecht, The Netherlands, 1991, pp. 71–94.
5. M. Ziv, in P.C. Debergh and R.H. Zimmerman, eds., *Micropropagation: Technology and Application*, Kluwer Academic Publishers, Dordrecht, The Netherlands, 1991, pp. 45–69.
6. T. Gaspar et al., in J.M. Bonga and D.J. Durzan, eds., *Cell and Tissue Culture in Forestry*, Vol. 1, Kluwer Academic Press, Dordrecht, The Netherlands, 1987, pp. 152–166.
7. M. Pâques, *Acta Hortic.* **289**, 283–290 (1991).
8. M. Ziv, G. Meir, and A. Halevy, *Environ. Exp. Bot.* **21**, 423 (1981).
9. M. Ziv, G. Meir, and A. Halevy, *Plant Cell, Tiss. Org. Cult.* **2**, 55–60 (1983).
10. P.C.A. Debergh, *Physiol. Plant.* **59**, 270–276 (1983).
11. B.W.W. Grout and H. Aston, *Hortic. Res.* **17**, 1–7 (1977).
12. B.W.W. Grout and H. Aston, *Hortic. Res.* **17**, 65–71 (1977).
13. C.H. Bornman and T.C. Vogelmann, *Physiol. Plant.* **61**, 505–512 (1984).
14. D. Beruto, M. Beruto, C. Ciccarelli, and P. Debergh, *Physiol. Plant.* **94**, 151–157 (1995).
15. B.J. Nairn, R.H. Furneaux, and T.T. Stevenson, *Plant Cell, Tiss. Org. Cult.* **43**, 1–11 (1995).
16. Belg. Pat. 904661 (April 23, 1986), M. Pâques and P. Boxus.
17. M.P. De Proft, L.J. Maene, and P.C. Debergh, *Physiol. Plant.* **65**, 375–379 (1985).
18. D.G. Matthys et al., in F. Carré and P. Chagvardieff, eds., *Ecophysiology and Photosynthetic in vitro Cultures*, Commisariat à l'énergie atomique, Cadarache, France, 1995, pp. 129–140.
19. W. Dillen and S. Buyssens, *Plant Cell, Tiss. Org. Cult.* **19**, 181–188 (1989).
20. P.L. Pasqualetto, R.H. Zimmerman, and I. Fordham, *Plant Cell, Tiss. Org. Cult.* **14**, 31–40 (1988).
21. T. Matsuhashi, in P. Harris, ed., *Food Gels*, Elsevier, London, 1990, pp. 1–51.
22. L.J. Maene and P.C. Debergh, *Acta Hortic.* **212**, 335–348 (1987).
23. T.W. Zimmerman and R. Scorza, *Mol. Breed.* **2**, 73–80 (1996).

See also ACCLIMATIZATION; MICROPROPAGATION OF PLANTS, PRINCIPLES AND PRACTICES.

MONOCOT CELL CULTURE

RICHARD BRETTELL
CSIRO Plant Industry
Darwin, Australia

OUTLINE

INTRODUCTION

The earliest studies in plant cell and tissue culture have noted genotypic differences in growth properties, both within species and between plant genera. Monocots have earned a reputation for being unresponsive or recalcitrant in culture; however, this is not an entirely deserved or fair generalization. For many monocot species it has been demonstrated that efficient methods for culture can be developed when account is taken of characteristics, such as cell physiology and developmental biology, which may differ from those of model dicot species such as tobacco.

With respect to their classification, it is recognized that monocots comprise a diverse group of plant genera and that the boundaries between monocots and dicots may not be absolute in terms of their evolutionary relationships. For example, certain dicotyledonous families such as the Aristolochiaceae possess attributes considered typical of monocotyledons. Similarly, some monocotyledonous families such as the Araceae and Dioscoreaceae resemble families that are assigned to the dicotyledons (1). The research effort in developing culture conditions for monocots has not been evenly spread across the major families. Interest is focused on plant species that have economic importance in agriculture and horticulture. Thus the Poaceae may have been given a disproportionate amount of attention owing to their ubiquity and significance as cereals and pasture grasses.

Research into monocot tissue and cell culture has largely been driven by applications of the technology, as opposed to academic curiosity. Applications of plant tissue and cell culture include micropropagation, embryo rescue, production of haploid plants, and genetic transformation. The major techniques include initiation of callus cultures and regeneration of plants, protoplast culture, anther and pollen culture, and meristem culture. The status of monocots will be summarized in this article with respect to these procedures. The description of monocot families will follow the treatment of Dahlgren et al. (2).

INITIATION OF CALLUS CULTURES AND REGENERATION OF PLANTS

Callus cultures are typically formed through the proliferation of tissue when plant cells multiply in a disorganized fashion, stimulated by growth-regulating substances added to the nutrient culture medium. The term *callus* is derived from the wound callus formed by many plants in response to damage. Although it is notable that this wound response is not typical of monocots, most species will form callus tissue when explants are placed on growth medium containing exogenous growth substances (auxin, or a mixture of auxin and cytokinin). However, these callus tissues are frequently not capable of sustained proliferation or plant regeneration.

In monocots, regeneration of plants can often be achieved through a process of somatic embryogenesis, which refers to the formation of embryonic structures from somatic cells. This is a commonly observed tissue culture response in monocots, and can be induced from a variety of immature tissues and meristems. As with disorganized callus growth, somatic embryogenesis is induced by applications of exogenous growth substances, but in this case plants are regenerated directly

from proliferating somatic embryos following their transfer to medium containing reduced levels of the growth substances. This mode of culture and regeneration has been reported for a very wide range of monocot families, including the Agavaceae, Alliaceae, Alstroemeriaceae, Arecaceae, Asparagaceae, Dioscoreaceae, Iridaceae, Liliaceae, Musaceae, and Poaceae.

A common characteristic of monocots is that tissue culture response is closely linked to the developmental state of the tissue being cultured. In members of the Poaceae, it has long been recognized that regenerable cultures could only be initiated from immature explants containing meristematic cells, or cells that still retained a capacity for active cell division. The competence to respond in culture is rapidly lost as tissues mature, as was demonstrated in several cereal species using leaf or inflorescence cultures. For example, in sorghum it was shown that very young leaf tissue could express totipotency to the extent of forming somatic embryos, but that the ability to respond was rapidly lost as the leaves matured (3). Similar gradients of culture response, associated with the developmental state of the tissue being cultured, have also been described in other monocot families such as the Alliaceae, Alstroemeriaceae, and Amaryllidaceae.

There exist monocots that show greater plasticity with respect to tissue culture response. For example, in *Anthurium spp.*, plants have been regenerated from cultures initiated from roots, as well as from leaves, petioles, spadices, spathes, lateral buds, and shoot tips (4). However, it is interesting to note that as a member of the Araceae, *Anthurium* is in a family that is considered to have strong affiliation with the dicots.

PROTOPLAST CULTURE

Protoplasts are isolated plant cells that have had their cell wall removed, generally following digestion in an enzyme solution with cellulase and pectinase activities. Monocot protoplasts were the focus of intense research activity in the 1980s, as they were an attractive target material for genetic transformation experiments as well as a means of producing somatic hybrid cells following protoplast fusion.

Exploitation of the potential of plant protoplasts requires an ability to regenerate plants, but in comparison to amenable dicot species, this has proved technically difficult in many monocot species. In part these difficulties can be attributed to the loss in competence to respond in culture that is observed in many monocots as the cells differentiate and the tissues mature. Thus, despite intensive experimental efforts over many years, there are no confirmed reports of plant regeneration from protoplasts isolated from expanded leaves of any member of the Poaceae. Plant regeneration in grasses and cereals has generally been achieved by initiating embryogenic suspension cultures as a source of totipotent protoplasts. Similarly in the Alliaceae and Musaceae, cell divisions have not been observed in protoplasts isolated directly from the plant, but only from protoplasts isolated from cells cultured in liquid suspension.

Protoplasts have been used successfully for the genetic transformation of a number of cereal and grass species, following direct gene transfer through the protoplast membrane using electroporation or chemical treatments. However, the technical problems associated with monocot protoplast culture mean that the use of protoplasts for genetic transformation has largely been superseded by other methods for gene transfer including microprojectile bombardment and *Agrobacterium*-mediated transformation.

The problems associated with routine culture of monocot protoplasts are also reflected in the limited application of protoplasts for the production of somatic hybrids in monocots. Exceptions are found in the Poaceae, where plants have been recovered in some novel intergeneric combinations following protoplast fusion, for example, with *Oryza sativa + Echinochloa oryzicola* (5).

ANTHER AND MICROSPORE CULTURE

Anther and microspore culture is one area of plant tissue culture in which monocots are well represented. These techniques follow from the discovery by Guha and Maheshwari in the 1960s that immature pollen of the dicot *Datura innoxia* could be induced to divide and form haploid embryos in cultured anthers. In subsequent studies, members of the Poaceae were also found to be responsive to anther culture for the production of pollen-derived plants. In cereal and grass species, anthers are generally collected when the microspores are at a middle or late uninucleate stage, and cultured under conditions that allow the development of embryos directly from the microspores through sustained cell division. Embryos are formed after three to five weeks aseptic culture of the anthers on solid or liquid nutrient media. The technique has been applied extensively, particularly in China, for the production of true-breeding doubled haploid lines for agriculture.

Refinements in the technique have enabled researchers to culture isolated microspores. In initial studies dividing microspores were isolated from precultured anthers. More recently these results have been extended so that in species such as rice, barley, and wheat, methods have been developed for inducing freshly isolated microspores to undergo cell division and produce viable embryos in culture. As with protoplasts, isolated cereal microspores have been used successfully as targets in genetic transformation experiments.

Success with monocot anther and microspore culture is not confined to the Poaceae. Examples of plant regeneration from microspores in cultured anthers are also found in the Liliaceae and Asparagaceae.

MICROPROPAGATION

Micropropagation using tissue culture is a widely applied method for producing large numbers of plants of a desired genotype. Orchids (Orchidaceae) were among the first plants to be micropropagated commercially. The technique involved the culturing of small explants from the mother plant under conditions that stimulate the explants to produce many shoot primordia. In most cases, micropropagation depends on the constant development of organized meristems rather than the proliferation of disorganised callus tissues. The maintenance of an organized plant structure is believed to favor clonal uniformity, and reduce the frequency of deleterious mutations that are commonly observed in plants derived from tissue culture. The phenomenon of genetic change occurring as a result of tissue culture has been termed *somaclonal variation*.

Micropropagation has been applied to many monocots of horticultural and ornamental interest. Examples include agave and yucca (Agavaceae), flowering bulbs (Amaryllidaceae and Iridaceae), oil palm and coconut palm (Arecaceae), pineapple (Bromeliaceae), yam (Dioscoreaceae), orchids (Orchidaceae), and ginger (Zingiberaceae).

Another technique that can be considered in the context of plant tissue culture and micropropagation is meristem culture, which involves the use of shoot meristems to initiate cultures. Since plants infected with virus frequently have virus-free meristems, the technique has been used as a method for virus elimination. Meristem culture was pioneered by Georges Morel in the 1950s and has been successfully applied to monocots, including members of the Agavaceae, Alliaceae, Asparagaceae, Orchidaceae, and Poaceae.

Both cultured meristem tips and larger micropropagules can be stored at low temperature or cryopreserved in a frozen state. Both approaches have been used successfully in monocots for the preservation and storage of valuable plant materials.

EMBRYO CULTURE

Embryo culture includes culture of both immature embryos and mature embryos. In monocots, immature embryos have been used as a convenient starting material for initiating embryogenic cultures capable of plant regeneration (see the section on initiation of callus cultures and regeneration of plants). Alternatively developing embryos may be brought to maturity in an aseptic environment, and this has led to the technique known as *embryo rescue*. Embryo rescue has found considerable application in interspecific crosses for recovering embryos that start to develop, but through incompatibility of the parents do not reach a viable maturity, for example, through a lack of endosperm. The embryo rescue technique has been widely applied in members of the Poaceae for the production of intergeneric as well as interspecific hybrids. It has also been used in wheat and barley for the rescue of haploid embryos formed following wide hybridization, for example, between *Hordeum vulgare* and *H. bulbosum* (6).

Embryos may also be cultured when they have reached physiological maturity. This has proved useful in species of banana (Musaceae) where seed germination is erratic, and many species of palm (Arecaceae) where germination is inhibited by strong dormancy, which can be broken when the embryo is excised from the seed.

CONCLUDING REMARKS

Tissue and cell culture of monocots accounts for a considerable body of work, in which the boundaries continue to be extended to include new species and new technologies. While not all techniques can be applied universally, it has been shown that methods can be effectively applied to monocots when account is taken of their particular physiological and developmental characteristics.

BIBLIOGRAPHY

1. R.M.T. Dahlgren, H.T. Clifford, and P.F. Yeo, *The Families of the Monocotyledons*, Springer-Verlag, Berlin, 1985, p. 47.
2. R.M.T. Dahlgren, H.T. Clifford, and P.F. Yeo, *The Families of the Monocotyledons*, Springer-Verlag, Berlin, 1985.
3. W. Wernicke and R. Brettell, *Nature (London)* **287**, 138–139 (1980).
4. F.-C. Chen, A.R. Kuehnle, and N. Sugii, *Plant Cell, Tisue Organ Cult.* **49**, 71–74 (1997).
5. R. Terada, J. Kyozuka, S. Nishibayashi, and K. Shimamoto, *Mol. Gen. Genet.* **210**, 39–43 (1987).
6. K.J. Kasha and K.N. Kao, *Nature (London)* **225**, 874–876 (1970).

See also Cryopreservation of plant cells, tissues and organs; Culture establishment, plant cell culture; Germplasm preservation of in vitro plant cultures; Plant cell culture, laboratory techniques.

MOSS, MOLECULAR TOOLS FOR PHENOTYPIC ANALYSIS

Celia D. Knight
University of Leeds
Leeds, United Kingdom

OUTLINE

INTRODUCTION

The moss species *Physcomitrella patens*, *Ceratodon purpureus*, and *Funaria hygrometrica* have been established in axenic culture for a number of years and have been developed as models for studying higher plant development (1–3). Other moss species, such as *Tortula ruralis*, have thus far been refractive to axenic culture but are nonetheless studied for specific features such as desiccation tolerance (4). Each species offers its own particular attraction, but all bryophytes provide a relatively simple cellular system with which to study plant developmental responses. With the establishment of conditions for transformation (5), a new age of research became applicable to moss, that of reverse genetics and the use of molecular tools to determine gene function and regulation in vivo. The purpose of this article is to review the technologies that exploit the simple cellular and genetic system of moss in the phenotypic analysis of single cells and multicellular complexes.

As early land plants, bryophytes evolved mechanisms to respond to pressures of the terrestrial environment, such as desiccation tolerance. Furthermore, as sessile organisms, in contrast to their aquatic algal predecessors, they evolved mechanisms to grow toward light (phototropism). Bryophytes are nonvascular plants, and therefore their size and complexity are limited. However, within these limitations, cellular differentiation occurs, and the resulting structures not only provide insight into how multicellular complexes arise, but also bear some remarkable similarities to analogous forms in angiosperms; for example, the leaf of a moss gametophore is a simple pinnate leaf shape, but comprises only a single layer of cells. By comparing moss and angiosperm development, we therefore have the opportunity to study evolutionary trends in morphogenesis. Recently, the evolutionary distinction between mosses and angiosperms was surprisingly highlighted by the demonstration that mosses possess an active homologous recombination system (6). By contrast, angiosperms do not recognize and recombine homologous sequences at high frequency (7). A possible explanation for this difference between the two classes of plants relates to ploidy. The dominant phase of the moss life cycle is the gametophyte, which is haploid. The dominant phase of the angiosperm life cycle is at least diploid and in many cases polyploid. Polyploidy could not have evolved in plants in which efficient homologous recombination occurred in mitotic cells, although whether the homologous recombination mechanism was lost or suppressed, thus allowing an increase in ploidy, is unknown. Of relevance to this article is how the discovery of homologous recombination is being exploited in moss research.

Previous work on the moss *P. patens* exploited haploidy in a genetic approach by the isolation of morphological and biochemical mutants (1). While the characterization of these classes of mutants has generated useful data, isolation of the genes mutated is greatly facilitated by a reverse genetic approach. The exploitation of endogenous homologous recombination mechanisms is called "gene targeting" and is an invaluable tool in functional genomics research, having been used successfully in bacteria, yeast, and some mouse cell lines (see Ref. 6). Over the past few years, evidence has been obtained in the moss *P. patens* for both the specific targeting of moss genes (Fig. 7) and significant sequence homology between mosses and angiosperms (8,9), and these will be reviewed. It is predicted that the targeting in moss of homologues of known angiosperm genes will generate a mutant phenotype and that the nature of the phenotype is indicative of gene function. An understanding of phenotypic analysis in moss and how molecular tools can be used is therefore crucial to this very powerful tool.

LIFE CYCLE OF *P. PATENS*

The life cycle of the moss *P. patens* has been reviewed previously (1,10,11). Comprehensive culture conditions for *P. patens*, which are largely suitable for *Ceratodon* and *Funaria* spp. also, are reviewed by Cove (12) and can be obtained by registration with the International Bryophyte Research Information Service (IBRIS) (email d.j.cove@leeds.ac.uk). Features of the life cycle included here will focus on morphogenesis from a single-cell spore or protoplast, through a branched single cell filamentous network to a multicellular three-dimensional bud, which develops into a leafy shoot. Since all these structures form part of the gametophyte and are haploid, they are all susceptible to altered development following gene disruption by homologous recombination.

The single-cell propagule is the spore. *P. patens* is a monoecious moss, normally producing female antheridia at the gametophore apex and male antheridia in the leaf axils. After appropriate gametogenesis induction, normally a reduction of growth temperature from 25 to 15 °C, the archegonium is fertilized following irrigation with sterile distilled water, and the diploid sporophyte develops from the archegonium at the apex. *P. patens* is typified by a short stalk called the seta. Mature sporophytes can be picked off and stored dry at 4 °C. For germination, the capsule is crushed in sterile distilled water and plated onto solid growth medium, each capsule generating approximately 10^3 viable spores. A technically convenient analogy for spore germination is protoplast regeneration. Protoplasts are easier to obtain than spores, since the production of spores takes at least 3 months. By contrast, tissue can be propagated vegetatively by blending, and a single 9-cm Petri dish culture of 7-day-old tissue, when treated with Driselase™ (Sigma) cell-wall degrading enzymes, yields approximately 10^6 protoplasts. Regeneration frequencies of up to 90% can be obtained.

That a single moss cell can develop into a multicellular complex containing forms similar in shape to higher plant leaves allows fundamental questions in plant development to be addressed in this species. For example, how does regulation of the cell cycle influence developmental events, and what are the consequences of changes in the plane of cell divisions? Although these questions and many others are being actively pursued in higher plant research, the analysis of appropriate structures in higher plants frequently depends upon sectioning and fixing procedures. The simplicity of the moss system offers the opportunity to answer some of these questions using noninvasive techniques.

The first event detectable visually following spore germination and protoplast regeneration is the establishment of asymmetry. In the case of protoplast regeneration, the pear-shaped regenerant has already undergone one cell division and responded to light and calcium cues to establish the polarity of outgrowth [Fig. 1(a)]. Cove et al. have used both *P. patens* and *C. purpureus* protoplasts to study both axis alignment and polarity (13), and more recent work shows a role for phytochrome (D.J. Cove, unpublished data). *C. purpureus* is an easier model to study the effects of light than *P. patens* since regeneration is not critically light dependent in this species. The cell emerging from a protoplast or spore is called a *protonema*, and there are normally between 1 and 3 protonemata for each spore or protoplast [Fig. 1(b)]. Growth is by apical extension and serial division of the apical cell. Subapical cells do not extend in length, although they undergo further divisions (normally no more than twice) to produce side branches. Such a growth pattern establishes an approximately planar network of single-cell filaments [Fig. 1(c)]. The primary protonemal cell type is called a *chloronema* and is typified by an apical cell cycle time of 24 h under continuous white light $(10-15 \text{ W m}^{-2})$ at 25 °C. Cells in chloronemal filaments are separated by perpendicular transverse cross walls and are densely packed with chloroplasts [Fig. 2(b)]. As the first cell arising from the spore, the primary role of these cells may be considered as assimilatory. After several days and with appropriate endogenous levels of the hormones cytokinin and auxin, the apical chloronemal cell differentiates into a caulonemal cell. This normally occurs over one or two cell divisions so that intermediate filaments may be observed. Caulonemal protonemata are typified by an apical cell cycle time of only about 6 h, the cross walls are oblique by contrast to chloronemata, and the cells are more vacuolate, with fewer spindle-shaped chloroplasts [Fig. 2(a)]. These protonemata represent the adventitious protonemal phase, in which growth away from the center of the colony supersedes photosynthesis as the primary role. Caulonemal cells continue to grow by apical cell extension and serial division. The relatively fast growth rate and reduced number of chloroplasts per cell means that several features are prominent in the apical cell of caulonema. The apical dome is generally free of chloroplasts and is granular in appearance, containing mitochondria and Golgi. The nucleus is often clearly visible at a constant distance from the apex for most of the cell cycle. Caulonemata also produce side branches, though by contrast to chloronemata, which produce only chloronemal side branches, there are four possible fates for caulonemal side branches. The majority are chloronemal (approximately 90%); less than 1% may be caulonemal; a variable percentage, up to 10%, are intermediate filaments switching from chloronemata to caulonemata, and about 2% will be buds (14). Buds represent a very crucial developmental transition, since they arise from a single-cell side-branch initial and develop into a three-dimensional multicellular structure, from which the shoot and its recognisable leaf-shaped structures develop [Fig. 2(c)].

Bud production is cytokinin induced (2,10). A role for calcium in cytokinin-induced bud formation in *F. hygrometrica* was suggested by Saunders and Hepler (15), although subsequent papers, reviewed by Schumaker and Dietrich (2), while demonstrating the involvement of calcium, have yet to determine fully the processes upon which it acts. Furthermore, experiments carried out by Russell did not show changes in calcium levels closely associated with cytokinin-induced bud formation in *P. patens* (14). A developing bud shows a difference in

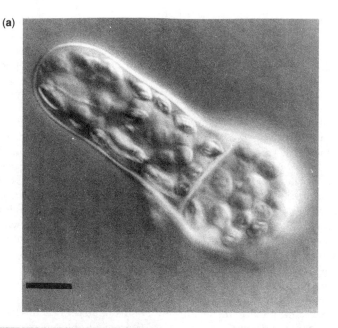

Figure 1. (**a**) Regenerating protoplast, approximately 24 h after isolation. Scale bar = 10 μm. (**b**) Sporeling, approximately 3 d after germination. Scale bar = 30 μm. (**c**) Caulonemal filament showing chloronemal side branches, approximately 7 d after tissue subculture. Scale bar = 50 μm.

the plane of cell division at the first cell division of the side-branch initial. This division takes place earlier than in a protonemal side branch and is oblique. The resulting two cells undergo a second division, approximately 5.5 h later, both being perpendicular to the first division cell wall. The four-cell bud [Fig. 2(c)] then takes on different developmental fates, the two basal cells becoming the bud stalk and the first rhizoid, respectively, and the two apical cells form leaf initials. Rhizoids are cell filaments that emerge 180° from the apex of the bud [Fig. 3(a)]. These filaments act to stabilize the gametophore, the growth of which is influenced by both light and gravity directions. Mature rhizoids are largely vacuolate and normally pigmented and appear to have no assimilatory function.

The analysis of moss development up to the stage of gametophore development has received the most attention to date, largely because these structures are easily identifiable by light microscopy. The diameter of a protonemal cell is approximately 20 μm, the length of a chloronemal cell approximately 120–150 μm, and a caulonemal cell approximately 300–400 μm. While it is clearly advantageous to observe these cells by noninvasive techniques, it is clearly less easy to section three-dimensional structures composed of cells of these dimensions in comparison to higher plant structures. Time-lapse microscopy has attempted to follow the process of bud development, though this becomes less informative after the 4- to 8-cell stage (14). It is likely that the use of

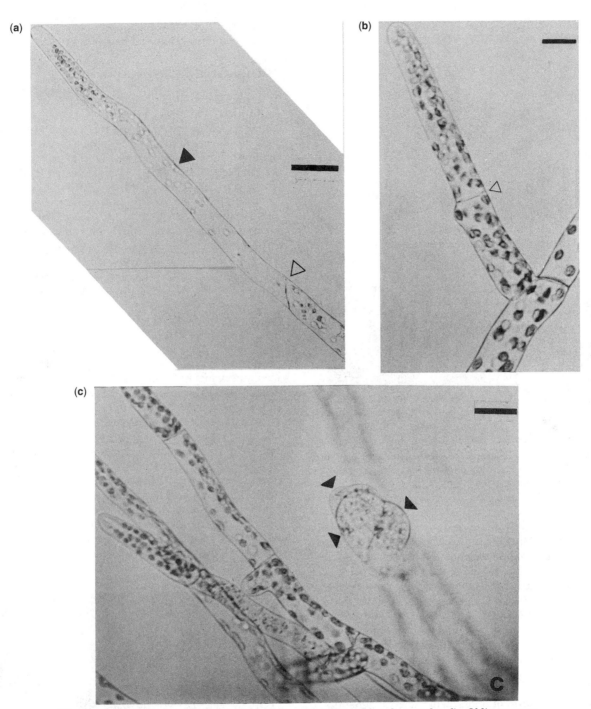

Figure 2. (**a**) Caulonemal apical cell. Position of nucleus (closed arrowhead). Oblique cross wall (open arrowhead). Scale bar = 40 μm. (**b**) Chloronemal cell. Transverse cross wall (open arrowhead). Side-branch initial (arrow). Scale bar = 20 μm. (**c**) Bud. 3 of 4 cells are visible (arrowheads). A chloronemal side-branch initial can be seen in comparison with the developing bud on a neighboring protonema. Scale bar = 40 μm.

cell-specific reporter genes such as *gfp* (green fluorescein protein) will find an application in the development of gametophores in future. It has already been mentioned that rhizoid development occurs early in gametophore development and the development of the first leaf is apparent soon after rhizoid emergence. Leaves are a single layer of cells with an apparent midrib region

and extension of the leaf occurs basally. As shown by the scanning electron micrograph in Figure 3(b), the phyllotaxy of leaves on the gametophore follows a spiral arrangement. It is known that dark-grown gametophores etiolate and produce scale leaves and these dark-grown gametophores, like apical dark-grown caulonemal cells, respond to gravity by growing away from the gravitational

(a)

(b)

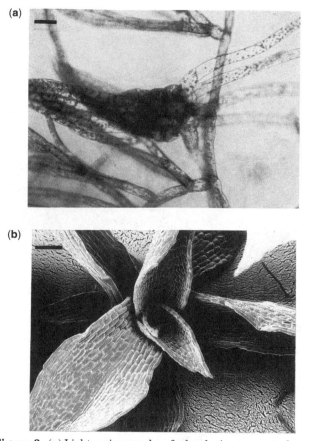

Figure 3. (**a**) Light micrograph of developing gametophore. Scale bar = 50 μm. (**b**) Scanning electron micrograph of mature gametophore. Scale bar = 100 μm.

vector. Genetic analysis of gravitropism in *P. patens* shows that the multicellular response is, at least in part, distinct from the single protonemal response (16). The study of gravitropism in moss therefore allows a link between response mechanisms in single and multicellular complexes. Mutants have been obtained with altered gametophore development, and these are termed *gad* mutants (1). One class of *gad* mutant, in which the leaf cells are rounded rather than elongate, also shows an abnormal protonemal gravitropic response, and this is most likely a pleiotropic effect of the same mutation.

Finally, it should be noted that, under standard growth conditions, a culture of moss will always generate a recognizable pattern of growth, although there is clearly wide variability. Indeed there have been attempts to model growth patterns mathematically (17). This implies that there is determination in the branching pattern and that factors influencing branching pattern could be identified. Analysis to date has revealed that this is not straightforward, and while there are likely to be factors controlling the distribution of buds, for example, there is also likely to be enormous plasticity in moss development. In this section, the basic development of moss from a single cell through to a multicellular complex has been covered. Many genes will undoubtedly participate in effecting this program, and molecular tools allow roles for candidate genes to be assessed. The first tool that will be reviewed,

however, is not a new technology but exemplifies how the simple cellular system can be studied.

FITC LABELING OF ANTIBODIES

One approach that lends itself to moss single-cell analysis is to determine the location of proteins, or protein homologues, known to play a role in signal transduction and development in other organisms. Antibodies raised against these proteins and labeled with Fluorescein IsoThioisocyanate (FITC) can be detected by fluorescence microscopy using standard fluorescein filter sets. This approach has been used to determine the location of the heterotrimeric G-α subunit in *P. patens*. Hutton et al. (18) showed evidence for specificity of a monoclonal antibody raised against the *Arabidopsis thaliana* G-α subunit for *P. patens*. FITC labeling of this antibody against protonemal cells indicated clear labeling to the protonemal cross-walls (Fig. 4). Given that heterotrimeric proteins are primary signal transducers, a location at an intercellular junction is not surprising.

It was previously indicated that a strength of moss phenotypic analysis is that much of the early development can be assessed noninvasively. The previous example using FITC-labeled G-α antibodies nonetheless requires moss protonemal cells to be fixed to allow the antibody access to the intracellular environment. Probing protonemal cells with FITC-labeled antibodies to cell-wall-specific proteins, however, does not require fixing, and the use of this technology on developing protonemata is a promising application that is in its infancy. Figure 5 shows data indicating that LM6, an antibody raised against an arabinan side chain of pectin (19), only labels the apices of primary protonema and their side branches (C.D. Knight and J.P. Knox, unpublished data). Patterns of labeling with various antibodies should be informative in the study of cell-wall dynamics during development.

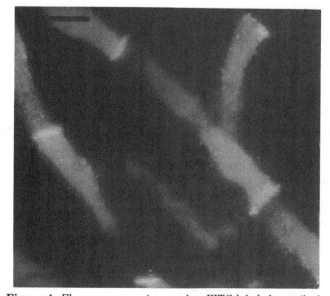

Figure 4. Fluorescence micrograph. FITC-labeled antibody raised against *Arabidopsis thaliana* Gα-subunit labels protonemal cross walls. Scale bar = 20 μm.

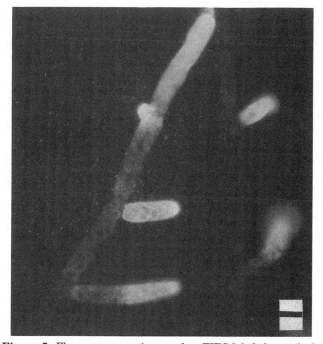

Figure 5. Fluorescence micrograph. FITC-labeled antibody (LM6) raised against an arabinan side chain of pectin. Scale bar = 20 μm.

TRANSGENIC MOSS

The altered expression of key genes, either by disruption or by overexpression, may generate a different developmental program. Exploitation of this approach requires an understanding of the transformation process in moss. Procedures for the transformation of *P. patens* were first described by Schaefer et al. (5). The procedure, which uses polyethylene glycol (PEG) -mediated DNA uptake by protoplasts and standard plant-selectable marker gene cassettes, carried in a pUC-based vector, is effective. Commonly, the neomycin phophotransferase gene (*npt*II) or the hygromycin phophotransferase gene (*hpt*II) is expressed under control of the cauliflower mosaic virus 35S promoter, or slightly less effectively, by the *nos* promoter. Selection is with 25–50 μg/mL Geneticin™ (Sigma) or 10–30 μg/mL hygromycin, respectively. Moss is not a host for *Agrobacterium* infection (C.D. Knight, unpublished data), thus distinguishing moss transformation from general dicotyledonous plant transformation procedures. Although, in principle, the use of binary vector components should be effective in generating transformants, in practice the frequencies obtained with these contructs are low and pUC-based vectors are recommended.

A typical plate of antibiotic-resistant regenerants after 14 days of selection is shown in Figure 6 (20). The single fast-growing colony in (b) represents a stable transformant. The remaining regenerants in (b) represent a class of transformant referred to as unstable. These are typified by slower growth rates and by their dependence on selection for maintenance of the plasmid. A procedure for distinguishing stable from unstable transformants is outlined in Figure 7. The precise nature of unstable

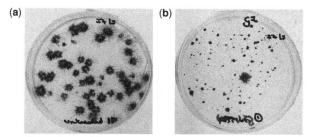

Figure 6. (a) Untreated protoplasts regenerating on a 9-cm Petri dish containing BCD + calcium medium (12) at 14 d. (b) Protoplasts transformed by plasmid pJIT 161 (20) regenerating on a 9-cm Petri dish containing BCD + calcium + G418 (50 μg/mL) medium at 14 d.

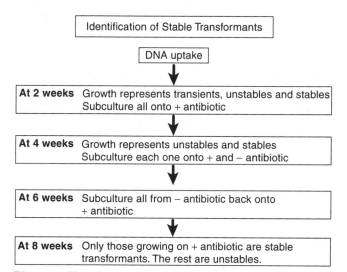
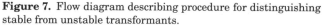

Figure 7. Flow diagram describing procedure for distinguishing stable from unstable transformants.

transformants is still under investigation, but it is clear that stable integrative transformation frequencies remain low (approximately 1 in 10^5 protoplasts, or 0.5–1/μg plasmid DNA). Schaefer and Zryd (6) have shown that this rate of integration may be increased approximately 10-fold by the inclusion of homologous genomic DNA, and this finding suggested efficient gene targeting, which has been subsequently confirmed elsewhere. It is clear though that the frequency of DNA uptake and expression is relatively high, with the unstable transformation frequency approaching 1 in 10^3 protoplasts, or 50–100/μg plasmid DNA. Therefore, these transgenics may have some uses if expression of a clone in moss is all that is required. Caution is advised at this stage in interpreting cell-specific expression patterns in unstable transgenics, since it is clear that expression levels vary between cells (C.D. Knight, unpublished data).

The PEG-mediated method works efficiently for transformation of *C. purpureus* (21) and although microprojectile bombardment is efficient at delivering DNA to *P. patens* and generating stable transformants, this procedure has been less successful to date at generating gene knockouts (C.D. Knight unpublished data). It is unclear whether this difference is significant.

REPORTER GENE ANALYSIS

The most widely used reporter gene in moss is the b-glucuronidase (*gus*) gene. Plasmids expressing *gus* and methods for histochemical staining and fluorometric analysis are described by Jefferson (22). Examples of GUS expression will be discussed in the next section.

A second useful reporter gene expressed in moss is the green fluorescent protein (*gfp*) gene (23). Recently a number of *gfp* mutations have become available that allow detection at different wavelengths and hence dual labeling. Details of these plasmids and how to obtain them can be obtained from the Arabidopsis Biological Resource Center (1060 Carmack Road, Columbus, OH 43210-1002. http://aims.cps.msu.edu/aims). An example of *gfp* expression in *P. patens* is shown in Figure 8, in which the plasmid pBASgfp (21) is expressed strongly in all protonemal cells.

INDUCIBLE PROMOTER–REPORTER GENE ANALYSIS

While an efficient gene targeting system in haploid tissue has the advantage of generating mutant phenotypes directly, it follows that disruption of an essential gene will be lethal. It is therefore essential that mechanisms be developed concomitantly to confirm lethality of a given gene. One way to do this is to develop functional inducible promoters. If a single cross-over occurs between the endogenous copy of an essential gene and a transforming plasmid carrying a 3'-truncated copy of the gene under control of an inducible promoter, the lethal knock-out will be rescued only in the presence of the inducer. Alternatively, transformation of a diploid may result in a non-lethal but abnormal phenotype.

Gatz (24) reviewed the inducible promoters available to date for plants. The tetracycline-repressible promoter has been shown to function in moss by Zeidler et al. (25). Transgenics selected for hygromycin resistance express the chimaeric TetR promoter–*gus* fusion only when cultures are not exposed to tetracycline. That is, these transgenics must be grown on medium containing tetracycline at 1 µg/mL for 2 weeks and then transferred to medium lacking tetracycline for 3 days, before assaying for *gus* expression. An example of *tet* repression is shown in Figure 9. Although this promoter functions, it would be preferable to use a system in which the conditions for induction or repression were less imposing on plant development. Other options outlined by Gatz are being tested.

EVIDENCE FOR GENE TARGETING

An increasing number of reports show that gene targeting in moss occurs at efficiencies greater than 10% and up to 100% of transgenics tested, whereas, in spite of considerable effort, the best-reported rate for gene targeting in angiosperms is 0.01% in *Arabidopsis* (26).

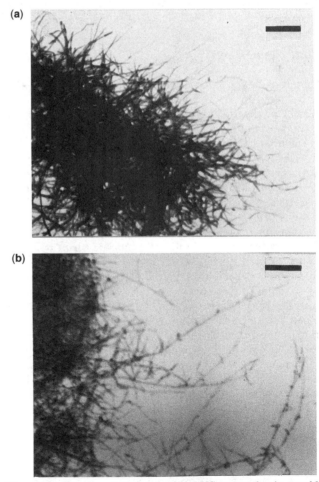

(a)

(b)

Figure 9. Histochemical staining for GUS expression in a stable transgenic transformed by pGL2tTGUS. (**a**) Transformant grown for 2 weeks on tetracycline (1 µg/mL), then transferred to medium without tetracycline for 3 d before staining. (**b**) Continuous growth on tetracycline. Scale bar = 500 µm.

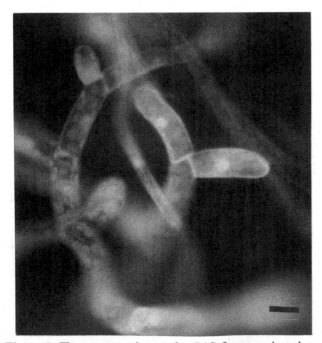

Figure 8. Fluorescence micrograph. pBASgfp expression, observed using a fluorescein filter set. Scale bar = 20 µm.

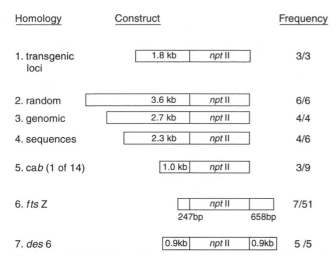

Homology	Construct	Frequency
1. transgenic loci	1.8 kb npt II	3/3
2. random	3.6 kb npt II	6/6
3. genomic	2.7 kb npt II	4/4
4. sequences	2.3 kb npt II	4/6
5. cab (1 of 14)	1.0 kb npt II	3/9
6. fts Z	npt II 247bp 658bp	7/51
7. des 6	0.9kb npt II 0.9kb	5/5

Figure 10. Published evidence for gene targeting in *Physcomitrella patens*. Details and references for Examples 1–7 are described in the text. Construct shows the length of sequence homology in kilobase pairs (kb) or base pairs (bp) present either on one side of the *npt*II gene (Examples 1–5) or flanking the *npt*II gene (examples 6–7). *Npt*II is the 35S-*npt*II-polyA expression cassette. Frequency refers to the number of transgenics integrated at the homologous site/total number of integrations.

Figure 10 lists the published evidence for *P. patens* to date. The results in Example 1 are due to retransformation of a transgenic, selecting for a second antibiotic resistance, the homology being provided by the transformation vector and the frequency of targeting assessed by segregation analysis (27). Examples 2, 3, and 4 are random genomic sequences; three single-copy random genomic sequences were shown by Southern hybridization to target the genomic locus with 90% efficiency (6). Example 5 is 1 of the 14 members of the chlorophyll A/B binding protein gene family; a 1.0-kb genomic sequence of 1 of the 14 genes was targeted in 30% of the transgenics, and targeting was specific to the gene member of the multigene family (28). Example 6 is the *fts*Z gene and is the first demonstration of a knockout phenotype; cDNA of the *fts*Z gene, known to be involved in bacterial cell division, was disrupted, generating defective chloroplast division (29). Finally, Example 7 is a novel desaturase gene that when disrupted generated a predictable change in fatty acid profile (30).

Two papers on *Physcomitrella*-expressed sequence tags (ESTs) indicate that there is sufficient sequence homology between moss genes and higher plant genes for many other moss homologues to be sought. Reski et al. (8) analyzed 80 sequences from a cytokinin-induced cDNA library, and Machuka et al. (9), 169 sequences from an abscisic acid–induced cDNA library. Further moss sequences will become available in the near future.

CONCLUDING REMARKS

Gene targeting clearly represents a very promising route towards the functional analysis of moss genes and moss homologues of higher plant genes. As mentioned in the introduction, the comparison of moss and angiosperm development will allow evolutionary trends in morphogenesis to be studied. This should be particularly enlightening if homologues of higher plant genes known to be functional in structures that mosses donot possess can be disrupted. For example, there are moss homologues of lignin-specific sequences (9), and yet mosses do not synthesise lignin. Perhaps functional analysis of higher plant genes in moss might reveal new functions for old genes as well as functions for genes for which there is no other route of analysis.

There remains much also to be gained from other experimental approaches using this simple system. Recently, some exciting work by Bruecker et al. (31) showed that an aphototropic mutant of *Ceratodon* could be repaired by microinjection of a rat heme oxygenase cDNA. The microinjection of other molecules, in addition to DNA, such as RNA, proteins, and antibodies into single target cells would open up a multitude of further experiments in which molecular tools can be applied to in vivo studies to modify the plant developmental program in a controlled way.

ACKNOWLEDGMENTS

I am most grateful to David Cove for providing Figures 1(a), 1(b), and 3(b) and for critically reviewing the manuscript. Thanks also to Mathias Zeidler (Frei Universität, Berlin) for providing plasmids pGL2tTGUS and pBASgfp; Paul Knox (University of Leeds) for antibody LM6; Paul Millner (University of Leeds) for anti-GPα1 antibody, and Jenna Hutton (for Fig. 4) and to Bev Merry for technical assistance.

BIBLIOGRAPHY

1. D.J. Cove, C.D. Knight, and T. Lamparter, *Trends in Plant Sci.* **2**, 99–105 (1997).

2. K.S. Schumaker and M.A. Dietrich, *Annu. Rev. Plant Physiol. Plant Mol. Biol.* **49**, 501–523 (1998).

3. T. Lamparter et al., *J. Plant Physiol.* **153**, 394–400 (1998).

4. M.J. Oliver, *Physiol. Plant* **97**, 779–787 (1997).

5. D. Schaefer, C.D. Knight, D.J. Cove, and J.-P. Zryd, *Mol. Gen. Genet.* **226**, 418–424 (1991).

6. D. Schaefer and J.-P. Zryd, *Plant J.* **11**, 1195–1206 (1997).

7. H. Puchta, *Trends Plant Sci.* **3**, 77–78 (1998).

8. R. Reski et al., *Bot. Acta* **111**, 141–151 (1998).

9. J. Machuka et al., *Plant Cell Physiol.* **40**, 98–238 (1999).

10. D. Cove, in V.E.A. Russo, S. Brody, D. Cove, and S. Ottolenghi, eds., *Development. The Molecular Genetic Approach*, Springer, Heidelberg, 1992, pp. 179–193.

11. R. Reski, *Bot. Acta* **111**, 1–16 (1998).

12. D. Cove, in eds., *Plant Tissue Culture Manual*, Kluwer Academic Publishers, Dordrechts The Netherlands, 1996, pp. 1–43.

13. D.J. Cove, R.S. Quatrano, and E. Hartmann, *Development* **122**, 371–379 (1996).

14. A.J. Russell, Ph.D. Thesis, University of Leeds, 1993.

15. M.J. Saunders, and P.K. Hepler, *Planta* **152**, 272–281 (1981).

16. C.D. Knight and D.J. Cove, *Plant, Cell Environ.* **14**, 995–1001 (1991).

17. F.D. Fracchia and N.W. Ashton, in *Proceedings of IEEE Visualisation '95*, IEEE Computer Society Press, New York, 1995 pp. 364–367.

18. J.L. Hutton, C.D. Knight, and P.A. Millner, *J. Exp. Bot.* **49**, 1113–1118 (1998).

19. W.G.T. Willats, S.E. Marcus, and J.P. Knox, *Carbohyd. Res.* **308**, 149–152 (1998).

20. R.R.D. Croy, *Plant Molecular Biology Labfax*, Bios Scientific, Oxford, U.K., 1993.

21. M. Zeidler, E. Hartmann, and J. Hughes, *J. Plant Physiol.* **154**, 641–650 (1999).

22. R.A. Jefferson, *Plant Mol. Biol. Rep.* **5**, 387–405 (1987).

23. J. Haseloff and B. Amos, *Trends Genet.* **11**, 328–329 (1995).

24. C. Gatz and I. Lenk, *Trends Plant Sci.* **3**, 352–358 (1998).

25. M. Zeidler, C. Gatz, E. Hartmann, and J. Hughes, *Plant Mol. Biol.* **30**(1), 199–205 (1996).

26. S.A. Kempin et al., *Nature (London)* **389**, 802–803 (1997).

27. W. Kammerer and D.J. Cove, *Mol. Gen. Genet.* **250**, 380–382 (1996).

28. A.H. Hofman et al., *Mol. Gen. Genet.* **261**, 92–99 (1999).

29. R. Strepp et al., *Proc. Natl. Acad. Sci. U.S.A.* **95**, 4368–4373 (1998).

30. T. Girke et al., *Plant J.* **15**, 39–48 (1998).

31. G. Brücker et al., *Planta* (in press).

See also FLUX ANALYSIS OF MAMMALIAN CELL CULTURE: METHODS AND APPLICATIONS; PLANT CELL CULTURE, LABORATORY TECHNIQUES.

O

OFF-LINE ANALYSIS IN ANIMAL CELL CULTURE, METHODS

Heino Büntemeyer
Institute of Cell Culture Technology
University of Bielefeld
Bielefeld, Germany

OUTLINE

INTRODUCTION

The cultivation of mammalian cells *in vitro* requires special environmental conditions. Except primary cells taken directly from an organ, cultured cells usually derive from immortal or immortalized cell lines. The cells may be genetically engineered or manipulated by transfection or fusion techniques. The behavior of this new cell depends very much on the origin of the basal cell line.

Whereas some requirements are general for every cell, others can be very special for one cell line. All cells need isotonic conditions of about 300 mosmol/kg. Usually the cells need oxygen and a carbon source (mostly glucose), too. As the cells cannot synthesize the essential amino acids and vitamins, they have to be supplied. Some additional components may basically not be needed for surveillance, but they can support the cells to optimize cell growth and productivity. This knowledge leads to complex media formulations that seldom contain less than 40 different components. During optimization of culture conditions and process strategies a detailed analysis of the nutrient requirements has to be performed. Many different analysis methods have to be established in a laboratory to comply with this extensive task.

In this article methods for almost all media compounds are described. All methods, which are described in detail in this article, were developed, adapted, or checked in the laboratory for suitability of analysis of cell culture media and supernatants. They should be easily transferable to similar laboratory conditions. In this article the methods for the analysis of proteins are only very briefly described. For each protein special conditions and methods may apply. In general, the characterization of proteins includes a variety of steps. Methods for the analysis of amino acid sequence, glycosylation, molecular weight, heterogeneity, and activity have to be employed. A description of all these procedures would be beyond the scope of this article. For this reason protein separation methods such as electrophoresis and protein and peptide chromatography are not included here.

For almost all suppliers of special equipment or chemicals cited here, a listing of the home pages (World Wide Web) can be found at the end of this article. All other products may be delivered by local suppliers. When a method is described in detail, an equivalent apparatus of another supplier may also be suitable.

Composition of Cell Culture Media

Cell culture media contain a multitude of components. In most cases a complete medium consists of a chemically well-defined basal medium with additions of more or less defined additives. The basal medium contains low-molecular-weight substances such as inorganic ions, amino acids, vitamins, and some other components (e.g., glucose, pyruvate, etc.). In Table 1 the formulations of the three main basal media are listed. All three media contain roughly the same substances. Differences can be found in the individual concentrations. Often some low-molecular-weight compounds like ethanolamine, diaminobutane, selene dioxide, glutathione, taurine, ascorbic acid, fatty acids, cholesterol, etc. are added to support the cells for distinct biochemical pathways. Particularly for continuous and high-density processes the concentrations of the main nutrients (glucose and amino acids) are elevated. Usually, even an enriched basal medium is not suitable for the growth of mammalian cells *in vitro*. High-molecular-weight supplements, in particular proteins, have to be added to fulfill the requirements of the cells. Besides proteins, these supplements may also contain peptides, lipoproteins, phospholipids, or lipids. Often it is necessary to use serum or serum substitutes as an additive to the basal medium, especially during development and establishment of new cell lines when the behavior and the requirements of the new cells are not known. The function of some of the proteins is known. Insulin stimulates glucose metabolism; transferrin is the carrier for iron ions and possibly other trace elements. Albumin acts as an adsorbent for free lipids and toxic pollutions. Lipoproteins supply the cells with cholesterol and fatty acids. All in all, mammalian cells *in vitro* require a complex medium, which consists of many chemically different components.

Table 1. List of Ingredients for the Three Basal Cell Culture Media DMEM, Ham's F12, and RPMI 1640

Substance	DMEM (mg/L)	HAM F12 (mg/L)	RPMI 1640 (mg/L)
Inorganic salts			
$Ca(NO_3)_2 \cdot 4\,H_2O$	—	—	100.00
$CaCl_2$ (anhyd.)	200.00	33.22	—
$CuSO_4 \cdot 5\,H_2O$	—	0.003	—
$FeSO_4 \cdot 7\,H_2O$	—	0.834	—
$Fe(NO_3)_2 \cdot 9\,H_2O$	0.10	—	—
KCl	400.00	223.60	400.00
$MgSO_4$ (anhyd.)	97.67	57.22	48.84
NaCl	6400.00	7599.00	6000.00
$NaHCO_3$	3700.00	1176.00	2000.00
Na_2HPO_4 (anhyd.)	—	142.04	800.00
$ZnSO_4 \cdot 7\,H_2O$	—	0.863	—
Other components			
Glucose	4500.00	1802.00	2000.00
Phenol red	15.00	1.20	5.00
Na-pyruvate	—	110.00	—
Hypoxanthine (Na salt)	—	4.77	—
Thymidine	—	0.73	—
Linolic acid	—	0.084	—
Liponic acid	—	0.21	—
Putrescine $\cdot$ 2 HCl	—	0.161	—
Glutathione	—	—	1.00
Amino acids			
Alanine	—	8.90	—
Arginine $\cdot$ HCl	84.00	211.00	241.86
Asparagine	—	15.01	50.00
Aspartic acid	—	13.30	20.00
Cysteine $HCl \cdot H_2O$	—	35.12	—
Cystine $\cdot$ 2 H_2O	62.75	—	65.15
Glutamic acid	—	14.70	20.00
Glutamine	584.00	146.00	300.00
Glycine	30.00	7.50	10.00
Histidine $HCl \cdot H_2O$	42.00	20.96	15.00
Hydroxyproline	—	—	20.00
Isoleucine	105.00	3.94	50.00
Leucine	105.00	13.10	50.00
Lysine $\cdot$ HCl	146.00	36.50	40.00
Methionine	30.00	4.48	15.00
Phenylalanine	66.00	4.96	15.00
Proline	—	34.50	20.00
Serine	42.00	10.50	30.00
Threonine	95.00	11.90	20.00
Tryptophan	16.00	2.04	5.00
Tyrosine (Na_2 salt)	104.20	7.81	28.94
Valine	94.00	11.70	20.00
Vitamins			
Biotin	—	0.007	0.20
Ca-pantothenate	4.00	0.48	0.25
Choline chloride	4.00	13.96	3.00
Folic acid	4.00	1.30	1.00
i-Inositol	7.20	18.00	35.00
Nicotin amide	4.00	0.037	1.00
Pyridoxine HCl	—	0.062	—
Pyridoxal HCl	4.00	—	1.00
Riboflavin	0.40	0.038	0.20
Thiamine HCl	4.00	0.34	1.00
Vitamin B_{12}	—	1.36	0.005
p-Aminobenzoic acid	—	—	1.00

Source: Cell Culture Catalogue, Life Technologies, Paisley, UK.

ANALYSIS OF CELL DENSITY

The determination of cell numbers is the main task during monitoring of cultivation progress. Besides total cell number, the ratio of viable and dead cells is also of particular interest. Methods using cell staining and optical means are faced methods measuring particle size or volume.

Cell Density Determination by Cell Staining

The most common method of cell staining is the trypan blue exclusion method. A cell suspension is mixed with a 0.4% trypan blue solution (isotonic, 0.81% sodium chloride, 0.06% potassium dihydrogen phosphate) and placed in a calibrated hemocytometer chamber (Neubauer chamber). Anchorage-dependent cells have to be removed from the surface prior to the staining procedure. For this removal the cells are incubated with a trypsin solution for some minutes. The cells are manually counted by using a phase-contrast microscope at a magnification of 100–400 times. The dye cannot pass the intact cell membrane. Therefore, viable cells are not stained. Dead cells are dyed blue. From cell count and calibrated chamber size the cell density and viability can be calculated.

In some special cases a direct cell counting is impossible. When the cells grow in aggregates (spheroids) or inside of macroporous carriers a representative aliquot cannot be taken to ensure correct counting. In those cases it may be useful to lyse the cells and stain the nucleus. For this purpose a cell pellet is resuspended in a crystal violet solution (0.08% crystal violet in 0.1 M citrate) and incubated at 37 °C for at least 3 h. Afterwards the nuclei can be counted microscopically using a hemocytometer chamber.

Cell Density Examination System, CeDeX2

An improvement in the cell staining method has been made recently in regard to automation procedures. The CeDeX2 system (Innovatis) consists of three functional units: the liquid management, the image capture optics, and the data processing system containing the user interface. The main parts of the liquid handling system are a syringe drive module, a modular valve positioner, and the flow chamber. The sample is picked from the sample port, stained by trypan blue, and pumped gradually through the flow chamber to take the images. Afterwards the system cleans and prepares itself automatically for the next analysis. The analyzed sample volume is constant and determined by the depth of the standardized flow chamber and the image region being processed. The sample image, also presented in the user interface, is similar to that obtained by manual sample analysis.

The detection and differentiation of viable and dead cells is carried out by software that considers the special demands of microscopic image analysis. First, the algorithm detects the cells and distinguishes them from other objects like cell debris. Once the cells are identified, they are differentiated into viable and dead cells according to their grade of staining. On user request the diameter spectrum and eccentricity histogram are presented. In addition to the cell densities and viability, these parameters are helpful to assess the condition of the culture. The liquid handling system together with the simple and effective user interface guarantees easy handling. User-independent results are achieved by the high degree of automation. The analysis process is based directly on the two-dimensional information of the cells. Therefore, much more precise and reliable results are obtained than from other methods using one single, indirect parameter.

Coulter Particle Counter

The Coulter method (Beckman Coulter) of sizing and counting particles is based on measurable changes in electrical resistance produced by nonconductive particles suspended in an electrolyte. A small opening (aperture) between anode and cathode is the sensing zone through which suspended particles pass. In the sensing zone each particle displaces its own volume of electrolyte. The volume displaced is measured as a voltage pulse. The height of each pulse is proportional to the volume of the particle, independent of shape, color, and density of the particle. The quantity of suspension drawn through the aperture is controlled to allow exact counting and sizing of particles for a reproducible volume. A differentiation between viable and dead cells can only be performed by examination of the particle (cell) size.

CASY® Particle Counter

The CASY® particle counter (Schärfe System) system combines the established resistance measuring principle with the pulse area signal processing method. This allows a very high dynamic range, high resolution, and excellent reproducibility for the volume determination. The cells are suspended in a weak electrolyte and driven through a capillary of predefined geometry at a constant stream velocity. Electricity is supplied to the capillary across two platinum electrodes. While passing through the capillary, the cell displaces an amount of electrolyte equal to its own volume. This change in resistance level becomes an indication of cell volume. The measuring signal is scanned by the system at a frequency of 1 MHz. The amplitude and width of the pulse is captured and the integral is determined (pulse area analysis). These integrals are stored for each particle. A size distribution over all particles is computed in a resolution of 1024 channels from the stored pulse area values (integrals) (1). Viable and dead cells can only be differentiated by their cell volume/size. The size ranges for viable and dead cells may vary from cell line to cell line. An adjustment has to be made by the analyst to compare the data.

ANALYSIS OF MEDIUM COMPONENTS

Analysis of Nutrients

Glucose. Glucose is the main nutrient for almost all mammalian cells. Therefore, the quantitative determination of the glucose concentration is very important. There are a multitude of established chemical and biochemical methods. Not all of them can be employed for a direct quantification in a complex mixture like cell culture medium. Only a specific method that is insensitive to interference with other compounds can be used. All common methods use enzymes as specific agent. Two of the most often employed determination methods will now be described.

Photometric Glucose Assay. D-Glucose is converted in the presence of ATP by the enzyme hexokinase to D-glucose-6-phosphate. This product is then converted by the second enzyme glucose-6-phosphate-dehydrogenase in the presence of $NADP^+$ to D-gluconate-6-phosphate. During this last reaction NADPH is formed. The concentration of NADPH can be easily monitored at a wavelength of 340 nm. The concentrations of produced NADPH and assayed glucose are proportional.

$$\text{D-glucose} + \text{ATP} \xrightarrow{\text{hexokinase}} \text{D-glucose-6-P} + \text{ADP}$$

$$\text{D-glucose-6-P} + NADP^+ \xrightarrow{\substack{\text{glucose-6-phosphate-} \\ \text{dehydrogenase}}} \text{D-gluconate-6-P} + NADPH + H^+$$

This assay test kit (e.g., Roche Diagnostics, former Boehringer Mannheim) (2) is desired to be used in a cuvette UV spectrophotometer and needs no further laboratory equipment. The method can be recommended when only few or sporadic measurements are necessary. Otherwise, the analysis is too time consuming and labor intensive. In that case, the acquisition of an automatic analyzer should be considered.

Enzyme Electrode-Based Biosensor. For such a biosensor (e.g., Model YSI 2700, Yellow Springs Instrument Co Inc.) (3), the enzyme electrode consists of an amperometric hydrogen peroxide sensitive electrode combined with immobilized glucose oxidase trapped between synthetic membranes (4). The electrode itself consists of a platinum anode and a Ag/AgCl cathode. The platinum anode is polarized at +700 mV relative to the cathode. At the electrodes, a current results from decomposition of hydrogen peroxide to water and oxygen. The membrane covering the electrodes consists of three layers (Fig. 1). The outer layer, made of polycarbonate, is in direct contact with the sample. The next layer is the immobilized glucose oxidase enzyme followed by a cellulose acetate membrane that readily passes H_2O_2 but excludes chemical compounds with a molecular weight above approximately 200 Da. This last cellulose acetate film also protects the electrode from fouling caused by proteins, detergents, lipids, and other substances. After applying a sample containing glucose, a dynamic equilibrium is achieved very rapidly, when the rate of peroxide production and peroxide diffusion to the electrode is equivalent, indicated by a steady-state current response from the electrode. The current is proportional to the hydrogen peroxide conversion and the glucose oxidation (reactions):

$$\text{D-glucose} + O_2 \xrightarrow{\text{glucoseoxidase}} \text{glucono-}\delta\text{-lactone} + H_2O_2$$

$$H_2O_2 \xrightarrow{\text{Pt anode}} 2H^+ + O_2 + 2e^-$$

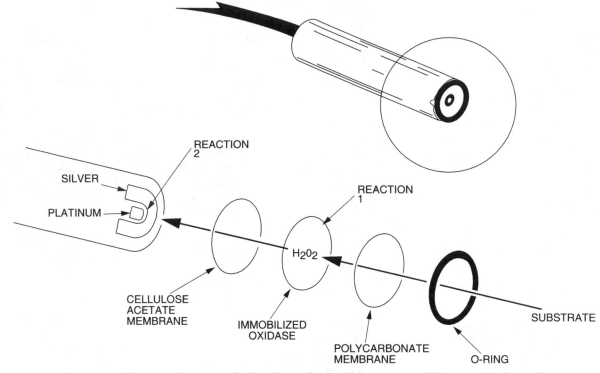

Figure 1. Schematic drawing of the glucose/lactate biosensor of YSI 2700 Biochemical Analyzer (reproduced from Operations Manual YSI 2700 Biochemical Analyzer, Yellow Springs Instruments).

The enzyme electrode is placed in a small chamber in an automatic system (YSI 2700). Calibration and maintenance procedures are performed routinely by a liquid handling system. The sample volume needed is a typically 25 μL (5–65 μL, adjustable), and the minimal sample glucose concentration is 0.05–0.1 g/L. The analysis of one sample lasts about 1 min. The sample can be applied without any prior preparation. Nevertheless, a removal of cells (e.g., by centrifugation) is strongly recommended in order to prolong the stability of the enzyme membrane. The membrane, once placed on the electrode, normally runs stable for some weeks. All in all, this method (and the apparatus) is a reliable glucose quantification method that can be recommended when a variable number of samples have to be analyzed daily.

Amino Acids. Besides glucose the amino acids are the major group of medium compounds from which cells generate energy and carbon. The amino acids can be divided into two groups, essential and nonessential amino acids. This classification comes from a gradation made for animals and human beings. This might not be completely valid for mammalian cells cultured *in vitro*. Dependent on donor and organ origin of each cell line, one or more amino acids formerly classified as nonessential might also be essential. Therefore, almost all amino acids are present in the defined basal medium formulations (Table 1), some in high and some in low concentrations. The amino acid with the highest medium concentration is glutamine, classified as a nonessential amino acid. For all cell lines that do not express the glutamine synthetase

gene, glutamine is essential. The cells can convert glutamine to α-ketoglutarate, which is introduced directly into the TCA cycle.

From a chemical point of view the amino acids are a very heterogeneous group of chemicals. Aliphatic, aromatic, polar, nonpolar, acidic, basic, and cyclic amino acids are present. Common to all acids are the carboxy and the primary (except proline and hydroxyproline) amino groups at the α-carbon. Except the three aromatic amino acids phenylalanine, tyrosine, and tryptophan, all other amino acids cannot be reasonably detected by spectrophotometrical means. An analysis method capable of quantification of all amino acids usually includes a separation procedure and a derivatization procedure to introduce a detectable group to the amino acid molecule.

A multitude of methods have been developed using different derivatization reagents and chromatographic separation techniques. Two principles have been established: the precolumn and the postcolumn derivatization techniques. In the precolumn method the amino acids are chemically modified first to introduce a chromophore or a fluorophore. The derivatization products are then separated on a chromatographic column and detected by an optical detector (spectrophotometer, fluorimeter). Usually an aromatic group is introduced to the amino acid molecule. The derivatives can be separated on a reversed-phase column and monitored with an UV or fluorescence detector. In the postcolumn method the amino acids are separated first on an ion exchange column and then modified just before detection. Almost every derivatization procedure modifies the amino acid at the amino group that is much more reactive in an aqueous solution, especially at alkaline pH. In this article only the most important and commonly used methods are described in more detail.

Ninhydrin Method. This method is the only commonly used postcolumn derivatization method (5,6). The amino acids are separated on specially developed cation exchange columns (heated to temperatures of 40–70 °C) by eluting stepwise with five different acidic lithium citrate buffers (also containing methanol and phenol) at a pH of 2.5–5.0. At the end of the column the elution stream is merged with the ninhydrin reagent (20 g ninhydrin, 1.7 g hydrindantin in 65% dimethylsulfoxide, 35% 4 M lithium acetate buffer), passed through a reaction coil ($T = 90$–120 °C) and applied to a VIS detector. Chromatograms are taken at wavelengths of 570 and 440 nm. Ninhydrin reacts under these conditions with all primary amino groups to form a dye that can be detected best at 570 nm. During this reaction only the amino group stays as part of the dye molecule (Ruhemann's purple). Secondary amino groups (proline, hydroxyproline) form other derivatives (yellow chromophores) than primary amino groups. These derivatives are detectable best at 440 nm. Although almost all biogenic amines and amino acids can be detected with this method, it is being replaced more and more by precolumn derivatization methods because of its very long analyzing time, more than 2 hours, the unstable ninhydrin reagent, and the toxic and corrosive elution buffers.

o-Phthaldialdehyde Method. Primary amino groups react at alkaline pH in the presence of selected thiol compounds with *o*-phthaldialdehyde (OPA) to form unstable isoindoles. These isoindoles can be immediately separated on C_{18} (ODS)–reversed-phase columns and detected with a fluorescence detector (7,8). The reaction is:

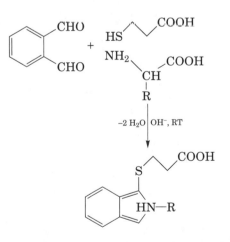

Dependent on the thiol used, the resulting derivative is more or less hydrophobic. Therefore, different elution buffers and profiles have to be used. The more hydrophilic the thiol is, the less hydrophobic the elution buffers can be. The following thiols were tested: 2-mercaptoethanol, mercaptoacetic acid, 2-mercaptopropionic acid, and 3-mercaptopropionic acid. Good fluorescence yields can only be achieved when using 2-mercaptoethanol or 3-mercaptopropionic acid.

Only primary amino groups of amino acids and amines can react with *o*-phthaldialdehyde. Secondary amino groups will not be modified. Therefore, proline and hydroxyproline cannot be analyzed. Furthermore, cysteine and cystine give only very poor fluorescent derivatives that are not quantitatively detectable. To overcome this last hint, it is possible to oxidize cysteine and cystine with a mild oxidant like jodoacetic acid to cysteic acid prior to OPA derivatization. The OPA derivative of cysteic acid is very well detectable. The reagent OPA itself is not fluorescent and produces no interfering signals.

Procedure: The complete analysis of amino acid in samples from cell cultures is performed with an automated HPLC system (Kontron Instruments). A programmable autosampler first mixes the prepared sample with the reagent mixture (OPA reagent) and then injects an aliquot onto a C_{18}-reversed-phase HPLC column after a reaction time of 1.5 min. The OPA derivatives are eluted in a binary gradient in less than 30 min and passed through a fluorescence detector. Data recording, evaluation, calculation, and device control is done with chromatography software (KromaSystem 2000, Kontron). A detailed description of this method follows.

Sample preparation: Cell-free supernatant is mixed 1:1 with 5% HCO_4 containing 300 µM of δ-amino-*n*-valeric acid as an internal standard. The mixture is centrifuged for 5 min to remove the precipitated proteins. An aliquot is mixed with two aliquots of 0.4 M sodium borate buffer pH 10.4 to alkalize and dilute the sample.

Derivatization: 20 µL of the prepared sample is filled into a sampler vial. The sampler (AS 465, Kontron) mixes with 70 µL of reagent (50 mg *o*-phthaldialdehyde, 1 mL methanol, 100 µL 3-mercaptopropionic acid, 9 mL 0.6 M sodium borate buffer, pH 10.4) and injects 20 µL onto the column after 1.5 min reaction time.

Elution: The mixture is separated on a C_{18}-reversed-phase column (Ultrasphere ODS, 5 µ, 4.6 × 150 mm, Beckman Coulter, Inc.) with a multistep binary gradient in less than 30 min. The column temperature is set to 27 °C. Buffer A consists of 0.085 M sodium acetate, pH 7.5, 1% tetrahydrofurane. Buffer B is a mixture of 70% methanol and 30% 0.085 M sodium acetate, pH 5.2. Total flow is set to 1.3 mL/min for the first 13 min after injection and to 2.2 mL/min for the rest of the analysis. The gradient is set as follows: 5% B at time 0, linear increase to 25% B in 15 min, linear increase to 51% B in 1 min, hold 51% B for 6 min, linear increase to 70% B in 1 min, hold 70% B for 3 min, linear increase to 85% B in 0.5 min, hold 85% B for 3 min.

Detection: The OPA derivatives are detected with a fluorescence detector (SFM 25, Kontron) set to excitation and emission wavelengths of 330 and 450 nm, respectively.

Figure 2 shows an example chromatogram obtained for a standard mixture. All amino acids are baseline separated and can be quantified by peak area integration.

Phenylisothiocyanate Method. Phenylisothiocyanate (PITC) reacts under alkaline conditions with both primary and secondary amino groups (Edman reaction). The derivatives can be separated on C_{18} (ODS)–reversed phase columns and detected with a UV detector at 254 nm (9). The reaction is:

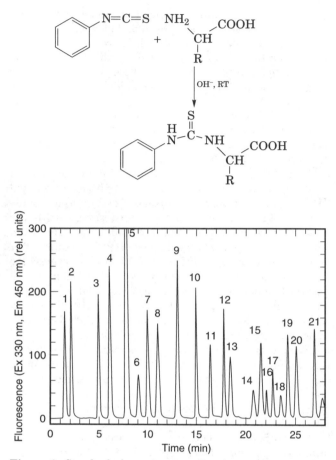

Figure 2. Standard chromatogram of amino acids processing the OPA method. Separation conditions apply as described in the text. List of amino acids: (1) aspartic acid, (2) glutamic acid, (3) asparagine, (4) serine, (5) glutamine, (6) histidine, (7) glycine, (8) threonine, (9) arginine, (10) alanine, (11) tyrosine, (12) ethanolamine, (13) δ-amino-n-valeric acid (internal standard), (14) methionine, (15) valine, (16) tryptophan, (17) phenylalanine, (18) by-product, (19) isoleucine, (20) leucine, (21) lysine.

The method of sample preparation and derivatization follows a stringent procedure that involves many labor-intensive stages and cannot be completely automated. An improvement was made by introducing the Pico Taq system (Waters), a semiautomatic apparatus to perform the drying and derivatization of the sample (10,11). However, the resulting phenylthiocarbamyl derivatives are very stable and easy to handle.

Procedure: The analysis of samples from cell cultures is done with an automated HPLC system (Kontron). An autosampler injects an aliquot of the prepared sample onto a C_{18}-reversed-phase HPLC column. The PITC derivatives are eluted in a binary gradient in less than 50 min and passed through a UV detector. Data recording, evaluation, calculation, and device control is done with chromatography software (KromaSystem 2000, Kontron). A detailed description of this method follows.

Sample preparation: Cell-free supernatant is mixed 1 : 1 with an internal standard solution of 300 µM norleucine. An aliquot of 100 µL is lyophilized with a vacuum concentrator.

Derivatization: 20 µL of mixture 1 (2 : 1 : 1 methanol: water:triethylamine) is added to the lyophilizate, vortexed, and dried again. For derivatization 20 µL of mixture 2 (7 : 1 : 1 : 1 methanol:water:triethylamine:PITC) is added and mixed during a reaction time of 20 min at room temperature (22 °C). The mixture is lyophilized again to remove excess PITC. The lyophilizate is dissolved in 100 µL elution buffer A, and 40 µL is injected onto the column.

Elution: The mixture is separated on a C_{18}-reversed-phase column (ODS Hypersil, 5 µ, 4.6 × 250 mm, Hypersil) with a multistep binary gradient in less than 50 min. The temperature of the column is set to 39.5 °C by use of a water bath. Buffer A consists of 98% 0.085 M sodium acetate, pH 5.2, 2% acetonitrile. Buffer B is a mixture of 70% acetonitrile and 30% 0.085 M sodium acetate, pH 5.2. The total flow is set to 1.4 mL/min. The gradient is set as follows: 2% B at time 0, hold 2% for 9 min, linear increase to 4% B in 1 min, linear increase to 10% B in 10 min, linear increase to 25% B in 9 min, linear increase to 31% B in 8 min, linear increase to 90% B in 3 min, hold 90% B for 4 min.

Detection: The PITC derivatives are detected with a UV detector (D 430, Kontron) set to a wavelength of 254 nm.

Figure 3 shows an example chromatogram obtained for a standard mixture. All amino acids are baseline separated and can be quantified by peak area integration.

FMOC Method. FMOC (9-fluorenylmethoxycarbonyl-chloride) reacts with both primary and secondary amino groups. Due to the introduction of the large hydrophobic fluorenylmethyl group, the derivatives can already be separated on a C_8-reversed-phase column. Detection is done with a fluorescence detector at excitation and emission wavelengths of 260 and 310 nm, respectively. The reaction is:

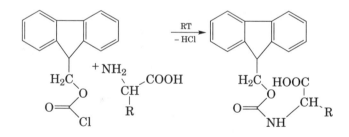

FMOC offers a sensitivity comparable to the OPA method when used with fluorescence detection. But FMOC and its hydrolysis products have similar fluorescence spectra to the FMOC amino acids. Excess FMOC remaining after derivatization reacts with water to form FMOC-OH (9-fluorenylmethylalcohol), which elutes as a large broad peak. Removal of FMOC-OH can be achieved by liquid–liquid extraction into pentane. A more elegant method of preventing interference of FMOC-OH is to react excess FMOC with a very hydrophobic amine (e.g., aminoadamantane) to form a derivative that elutes after all amino acids.

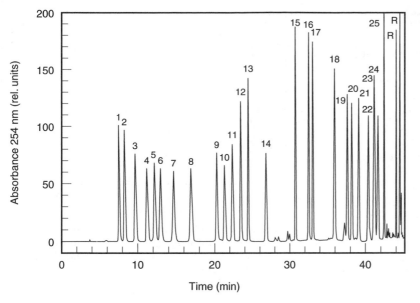

Figure 3. Separation of standard mixture amino acids using the PITC method. Amino acids identified as follows: (1) aspartic acid, (2) hydroxyproline, (3) glutamic acid, (4) serine, (5) asparagine, (6) glycine, (7) glutamine, (8) taurine, (9) histidine, (10) threonine, (11) alanine, (12) arginine, (13) proline, (14) ethanolamine, (15) tyrosine, (16) valine, (17) methionine, (18) cytine, (19) isoleucine, (20) leucine, (21) norleucine (internal standard), (22) phenylalanine, (23) ornithine, (24) tryptophan, (25) lysine, (R) reagent.

Analysis of other Ingredients

Pyruvate. Pyruvate is the end product of aerobic glycolysis. At this point it can undergo several reactions, especially oxidative decarboxylation to produce acetyl-CoA or reduction to lactate (the end product of anaerobic metabolism). Although free pyruvate is consumed by mammalian cells rapidly, probably to bypass glycolysis, no significant effect on cell growth and productivity was reported. Nevertheless, some basal medium formulations (e.g., F12) already contain pyruvate in a concentration of 1 or 2 mM.

The determination of pyruvate cannot be performed without any molecular modification, since no chromophore is present, except when employing an enzyme assay (using lactate dehydrogenase). On the other hand, pyruvate possesses an α-keto group that is reactive enough to react with primary amines under aqueous conditions. With o-phenylendiamine (OPD) (12) or 1,2-diamino-4,5-dimethoxybenzene (13) fluorescent products (2-quinoxalinol derivatives) are formed that can be separated on reversed-phase columns and detected in a fluorescence detector. The reaction is:

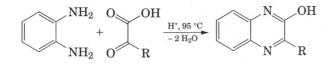

Procedure: The analysis of pyruvate in samples from cell cultures is performed with an automated HPLC system (Kontron Instruments). The OPD derivatives are eluted in a binary gradient in less than 20 min and passed through a fluorescence detector. Data recording, evaluation, calculation, and device control is carried out by chromatography software (KromaSystem 2000, Kontron).

Sample preparation: Cell-free supernatant is mixed 1:1 with 3% $HClO_4$ containing α-ketoglutarate as an internal standard. The mixture is centrifuged for 5 min to remove the precipitated proteins.

Derivatization: 50 μL of prepared sample is mixed with 500 μL of the OPD reagent (0.1 g o-phenylendiamine and 250 μL 2-mercaptoethanol in 100 mM 2 N hydrochloric acid) and derivatized for 2 hours at 95 °C. After cooling, 100 μL of the solution is mixed with 100 μL of 0.4 M sodium borate buffer pH 9.5 and 20 μL is injected onto the column.

Elution: The mixture is separated on a C_{18}-reversed-phase column (Ultrasphere ODS, 5 μ, 4.6 × 150 mm, Beckman Coulter, Inc.) with a binary gradient in less than 20 min. The column temperature is set to 27 °C. Buffer A consists of 0.085 M sodium acetate pH 7.5, 1% tetrahydrofurane. Buffer B is a mixture of 70% methanol and 30% 0.085 M sodium acetate, pH 5.2. Total flow is set to 1.0 mL/min. The gradient is set as follows: 20% B at time 0, linear increase to 100% B in 9 min, hold 100% B for 4 min.

Detection: The OPD derivatives are detected with a fluorescence detector (SFM 25, Kontron) set to excitation and emission wavelengths of 340 and 412 nm, respectively.

Inorganic Salts. Cell culture media contain inorganic cations and anions. The predominant salt in the medium is sodium chloride in a concentration of 6–7.5 g/L. This high concentration is necessary to maintain an osmotic pressure of about 300 mosmol/kg to ensure isotonic conditions for the cells. Besides sodium, only potassium, magnesium, and calcium cations are present in considerable concentrations. Sulfate, phosphate, and nitrate are the anions along with chloride. Some trace elements like iron, zinc, copper, and selenium, each in a very low concentration, may also be present. Sodium bicarbonate/carbondioxide is usually the main pH buffer of the medium.

Ionic substances including inorganic cations and anions can be well separated by ion-exchange chromatography. The separated ions can easily be detected by using a conductivity detector, if the ion concentration is high enough to compensate the poor sensitivity. Conductivity detection is not suitable for the detection of trace elements. In that case methods like mass spectrometry (ICP-MS) or atomic absorption spectroscopy may apply.

Procedure: The ion separation can be performed with an ion chromatograph (e.g., Dionex, Metrohm) or an HPLC system equipped with a conductivity detector (ICM300, Kontron). The temperatures of the column and the flow cell of the detector have to be monitored constantly, since conductivity is extremely temperature sensitive.

Sample preparation: Cell-free supernatant is mixed with an internal standard (e.g., cesium bromide) and filtered (0.45 μm). The mixture has to be diluted with ion-free water to meet the detection range (e.g., 1 : 100).

Cation Separation. Inorganic cations can be separated on a cation exchange column (IC Cation SuperSep (silica, polybutadiene–malic acid), 125 mm × 4.0 mm, Metrohm) and eluted isocratically with a buffer consisting of 4 mM tartaric acid and 0.7 mM pyridine-2,6-dicarboxylic acid in less than 20 min. The column temperature is set to 30 °C; total flow is set to 1.0 mL/min. A chromatogram obtained under these conditions is shown in Figure 4.

Anion Separation. The anions are separated on a anion exchange column (Anion/R [polystyrene, $N(CH_3)^{3+}$], 10 μ, 0, 19 meq/g, 250 mm × 4.1 mm, Alltech) and eluted with 5 mM p-hydroxybenzoic acid, pH 8.5 (adjusted with LiOH) in 30 min. The column temperature and total flow are set to 30 °C and 2.5 mL/min, respectively. Figure 5 shows an example of a chromatogram.

Vitamins. Cell culture basal media contain about ten different vitamins and precursors (Table 1). Sometimes special media recipes contain additional vitamins or provitamins such as vitamin C (ascorbic acid), retinoic acid (vitamin A acid), or E (α-tocopherol). From a chemical point of view the group of vitamins is an extremely heterogeneous collection of substances with different chemical properties. Most of the vitamins are water soluble, but some are only fat soluble. A uniform analysis method cannot be achieved. A second problem for the determination derives from the very low concentrations, generally far below 10 mg/L. Nevertheless, the knowledge of vitamin requirements during cell cultivation (especially

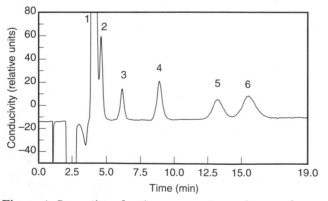

Figure 4. Separation of cations on a cation exchange column. Cell culture basal medium was diluted 1 : 100 prior injection. Identified cations are (1) sodium, (2) ammonium, (3) potassium, (4) cesium (internal standard), (5) calcium, (6) magnesium.

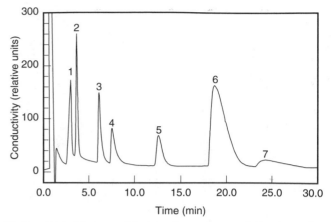

Figure 5. Anion separation by anion exchange chromatography. Separated anions of 1 : 100 prediluted basal medium are identified as follows: (1) bicarbonate, (2) chloride, (3) bromide, (4) nitrate, (5) phosphate, (6) sulfate, (7) iodide.

long-term and high-density cultures) may improve cell growth and productivity.

Analysis of vitamins is often performed in the food industry for quality control of multivitamin preparations, juices, engineered food, and other materials (14). In general, the vitamin concentrations in these matrices are much higher than in culture medium. However, some progress has been made in adapting methods for the analysis of certain vitamins to cell culture conditions. In the following, determination methods for some vitamins are described that have been recently developed in our laboratory.

Pantothenate. Pantothenate, a member of the vitamin B_2 group, is a dipeptide formed from 2,4-dihydroxy-3,3-dimethylbutyric acid and β-alanine. In conjunction with cysteamine, adenosine, and diphosphate, pantothenate forms the coenzyme A.

The pantothenate molecule contains no chromophore or fluorophore. An analysis method was developed using a refractometer as detector (15). The low concentration in medium in a range of 0.4 to 4 mg/L and the many other medium ingredients make the use of such a detection method impossible. A more promising alternative seems to be an acidic hydrolysis with later analysis of the released β-alanine. The β-amino acid β-alanine can be derivatized with one of the reagents described in the amino acid section. The second product of the hydrolysis is pantolactone. Pantolactone may be analyzed by gas chromatography after liquid–liquid extraction from the hydrolysis mixture using dichloromethane as organic solvent.

Procedure: The quantification of β-alanine after hydrolysis of pantothenate can be carried out with an HPLC system.

Sample preparation: 100 μL of sample and 200 μL concentrated hydrochloric acid is boiled for 15 min in a water bath. The mixture is lyophilized in a vacuum concentrator and resolved in 100 μL of 0.4 M sodium borate buffer, pH 9.5.

Derivatization: 40 μL of the prepared sample is filled into a sampler vial. The sampler mixes with 70 μL of reagent (50 mg o-phthaldialdehyde, 1 mL methanol, 100 μL 2-mercaptoethanol, 9 mL 0.6 M sodium borate buffer, pH 10.4) and injects 60 μL onto the column after 1.5 min reaction time.

Elution: The mixture is separated on a C_{18}-reversed-phase column (Ultrasphere ODS, 5 μ, 4.6 × 150 mm, Beckman Coulter, Inc.) with a multistep binary gradient in less than 20 min. The column temperature is set to 39.5 °C. Buffer A consists of 0.1 M sodium acetate pH 7.5, 1% tetrahydrofurane. Buffer B is a mixture of 70% methanol and 30% 0.1 M sodium acetate pH 5.2. Total flow is set to 1.8 mL/min. The gradient is set as follows: 25% B at time 0, linear increase to 50% B in 3 min, hold 50% B for 10 min, linear increase to 80% B in 1 min, hold 80% B for 4 min. This gradient has to be chosen to separate the β-alanine derivative from all other amino acid derivatives present in the sample at much higher concentrations.

Detection: The OPA derivatives are detected with a fluorescence detector (SFM 25, Kontron) set to excitation and emission wavelengths of 330 and 450 nm, respectively.

Riboflavin. Riboflavin (7,8-dimethyl-10-ribityl-isoalloxazin), a member of the vitamin B_2 group, is contained in prosthetic groups (FMN, FAD) of flavoproteins. Aerobic and anaerobic dehydrogenases often belong to the group of flavoproteins. Such enzymes are involved especially in the respiratory chain. The isoalloxazin structure in riboflavin acts in this context as a reversible redox system.

Riboflavin itself is fluorescent without any modification, and an analysis is easy when the concentration is high enough (16–18). Usually the riboflavin concentration in cell culture media is in a range of 0.04–0.4 mg/L, which is too low for direct measurement. But a tenfold concentration is sufficient for quantitative determination.

Procedure: The quantification of riboflavin can be performed with an HPLC system. Riboflavin is separated from contaminant substances on a C_{18} column and detected with a fluorescence detector.

Sample preparation: 1 mL of sample is lyophilized in a vacuum concentrator and resolved in 100 μL buffer.

Elution: The concentrated sample is injected onto a C_{18} reversed-phase column (Ultrasphere ODS, 5 μ, 4.6 × 150 mm, Beckman Coulter, Inc.) and eluted with a buffer consisting of 87% 0.01 M sodium acetate, pH 5.5, and 13% acetonitrile. Total flow is set to 2 mL/min.

Detection: Riboflavin is detected in a fluorescence detector (SFM25, Kontron) set to excitation and emission wavelengths of 436 and 535 nm, respectively. At these wavelengths only a low interference was observed.

Thiamine. Thiamine, vitamin B_1, is in its diphosphate form the prosthetic group of the enzyme decarboxylase–dehydrogenase, one of three units of a multienzyme complex performing the oxidative decarboxylation.

The thiamine concentration in cell culture media is in a range of 0.3 to 4 mg/L, which is sufficient for quantitative determination, if a sensitive detection method is used. Although thiamine contains a pyrimidine and thiazole ring in the molecule, a much more sensitive detection can be achieved when the thiazole ring is oxidized. The resulting thiochrome is fluorescent (19–21).

Procedure: The quantification of thiamine can be carried out with an HPLC system. Thiamine is oxidized by potassium hexacyanoferrate in alkaline solution to thiochrome. Thiochrome can be separated on a C_{18} column and detected with a fluorescence detector.

Sample preparation: 0.5 mL of sample is mixed with 0.5 mL of 1% $K_3Fe(CN)_6$ in 15% NaOH. After 45 sec the reaction is stopped by adding 75 μL phosphoric acid.

Elution: The reaction mixture is injected immediately onto a C_{18} reversed-phase column (Ultrasphere ODS, 5 μ, 4.6 × 150 mm, Beckman Coulter, Inc.) and eluted with a buffer consisting of 87% 0.01 M sodium acetate, pH 5.5, and 13% acetonitrile. Total flow is set to 1.2 mL/min.

Detection: Thiochrome is detected in a fluorescence detector (SFM25, Kontron) set to excitation and emission wavelengths of 364 and 436 nm, respectively.

Lipids. The cell membrane of mammalian cells consists basically of a lipid bilayer of phospholipids. The phospholipids (e.g., phosphatidyl choline, phosphatidyl ethanolamine, phosphatidyl serine) themselves are diesters of phosphoric acid with glycerine on one side and choline, ethanolamine, or serine on the other side. Glycerine is esterified at its two other hydroxyl groups with fatty acids. The fatty acids (saturated and unsaturated) can be synthesized by an enzyme complex (fatty acid synthetase complex) located in the cytosol starting from acetyl-CoA. Another main component of the cell membrane is the steroide cholesterol. It has a rigid structure and can strengthen the cell membrane if it is incorporated into the lipid bilayer. Cholesterol can also be synthesized from acetyl-CoA by another pathway.

Although the cells can prepare their lipids, special additives to basal cell culture media can contain fatty acids, cholesterol, and phospholipids to support the cell status. In medium additives like serum, lipoprotein mixtures, and protein/fatty acid mixtures these components may be included.

Fatty Acids. Fatty acids may be analyzed either by liquid or by gas chromatography. Generally present in low concentrations, a concentration step is necessary. This concentration can be carried out by liquid–liquid extraction with a lipophilic solvent and subsequent lyophilization.

Procedure: The lyophilized fatty acids can either be dissolved and applied directly to a gas chromatograph equipped with a special column or be derivatized prior to HPLC analysis (15). In each case the same sample preparation procedure may be used.

Sample preparation: 0.4 mL of sample, 10 μL internal standard solution (5 mM heptadecanoic acid), and 1 mL of extracting agent (Dole mixture; isopropanol/n-heptane/2 M phosphoric acid 40 : 10 : 1) are vortexed for 10 min. 0.4 mL n-heptane and 0.6 mL pure water are added and mixed again. 0.4 mL of the upper (organic) phase are taken and lyophilized.

GC analysis: The lyophilized fatty acids are dissolved in n-heptane, dried with sodium sulfate, and applied to the gas chromatograph. The gas chromatograph (e.g., CP9000, Chrompack) may be equipped with a split injector, a flame ionization detector (FID), and a polar capillary column (e.g., FFAP-CB, 25 m, Chrompack). The temperatures of injector and detector are both set to 300 °C. The fatty acids elute at temperatures of 200–270 °C.

HPLC analysis: Before injection the fatty acids have to be derivatized to add a chromphore. The lyophilized fatty acids are dissolved in 200 µL acetonitrile. 12 µL of reagent (50 mM p-bromophenacylbromide, 5 mM 18-crown-6) and 1 mg $KHCO_3$ are added and held for 45 min at 85 °C. The fatty acid derivatives can be separated on a C_6-reversed-phase column (Spherisorb Hexyl, 5 µ, 125 × 4.6 mm, Bischoff) by binary gradient elution in less than 30 min. Solvent A consists of 50% acetonitrile, 50% water, and solvent B of 90% acetonitrile, 10% water. The total flow is set to 1.3 mL/min. The gradient is set as follows: 0% B at time 0, linear increase to 100% B in 30 min, hold 100% B for 2 min. Detection is carried out by UV absorption at 254 nm. Figure 6 shows an example chromatogram.

Cholesterol and Cholesteryl Esters. Cholesterol may be analyzed by gas chromatography. After liquid–liquid extraction from the aqueous sample with an organic solvent and subsequent lyophilization, it can be acetylated and chromatographed on a non polar column. Cholesteryl esters can be hydrolyzed prior to acetylation.

Procedure: The analysis of cholesterol acetate may be carried out with a normal gas chromatograph (e.g., CP9000, Chrompack) equipped with a split injector, an FID, and a non polar capillary column (e.g., CP-5-Sil CB, 10 m, Chrompack).

Sample preparation: 2 mL of sample are added to 2 mL of extracting agent (75% diisoproylether, 25% n-butanole) and mixed for 3 h in an end-over-end mixer. The non aqueous phase is taken and lyophilized. The cholesteryl esters can now be hydrolyzed with ethanolic KOH (0.6 mL 33% KOH, 9.4 mL ethanol) for 1 h at 60 °C. After neutralization (HCl) and extraction (hexane, three times) cholesterol can be derivatized.

Derivatization: The solvent (hexane) is removed and acetic anhydride is added. After 1 h at 100 °C the reaction is stopped by adding ice water. Cholesterol acetate is extracted into hexane (three times). The joined organic phases are washed with pure water and lyophilized afterwards.

Chromatography: The dried extract is dissolved in hexane, and an aliquot is applied to the gas chromatograph. The temperatures of injector and detector should be set to 270 and 300 °C, respectively. Cholesterol acetate elutes at a temperature of 240–270 °C. For improved reproducibility an internal standard (e.g., stigmasterol acetate) may be added early during sample preparation.

ANALYSIS OF METABOLIC END PRODUCTS

During metabolism of glucose, amino acids, and other compounds the cells also produce substances that are released into the surrounding medium. The main end products of metabolism are lactic acid (lactate) and ammonia. Both substances are known to affect cell viability and product formation. Therefore, it is necessary to monitor the concentrations in the culture supernatant to be able to maintain low concentrations by use of special means or process procedures.

Lactate. Lactate is the end product of anaerobic metabolism of glucose. Almost all cells *in vitro* produce lactate also under aerobic conditions. Lactate is formed from pyruvate by the enzyme lactate dehydrogenase. A maximum of two moles lactate can be produced from one mole glucose under completely anaerobic conditions. Additionally, lactate may also be synthesized by other pathways, especially amino acid metabolism. The two most common methods of lactate analysis are described in the following.

Photometric Lactate Assay. Lactate is converted in the presence of NAD^+ by the enzyme L-lactate dehydrogenase to pyruvate. During this reaction NADH is formed, which can be monitored at a wavelength of 340 nm. The reaction is reversible, and the equilibrium is more on the lactate side than on the pyruvate side. Therefore, pyruvate has to be removed. This can be achieved by adding the second enzyme, glutamate–pyruvate transaminase, which converts pyruvate in the presence of glutamate to alanine and 2-oxoglutarate. The assay (e.g., Roche Diagnostics) (22,23) is desired to be used in a cuvette UV spectrophotometer and needs no further laboratory equipment. The reactions are:

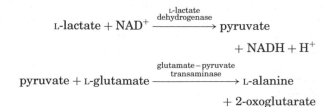

Enzyme Electrode-Based Biosensor. The principle of an enzyme electrode-based biosensor (e.g., Model YSI 2700, Yellow Springs Instrument Co. Inc.) (3) is already described in detail in the section on glucose analysis. In the case of lactate determination the immobilized enzyme

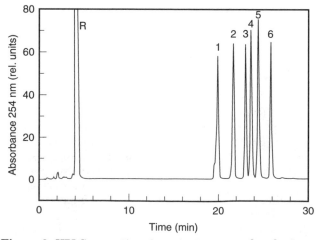

Figure 6. HPLC separation of standard mixture of predominant fatty acids. All conditions as described in the text. Identified fatty acids: (1) linolenic acid (18:3), (2) linoleic acid (18:2), (3) palmitic acid (16:0), (4) oleic acid (18:1), (5) heptadecanoic acid (17:0) (internal standard), (6) stearic acid (18:0), (R) reagent.

is lactate oxidase, which oxidizes lactate and generates hydrogen peroxide. The reactions are:

$$\text{L-lactate} + O_2 \xrightarrow{\text{lactate oxidase}} \text{pyruvate} + H_2O_2$$

$$H_2O_2 \xrightarrow{\text{Pt anode}} 2H^+ + O_2 + 2e^-$$

The YSI 2700 analyzer is capable of holding and maintaining two enzyme electrodes in its chamber. Therefore, from the same sample volume (25 µL) two determinations (e.g., glucose and lactate) can be made at the same time.

Ammonia. In animal cell culture, other than in mammals, ammonia is the main end product of nitrogen metabolism. Beside ammonia, alanine is also produced in a remarkable amount, while only little urea is secreted by the cells. Especially when high glutamine and other amino acid concentrations have to be used to supply the cells, an ammonia concentration of several millimolar can be found. High ammonia concentrations can affect cell growth, productivity, and product integrity very drastically. Several analytical methods have been used for the quantification of ammonia, including enzyme assay systems (e.g., Roche Diagnostics) (24,25), gas-sensitive electrodes (e.g., Mettler-Toledo), ion chromatography (e.g., Metrohm, Dionex), and derivatization. The methods are discussed in the following. Each of these methods have advantages and disadvantages.

Enzyme Assay. Due to the use of a special enzymatic reaction (glutamate dehydrogenase), the enzyme assay is highly specific for ammonia. The concentration of NADH can be easily monitored at a wavelength of 340 nm. The concentrations of reacted NADH and assayed ammonium are inversely proportional. The necessity of the coenzyme NADH and the consumption of enzyme makes this method a cost-intensive analysis procedure. The reaction is:

$$\text{2-oxoglutarate} + \text{NADH} + \text{NH}_4^+ \xrightarrow{\substack{\text{glutamate} \\ \text{dehydrogenase}}} \text{L-glutamate} + \text{NAD}^+ + H_2O$$

This assay test kit is desired to be used in a cuvette UV spectrophotometer and needs no further laboratory equipment. The method can be recommended when only a few or sporadic measurements are necessary.

Gas-Sensitive Ammonia Electrode. An ammonia electrode works by the principle that under alkaline conditions ammonia degasses from aqueous solutions, passes through a hydrophobic membrane (PTFE), and dissolves in an acidic solution, where the resulting pH shift can be measured and quantitatively evaluated. In most cases this is also a specific detection method. The main disadvantages are the size of the electrode and the fragile membrane adapter. Depending on the ammonia concentration in the sample and a predilution possibility, a sample volume of up to 10–20 mL may be necessary for analysis.

Procedure: 2 mL of cell-free sample are diluted with water to a volume of 20 mL. The ammonia electrode is placed into the solution. After obtaining a stable value,

0.5 mL of 10 M NaOH is added, and the highest value is registered.

Ion Chromatography. The ion chromatography analysis of ammonia is based on cation exchange chromatography (26) and conductivity detection. Due to the chemical similarity of ammonium and potassium cations and the high sodium concentration, a good resolution may be difficult to obtain. A small sample volume requirement and an automatic analysis procedure are advantages of this method, whereas the high equipment requirement (chromatography system) is the main disadvantage. For details please refer to the section on cation analysis.

Fluorescence Detection. o-Phthaldialdehyde reacts with primary amines, including ammonia, in the presence of mercaptoacetic acid (thioglycolic acid) at basic conditions to unstable, fluorescent isoindole derivatives (see also the section on amino acid analysis, OPA method). The reaction product is analogous to the products formed with 3-mercaptopropionic acid and amino acids, but its fluorescent property is quite different. Whereas the fluorescence intensity at excitation and emission wavelengths of of 330 and 450 nm (amino acids), respectively, is very poor, the fluorescence yield can be increased greatly by shifting to wavelengths of 415 and 485 nm, respectively. On the other hand, the fluorescence intensity of the amino acid derivatives is negligible at those wavelengths. Therefore, this method has good selectivity for ammonium quantification.

Procedure: The reagent is prepared by dissolving 1.85 mmole o-phthaldialdehyde and 4 mmole mercaptoacetic acid (thioglycolic acid) in 2 mL methanol and adding 100 mL 0.4 M sodium borate buffer, pH 10.4. The mixture can be stored at 4 °C in 10-mL aliquots. Before measurement one aliquot was allowed to reach room temperature (20 °C). The reaction is directly carried out in half-microquartz cuvettes by adding 1–1.3 mL reagent to 20 µL of cell-free sample. After a brief mixing the cuvette is immediately placed in a spectrofluorimeter (RF551, Shimadzu) set to excitation and emission wavelengths of 415 and 485 nm, respectively. The highest emission value is reached in approximately 1 min. This value is used for calculation.

Urea. Urea is the end product of nitrogen metabolism in mammals. Normally it is produced in the liver and secreted by the kidney into the urine. Cells *in vitro* are usually not able to synthesize urea. Therefore, the predicted urea concentration in the supernatant may be very low. On the other hand, a considerable amount of urea may be found in medium additives like serum or plasma.

Urea may be quantified by using a two-step enzyme assay (27,28). The reaction may be monitored by following the NADH conversion at 340 nm. The reaction is specific for urea, but the method is not very sensitive.

$$\text{urea} + H_2O \xrightarrow{\text{Urease}} 2\text{NH}_3 + CO_2$$

$$\text{2-oxoglutarate} + \text{NADH} + \text{NH}_4^+ \xrightarrow{\substack{\text{glutamate} \\ \text{dehydrogenase}}} \text{L-glutamate} + \text{NAD}^+ + H_2O$$

ANALYSIS OF OTHER SUBSTANCES AND PARAMETERS

Pyroglutamic Acid. Pyroglutamic acid (5-oxo-2-pyrollidone carboxylic acid) is a molecule that is formed from glutamine in a spontaneous thermal intramolecular cyclization reaction.

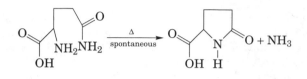

Under cultivation conditions glutamine has a half-life of about 6 to 8 days (29). Therefore, when high glutamine concentrations are used and maintained under such conditions (e.g., high-density batch and perfusion cultivations), a considerable amount of pyroglutamate is produced.

In principle, pyroglutamate can be analyzed using the same derivatization procedure as described for HPLC analysis of fatty acids. But sample preparation and elution conditions distinguish clearly because the formed derivative is much more hydrophilic and cannot be separated on a C_6-reversed-phase column.

Procedure: The analysis may be carried out using a binary gradient HPLC system with UV detection.

Sample preparation: The cell-free sample is adjusted to pH 3. 50 µL thereof are lyophilized and resolved in 180 µL acetonitrile.

Derivatization: 20 µL reagent (50 mM *p*-bromophenacylbromide, 5 mM 18-crown-6) and 1 mg KHCO$_3$ are added to the solution and heated for 90 min to 85 °C. The reaction mixture is rapidly cooled with ice water and 15–30 µL are injected.

Elution: The pyroglutamate derivative can be separated on a C_{18}-reversed-phase column (Ultrasphere ODS, 5 µ, 4.6 × 150 mm, Beckman Coulter, Inc.) by binary gradient elution in less than 30 min. Solvent A consists of 20% acetonitrile, 80% water, and solvent B of 90% acetonitrile, 10% water.

The total flow is set to 1.3 mL/min. The gradient is set as follows: 0% B at time 0, linear increase to 100% B in 30 min, hold 100% B for 2 min. Detection is carried out by UV absorption at 254 nm. Besides pyroglutamate, lactate can also be analyzed quantitatively with this method. Figure 7 shows an example chromatogram.

Enzyme Activities. Several enzymes are released from necrotic and apoptotic cells and cell membranes into the cell culture medium during cultivation. These enzymes may also be active in medium, influencing cell behavior or product quality. Monitoring these enzyme activities may be necessary to assess culture status or product quality.

Lactate Dehydrogenase Activity. Lactate dehydrogenase is a cytosolic enzyme. The detection of lactate dehydrogenase activity in the cell culture supernatant indicates cell damage by defective membranes or cell lysis. This enzyme is often used as marker enzyme for cell death.

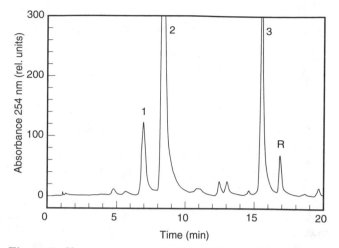

Figure 7. Chromatogram obtained by following the pyroglutamate derivatization procedure. Derivatization and separation conditions apply as described in the text. Identified substances are (1) pyroglutamate, (2) lactate, (3) unresolved amino acids (mainly glutamine), (R) reagent.

As described in the section on lactate analysis, lactate dehydrogenase converts pyruvate in the presence of NADH into lactate (or vice versa). The enzyme activity can be monitored by following the NADH conversion in a temperature-controlled spectrophotometer at a wavelength of 340 nm. A standardized procedure can be performed as follows: 100 µL cell-free supernatant is mixed with 700 µL of 30 mM sodium phosphate buffer, pH 7.4, 100 µL of 10 mM sodium pyruvate solution (in phosphate buffer) and 100 µL 2.7 mM NADH solution (in phosphate buffer) in a quartz half-microcuvette. The cuvette is placed in a temperature-controlled (37 °C) photometer. The linear extinction decrease at 340 nm is monitored for 1 min. The enzyme activity can be calculated from the slope.

Neuraminidase Activity and Sialic Acids. Many of the therapeutic proteins produced by cell culture are glycosylated. Variability in the oligosaccharide pattern can affect their behavior after application to a patient (half-time, biodistribution, biological activity). Terminally linked sialic acids are particularly involved in various biological events. Sialic acids are easily cleaved off the oligosaccharide by neuraminidases. Neuraminidase activity has been localized on the subcellular level in the plasma membrane, the Golgi apparatus, the lysosomes, and the cytosol. Moreover, neuraminidase activity has also been detected in cell culture fluids (30).

Determination of Neuraminidase Activity. The neuraminidase activity is determined fluorometrically with 4-methylumbelliferyl-α-D-N-acetylneuraminic acid substrate (MUF-NeuAc5) (31). A standardized assay can be performed as follows (32). After centrifugation (15000 × g, 15 min), 250 µL of supernatant, 25 µL of 4 mM MUF-NeuAc5 solution, and 25 µL of 1 M phosphate buffer, pH 7.0, are mixed and heated for 1 h at 37 °C. The reaction is stopped by adding 700 µL 0.375 glycine/KOH buffer, pH 10.4. The mixture is centrifuged again (15000 × g,

5 min), and the fluorescence is determined at excitation and emmision wavelengths of 362 and 448 nm, respectively.

Determination of Sialic Acids. Free sialic acids can be derivatized with 1,2-diamino-4,5-methylenedioxybenzen (DMB) into fluorescent derivatives that can be separated on a C_{18}-reversed-phase column (33,34). 20 µL cell-free supernatant is mixed with 40 µL ice-cold acetone to precipitate soluble proteins. After centrifugation (15000 × g, 5 min) 15 µL of the mixture is lyophilized in a vacuum concentrator. The lyophilizate is dissolved in 200 µL of 25 mM H_2SO_4. 200 µL DMB reagent (7 mM DMB, 18 mM disodium dithionite, 1 M 2-mercaptoethanol in water) are added and heated for 2.5 h at 60 °C. The reaction is stopped by cooling to 0 °C (ice water). After centrifugation (15000 × g, 5 min) 20 µL of the mixture are injected onto the column (Ultrasphere ODS, 5 µ, 4.6 × 150 mm, Beckman Coulter, Inc.). The sialic acid derivatives are eluted isocratically (1.2 mL/min) with a solvent consisting of 5% acetonitrile, 7% methanol, and 88% water and quantitatively detected with a fluorescence detector at excitation and emission wavelengths of 373 and 448 nm, respectively.

Osmolality. The cytosol interacts with the medium through the water-permeable cell membrane. Dependent on the concentration ratio of all substances on both sides of the cell membrane, the cell is exposed to an osmotic pressure. The osmotic pressure of a solution is given by its osmolality. The osmolality of the medium should be in a range of approximately 300 mosmol/kg ±50 mosmol/L to provide isotonic conditions. For the determination of the osmolality, the molar lowering of the freezing point (Raoult's Law) by a dissolved substance can be measured. The osmolality is independent of the kind of the dissolved substance, but cumulative for all dissolved substances. The measurement can be performed with a freezing point osmometer (e.g., semiautomatic half-micro-osmometer, Knauer). 150 µL cell-free supernatant is needed for a determination.

Analysis of Proteins. There are several proteins present in cell culture fluids. Some are added to the medium to support cell growth and product formation. The others are produced by the cells, among which the desired product can be found. For this reason an overall, unspecific protein assay can usually not be used to determine product quantity. For each product a special assay, regarding the properties of that protein, has to be established, if not only quantity but also activity has to be analyzed. Nevertheless, the total protein content in the medium is often a useful parameter.

Unspecific Protein Assays. A number of methods have been developed to determine total protein concentration. Besides direct UV absorbance and fluorescence, dye staining and reaction with a copper-containing reagent are the most common methods. The main problem of all those methods is that the response for different proteins may vary widely. With a complex mixture of unknown proteins this may lead to completely wrong results. Much care must be taken when choosing a method for a special purpose. The most common methods are discussed briefly in the following overview. A detailed description of all methods including working instruction can be found in Dunn (35).

UV absorbance at 280 nm: Determination of absorbance of aromatic amino acids in the protein (phenylalanin, tyrosine, tryptophan).

UV absorbance at 205 nm: Determination of absorbance of peptide bonds.

Fluorescence (excitation 280 nm, emission 340 nm): Determination of tryptophan fluorescence in the protein.

Dye staining: The dye coomassie blue G 250 binds in strong acidic solution to positively charged protein molecules, forming a blue product that can be detected at 595 nm (36).

Biuret reaction: Copper(II) ions in alkaline solution form a purple complex with proteins (peptide bonds). Detection at 540 nm (37).

Lowry method: The method is based on the Biuret reaction and the Folin–Ciocalteau phosphormolybdiphosphotungstic acid reduction to heteropolymolybdenum blue by the copper-catalyzed oxidation of aromatic amino acids (38). Detection at 750 nm.

BCA reagent: An alternative detection reagent, bicinchoninic acid (available from Pierce), has been developed for use with the Lowry method. Detection at 562 nm (39).

Protein assay ESL: The method is an improvement of the Biuret method. Spare copper(II) ions are reduced to copper(I) ions by ascorbic acid. These copper(I) ions form a complex with bathocuproin that can be detected at 485 nm (40). Since spare copper ions are measured, the extinction is inversely proportional to the protein concentration. An assay kit is commercially available (Roche Diagnostics).

Enzyme-Linked Immunoassays. For highly specific determinations antibody–antigen binding is very useful. Whenever an antibody against a substance (protein) is available or can be produced, an immunoassay is a method of choice. An immunoassay may be performed in a multiwell microtiter plate as an enzyme-linked immunosorbent assay (ELISA), as a radio immunoassay (RIA), as an affinity chromatographic analysis, or otherwise (41).

A standard sandwich ELISA procedure usually provides sufficient selectivity and sensitivity. Sensitivity may be improved by use of the (strep)avidin biotin amplification method. Sandwich ELISA is performed in four steps. First, the multiwell microtiter plate is coated with a primary antibody. Remaining binding sites on the plate are saturated with inert protein (albumin, serum). Second, the samples and standards containing the desired protein are applied. After incubation and removal of supernatant, an enzyme-labeled antibody (secondary antibody, conjugate) is added in a third step. The fourth step is carried out by adding a substrate of the enzyme. The conversion of the substrate by time is monitored photometrically. By comparison to standard concentrations a quantitative determination can be obtained. Commonly labelled enzymes are horseradish peroxidase and alkaline phosphatase. The most appropriate substrates for the peroxidase may be *o*-phenylendiamine or 2,2′-azino-di-[3-ethylbenzthiazolinesulfonate(6)] diammonium salt) ABTS. For the phosphatase *p*-nitrophenylphosphate is a useful substrate.

ANALYSIS WITH CLINICAL ANALYZERS

Fully automated analyzers are widely used in central hospital laboratories. These systems often have a sample throughput of up to several hundred measurements per hour. A wide variety of parameters of clinical interest can be analyzed. These parameters can be categorized in groups of basal substrates, enzymes, electrolytes, or immunochemicals. In the group of basal substrates the following substances and parameters are compiled: albumin, bilirubin, cholesterol, creatinine, glucose, urea, uric acid, triglycerides, and total protein. Among others, the activity of the following important enzymes can be quantified: alkaline phosphatase (ALP), amylase (AMYL), cholinesterase (CHE), creatin kinase (CK), glutamate dehydrogenase (GLDH), aspartate aminotransferase (AST/GOT), alanine aminotransferase (ALT/GPT), γ-glutamyl transferase (GGT), lactate dehydrogenase (LDH), lipase (LIP). Additionally, analytical methods for electrolytes such as sodium, potassium, calcium, magnesium, chloride, iron, and inorganic phosphate are integrated in the clinical autoanalyzer systems. Some of these analyzers are also able to perform immunological quantifications for immunoglobolins (A, G, M), lipoproteins (APO), transferrin, etc. All these methods are based either on reactions followed by photometrical detection or on measurements with ion-selective electrodes. An alternative to these methods based on liquid chemistry is a system using strip technology. All chemicals needed for one special detection are placed and fixed on a prepared area on the strip. The strip is dipped into the sample or wetted with a sample drop. With ongoing reaction a color or change in color is produced. Depending on the special strip used, this color can be evaluated either by comparison with a color table or by using a strip photometer. Fully automated analyzers based on this strip technology have also been developed for use in a clinical laboratory.

To explain each method in detail in this article would lead too far, but a complete description of each detection and quantification method can be obtained from the manufacturers of the clinical analyzers. These clinical systems are offered from companies such as Roche Diagnostics/Hitachi Instruments, Bayer Diagnostics, Beckman Coulter, or Olympus Diagnostica.

All methods used in the clinical analyzer systems, as described, are optimized and established to meet the requirements of clinical samples such as whole blood, serum, plasma, urine, or other body liquids. If these conditions are satisfied, a cell culture technologist in analyzing his samples from culture supernatants or cell extracts has exactly and independently prove each single method. Special attention has to be drawn to detection limit, sensitivity, reproducibility, and the presence of disturbing substances. When all these parameters are satisfactory, the use of a clinical analyzer may be a substantial help for routine analysis. Some methods used in the autoanalyzers are also offered as complete analyzing kits optimized for manual operation (Roche Diagnostics).

ACKNOWLEDGMENTS

The excellent technical assistance of Mrs. Angela Ehrlich and the help of Mrs. Ulrike Baillie during preparation of this manuscript is gratefully acknowledged. Furthermore, I thank Prof. Dr.-Ing. Jürgen Lehmann for his generous support and all other current and former members of the institute who contributed to the development of certain methods.

SERVICE INFORMATION

Most of the suppliers cited in this article are present on the internet. In the following a list of the internet home pages is given.

Alltech Assoc., Inc.	http://www.alltechweb.com/
Beckman Coulter, Inc.	http://www.beckmancoulter.com
Bayer Diagnostics	http://www.bayerdiag.com
Bio-Tek Kontron Instruments	http://www.biotek-kontron.com
Chrompack Intl. BV	http://www.chrompack.com
Dionex Corporation	http://www.dionex.com
Hypersil	http://www.hypersil.com
Innovatis GmbH	http://www.innovatis.com
Knauer GmbH	http://www.knauer.net
Metrohm Ltd.	http://www.metrohm.com
Mettler-Toledo	http://www.mt.com
Olympus Diagnostica	http://www.olympus-diagnostica.com/
Pierce	http://www.piercenet.com/
Roche Diagostics	http://biochem.roche.com http://www.roche.com/diagnostics
Schärfe System GmbH	http://www.casy-technology.com/
Shimadzu, Inc.	http://www.shimadzu.com
Waters Corporation	http://www.waters.com
Yellow Springs Instruments Inc.	http://www.ysi.com

BIBLIOGRAPHY

1. *CASY® 1 Cell Counter TTC*, Operations Manual, Schärfe System GmbH, Rentlingen, Germany.

2. *Roche Diagnostics*, 1998 Biochemicals Catalogue, Roche Diagnostics, Mannheim, Germany, p. 606.

3. *Biochemical Analyser YSI 2700*, Operations Manual, Yellow Springs Instrument, Yellow Springs, OH, USA.

4. F.T. Williams, *Biotech. Forum Europe* **9**(5), 302 (1992).

5. S. Moore, D.H. Spackman, and W.H. Stein, *Anal. Chem.* **30**, 1185 (1958).

6. P.B. Hamilton, *Anal. Chem.* **35**, 2055 (1963).

7. M. Roth, *Anal. Chem.* **43**, 880 (1971).

8. H. Büntemeyer, D. Lütkemeyer, and J. Lehmann, *Cytotechnology* **5**, 57 (1991).

9. D.R. Koop, E.T. Morgan, G.E. Tarr, and M.J. Coon, *J. Biol. Chem.* **257**, 8472 (1982).

10. B.A. Bidlingmeyer, S.A. Cohen, and T.L. Tarvin, *J. Chromatogr.* **336**, 93 (1984).

11. S. Reid, D.H. Randerson, and P.F. Greenfield, *Aust. J. Biotechnol.* **2**, 69 (1987).

12. T. Hayashi, H. Tsuchiya, and H. Naruse, *J. Chromatogr.* **273**, 245 (1983).

13. S. Hara, Y. Takemori, M. Yamaguchi, and M. Nakamura, *J. Chromatogr.* **344**, 33 (1985).

14. P. Jonvel, G. Andermann, and J.F. Barthelemy, *J. Chromatogr.* **281**, 371 (1983).

15. M. Püttmann, H. Krug, E. von Ochsenstein, and R. Kattermann, *Clin. Chem. (Winston. Salem, N.C.)* **39**, 825 (1993).

16. M.D. Smith, *J. Chromatogr. B* **182**, 285 (1980).

17. V.J. Gatautis and H.K. Naito, *Clin. Chem.* **27**, 1672 (1981).

18. P. Pietta, A. Calatroni, and A. Rava, *J. Chromatogr. B* **229**, 445 (1983).

19. J. Bontemps et al., *J. Chromatogr. B* **307**, 283 (1984).

20. J.P.M. Wielders and C.J.K. Mink, *J. Chromatogr. B* **277**, 145 (1983).

21. S.M. Fernando and P.A. Murphy, *J. Agric. Food Chem.* **38**, 163 (1990).

22. I. Gutmann and A.W. Wahlefeld, in H.U. Bergmeyer, et al., eds., *Methods of Enzymatic Analysis*, Vol. 3, Verlag Chemie, Weinheim, 1974, p. 1464.

23. *Roche Diagnostics*, Biochemical Catalogue, see also 2. 1998, p. 613.

24. *Roche Diagnostics*, Biochemical Catalogue Analog, 1998, p. 599.

25. H.U. Bergmeyer and H.-O. Beutler, in Bergmeyer, et al., eds., *Methods of Enzymatic Analysis, Vol. 8*, Verlag Chemie, Weinheim, 1985, p. 454.

26. W.S. Gardner, H.A. Bootsma, C. Evans, and P.A. St. John, *Mar. Chem.* **48**, 271 (1995).

27. I. Gutmann and H.U. Bergmeyer, in H.U. Bergmeyer, et al., eds., *Methods of Enzymatic Analysis*, Vol. 2, Verlag Chemie, Weinheim, 1974, p. 1794.

28. *Roche Diagnostics*, Biochemical Catalogue, see above. 1998, p. 629.

29. G.L. Tritsch and G.E. Moore, *Exp. Cell Res.* **28**, 360 (1962).

30. E. Munzert et al., *Biotechnol. Bioeng.* **56**, 441 (1997).

31. M. Potier et al., *Anal. Biochem.* **94**, 287 (1979).

32. E. Munzert, J. Müthing, H. Büntemeyer, and J. Lehmann, *Biotechnol. Prog.* **12**, 559 (1996).

33. S. Hara et al., *Anal. Biochem.* **194**, 138 (1987).

34. E. Munzert Ph.D. Thesis, University of Bielefeld, Bielefeld, Germany, 1996.

35. M.J. Dunn, in E.L.V. Harris and S. Angel, eds., *Protein Purification Methods: A Practical Approach*, IRL Press, Oxford, U.K., 1989, p. 10.

36. M.B. Bradford, *Anal. Biochem.* **72**, 248 (1976).

37. M.L. Goldberg, *Anal. Biochem.* **51**, 240 (1973).

38. O.H. Lowry, N.J. Rosenbrough, A.L. Farr, and R.J. Randall, *J. Biol. Chem.* **193**, 265 (1951).

39. P.K. Smith et al., *Anal. Biochem.* **150**, 76 (1985).

40. M. Matsushita, T. Irino, T. Komoda, and Y. Sakagishi, *Clin. Chim. Acta* **216**, 103 (1993).

41. P. Tijssen, *Laboratory Techniques in Biochemistry and Molecular Biology*, Vol. 15. Elsevier, Amsterdam, 1988.

See also FLOW CYTOMETRY OF PLANT CELLS; IMMUNO FLOW INJECTION ANALYSIS IN BIOPROCESS CONTROL; OFF-LINE IMMUNOASSAYS IN BIOPROCESS CONTROL; ON-LINE ANALYSIS IN ANIMAL CELL CULTURE.

OFF-LINE IMMUNOASSAYS IN BIOPROCESS CONTROL

BIRGITT PLÄSIER
School of Chemical Engineering
University of Birmingham
Edgbaston, Birmingham

OUTLINE

INTRODUCTION

Immunoassays are based on the specific antibody–antigen reaction. From the analytical point of view, antibodies are specific biorecognition molecules. In principle, they can be prepared against any chemical structure using either the immunization of animals or novel recombinant techniques. Yalow and Berson introduced antibodies for analytical purposes at the end of the 1950s (1). In the following years, immunoassays were widely applied in biochemistry, clinical chemistry, and environmental monitoring. At present, polyclonal antibodies produced by immunization of animals are being replaced by monoclonal antibodies. The introduction of the monoclonal antibody technology by Köhler and Milstein in 1975 (2) made large quantities of homogeneous mono molecular antibodies available by cell culture. Recombinant antibodies produced by biotechnological processes can reduce the use of experimental animals for antibody production and offer antibodies designed for a particular analytical problem.

In biotechnological processes, immunoassays can be used for the quantification of active ingredients and of protein contaminants, for instance, in pharmaceutical products (3). Immunoassays are qualified by their sensitivity, specificity, accuracy, and reproducibility as well as their suitability in routine test systems. Immunoassays are an effective analytical tool for the quantification

Table 1. Overview of Immunoassay Categories

Assay	Acronym	Refs.
1. Assays with antibody limitation		
Chemiluminescence immunoassay	CIA	(5,6)
Enzyme immunoassay	EIA	(7–9)
Fluorescence immunoassay	FIA	(10,11)
Radioimmunoassay	RIA	(12,13)
2. Turbidimetric, nephelometric, and agglutination immunoassays		
Immunonephelometric assay		(14)
Immunoturbidimetric assay		(15,16)
Latex agglutination test	LAT	(17)
Particle counting immunoassay	PACIA	(18)
3. Assays without limitation		
Enzyme-linked immunosorbant assay	ELISA	(8,19,20)
Immunochemiluminometric assay	ICLMA	(5,21,22)
Immunofluorimetric immunoassay	IFMA	(23)
Immunoradiometric assay	IRMA	(24)
4. Homogene assays with detection of the antigen–antibody binding		
Chemiluminescence fluorescence energy transfer	CLETIA	(25)
Enzyme-monitored immunoassay	EMIT	(26)
Fluorescence energy transfer immunoassay	FETI	(27,28)
Fluorescence polarization immunoassay	FPIA	(29)
Fluorescence quenching immunoassay	FQIA	(30)
Substrate-labeled fluorescence immunoassay	SLFIA	(31)

of active ingredient in complex protein mixtures, such as the determination of product titers in cell culture fluids or product concentration in early steps of protein recovery. Another application is the quantification of specific trace-protein contaminants in products derived from biotechnological production. In addition, it is possible to differentiate between a native and a denatured protein form if sensitive antibodies are available. Pharmaceutical products received from biotechnological production can include host cell proteins. The quantification of host cell proteins can be detected by multiantigen immunoassays (3).

Immunoassays are an analytical tool to measure a large number of samples in a short period of time (several hours). It is labor intensive because most steps are carried out manually. Major cost factors are the price of the antibody and staff salary. For routine use immunoassays can be automated. A great variety in immunoassay analyzers exist, especially for use in clinical chemistry (4). Immunoassays are classified by whether they are in competitive or noncompetitive assays and by the reporting molecule that is conjugated to the antibody or antigen [radioimmunoassay (RIA), radiolabeled analyte/antibody; fluorescence immunoassay (FIA), fluorophore-labeled analyte/antibody; enzyme immunoassay (EIA), enzyme-conjugated analyte/antibody]. The term *homogeneous* means that an immunoassay is carried out in solution, and heterogeneous immunoassays implies the use of plates or cartridges where, for example, antibodies can be immobilized. The term *antigen* is used for larger molecules like proteins that can give an immune response. Hapten is the part of an antigen where the specific antibody binds and as well for small molecules. Table 1 gives an overview of the different types of immunoassays (5–31).

In the following paragraphs different immunoassays and their applications are discussed in detail. The main focus is on immunoassays, which can be run in the off-line mode. On-line detection will be discussed in another section of this encyclopedia.

COMPETITIVE AND NONCOMPETITIVE IMMUNOASSAYS; RADIOIMMUNOASSAY

All immunoassays depend on the measurement of fractional binding site occupancy of the antibody by analyte. Noncompetitive immunoassays directly measure occupied sites, while competitive assays are based on the detection of total and unoccupied sites by analyte (32). In competitive immunoassays, labeled and unlabeled analyte (sample) are simultaneoulsy exposed to the antibody (Fig. 1). Instead of a labeled analyte, a labeled anti-idiotypic antibody could be used. In noncompetitive immunoassays the labeled antibody detects the bound analyte (Fig. 2). Maximal sensitivity will be reached by decreasing the amount of antibody in competitive assays and increasing the antibody concentration in noncompetitive assays (32).

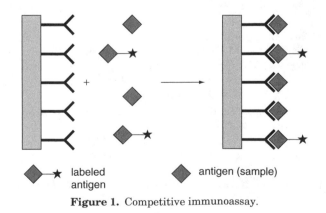

labeled antigen   antigen (sample)

Figure 1. Competitive immunoassay.

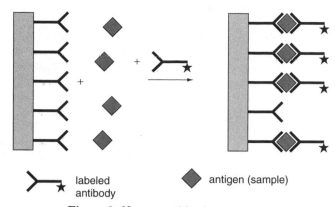

Figure 2. Noncompetitive immunoassay.

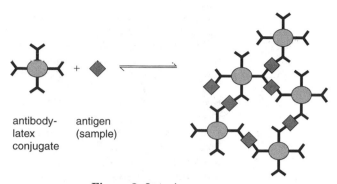

Figure 3. Lateximmunoassay.

The radioimmunoassay and analogous protein binding assays were independently developed in the late 1950s and early 1960s for the measurement of insulin by Yalow and Berson (33) and thyroxine and vitamin B12 by Ekins (34,35). These RIAs relied on the competition between the radioactive labeled antigen and the unlabeled analyte in the sample following the schematic shown in Figure 1. Radiolabeled antibody methods (immunoradiometric assay, IRMA; 24) followed as noncompetitive assays. Commonly used radiolabels are ^{125}I, ^{131}I, and ^3H. However, work with radioactive isotopes is subject to strict safety regulations and can only be undertaken in specialized laboratories. The preparation of radiolabeled antigen involves risks that are substantial. Even when these are prepared commercially, the product shows batch-to-batch variation and generally has a half-life limited to 2 months. Furthermore, major difficulties arise with the disposal of radioactive waste. For these reasons the RIA lost importance when other methods like fluorescence immunoassays and enzyme immunoassays were developed.

NEPHELOMETRIC AND TURBIDIMETRIC IMMUNOASSAYS

When a light beam is directed at a fluid that contains suspended particles, light is absorbed, scattered, reflected, and transmitted. Quantification of the residual transmitted light is the basis of turbidimetry, while the measurement of scattered light is used in nephelometry. Polyclonal antibodies and soluble proteins have multiple interaction sites and built first soluble complexes, which further associate to form insoluble precipitates. In the range of antibody excess, adding further antigen results in an increasing number of scattering centers up to the equivalence point. In antigen excess, particles continue to increase in number but decrease in size and scattering potential, until finally only complexes of a single antibody bound to two antigen molecules exist. Under antibody excess, this process results in light scattering being direct proportional to the antigen concentration, giving a scatter curve similar to the precipitation curve of Heidelberger (36). Therefore, analyses are run in antibody excess, since light scatter from a sample in large antigen excess may not be differentiated from the response given by a lower antigen concentration.

For detecting the immuncomplexes three different types of measurement exist: end-point detection, fixed-time method (two measurements in a fixed time interval), and peak-rate method (for detecting the reaction rate). The last two measure reaction kinetics. Turbidimetric and nephelometric immunoassays are homogeneous (no separation steps are required), without sample pretreatment, antigens and antibodies can be used without modification (as opposed to lateximmunoassays), results are available within 3–30 min, and these assays are easy to automate. By adding nonionic polymers (e.g., polyethyleneglycol), the speed of the reaction and the measurement range increase. A breakthrough in sensitivity came with the introduction of particle-enhanced lateximmunoassays (measurement range µg/mL) (37,38). Figure 3 shows the schematic of a lateximmunoassay. The signal increases with increasing antigen content in the sample. Nonlabeled immunoassays are still popular in clinical testing. Based on latex agglutination assays a multiple analytical system has been developed. Its main use is the rapid analysis (10 min) of body fluids for routine use in blood transfusions, diabetes, or for detecting sexually transmitted diseases (39). Recent advances in nonlabled immunoassays include the use of alternating currents to increase the speed of latex agglutination assays for myoglobin (40) and α-fetoprotein (41). Haptens cannot build precipitates because of their monovalence. Successful detection of haptens is offered by the latex inhibition immunoassay. The signal decreases on addition of the analyte (38,42).

ENZYME IMMUNOASSAYS

Enzyme immunoassays exploit an enzymatic reaction for detecting the immunreaction. In 1971 Engvall and Perlmann (43) and van Weemen and Schuurs (44) described independently the use of enzyme-labeled agents. Methods based on enzyme labels are the most common types of immunoassays in use at present. This group of techniques includes the enzyme-linked immunosorbent assays (ELISA), the enzyme-monitored immunotest (EMIT), the competitive binding enzyme immunoassay, and the immunoenzymometric assay (IEMA). Horseradish peroxidase and alkaline phosphatase remain the most common labels for enzyme immunoassays. The competitive EIA is analogous to the classical RIA described above, and the schematic is shown in Figure 1. Enzyme-labeled antigen is mixed with antigen from the sample and added to the limited amount of antibody (7–9). For this assay a separation step is required. The easiest way is to absorb or bind the antibody to a solid phase, which then allows washing of the antibody–antigen complex prior to measurement. An alternative assay for antigens depends on the competition between a fixed amount of solid-phase antigen and antigen in the sample for a limited amount of specific enzyme-labeled antibody. This assay is also called an inhibition assay because the amount of enzyme-labeled antibody that will be bound to the solid phase decreased with increasing concentration from antigen in the sample. This type of assay can be used to measure haptens as well. The ELISA belongs to the group of heterogeneous immunoassays and is an example of a noncompetitive assay (19,20). The schematic of a sandwich ELISA is shown in Figure 4. The excess of solid-phase antibody is first incubated with the sample containing the antigen. After washing, the enzyme-labeled antibody is added, and after a further washing step the enzyme activity retained is measured. In the sandwich-type immunoassay the analyte has to be large enough to present two reactive antigenic sites. This excludes the use of this assay for measuring hapten concentration. A sensitive sandwich ELISA for the detection of recombinant human antithrombin III produced in tissue culture was reported in Ref. 45, and an ultrasensitive enzyme immunoassay for antibodies (immune complex transfer enzyme immunoassay) has been reviewed in Ref. 46.

Many enzyme immunoassays are based on the modulation of enzyme activity. The enzyme activity increases or decreases during the immunoreaction. To the group of homogeneous assays belong the enzyme-multiplied immunoassay (Fig. 5). Enzyme-labeled antigen and antigen from the sample compete for a limited amount of antibody. Antibody bound to the enzyme-antigen conjugate minimises the enzyme activity. The EMIT was introduced by Rubenstein in 1972 (47). A new enzyme

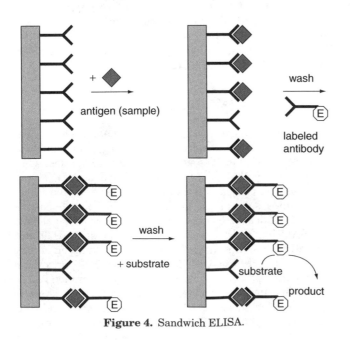

Figure 4. Sandwich ELISA.

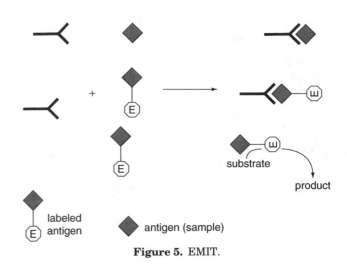

Figure 5. EMIT.

modulator-mediated immunoassay (EMMIT) was presented by Brillhart and Ngo (48). The competitive EMMIT is an enzyme-amplified immunoassay. Analyte from the sample and the modulator–antigen conjugate compete for free antibody. The modulator–antigen conjugate loses its enzyme modulation activity when bound to the antibody. The activity of the enzyme in solution will be influenced by the unbound modulator–conjugate complex. The enzyme activity can be modified either by reversible, noncovalent (reversible enzyme inhibitors or activators, allosteric effectors, antibodies to the enzyme, and transition-state analogues), or irreversible (enzyme inhibitors directed to the active site, enzyme modifications as phosphorylation or dephosphorylation of amino acid side chains), covalent interactions with the modulator. The cloned enzyme–donor immunoassay (CEDIA®; 49) combines the application of recombinant DNA technology with standard immunochemical principles. The CEDIA® technology makes use of two genetically engineered fragments of *E. coli* β-galactosidase. The smaller fragment is called the enzyme donor and the larger fragment, the enzyme acceptor. The enzyme donor contains a short sequence that is missing from the amino-terminal end of the enzyme receptor. The two fragments can build associated subunits (inactive) and then recombine spontaneously to form active β-galactosidase (tetramer). The antigen is conjugated to the enzyme donor in a way that it does not affect the complementation. Antibody directed against the antigen can inhibit the complementation reaction. Antigen from the sample and the enzyme donor–antigen conjugate compete for the limited number of antibody sites. The resulting unbound enzyme donor and acceptor can combine to build active β-galactosidase. The amount of β-galactosidase formed and measured using a chromogenic substrate is proportional to the antigen concentration in the sample.

A new analytical system, the expression immunoassay, which uses an expressible enzyme coding DNA fragment as a reporter molecule, was introduced in 1995 (50). The antibody was labeled with a DNA fragment encoding luciferase. After completion of the immunoreaction the DNA label was subjected to a cell-free (in vitro) coupled transcription/translation reaction that produced luciferase molecules in solution. There was a linear relationship between the enzyme activity and the amount of analyte in the sample. The expression immunoassay involves an increase in the number of enzyme molecules, thus introducing an additional level of amplification.

Enzyme immunoassays play an important role not only in detecting proteins but also in the quantification of DNA/RNA and in detecting specific sequences. The ability of the polymerase chain reaction specifically to amplify minute amounts of DNA or RNA opens a new approach to diagnosis. The quantification of native or modified nucleic acids can be undertaken for the simple purpose of measuring their concentration in solution, or through a hybridization process with a labeled probe for detecting certain sequences. Polyclonal and monoclonal antibodies have proven able to target DNA and RNA. They were shown to be capable of detecting particular structures, including codons, Z-shaped DNA, or DNA/RNA hybrids and to distinguish between labeled and unlabeled DNA (51). Even though the following assay strictly belongs to the group of fluorescence immunoassays, it is described here because it is also related to the hybridization assays. A sandwich-type DNA hybridization assay using enzyme-amplified time-resolved fluorometry of lanthanide chelates was reported (52). The target DNA was hybridized with two adjacent and nonoverlapping oligonucleotide probes, one oligonucleotide serving as the capture probe and the other as the detection probe. Two ligand-specific protein binding pairs (biotin–strepavidin and digoxigenin–antidigoxigenin) were used alternately for capture of the hybrids to the solid phase and detection. In both cases alkaline phosphatase was used as a reporter molecule and phosphatase as a substrate. The catalytic hydrolysis of the substrate produces diflunisal, which forms a ternary fluorescent complex. This hybridization assay combines enzymatic amplification and time-resolved fluorescence to produce an ultrasensitive assay for oligonucleotide probes.

Enzyme immunoassays have been mainly used for the detection of the expression products of the gene cloning technology. The detection of proteins and or peptides by specific monoclonal antibodies can be used early in the cloning process either in partially purified culture media, or by quantification of these products in solution when released into the medium. Monoclonal antibodies are a powerful tool for the detailed characterization of the presence of the full gene length in the clone, determination of the size of the insert, or for instance, of the presentation of expressed epitopes in fusion proteins or for the measurement of contaminating DNAs.

FLUORESCENCE IMMUNOASSAY

In fluorescence immunoassays the marker can be an enzyme conjugate, which changes a fluorogen into a fluorescent molecule, antigen, or antibody directly conjugated to a fluorescent dye, or the natural fluorescence of the analyte is detected. Some of the techniques for enzyme immunoassays can be directly transferred into fluorescence immunoassays by changing the reporting molecule. For a highly fluorescent molecule like fluorescein

the detection limit of 0.5×10^{-14} mol/L can be reached in distilled water, but in practice, the detection limit is in the range of 10^{-9} to 10^{-12} mol/L. This is due to the backround fluorescence in biological samples and fluids and because fluorescence efficiency or quantum yield is dependent on solvent characteristics (pH, polarity) and temperature. The fluorescence polarization immunoassay (FPIA) is a simple and quick homogeneous assay, which can be easily automated (29), although the sensitivity is less than heterogeneous fluorescence immunoassay methods. The principle behind the FPIA is as follows. The light is resolved with a fixed polarization lens or prism into rays with their electrical vectors in a single plane. When fluorescent substances in solution are excited with the polarized light, they emit partially polarized fluorescence, which can be detected at 90° to the incident beam. The emission is monitored by a rotating polarizer. The competitive fluorescence immunoassay (10,11) is related to the EIA (schematic shown in Fig. 1). Fluorescent-labeled analyte competes with the sample antigen for free antibody binding sites. This assay requires a separation step. The fluorigenic substrate-labeled separation free enzyme-mediated immunoassay (FSIA) (53) makes use of a fluorigenic enzyme substrate conjugated to the antigen. As in the FIA, labeled and unlabeled antigen compete for free antibody binding sites. The fluorigenic substrate is inactivated when bound to the antibody. The enzyme acts on the remaining free fluorigenic substrate–antigen conjugate, yielding a fluorescent product, which is directly related to the sample antigen.

Many fluorescence immunoassays are competitive assays, which can be subdivided into quenching and enhancement assays. An example is the fluorescence energy transfer immunoassay (FETI; 27,28). The assay is based upon dipole–dipole coupled electron energy transfer between two chromophores brought into proximity by interaction of an antibody with cognate antigen. Energy transfer occurs when the fluorescence emission spectrum of one chromophore (donor) overlaps the excitation spectrum of the second chromophore (acceptor). Two different fluorophores, such as FITC (fluorescein isothiocyanate) and TMRITC (tetramethylrhodamine isothiocyanate) are used as donor and acceptor pair. The decreasing emission spectra of the first fluorophore or the increasing light intensity of the second fluorophore is detected. This effect is increased the closer the donor and acceptor pair get. In the competitive, homogeneous FETI shown in Figure 6, labeled antigen competes with sample antigen for labeled antibody. Energy transfer takes place when the antigen conjugate reacts with the antibody. This assay is suited to measuring haptens as well. A sandwich-type FETI has also been examined. Donor-labeled antibody and acceptor-labeled antibody are mixed with sample. Quenching takes place when immuncomplexes are formed. In the case of antigen access a hook effect is seen in the response curve, and immuncomplexes are not informed.

A separate group of immunoassays are time-resolved immunoassays (TR-FIA; 54). The principle of the time-resolved monitoring and especially the use of lanthanide ions as labels are exploited in these types of measurements. The difference between the fluorescence lifetime

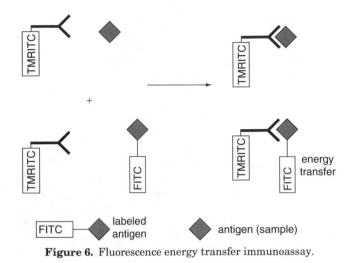

Figure 6. Fluorescence energy transfer immunoassay.

of the specific signal and the nonspecific background has been used to increase assay sensitivity by the improvement of signal-to-noise ratio. When the fluorescence decay time of the label is sufficiently longer than the average background decay, the specific signal of the label can be measured after the background signal has decayed. Lanthanide chelates, for which the fluorescence decay time ranges from 10 to 1000 µs, present interesting possibilities for increasing the sensitivity of fluorescence immunoassays. New ultrasensitive bioanalytical assays exploit lanthanide fluorescence and are based on the detection of dissociative enhancement of lanthanide ions, direct labeling with luminescent chelates, enzyme-amplified lanthanide fluorescence (described under enzyme immunoassays), lanthanide fluorescence quenching, and energy transfer (55). Dissociative enhancement with lanthanide ions has a great advantage over direct labeling with fluorescent chelates. It is not necessary to combine optimum binding and fluorescence properties of the lanthanide chelate into one label. The lanthanide chelate bound to the antigen or antibody has strong binding properties but is not itself fluorescent in the assay medium. The lanthanide ion must be dissociated from the chelator and released into the enhancement solution in which it is fluorescent and can be detected. An immunoassay by fluorescence energy transfer from europium chelate in liposomes to allophycocyanin was reported in Ref. 56 and the exploitation of time-resolved fluorescence of the rare earth lanthanides in high-throughput screening is reviewed in Ref. 57.

CHEMILUMINESCENCE AND BIOLUMINESCENCE IMMUNOASSAYS

Light emission produced in a chemical reaction from the decay of chemiexcited species to the electronic ground state is known as chemiluminescence. Light-emitting reactions are also found in nature in a diverse range of organisms, and this type of light is termed bioluminescence. Detection in chemiluminescence immunoassay may be based on either direct monitoring of the conjugated labels (e.g., luminol) or enzyme-mediated

formation of luminescent products. Common assays are the competitive chemiluminescence immunoassay (CIA; 5,6) and the immunochemiluminometric assay (ICMA) reviewed in Ref. 58.

One of the most efficient light-producing systems so far is the firefly luciferase bioluminescence. A fusion protein of protein A and firefly luciferase has been engineered that retains the binding properties of protein A (binds to the Fc region of IgG) and the enzyme activity of luciferase. This has been exploited in bioluminescence immunoassays for human IgG (59). Reporter-gene-based assays have been developed following advances in the genetics of bioluminescent organisms, including the use of genes for bioluminescent enzymes (luciferase) and proteins (apoaequorin) as reporter genes (60).

SURFACE PLASMON RESONANCE AND IMMUNOASSAYS

Since the introduction of the BIAcore instrument by Pharmacia in 1990 (61), the use of biosensors for immunoassays has gained increasing popularity. This system makes use of surface plasmon resonance (SPR) for monitoring interactions between molecules of interest, essentially as an increase in the mass of the material immobilized on the sensor surface. Such SPR-based sensors usually employ a thin glass slide (0.2–0.8 mm) with a gold coating (20–60 nm). This is functionalized with chemicals having ligands or receptors (e.g., antibodies) for biomolecules (antigens). New functionalized sensor chips are described in Refs. 62 and 63 for an improved antibody attachment.

The surface plasmon resonance is based on the principle that the evanescent wave penetrating the glass resonates with the surface plasmon of the gold layer. Surface plasmons are collective oscillations in free-electron plasma at a metal boundary. Normally, these oscillations are due to an electric field, but under certain conditions, they can be optically induced. This resonance is affected by the refractive index at the gold surface. This method is sufficiently sensitive for monitoring reactions occurring at the gold surface, and the use of labeled molecules is not required. Its main applications are concentration measurement, rate constant determination, and affinity ranking (64,65). In biotechnology, this technique is used for real-time monitoring of recombinant protein concentration in animal cell cultures (66) to replace the labor-intensive ELISA.

IMMUNOAFFINITY CHROMATOGRAPHY; CAPILLARY ELECTROPHORETIC IMMUNOASSAYS

Methods that use immunoaffinity chromatography (IAC) for sample preparation or detection are becoming increasingly popular tools in the analysis of biological compounds. Potential advantages of this flow-based immunoassay include speed and ease of automation. A simple format for IAC is shown in Figure 7. The sample is injected onto the IAC column under mobile-phase condition. The analyte will be bound to the immobilized antibody in the column. Due to the specificity of the antibody–antigen interaction, other solutes present in the sample are washed

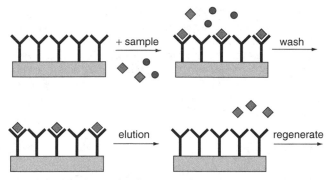

Figure 7. Principle of immunoaffinity chromatography.

out of the column by the application buffer. To elute the antigen for detection, a second buffer that causes a dissociation of analyte and antibody is used. After the fully eluting the antigen, the initial application buffer is reapplied to regenerate the column. The advantages of using this approach in analytical applications, particularly when performed by high-performance immunoaffinity chromatogaphy (HPIAC), include its simplicity, fight precision, and the possibility for fast sample analysis. Examples for the case of HPIAC include a great variety of biological and clinical samples (body fluids, cell or tissue extracts, aliquots from bioreactors). When used with appropriate elution schemes, the columns are stable for several hundred sample applications. Examples for possible applications are the detection of antithrombin III and tissue-type plasminogen activator in cell cultures by fluorescence (67) and interleukin-2 in tissue samples (68).

The IAC technique is used for immunoextraction to remove a specific solute or a group of solutes from a sample prior to analysis. Therefore, IAC is combined with HPLC (high performance liquid chromatography), GC (gas chromatoghraphy), or CE (capillary electrophoresis). Interferon α-2 was monitored by IAC/HPLC in cell extracts (69), steroids were detected by IAC/GC in urine (70), and serum insulin was measured by IAC/CE (71).

A newly emerged analytical technique is the capillary electrophoretic immunoassay (CEIA). The method offers several advantages over classical immunoassays such as rapid separation with high mass sensitivity and simultaneous determination of multiple analytes. CE can separate free antigen and antibody from the antigen–antibody complex. In conjunction with laser-induced fluorescence (LIF) detection, CEIA can readily measure analytes at a concentration as low as 10^{-11} M, which is comparable with most conventional immunoassays. CE can combine the immunologic recognition of the analyte, with on-line quantitation, microscale analysis, and automatic instrumentation. CEIA requires less sample and reagent than used in conventional immunoassays and can use all existing CE detection techniques from UV (ultraviolet light) and LIF to MS (mass spectrometry). In enzyme-labeled CEIA it is possible to determine the analyte of interest by separating and detecting the substrate and the product of the labeled enzymes. One disadvantage of the CEIA is that CE is a serial analytical method, and it is only possible to analyze one sample at a time.

A CE-based affinity assay was presented by Lausch et al. (72) for monitoring IgG in cultivation media. Protein A conjugated with a fluorescent dye was used as an affinity ligand. The protein A formed a fluorescent complex with the IgG from the sample, and the complex was separated from excess protein A by capillary zone electrophoresis (CZE). The CE affinity assay was successfully used to monitor monoclonal antibodies in cultivation processes. Reif et al. (73) analyzed human IgG with fluorescent-labeled protein G.

A noncompetitive CEIA is based on the separation of the antigen–antibody complexes from free antigen (or antibody). If the analytes can be analyzed by UV or native fluorescence detection, the amount of immunocomplex can be directly quantified. However, in most assays the analyte or antibody needs a fluorescent label to increase the detection sensitivity. Karger and co-workers presented CEIA for antigens using fluorescent-labeled antibody or antibody fragments (74).

As in conventional immunoassays, one reagent is limited in a competitive CEIA. The analyte in the sample competes with a labeled analogue for free antibody binding sites. CE-LIF will separate this mixture, and the result is two distinctive peaks coresponding to free-labeled analyte and the immunocomplex with labeled analyte. The more sample analyte is present, the more fluorescent-labeled analogue will remain and fewer immunocomplexes with the fluorescent-labeled antigen will be formed. These assays can also be used for detecting multiple anlytes in a sample assuming that no cross-reactivity takes place. Schulzt and Kennedy first reported competitive CEIA (75), and a method for analyzing insulin within 6 sec was presented by this group (76). The CEIA can be used as an on-line method. A multiple capillary system has already been marketed by Beckman for clinical diagnosis and microchip-based CEIA with multiple microfabricated channels will improve the throughput of CEIA significantly (77).

MISCELLANEOUS IMMUNOASSAYS

Alternative immunoassay types are assays based on electrochemical detection. Speed, accuracy, and precision are characteristics of electrochemical detection. Enzyme labels can be used that generate an electrochemically active product. Other techniques involve nonenzymatic labels like voltametric measurement of 2,4-dinitrophenol, or various metal ions, as reviewed in Refs. 78 and 79.

Liposome-amplified immunoanalysis exploits the advantages of liposome-encapsulated dye or enzyme, which is later released as a result of the immunoreaction. Liposomes are lipid bilayer vesicles that are formed when lipids are dispersed in water. During vesicle formation they encapsulate a portion of aqueous solution that contains the marker molecule. When the analyte of interest is conjugated to a lipid, this can be incorporated into the liposome surface. Competition takes place when the free and bound analyte compete for free antibody binding sites. The number of liposomes that bind to the antibodies is inversely proportional to the amount of free analyte. Liposomes can also be used in other immunoassay variations. The advantage of liposomes over the more popular enzyme label is that any water-soluble marker can be encapsulated. The physical characteristics of the liposomes can be changed by the lipid composition. The size of the liposomes and the number of analytes presented at the surface are variable. The enhancement is instantaneous. A further enzymatic incubation step can be avoided. Examples for liposome immunoassays are the detection of human interferon (80) and ferritin (81); for a review see Ref. 82.

Multispot immunoassays can be used to measure an array of analytes. The basic concepts were developed by Ekins et al. (83). Microspot assays can be characterized by the use of small amounts of an antibody (binding agent) localized at a high surface density on a solid support in form of a microspot. When the binding-site concentration is so low that it does not affect the analyte concentration in the medium, this implies that not more than 5% or ideally 1% of the total analyte is bound. Under these circumstances the binding-site fractional occupancy is independent of both the amount of binding agent and the sample volume (ambient analyte condition). The microspot acts as an analyte sensor, and the amount of bound analyte is indicative of the analyte concentration in the sample. The bound analyte can be detected by a labeled antibody (sandwich immunoassays, noncompetitive) or by an antibody against free binding sites (competitive). Another possibility is the use of two different labeled antibodies against the bound analyte and free binding sites (competitive and noncompetitive mode). Such assays have been used in endocrinology, allergies, infectious diseases, and therapeutic drugs (84).

CONCLUSION

Immunoassays play an important part in biotechnology. They are used in bioprocess control during cultivation processes for monitoring product titers. First used as off-line technology, real-time or on-line detection has become more and more popular. The immunoassay data provide a control for cultivation processes and required information for documentation purposes. Immunoassays and DNA/RNA-hybridization assays can be exploited in testing the genetic stability of a genetically modified organism or virus infection (85). Following protein recovery, immunoassays are used to detect active ingredients. Immunoassays can distinguish between native and denatured protein, detect protein contaminants, and host cell proteins. Stereoselective antibodies can be used for measuring the concentration of chiral drugs (86). Immunoassays are used in clinical testing and studying of pharmacokinetics of biotechnology-derived pharmaceutical products (87). An immunoassay based on a fiber-optic system for recombinant hirudin is presented in Ref. 88 for pharmacokinetic studies.

Enzyme amplification and chemiluminescent reporters allow detection limits to the attomole level (10^{-18} M), which meets the requirements of most applications. Detection limits down to the single molecule level can be reached with the development of new instrumentation techniques (confocal and near-field scanning optical microscopy, photon counting cameras, fluorescence-correlation and time-gated spectroscopy) (89). These developments can increase the rate of DNA sequencing, increase the capacity of screening libraries for products of evolutionary biotechnology, and facilitate the characterization of compounds in drug discovery.

BIBLIOGRAPHY

1. R.S. Yalow and S.A. Berson, *Nature (London)* **184**, 1648–1649 (1959).
2. C. Köhler and C. Milstein, *Nature (London)* **265**, 495–497 (1975).
3. R.G. Werner et al., *Immunol. Tech.* **20**, 221–226 (1992).
4. D.W. Chan, *Anal. Chem.* **67**, 519R–524R (1995).
5. L.J. Kricka and G.H.G. Thorpe, *Ligand Rev.* **3**, 17–24 (1981).
6. J. de Boever, F. Kohen, and D. Vandekerckhove, *Clin. Chem. (Winston-Salem, N.C.)* **29**, 2068–2072 (1983).
7. M. Oellerich, *J. Clin. Chem. Clin. Biochem.* **20**, 895–894 (1984).
8. P. Tijssen, *Practice and Theory of Enzyme Immunoassay*, Elsevier, Amsterdam, (1985).
9. J. Folan, J.P. Gosling and P.F. Fottrell, *Clin. Chem. (Winston-Salem, N.C.)* **34**, 1843–1846 (1988).
10. I. Hammamiliä, *Clin. Chem. (Winston-Salem, N.C.)* **31**, 359–370 (1985).
11. S. Rasi, E. Suvanto, L.M. Vilpo, and J.A. Vilpo, *J. Immunol. Methods* **117**, 33–38 (1989).
12. T. Chard, *An Introduction to Radioimmunoassay and Related Techniques*, Elsevier, Amsterdam, (1987).
13. S.J. Grange, A. Munoy, J.S. Wang, and J.D. Groopman, *Cancer Epidemiol. Biomarkers Prev.* **5**, 57–61 (1996).
14. M. Marre, J.P. Claudel, and P. Ciret, *Clin. Chem. (Winston-Salem, N.C.)* **33**, 209–213 (1987).
15. Y. Maynard, M.G. Scott, M.H. Nahm, and J.H. Ladenson, *Clin. Chem. (Winston-Salem, N.C.)* **32**, 752–757 (1986).
16. D. Collet-Cassert, J.N. Limet, L. Van Krieken, and R. De Hertogh, *Clin. Chem. (Winston-Salem, N.C.)* **35**, 141–143 (1989).
17. S.G. Hadfield, A. Lane, and M.B. McIllmurray, *J. Immunol. Methods* **97**, 153–158 (1987).
18. T.A. Wilkens, G. Brouwers, J.C. Mareshal, and C.L. Cambasio, *Clin. Chem. (Winston-Salem, N.C.)* **34**, 1749–1752 (1988).
19. R.M. Nakamura, Y. Kasahara, and G.A. Rechnitz, *Immunochemical Assay and Biosensor Technology for the 90's*, Am. Chem. Soc., New York, (1992).
20. E. Ishikawa, *Clin. Biochem. (Winston-Salem, N.C.)* **20**, 209–327 (1983).
21. F. Kohen et al., in T.T. Ngo, ed., *Nonisotopic Immunoassays*, New York, 1990, pp. 271–286, Plenum Press.
22. I. Weeks and J.S. Woodhead, *J. Clin. Immunoassay* **7**, 82–89 (1984).
23. E.P. Diamandis, *Clin. Biochem.* **21**, 139–150 (1988).
24. S. Schwarz, P. Berger, and G. Wick, *Clin. Chem. (Winston-Salem, N.C.)* **31**, 48–51 (1985).
25. A. Patel and A.K. Cambell, *Clin. Chem. (Winston-Salem, N.C.)* **29**, 1604–1608 (1983).

26. J. Chang, S. Gotcher, and J.B. Gushaw, *Clin. Chem. (Winston-Salem, N.C.)* **30**, 231–234 (1981).

27. P.L. Khanna, in T.T. Ngo, ed., *Nonisotopic Immunoassays*, New York, 1990, pp. 211–230, Plenum Press.

28. J. Calvin, K. Burling, and C. Blow, *J. Immunol. Methods* **86**, 249–256 (1986).

29. D.L. Colbert, G. Gallacher, and R.W. Mainwearing-Burton, *Clin. Chem. (Winston-Salem, N.C.)* **31**, 1193–1195 (1985).

30. G. Barnard, F. Kohen, H. Mikola, and T. Lövgren, *Clin. Chem. (Winston-Salem, N.C.)* **35**, 555–559 (1989).

31. P. Allain, A. Turcant, and A. Premel-Cabic, *Clin. Chem. (Winston-Salem, N.C.)* **35**, 469–470 (1989).

32. R. Ekins, in R.F. Masseyeff, W.H. Albert, and N.A. Staines, ed., *Methods of Immunological Analysis*, VCH, Weinheim, 1993, pp. 227–257.

33. R.S. Yalow and S.A. Berson, *J. Clin. Invest.* **39**, 1157–1175 (1960).

34. R.P. Ekins, *Clin. Chim. Acta* **5**, 453–459 (1960).

35. R.M. Barakat and R.P. Ekins, *Lancet* **2**, 25–26 (1961).

36. H. Heidelberger and F.E. Kendell, *J. Exp. Med.* **62**, 697–720 (1935).

37. L.B. Bangs, *Am. Biotechnol. Lab.* **5**, 10–16 (1987).

38. A.M. Gressner, *GIT Lab. Med.* **9**, 419–429 (1990).

39. EP 0397424A2 (May 4, 1990), J.D. Allan et al. (to Biotrack Inc.)

40. M.I. Song et al., *Anal. Chim. Acta* **282**, 193–198 (1993).

41. M.I. Song et al., *Anal. Chem.* **61**, 895–898 (1994).

42. J.E. Craine, *Am. Biotechnol. Lab.* **5**, 34–41 (1987).

43. E. Engvall and P. Perlmann, *Immunochemistry* **8**, 871–874 (19971).

44. B.K. van Weemen and A.H.W.M. Schuurs, *FEBS Lett.* **15**, 232–236 (1971).

45. M. Schröder, D. Kaiser, R. Schäfer, and P. Friedel, *Genet. Eng. Biotechnol.* **16**, 211–225 (1996).

46. E. Ishikawa, *Acta Histochem. Cytochem.* **29**, 273–281 (1996).

47. K.E. Rubenstein, R.S. Schneider, and E.F. Ullmann, *Biochem. Biophys. Res. Commun.* **47**, 846–851 (1972).

48. K.L. Brillhart and T.T. Ngo, in R.F. Masseyeff, W.H. Albert, and N.A. Staines, eds., *Methods of Immunological Analysis*, VCH, Weinheim, 1993, pp. 406–415.

49. P.L. Khanna and W.A. Coty, in R.F. Masseyeff, W.H. Albert, and N.A. Staines, eds., *Methods of Immunological Analysis*, VCH, Weinheim, 1993, pp. 416–426.

50. T.K. Christopoulos and N.H.L. Chiu, *Anal. Chem.* **67**, 4290–4294 (1995).

51. F. Traincard and J.-L. Guesdon, in R.F. Masseyeff, W.H. Albert, and N.A. Staines, eds., *Methods of Immunological Analysis*, VCH, Weinheim, 1993, pp. 549–564.

52. N.H.L. Chiu, T.K. Christopoulos, and J. Peltier, *Analyst (London)* **123**, 1315–1319 (1998).

53. K.L. Brillhart and T.T. Ngo, in R.F. Masseyeff, W.H. Albert, and N.A. Staines, eds., *Methods of Immunological Analysis*, VCH, Weinheim, 1993, pp. 435–453.

54. E. Soini and T. Lofgren, in T.T. Ngo, ed., *Nonisotopic Immunoassays*, New York, 1990, pp. 231–243, Plenum Press.

55. E.F.G. Dickson, A. Pollak, and E.P. Diamandis, *J. Photochem. Photobiol. B: Biol.* **27**, 3–19 (1995).

56. Y. Okabayashi and I. Ikeuchi, *Analyst (London)* **123**, 1329–1332 (1998).

57. J. Burbaum and N.H. Sigal, *Curr. Opi. Chem. Biol.* **1**, 72–78 (1997).

58. H.A.H. Rongen, R.M.W. Hoetelmans, A. Bult, and W.P. van Bennekom, *J. Pharm. Biomed. Anal.* **12**, 433–462 (1994).

59. E. Kobatake, T. Iwai, Y. Ikariyama, and M. Aizawa, *Anal. Biochem.* **208**, 300–305 (1993).

60. I. Bronstein, et al., *J. Anal. Biochem.* **219**, 169–181 (1994).

61. U. Jönsson, et al., *Biotechniques* **11**, 620–627 (1991).

62. S. Sasaki, R. Nagata, B. Hock, and I. Karube, *Anal. Chim. Acta* **368**, 71–76 (1998).

63. R. Nakamura, et al., *Anal. Chem.* **67**, 4649–4652 (1997).

64. C.A.K. Borrebaeck, et al., *Bio/Technology* **10**, 697–698 (1992).

65. D. Neri, S. Montigiani, and P.M. Kirkham, *Trends Biotechnol.* **14**, 465–470 (1996).

66. K. Baker, A. Ison, R. Freedman, and W. Jones, *Genet. Eng. Biotechnol.* **17**, 69–74 (1997).

67. K. Beyer, M. Reinecke, W. Noé, and T. Scheper, *Anal. Chim. Acta* **309**, 301–305 (1995).

68. T.M. Philips, *Biomed. Chromatogr.* **11**, 200–205 (1997).

69. L. Ryback, M. D'Andrea, and S.J. Tarnowsky, *J. Chromatogr.* **397**, 355–361 (1987).

70. A. Farjam, et al., *Anal. Chem.* **63**, 2481–2487 (1991).

71. L.J. Cole and R.T. Kennedy, *Electrophoresis* **16**, 549–556 (1995).

72. R. Lausch, O.-W. Reif, P. Riechel, and T. Scheper, *Electrophoresis* **16**, 636–641 (1995).

73. O.-W. Reif, R. Lausch, T. Scheper, and R. Freitag, *Anal. Chem.* **66**, 4027–4033 (1994).

74. K. Shimura and B.L. Karger, *Anal. Chem.* **66**, 9–15 (1994).

75. N.M. Schultz and R.T. Kennedy, *Anal. Chem.* **65**, 3161–3165 (1993).

76. L. Tao and R.T. Kennedy, *Anal. Chem.* **68**, 3899–3906 (1996).

77. T. Pritchett, R.A. Evangelista, and F.-T.A. Chen, *Bio/Technology* **13**, 1449–1450 (1995).

78. O.A. Sadik and J.M. van Emon, *ACS Symp. Ser.* **646**, 127–147 (1996).

79. P. Skaldal, *Electroanalysis* **9**, 737–745 (1997).

80. H.A. Rongen, et al., *Anal. Chim. Acta* **287**, 527–534 (1994).

81. Y. Ishimori and K. Rokugawa, *Clin. Chem.* **39**, 1439–1443 (1993).

82. H.A.H. Rongen, A. Bult, and W.P. van Bennekom, *J. Immunol. Methods* **204**, 105–133 (1997).

83. R.P. Ekins, F. Chu, and J. Micallef, *J. Biolumin. Chemilumin.* **4**, 59–78 (1989).

84. F.W. Chu, et al., *ACS Symp. Ser.* **657**, 170–184 (1997).

85. J.K. Khan, R.S.K. Aminuddin, and B.P. Singh, *Indian J. Exp. Biol.* **36**, 546–552 (1998).

86. P.A. Got and Scherrmann, *Pharm. Res.* **14**, 1516–1523 (1997).

87. S. Toon, *Eur. J. Drug Metab. Pharmacokinet.* **21**, 93–103 (1996).

88. D. Gyax, et al., *Ther. Drug Monit.* **18**, 405–409 (1996).

89. D.M. Kelso, *Proc. SPIE — Int. Soc. Opt. Eng.* **2985**, 206–212 (1997).

See also IMMUNO FLOW INJECTION ANALYSIS IN BIOPROCESS CONTROL; OFF-LINE ANALYSIS IN ANIMAL CELL CULTURE, METHODS; ON-LINE ANALYSIS IN ANIMAL CELL CULTURE.

ON-LINE ANALYSIS IN ANIMAL CELL CULTURE

GERLINDE KRETZMER
Institut für Technische
Chemie der Universität
Hannover, Germany

OUTLINE

INTRODUCTION

Cultivating animal cells still requires a rather complex artificial environment. These requirements include not only physical parameters like temperature, dissolved oxygen concentration, pH, and stirrer speed, but also chemical parameters like nutrients, metabolites, and products. None of these parameters should be neglected, but for some of them a close surveillance is demanded. The viability and/or the productivity of the cells and, therefore, the economical benefit of the whole process depend on the mentioned parameters. On the one hand, good manufacturing practice (GMP) requires well-documented processes for control and safety reasons; on the other hand, comprehensive characterization of the process is necessary for a better understanding. Even after several years of research there are still quite a lot of obstacles and obscurities concerning cell growth, cell viability, and especially product quantity and quality. A detailed analysis of the cell's environment is the basis for control, and this leads to process optimization and the enhancement of product quality.

Analysis of the environment can be done off-line or "on-line." The term "on-line" will include *in-line, in situ, on-line*, and noninvasive analysis methods. In animal cell technology off-line analysis is the most common method to get information about the environment. There are two main obstacles hindering the broad use of on-line analysis methods in animal cell production processes. Animal cell cultures are extremely susceptible to contamination with bacteria and yeasts. The monoseptic operation of the bioreactors requires their wet steam sterilization. These extreme conditions restrict the number of analysis tools used in-line mainly to temperature, pH, and pO_2 meters. These instruments withstand steam sterilization and have long-term stability and selectivity. All other methods work outside the reactor in a nonsterile area. This leads us to the second obstacle: Operating the analyzers outside the reactor requires an aseptic sampling device that will prevent back contamination but also give a realistic and reliable insight into the reactor. Although in-line analysis instruments are desirable, most of the methods have to deal with enzymes, and this restricts their use. On-line monitoring will be the method of choice at the moment. For the optimal usage of these analyzers the sample should be representative of the process at that certain moment and the sample should be ready to use within the analyzer. That means dilution, concentration, chemical modification, and so on should be done automatically between sampling and analyzing. The nature of the sample depends on the analysis being performed; therefore, the aseptic sampling device is an important element for a reliable on-line analysis system.

In the future on-line monitoring will become more and more important for process understanding, process optimization, and process safety. This article will give an overview on sampling devices and on-line analysis methods used in the laboratory and industry.

ASEPTIC SAMPLING DEVICES

Off-Line Sampling

In spite of increasing on-line analysis many parameters in animal cell culture are still ascertained using off-line methods such as cell density, cell viability, but also nutrient and product concentration; a brief résumé on off-line sampling systems will be presented.

Withdrawing samples from small culture vessels like T-flasks, spinner flasks, and hollow-fiber reactors is carried out with sterile pipettes under laminar hood conditions. It is important that the sample be representative of the status of the culture. The cell suspension should be well mixed before sampling.

Every reactor is equipped with inclusive discontinuous sterile sampling systems like steam-sterilizable bottom harvesting valves for dissolved and suspended substances, hooded samplers, and glass traps (1–4). The samples are obtained manually, and the first 5 to 10 mL is discarded to ensure a representative sample. Volatile compounds are determined in the headspace.

Automated sampling devices have been described by Lenz et al. (5) and Ghoul et al. (6). These devices are constructed to connect an analyzer (e.g., HPLC) to the process. They consist of an automatically steam-sterilized valve followed by a filtration unit for removal of particles. Between measurements the filtration membrane is automatically scrolled forward to avoid clogging by a filtration cake. These devices are used for different culture types, mainly in the microbial area.

On-Line Sampling Devices

There are three different types of samples to be taken out of the reactor:

- culture medium with cells
- culture medium without cells
- dissolved gas and volatile medium compounds

Therefore, different types of on-line sampling devices exist. Cell-free samples and the dissolved and volatile compounds are mainly taken via membranes (dialysis, ultra- or microfiltration membranes), whereas for cell-containing samples various devices exist.

One crucial point concerning the on-line determination of substrates, metabolites, products, etc. is the presence of biomass in the sample. The cells will continue to metabolize and produce under conditions different from those in the reactor and therefore falsify the obtained data.

Furthermore, the cells will, with great likelihood, attach themselves to the connecting tubes and other parts of the analyzer. Especially mammalian cells with their relative large diameter will settle down and form active layers or block the system. For biotechnological processes cell-free sampling is preferential for most analysis problems.

Cell-Free Sampling Devices. Despite the problems with the biomass mentioned above, the nature of the molecular species is decisive for the choice of sampling device and membrane, respectively. Analyzing low-molecular-weight substances like glucose and lactate, ultrafiltration or dialysis membranes are used. These membranes prevent cell debris and large biomolecules passing into the analyzer. The pore size is determined by the demand of the aseptic flow stream. The membrane acts as a barrier to both sides: The cells growing in the reactor are prevented from leaving, and, more important, contamination with organisms coming from outside the reactor is prevented. Especially the slow-growing mammalian cell culture with the rich medium is susceptible to contamination with bacteria. To ensure a complete exclusion of contamination, membranes must have a pore size of $0.2\,\mu m$ or lower. Additionally the membranes have to withstand sterilization, which reduces the number of materials suitable for this purpose. Membrane materials often used in mammalian cell cultivation are cellulose acetate, cellulose nitrate, polysulfone, and most commonly polypropylene. Using this type of sampling device the analyzer may work under nonsterile conditions, which is the only possibility for many analyzers using biological sensors based on enzymes and antibodies. This kind of sensor prohibits sterilization either with heat or with chemicals. The disadvantage of this type of sampling device is the restricted standing time, because of membrane fowling and clogging. Mixing in mammalian cell reactors is restricted to slow stirrer speed, to avoid damage of the cells by mechanical and physical forces. This too will promote membrane fowling and clogging, and therefore the position of the sampling device inside the reactor is of great importance. Another important point is the filtration process characteristics, which concern, for example, transmembrane pressure, pore geometry, time lag, sample dispersion, etc. This will influence the reliability of the obtained data (7,8). Another risk that limits the use of these sampling devices for genetically engineered cell cultures is the possibility of membrane damage and the escape of engineered material into the environment.

In principle two different types of filtration module are possible. The modules may be placed inside the reactor (in-line or *in situ* modules) or in an external loop outside the reactor (external modules). In-line modules have the advantage of short response times, and the "sterile barrier" is inside the reactor. This means fewer possibilities of contamination because of the absence of tubing, pumps, and valves between the reactor and the sterile barrier. On the other hand, if the membrane is blocked, there is no possibility of exchanging the module during the cultivation run. Due to the low stirrer speed in mammalian cell cultivation, the location of these in-line modules in the reactor is crucial and influences their performance. Mammalian cells tend to attach themselves to the membranes as well as the macromolecules present in the culture medium, and so they may clog the filtration unit. Therefore, the sampling module should be in the area of greatest turbulence.

The membranes described below are widely used in microbial fermentation. For details see Freitag (9), Scheper et al. (10), and Schügerl (11).

In-Line Modules. Early types of *in situ* modules were equipped with ultra- or microfiltration membranes and were disc shaped (12,13). These devices, steam sterilizable and stable long term, were used for microbial but not for mammalian cell culture. Their big disadvantage is their shape: They can only be inserted into the reactor from the inside. Rod-shaped devices with tubular membranes overcome this problem (14–16). They can be inserted using the standard ports of the fermentor. The module (Fig. 1) originally developed by the University of Hannover (17) and currently distributed by ABC (Advanced Biotechnology Corporation, Munich, Germany) and Eppendorf-Netheler-Hinz (Hamburg, Germany) has been successfully used for monitoring mammalian cell cultures (Hybridoma, BHK) (15,17,18). The advantage of short response times of rod-shaped modules is the combination of large filtration area with a small internal volume. For monitoring low-molecular-weight substances this sampling device is also suitable. Using this device for monitoring high-molecular-weight substances that should pass through the membrane will falsify the data, since these substances will form a secondary filtration area (19).

Systems used for perfusion of medium during mammalian cultivation processes (e.g., silicone tubing or spin filters) can also be used for connecting to an on-line analysis system (20,21). As long as the viability of the cultures is high, spin filters work satisfactorily for micro-carrier cultures as well as for suspension cultures. With decreasing culture viability, the amount of cell debris in the reactor increases, and therefore the amount of debris passing the spin filter increases after leading to filter clogging.

External Modules. External sampling modules are more commonly used in mammalian cell culture. They are placed into an external loop through which the culture medium is recirculated. This simplifies the accessibility and the exchangeability in cases were it is necessary; for example, it is possible to have several modules in parallel. Any type of sterilizable filter module can be used as

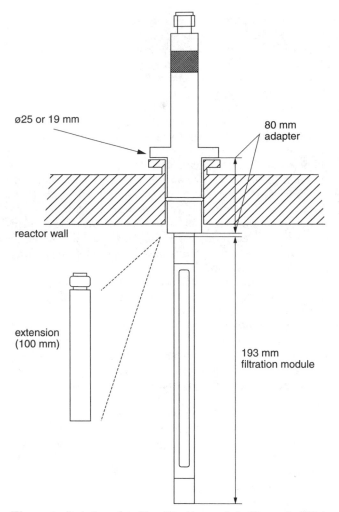

Figure 1. Rod-shaped in-line filtration module (Eppendorf/University of Hannover).

an external sampling module (e.g., a hollow-fiber unit). Tangential or cross-flow modules are used preferentially to minimize membrane fouling. However, the rapid flow of the reactor contents over the membrane may cause problems with cultures where the cells are sensitive to shear stress. Slowing down the circulation speed increases fowling as mammalian cells settle down and attach to the module and furthermore the cell's environment in the loop may change considerably, such as with oxygen depletion and/or temperature drop. Therefore, when using external sampling modules, these variations have to be followed carefully in order not to measure artefacts caused by the loop.

Another disadvantage compared to the in-line modules is reliability. The "sterile barrier" is outside the reactor, and the tubing and pumps between reactor and module are known to be the least reliable parts in such a system. Blocking of the tubing by biomass or erosion of the tubes in the pumps may lead to breakage and contamination of the culture. It is, therefore, good practice to use new tubes for each extended vessel operation.

Disc-shaped modules with different types of flat membranes have been described by Graf (19) and Fenge et al. (22) for continuous hybridoma cultures. Graf used

a cross-flow module distributed by Millipore (Eschborn, Germany) to acquire samples for glucose analysis, while Fenge et al. used a home-made tangential filtration unit to acquire samples for monoclonal antibody analysis. Rapid circulation did not cause problems in Fenge's case, since the biomass was kept in the reactor by a perfusion system.

Several tubular shaped modules have been described for microbial systems (23–25) but only few were used for mammalian cell cultivation. A commercially available tangential flow module is the A-sep from Applicon (Fig. 2) (26–28). The reactor content is pumped through a length of silicon tubing which meanders backwards and forwards several times. Dubois et al. described a 19-day Hela-culture with a continuous sample flow of 50 ml/min.

To evade the rapid circulation used to avoid membrane clogging, modules with secondary flows are developed. Different types were used for microbial fermentations (29,30) but the most successful one is the BIOPEM developed by GBF (Gesellschaft für Biotechnologische Forschung) and B.Braun Biotech International (31,32). The round filter cell (Fig. 3) is equipped with a magnetic stirrer reducing membrane fouling because of the high shear effect close to the membrane. Another commercially available module is the PERSEP-system (TECHSEP, Germany), a rotating rod-shape module is inserted into the fermentor. Because of the high rotation speeds (3,000 to 5,000 rpm) membrane fowling is not a problem.

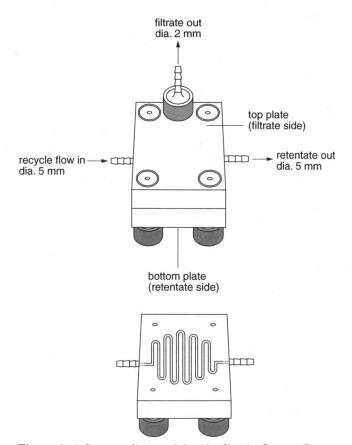

Figure 2. A-Sep-sampling module (Applicon). *Source*: Reproduced with permission from Schulze B., Ph.D. Thesis, University of Hannover, Germany, 1994 (28).

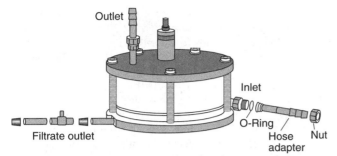

Figure 3. Biopem sampling module (B. Braun International, Germany).

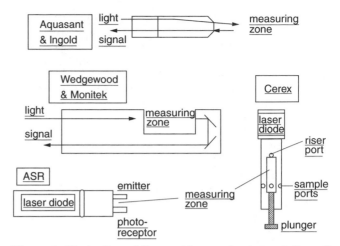

Figure 4. Illustration of the working mechanisms of the cell density probes (35).

CELL CHARACTERIZATION

For characterization and optimization of a bioprocess parameter such as the biomass, cell density, viability, metabolic status, and morphology are of great interest. On-line measurement of cell density and viability are useful since continuous cultures with sophisticated feeding strategies are often used in more sophisticated research environments.

Optical sensors are the method of choice. In principle there are two types of noninvasive sensors: nephelometric and fluorescence sensors. Recently developed equipment that delivers microscopic images with automated image analysis is also under investigation.

Nephelometric Sensors

Nephelometric sensors measure the turbidity of the cultivation medium (33). Suspended biomass, particles, and air bubbles contribute to the turbidity of the liquid phase. Turbidity can be used as a measure of the cell density, using the appropriate calibration curve for the number of cells as a function of turbidity. These data are only reliable when there is no interference from other particles. This results in some restrictions for the application of this method. Cultures with entrapped cells (e.g., hollow-fiber cultures) as well as microcarrier cultures cannot be monitored with this method. Data obtained with nephelometric sensors are reliable up to the point when the viability of the cell culture drops. The sensor cannot distinguish between viable and nonviable cells, and cell debris also increases the turbidity of the culture medium. This has to be taken into account when using nephelometric sensors for the determination of cell number or cell concentration.

Two different types of sensor are used in biotechnology: transmission and retroflective sensors (34). Transmission sensors are reliable when monitoring high cell densities, but since they often work at one defined wavelength, they are insensitive to low cell concentrations. *In situ* types of transmission sensors may be installed in an external loop (Monitek) with all the problems of external loops. Other sensors interfaced via standard ports into the bioreactor (BTG, Bonnier Technology Group) may cause problems as a result of the hydrodynamic behavior of the medium in the flow-through cell. Data obtained with transmission sensors may not reflect the actual situation in the bioreactor.

Fiber optics are used for retroreflective sensors to guide the excitation light into the reactor and collect the backward-scattered light (Aquasant, Mettler). Therefore, the collected light increases with increasing cell concentration. The system is reliable, easy to install, and low cost. Wu et al. (35) used this system for monitoring industrial mammalian cell culture and performed a comparison of several commercially available optical systems (Fig. 4). A comparison of data obtained using microscope and graduated slides, Coulter counter, and the various probes shows a high correlation. The Aquasant data are always slightly lower than the microscopic data, especially at higher cell densities, but they can be obtained continuously.

Nephelometric sensors are low cost and easy to install. The response time is small (seconds), and the data are easy to interpret. The main disadvantage is that other particles of cellular origin interfere, and dying cells or cell debris cause high values of optical density. Also it is not possible to distinguish between viable and nonviable cells.

Fluorescence Methods

Another way of obtaining information about the biomass during the cultivation is the measurement of the culture fluorescence. Biologically active cells contain the dinucleotides NADH and NADPH. If the culture conditions are optimal and the cells are growing well, the NADH and NADPH concentrations increase. These reduced dinueotides can be irradiated with UV light (340–360 nm), and the induced fluorescence can be registered with suitable detectors (460 nm). Zabriskie and Humphrey (36) were the first to use culture fluorescence to monitor living cells. They used the correlation between biomass concentration (X) and fluorescence intensity (I_f):

$$X = (e^{-b}I_f)^{1/a}$$

where a and b are constants characteristic of the biological system and the reactor, but only in a few cases is this correlation linear.

Various types of *in situ* sensors using the same optical system for the irradiation of the cells and the detection of the fluorescence are available (Fluoromeasure from BioChem Technology, Fluorosensor from Ingold). In the literature there is a variety of data available derived by using these sensors to estimate biomass concentration, reactor characterization, medium composition, and the metabolic state of the cells (37–41). Most of the applications are carried out with microorganisms, but there are several papers describing data obtained with animal cells (42–46). Two facts hamper the broad use of *in situ* fluorescence sensors in monitoring animal cell cultures: the low cell concentration at least at the beginning of the cultivation and therefore the low NADH signal and the broad variety of fluorescence-active substances in the culture medium. The interpretation of the signals is nontrivial and has to be done in comparison with other process data obtained. Srinivas and Mutharasan (41) could show with hybridoma cells that metabolic studies such as nutrient depletion can be monitored and explained. Akhnoukh et al. (46) used the culture fluorescence to monitor virus production with *Spodoptera frugiperda* Sf9. By plotting 1/X vs. 1/fluorescence (where X is a measure of the cell concentration), the phases of growth, virus infection, expression of virus genome, and lysis of cells can be identified (Fig. 5). Akhnouk et al. (46) also showed that it is necessary to measure the background fluorescence to get reliable data.

In situ fluorescence sensors detect only viable cells and give an insight into the metabolic state of the culture. The technique is simple and noninvasive, but the signal interpretation is nontrivial. For animal cells the low cell density and the fluorescence-active medium compounds bring additional problems.

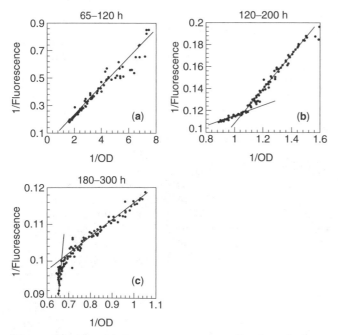

Figure 5. Reciprocal fluorescence and turbidity data during a batch cultivation of Spodoptera frugiperda for the determination of growth phase, infection phase, and cell lysis.

This may be overcome by using 2-dimensional fluorescence measurement systems. The 2D-fluorescence spectroscopy enables rapid detection of fluorescence spectra over a broad range of excitation and emission wavelengths. Simultaneously, several analytes will be registered qualitatively and quantitatively. The method is sensitive enough to give information about the chemical and physical environment of the cells as well as intracellular data. Measurements will be carried out with a fiber optical light guide on-line at the bioreactor in real-time. The metabolism of the cells will not be disturbed and the risk of contamination is low. The changes in fluorescence intensity show high correlation with other on-line or off-line measured data (47–51). A commercially available Fluorescence spectrometer can be used for detection of 2D-fluorescence spectra. Samples can be taken off-line and on-line using fiber optical sensors (52). The latter has significant advantages since the fiber optical sensor does not penetrate the reactor and can be installed and removed without sterilization.

The fluorescence intensity at particular wavelengths is dependent on chemical, physical and biological factors e.g., pH-Value, temperature, Quenching effects (53,54). Especially due to the phenol red dye used to check the pH of the mammalian cell culture medium causes serious quenching problems.

2D-Fluorescence spectroscopy is used to monitor various microorganisms. For mammalian cell cultures only preliminary measurements were carried out, such as the experiments to monitor the viability of CHO-cultures and to control the quality of produced protein (55,56).

ON-LINE MONITORING OF THE CELL'S ENVIRONMENT

During the past decades the environment of the cells was only monitored and controlled for temperature, pH value, and oxygen. It soon became obvious that this is not sufficient and that productivity can be vastly improved if knowledge regarding the optimal environmental conditions is taken into account. This means an extensive analysis of the cell environment is necessary.

One problem in mammalian cell culture is the strict requirement for contamination prevention. The bioreactor and its equipment have to be sterilized before use. Any contamination negates the culture. Putative in-line sensors have to withstand harsh sterilization conditions, which has restricted the detectable parameters to temperature, pH value, and oxygen. Since mammalian cell cultures may last for several days or months, even for these sensors their long-term stability was questionable with respect to their original calibration. The analysis of other important parameters like sugars, amino acids, metabolites, and proteins such as the product is restricted to off-line methods, which are time and labor consuming and will always have the disadvantage of a time delay.

Since fed-batch and perfusion techniques are included in process optimization, control of the environmental parameters becomes important. These techniques are based on changes in the environmental conditions and efforts to keep optimal conditions by adding or exchanging medium.

The growth rate of mammalian cells is slow, and therefore the changes in the nutrient and metabolite environment are not rapid compared to other microbial processes; so monitoring these changes by on-line methods is desirable.

During the past decade biosensors have become increasingly important. This technology has provided simple, rapid, and sensitive methods for the measurement of low- and high-molecular-weight substances. By using biological reactions, they combine the specificity of the biological compound with the capabilities of the modern transducer technology. The reaction can either be a catalytic one using enzymes or an affinity one using antibodies or receptors. During the reaction with the analyte the microenvironment of the transducer is changed. These changes can be changes in temperature, optical properties, proton, electron, gas, or ion concentration, which are sensed by the transducer, which sends an electrical signal to a recording or display device. The amount of the change correlates with the concentration of the analyte. For further information see Refs. 57 and 58.

A variety of publications deal with biosensors used for process monitoring (59–74). Most of these sensors are used on-line but outside the reactor in a sampling stream due to problems with the sterilization of the sensors. The sterilization and maintenance of the properties of the biological compound is impossible. This means that when using the sensor *in situ*, the biological compound has to be applied to the sensor after sterilization. Furthermore the conditioning of the analyte has to take place inside the sensor. This makes *in situ* sensors rather complicated, but they are described in the literature for use in penicillin and glucose estimations (60,75). Other aspects regarding *in situ* sensors are regulatory requirements, since some of the sensors need toxic mediators like ferrocene derivatives, which might bleed out into the culture medium.

Therefore, most of systems described in the literature and mentioned above incorporate the biosensor in a flow injection analysis (FIA) system. The use of a flow injection analysis system to automate the quantification of the analyte by these biosensors results in analytical methods that combine the selectivity of the biological reaction with speed, simplicity, and flexibility.

In the next section the focus will be on the most important variables that need to be analyzed. First of all techniques for analyzing standard variables like temperature, pH value, oxygen, and exhaust gas will be summarized briefly. Furthermore, on-line techniques for the nutrients (glucose, amino acids) and metabolites (lactate, ammonia) will be described. On-line monitoring of proteins can be found in the article "Immuno Flow Injection Analysis in Bioprocess Control" by Katja Klockewitz.

Physical Parameters

In industrial processes only a few process parameter are monitored, since each probe inserted into the bioreactor adds to the risk of contamination. However, it is necessary to monitor a set of control parameters, and each reactor is equipped with standard probes for those parameters in order to control the process. Reliable *in situ* measurement systems for the most important parameters (temperature, stirrer speed, pH value) are

taken from those in common use in the chemical industry. Additionally a bioreactor is equipped with a probe to measure dissolved oxygen concentration, and sometimes additional sensors are used for a determination of the composition of the exhaust gas. Since these systems are well known and described (76), only a short summary will be given.

Temperature. Temperature, the most important parameter for cultivation and sterilization, is measured by a platinum-resistance thermometer Pt-100 (100 ohm at 0 °C and 123.2 ohm at 60 °C) with an accuracy of ±0.5%. This sensor is very reliable and can be used without calibration.

pH Value. The pH value has a substantial influence on cell growth and metabolism. In order to achieve optimal conditions for growth and production, the optimal pH value has to be maintained. The pH value can be controlled by a high buffer capacity of the culture medium or by addition of acid and alkali solutions. In mammalian cell culture the culture medium's buffer capacity is based either on $CO_2/NaHCO_3$ or HEPES buffer.

If the hydrogen-ion concentration equals the hydroxide ion concentration, the solution is neutral. This is achieved at pH $7 = -\log[H^+]$. Media with higher pH values are alkaline, and those with lower pH values are acid. Mammalian cells prefer pH values in a range between 6.8 and 7.4. The measurement of the pH value is done with galvanic elements. The electrical potential E is given by the Nernst equation:

$$E = E_0 + 2.3(RT/F)\log[H^+]$$

were E_0 is the standard potential and F is the Faraday constant.

The absolute potential is not detectable; therefore, the difference of the potential U between the measuring and the reference electrode is detected.

The measurement is carried out with standard steam-sterilizable silver–silver chloride electrodes (Fig. 6). The potential is measured at the outer surface of the glass membranes of the electrodes, which depends on the pH value of the solution. The measured potential decreases with the age of the electrodes, and steam sterilization adds to the age of the electrodes. Therefore, the pH electrode has to be calibrated after each sterilization. Standard pH electrodes with high accuracy are the Ingold electrode (Mettler-Toledo) and the pH electrode by Broadly-James.

Dissolved Oxygen. The dissolved oxygen concentration of the cultivation medium is measured using a amperometric probe. The Clark electrode consists of cathode, anode, and electrolyte separated from the culture medium by a oxygen-permeable teflon membrane. The oxygen is reduced at the cathode. A linear correlation between the partial pressure of the oxygen and the intensity of current exists (77). These electrodes are commercially available (Ingold electrode Mettler-Toledo), are steam sterilizable, and fit through a standard port into the reactor. Several authors describe monitoring and control of oxygen tension in the culture medium during animal cell culture (78,79).

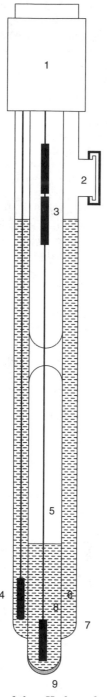

Figure 6. Illustration of the pH electrode with inserted reference (Ingold, Mettler-Toledo): 1: plug; 2: refill opening; 3: plug contact; 4: reference element; 5: measuring element; 6: reference electroyte; 7: diaphragm; 8: inner buffer; 9: gas-permeable membrane.

Singh (80) studied the oxygen uptake of hybridoma cells, and using a dynamic model for calculations could show that the specific oxygen demand is 0.15 mM $O_2/10^{-9}$ cells/h.

Carbon Dioxide. In mammalian cell cultures a carbonate buffer is used to maintain the pH value almost constant; therefore, it is not meaningful to measure the dissolved CO_2 concentration. If desired *in situ* electrodes using the Severinghaus principle are commercially available (Ingold, Mettler-Toledo). They consist of a pH electrode immersed in a bicarbonate buffer, which is separated from the culture medium by a gas-permeable membrane. Dissolved CO_2 diffuses through the membrane and changes the pH value in the external buffer solution. This change in the pH value relates to the dissolved CO_2 concentration in the bioreactor.

Exhaust Gas. Analysis of the exhaust gas is easy since there is no special sampling probes necessary. The exhaust gas is cooled and dried to remove the water vapor. Oxygen is measured with a paramagnetic oxygen analyzer and CO_2 with an infrared analyzer. Both types of analyzers are commercially available. A critical comparison of various analyzers was carried out by Heinzele and Dunn (81). Measuring the exhaust gas composition is not common in mammalian cell cultivation, since the cell density is not high and therefore the changes are small and near the detection limit. Additionally the pH value is often maintained by adding CO_2 gas to the cultivation medium, and the concentration of CO_2 produced as a result of metabolism is small.

Nutrients and Metabolites

Most commercially available cell culture media contain glucose as the main carbon source, since glucose is a low-cost ingredient and is easily metabolized by mammalian cells. However, an oversupply of glucose may cause problems with toxic metabolites like lactate. For this reason monitoring glucose concentration is of great importance for optimization of mammalian cell processes. There is a similar connection between glutamine, which is an important nitrogen source, and its toxic metabolite, ammonia. Ammonia can cause regression in cell growth but also changes in glycosylation of the desired product protein.

Off-line analysis is sufficient for every batch cultivation, but fed-batch or even perfusion cultivation needs a more frequent determination. It is necessary to effect the on-line monitoring every few minutes, if, for example, the glucose concentration is meant to be constant. Then it is possible to feed small amounts of glucose and keep the concentration as low as possible to avoid byproducts and the accumulation of toxic concentrations of lactate.

Most known on-line systems for monitoring glucose, lactate, glutamine, and ammonia are based on the flow injection analysis principle. Figure 7 shows the principle of such equipment. A sampling device is installed next to the fermenter, and a cell-free sample is withdrawn continuously. Next, the sample is conditioned (e.g., dilution, addition of cosubstrates, adjustment of pH or buffer capacity) as the analysis protocol requires. An aliquot of the conditioned sample is then injected into a continuously flowing carrier stream, the characteristic feature of the FIA system. The carrier stream transports the sample through the reaction coil, where the analysis reaction starts. After detection the signal is processed by

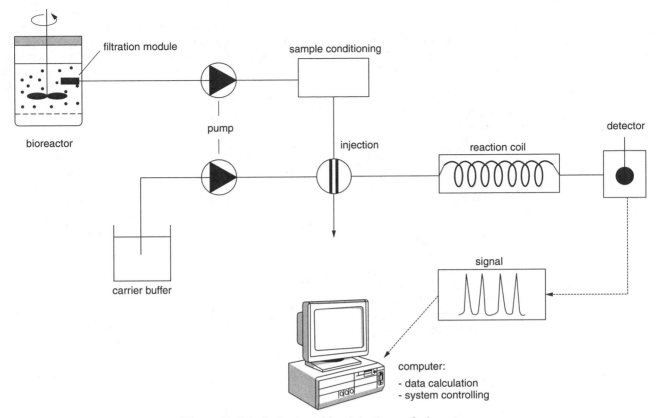

Figure 7. Principal setup of flow injection analysis systems.

a computer, giving the concentration of analyte in g/L. In sophisticated systems this computer can be used to control the flow of analyte into the bioreactor so as to maintain required concentrations of the analyte in the culture medium.

A drawback of this FIA system is the time delay incurred between withdrawing the sample and getting the results. On the other hand, the time delay is neglectable due to the slow growth rate of the cells.

The bottleneck of this kind of system is the cell-free sample. The sampling device must retain a sterile barrier between the reactor and the analysis system and at the same time withdraw a representative sample. This is fulfilled for low-molecular-weight components such as glucose, lactate, ammonia, etc., but not for high-molecular-weight components like proteins. Analyzing proteins needs a different setup (see article "Immuno Flow Injection Analysis in Bioprocess Control" by Katja Klockewitz).

Glucose. Several biosensors used for measuring glucose are described in the literature. These can be adapted to monitor glucose concentrations in animal cell cultures. All of them are based upon enzymatic reactions, and most of them rely on the conversion of glucose to gluconic acid using the enzyme glucose oxidase (GOD).

$$\beta\text{-D-glucose} + O_2 \xrightarrow{\text{GOD}} \text{gluconic acid } (H^+) + H_2O_2$$

The main difference between the described systems is the mode of detection. Graf and Schügerl (15) implemented a

YSI (Yellow Springs Instrumental) analyzer as a reaction coil and detector in the FIA system to monitor glucose.

The enzyme membrane is a trilayered deck; the enzyme (glucose oxidase GOD) is immobilized between a polycarbonate and a cellulose acetate membrane. The detection was done by measuring the current resulting from the oxidation of H_2O_2 at a platinum electrode. This system was stable over a period of 250 h of monoclonal antibody production from a rat–mouse hybridoma (15).

A fiber optic sensor was used by Dremel et al. (68) to detect the oxygen consumed by the immobilized enzyme (glucose oxidase). Several other systems were described to measure glucose like chemiluminescence detection of the produced H_2O_2 (82,83).

Another possibility is the immobilization of the enzyme in cartridges (21,83). Again the system relies on the enzymatic oxidation of glucose by glucose oxidase. The quantification was done by measuring the decrease of the oxygen in the carrier stream with an oxygen-sensitive electrode.

Lactate. The systems measuring lactate are again based on enzymatic reactions. Scheper (84) described a sensor system detecting the fluorescence of NAD$^+$ (nicotinamide adenine dinucleotide) using the coenzyme in the enzymatic reaction.

$$\text{lactate} + NAD^+ \xrightarrow{\text{lactate dehydrogenase}} \text{pyruvate} + NADH + H^+$$

Only the reduced form NADH expresses fluorescence. The increase of the fluorescence is correlated to the decrease of

NAD^+ and therefore with the concentration of lactate in the medium. The only drawback in using this method in cell culture is the presence of the pH indicator, phenol red, in the medium to double check for pH stability. The indicator tends to bias and disturb the fluorometric measurements.

Methods used for animal cell monitoring with high reliability are based upon the enzymatic reaction of lactate with lactate oxidase (68,85,86). These systems are similar to those used for measuring glucose.

Amino Acids. Different approaches can be used to determine amino acids during the cultivation of animal cells. Jürgens et al. (85) used an enzyme cartridge with immobilized L-amino acid oxidase for quantification of L-amino acids. With this system L-methionine can be determined during the cultivation of *Spodoptera frugiperda* as well as the total L-amino acid concentration.

A variety of methods are used to detect glutamine, as this is the most important amino acid in animal cell cultivation: amperometric biosensors (69,87), chemiluminescence fiber optic biosensors (72,88), and enzyme electrodes (62,89). All methods are based on the following reaction

$$\text{glutamine} \xrightarrow{\text{glutaminase}} \text{L-glutamic acid} + NH_4^+$$

The methods differ in the way the resulting ammonium is measured. One possibility is the conversion of the ammonium ion into ammonia, which can be detected with an ion-sensitive electrode (83). Blankenstein et al. (72) described an amperometric detection after oxidation of the produced glutamate with the enzyme glutamate oxidase. The decrease of oxygen in the carrier stream during that reaction was measured by an oxygen electrode. The authors also reported chemoluminescence detection of the H_2O_2 produced after reaction with luminol, which results in the production of a substance with a blue color.

A small-volume L-glutamate on-line sensor was developed by Niwa et al. (90) to monitor changes in the local concentration of L-glutamate released from nerve cells in culture. A syringe pump in the suction mode is used to sample extracellular fluid continuously from a glass microcapillary, and the concentration of L-glutamate can be determined by using a glassy carbon (GC) electrode modified with an Os-polyvinylpyridine mediator bottom film containing horseradish peroxidase and a bovine serum albumin top layer containing L-glutamate oxidase. Eyer et al. (91) described a method for the indirect control of the glutamine level in the reactor. They measured the oxygen uptake rate (OUR).

Multidetection of Different Compounds. Glucose, lactate, and glutamine are the most interesting low-molecular-weight compounds in animal cell cultivation. Therefore, the simultaneous monitoring of these components with one system is most desirable. This would minimize the risk of contamination while increasing dramatically the amount of information on the culture. Van der Pol et al. (92) described a multichannel on-line system for the detection of glucose, lactate, glutamine, and ammonia. They combined enzymatic reactions with chemical reactions. Glucose, lactate, and glutamine were detected using immobilized, dehydrogenases, whereas ammonia was detected using an o-phthaldialdehyde solution. The results were reliable, but the detection of all components required 42 min. Similar systems are described in literature based on an enzymatic reaction with oxidases (21,85,93,94).

Dremel et al. (68) reported a system where glucose and lactate could be determined simultaneously in two separate channels. It yielded reliable results for animal cell cultures with a sampling frequency of 20 samples per hour.

Weidemann (21) used a two-channel–two-selector system for monitoring glucose and lactate during perfusion cultures of adherent recombinant BHK cells. He kept the glucose and lactate concentration at a low level (glucose 0.5 g/L and lactate 1.5 g/L) using the signals from the FIA system for controlling the feeding pumps.

BIBLIOGRAPHY

1. N. Ahlmann et al., *Anal. Chim. Acta* **190**, 221–226 (1986).

2. G. Imming, H. Schaller, and M. Meiners, in A. Holme ed., *First IFAC (International Federation of Automatic Control) Workshop on Modelling and Control in Biotechnological Processes*, Pergamon, Helsinki, 1982, p. 27.

3. B. Mattiasson et al., *Ann. N.Y. Acad. Sci.* **413**, 193–196 (1983).

4. R. Freitag, Th. Scheper, and K. Schügerl, *Enzyme Microb. Technol.* **13**, 969–975 (1991).

5. R. Lenz, C. Boelcke, U. Peckmann, and M. Reuss, (1985) A new automatic sampling device for the determination of filtration characteristics and the coupling of an HPLC to fermentors, in A. Holme, ed., *First IFAC (International Federation of Automatic Control) Symposium on Modelling and Control in Biotechnological Processes*, Halme, Pergamon, Noordwijkerhout, 1985, pp. 55–60.

6. M. Ghoul, E. Ronat, and J.-M. Engasser, *Biotechnol. Bioeng.* **28**, 119–121 (1986).

7. U. Spohn and H. Voss, *BTF—Biotechnol. Forum* **6**, 274–288 (1989).

8. L.H. Christensen, J. Nielsen, and J. Villadsen *Chem. Eng. Sci.* **46**(12), 3304–3307 (1991).

9. R. Freitag, in R. Freitag, ed., *Biosensors in Analytical Biotechnology*, Academic Press, San Diego, Calif., 1996, pp. 1–21.

10. Th. Scheper, R. Freitag, and F. Scrienc, in H. Hauser and R. Wagner, eds., *Mammalian Cell Biotechnology in Protein Production*, de Gruyter, Berlin, 1997, pp. 373–410.

11. K. Schügerl, *Bioreaktionstechnik: Bioprozesse mit Mikroorganismen und Zellen*, Birkhäuser, Basel, 1997.

12. Th. Lorenz, W. Schmidt, and K. Schügerl, *Chem. Eng. J.* **35**, B15–B22 (1987).

13. Th. Bayer, W. Zhou, K. Holzhauer, and K. Schügerl, *Appl. Microbiol. Biotechnol.* **30**, 2–33 (1989).

14. Eur. Pat. Appl. 85 308,834.2, Publ. No. 0184441 (December 4, 1985), T.L. Waarrik (to Eli Lilly & Company, Indianapolis, Id.).

15. H. Graf and K. Schügerl, *Appl. Microbiol. Biotechnol.* **35**, 165–175 (1991).

16. I. Marc, F. Blanchard, J.-M. Engasser, and S. Taha, *Workshop Aseptic Sampling, 5th Eur. Congr. Biotechnol. (ECB5)*, Copenhagen, 1990.

17. H. Graf, D. Wentz, and K. Schügerl, *Biotechnol. Biotech.* **5**, 183–186 (1991).

18. D. Wentz, Ph.D. Thesis, University of Hannover, 1989.

19. H. Graf, Ph.D. Thesis, University of Hannover, 1989.

20. E. Fraune, Ch. Fenge, and W. Kuhlmann, *8th Int. Biotechnol. Symp.*, Paris, 1988, Abstr. Book, p. 115.

21. R. Weidemann, Ph.D. Thesis, Germany Universität Hannover, 1995.

22. Ch. Fenge et al., *Cytotechnology* **6**, 55–63 (1991).

23. S. Mitzutani et al., *J. Ferment. Technol.* **65**, 325–331 (1987).

24. R. Freitag, Th. Scheper, A. Spreinat, and G. Antranikian, *Appl. Microbiol. Biotechnol.* **35**, 471–476 (1991).

25. J. Gram, M. de Bang, K. Nikolajsen, and K.A. Holm, *Workshop: Aseptic Sampling, 5th Eur. Congr. Biotechnol. (ECB5)*, Copenhagen, 1990.

26. D. Dubois et al., *Bioknowledge* **2**, 7–10 (1991).

27. L.W. Forman, B.D. Thomas, and F.S. Jacobsen, *Anal. Chim Acta* **249**, 101–111 (1991).

28. B. Schulze, Ph.D. Thesis, University of Hannover, 1994.

29. H.B. Winzeler *Chimia* **44**, 288–291 (1990).

30. K.H. Kroner, V. Nissinen, and H. Ziegeler, *Bio/Technology* **5**, 921–926 (1987).

31. K.H. Kroner, W. Stach, and W. Kuhlmann, *Chem.-Tech. (Heidelberg)* **15**, 74–77 (1986).

32. R. Freitag et al., *Anal. Chim. Acta* **249**, 113–122 (1991).

33. R.D. Vanous, *Am. Lab.* **6**, 17–23 (1978).

34. K. Reardon and Th. Scheper, in K. Schügerl, ed., *Biotechnology, Measuring, Modelling and Control*, 2nd rev. ed., Vol. 2, VCH, Weinheim, 1991, pp. 181–223.

35. P. Wu et al., *Biotechnol. Bioeng.* **45**, 495–502 (1995).

36. D.W. Zabriskie and A.E. Humphrey, *Eur. J. Appl. Microbiol.* **35**, 337–343 (1978).

37. W. Beyeler, A. Einsele, and A. Fiechter, *Eur. J. Appl. Biotechnol.* **13**, 10–14 (1981).

38. W. Beyeler, K. Gschwend, and A. Fiechter, *Chem.-Ing.-Tech.* **55**(5), 869–871 (1983).

39. Th. Scheper and K. Schügerl, *J. Biotechnol.* **3**, 221–229 (1986).

40. K.F. Reardon, Th. Scheper, and J.E. Bailey, *Biotechnol. Prog.* **3**(3), 153–167 (1987).

41. S.P. Srinivas and R. Mutharasan, *Biotechnol. Lett.* **9**(2), 139–142 (1987).

42. C. Leist, H.P. Meyer, and A. Fiechter, *J. Biotechnol.* **4**, 235–246 (1986).

43. G. MacMichael, W.B. Arminger, J.F. Lee, and R. Mutharasan, *Biotechnol. Tech.* **4**, 213–218 (1987).

44. S.P. Srinivas and R. Mutharasan, *Biotechnol. Bioeng.* **30**, 769–774 (1987).

45. S.A. Siano and R. Mutharasan, *Biotechnol. Bioeng.* **37**, 141–159 (1991).

46. R. Akhnoukh, G. Kretzmer, and K. Schügerl, *Enzyme Microb. Technol.* **18**, 220–228 (1996).

47. Th. Scheper, R. Freitag, and F. Scrienc, in H. Hauser and R. Wagner, eds., *Mammalian Cell Biotechnology in Protein Production*, 1997, pp. 373–410.

48. B. Hitzmann et al., *Anal. Chim. Acta* **348**, 135–141 (1997).

49. A. Ritzka, P. Sosnitza, R. Ulber, and T. Scheper, *Curr. Opin. Biotechnol.* **8**, 160–164 (1997).

50. C. Müller, B. Hitzmann, F. Schubert, and T. Scheper, *Sensors Actuators* **B40**, 71–77 (1997).

51. S. Marose, C. Lindemann, and Th. Scheper, *Biotechnol. Prog.* **14**(1), 63–74 (1998).

52. S. Marose, C. Lindemann, R. Ulber, and Th. Scheper, *Trends Biotechnol.* **17**, 30–34 (1999).

53. J.M. Hilmer, Ph.D. Thesis, University of Hannover, 1996.

54. X.F. Wang and B. Herman, *Fluorescence Imaging Spectroscopy and Microscopy*, Wiley, New York, 1996.

55. R. Finke, Thesis, University of Hannover, 1998.

56. M. Hüners, Thesis, University of Hannover, 1996.

57. A.P.F. Turner, I. Karuber, and G.S. Wilson, eds., *Biosensors: Fundamentals and Applications*, Oxford Science Publication, Oxford, U.K., 1987.

58. J.V. Twork and A.M. Yacynych, eds., *Sensors in Bioprocess Control*, Dekker, New York, 1990.

59. O.W. Merten, G.E. Palfi, and J. Steiner, *Adv. Biotechnol. Processes* **6**, 11–178 (1986).

60. D.G. Kilburn, in M. Butler, ed., *Mammalian Cell Biotechnology*, Oxford University Press, Oxford, U.K., 1991, pp. 159–185.

61. B. Griffiths, in R.I. Freshney, ed., *Animal Cell Culture*, IRL Press, Oxford, U.K., 1986, pp. 3–69.

62. J.-L. Romette and C.L. Cooney, *Anal. Lett.* **20**, 1069–1081 (1987).

63. E.J. Fernandez, A. Mancuso, and D.S. Clark, *Biotechnol Bioeng.* **22**, 457–462 (1988).

64. M. Gotoh, E. Tamiya, and A. Seki, *Anal. Lett.* **22**(2), 309–322 (1989).

65. J. Bradley, W. Stöcklein, and R.D. Schmid, *Process Control Qual.* **1**, 157–173 (1991).

66. R. Renneberg et al., *J. Biotechnol.* **21**, 173–186 (1991).

67. C. Filippini, B. Sonnleitner, and A. Fiechter, *J. Biotechnol.* **18**, 153–160 (1991).

68. B.A.A. Dremel, S.-Y. Li, and R.D. Schmid, *Biosens. Bioelectron.* **7**, 133–139 (1992).

69. M.V. Cattaneo, J.H.T. Luong, and S. Mercille, *Biosens. Bioelectron.* **7**, 329–334 (1992).

70. B. Mattiasson and H. Hankanson, *Adv. Biochem. Eng. Biotechnol.* **46**, 81–102 (1992).

71. Th. Scheper, *J. Ind. Microbiol.* **9**, 163–172 (1992).

72. G. Blankenstein, F. Preuschoff, and U. Spohn, *Anal. Chim. Acta* **271**, 231–237 (1993).

73. G. Kretzmer, in R. Freitag, ed., *Biosensors in Analytical Biotechnology*, R.G. Landes, Austin, Tex., Academic Press, San Diego, Calif. 1996.

74. J.I. Rhee et al., *Anal. Chim. Acta* **374**, 177–183 (1998).

75. J. Bradley et al., *Analyst (London)* **114**, 375–379 (1989).

76. W.G. Andrew and O. Williams, eds., *Applied Instrumentation in the Process Industries*, 2nd ed., Vol. 1, Gulf Publ. Co., Houston, Tex., 1979.

77. H. Buehler and W. Ingold, *Process Biochem.* **11**, 19–24 (1976).

78. C.M. Kussow, W.C. Zhou, D.M. Gryte, and W.S. Hu, *Enzyme Microb. Technol.* **17**, 779–783 (1995).

79. A. Oeggerli, K. Eyer, and E. Heinzle, *Biotechnol. Bioeng.* **45**(1), 42–53 (1995).

80. V. Singh *Biotechnol. Bioeng.* **52**(3), 443–448 (1996).

81. E. Heinzele and I.J. Dunn, in H.J. Rehm, G. Reed, A. Pühler, and P. Stadler, eds., VCH, *Biotechnology*, 2nd ed., Vol. 4, Weinheim, 1991, pp. 27–74.

82. K.B. Male, P.O. Gartu, A.A. Kamen, and J.H.T. Luong, *Biotechnol. Bioeng.* **55**, 497–504 (1997).

83. Y.L. Huang et al., *Anal. J. Biotechnol.* **18**, 161–172 (1991).

84. Th. Scheper, *Bioanalytik*, Vieweg Verlag, Braunschweig, 1991.

85. H. Jürgens et al., *Anal. Chim Acta* **298**, 141–149 (1995).

86. K.B. Male, P.O. Gartu, A.A. Kamen, and J.H.T. Luong, *Anal. Chim. Acta* **351**, 159–167 (1997).

87. K.B. Male, J.H.T. Luong, R. Tom, and S. Mercile, *Enzyme Microb. Technol.* **15**, 26–32 (1993).

88. M.V. Cattaneo and J.H.T. Luong, *Biotechnol. Bioeng.* **41**, 659–665 (1993).

89. C. Campmajó et al., *Cytotechnology* **14**, 177–182 (1994).

90. O. Niwa, T. Horiuchi, and K. Torimitsu, *Biosensors Bioelectron.* **12**(4), 311–319 (1997).

91. K. Eyer, A. Oeggerli, and E. Heinzle, *Biotechnol. Bioeng.* **45**, 54–62 (1995).

92. J.J. van der Pol et al., *J. Biotechnol.* **37**, 253–264 (1994).

93. G. Blankenstein et al., *Biotechnol. Bioeng.* **20**, 291–307 (1994).

94. S.F. White et al., *Biosens. Bioelectron.* **10**, 543–555 (1995).

See also BIOREACTOR OPERATIONS—PREPARATION, STERILIZATION, CHARGING, CULTURE INITIATION AND HARVESTING; BIOREACTOR SCALE-UP; BIOREACTORS, STIRRED TANK; IMMUNO FLOW INJECTION ANALYSIS IN BIOPROCESS CONTROL; OFF-LINE ANALYSIS IN ANIMAL CELL CULTURE, METHODS; OFF-LINE IMMUNOASSAYS IN BIOPROCESS CONTROL.

P

PHYSIOLOGY OF PLANT CELLS IN CULTURE

TETSURO MIMURA
Hitotsubushi University
Tokyo, Japan

HIROSHI ASHIHARA
Ochanomizu University
Tokyo, Japan

OUTLINE

UPTAKE OF SUGARS, NITROGEN AND PHOSPHATE

Carbon, nitrogen, and phosphorous are major constituents of cells, and in typical plant cells in culture they account for 40%, 7%, and 0.3% of dry weight, respectively (1). Plants are autotrophs, and therefore, inorganic carbon, nitrogen, and phosphorous can be utilized for growth. However, a limited number of cultured plant cells can grow with only CO_2 as a carbon source. Most cultured cells grow heterotrophically. Sugars, such as sucrose and glucose, are usually supplied as carbon sources in the culture medium. Nitrogen is supplied to cultured plant cells as a combination of ammonium and nitrate salts. The most common nitrogen compounds used for this purpose are KNO_3, $NaNO_3$, $Ca(NO_3)_2$, $(NH_4)_2SO_4$, $NH_4H_2PO_4$, and NH_4NO_3. In addition, some organic nitrogen compounds, such as amino acids, are occasionally included in culture media. Phosphorus is usually supplied as inorganic phosphate in the form of KH_2PO_4, NaH_2PO_4, or $NH_4H_2PO_4$.

Uptake and Utilization of Sugars

Various sugars are used as nutrients for cultured plant cells (Table 1). A comprehensive list of carbon sources and their ability to support the growth of plant cells in suspension culture has been discussed previously (2).

Sucrose (2–3% w/v in concentration) is the most common sugar used as a carbon source. There are several reports on the uptake of sugars by the suspension-cultured plant cells. In various culture systems, sucrose in the culture medium is hydrolyzed to glucose and fructose before entry into the cells, although such a degradation step is not always obligatory for utilization of sucrose by plant cells (2). Figure 1(a) shows changes in levels of sucrose and reducing sugars in the medium of batch suspension cultures of *Catharanthus roseus* cells. Substantially all the sucrose in the culture medium was hydrolyzed by cell wall-bound invertase to glucose and fructose before it was taken up by the cells (3). The highest rate of degradation of sucrose was observed at lag phase of cell growth (1 day after inoculation to the fresh medium). A pronounced reduction in total sugar levels in the medium was observed in the logarithmic phase of cell growth (day 4). Glucose was more readily taken up by the cells than was fructose in several culture systems including *C. roseus* (3) and carrot cells (4). However, both hexoses were taken up at equal rate by cultured rice cells (5). In addition to cell wall-bound invertase, excreted invertase may participate in the degradation of sucrose. The level of extracellular invertase in the culture medium was rather low during the initial phase of culture, where rapid degradation of sucrose was observed. Both wall-bound and excreted plant invertases have acidic pH optima (4.0–4.7). The pH of culture medium usually decreased at the early phase of culture [Fig. 1(b)]. Thus hydrolysis of sucrose by the acid invertases may be stimulated at this phase.

Glucose and fructose taken up by the cells are metabolized via glycolysis, the tricarboxylic acid (TCA) cycle, and the pentose phosphate pathway. Their intermediates, sugar phosphates and organic acids, are utilized as carbon skeletons of cellular constituents (Fig. 2). The ATP produced in glycolysis and respiration is used as an energy supply. The metabolic fate of glucose and fructose is slightly different in *C. roseus* cells. Glucose is a better precursor for respiration than fructose, while fructose is preferentially utilized for the resynthesis of sucrose, especially in the early phase of cell growth (3).

Table 1. Carbon Sources Examined for Cultured Cells from Various Plant Species

Class	Carbon source
Class 1	(effective for most plant cultures) Sucrose, glucose, galactose, fructose, maltose, raffinose, stachyose
Class 2	(effective for limited plant cultures) Cellobiose, glycerol, lactose, melezitose, starch, trehalose
Class 3	(poor) Arabinose, inositol, mannitol, rhamnose, ribose, sorbitol, xylose

Source: Data from Ref. 2.

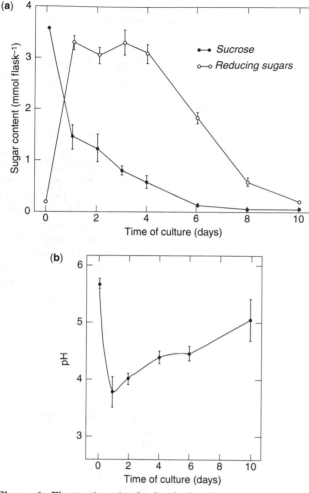

Figure 1. Fluctuations in the level of carbon sources (**a**) and in the pH (**b**) of the culture medium of suspension cultures of *Catharanthus roseus*. *Source*: Redrawn from Ref. 3.

Metabolism of other carbon sources by plant cells in culture has not been examined extensively. However, these compounds may be phosphorylated and converted to glucose-6-phosphate or fructose-6-phosphate; next they enter the glycolytic pathway and are then further metabolized, as shown in the pathways represented in Figure 2.

Uptake and Utilization of Nitrogen

Nitrogen is supplied as NO_3^- and NH_4^+ in the culture medium. NH_4^+ is a direct substrate for the formation of organic nitrogen (amino acid), but the concentration of NH_4^+ ions in culture media is usually 2–10 times lower than that of NO_3^- ions. Nitrate can be stored in vacuoles without a detrimental effect. However, NH_4^+ ions and in particular its equilibrium partner, ammonia, are toxic even at quite low concentrations (5).

In batch suspension culture, NH_4^+ ions in the culture medium are initially absorbed and subsequently NO_3^- ions are taken up by the cells. A decrease in medium pH just after cell inoculation [Fig. 1(b)] may depend upon the cell uptake of NH_4^+ ions by the cells. NO_3^- ions are reduced to ammonia by the action of nitrate

reductase and nitrite reductase in the cells (Fig. 3). As is generally the case for plant life, most NH_4^+ ions in the cells are assimilated by the glutamine synthetase (GS) and glutamate synthase (glutamate:oxoglutarate amino transferase, GOGAT) system. In addition, the reversible glutamate dehydrogenase system may also be operative when higher concentrations of NH_4^+ ions are present in the cells. Glutamate, the product of ammonia assimilation, is utilized for the synthesis of other amino acids and nucleotides, and is finally consumed during the synthesis of proteins and nucleic acids.

Uptake and Utilization of Phosphorus

Phosphorus is an essential constituent of nucleotides, nucleic acids, phospholipids, and sugar phosphates (6). In addition, inorganic phosphate (Pi) and organic phosphate compounds, such as ATP, act as regulators of several important metabolic processes. In contrast to sugars and nitrogen, the uptake of Pi by plant cells in culture is usually very fast. Tracer experiments with ^{32}Pi revealed that nearly half of the Pi in the standard Murashige–Skoog medium (1.25 mM) was taken up by *C. roseus* cells within 24 h after inoculation (6). Free Pi in the cells decreased with cell growth, and more than 85% of the absorbed Pi was found as organic phosphates at the stationary phase of cell growth. A large proportion of the absorbed Pi was incorporated into nucleic acids (45%) and phospholipids (30%), 5–10% was incorporated into nucleotides, and less than 3% was into sugar phosphates and proteins (Fig. 4).

Intracellular compartmentation of Pi has been investigated using ^{31}P-NMR (7). As soon as stationary-phase cells were transferred to a fresh medium, Pi entered the cells and accumulated in the cytosol. When the cytoplasmic pool of Pi was filled, the Pi was then taken up by the vacuoles. As the cytoplasmic pool of Pi was consumed for organic phosphate synthesis, Pi was moved from vacuoles to the cytoplasm. Thus the cytoplasmic Pi concentration was usually maintained between 5 and 6 mM.

Cytoplasmic Pi concentration is one of the most effective signals for cellular metabolism. Metabolic changes induced by Pi include the initiation of cell division (8) and depression of the formation of indole alkaloids and phenolic compounds (9) in plant cells in culture. In Pi-deficient cells, the level of ATP is extremely low, and biosynthetic reactions cannot function. The addition of Pi to the Pi-deleted suspension-cultured *C. roseus* cells resulted in a marked increase in ATP within a few hours (10). Furthermore, biosynthesis of nucleic acids and proteins commenced, and finally cell division occurred (11,12). Free amino acid pools were reduced by Pi, which is mainly due to an increase in the rate of protein synthesis induced by increased ATP supply. A decrease in the rate of formation of secondary metabolites, such as phenolic compounds, by Pi seems at least partially due to reduced availability of free amino acids.

Thus phosphate concentration in culture media influences growth and formation of secondary metabolites of plant cells in culture. Pi also acts as an important effector of enzymes of carbohydrate metabolism in plant cells in culture (7).

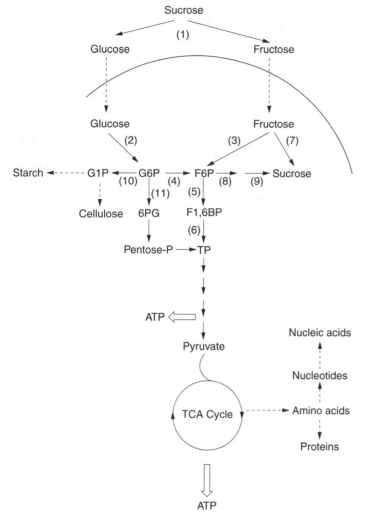

Figure 2. Uptake and metabolism of sucrose by cultured plant cells. Enzymes are represented by numbers as follows: (1) invertase; (2) hexokinase; (3) hexokinase and/or fructokinase; (4) phosphoglucoisomerase; (5) phosphofructokinase and/or pyrophosphate: fructose-6-phosphate 1-phosphotransferase; (6) aldolase; (7) sucrose synthase; (8) sucrose-6-phosphate synthase; (9) sucrose-6-phosphate phosphatase; (10) phosphoglucomutase; (11) glucose-6-phosphate dehydrogenase. Abbreviations: F6P, fructose-6-phosphate; F1,6BP, fructose-1,6-bisphosphate; G1P, glucose-1-phosphate; G6P, glucose-6-phosphate; 6PG, 6-phosphogluconate; TCA, tricarboxylic acid; TP, triose phosphate. *Source*: Adapted from Ref. 3.

MECHANISMS OF MEMBRANE TRANSPORT SYSTEMS

Transport processes across membranes are strictly dependent on the energetic situation of the membrane. We deal with the energetics of the plasma membrane and tonoplast, and then the transport activities of each substance. Figure 5 shows a schematic diagram of membrane transport systems in plant cells. The molecular structure of some transporters has been already identified. Studies on the other transporters and on the mechanisms regulating transport are important subjects for the near future (13).

Energetics of Membrane Transport

Transport of all substances across membranes is basically driven by a chemical potential gradient (for neutral substances like sugars) or electrochemical potential gradient (for ionic compounds such as nitrate, ammonium ion, and phosphate).

Since the biological membrane is composed of a lipid bilayer and proteins, when substances are lipid soluble (that is, mainly hydrophobic), they can directly pass through the lipid part. For example, NH_3, being a small, neutral molecule, has been considered to be permeable across the lipid membrane. Otherwise, protein transporters are needed for substances to cross the membrane. There are two kinds of transporters, one facilitating transport along an electrochemical potential gradient (channel or facilitated diffusion carrier), and the other working for transport against an electrochemical potential gradient (pump, secondary active carrier, or ABC transporter).

The electrochemical potential gradient across a biological membrane is mainly composed of three parameters, the concentration outside (one side), the concentration inside (the other side), and the electrical potential difference. In the plasma membrane, they correspond to the extracellular concentration, the cytoplasmic concentration, and the ordinal membrane potential. When the substance is neutral, we do not have to consider the electrical potential gradient. The concentrations of each substance in various compartments will be considered later. It should be noted that in case of water, a parameter of pressure is also important, but this is not the case in this section (14).

The electrical potential gradient (or difference) is usually called the membrane potential. In the plasma membrane, the potential of the extracellular medium becomes the zero standard. The intracellular potential

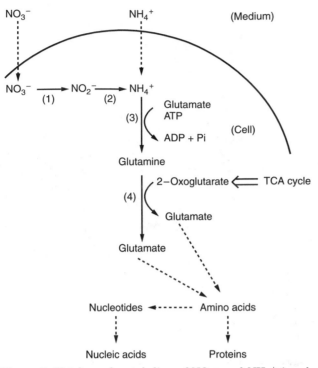

Figure 3. Uptake and metabolism of NO_3^- and NH_4^+ ions by plant cells in culture. Enzymes are represented by numbers as follows: (1) nitrate reductase; (2) nitrite reductase; (3) glutamine synthetase; (4) glutamate synthase.

There are several different methods to measure the membrane potential. The most conventional method is to use the glass microelectrode connected to the electrical amplifier. A glass microelectrode is inserted into the cell, and the intracellular potential is measured. Usually, the inserted glass electrode penetrates both the plasma membrane and the tonoplast. The potential difference measured by the electrode is a sum of the plasma membrane potential and the tonoplast potential. Since the potential in the vacuole is a about 20 mV positive against the cytoplasm, the real membrane potential of the plasma membrane is more negative than the measured value. The second method is the use of membrane permeable ionic substances, for example, TPP^+ or $TPMP^+$. These substances are distributed according to the membrane potential. When we measure their distribution between extracellular and intracellular compartments, we can estimate the membrane potential. In order to measure their distribution, we usually use radio-labeled compounds. Third, we can measure the membrane potential using fluorescent substances whose fluorescence changes dependent on the membrane potential, such as oxonol or $DiOC_5$. For the glass electrode measurements, technical training is needed. Using the final two methods, we can measure the membrane potential of cultured plant cells easily. Recent developments in fluorescent microscopic measurements have greatly improved the temporal and spatial resolutions of the potential measurements.

The membrane potential of plant cells is composed of two parts, one is a diffusion potential (passive potential) and the other is an electrogenic potential (active potential). In most plant cells, K^+ is a major permeable ion across the plasma membrane. There is a large concentration gradient

of plant cells ranges from about -100 mV to more negative than -200 mV. In cultured cells or protoplasts, slightly smaller (more positive) potentials have also been reported.

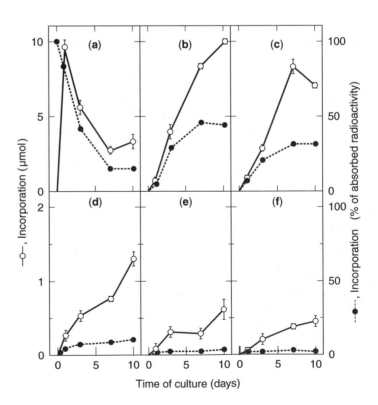

Figure 4. Uptake of ^{32}P by suspension-cultured *Catharanthus roseus* cells. (Redrawn from Ashihara and Tokoro, [7].) (**a**) Pi; (**b**) nucleic acids; (**c**) phospholipids; (**d**) nucleotides; (**e**) sugar phosphates; (**f**) proteins.

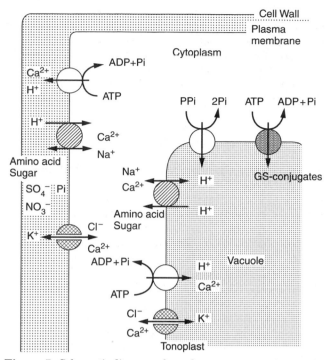

Figure 5. Schematic diagram of membrane transport systems in plant cells. ○, a molecule acting as a pump; ◑, a molecule acting as a carrier; ●, a molecule acting as a channel; ◕, a molecule acting as an ABC transporter.

of K^+ between the inside and outside of the cell. The K^+ concentration of the cytoplasm is around 100–200 mM and that of the extracellular space is less than around 1 mM. Thus the diffusion potential of K^+ of the plasma membrane becomes about −100 mV or more. In suspension cultured cells, the culture medium often contains a high concentration of K^+. In these cases, the diffusion potential may change dependent on the medium composition.

The electrogenic component of the plasma membrane potential is generated by an H^+ extruding ATPase (P-type H^+ pump). The H^+ pump carries H^+ as an outward current. It hyperpolarizes the plasma membrane. The amount of this component often corresponds to the diffusion potential. The electrogenic potential is strongly sensitive to the metabolic activities. If we treat cells with metabolic inhibitors such as KCN or arsenate, the active potential is immediately lost and the membrane depolarizes. The other function of the H^+ pump is to construct the H^+ gradient across the plasma membrane. The pH of the extracellular space is usually acidic and the pH of the cytoplasm is neutral to weakly alkaline. The pH is partly maintained by the action of the plasma membrane H^+ pump. Thus the plasma membrane H^+ pump is functioning to generate the proton motive force composed of both the membrane potential and the H^+ concentration gradient. The proton motive force is the most important factor that drives the secondary active carriers.

The plasma membrane H^+ pump is well characterized both biochemically and molecular biologically. The molecular weight of H^+ pump is about 100 kDa, and it functions as a dimer. Genes of the H^+ pump belong to a multiple gene family (13).

Concerning pumps in the plant plasma membrane, besides the H^+ pump, a Ca^{2+}-extruding ATPase has also been reported.

The vacuole is one of the most important organelles for solute metabolism in plant cells. Its volume usually occupies more than 80% of the total cell volume. Accumulation of sugars, amino acids, and inorganic substances in the vacuole functions as a source of osmotic pressure and as a reservoir or a buffer of the cytoplasmic activities.

Transport into the vacuole is also mediated by different kinds of proteins in the tonoplast. Pumps, carriers, channels, and ABC transporters are known to be in the tonoplast. The tonoplast is energized by two kinds of H^+ pumps; that is, V-type H^+-ATPase and H^+-PPase. Both transport H^+ from the cytoplasm to the vacuole. The vacuolar pH is around 5 to 5.5. As the vacuolar potential is usually more positive than the cytoplasmic potential (about 20–50 mV), an electrochemical potential gradient of H^+ across the tonoplast is formed from the vacuole to the cytoplasm.

Transport Mechanisms of Sugars

Sucrose, glucose, and fructose are well known as sugars taken up into plant cells. The sucrose transport system has been fully investigated (15). The cytoplasmic sucrose concentration varies considerably dependent on the cellular metabolism from a few to several hundred mM. The uptake of sucrose is an active energy-dependent process. Sucrose uptake through the plasma membrane is driven by co-transport with H^+. A pH jump of the medium containing the plasma membrane vesicles induces sucrose accumulation in them. The apparent K_m of sucrose transport is about 1 mM. The stoichiometry of proton and sucrose is supposed to be 1 : 1. Since sucrose is an electroneutral substance, its transport with H^+ is electrogenic. Transport of the positive charge depolarizes the membrane potential. Electrophysiological measurements support this phenomenon.

The proton–sucrose co-transport is inhibited by diethyl pyrocarbonate (DEPC), which modifies the histidine residue, or by p-chloromercuribenzenesulfonic acid (PCMBS), which modifies the cysteine residue. Sucrose transport is also inhibited by phlorizin and cytochalasin B, which are potent inhibitors of glucose transporters of animal cells.

Vanadate and DES, which inhibit the H^+-extruding pump of the plasma membrane, also inhibit H^+-coupled sucrose uptake. Uncouplers like CCCP, FCCP, and DNP, which collapse the H^+ electrochemical gradient across the membrane, inhibit H^+-coupled uptake.

Biochemical characterization of sucrose transporter protein revealed that a 40–60-kDa protein was a good candidate for a transporter in various materials. Simultaneously the cloning of the sucrose transporter gene was successful using a complementation of yeast sucrose transport mutant. The spinach sucrose transporter codes for a protein of 525 amino acids. Its molecular weight is about 55 kDa. The sucrose transporter is composed of twelve membrane-spanning domains divided to two six-domains with a hydrophilic part. It belongs to a superfamily of glucose transporters.

In cells in culture, along with sucrose, glucose is also an important nutrient. After extracellular invertase hydrolyzes sucrose to glucose and fructose, glucose is transported into the cell. Glucose uptake into the cell is also H^+-coupled co-transport. The glucose transport system of *Chlorella* has been well characterized. Later, this was also demonstrated in plasma membrane of higher plants. The proton–glucose transport system has been investigated using the plasma membrane vesicles of sugar beet. It is dependent on both pH and membrane potential gradients. The K_m of glucose is a few hundred μM. The glucose transporter gene of *Chlorella* was cloned before the sucrose transporter. It coded a protein of 533 amino acids. The estimated molecular weight is 57 kDa. The hydropathy plot predicts twelve membrane-spanning domains, the same as for the sucrose transporter. Later, genes of similar transporters were isolated from higher plants, such as *Arabidopsis*.

Sugar is also one of the main components of the vacuole. The sucrose concentration in the vacuole sometimes can be up to 100 mM. There are transporters for sugars in the tonoplast. Sucrose is transported through a facilitated transporter or sucrose/H^+ antiporter. Glucose is also transported via similar mechanisms. However, the details remain unknown.

Transport Mechanisms for Nitrogen Compounds

The nitrogen compounds plant cells can utilize include nitrate, nitrite, ammonium, amino acids, and urea (16). Most media for cultured cells contain nitrate and/or ammonium salt as a nitrogen source. When the culture medium contains both nitrate and ammonium ion, ammonium ion is preferentially consumed by cells. Amino acids are the main nitrogen source in some media. Cultured cells of rice are often maintained in amino acid containing medium.

The transport mechanism of NH_4^+ has been a controversy for a long time: whether NH_4^+ itself can cross the membrane or whether only NH_3 is transported. Compared with NH_4^+, NH_3 is highly permeable to the lipid bilayer of biomembranes. However, the equilibrium pH between NH_4^+ and NH_3 is high (around 9) compared with the ordinary pH of the extracellular space, and NH_4^+ uptake is not strongly dependent on the medium pH and is sometimes lower at a higher pH (NH_3 concentration increases). These findings indicate that NH_4^+ may also be transported across the plant plasma membrane.

Since NH_4^+ has a positive charge, the potential difference (usually inside negative) accelerates the inward transport. The NH_4^+ concentration in the cytoplasm is believed to be very low, because NH_4^+ is very toxic for the biological activities. Also the enzyme activities that assimilate NH_4^+ are high enough in plant cells to keep the level of NH_4^+ low. Interestingly, recent studies indicate that the intracellular NH_4^+ level may be higher than a few mM (17). In the latter case, it is not clear whether the transport of NH_4^+ across the plasma membrane is passive or active.

By complementation of yeast NH_4^+ transport mutant, a putative NH_4^+ transporter gene (*AMT1*) was cloned from *Arabidopsis*. It encoded a highly hydrophobic protein composed of 501 amino acids with 9–12 membrane spanning domains. The yeast expressing this protein could take up methylamine as an analogue of NH_4^+. Methylamine uptake is effectively competed by NH_4^+. The K_i for NH_4^+ is about 10 μM. Methylamine uptake is also inhibited by protonophores. This indicates that NH_4^+ is co-transported with H^+. NH_4^+ may also be a substrate for a cation-permeable channel.

NO_3^- transport has different characteristics from NH_4^+ transport. The cytoplasmic concentration of NO_3^- is reported to be around 10 mM. Furthermore, since NO_3^- has a negative charge, the electrochemical potential gradient across the plasma membrane of NO_3^- is uphill. Uptake of NO_3^- into the cell against an electrochemical potential gradient should be an active process. Most data indicate that NO_3^- is also co-transported with H^+. Transport of NO_3^- is often followed by the cytoplasmic acidification and membrane depolarization. The former indicates the transport of H^+ and the latter the transport of positive charge together with NO_3^-. A stoichiometry of H^+ to NO_3^- is reported to be 2.

Different transporters are known to function in NO_3^- transport. They are constitutive or inducible, and have high or low affinity for NO_3^-. When plants are growing in the absence of NO_3^-, the apparent NO_3^- uptake rate is very low. However, once they are exposed to enough NO_3^-, the uptake rate greatly increases. The initial small uptake when plants are exposed to NO_3^- is supported by constitutive transporters, and the induced transporters work for the successive uptake of NO_3^-. The K_m of high-affinity transporters is about 20 μM. In addition to NH_4^+, genes of some putative NO_3^- transporters have been identified.

Transport of amino acids has been extensively investigated physiologically, biochemically, and molecular biologically. With plants in nature, nitrate and ammonium ions are the major source of nitrogen. However, in plants (for example, phloem loading) or in cultured cells, amino acids are also important substrates for membrane transport.

Amino acids are also co-transported with H^+. H^+ uncouplers effectively inhibit the amino acid transport. Treatment with potassium, which depolarizes the membrane, also decreases amino acid transport.

In sugar-cane suspension cultured cells, three distinct transport systems have been found: those for neutral amino acids, acidic amino acids, and basic amino acids (18). It is clear that multiple transporters function with different substrate specificity. In *Arabidopsis*, the complementation of yeast mutants deficient of amino acid transport has revealed several transporter genes. They belong to the amino acid permease (AAP) family (15).

Transport Mechanisms for Phosphate

Phosphorus is transported as inorganic phosphate (Pi) by plant cells. The Pi concentration in the cytoplasm is likely to be a few to ten mM. The Pi level in culture medium is usually much higher than that in nature. Normally, the Pi level in soil is less than 10 μM. Thus Pi uptake is also an active process (19).

P nutritional status is one of the most important determinants of Pi uptake rate; under Pi deficiency, the capacity for Pi uptake increases. This shows that plant cells have a variety of Pi uptake systems with different K_ms. In more recent studies, influx isotherms for Pi have been commonly interpreted in terms of two uptake systems, one having a low K_m (high affinity) and the other a high K_m (low affinity) and differing also in their V_{max} composed of two saturating systems. In *Catharanthus* and tobacco suspension cultured cells, only one kind of Pi transporter can be found irrespective of Pi condition. Pi deficiency changed the V_{max}, but not K_m in tobacco.

Pi is also transported into cells across the plasma membrane via co-transport with H^+. When Pi is taken up into the cell, the extracellular pH increases. Accumulation of Pi is usually associated with membrane depolarization. It seems reasonable to presume that the positive charges transported with Pi are protons. Figure 6 shows an example of simultaneous measurements of extracellular and intracellular pH during Pi uptake in *Catharanthus* cells. After addition of phosphate, the extracellular pH increased until the exhaustion of added Pi. At the same time, the cytoplasmic pH first decreased and then maintained a lower value. After the exhaustion of extracellular Pi, both the extracellular and the intracellular pH recovered their original values (20).

Pi is a multivalency molecule. Its valency changes dependent on the medium pH, but we do not know which ionic species of Pi is transported across the plasma membrane. There has been much debate over the stoichiometry of the plasma membrane transporter, with numbers ranging between 2 and 4.

Pi influx across the plasma membrane is sensitive to many inhibitors, but none is very specific in its action. Inhibitors that collapse the electrochemical potential gradient for H^+ also inhibit Pi uptake across the membrane. Arsenate is used as an analogue of the Pi molecule and competes with Pi for uptake. Substances that directly affect Pi co-transporters have not yet been found. SH reagents like $HgCl_2$ and PCMBS that are known to inhibit H^+-co-transport systems also inhibit Pi

uptake. Furosemide is reported to inhibit Pi transport without inhibition of proton pumping in *Catharanthus* cultured cells.

The first plasma membrane Pi transporter to be identified in eukaryotic cells was in yeast; *PHO84* as the gene encoding the Pi transporter. Pi was co-transported with H^+ by the *PHO84* protein with a K_m for Pi of about 8 μM. The *PHO84* protein has 596 amino acids, 12 membrane-spanning domains. They are separated into two 6 domains by 74 amino acid residues. This is classified in a group of glucose transporters. In higher plants, genes of Pi transporters have been isolated from *Arabidopsis*, potato, *Catharanthus*, and tomato. Unlike *Catharanthus*, these plants have multiple Pi transporter genes. The Pi transporter has 12 membrane-spanning domains. Pi transporter proteins from higher plants have not yet been purified. Mitsukawa et al., (21) introduced *PHT1* from *Arabidopsis* into tobacco suspension cultured cells BY2 and succeeded in increasing Pi uptake activity of those cells.

Pi taken up into the cytoplasm across the plasma membrane is partly metabolized, and most of the rest is transported into the vacuole. Pi accumulated in the vacuole is used to buffer the cytoplasmic Pi level against fluctuations caused by variable external supply. In sycamore suspension cultured cells, in Pi-depleted culture medium, the vacuolar Pi level gradually decreased over 50 h until it coincided with the cytoplasmic Pi level. When Pi was added to the Pi-deficient cells, the Pi level of the cytoplasm increased within 2 h; then the vacuolar Pi level gradually increased. There are few reports dealing with the mechanism of Pi transport across the tonoplast (19).

MEASUREMENT AND CONTROL OF CYTOPLASMIC pH

The cytoplasmic pH is the most important factor of physical environments of living cells, not only for enzymatic activities, but also H^+-coupled membrane transport, equilibrium of various substances and reactions, etc. The cytoplasmic pH of plant cell is strictly regulated around 7.5, even under various environmental disturbances, for example, acid or alkaline load. On the other hand, the vacuolar pH is maintained around 5. The vacuole as an acid compartment is working as a reservoir for many degrading enzymes. Both compartments have respectively specific mechanisms to keep pH at constant values (22). In this section, we first deal with how the intracellular pH values are measured, and then the mechanisms of the pH regulation in plant cells.

Measurement of Cytoplasmic pH

The cytoplasm usually occupies about less than 20% of the total cell volume. Thus the pH of solutes of cells or tissues measured as a whole is similar to the vacuolar pH. In order to measure the cytoplasmic pH, we must use in vivo measurements of living cells. Thus far, the following techniques have been applied to measure the cytoplasmic pH. The first method uses the membrane-permeable substances that distribute between the cytoplasm and the extracellular space dependent on their pH values. $^{14}C - DMO$ is a well-used substance. The nonionic form of

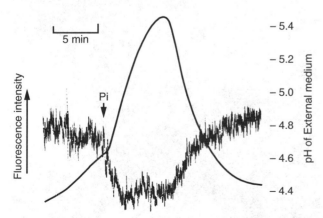

Figure 6. Pi-induced changes in pH of external medium (straight line) and fluorescence intensity (noisy trace) of BCECF loaded into the suspension-cultured *Catharanthus* cells. Decrease in fluorescence intensity means acidification of the cytoplasm. Fluorescence intensity began to increase as soon as the external medium pH reached its peak, when medium Pi has been completely exhausted by cells. *Source*: From Ref. 20.

DMO is membrane permeable, and DMO is equilibrated between each compartment dependent on pH. We can determine the pH by measuring the DMO concentration of each compartment. This is one of the easiest method of pH measurement, but there remain some ambiguities. The determination of DMO distribution between the cytoplasm and the vacuole is usually difficult.

The second method is the use of a pH-sensitive microelectrode, which has a pH-sensitive resin in the tip of the pipet and is inserted into the cytoplasm by a micromanipulator. It should be noted that the value measured with a pH-sensitive microelectrode is the sum of the membrane potential and pH gradient. Therefore, we must subtract the membrane potential measured together with a usual glass microelectrode to obtain the real pH value. Although it is not easy to apply a glass microelectrode to measure the pH, the measured values are more reliable.

During the past 20 years, the ^{31}P-NMR method has been extensively used to measure the in vivo pH of both plant and animal cells. ^{31}P-NMR can detect Pi in vivo, distinguishing Pi pools in different compartments, mostly because of the different pHs in these compartments. The pH affects the degree of dissociation of Pi and thereby alters the chemical shift of Pi peaks. Thus we can estimate the pH value of each compartment by the chemical shift of Pi. In plant cells, the vacuole is a large compartment with a pH around 5, compared to the cytoplasm, which is usually maintained around pH 7.5. The Pi signals from these two pools are therefore quite different, as shown in Figure 7 for *Catharanthus* suspension cultured cells, in which Pi in the cytoplasm and vacuole are clearly distinguishable dependent on each pH. For the NMR measurements, suspension-cultured cells are one of the most suitable materials, because the NMR-measurement tube has only a quite limited space.

Finally, a recently developed method to measure the cytoplasmic pH is the pH-sensitive fluorescent dye. Since the fluorescence changes depending on pH, we can detect the pH value or its change with a fluorescent microscope or fluorescence photometer. Figure 8 shows a typical example of a fluorescent image of *Catharanthus* suspension cultured cells stained with the pH-sensitive dye; 2′,7′-bis-(2-carboxyethyl)-5 (and -6) carboxyfluorescein (BCECF). The fluorescence of BCECF is strong around pH 7 and weak in an acid region. The fluorescence is strong in cytoplasm having a neutral pH but weak from the vacuole expressing a pH of 5. The pH values are estimated from the degree of brightness. At present, there are many kinds of fluorescent dyes for not only measurement of the cytoplasmic pH, but also the vacuolar pH, the membrane potential, Ca^{2+} or other ion concentrations (23). Acetoxymethylester derivatives of these pH-sensitive fluorescent dyes are membrane permeable. After loading, the intracellular esterase digests the acetoxymethylester part, and the dye stays in the cell. Since the membrane permeabilities of these dyes sometimes vary with the material, it might be difficult to load dyes into the cell. Furthermore, dyes loaded into cells are distributed not only in the cytoplasm but also the in the vacuole and other organelles. Thus it would also be difficult to estimate the pH value of each compartment.

Control of Cytoplasmic pH

Figure 6 shows a typical example of cytoplasmic pH regulation induced by acidification during Pi uptake with

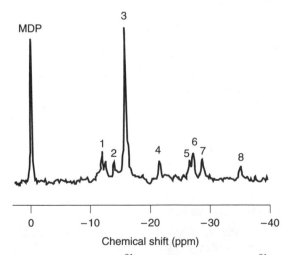

Figure 7. An example of ^{31}P-NMR measurements. ^{31}P-NMR spectrum of *Catharanthus* suspension-cultured cells. MDP (methylene diphosphonic acid); chemical shift standard. Peak assignments: 1, G6P; 2, cytoplasmic Pi; 3, vacuolar Pi; 4, γ-nucleotide triphosphates; 5, α-nucleotide phosphates; 6 and 7, UDPG; 8, β-nucleotide phosphates. Cytoplasmic and vacuolar pH values are calculated from Pi resonances of peaks 2 and 3, respectively. The Pi content of each compartment is calculated from the area under each peak. *Source*: From Ref. 20.

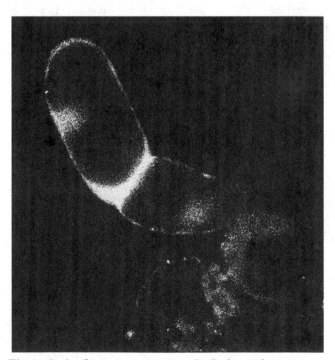

Figure 8. A fluorescent image of *Catharanthus* suspension-cultured cells loaded with BCECF-AM. The fluorescence of BCECF is strong around pH 7 and is weak in an acidic region. The fluorescence from the cytoplasm having a neutral pH becomes bright, but that from the vacuole around pH 5 becomes dark. The pH values are estimated from the degree of brightness.

H$^+$ in suspension cultured cells of *Catharanthus roseus*. The cytoplasmic pH was measured by BCECF loading. Such control of the cytoplasmic pH may be achieved by a variety of mechanisms. One possible mechanism is the extensive pH buffering capacity of the cytoplasm. For example, phosphoric acids, amino acids, and organic acids act as buffering agents. The second mechanism is a so-called biochemical pH stat (24). With this mechanism, the activities of PEP carboxylase and malic enzyme change in response to changes in the cytoplasmic pH. By the action of these enzymes, the numbers of carboxyl residues (i.e., malate concentration) are controlled (25). Recently, Sakano (25) modified this biochemical pH stat on the basis of H$^+$ production or consumption of each reaction.

The third mechanisms is the biophysical pH stat. With this mechanism, the cytoplasmic pH is controlled by H$^+$ transport systems, including primary H$^+$ pumps and secondary H$^+$ co-transport systems (22). There are many H$^+$ transport systems in the plasma membrane and the tonoplast, and only changes in the activities of these transport systems directly affect the pH of the cytoplasm.

BIBLIOGRAPHY

1. G.F. Payne, V. Bringi, C. Prince, and M.L. Shuler, *Plant Cell and Tissue Culture in Liquid System*, Hanser Publishers, Munich, 1991.
2. G. Stepan-Sarkissian and M.W. Fowler, in M.J. Morgan, ed., *Carbohydrate Metabolism in Cultured Cells*, Plenum, New York, 1986, pp. 151–181.
3. K. Sagishima, K. Kubota, and H. Ashihara, *Ann. Bot. (London)* [N.S.] **64**, 185–193 (1989).
4. J. Kanabus, R.A. Bressan, and N.C. Carpita, *Plant Physiol.* **82**, 363–368 (1986).
5. S. Amino and M. Tazawa, *Plant Cell Physiol.* **29**, 482–487 (1988).
6. H. Marschner, *Mineral Nutrition of Higher Plants*, 2nd ed., Academic Press, London, 1995, pp. 229–312.
7. H. Ashihara and T. Tokoro, *J. Plant Physiol.* **118**, 227–235 (1985).
8. F. Rebeille, R. Bligny, J.-B. Martin, and R. Douce, *Arch. Biochem. Biophys.* **225**, 143–148 (1983).
9. S. Amino, T. Fujimura, and A. Komamine, *Physiol. Plant.* **59**, 393–396 (1983).
10. K.-H. Knobloch and J. Berlin, *Plant Cell Tissue Organ Cult.* **2**, 333–340 (1983).
11. H. Ashihara and T. Ukaji, *J. Plant Physiol.* **124**, 77–85 (1986).
12. T. Ukaji and H. Ashihara, *Z. Naturforsch. C* **41C**, 1045–1051 (1986).
13. M.R. Sussman, *Annu. Rev. Plant Physiol. Plant Mol. Biol.* **45**, 211–234 (1994).
14. U. Lüttge and N. Higinbotham, *Transport in Plants*, Springer-Verlag, New York, 1979.
15. D.R. Bush, *Annu. Rev. Plant Physiol. Plant Mol. Biol.* **44**, 513–542 (1993).
16. W.B. Frommer et al., *Plant Mol. Biol.* **26**, 1651–1670 (1994).
17. M.Y. Wang, M.Y. Siddiqi, T.J. Ruth, and A.D.M. Glass, *Plant Physiol.* **103**, 1249–1258 (1993).
18. R.E. Wyse and E. Komor, *Plant Physiol.* **76**, 865–870 (1984).
19. T. Mimura, *Plant Cell Physiol.* **36**, 1–7 (1995).
20. K. Sakano, Y. Yazaki, and T. Mimura, *Plant Physiol.* **99**, 672–680 (1992).
21. N. Mitsukawa et al., *Proc. Natl. Acad. Sci. U.S.A.* **94**, 7098–7102 (1997).
22. A. Kurkdjian and J. Guern, *Annu. Rev. Plant Physiol. Plant Mol. Biol.* **40**, 271–303 (1989).
23. R.P. Haugland, *Handbook of Fluorescent Probes and Research Chemicals*, 6th ed., Molecular Probes, Au: Location, 1996.
24. D.D. Davies, *Physiol. Plant.* **67**, 702–706 (1986).
25. K. Sakano, *Plant Cell Physiol.* **39**, 467–473 (1998).

See also CHARACTERIZATION AND DETERMINATION OF CELL DEATH BY APOPTOSIS; PLANT CELL CULTURE, EFFECT ON GROWTH AND SECONDARY PRODUCT ACCUMULATION OF ORGANIC COMPOUNDS AND SURFACTANTS; PLANT CELL CULTURES, PHOTOSYNTHETIC; PLANT CELL CULTURES, PHYSIOCHEMICAL EFFECTS ON GROWTH; PLANT CELL CULTURES, SECONDARY PRODUCT ACCUMULATION; PROGRAMMED CELL DEATH (APOPTOSIS) IN CULTURE, IMPACT AND MODULATION.

PLANT CELL CULTURE BAG

HIROSHI FUKUI
Kagawa University
Kagawa, Japan

MICHIO TANAKA
Kagawa University
Kagawa, Japan

OUTLINE

Introduction
Preparation of the Culture Bag and the Culture Method
Growth of Plant Cells and Tissue in a Culture Bag
Production of Metabolites in Culture Bags
Bibliography

INTRODUCTION

For effective proliferation of plant tissue and cells in a liquid medium, it is usually necessary to provide agitation or forced aeration to exchange gases. For this purpose, various types of culture vessels have been devised for supporting cell growth: for example, conical and flat-bottom round flasks placed on reciprocal or gyratory shakers, bubble-type reactors (1), stirred-jar fermentors (2), flat-bladed impeller bioreactors (3), roller-bottle systems (4), air-lift column bioreactors (5), cell-lift impeller bioreactors (6), and helical-ribbon impeller systems (7) (reviewed in Refs. 8 and 9). In these systems, the cultured cells and tissues cannot survive without agitation for sufficient gas exchange. Recently, Tanaka (10) reported that an envelope-shaped (named a "culture bag") and a box-shaped ("culture pack") culture vessel developed using fluorocarbon polymer film can be effectively and conveniently used for micropropagation of ornamental plants. The fluorocarbon polymer film possesses superior properties such as a high melting point (265–310 °C) and high gas (O_2, CO_2, and N_2) permeability as needed for plant cells and tissues. This culture bag system makes it possible for plant cells and tissues to grow in a stationary liquid medium without agitation. The cultured cells and tissues in the culture bag may express their yet uncovered biosynthetic capability. In addition, the culture bags can save space because they can be placed in layers with small spaces between the bag surfaces.

This article introduces a novel film culture vessel, the culture bag, suitable for the growth of plant cells and tissues as well as for their metabolite production.

PREPARATION OF THE CULTURE BAG AND THE CULTURE METHOD

Sheets of fluorocarbon polymer film (Neoflon PFA®, Daikin Industries, Ltd., Osaka, Japan; 12.5, 25, 50, and 100 μm thick) are shaped into an envelope (for example, 15 cm long by 17 cm wide) (Fig. 1; for further details, refer to Ref. 10). The upper edge of the envelope is cut on a slant for temporary closing of the opening. After autoclaving the culture bag, the opening, which is covered with

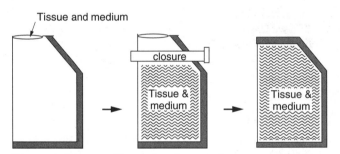

Figure 1. Diagram illustrating the procedure to make and use the culture bag. The shadowed sides are heat sealed.

aluminum foil, is used to introduce autoclaved medium. The homogeneous growth in this shape of culture bag into which *Nicotiana* BY-2 cells (480 mg fr. wt), *Lithospermum erythrorhizon* cells (750 mg fr. wt), or its hairy roots (200 mg fr. wt) are inoculated can be obtained with 25 to 30 ml. After pushing out the air trapped in the upper space in the culture bag, the opening is temporarily sealed with a closing device (Spectrum Medical Industries), before heat sealing.

The heat-sealed culture bags are laid on a sheet of 1-cm mesh net without overlapping each other to make the air-permeable film area as large as possible, and then the nets are piled on one another with 1 cm or more space between the nets and incubated under the culture conditions (25 °C in the dark) without shaking. Control cultures are carried out in 100-ml flasks containing the same volume of the same medium as the culture bag and agitated on a rotatory shaker (70 ~ 100 rpm) under the same condition for the same period as the culture bag.

GROWTH OF PLANT CELLS AND TISSUE IN A CULTURE BAG

The growth of tobacco BY-2 cells, one of the most prolific plant cell cultures (11), and the shikonin-producing *Lithospermum* M-18 (12) cells, and hairy roots (13) in the culture bag were compared with that in shaken flasks (Figs. 2–4).

Figure 2 shows that the growth of tobacco BY-2 cells in the culture bag made of 12.5-μm film was almost equal to that of the shaken flask, indicating that the film permeate sufficient oxygen for the cell growth. The cell growth varied inversely with the film thickness. This indicates that the growth depends on the exchange rates of gases, especially oxygen, because the gas permeability of the film is inversely proportional to the thickness (10). The thickest film (100 μm) also enables the cells to grow without cell death from oxygen shortage, although the growth rate was much lower than that of the thinner film. The same result was observed in shoot development of *Cymbidium* (14)

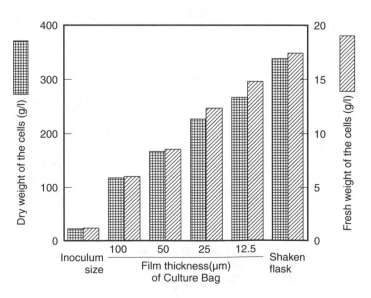

Figure 2. The effect of the film thickness on the growth of tobacco BY-2 cells. The cells (480 mg fr. wt) were inoculated into the culture bags and 100-ml flasks containing 25 ml of LS medium. The former was cultured on a net without shaking, and the latter was shaken at 100 rpm for a week in the dark at 25 °C.

and *Spathiphyllum* (15) on agar medium in a box-shaped vessel, a culture pack made of fluorocarbon polymer film.

Figure 3 shows that the dry mass of shikonin-producing *Lithospermum* cells (M-18) cultured in the culture bag of the thinner films (12.5 and 25 μm) for 4 weeks was larger than that in shaken flasks. The culture bag of 100-μm film that reduced the proliferation of the fast-growing tobacco cells (Fig. 2) supported the good growth of *Lithospermum* cells having a doubling time of about a week. Such doubling times are observed in various types of plant cell cultures used for metabolite production. These results indicate that the culture bag is suitable for plant cell suspension cultures without shaking, although the shaking stress and the nutrient gradient might participate in the regulation of growth.

The hairy root cultures are known to be useful for the metabolite production. *Lithospermum* hairy roots that produce shikonin, red naphthoquinone derivatives, in a shaken flask (16) proliferated in the culture bag containing ammonium nitrate-depleted MS medium without agitation (Fig. 4), although the growth rate in the culture bag was about half that in a shaken flask, and strongly reduced by the presence of ammonium ion as shown in the shaken flasks. The hairy roots showed the same tendency as tobacco cells to grow more vigorously in the culture bag of thinner film containing MS-NH₄ NO₃ medium, probably due to the lack of a sufficient oxygen supply. These data suggest that the hairy roots need sufficient oxygen without ammonium ion for good growth.

PRODUCTION OF METABOLITES IN CULTURE BAGS

Lithospermum cells in the culture bag of thinnest film (12.5 μm) produced almost the same amount of shikonin, red naphthoquinone derivatives, as those in the shaken flask (Fig. 3). The productivity of the culture bag varied inversely with the film thickness. Much less shikonin was produced in the culture bags of thicker film (50 and 100 μm) compared with shaken flasks, while the cell growth in the culture bag was not so much repressed as shikonin formation, suggesting that the environmental factors suitable for the secondary metabolism are different from those for the cell growth.

The red pigments consist of several kinds of shikonin derivatives (17). HPLC analysis showed that the pigments from the cells in the culture bag contained the same derivatives as those from the shaken flask. It is noted, however, that a much lower amount of benzoquinone derivatives, abnormal stress metabolites in shikonin biosynthesis (18), were produced in the culture bag than in the shaken flask. This means that the former system might give much less stress to the metabolism of cultured cells due to the fact that they are not moved in the culture bag.

Lithospermum hairy roots also produced shikonin derivatives in the culture bag containing ammonium

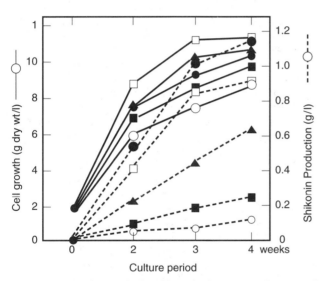

Figure 3. The effect of the film thickness on the growth and shikonin formation in *Lithospermum erythrorhizon* cells (inoculum size: 750 mg) cultured in the culture bags and 100-ml flasks containing 30 ml medium. The former was cultured on a net without shaking and the latter on a shaker at 70 rpm in the dark at 25 °C for 3 weeks. Culture bag with film thickness □: 12.5 μm, ▲: 25 μm, ■: 50 μm, ○: 100 μm; ●: shaken flasks.

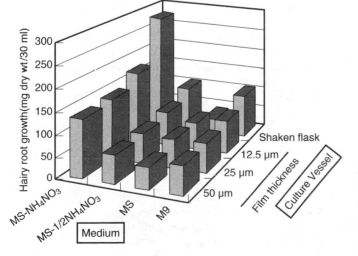

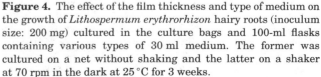

Figure 4. The effect of the film thickness and type of medium on the growth of *Lithospermum erythrorhizon* hairy roots (inoculum size: 200 mg) cultured in the culture bags and 100-ml flasks containing various types of 30 ml medium. The former was cultured on a net without shaking and the latter on a shaker at 70 rpm in the dark at 25 °C for 3 weeks.

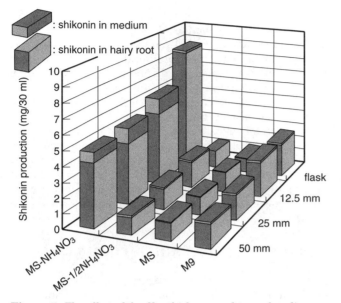

Figure 5. The effect of the film thickness and type of medium on shikonin production in *Lithospermum erythrorhizon* hairy roots cultured in the culture bags and 100-ml flasks containing various types of 30 ml medium. The upper part of each column is the amount of shikonin secreted into the medium, and the lower is the amount of shikonin in the hairy roots. Culture conditions are the same as those in Figure 4.

nitrate-depleted MS medium (Fig. 5). The amount of shikonin produced tended to be larger in culture bags made of thinner film, suggesting that the productivity depends on the gas exchange rate. The same result was observed in the production of anthocyanin by *Euphorbia milli* cells (19) and artemisinin production in *Artemisia annua* cells (20) grown in the culture bag. The shikonin production in the culture bag was strongly inhibited by the presence of the ammonium ion as reported for the cell cultures (12). However, M-9 medium that was devised for effective shikonin production in the dedifferentiated cells (12) was not suitable for the production in the hairy roots. The hairy roots showed a good relationship between shikonin production and cell proliferation (Figs. 4 and 5), in contrast to the dedifferentiated cell cultures. This suggests that shikonin production in the hairy roots is in direct connection with the primary metabolism, while the cell cultures that accumulate the biosynthetic intermediates such as *p*-hydroxybenzoic acid glucoside (21) in the MS medium (growth medium of two-stage culture) is transferred to the M-9 medium (production medium) to produce a large amount of shikonin from the intermediate. Thus the production medium for the hairy roots could be different from that for the dedifferentiated cells.

Shikonin produced is secreted outside the cell wall (16,22). Figure 5 showed that the amount of shikonin secreted into the medium was several times larger in the culture bag than in the shaken flasks, and higher in culture bags made of thinner film. This suggests that the plant cells and tissues in the culture bag could display a metabolic capability different from those in the shaken flasks.

The experimental results described herein indicate that the culture bag is useful for the production of secondary metabolites in plant cell cultures and hairy root cultures without agitation, as well as for studies on the physiological effect of shaking or agitation on plant tissue and cell culture in a liquid medium.

BIBLIOGRAPHY

1. W. Tulecke and L.G. Nickell, *Science* **130**, 863–864 (1959).
2. A.F. Byrne and M.B. Koch, *Science* **135**, 215–216 (1962).
3. B.S. Hooker, J.M. Lee, and G. An, *Biotechnol. Bioeng.* **35**, 296–304 (1990).
4. D.T.A. Lamport, *Exp. Cell Res.* **33**, 195–201 (1964).
5. F. Wagner and H. Vogelmann, in W. Barz, E. Reinhard, and M.H. Zenk, eds., *Plant Tissue Culture and its Biotechnological Application*, Springer-Verlag, Berlin, 1977, pp. 245–252.
6. W.J. Treat, C.R. Engler, and E.J. Soltes, *Biotechnol. Bioeng.* **34**, 1191–1202 (1989).
7. M.Jolicoeur, C. Chavarie, P.J. Carreau, and J. Archambault, *Biotechnol. Bioeng.* **39**, 511–521 (1992).
8. F. Kargi and M. Rosenberg, *Biotechnol. Prog.* **3**, 1–8 (1987).
9. E.B. Herman, *Recent Advances in Plant Tissue Culture II (Secondary Metabolite Production 1988–1993)*, Agritech Consultants, Shrub Oak, N.Y., 1993, pp. 8–12.
10. M. Tanaka, in Y.P.S. Bajaj, ed., *Biotechnology in Agriculture and Forestry*, Vol. 17 Part I, Springer-Verlag, Berlin, 1991, pp. 212–228.
11. M. Noguchi et al., in W. Barz, E. Reinhard, and M.H. Zenk, eds., *Plant Tissue Culture and its Biotechnological Application*, Springer-Verlag, Berlin, 1977, pp. 85–94.
12. Y. Fujita, Y. Hara, C. Suga, and T. Morimoto, *Plant Cell Rep.* **1**, 61–63 (1981).
13. H. Fukui, A.F.M. Feroj Hasan, Y. Ishii, and M. Tanaka, *Phytochemistry* (1998).
14. M. Tanaka, M. Goi, and T. Higashiura, *Acta Hortic.* **226**, 663–670 (1988).
15. M. Tanaka, K. Jinno, M. Goi, and T. Higashiura, *Acta Hortic.* **230**, 73–80 (1988).
16. K. Shimomura, H. Sudo, H. Suga, and H. Kamada, *Plant Cell Rep.* **10**, 282–285 (1991).
17. Y. Fujita, Y. Maeda, C. Suga, and T. Morimoto, *Plant Cell Rep.* **2**, 192–193 (1983).
18. H. Fukui, N. Yoshikawa, and M. Tabata, *Phytochemistry* **23**, 301–305 (1984).
19. R. Hamada et al., *Biol. Biotechnol. Biochem.* **58**, 1530–1531 (1994).
20. C.K.H. Teo, A.W. Yap, E.K. Chan, and M. Tanaka, *Asian Pac. J. Mol. Biol. Biotechnol.* **3**, 317–321 (1995).
21. K. Yazaki, H. Fukui, and M. Tabata, *Chem. Pharm. Bull.* **34**, 2290–2293 (1986).
22. M. Tsukada and M. Tabata, *Planta Med.* **50**, 338–340 (1984).

See also CULTURE ESTABLISHMENT, PLANT CELL CULTURE; MICROPROPAGATION OF PLANTS, PRINCIPLES AND PRACTICES; PLANT CELL CULTURE, LABORATORY TECHNIQUES.

PLANT CELL CULTURE, EFFECT ON GROWTH AND SECONDARY PRODUCT ACCUMULATION OF ORGANIC COMPOUNDS AND SURFACTANTS

ALAN SCRAGG
University of the West of England
Frenchay, Bristol
United Kingdom

OUTLINE

Solvent Addition
Artificial Accumulation Sites
Two Phase Cultures
Addition of Surfactants
Bibliography

A range of compounds not normally used in culture media has been added to plant-cell cultures to improve growth or secondary product accumulation. These compounds have included solvents, ion-exchange resins, surfactants, and perfluorocarbons. Many of these compounds have been added to increase the accumulation of secondary products in plant-cell cultures. One approach has been to reduce the feedback inhibition upon secondary product accumulation by removing the secondary products from the cells as they are formed. Once synthesized, secondary products can be released into the medium but more frequently they are stored in the vacuole. Thus to release these compounds, the the tonoplast and cell membrane have to be crossed. Chemical agents, including organic solvents and detergents, have been used to permeabilize cells (1). Table 1 gives the concentrations of some agents required to extract 90% of the stored secondary product. For dimethyl sulfoxide (DMSO) and chloroform, the levels required can be high. In almost all cases, the viability of the cells was low after treatment which resulted in the loss of the culture or a considerable reduction in productivity.

SOLVENT ADDITION

The effect of solvents on the growth and thiophene accumulation in hairy root cultures of *Tagetes patula* was one of the first studies reported (2). The cultures were grown in a two-phase culture with an immiscible solvent which can act as a sink for the secondary product formed. To function correctly, the solvent requires four characteristics. The solvent must not be toxic to the cell culture, the product must be excreted from the cells, there must be good phase separation, and the secondary product must be preferentially extracted into the solvent. A number of solvents were tested for their ability to affect cell growth, respiration, and thiophene accumulation in *T. patula* cultures. Thiophenes are intracellular compounds and are hydrophobic, so that they partition well into solvents if released from the cells. The results are shown in Table 2. The solvents were selected on the basis of the empirical correlation between biocompatability and the parameter $\log P$ (3). $\log P$ is the log of the partition coefficient of the solvent over a standard octanol/water two-phase system. $\log P$ values can be found in the literature (4) or can be calculated by using the hydrophobic-constant method (5). $\log P$ values can be seen in the table and range from 0.7 to 11. The dry weights, respiration, and thiophene accumulation were determined after 10-days' growth. Those solvents with $\log P$ values above 5 appeared to be compatible with the hairy roots. The density of the phthalates was too close to that of water to give good phase separation, so that hexadecane and FC-40 (a halogenated hydrocarbon available from 3M company) were preferred. These two solvents were used in two-phase culture grown in either stirred-tank or liquid-impelled loop reactors. The design of the liquid-impelled loop reactor is shown in Figure 1. The *T. patula* cultures grew well in the loop reactor and had growth rates superior to those in the stirred-tank reactor. In a normal single-phase system, less than 1% of the thiophenes were found in the medium. However, with the two-phase systems using hexadecane, 28% of the thiophenes in the loop reactor and 68% in the stirred-tank were found in the solvent phase. With FC 40, the extraction was considerably less at between 10–20%. The toxicity of a wider range of solvents has been investigated using suspension cultures of *Morinda citrifolia* (6). *M. citrifolia* produces high levels of anthraquinones that are relatively hydrophobic. The cultures of *M. citrifolia* were grown in media saturated with one of 33 solvents, and growth and anthraquinone accumulation were followed for 18 days. The specific growth rates and anthraquinone accumulation

Table 1. Concentration of Agent Required to Release 90% of Betacanins from *Chenopodiun rubrum* and Berberine from *Thalictrum rugosum*[a]

Agent	C. rubrum	T. rugosum
Dimethyl sulfoxide (%)	35	30
Phenethyl alcohol (%)	0.98	0.80
Chloroform (% sat.)	64	67
Triton X-100 (ppm)	230	210
Hexadecyltrimethylammonium bromide (ppm)	84	60

[a]Data from Ref. 1.

Table 2. Growth, Respiratory Activity, and Thiophene Production in *Tagetes patula* Hairy Root Cultures[a]

Solvent	Log P	Growth	O2 Uptake	Thiophene
Ethyl acetate	0.7	−	−	−
Diethyl phthalate	3.3	−	−	+
Hexane	3.5	−	−	−
Decanol	4.0	−	−	−
Dibutyl phthalate	5.4	+	+	+
Decane	5.6	+	+	+
Hexadecane	8.8	+	+	+
Dioctyl phthalate	9.6	+	+	+
FC40	11.0	+	+	+

[a]Data from Ref. 2.

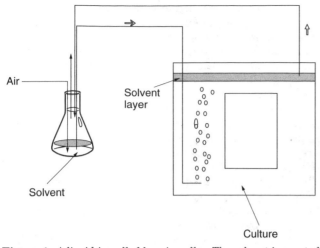

Figure 1. A liquid-impelled loop impeller. The solvent is aerated in a separate vessel and then pumped to the base of the loop reactor. In this case the solvent is lighter than water, so it rises to the surface. A solvent whose density is greater than water would be added at the surface. The flow of solvent causes a circulation within the reactor which mixes the culture. The solvent layer at the surface of the vessel is pumped back to the aeration vessel. Modified from Ref. 2.

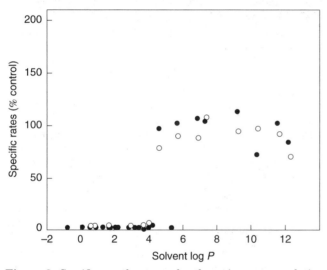

Figure 2. Specific growth rates and anthraquinone accumulation in suspension cultures of *Morinda citrifolia* in the presence of saturating concentrations of organic solvents. (●) anthraquinone; (○) growth. Data from Ref. 6.

in relation to the log P values are shown in Figure 2. The results are similar to those obtained with the hairy roots of *T. patula* where solvents with log P values of less than 5 were toxic. Previous research (3) indicates that plant cells are more sensitive than bacterial cells which have a log P limit of 4. The critical solvent concentrations were also determined by using critical concentrations (LD) which are the minimum amount of solvent needed to kill a fixed amount of cells within 48 hours. The LD values decrease as the chain length increases, plant cell membranes are extremely sensitive to solvents, and log P values can be use to predict sensitivity.

ARTIFICIAL ACCUMULATION SITES

An alternative strategy for increasing secondary product accumulation is to provide an artificial accumulation site. This site can be either a solid or a liquid, examples of which are shown in Table 3. One of the first solid-phase additions was RP-8, a lipophilic silica gel. When added to suspension cultures of *Valeriana wallichii*, this compound accumulated valpotriates whereas none could be detected in the control culture (7). The same was found with suspension cultures of *Pimpinella anisum* where the phenylpropanoid anethole was detected only in the presence of RP-8 (8). Ion-exchange resins have been extensively used to collect secondary products from plant cell suspensions and hairy root cultures (Table 3). Ion-exchange resins such as XAD-2, 4, and 7 have little effect on growth but increase the yield of secondary products in suspension cultures of *Catharanthus roseus* (4), *Nicotiana rustica* (9), *Cinchona ledgeriana* (10), and *Papaver somniferum* (11). These resins are also ideal for continuously removing exported secondary products from hairy root cultures such as *C.roseus* (12), *T.petula* (13), and *Duboisia leichhardtii* (14). In cultures grown in shake flasks, the resin can be added in 30-μm nylon mesh bags, whereas in bioreactors the medium can be passed through a column of resin. The provision of a column is particularly suitable for hairy root cultures where the medium is passed through the roots during normal culture.

The introduction of an immiscible liquid to a plant cell culture can also act as a site for accumulating secondary products. Myglyol, a nontoxic triglyceride, was added to cultures of *Thuja occidentalis* (15), and monoterpenes were detected in the Myglyol, whereas they had not been found previously in the culture. The same effect was observed in cultures of *Matricaria chamomilla* and appeared to be due to Myglyol retaining the volatile monoterpenes normally lost during culture. Polysiloxane, a silicone-based antifoam, was added to cultures of *Eschscholtzia californica* and appeared to stimulate the accumulation benzophenanthrene alkaloids (16). One of the benzophenanthridine alkaloids, sanguinarine, is commercially interesting as a mild antibiotic in toothpaste. The use of immiscible solvents has been discussed in an earlier section.

TWO PHASE CULTURES

The use of two-phase culture for cultivating plant cells has also been investigated using polyethylene glycols as the second phase. Cultures of *N. tabacum* grew well, and the best growth rate was in the presence of 3% polyethylene glycol 2000 (17). Two-phase culture has been used for bioconversion where the second phase is used to remove potential toxic concentrations of the products of the biocoversion. This has been successfully been carried out with a culture of *Vitis vinifera* where the addition of Myglyol increased the conversion of geraniol (18).

ADDITION OF SURFACTANTS

Surfactants have been added to plant-cell cultures to improve secondary product accumulation and also to

Table 3. Extraction Systems Used for Plant-Cell Cultures

Exraction Phase	Plant-Cell System	Metabolite	Ref.
Solid Phase (suspension cultures)			
RP-8	*Valriana wallichii*	Valepotriates	7
XAD-4	*Nicotiana rustica*	Nicotine	9
XAD-7	*Catharanthus roseus*	Alkaloids	4
XAD-7	*Cinchona ledgeriana*	Anthraquinones	10
XAD-7	*Papaver somniferum*	Sanguinarine	11
(hairy root cultures)			
XAD-2,-4,-7	*Catharanthus roseus*	Alkaloids	12
XAD-7	*Tagetes petula*	Thiophenes	13
XAD-2	*Duboisia leichhardtii*	Berberine	14
Liquid Phase (suspension cultures)			
Myglyol	*Thuja orientalis*	Monoterpenes	15
Myglyol	*Matricaria chamomila*	Essential oils	8
Polysiloxane	*Eschscholtzia californica*	Alkalids	16

improve growth. Pluronic F-68, a polymeric surfactant, has been used in animal-cell cultures as a shear-stress protectant and was shown to react with the cell membrane. For this reason, it was added to plant-cell cultures. Suspension cultures of *M. citrifolia* produced higher yields of anthraquinones in the presence of Pluronic F-68 (19). A two-phase culture was used where the second phase was hexadecane because it had been shown that this was nontoxic and capable of accumulating compounds like anthaquinone which may be released from the cells. Figure 3 shows the effect of increasing levels of Pluronic F-68 on growth and anthraquinone accumulation. It can be seen that the addition of Pluronic acid had a stimulating effect on both growth and anthraquinone accumulation. When the second phase of hexadecane was added, the growth rate increased from 0.3 to 0.7 days^{-1}, and the anthraquinone production rate increased from 0.7 to 1.2 days^{-1}.

Successful cultivation of plant protoplasts requires an adequate supply of gases. Approaches using oxygen-enriched atmospheres and liquid over solid media have had some success. An alternative has been the use of oxygen-gassed perflurocarbons (PFCs) which are inert, highly fluorinated organic compounds that have the capacity to dissolve large quantities of gases. Addition of PFCs enhanced the division of *Petunia hybrida* protoplasts (20). More recently, PFCs were combined with commercial bovine hemoglobin (Erythrogen) and produced a synergistic effect on division rates (21). Erythrogen has also been added to *P. hybrida* protoplasts in combination with Pluronic F-68, and the combination of these two increased the division of the protoplasts (22). A PFC has also been used to increase the supply of carbon dioxide to cultured shoots of rose (*Rosa chinesis*) (23).

BIBLIOGRAPHY

1. P. Brodelius and H. Pedersen, *Trends Biotechnol.* **11**, 30–36 (1993).

2. R.M. Buitelaar, A.A.M. Langenhoff, R. Heidstra, and J. Tramper, *Enzyme Microb. Technol.* **13**, 487–494 (1991).

3. C. Laane, S. Boeren, S. Vos, and C. Veeger, *Biotechnol. Bioeng.* **30**, 81–87 (1987).

4. M. Asada and M.L. Schuler, *Appl. Microbiol. Biotechnol.* **30**, 475–481 (1989).

5. R.F. Rekker and H.M. de Kort, *Eur. J. Med. Chem. Chim. Ther.* **6**, 479–488 (1979).

6. L. Bassetti and J. Tramper, *Enzyme Microb. Technol.* **16**, 642–848 (1994).

7. H. Becker and S. Herold, *Planta Med.* **49**, 191–192 (1983).

8. W. Bisson, R. Biederbeck, and J. Rechling, *Planta Med.* **47**, 164–168 (1983).

9. R. Maisch, B. Knoop, and R. Biederbeck, *Z. Naturforch., C. Biosci.* **41C**, 1040–1044 (1986).

10. R.J. Robins and M.J.C. Rhodes, *Appl. Microbiol. Biotechnol.* **24**, 35–41 (1986).

11. R.D. Williams, N. Chauret, C. Bédard, and J. Archambault, *Biotechnol. Bioeng.* **40**, 971–977 (1988).

12. S.J. Sim, H.N. Chang, J.R. Liu, and K.H. Jung, *J. Ferment, Bioeng.* **78**, 229–234 (1994).

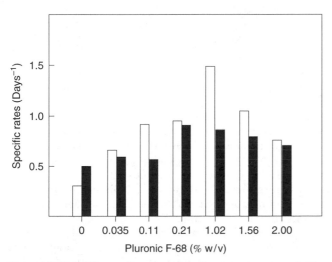

Figure 3. Specific growth rates and anthraquinone accumulation in the presence of increasing concentrations of Pluronic F-68 in suspension cultures of *Morinda citrifolia*. (□) growth; (■) anthraquinone. Data from Ref. 19.

13. R.M. Buitelaar et al., *Enzyme Microb. Technol.* **15**, 670–676 (1993).

14. T. Muranaka, H. Ohkawa, and Y. Yamada, *Appl. Microbiol. Biotechnol.* **40**, 219–223 (1993).

15. J. Berlin, L. White, W. Schubert, and V. Wray, *Phytochemistry* **23**, 1277–1279 (1984).

16. S.Y. Byun, H. Pedersen, and C.K. Chin, *Phytochemistry* **28**, 1101–1104 (1990).

17. B.S. Hooker and J.M. Lee, *Plant Cell Rep.* **8**, 546–549 (1990).

18. F. Cormier and C. Ambid, *Plant Cell Rep.* **6**, 427–430 (1987).

19. L. Bassetti and J. Tramper, *Enzyme Microb. Technol.* **17**, 353–358 (1995).

20. P. Anthony et al., *Plant Cell Rep.* **13**, 251–255 (1994).

21. P. Anthony, M.R. Davey, J.B. Power, and K.C. Lowe, *Biotechnol. Tech.* **11**, 581–584 (1997).

22. P. Anthony, K.C. Lowe, M.R. Davey, and J.B. Power, *Plant Cell Rep.* **17**, 13–16 (1997).

23. J. Wardrop et al., *Plant Cell Rep.* **17**, 17–21 (1997).

See also Physiology of plant cells in culture; Plant cell cultures, secondary product accumulation; Plant cell cultures, selection and screening for secondary product accumulation.

PLANT CELL CULTURE, LABORATORY TECHNIQUES

M.R. Fowler
The Norman Borlaug Institute for Plant Science
Research De Montfort University
Leicester, United Kingdom

OUTLINE

INTRODUCTION

Plant cell cultures are proving to be extremely useful model systems in a wide variety of investigations. They have several advantages over the use of whole plants, conceptually the most important being the ability to precisely control and manipulate the growth environment of a homogeneous population of cells. The effects of specific treatments on metabolism, growth, and division can be investigated without the complicating factors present when working with whole plants. Cell cultures therefore find widespread use as systems to study gene expression (particularly during the cell division cycle and in studies of plant growth regulator function), the degradation or biotransformation of xenobiotics, and the production of secondary metabolites.

As with any model system, results obtained using plant cell cultures must be interpreted with some caution. The formation of cell cultures involves a degree of dedifferentiation and reprogramming of gene expression. Cell cultures may not therefore be a true representation of the situation in planta. However, for fundamental studies and applied research they often remain the system of choice.

This article will cover the basic techniques (and facilities) required to establish, maintain, and monitor plant cell cultures. Where possible, the theoretical background will be given to help the reader fully appreciate the advantages and limitations of plant cell cultures.

LABORATORY FACILITIES

The growth of plant cell cultures places some novel technical and infrastructure problems on the laboratory (1,2). In order successfully to grow plant cell cultures certain facilities must be available. The equipment needed must not only include items needed for the maintenance of the cell cultures themselves, but also facilities for the growth of donor material if cell cultures are to be established routinely. The laboratory should therefore provide areas suitable for:

1. growth media production, sterilization, and storage
2. the manipulation of plant material under aseptic conditions
3. the growth of both donor plant material and the cell cultures themselves under controlled conditions

A media room suitable for producing plant cell culture media need not be very complicated, as it requires little equipment that would not be present in any laboratory. Required items include both a top pan balance and a fine analytical balance, stirrer plates (heated ones can be useful), a source of high-purity water, pH meters, an autoclave (a large pressure cooker can be used, but only if small volumes of media are to be used), and refrigerators and freezers. Useful additions to this list would include a steamer or microwave oven (for melting agar gelled media) and an automatic pipetter unit.

Growth rooms or growth chambers should be used to provide areas where plant cell cultures and donor plant material can be grown in controlled conditions. Growth rooms are ideal if a large volume of plant cell culture work is to be undertaken, and with cultures that grow in the same conditions. Growth chambers provide smaller areas for the growth of plants or cell cultures, but are self-contained and can therefore provide facilities dedicated to a particular plant or cell culture type. The growth rooms or growth chambers should be equipped with time-controllable lights, a temperature control system (capable of dealing with the large amount of heat given out by any lighting), and some way of controlling humidity. Plant cell cultures are usually grown at about 25 °C, and the humidity should not be lower than 50% or culture media will dry out very quickly (3). There should also be areas where cultures can be grown in complete darkness. Conditions in growth rooms used for growing donor plants should match as closely as possible the natural conditions for that particular plant (although this may be less important for plants that are to be used eventually to establish cell cultures, as they are not normally required to flower or set seed, unless specialized cell types such as endosperm or pollen are required), as the condition of the donor material may prove to be critical in being able to establish a cell culture.

Cell suspension cultures require constant agitation and therefore a shaker bed in a controlled environment room must be available. Shaker beds are gyratory (orbital) with platforms with clips of various sizes to hold conical flasks. They should have variable speed settings.

Areas for the manipulation of plant material under aseptic conditions should ideally be self-contained rooms in which laminar-flow transfer cabinets can be placed. Laminar-flow transfer cabinets should be used for all manipulations that require an aseptic environment. Transfer cabinets are available in a variety of sizes, and consist basically of a high-efficiency filter to remove air-borne contaminants and a fan to produce a laminar flow of air from the back of the cabinet toward the user (or from the top to the bottom of the cabinet). They are made of a variety of materials, stainless steel probably being the best as it is robust and easy to keep clean and surface sterilize. The cabinets can also be supplied with a gas source for a burner, although self-contained gas burners can be used. Items within the cabinet should ideally be kept to a min-imum, as anything that interferes with the laminar flow of the filtered air can compromise performance. Laminar-flow cabinets should be serviced regularly to ensure that the filter is working correctly. The performance of transfer cabinets can also be checked by placing unlidded Petri dishes of media in the cabinet and checking for the growth of any microorganisms. If genetically manipulated plant material that may still be harboring microorganisms is to be used, a transfer cabinet specially designed to pre-vent contamination of the environment should be used. Laminar-flow cabinets may be provided with a UV light source to maintain a sterile environment, although the use of such devices is of questionable efficiency and can present some health risks (4).

Additional equipment that should be present in a plant cell culture laboratory includes both binocular (dissecting) and high-magnification microscopes, the latter preferably with a UV light source. The binocular microscopes should be portable so as to allow their use in a laminar-flow transfer cabinet. Both types of microscope should have attachments to allow photography.

PLANT CELL CULTURE MEDIA

The culture media must provide all the essential elements and nutrients necessary for the growth of the cell culture. As such, plant culture media are composed of three basic components:

1. A supply of essential elements, which is supplied in the form of a complex mixture of salts
2. An organic supplement that supplies essential vitamins and other organic supplements (although plants are capable of synthesizing vitamins and amino acids, the biosynthetic capability of plant cell cultures often differs from that of whole plants, necessitating the supply of these in the culture medium)
3. A carbon source (again, although whole plants are capable of fixing carbon from atmospheric carbon dioxide, plant cell cultures are, except in specialized cases, not autotrophic; this necessitates a supply of carbon in the medium)

The three basic components of plant cell culture media can be further divided, divisions that become apparent if the formulations of particular media are examined (Tables 1–3). The supply of essential elements falls into three groups:

1. Macroelements (or macronutrients)
2. Microelements (or micronutrients)
3. Iron source

Plant cell culture medium is therefore usually made by combining several different components to give a complete medium. Concentrated stock solutions of macroelements, microelements, iron source, and organic supplement are commonly made, while the carbon source is usually added as a solid.

Stock Solution Components

Macroelements. As the name suggests, this stock solution contains the elements required in large amounts for plant growth (these are elements that generally comprise at least 0.1% by dry weight of plants) (5). The macronutrients are usually considered to be carbon (which is supplied as a separate component and is considered later), nitrogen, phosphorus, potassium, magnesium, calcium, and sulfur.

Nitrogen is usually supplied as nitrate and/or ammo-nium salts. To be incorporated into biological macro-molecules nitrogen must be in the reduced form (such as ammonium ions). Nitrate ions present in media must therefore be reduced in order to be incorporated in molecules, an energetic process. There is therefore a the-oretical advantage in supplying nitrogen solely as ammo-nium ions. Ammonium ions, however, can be toxic in high concentrations (although plant cell cultures are generally less susceptible to ammonium toxicity than are animal cell cultures, for example) and uptake of ammonium ions causes acidification of the medium. The use of ammonium ions as the sole nitrogen source therefore requires that

Table 1. Formulations of Gamborg's B5 Medium

Essential element	Concentration in stock (mg l^{-1})	Concentration in medium (mg l^{-1})
Macronutrients (50 ml)		
KNO$_3$	50000	2500
CaCl$_2 \cdot$ 2H$_2$O	3000	150
(NH$_4$)$_2$SO$_4$	2680	134
MgSO$_4 \cdot$ 7H$_2$O	5000	250
NaH$_2$PO$_4 \cdot$ H$_2$O	3000	150
Micronutrients (25 ml)		
KI	30	0.75
H$_3$BO$_3$	120	3
MnSO$_4 \cdot$ 4H$_2$O	400	10
ZnSO$_4 \cdot$ 7H$_2$O	80	2
Na$_2$MoO$_4 \cdot$ 2H$_2$O	10	0.25
CuSO$_4 \cdot$ 5H$_2$O	1	0.025
CoCl$_2 \cdot$ 6H$_2$O	1	0.025
Iron source (10 ml)		
FeNaEDTA	3670	36.7
Vitamins (1 ml)		
myo-inositol	add as solid	100
pyridoxine-HCl	1000	1
thiamine-HCl	10000	10
nicotinic acid	1000	1
Carbon source		
Sucrose	add as solid	20000
pH 5.5		

Note. Formulations of plant cell culture media have been adapted from Refs. 5 and 20. The composition of the various stock solutions is given, as is the amount of each stock solution needed for 1 liter of medium. It should be noted that the composition of plant cell culture media varies to some degree from source to source. A full list of media formulations can be found in Ref. 8.

Table 2. Formulations of Murashige and Skoog Medium

Essential element	Concentration in stock (mg l^{-1})	Concentration in medium (mg l^{-1})
Macronutrients (50 ml)		
NH$_4$NO$_3$	33000	1650
KNO$_3$	38000	1900
CaCl$_2 \cdot$ 2H$_2$O	8800	440
MgSO$_4 \cdot$ 7H$_2$O	7400	370
KH$_2$PO$_4$	3400	170
Micronutrients (5 ml)		
KI	166	0.83
H$_3$BO$_3$	1240	6.2
MnSO$_4 \cdot$ 4H$_2$O	4460	22.3
ZnSO$_4 \cdot$ 7H$_2$O	1720	8.6
Na$_2$MoO$_4 \cdot$ 2H$_2$O	50	0.25
CuSO$_4 \cdot$ 5H$_2$O	5	0.025
CoCl$_2 \cdot$ 6H$_2$O	5	0.025
Iron source (5 ml)		
FeSO$_4 \cdot$ 7H$_2$O	5560	27.8
Na$_2$EDTA $\cdot$ 2H$_2$O	7460	37.3
Vitamins (5 ml)		
myo-inositol	20000(2000)	100(100)
nicotinic acid	100	0.5
pyridoxine-HCl	100	0.5
thiamine-HCl	100(80)	0.5(0.4)
glycine	400	2
Carbon source		
sucrose	add as solid	30000
pH 5.7–5.8		

Note: Linsmaier and Skoog (LS) medium is basically the same except for the vitamins, which are given in brackets.

the culture medium be buffered. Most plant cell culture media therefore supply nitrogen as a mix of nitrate and ammonium salts. A supply of nitrate and ammonium salts also has the advantage of weakly buffering the media. Uptake of ammonium ions causes H$^+$ ions to be excreted into the culture medium, whereas nitrate uptake causes OH$^-$ ion excretion. The buffering depends on both nitrate and ammonium ions being present in the medium and the fact that ammonium ion uptake is reduced at acidic pH while the uptake of nitrate ions is reduced at alkaline pH (5).

Phosphorus (involved in energy transfer and a component of RNA and DNA) is usually supplied as the phosphate ion and is present at lower concentrations than nitrate/ammonium ions. High concentrations of phosphorus in media can lead to precipitation of other elements as insoluble phosphates.

Potassium is usually supplied as the chloride, nitrate, or orthophosphate salt, and is an important cellular cation involved in many processes.

Magnesium is usually supplied as magnesium sulfate. Like potassium it is an important cellular cation, and can in some cases substitute for potassium.

Calcium is usually supplied as the chloride salt (although calcium nitrate is used in some medium formulations). Calcium has important structural and regulatory roles.

Sulfur is usually supplied as magnesium sulfate or occasionally ammonium sulfate (many micronutrients are also supplied as sulfates). Sulfur is an important component of some amino acids and as such helps to determine protein structure.

A 10X or 20X stock solution of macroelements is usually made in deionized water and can be stored at 4 °C for several months.

Microelements. These are elements required in trace amounts for plant growth and development and have diverse roles. Microelements comprise manganese, copper, cobalt, boron, molybdenum, and zinc, which are usually considered to be essential (5,6). Nickel is included in the microelement formulations of some media (such as Heller's medium) and as a component of urease (5) may be

Table 3. Formulations of Schenk and Hildebrandt Medium

Essential element	Concentration in stock (mg l^{-1})	Concentration in medium (mg l^{-1})
Macroelements		
KNO$_3$ (25 ml)	101000	2525
MgSO$_4 \cdot$ 7H$_2$O (15 ml)	24640	36.6
NH$_4$H$_2$PO$_4$ (25 ml)	11500	287.5
CaCl$_2 \cdot$ 2H$_2$O (15 ml)	14680	220.2
Microelements (10 ml)		
MnSO$_4$	1320	13.2
H$_3$BO$_3$	500	5
ZnSO$_4 \cdot$ 7H$_2$O	100	1
KI	100	1
CuSO$_4 \cdot$ 4H$_2$O	20	0.2
Na$_2$MoO$_4$	10	0.1
CoCl$_2 \cdot$ 6H$_2$O	10	0.1
Iron source (10 ml)		
FeSO$_4 \cdot$ 7H$_2$O	1500	15
Na$_2$EDTA	2000	20
Vitamins (10 ml)		
thiamine-HCl	500	5
nicotinic acid	500	5
pyridoxine-HCl	50	0.5
myo-inositol	add as solid	1000
Carbon source		
sucrose	add as solid	30000

necessary for the growth of some cell cultures (7). Other elements (such as aluminum and iodine) are also often present in microelement formulations, but whether these are strictly necessary is doubtful.

A more concentrated (100X or 200X) stock solution can be made, as these elements are present at much lower levels than the macroelements. Store the stock solution at 4 °C, where it should be stable for several months.

Iron source. Iron is usually supplied as iron sulfate (iron citrate can also be used) and is generally considered to be the most important micronutrient. EDTA (the disodium salt) is usually used in conjunction with the iron sulfate to chelate the iron so as to allow a slow and continuous release into the medium (the commercially obtainable ferric-sodium salt of EDTA can also be used as the iron is already complexed). Uncomplexed iron can undergo rearrangement and precipitate out of the medium as ferric oxide (5). The iron source should be specially prepared so as to ensure chelation of the iron. The Na$_2$EDTA should be dissolved in almost boiling water, after which the iron sulfate is added and the solution allowed to cool, then made up to volume (8). The Fe/EDTA stock solution (100X) should be protected from light (9) and stored at 4 °C. It has been observed that EDTA, which chelates other

divalent cations, can have inhibitory effects on some plant cultures (10).

It has been reported that Fe/EDTA produced by this method can lead to precipitation of iron from media (such as Murashige and Skoog) if used at standard concentrations. One-third of the original amount of iron (with the same amount of EDTA) can be used in order to avoid this problem (8).

Vitamins/organic supplements. These are often included in plant cell culture media, often for historical reasons. Only two vitamins are considered to be essential, thiamine (vitamin B$_1$) and myo-inositol, although this may vary from culture to culture (5,7,11). Other vitamins, although not essential, may improve the growth of certain cell cultures (12).

Reduced nitrogen can also be supplied to plant cell cultures in the form of amino acids (usually arginine, glutamic acid, glutamine, and glycine). The uptake of amino acids, like the uptake of ammonium ions, causes acidification of the medium (5). Glycine is a standard component of many media, but in most cases is not required. Casein hydrolysate can be used as a source of amino acids (and therefore reduced nitrogen) and is also rich in calcium and phosphate (5).

Stock solutions of organic supplements (100X−1000X) should be stored in the freezer (in suitable aliquots). Generally, the vitamin/organic supplement stock is added before the media is autoclaved; however, if specific studies on vitamins are being conducted, they should be filter sterilized and added after the medium has been autoclaved (8).

Carbon source. Sucrose is by far the most used carbon source, for several reasons. It is cheap, readily available, relatively stable to autoclaving, and readily assimilated by plant cells. Other carbohydrates can be used, such as glucose (glucose is easily caramelized though), maltose, galactose, as can the sugar-alcohols glycerol and sorbitol. Many of the latter are only used in specialized circumstances though. The carbon source is added to the medium as a solid.

These then are the basic components of most plant cell culture media formulations. However, other components are commonly added for specific purposes.

Gelling agents. These are used to "solidify" the plant culture medium so plant cells can be grown on the surface of the medium. Agar is the most common agent used for gelling (incorrectly called solidifying) media. A natural product from seaweed it is relatively cheap. Agar is insoluble in cold water, but produces relatively inert gels at about 100 °C and "solidifies" at around 45 °C. Agar is used at concentrations of 0.6−0.8% (w/v). Low pH inhibits gelling. Agar is relatively impure, and the use of special "Plant Cell Culture" grade agar is recommended. Being a natural product the quality can vary from batch to batch and manufacturer to manufacturer; so it is best to stick to one supplier. Some agar preparations also contain significant amounts of some salts, which can alter the composition of the medium (13). Purified agar or agarose can be used for more demanding procedures (such as protoplast culture). The routine large-scale use of agarose is expensive.

Alternative gelling agents such as the gellan (a bacterial product) gums Gelrite or Phytogel are becoming more popular as they may be more suited to the growth of some cells. These gellan gums are more expensive (per unit weight) than agar, but can be used at concentrations as low as 0.2% (w/v). Gellan gums are used in the same way as agar. A variety of other gelling agents are also available commercially. All gelling agents have effects on the water potential of the medium and affect the rate of diffusion of nutrients (and toxic byproducts).

For plant cell cultures to proliferate, further additions to the medium may be required. Plant growth regulators are often required by plant cell cultures for cell division and expansion (and other developmental pathways). These plant growth regulators are most commonly plant hormones or their synthetic analogues, and thus give the cells the correct signals for proliferation. These are supplied in the medium because the biosynthetic capability may not be present in plant cell cultures. Plant growth regulators can be divided into several groups (Table 4).

1. Auxins
2. Cytokinins
3. Gibberellic acid
4. Abscisic acid
5. Ethylene
6. Others

Auxins. Indole-3-acetic acid (IAA) is the only (or predominant) natural auxin, but its use in cell cultures in vitro is complicated. IAA is not very stable to heat and is also photolyzed (stock solutions are degraded within a few days) (14). In order to partially alleviate this problem, relatively stable amino acid conjugates of IAA (such as indole-acetyl-L-alanine and indole-acetyl-L-glycine) can be used, although their use is not widespread (5). Stable chemical analogues of IAA are therefore usually used in plant cell culture media. 2,4-Dichlorophenoxyacetic acid (2,4-D) is perhaps the most commonly used auxin and is very effective. Others, such as indole-3-butyric acid (IBA), 1-napthylacetic acid (NAA), 2-napthyloxyacetic acid (NOA), 2,4,5-trichlorophenoxyacetic acid (2,4,5-T), 2-methyl-4-chlorophenoxyacetic acid (MCPA), 2-methoxy-3,6-dichlorobenzoic acid (dicamba), and 4-amino-3,5,6-trichloropicolinic acid (piclorom) are also available. Not all are equally efficient at promoting growth and cell division and there may be species-to-species variation in efficacy. Synthetic auxins should be handled with care as many (or contaminants present in the preparation) are mammalian carcinogens. Synthetic auxins are also known to promote somaclonal variation (5).

There also exists a class of compounds that are known to antagonize auxin action, the so-called anti-auxins. Anti-auxins act either by inhibiting auxin transport or the correct recognition of auxin molecules by cells and so can prove useful in studies of auxin action. Commonly used anti-auxins include 2,3,5-triiodobenzoic acid (TIBA), p-chlorophenoxyisobutyric acid (PCIB), and 2,4,6-trichlorophenoxyacetic acid (2,4,6-T).

Auxins are usually included in plant cell culture media in order to promote cell division and cell growth.

Cytokinins. The natural cytokinins are a wide variety of related (purine derivatives) compounds. Some naturally

Table 4. Plant Growth Regulators Commonly Used in Plant Cell Culture Medium

Regulator	Molecular weight
Auxins[a,b]	
IAA (indole-3-acetic acid)	175.2
IBA (3-indolebutyric acid)	203.2
2,4-D (2,4-dichlorophenoxyacetic acid)	221
2,4,5-T (2,4,5-trichlorophenoxyacetic acid)	255.5
NAA (1-naphthylacetic acid)	186.2
NOA (2-naphthyloxyacetic acid)	202.2
Picloram (4-amino-3,5,6-trichloropicolinic acid)	241.5
Dicamba (2-methoxy-3,6-dichlorobenzoic acid)	221
MCPA (2-methyl-4-chlorophenoxyacetic acid)	200.6
Cytokinins[b,c]	
Zeatin (4-hydroxy-3-methyl-trans-2-butenylaminopurine)	219.2
IPA [N^6-(2-isopentyl)adenine]	203.3
BAP (6-benzylaminopurine)	225.2
Kinetin (6-furfurylaminopurine)	215.2
Thidiazuron (N-phenyl-N′-1,2,3-thiadiazol-5-ylurea)	220.25
Gibberellic acid (GA$_3$)[d]	346.4
Abscisic acid[d]	264.3

[a]Auxins are usually titrated into solution with NaOH (0.1 M). DMSO can also be used, as can 95% ethanol.
[b]If auxins and cytokinins are dissolved in alkali and acid, the pH of the stock solutions should be brought to the pH of the medium before use.
[c]Cytokinins are usually dissolved in a small volume of HCl. Cytokinins can also be dissolved in DMSO.
[d]Gibberellic acid and abscisic acid are soluble in water.

occurring cytokinins used in cell culture media are 4-hydroxy-3-methyl-trans-2-butenylaminopurine (zeatin) and N[6]-(2-isopentyl) adenine (2iP or IPA). These naturally occurring compounds are very expensive (especially zeatin) and relatively unstable. The synthetic analogues 6-furfurylaminopurine (kinetin) and 6-benzylaminopurine (BA or BAP) therefore find widespread use in plant cell culture media. Other, non-purine-based chemicals (such as substituted phenylureas) also find use as cytokinins (7). Cytokinins are often included in plant cell culture media along with auxins in order to promote cell division.

Combinations of auxins and cytokinins can be used to initiate specific forms of organogenesis in plant tissue cultures. Generally, high levels of cytokinin coupled with low levels of auxins promote shoot formation, while high levels of auxin in conjunction with low levels of cytokinins promote root formation.

Gibberellins or gibberellic acids (GAs). There are many variations on the gibbane carbon skeleton that, in planta, are involved in regulating cell elongation. Commercially, only a few of the possible gibberellins are available. Anti-gibberellins, which act by preventing synthesis (such as ancymidol), are available.

Abscisic acid (ABA). ABA is generally regarded as inhibiting cell growth. It is most commonly used in media to promote specialized developmental pathways such as somatic embryogenesis.

Ethylene. A naturally occurring gaseous plant growth regulator, most commonly associated with controlling fruit ripening in climacteric fruits. It is not often used in plant cell tissue cultures, but can be supplied to cultures as a gas or by ethephon (2-chloroethylphosphoric acid). Ethylene action can be antagonized by silver ions, and aminoethoxyvinylglycine (AVG) inhibits ethylene biosynthesis.

A bewildering array of other compounds (polyamines, phenolic compounds, and jasmonic acid, among others) have been postulated to have growth regulatory properties. In general, it is the auxins and cytokinins that find the most widespread use in plant cell culture.

Stock solutions (10 mg ml^{-1} or 10 mM) of plant growth regulators are usually prepared. If the plant growth regulators are to be added after the culture medium has been sterilized, the pH of the stock solutions should be brought to the pH of the medium.

Plant cell culture media can be bought from a variety of commercial suppliers, and may offer some advantages for routine cell culture work. But, buying premade media is relatively expensive, and does not allow the easy manipulation of individual media components. It has also been observed that some commercial plant cell culture media has a tendency to precipitate out during autoclaving.

Preparation of Media

Stock solutions of the basic medium components (macronutrients, etc.) can be prepared and stored as indicated. They are then added to deionized water (about half the final volume) in the indicated proportions, along with the sucrose. Any other heat-stable components can also be added. When the sucrose has dissolved, the volume is brought to about 90% of final, and the pH of the medium adjusted to the desired value. The medium is then brought to the correct final volume (with thorough mixing) and dispensed into suitable containers for autoclaving. After autoclaving the media should be clear with a slight yellow color from the iron source. Any browning of the medium indicates that the carbon source has caramelized and should therefore be discarded.

It is important to remember that while most components of plant cell culture medium are considered to be thermostable, certain are not and there are conflicting data on others. Gibberellins are rapidly degraded by autoclaving and therefore should be filter sterilized and added to the medium after autoclaving (15). Auxins are generally considered to be thermostable (although there is some disagreement, and for some applications better results have been achieved using filter sterilized auxins) (8,14,16). Cytokinins (except zeatin) are also considered to be thermostable (although some substituted phenylureas are not), as are most vitamins (calcium pantothenate excepted and thiamine is destroyed if the medium pH is too high) (7,8). Sucrose is also added to medium before autoclaving, although this results in a degree (approximately 5%, depending on the duration of autoclaving) of hydrolysis to a mixture of D-glucose and D-fructose (17).

Media Sterilization

In most cases plant cell culture media is sterilized by steam in an autoclave. This is usually done for 20–30 min at 121 °C (103 kPa). These criteria are set on the general rule that 121 °C must be maintained for at least 15 min in order to kill thermophilic indicator microorganisms such as *Bacillus steriothermophilus*. It should be remembered that this standard autoclave regime will be insufficient to ensure sterilization of large volumes of media (5). However, thermophilic organisms are rarely a problem in plant cell cultures, and standard autoclave cycles of 20–30 min at 121 °C are widely used regardless of culture vessel size. Excessively long autoclave cycles should be avoided, as they result in caramelization of the carbon source and may well result in the breakdown of other medium components.

The efficacy of steam sterilization can be checked by the use of special indicator tubes, which change color when they have been exposed to a certain temperature for a set length of time (various combinations can be obtained). Ideally they should be placed in a vessel containing a similar volume liquid if media is being sterilized to ensure that the media is sterile. A cheaper alternative is to use special tape that has indicator strips on it that change color when autoclaved. However, this tape only indicates that the vessel has been autoclaved, not whether the contents are sterile.

The heat-labile components of media can be sterilized by filtration through a sterile fine-pore membrane (0.45 or 0.22 µm). These are available commercially, either as presterilized sealed units or as self-assembly units that are autoclaved before use. They are simple to use, as either the liquid is forced through the membrane into a sterile receptacle from a syringe or on larger units a vacuum source is used. These filter units will remove bacteria and fungi, but not viruses, viroids, and mycoplasma.

Aseptic Technique

It is obviously important to ensure that any plant cell cultures are sterile, in order to avoid loss of the culture and invalidating any experimental results. It is vital then that all possible precautions against contamination are taken. We have already seen that plant cell culture media can be sterilized by autoclaving and that any heat-labile components can be filter sterilized. However, when manipulating plant material and/or plant cell cultures, the whole environment should be as free from contamination as is possible.

Hands should thoroughly washed before any work is commenced, and latex gloves can be worn. These gloves can be occasionally swabbed with 70% ethanol to ensure that they are sterile. Face masks can also be worn to prevent airborne contaminants spreading, and long hair should be tied back (or a hair net used).

Any surfaces where aseptic techniques are to be used should be surface sterilized before and after use. This is usually done by swabbing the area with a 70% (v/v) solution of ethanol or isopropanol, although industrial methylated spirit can be used and is much cheaper. Acidified alcohol (70%, pH 2) or a solution of phenolic disinfectant can also be used. As a further precaution any manipulations can be carried out on autoclaved ceramic tiles, that can be changed regularly to ensure asepsis.

Any vessels/surfaces etc. that are going to be used within the aseptic environment should be sterile. This can be achieved by autoclaving or by dry heat. If items are autoclaved, any openings should not be sealed so tightly so as to prevent the steam from penetrating into them. This is because steam sterilizes by transfer of its thermal energy to any surfaces in contact with it. Simply heating to 121 °C will not ensure sterility. Dry heat can also be used to sterilize items (check they will withstand the temperature), but is less efficient and therefore requires longer times. Any small items to be sterilized by dry heat can be wrapped in aluminum foil. The total time taken for dry heat sterilization is considered to be well over 3 hours (5) at about 180 °C (1 hour for the load to reach the sterilization temperature, 2 hours at the sterilization temperature and a cooling-down period).

Instruments used for the manipulation of plant material should initially be sterilized by autoclaving or dry heat (dry heat will blunt scalpels). They can be kept sterile during use by placing them in a container of 80% (v/v) ethanol which is quickly flamed off. There is no need to heat instruments in a flame for a long period; this will blunt scalpel blades and cause delays while instruments are allowed to cool down. Obviously precautions need to be taken to ensure that the ethanol does not ignite (this is particularly so with transfer cabinets, where the flow of air will blow the fire toward the user); so it should be kept capped when possible and kept in a container that will not smash or tip over (a boiling tube with cotton wool in the end, which is then placed in a weighted beaker to prevent tipping over works well).

Any plant material that is going to be used to establish a cell culture needs to be sterile. This is usually achieved by treating the plant material with chemicals such as bleach. The conditions needed to ensure sterility have to be determined on a case-by-case basis. It will depend on many factors such as the initial degree of contamination, the type of contaminating microorganism, the morphology of the material to be sterilized, and the susceptibility of the plant material itself to damage from the bleach. It is important that the plant material is not exposed to the sterilizing agent for too long a period, as this will have detrimental effects. If explants can be taken from seedling tissue, a good way of producing sterile donor material is to sterilize seeds and produce sterile plants in vitro; otherwise the explant source must be surface sterilized.

Most workers use a commercial bleach (such as Domestos), which contains approximately 5% sodium hypochlorate. The commercial bleach is usually diluted before use with water, but the precise dilution used needs to be determined. The addition of surfactants (0.1–1% v/v) such as Tween or Triton (or Teepol, which is cheaper, though less pure) can improve sterilization, presumably by improving contact with the bleach solution. A 70% solution of ethanol is also commonly used in conjunction with bleach to sterilize explants. If treatment with bleach proves ineffective at ridding contamination, the tissue can also be treated with Virkon (a commercial disinfectant that has a different pH than that of bleach). In cases where this proves ineffective, alternative chemical sterilization agents include hydrogen peroxide (about 10%), bromine water (about 1–2%), and mercuric chloride (0.1–1%), although some of these are extremely dangerous (such as mercuric chloride). After treatment with chemical sterilizing agents, the plant tissue must be washed thoroughly with copious amounts of sterile distilled water to ensure removal of the chemical. Some surface sterilization methods are given:

Tobacco or Arabidopsis Seeds (or Other Small, Smooth Seeds)
1. Submerge in 70% ethanol for 10 sec
2. Submerge in 10% Domestos for 20 min
3. Wash three times in sterile distilled water

Sugar Beet Seeds (Seeds with a Rough Seed Coat)
1. Submerge in 70% ethanol for 10 sec
2. Submerge in 50% Domestos/0.1% Teepol for 30 min
3. Wash three times in sterile distilled water

Tobacco Leaves
1. Submerge in 10% Domestos for 15 min
2. Wash three times in sterile distilled water

Vessels for Cell Culture In Vitro

A wide variety of vessels for cell cultures can be obtained commercially, and so long as they are capable of fulfilling the basic needs of containing the cell culture and its medium and excluding contaminants, all are acceptable. Unless they are disposable and purchased presterilized, the culture vessels must be capable of being sterilized.

Petri dishes are widely used vessels for plant cell cultures. They are cheap, can be stacked (and therefore occupy little space), and can be bought presterilized. Originally designed for work with microorganisms, their main drawback is the lack of space for growth vertically. They are, however, ideal for the initiation of callus cultures. Petri dishes must be sealed with a plastic film such as "cling-film" (plastic food wrap), Nescofilm, or Parafilm to prevent the medium from drying out and the entry of contaminants.

A variety of plastic containers for the growth of plants in vitro can be obtained commercially. These are either disposable or made from autoclavable plastic. They have the advantage of offering more height than Petri dishes. Glass "jam" or "powder" jars can be used in the same way. These vessels have tighter-fitting lids than Petri dishes, but it may still be necessary to seal them with a plastic film.

Cell suspension cultures are usually grown in glass conical flasks (Erlenmyer), which are stoppered with foam, paper, or cotton wool bungs and aluminum foil.

CELL CULTURE SYSTEMS

Callus Cultures and Cell Suspensions

Cell suspension cultures are usually initiated by producing a callus (an unorganized mass of cells) culture from a suitable explant (a piece of plant tissue such as leaves, root, or cotyledon) or from a specific cell type (such as endosperm). The size of the explant used to initiate the callus is not usually considered to be critical (although explants of a very small size may not be viable). Callus is usually produced by placing explants on a suitable medium gelled with agar which contains an auxin and/or a cytokinin. No hard-and-fast rule indicates which medium will prove successful, but general-purpose media such as Murashige and Skoog (18), Gamborg's B5 (11), or Schenk and Hildebrandt (19) are good starting points. Again, no hard-and-fast rules indicate the precise nature or concentration of the plant growth regulators that will be needed in order for callus to form. A grid of various concentrations (0 to 10 µM) of an auxin (often 2,4-D) and a cytokinin (often BAP or kinetin) is usually set up in order to establish the levels of plant growth regulators needed (20). The plant growth regulator regime necessary to induce callus formation must be determined empirically because of the difference in biosynthetic capability of different plant cell types, and it will composition and depend, at least partly, on the plant hormone composition and levels in the donor material. Therefore, the age of the explant material, its position on the plant, and which cell type forms the callus will all have an effect on the conditions needed for callus initiation. Sterile explants are gently pressed on to the surface of the medium to ensure good contact and left (often in the dark). Callus, which is observed as a lump of unorganized cell growth, usually at the cut surface (wounding the explant may be beneficial for callus formation) will then form on media of the correct composition, usually within two months.

Cell suspension cultures are usually then initiated by transferring lumps of callus into liquid medium of the same composition, which is then shaken to encourage the formation of a cell suspension culture. The callus transferred into the liquid medium should be friable (easily broken up into smaller cell clumps), and a relatively large inoculum should be used, so that cell density builds up quickly. However, if the inoculum is too large, toxic products (presumably from the stress of transfer to liquid medium) can quickly build up to lethal levels. Callus established from some plants or from some particular cell types may not be friable, and will not therefore easily form a good cell suspension, growing instead as large cell clumps. The friability of the callus may be improved by changes to the composition of the medium or by repeated subculturing (21). Alternatively the formation of cell suspensions can sometimes be encouraged by culturing the callus on lower concentrations of agar before transfer to liquid medium, or by placing a small amount of liquid on the surface of the solid medium. After the initial cell suspension culture has formed any remaining large cell clumps can be removed by filtering the suspension, allowing large clumps to settle out or by transferring the suspension with a small bore pipette.

Cell suspensions are most easily grown as batch cultures, usually in conical flasks. The cell suspension culture usually occupies 20–33% of the total graduated volume of the conical flask. If the culture volume occupies a greater proportion of the culture vessel, then problems with gaseous exchange across the surface of the media can be encountered, leading to anoxia. Cell suspension cultures are continually propagated by transferring a small volume of the culture into fresh medium, a process called subculture. This subculturing results in the dilution of the cell suspension culture (the amount of culture added to fresh medium during subculture; therefore, the degree of dilution depends on the individual culture and must be determined empirically) after which the biomass of the culture increases in a characteristic fashion until the nutrients present are used up and/or toxic byproducts accumulate to inhibitory levels (22). This is called the stationary phase, where no further increase in biomass or cell number is evident. Cells left in the stationary phase of the batch growth cycle for extended periods usually lose viability and die, leading to loss of the cell suspension or an extension of the subsequent lag phase upon subculturing. It is therefore important that the growth of the culture is monitored in order to determine the optimum batch culture cycle length. The degree of dilution of the culture at subculture also has to be determined (one part in five is a good starting point) as too great a dilution will result in an extension of the lag phase, the death of the culture or the need for the use of culture medium with special supplements (23,24). Cells can be transferred by using a simple plugged pipette (the ends may be removed if large cell aggregates are present) or a "Howell" syringe equipped with a large-diameter cannula.

Although termed cell suspension cultures, plant cell suspension cultures very rarely consist of separated single cells. Usually small clumps of cells are formed. These clumps can cause problems in some experiments as the metabolism of individual cells in these clumps may vary (25–27). Cell suspensions can be filtered in an attempt to reduce the size of these cell clusters; however, it is often observed that this filtering has an inhibitory effect on the growth of the culture, often until cell clumps are formed again. Alternatively, low concentrations of macerozyme and cellulase can be added to the culture medium to reduce cell clumping (25). Cell suspension cultures need to be aerated, which is usually achieved by placing the cultures on a gyratory (orbital) shaker. Speeds are usually around 30–150 rpm, with displacements of 2–4 cm. Again the precise speed needs to be determined for each cell suspension culture, as it will depend on the size of the cell clusters and cell density. However, speeds much above the higher limit quoted are likely to cause excessive cell damage, and speeds below 30 rpm will almost certainly result in the cells settling out and not being properly aerated.

Like many plant cultures, cell suspension cultures are prone to contamination due to the rich nature of the medium and the relatively slow growth rate of plant cells. Sometimes this contamination will be obvious, the culture may take on a cloudy appearance, a "slime" may be visible on the sides of the culture vessel, or small balls of fungi may be found floating in the medium. Surprisingly, a strange smell noticed at subculture or during experimental sampling can also be a good indicator of contamination problems that are not yet evident. Experience will indicate the strange smell!. It is, therefore, worth testing the cell suspension culture for latent contamination at regular intervals. This can be done by plating out small aliquots of the cell suspension culture on microbiological media designed for the growth of fungi and bacteria (such as nutrient agar, malt extract, potato dextrose, and corn meal agars). Incubation of the plates in suitable conditions will reveal the presence of any contamination. See Contamination Detection and Elimination.

One source of contamination that is altogether more difficult to detect and deal with is mycoplasma infection. Mycoplasma infection will not usually be fatal to the cell suspension culture, but can have deleterious effects on growth and may distort experimental data. Some antimycoplasma agents are now available, as are some detection kits. These are often designed to treat and detect mycoplasma contamination in mammalian cell cultures and should therefore be used with due caution.

In batch culture systems the culture environment never stabilizes (as they are closed systems). Thus efforts to couple cellular metabolism to cell growth over a long culture period cannot succeed (24,25,28). This is a major drawback of batch culture systems and means that any investigations should be conducted over as short a time period as possible.

Cell suspensions can also be grown as continuous cultures, either in a chemostat or a turbidostat, which to some extent overcomes the problems of batch cultures. Continuous cultures are used when investigations are conducted that require that cells are kept in a constant steady state of growth. The setup of continuous cultures is technically much more demanding than the growth of batch cultures, and the use of continuous cultures is therefore limited.

The plant growth regulator requirements of cell suspension cultures should be periodically checked to see whether such additions are still required. This is because cell suspensions (and indeed callus cultures) can develop the ability to grow in the absence of an external supply of plant growth regulators, a process referred to as habituation. This phenomenon is not noted with all cell cultures, but is prevalent in, for instance, cell cultures of *Beta vulgaris* (29,30). The mechanism by which habituation occurs has not been clearly established, although factors such as the plant growth regulators used to establish the culture and changes in cellular biochemistry have all been implicated (31,32).

Plant growth regulator autonomy, or habituation, may be of value in specific circumstances. Synthetic auxins such as 2,4-D can interfere with the assembly of the mitotic spindle and increase the duration of the cell cycle (33–35).

Assessing Cell Growth

We have seen that it is vital that the growth of the cell suspension is monitored in order to establish a batch growth cycle. The growth of cell suspension cultures can be assessed in several ways.

1. Packed cell volume (PCV)
2. Cell number
3. Fresh (or wet weight)
4. Dry weight
5. Medium conductivity
6. Macromolecule content

The determination of packed cell volume is a quick and simple way of assessing the growth of cell suspension cultures, although it will not determine between cell division and cell expansion (without further examination of cell size). A known volume of cell suspension culture is centrifuged at low speed (approximately 500 g) in a graduated centrifuge tube. The results are expressed as the percentage of the total volume occupied by the cell pellet.

Cell number. As its name suggests, this is a fairly simple (though time-consuming) technique where the number of cells per unit volume are counted by using a microscope and a suitable graticule-etched slide. In cell suspensions that grow as very finely divided small cell clumps or as single cells a haemocytometer can be used. A Sedgewick–Rafter counting slide or a "homemade" counting cell with a receptacle of known volume can also be used. However, as cell suspensions usually grow as cell clumps, which makes counting individual cells impossible, the accuracy of this technique can be improved by treating the cell suspension culture to remove or reduce these cell clumps. This can be done in two ways, by either treating the cell suspension culture with enzymes (such as pectinase at 0.25%) or more commonly by treatment with chromium trioxide at 70 °C. The exact treatment needed will have to be determined empirically, as it will depend on the degree of cell clumping [two volumes of 10% (w/v) chromium trioxide for 15 min is a good starting point, but if the cell clumps are large, a longer incubation time may be required]. After the mixture has cooled, vortex mixing can be used to aid the breakup of the clumps into single cells. Care must be taken that the cells are not overtreated, as single cells or small cell clumps may be destroyed by harsh treatments.

Fresh weight can be determined fairly simply by filtering, under reduced pressure, a known volume of cell suspension culture onto a glass or nylon fiber filter paper (weighed in the wet condition), which can then be reweighed and the weight of the cells calculated by difference.

Dry weight can be determined after wet weight by drying the filter papers and cells to a constant mass in an oven (at 60–80 °C).

Combinations of these techniques allow average cell volume and cell mass to be calculated and to determine increases in biomass. Cell division and cell expansion can also be distinguished.

Other techniques are also used, although less often. In some cell suspensions the conductivity of the medium has been found to be related to the fresh weight of the cells in suspension culture. The protein and DNA content of a known aliquot of cell suspension culture can also be used to assess growth, although this is a relatively time-consuming approach.

Assessing Cell Viability

These techniques (with the exception of identifying obviously dead cells while counting) do not, however, directly indicate whether cells are alive or dead. Not all the cells in a culture will be viable, and some measure of viability gives useful insights into the health of the cell suspension culture. A simple method to determine cell viability is to use a dilute solution (0.025% w/v) of Evan's blue. Healthy cells will exclude this dye, whereas damaged/dead cells will stain blue. These can be scored under a microscope and the results expressed as a percentage of total cell number. Fluorescein diacetate can also be used to assess viability. This method relies on functioning esterases being present in healthy cells, which produce fluorescein, which can be observed with the aid of a UV microscope. A simple method is given as [20]:

1. Add fluorescein diacetate to a concentration of approximately 0.01% (make a 0.5% stock solution in acetone and store at 4 °C)
2. Leave for 5 min
3. Examine the cells under a UV microscope; living cells fluoresce green; score as a percentage of total cell number

Other methods rely on the reduction of tetrazolium salts such as 2,3,5-triphenyltetrazolium chloride (TTC) (respiratory efficiency is monitored by spectrophotometric measurement of the red dye formazan). The TTC method is more labor intensive, and it should be optimized with respect to pH, time, and % TTC [20].

Synchronization of Cell Suspension Cultures

One area where plant cell suspension cultures find widespread use is in studies of gene expression during the cell division cycle. Cell suspensions are particularly suited to this type of investigation, as a homogenous population of cycling cells can be produced.

Early attempts at synchronizing the cell division cycle of suspension cultured plant cells relied either on the withdrawal and subsequent resupply of a nutrient [36–38] or a plant growth regulator [39,40]. These treatments caused the cells to arrest at a particular point in the cell division cycle and, following addition of the substance back to the medium, resume cell division in a synchronous fashion. However, these techniques may not be universally applicable or result in arrest at more than one point in the cell cycle [35,41]. More recent work has focused on the use of chemicals that prevent either DNA replication, such as aphidicolin and hydroxyurea [42,43], or mitosis, such as colchicine, oryzalin, or other antimicrotubule drugs [44].

SUMMARY

Plant cell cultures provide excellent experimental model systems. Unfortunately, due to the wide variation in the requirements of individual plant cell cultures, there is no real substitute for experience in plant cell culture. However, with the knowledge from this article it should be possible to initiate, maintain, and monitor the growth of cell cultures from most plant species. These provide the basic steps necessary for any investigations involving the use of cell cultures.

BIBLIOGRAPHY

1. O.L. Gamborg and G.C. Phillips, in O.L. Gamborg and G.C. Phillips, eds., *Plant Cell, Tissue and Organ Culture*, Springer-Verlag, Berlin, 1995, pp. 3–20.
2. H.E. Street, in H.E. Street, ed., *Plant Tissue and Cell Culture*, Blackwell, Oxford, 1973, pp. 11–30.
3. S.S. Bhojwani and M.K. Razdan, *Plant Cell Culture: Theory and Practice*, Elsevier, Amsterdam, 1983, pp. 11–24.
4. J.H. Dodds and L.W. Roberts, *Experiments in Plant Cell Culture*, Cambridge University Press, Cambridge, U.K., 1995, pp. 25–41.
5. F.W. Rayns and M.R. Fowler, in C.F. Hunter, ed., *In Vitro Cultivation of Plant Cells*, Butterworth-Heinemann, Oxford, 1993, pp. 43–64.
6. H. Marschner, *Mineral Nutrition of Higher Plants*, Academic Press, Orlando, Fla., 1986.
7. J.H. Dodds and L.W. Roberts, *Experiments in Plant Cell Culture*, Cambridge University Press, Cambridge, U.K., 1995, pp. 42–66.
8. E.F. George, D.J.M. Puttock, and H.J. George, *Plant Culture Media*, Vol. 2., Exegetics Ltd., England, 1988, pp. 398–405.
9. R.P. Hangarter and T.C. Stasinopoulos, *Plant Physiol.* **96**, 843–847 (1991).
10. J.M. Bonga, in J.M. Bonga and D.J. Durzan, eds., *Tissue Culture in Forestry*, Martinus Nijhoff, The Hague, 1982, pp. 4–35.
11. O.L. Gamborg, R.A. Miller, and K. Ojima, *Exp. Cell Res.* **50**, 151–158 (1968).
12. O.L. Gamborg and G.C. Phillips, in O.L. Gamborg and G.C. Phillips, eds., *Plant Cell, Tissue and Organ Culture*, Springer-Verlag, Berlin, 1995, pp. 21–34.

13. R.L.M. Pierik, in J. van Bragt, D.A. Mossel, R.L.M. Pierik, and H. Veldstra, eds., *Effects of Sterilization on Components in Nutrient Media*, Veenman and Zonen, Wageningen, 1971, pp. 3–13.

14. S.J. Nissen and E.G. Sutter, *HortScience* **25**, 800–802 (1990).

15. J. van Bragt and R.L.M. Pierik, in J. van Bragt, D.A. Mossel, R.L.M. Pierik, and H. Veldstra, eds., *Effects of Sterilization on Components in Nutrient Media*, Veenman and Zonen, Wageningen, 1971, pp. 133–137.

16. J.R. Dunlap, S. Kresovich, and R.E. McGee, *Plant Physiol.* **81**, 934–936 (1986).

17. S.R. Hagen, P. Muneta, J. Augustin, and D. LeTourneau, *Plant Cell, Tissue Organ Cult.* **25**, 45–48 (1991).

18. T. Murashige and F. Skoog, *Physiol. Plant.* **15**, 312–313 (1962).

19. R.U. Schenk and A.C. Hildebrandt, *Can. J. Bot.* **50**, 199–204 (1972)

20. R.A. Dixon, in R.A. Dixon, ed., *Plant Cell Culture: A Practical Approach*, IRL Press, Oxford, 1985, pp. 1–20.

21. H.M. Wilson and H.E. Street, *Ann. Bot.* **39**, 671–682 (1975).

22. E.F. George and P.D. Sherington, *Plant Propagation by Tissue Culture*, Exegetics Ltd., England, 1984.

23. R. Stuart and H.E. Street, *J. Exp. Bot.* **64**, 556–571 (1969).

24. H.E. Street, in H.E. Street, ed., *Plant Tissue and Cell Culture*, Blackwell, Oxford, 1973, pp. 59–99.

25. P.J. King, K.J. Mansfield, and H.E. Street, *Can. J. Bot.* **51**, 1807–1823 (1973).

26. D.E. deJong, E. Jansen, and A. Olson, *Exp. Cell Res.* **47**, 139–156 (1967).

27. D. Verma and R. Van Huystee, *Can J. Bot.* **48**, 429–431 (1970).

28. M.W. Fowler, in W. Barz, ed., *Plant Tissue Culture and its Bio-technological Application*, Springer-Verlag, Berlin, 1977, pp. 253–265.

29. H. Masuda, R. Nakagawa, and S. Sugawara, *Plant Cell Physiol.* **29**, 75–78 (1988).

30. W.P. Doley and J.K. Saunders, *Plant Cell Rep.* **8**, 222–225 (1989).

31. W. deGreef and M. Jacobs, *Plant Sci. Lett.* **17**, 55–61 (1979).

32. C. Kevers et al., *Physiol Plant.* **51**, 281–286 (1981).

33. M.W. Bayliss, *Plant Sci. Lett.* **8**, 99–103 (1977).

34. M.W. Bayliss, in J.A. Bryant, ed., *The Cell Division Cycle in Plants*, pp. 157–177.

35. J. Dolezal, S. Lucretti, and F.-J. Novak, *Biol. Plant.* **29**, 253–257 (1988).

36. M.W. Bayliss and A.R. Gould, *J. Exp. Bot.* **25**, 772–783 (1974).

37. A.R. Gould, N.P. Everett, T.L. Wang, and H.E. Street, *Protoplasma* **106**, 1–13 (1981).

38. S. Amino, T. Fujimura, and A. Komomine, *Physiol. Plant.* **59**, 393–396 (1983).

39. J.P. Jouanneau, *Exp. Cell Res.* **77**, 167–174 (1971).

40. A. Nishi, K. Kato, M. Takahashi, and R. Yoshida, *Physiol. Plant.* **39**, 9–12 (1977).

41. K.Z. Gamburg, in P.F. Wareing, ed., *Plant Growth Substances*, Academic Press, London, 1982, pp. 59–67.

42. L.-X. Qin et al., *Plant Mol. Biol.* **32**, 1093–1101 (1996).

43. R. Soni, J.P. Carmichael, Z.H. Shah, and J.A.H. Murray, *Plant Cell* **7**, 85–103 (1995).

44. O. Shaul et al., *Proc. Natl. Acad. Sci. U.S.A.* **93**, 4868–4872 (1996).

See also Culture establishment, plant cell culture; Equipment and laboratory design for cell culture; Micropropagation of plants, principles and practices; Physiology of plant cells in culture; Plant protoplasts; Protoplast fusion for the generation of unique plants.

PLANT CELL CULTURES, PHOTOSYNTHETIC

Jack M. Widholm
University of Illinois at Urbana-Champaign
Urbana, Illinois

OUTLINE

INTRODUCTION

Photosynthetic plant cell cultures are cultured plant cells that utilize light energy to carry out photosynthesis to obtain at least a portion of their required carbon and energy. The presence of chlorophyll (Chl) would be a visible marker for this capacity. The well-established photosynthetic cultures grow relatively rapidly as fine suspensions with relatively high Chl and CO_2-fixing enzyme levels. These cultures have many possible uses, ranging from basic photosynthesis and molecular biology studies to the testing of herbicides or production of valuable secondary compounds, as will be discussed in the following. In general, these cultures have not been exploited very extensively at this time, even though the potential seems clear.

BACKGROUND

Despite the fact that most plants depend upon photosynthesis to use light energy to obtain carbon and energy for growth, photosynthetic plant tissue and cell cultures are relatively rare and usually require time and patience to initiate (1). Most plant tissue cultures are grown in a medium containing 3% sucrose [heterotrophic (H) conditions] where the energy and carbon needs are saturated; so photosynthesis is not needed and the cells usually contain no Chl even if grown in the light. If the sucrose level is lowered to 1% [photomixotrophic (PM) conditions], some additional energy is needed for maximal growth; so the cells often contain Chl and carry out photosynthesis, especially if the growth regulator, cytokinin, is present in the medium. If all sugar and other carbon sources are removed from the medium [photoautotrophic (PA) conditions], then the cells must photosynthesize to survive. As summarized in the most recent comprehensive review on PA plant cell cultures (1), such cultures have been initiated from only 24 species, and only 11 of these have ideal characteristics such as continuous relatively rapid growth, relatively high Chl and photosynthetic enzyme levels, and the ability to grow on a minimal medium. The PA cultures should have more utility than the PM cultures, since all available carbon is fixed CO_2 and none comes from any component of the medium. Cultures grown under PA conditions generally grow more slowly, however.

The first PA suspension culture initiated was *Nicotiana tabacum* (tobacco) (2), as might be expected since tobacco is a favorite tissue culture species. One percent CO_2 was bubbled through the medium to obtain growth. One of the next PA cultures described was a *Chenopodium rubrum* suspension culture that was grown in a sealed two-tiered flask where the CO_2 level was maintained at 1% using a mixture of K_2CO_3 and $KHCO_3$ (2M) in the lower flask (3). Later a *Glycine max.* (soybean) suspension culture (SB-P) was initiated and grown in a 5% CO_2 atmosphere provided by blowing the CO_2 into the space over the culture in an Erlenmeyer flask through a Millipore filter connected to a syringe needle stuck through a rubber stopper (4). Another syringe needle with Millipore filter served as an exit for the gas. These cultures are described since these lines, tobacco in general and the specific *C. rubrum* and SB-P lines, are the most widely used in the numerous studies reported in the literature (1). In addition, the culture methods used are good examples of the variety of typical systems.

This article will rely on the references listed in the 1992 review (1) in many cases to save space and will emphasize information found in more recent publications for most of the specific examples.

General Characteristics

The initiation of PA cultures typically begins by placing green callus, obtained on a solid medium containing a cytokinin like benzyladenine, into liquid medium with 1% sucrose. The cultures are then incubated under continuous light (100–250 $\mu Em^{-2} s^{-1}$) on a gyrotory shaker at about 130 rpm. The cell clumps that remain alive and grow are transferred successively to fresh medium and then to a medium without any sucrose. Following more transfers, a PA culture should be obtained. Typically this process takes a year, and a clear selection occurs, since many cells die.

That the selected PA cultures are different from the cultures they were selected from is shown by bleaching and regreening studies. A total of eight different PA cultures of six different species have been grown under H conditions (adequate sugar or starch in the medium and darkness) for a period of time until all Chl had disappeared (1,5). These H-grown cells were then placed back into PA conditions where all the lines formed Chl quickly and began to grow. These characteristics are quite different from those of the original cultures, where long periods of time were needed to obtain the growing green cultures.

The newly initiated PA cultures are clearly not leaf-like, since their Chl levels are lower and the ratios of the CO_2-fixing enzyme activities, ribulose bisphosphate carboxylase (rubisco), and phosphoenolpyruvate carboxylase (PEPcase) are usually in favor of PEPcase rather than rubisco. After several years of culture, however, the Chl levels come closer to the leaf levels, and rubisco activity predominates over that of PEPcase, as is normally found in C_3 (photosynthesis where CO_2 is fixed by rubisco into a C_3 compound, 3-phosphoglycerate) plant leaves. One can speculate, however, that the lower Chl and altered CO_2-fixation enzyme activity ratios may be due, at least in part, to the fact that the PA cultures are growing while the mature leaf, which is the plant tissue usually used in photosynthesis studies, is not growing. The high PEPcase is thought to be important for anaplerotic CO_2 fixation to feed into the tricarboxylic acid cycle and glycolysis for amino acid and related compound synthesis. The rubisco levels are still only about half that of leaves on a per milligram Chl basis.

Overall the studies of PA cultures have shown that the medium should contain a cytokinin that stimulates chloroplast development and an auxin other than 2,4-dichlorophenoxyacetic acid, which has been shown to cause bleaching. Some cultures require no auxin or cytokinins. Usually no vitamins are needed, but in some cases thiamine is required for growth. Most cultures grow well on MS (Murashige and Skoog) or LS (Linsmaier and Skoog) basal minerals (1) that consist of a mixture of elements found to be necessary for plant growth. The growth of the PA cultures is usually stimulated greatly by the use of 1% or higher CO_2 atmospheres, although a few cultures will grow with ambient CO_2. The PA cultures grow relatively slowly, with doubling times of several days, in contrast to some heterotrophically grown cultures that can divide in less than 24 h.

Some cultures can grow slowly with the ambient CO_2 levels of about 700 ppm typically found in a culture room. These CO_2 levels are about double the air level of 350 ppm (0.035%). The growth stimulation usually observed by elevated CO_2 would be expected since the CO_2 compensation concentrations (the CO_2 level at which CO_2 fixation equals CO_2 evolution) of the cultures are usually from 0.015 to 0.035%, which are at least twice that of leaves. This higher CO_2 compensation concentration appears to be due not only to photorespiration (light-induced CO_2 release) but also to higher respiration that occurs both in the light and in the dark. The high dark respiration rate appears to be related to growth. The photorespiratory consequences, CO_2 evolution, and the decrease in CO_2 fixed caused by the competitive fixation of O_2 would be prevented by the use of elevated CO_2 levels, as is the common practice.

The growth of the PA cells would appear to be limited by rubisco enzyme activity, which is normally only half that of leaves on a mg^{-1} Chl basis, and in addition the rubisco activation level is 50% or less, while in leaves this is usually near 90%. The activation of rubisco is several cell lines can be increased to almost 100% by a 5-min 350 $\mu Em^{-2} s^{-1}$ light treatment (6), indicating that light is limiting. However, attempts to increase the light intensity for growing the cells above 300 $\mu Em^{-2} s^{-1}$ have not been successful, as the cells do not survive under these conditions.

The only C_4 (photosynthesis where CO_2 is fixed initially by PEPcase into a C_4 compound, oxaloacetate) species that have produced PA cultures are *Amaranthus powellii* and *A. cruentus*, but the cultures have 3–5 times higher rubisco than PEPcase activity; so they are not utilizing the C_4CO_2 fixation pathway. No PA cultures have been initiated from cereals, possibly because the Chl found in cultured tissues is not generally uniformly distributed but is usually localized in small differentiated regions.

Simplified Culture Maintenance

This laboratory has developed seven different lines of five species that need to be maintained continually. The maintenance of these lines as PA suspension cultures requires labor, shaker space, media, energy, and CO_2 gas, and there is always a chance of equipment malfunction or microbial contamination that can cause losses. Thus over the past few years we have been investigating methods to simplify the maintenance of these cultures.

We already often maintain the lines under PM conditions with 1% sucrose or starch in the liquid medium to act as a partial carbon and energy source, and this simplifies the culturing somewhat. The lines can also be grown as callus under PM conditions, where they maintained high Chl levels when kept on agarose-solidified media for at least one year (7). In all cases PM suspension cultures with high Chl levels could be reinitiated from the calli. PM suspension cultures of all lines, except SB1 (*Glycine max.*), were also able to grow well when placed back under PA conditions. Most of the lines were also capable of forming PA cultures directly from the calli. Thus six of these seven PA cell lines can be maintained as PM calli and then be recovered again as PA suspension cultures.

An even easier method to store the cultures would be to cryopreserve them in liquid nitrogen so that a sample could be thawed when needed to recover growing cultures. To this end we attempted to cryopreserve six of the lines after high osmoticum pretreatments that are normally necessary for recovery of growing cultures after thawing. Only the *D. innoxia* line, DAT, and the soybean line, SB1, could be successfully recovered as viable, growing, dark green cultures (8). The successful method utilized a preculture treatment of from 2 to 8 days in a medium containing 3% starch and 3% sorbitol for DAT and 3% sucrose and 3% sorbitol for SB1 cells. The cells survived if frozen with the cryoprotectants 10% dimethylsulfoxide (DMSO) and 9.1% sorbitol or with 10% DMSO and 8% sucrose. Following a programmed slowcooling to $-40\,°C$ and one hour holding at this temperature, the cells were stored in liquid nitrogen. The cells were thawed in a $40\,°C$ bath and could be recovered directly when added to fresh liquid medium. We previously had used feeder plates, using live cells as feeder layers, to recover thawed

H cultures, but here we found the direct transfer into liquid medium to be just as effective and much simpler.

Additional experimentation using higher concentrations of sorbitol in the preculture treatments and longer preculture treatment times in combination with a cryoprotectant solution with DMSO and sorbitol or sucrose but not glycerol allowed the successful cryopreservation in liquid nitrogen of the SB-P (9) and the tobacco (NTG-P) cell lines. We can now maintain all the photosynthetic cell lines as callus, which requires less labor and equipment and can also cryopreserve four of the lines (the two soybean, the *Datura*, and the tobacco line).

SPECIFIC USES

Biochemical Studies

The PA cultures provide an ideal system for various biochemical studies, including pulse-chase experiments to study cell wall turnover, for example. When the SB-P cells were given a 30-min pulse of $^{14}CO_2$, about 25% of the $^{14}CO_2$ fixed was in the wall components, and after a 96-h chase in $^{12}CO_2$ the amount increased to 80% (10). The pectin and hemicellulose fractions turned over, especially in cells labeled early in the batch culture cycle, while cellulose did not turn over at all during the chase. Many earlier studies followed the early C fixation products and the flow of ^{14}C through pathway intermediates (1). These studies showed that some cultures fixed a large proportion of the $^{14}CO_2$ into C_4 compounds due to high PEPcase activity, but these ^{14}C-labeled compounds were utilized slowly, indicating that true C_4 photosynthesis was not occurring where the initially fixed C in C_4 compounds would be rapidly refixed by rubisco.

Both CO_2 and O_2 gas exchange have been measured in several studies with PA cultures using $^{18}O_2$ and $^{13}CO_2$ and mass spectrometry. These studies showed that photorespiration does occur and that mitochondrial respiration also occurs both in the light and the dark (11).

Protoplasts have been prepared from PA cultures of *C. rubrum*, SB-P, and tobacco that were ruptured osmotically or by passage through a fine mesh in a syringe. Organelles were then isolated by differential or density gradient centrifugation to be used in a number of studies, including measurement of compounds, enzymes, and lipids in the different compartments or DNA amounts and repair.

The PA cells provide materials that are also much easier to use in Chl fluorescence studies, where less spectral distortion occurs in comparison with leaves (12).

Molecular Biology

A number of molecular studies have been carried out with PA cultures, including, on the effect of light quality and plant hormones on specific gene expression, DNA methylation and synthesis, DNA helicases and polymerases, and a number of genes have also been cloned from these cells (1). It may be of particular interest to note that the PA tobacco and SB-P cells have about twice as many copies of plastid DNA per cell as leaves of the same species (13,14). This seems to be related to an increase in the plastid DNA polymerases as well, so that the PM SB-P cells are very rich sources of these enzymes (G.C. Cannon, personal communication). The Cannon lab has used the SB-P cultures in recent studies of chloroplast DNA replication intermediates (15) and nuclear and chloroplast DNA repair mechanisms (16).

The SB-P cells were also used recently to demonstrate that there may be two distinct signaling pathways for jasmonic acid-inducible gene expression, one that is light dependent and one that is light independent (17).

Genetic Engineering

The PA cells would seem to be ideal for genetic engineering, since they grow well as fine suspensions, grow with CO_2 as the sole carbon source, should be selectable using a number of markers including agents that affect photosynthesis, and can be manipulated quite readily in culture. Protoplasts have been prepared from the SB-P cells, and up to 25% formed colonies that could be placed back under PA conditions where the Chl levels and growth rates were similar to the original culture (18). Protoplasts are usually easily transformed by electroporation or direct DNA uptake; so the protoplast system, which should also be feasible with many other cell lines, would allow rapid, efficient production of transgenic cells. Protoplasts have also been prepared from several PA cultures to prepare organelles for various studies, as mentioned previously.

One limitation to genetic engineering is that most PA cultures will not regenerate plants; so the end product would be transgenic cells and not whole plants. However, the tobacco leaf system used by Svab et al. (19) can produce green callus that will regenerate plants, and the *N. plumbaginifolia* protoplast PA system (20) will also regenerate plants.

To date there have been no reports of the transformation of PA cultures, but there have been many descriptions of the transformation of chloroplasts in tobacco leaf disks. The first system involved the bombardment with a plastid 16S ribosomal RNA carrying a mutation imparting resistance to spectinomycin and streptomycin (19). The gene could integrate into the chloroplast chromosome by homologous recombination at low frequency, and the rare transformants could be selected as green sectors using the antibiotics. Plants were regenerated that passed the transformed DNA to progeny by maternal inheritance as expected, since chloroplast DNA is normally maternally inherited in tobacco. The system has been improved by using a gene that detoxifies spectinomycin that is inserted in the chloroplast DNA by homologous recombination between two homologous DNA segments (21). A number of foreign DNA fragments have been inserted in this way to allow the study of many phenomena. So far chloroplast transformation has only been accomplished with tobacco, however.

Batch and Continuous Culture Systems

Most of the PA cultures are grown as batch cultures in shake flasks in 30–50 ml of liquid medium with 1% or higher CO_2 in air blown into the atmosphere above the medium or through the medium in tubes. The two-tiered flask system maintains the elevated CO_2 in a closed system using a K_2CO_3 and $KHCO_3$ buffer. Typically at each transfer, a small volume of cells are added to the fresh medium in the flasks or tubes, where they are allowed to grow up to stationary phase before transfer again to fresh medium.

The PA cultures have also been grown in fermenters as batch cultures in larger volumes. Yamada et al. (22) were able to grow a tobacco PA culture in a 5-L fermenter with a slow growth rate. The PA *C. rubrum* culture was grown in a 1.5-L fermenter, where the cells grew somewhat more slowly than in the smaller shake flask with 30 ml of medium (23).

PA cultures have also been grown in continuous culture systems. The *C. rubrum* PA culture was also grown in a 1.5-L airlift fermenter with a system simultaneously to remove medium containing cells and add fresh medium (24). A stable 100-h doubling time was reached within 8 d. A green *Spinacia oleracea* (spinach) suspension culture was placed in a 1.7-L fermenter with 1% fructose (25). As the fructose level was decreased stepwise to zero, the Chl level and photosynthesis rate increased, and the cells became PA. The lowest doubling time attained was about 5 d with the different dilution rates and light intensities used. A PA *Asparagus officinalis* (asparagus) culture was grown in steady-state turbidostats with 16-h light (120 μEm^{-2} s^{-1}) and 8-h darkness (26). The cultures were grown at a high (5 mg DW/ml) or a low (2 mg DW/ml) cell density. The low-density cells had higher Chl and grew more rapidly (doubling time 1.9 d) than those grown at high density. *Euphorbia characias* PA suspension cultures were grown in several different batch and semicontinuous culture systems for over 2 years in volumes up to 1.7 L with 18 h light (100–130 μEm^{-2} s^{-1}) (27).

These examples indicate that it should be possible to scale up the PA culture systems and that these cultures can grow in fermenters under continuous culture conditions for long periods of time, which could be useful for cell and/or compound production.

Secondary Compound Production

Since plants have produced many of the drugs, fragrances, colorings, and flavorings used in the past as well as today, many attempts have been made to find H tissue cultures that produce high levels of the desired compound. Most of the attempts have been disappointing, but the use of photosynthetic cultures might give different results, especially if the desired compounds are normally synthesized in green tissues. The studies summarized in Widholm (1) show mixed results from a number of different H, PM, and PA cultures, however, and at this time none of the examples gives a high enough yield of a valuable enough compound to be near the point of commercialization. The use of new techniques such as elicitation or transformation with genes for key biosynthetic enzymes could still lead to commercial success.

Herbicide Studies

A number of studies have used photosynthesis-inhibiting herbicides like diuron or atrazine to demonstrate how reliant the photosynthetic cultures are on photosynthesis for growth; that is, the growth of PA cultures was completely inhibited, the growth of the PM cultures was partially inhibited, and the H cultures were unaffected.

When 12 different herbicides with different mechanisms of action were applied to PA, PM, and H tobacco suspension cultures and seedlings, the PA cells and seedlings responded similarly (28). The PA cells were especially more sensitive than the H and PM cells to the five photosynthetic herbicides used. The best example of a correlation between photosynthesis and the 50% growth inhibition concentration was found with the photosynthetic electron transport inhibitor diuron, where the values for PA, seedlings, PM, and H systems were 0.02, 0.03, 1.0, and 200 μM, respectively. The seven other nonphotosynthetic herbicides inhibited the growth of the four different systems at similar concentrations.

The PA *C. rubrum* cells were grown in 1.5-mL volumes in a 24-well microtiter plate and were treated with four herbicides and a fungal toxin (29). The cells could be monitored for growth, viability, Chl content and fluorescence, and O_2 evolution easily in order to determine the effects of the compounds. This system would seem to be ideal to study the effects of many different compounds on the PA cells.

The PA cultured cell systems have been used in a number of herbicide resistance selection experiments and many triazine-resistant lines identified. The mutation in the target D1, quinone-binding, Q_B protein, encoded by the plastid *psbA* gene was found in all cases to be different from that found in five triazine-resistant weeds that all have the serine residue at position 264 changed to glycine (30). This change found in the weeds is known to decrease photosynthetic electron transport through the altered Q_B protein that leads to slower growth and lower competitive ability. Studies of the triazine-resistant *C. rubrum* (31) and potato lines (32) indicate that photosynthesis is not altered, however, so that it is possible to obtain triazine herbicide resistance without impairing plant performance.

CONCLUSIONS

It would seem that PA or PM plant cell cultures should provide systems useful for a wide range of cell technologies, since many lines are currently available and the methods for initiating new lines are developed. While PA cultures are not exactly like leaves, since they are growing and do not form a tissue with the abilities to translocate, etc., they are homogeneous, grow on simple medium, and are so readily manipulable that they have numerous exploitable uses. Their unstructured form also means that there are no stomates that can complicate certain studies with leaves.

The PA cultures are clearly different from the cells they were initiated from, since they readily regreen and become PA following bleaching, in contrast to the slow adaptation found initially. All the PA culture triazine-resistant mutants described so far have DNA changes different from those found in the triazine-resistant weeds. At least some of the PA cultures also have increased levels of chloroplast DNA and DNA biosynthetic enzymes.

These cultures should be ideal for selection and genetic engineering studies to attempt to manipulate photosynthesis, other metabolic processes, and valuable secondary compound production. Such studies should provide insight into basic biochemical processes and determine if valuable compounds can be produced.

Due to the ease of manipulation and analysis, these cultures are ideal for studying the effects of stress and other external effectors and to study the mechanism of action of chemicals.

BIBLIOGRAPHY

1. J.M. Widholm, *Int. Rev. Cytol.* **132**, 109–175 (1992).
2. L. Bergmann, *Planta* **74**, 243–249 (1967).
3. W. Husemann and W. Barz, *Physiol. Plant.* **40**, 77–81 (1977).
4. M.E. Horn, J.H. Sherrard, and J.M. Widholm, *Plant Physiol.* **72**, 426–429 (1983).
5. V.V. Lozovaya, X. Luo, and J.M. Widholm, *In Vitro Cell Dev. Biol. Plant* **32**, 295–298 (1996).
6. C.A. Roeske, J.M. Widholm, and W.L. Ogren, *Plant Physiol.* **91**, 1512–1519 (1989).
7. V.V. Lozovaya, X. Luo, and J.M. Widholm, *Plant Tissue Cult. Biotechnol.* **2**, 131–135 (1996).
8. X. Luo and J.M. Widholm, *Plant Cell, Tissue Organ Cult.* **47**, 183–187 (1997).
9. X. Luo and J.M. Widholm, *In Vitro Cell Dev. Biol. Plant.* **33**, 297–300 (1997).
10. V.V. Lozovaya, O.A. Zabotina, and J.M. Widholm, *Plant Physiol.* **111**, 921–929 (1996).
11. P. Chagvardieff, M. Pean, P. Carrier, and B. Dimon, *Plant Physiol. Biochem.* **28**, 231–238 (1990).
12. C. Xu et al. *Photosynth. Res.* **21**, 93–106 (1989).
13. G. Cannon, S. Heinhorst, J. Siedlecki, and A. Weissbach, *Plant Cell Rep.* **4**, 41–45 (1985).
14. G. Cannon, S. Heinhorst, and A. Weissbach, *Plant Physiol.* **80**, 601–603 (1986).
15. L.A. Hedrick, S. Heinhorst, M.A. White, and G.C. Cannon, *Plant Mol. Biol.* **23**, 779–792 (1993).
16. G.C. Cannon, L.A. Hedrick, and S. Heinhorst, *Plant Mol. Biol.* **29**, 1267–1277 (1995).
17. H. Ohta et al., *Physiol. Plant.* **100**, 647–652 (1997).
18. V.K. Chowdhury and J.M. Widholm, *Plant Cell Rep.* **4**, 289–292 (1985).
19. Z. Svab, P. Hajdukiewicz, and P. Maliga, *Proc. Natl. Acad. Sci. U.S.A.* **87**, 8526–8530 (1990).
20. P. Rey, F. Eymery, G. Peltier, and A. Silvy, *Plant Cell Rep.* **8**, 234–237 (1989).
21. Z. Svab and P. Maliga, *Proc. Natl. Acad. Sci. U.S.A.* **90**, 913–917 (1993).
22. Y. Yamada, K. Imaizumi, F. Sato, and T. Yasuda, *Plant Cell Physiol.* **22**, 917–922 (1981).
23. W. Husemann, *Protoplasma* **113**, 214–220 (1982).
24. W. Husemann, *Plant Cell Rep.* **2**, 59–62 (1983).
25. C.C. Dalton, *J. Exp. Bot.* **31**, 791–804 (1980).
26. E. Peel, *Plant Sci. Lett.* **24**, 147–155 (1982).
27. T. Hardy, D. Chaumont, and C. Gudin, *J. Plant Physiol.* **128**, 11–19 (1987).
28. F. Sato, S. Takeda, and Y. Yamada, *Plant Cell Rep.* **6**, 401–404 (1987).

29. C. Schwenger-Erger et al., *FEBS Lett.* **329**, 43–46 (1993).

30. Y. Sigematsu, F. Sato, and Y. Yamada, *Plant Physiol.* **89**, 896–992 (1989).

31. J. Thiemann, A. Nieswandt, and W. Barz, *Plant Cell Rep.* **8**, 399–402 (1989).

32. R.J. Smeda et al., *Plant Physiol.* **103**, 911–917 (1993).

See also ANGIOSPERMS; CULTURE ESTABLISHMENT, PLANT CELL CULTURE; DICOTYLEDONS; MICROPROPAGATION OF PLANTS, PRINCIPLES AND PRACTICES; PLANT CELL CULTURES, PHYSIOCHEMICAL EFFECTS ON GROWTH.

PLANT CELL CULTURES, PHYSIOCHEMICAL EFFECTS ON GROWTH

ALAN H. SCRAGG
University of the West of England
Frenchay, Bristol
United Kingdom

OUTLINE

Introduction

Light

pH

Temperature

Dissolved Oxygen

Osmotic Pressure

Foam

Agitation

Bibliography

INTRODUCTION

The growth of plant cells cultures is principally dependent on the medium, which contains plant growth regulators, but the physicochemical environment can also affect the growth of plant cells. The main parameters involved in the physicochemical environment are: light, pH, temperature, dissolved oxygen, dissolved carbon dioxide, osmotic pressure, agitation, and foam formation. These parameters can affect growth but do not often operate in isolation, as they are often linked, such as agitation and foam formation. In many cases physicochemical conditions such as temperature it has been generally assumed that all plant cultures have the same optimum, and therefore little research has been reported on the variation of growth produced by altering these parameters. Much of the research that has been reported has involved the effects of physicochemical conditions on the accumulation of secondary products.

LIGHT

The characteristics of light that influence plant tissues and cell cultures are those of intensity, spectral quality,

and length of exposure. Plant cell cultures are normally grown on a salt-based medium containing sucrose as the carbon and energy source so that photosynthesis is not required and is generally not functioning, although the culture may be green. The light intensities are too low at around 5 W/m^2 compared with peak solar irradience (1000 W/m^2) to supply sufficient energy for photosynthesis. However, photosynthetic cultures can be developed if the light levels are increased and the sugar removed gradually (1). Although plant cell cultures are not generally photosynthetic, the photoperiodicity, light quality, and intensity appear to influence the growth of plant cell cultures even when used at low levels, although many plant cultures are grown in the dark. Much of the work on the effects of light on growth was carried out some time ago, and more recent work has concentrated on the effects of light on secondary product accumulation. In general during the development of a callus or suspension culture the ability to grow in the light or dark is generally determined, but the parameter is not investigated further. The light intensity used for plant tissue culture is in the range of 50–200 µmole m^{-2} s^{-2}, which is lower than the intensity required for photosynthesis at 1000 µmole m^{-2} s^{-1}. Light has been shown to increase callus growth (2), and many investigators have tried to determine whether light of different wavelengths has different effects, but the results are conflicting. The same results have been obtained with suspension cultures. Suspension cultures of *Nicotiana labaccum* have been shown to be slightly inhibited by light (3), whereas *Taxus cuspidata* exhibited better growth in the dark (4), as shown in Figure 1. In contrast with suspension cultures of strawberry *Fragaria ananassa*) and *Vitis* spp, light had no effect on growth, even when the intensity was varied (5,6). In the case of callus culture of *Oxalis reclinata*, the effect of light on growth depended on the cell line (7).

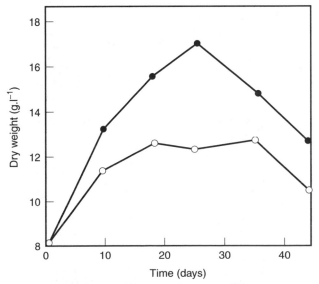

Figure 1. The effect of light on the growth of suspension cultures of *Taxus cuspidata*. The culture were grown in constant light of 85 µmol M^{-2} s^{-1} intensity (○) or in the dark (●). Data from Ref. 4.

pH

Callus and suspension cultures are generally grown on or in medium, which is not buffered. The initial pH of the medium is normally adjusted to between 5 and 7, and this can change upon autoclaving or after inoculation. It has been suggested that some of the media components such as EDTA and coconut milk may have a buffering capacity, but this will only be very small. The pH of the medium is normally allowed to find its own level and can vary during the culture growth period as components of the medium are metabolized such as the preferential utilization of ammonia when this is used in combination with nitrate as a nitrogen source in medium. Cultures become more acid when ammonia is utilized or when organic acids are produced and alkaline with the nitrate is used and ammonia released. Early research showed that culture initiated at different pH values rapidly reached the same pH (3 days) and that growth was little affected (8). This can be illustrated by the effect of various initial pH values on the growth of *Digitalis purpurea* L (9) and *Hyoscymus muticus* (10) as shown in Table 1. The initial pH had little effect on growth and the final pH values. The cultures of *H. muticus* initiated at different pH values did show differences in the final growth yield (10) after 2 weeks culture, and the final pH values were between 5.3 and 6.0. More recently different initial pH values of between 3.7 and 8.7 were shown not to affect the growth curves of strawberry (*F. ananassa*) suspension cultures, but anthocyanin accumulation was affected (11). Cultures of grape (*Vitis* hybrids) cultured at different initial pH values showed a steady decline in cell number after 12 days incubation from 10×10^6 at pH 4.5 to 3×10^6 cells/ml at pH 7.0 (12). pH values above 5.5 appeared to be inhibitory to growth, as shown by the growth curves, but the changes in pH values over the 12 days were not followed, nor was the final pH value recorded so that it is not clear how or if the pH values changed. Little work has been carried out on the incorporation of buffers into the medium in order to control pH, but one report has shown that callus cultures of *Tanacetum parthenium* buffered at pH 5.8 grew much better than cultures buffered at other pH values of 5 to 8 (13). The buffered values were maintained within 0.2 pH units over the culture period so that it is clear that growth is affected by pH. This has proved difficult to repeat in suspension cultures as, despite buffering, plant cells appear to control their pH.

TEMPERATURE

Traditionally plant cell cultures are grown at a temperature of 20–25 °C irrespective of the temperature that the plant normally grows. Most research on the effects of temperature has been carried out to determine the effects on the accumulation of secondary products. The influence of temperature on the doubling times of *Catharanthus roseus* has shown that temperature does influence growth with a broad peak of maximum growth between 27 and 35 °C and death occurring at 40 °C (14). In another study with *C. roseus* Morris (15) showed that cultures maintained at 25 °C had a maximum growth rate at 35 °C, which declined rapidly above 35 °C (Fig. 2). The cell yield in terms of dry weight had a broader peak with the maximum at 25 °C so that although the growth rate is greater at 35 °C, the yield is less than at 25 °C. In contrast, callus cultures of *Cephalotaxus fortunei* showed an optimum dry weight at 25 °C in accordance with accepted practice (16).

Table 1. The Effect of Initial pH on the Growth of Plant Cell Cultures

Digitalis purpurea

pH after autoclaving	pH at harvest	Dry wt/flask (% control)
4	5.1	104
4.5	5.2	103
5.5	5.1	100
6.5	5.1	98
7.6	5.4	99

Hyoscymus muticus

Initial pH	Dry wt g/flask
2.5	1.25
3.0	1.45
3.5	1.50
4.0	1.55
4.5	2.15
5.0	2.17
5.5	1.73
6.0	1.73

Source: Data from Refs. 9 and 10.

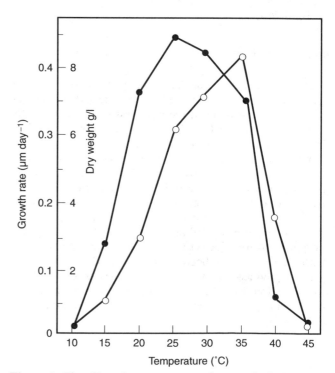

Figure 2. The effect of temperature on the growth of suspension culture of *Catharanthus roseus*: (○) growth rate days^{-1}; (●) final cell yield gL^{-1} dry weight. Data from Ref. 15.

DISSOLVED OXYGEN

Plant cells in culture are aerobic, but because of their low metabolic rate they have a much lower oxygen demand than microbial cultures. Maximum oxygen demands are in the range of 0.2 to 0.6 mmol g^{-1} dry wt. h^{-1} (17). In callus cultures oxygen supply is achieved by diffusion into the callus mass, and if the growth vessel is sealed, oxygen renewal will be limited. Suspension cultures are generally grown in shake flasks where shaking both mixes and supplies oxygen by surface agitation. The more vigorous the shaking or mixing, the better the oxygen transfer, but the more vigorous shaking will increase the shear stress. The influence of shaker speed on the fresh weight obtained by a culture of *C. roseus* where the oxygen supply was controlled by shaker speed (18) is shown in Figure 3. The study correlated oxygen supply (oxygen transfer rate) with shaker speed, but no allowance was made for the increased shear that the high shaker speeds would generate.

The effect of oxygen supply on the growth of plant suspension cultures has been studied using flasks fitted with different closures. An example is shown in Table 2, where suspension cultures of *C. roseus* were cultivated using three types of closure (19). The diffusion of oxygen was restricted by aluminum foil (two layers) of parafilm, and over a period of 9 days cultivation the carbon dioxide level reached 11–13% compared with 0.03% in air and 0.5% with polyurethane foam closures where diffusion is rapid. The oxygen levels are 6.8–13% in the flasks compared with 21% in the normal atmosphere. Thus conditions in the flask are different from those in normal atmosphere, and this may affect plant growth. The type of closure has been shown to affect the growth of *Panax notoginseng* cultures (20). Flasks can be very

Table 2. Effect of Closure on Gas Composition in Shake Flasks Containing Suspension Cultures of *Catharanthus roseus*

Closure	CO_2 (v/v)	O_2 (v/v)
Silicone foam	0.5	21.8
Silicone foam (parafilm covered)	12.9	6.8
Aluminum foil	11.6	13.1

Source: Data from Ref. 20.

different from normal atmospheric conditions. This has been confirmed by maintaining different gaseous condition in shake flasks where oxygen-limiting conditions for *C. roseus* reduced growth and oxygen above 50% inhibited growth (Fig. 4) (21).

The best method for the control and study of the effect of oxygen is the use of bioreactors, which allow a precise control of the gaseous condition not really possible in flasks. In addition, the effect of other gaseous components such as carbon dioxide and ethylene can also be studied. Carbon dioxide is the most abundant gaseous metabolite, and the first report on the effects of carbon dioxide was initiated by studies that showed that high aeration rates reduced the growth of plant cell cultures, probably by the removal of carbon dioxide (22,23). It was shown with cultures of *Datura stramonium* that aeration at 1 vvm (volume of gas/volume of reactor/minute) inhibited growth and 0.6 vvm was optimum (24). It was demonstrated that at high aeration rates (1.5 vvm) the addition of carbon dioxide to the gas eliminated the growth reduction of cultures of *C. roseus* at high aeration rates (22). The production of berberine by cultures of *Thalictrum ruguosum* (25) was affected by continuous gas stripping in an airlift bioreactor, but the addition of 2.08% CO_2 and 21.5 ppm ethylene, which were the

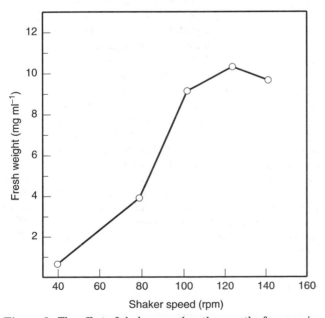

Figure 3. The effect of shaker speed on the growth of suspension cultures of *Catharanthus roseus* grown in 100 mL Erlenmeyer flasks. Data from Ref. 18.

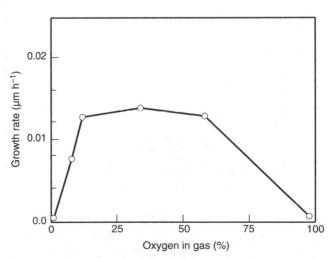

Figure 4. The influence of the gas-phase oxygen concentration passing through shake flasks on the growth rate of suspension culture of *Catharanthus roseus*. Data from Ref. 21.

values found in shake flasks, restored the berberine accumulation. The growth was not affected in either case. When carbon dioxide of up to 5% was added to the air supplied to a 7-L airlift bioreactor, growth reduction of *C. roseus* was seen at 3% (26). Values of between 5 and 20% reduced the growth of *C. roseus* in an airlift bioreactor (27) (Fig. 5) (28). Cultures of *Atropa belladonna* grown in the presence of 10 and 15% CO_2 showed growth inhibition at 15% but not at the other level (29). In a more recent study (30) the dissolved gaseous metabolites were seen as important parameters in the growth and secondary product accumulation in cultures of *C. roseus*. The two main components are ethylene and CO_2, and there was no difference in biomass accumulation at various flow rates irrespective of changes in dissolved gaseous metabolites, although secondary product accumulation was affected.

OSMOTIC PRESSURE

Plant cell cultures generally use between 1 and 2% sucrose as the carbon source in the growth medium. It has been shown that using higher sucrose concentrations can stimulate secondary product accumulation. However, the higher concentrations will impose an osmotic stress on the culture, and osmotic pressure has been shown to affect growth. Much of the research on the effects of osmotic stress has been in order to select drought tolerance in cultures (31). Suspension cultures of *C. roseus* growing in the presence of higher levels of sucrose give a higher final yield of biomass, but the growth rate is lower, probably due to osmotic stress (32). With *P. notoginseng* suspension cultures it has been shown that increasing the sucrose levels alters the dry weight to wet weight ratio up to 0.2 M (6.84%) sucrose (33) (Fig. 6). Much of the research on the effects of osmotic stress has used nonmetabolizable compounds such as mannitol to alter the osmotic strength. Rudge and Morris (31) showed

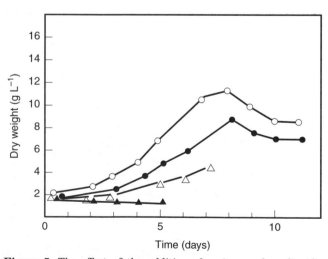

Figure 5. The effect of the addition of various carbon dioxide concentrations to the air supplied to a 7−1 airlift bioreactor containing a suspension of *Catharanthus roseus*: (○) control; (●) 5% carbon dioxide; (△) 10% carbon dioxide; (▲) 20% carbon dioxide. Data from Ref. 28.

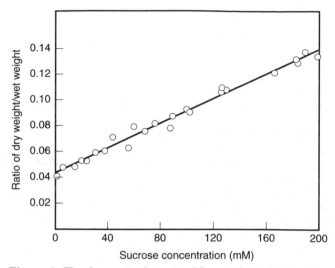

Figure 6. The changes in the ratio of dry weight to fresh weight with alteration in sucrose concentration in suspension cultures of *Panax notoginseng*. Data from Ref. 33.

that at low mannitol levels (0.05–0.2 M) the cells grew more rapidly than the control, but at higher levels of (0.3–0.6 M) growth was restricted, and at the highest levels growth was severely limited. The cells under moderate stress were smaller and contained densely packed starch granules, which would affect their wet-to-dry weight ratio. In a later study (34) also using mannitol to control the osmotic pressure the higher mannitol values giving an osmotic pressure of 6.62 atm reduced growth and gave smaller cells. The osmotic pressure of the medium was calculated using the following formula (33);

$$P = [C_1/M_1 + C_2/M_2 + C_i/M_i]RT$$

where C_i is the concentration of the solute i (gl^{-1}), M_i is the molecular weight of the solute i, R the gas constant (0.082 l atm mol^{-1} K^{-1}), and T the temperature (K). The initial osmotic pressure due to the use of 3% (30 g/L) sucrose (MW 342.3) in medium at 25 °C (298 K) is $P = 30/342.3 \times 0.082 \times 298 = 2.14$ atm. With normal medium containing 3% (30 gl^{-1}) sucrose at 25 °C at 25 °C or 298 K the osmotic pressure is 4.45 atm with 2.14 atm from the sucrose and 2.31 atm from the salts. Cultures of *Vitis* spp when exposed to various mannitol concentrations showed a reduced cell number after 12 cultures over the range of concentrations used (12) (Fig. 7). Figure 8 shows the effect of increasing sucrose on the wet weight of strawberry (*F. ananassa*) suspension cultures after 13 days of treatment and the effect of mannitol under the same conditions (5). It is clear that there is an effect of stress and at the same time anthocyanin accumulation increased.

FOAM

Cultures, which are shaken or aerated as in airlift bioreactors, will produce foam if the medium contains proteins and peptides. As plant cell cultures do in general

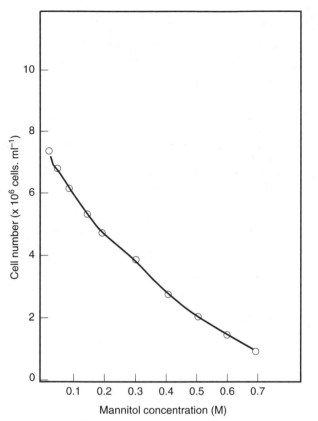

Figure 7. The effect of various mannitol concentrations on the cell numbers of a suspension of *Vitis* spp after 12 incubations. Data from Ref. 12.

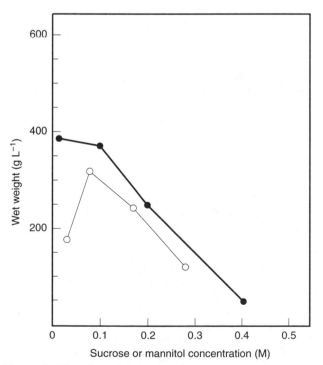

Figure 8. The effect of sucrose and mannitol concentration on the wet weight of suspension cultures of strawberry (*Fragaria ananassa*) after 13 days incubation: (○) sucrose; (●) mannitol. Data from Ref. 5.

export both proteins and polysaccharides into the medium, foam will form. The formation of foam in shake flasks is not a problem, but it does constitute a problem in highly aerated cultures as found in airlift bioreactors. A number of antifoams have been used including the silicone-based and polypropylene glycol and only silicon antifoam was found to inhibit spinach cultures (35) (Table 3). In order to reduce possible inhibitory effects of antifoams, mineral oil has been used to reduce foam in cultures of *N. tabacum* (36). The optimum concentration was found to be 5% when the cells were cultivated in a 5-L stirred-tank bioreactor and a reduction in growth was not seen.

AGITATION

Plant cells are large and are often found in aggregates so that without some form of stirring the cells or aggregates will settle out rapidly. However, because of the large size of plant cells (10–200 μm), the presence of a rigid cell wall and large vacuole plant cells have been regarded as sensitive to shear stress (37). Agitation by shaking flasks and in bioreactors by stirring and aeration increases the level of shear stress that the cells are exposed to. Shear produced in shake flasks has been shown to affect the growth of *N. tabaccum* cells and *Cudrania tricuspidata* (38). By including baffle plates in shake flasks, the level of shear can be increased and the effect can be seen on culturing *C. roseus* (Fig. 9) (39). The growth of plant cell suspensions in stirred tank bioreactors, which can have high rates of shear, has shown inhibition in some cases (37), but the sensitivity of plant cells to shear appears to be far less than was at first thought (37,40). The variation in shear sensitivity is variable and is dependent on the cell line. The effects of shear on plant cell cultures appears to increase the uptake of oxygen in the case of strawberry cultures (41), but with cultures of safflower and eucalyptus there was a decrease in respiration rate and ATP (42). The effects of shear appear to be mediated by cytoplasmic calcium. The shear stress required for growth inhibition was shown to be five orders of magnitude less than that required for cell rupture in cultures of *Daucus carota* and *Petunia mitchell* suspension cultures (42). However, growth inhibition was not observed in a number of cultures (37,40).

Table 3. Effect of Antifoam on Growth Rates of *Catharanthus roseus*

Antifoam concentration (mg/L)	Growth rate (days^{-1})	
	Dow Corning 1510	Polypropylene glycol
0	0.257	0.241
100	0.202	0.267
200	0.260	0.261
500	0.170	0.225
1000	0.231	0.205

Source: Data from Ref. 35.

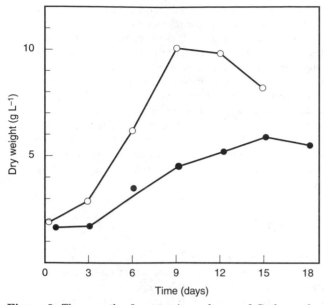

Figure 9. The growth of suspension cultures of *Catharanthus roseus* in flasks with or without baffles: (○) without baffles; (●) with baffles. Data from Ref. 40.

BIBLIOGRAPHY

1. J.M. Widholm, *Int. Rev. Cytol.* **132**, 109–175 (1992).

2. M. Seibert and P.G. Kadkade, in E.J. Staba, ed., *Plant Tissue Culture as a Source of Biochemicals*, CRC Press, Boca Raton, Fl., 1980, pp. 123–142.

3. S.H. Mantell and H. Smith, in S.H. Mantell and H. Smith, eds., *Plant Biotechnology*, Cambridge University Press, London, 1983, pp. 75–108.

4. A.G. Fett-Neto, J.J. Pennington, and F. DiCosmo, *J. Plant Physiol.* **146**, 584–590 (1995).

5. K. Sato, M. Nakayama, and J. Shigeta, *Plant Sci.* **113**, 91–98 (1996).

6. T. Yamakawa et al., *Agric. Biol. Chem.* **47**, 2185–2191 (1983).

7. N.P. Makunga, J. van Staden, and W.A. Cress, *Plant Growth Regul.* **23**, 153–158 (1997).

8. S.M. Martin, in E.J. Staba, ed., *Plant Tissue Culture as a Source of Biochemicals*, CRC Press, Boca Raton, Fl., 1980, pp. 143–148.

9. M. Hagomori, T. Matsumoto, and Y. Obi, *Agric. Biol. Chem.* **47**, 565–571 (1983).

10. S. Koul, A. Ahuja, and S. Grewal, *Planta Med.* **47**, 11–16 (1983).

11. W. Zang and S. Furusaki, *Biotechnol. Lett.* **19**, 1057–1061 (1997).

12. M. Suzuki, *J. Plant Physiol.* **147**, 152–155 (1995).

13. D.V. Banthorpe and G.D. Brown, *Plant Sci.* **67**, 107–113 (1990).

14. D. Courtois and J. Guern, *Plant Sci. Lett.* **17**, 473–482 (1980).

15. P. Morris, *Plant Cell Rep.* **5**, 427–429 (1986).

16. W. Zang et al., *Biotechnol. Lett.* **20**, 63–66 (1998).

17. R.A. Taticek, M. Moo-Young, and R.L. Legge, *Plant Cell Tissue Organ Cult.* **24**, 139–158 (1991).

18. J.B. Snape, N.H. Thomas, and J.A. Callow, *Biotechnol. Bioeng.* **34**, 1058–1062 (1989).

19. C.W.T. Lee and M.L. Shuler, *Biotechnol. Tech.* **5**, 173–178 (1991).

20. Y.-H. Zhang and J.-J. Zhong, *Enzyme Microb. Technol.* **21**, 59–63 (1997).

21. J.L. Tate and G.F. Payne, *Plant Cell Rep.* **10**, 22–25 (1991).

22. J.P. Ducos and A. Pareilleux, *Appl. Microbiol. Biotechnol.* **25**, 101–105 (1986).

23. N.J. Smart and M.W. Fowler, *Biotechnol. Lett.* **3**, 171–176 (1981).

24. R. Ballica and D.D.Y. Ryu, *Biotechnol. Bioeng.* **42**, 1181–189 (1993).

25. D. Kim, H. Pedersen, and C.-K. Chin, *Biotechnol. Bioeng.* **38**, 331–339 (1991).

2 6. P.K. Hegarty, N.J. Smart, A.H. Scragg, and M.W. Fowler, *J. Exp. Bot.* **37**, 1911–1920 (1986).

27. A.H. Scragg, in B.V. Charlwood and M.J.C. Rhodes, eds., *Secondary Products from Plant Tissue Culture*, Oxford University Press, Oxford, U.K., 1990, pp. 243–263.

28. A.H. Scragg, in B.V. Charlwood and M.J.C. Rhodes, eds., *Secondary Products from Plant Tissue Culture*, Oxford University Press, Oxford, U.K., 1990, pp. 243–263.

29. R. Wongsamuth and P.M. Doran, *J. Chem. Tech. Biotechnol.* **69**, 15–26 (1997).

30. J.E. Schlatmann et al., *Enzyme Microb. Technol.* **20**, 107–115 (1997).

31. K. Rudge and P. Morris, in P. Morris, A.H. Scragg, A. Stafford, and M.W. Fowler, eds., *Secondary Metabolism in Plant Cell Cultures*, Cambridge University Press, Cambridge, U.K., 1986, pp. 75–81.

32. A.H. Scragg et al., *Enzyme Microb. Technol.* **12**, 292–298 (1990).

33. Y.-H. Zhang et al., *Biotechnol. Lett.* **19**, 943–945 (1997).

34. Y.-H. Zhang, J.J. Zhong, and J.-T. Yu, *Biotechnol. Lett.* **17**, 1347–1350 (1995).

35. P.A. Bond, P. Hegarty, and A.H. Scragg, in H.J.J. Nijkamp, L.H.W. van der Plas, and J. van Aartrijk, eds., *Progress in Plant Cellular and Molecular Biology*, Kluwer Academic Publishers, Dordrecht, The Netherlands, 1987, pp. 440–443.

36. G.-Q. Li, J.H. Shin, and J.M. Lee, *Biotechnol. Tech.* **9**, 713–718 (1995).

37. J.J. Meijer et al., *Enzyme Microb. Technol.* **16**, 467–477 (1994).

38. H. Tanaka, *Biotechnol. Bioeng.* **23**, 1203–1218 (1981).

39. A.H. Scragg, E.J. Allan, and F. Leckie, *Enzyme Microb. Technol.* **10**, 361–367 (1988).

40. H. Tanaka, H. Senba, T. Jitsufuchi, and H. Harada, *Biotechnol. Letters* **10**, 485–490 (1988).

41. T. Takeda et al., *Can. J. Chem. Eng.* **76**, 267–275 (1998).

42. E. Dunlop, P.K. Namdev, and M.Z. Rosenberg, *Chem. Eng. Sci.* **49**, 2263–2276 (1994).

See also ANIMAL CELL CULTURE, EFFECTS OF AGITATION AND AERATION ON CELL ADAPTATION; ANIMAL CELL CULTURE, PHYSIOCHEMICAL EFFECTS OF DISSOLVED OXYGEN AND REDOX POTENTIAL; ANIMAL CELL CULTURE, PHYSIOCHEMICAL EFFECTS OF OSMOLALITY AND TEMPERATURE; ANIMAL CELL CULTURE, PHYSIOCHEMICAL EFFECTS OF pH; PHYSIOLOGY OF PLANT CELLS IN CULTURE; PLANT CELL CULTURE, EFFECT ON GROWTH AND SECONDARY PRODUCT ACCUMULATION OF ORGANIC COMPOUNDS AND SURFACTANTS; PLANT CELL CULTURES, PHOTOSYNTHETIC; TRANSCRIPTION, TRANSLATION AND THE CONTROL OF GENE EXPRESSION.

PLANT CELL CULTURES, SECONDARY PRODUCT ACCUMULATION

NIESKO PRAS
University Centre for Pharmacy
Groningen Institute for Drug Studies
University of Groningen
Groningen, The Netherlands

OUTLINE

INTRODUCTION

Higher plants are a source of a large number of biochemicals. These plant-derived organic compounds can be classified as primary and secondary metabolites or products. Primary products generally occur in nearly all organisms, and include the synthesis of DNA, RNA, proteins, lipids, and carbohydrates. Higher plants use these compounds (e.g., oils, fatty acids, starch, and sucrose) for general growth and physiological development. Primary products are those that are necessary for the cell's survival and reproduction, whereas secondary products may be eliminated without harming cell survival and reproduction. Secondary products are biosynthetically derived from primary products, occurring mostly in a particular taxonomic group (e.g., species or genus). Secondary products are divided into several groups, on the basis of their biosynthetic origin. Primary products from the glycolysis and the pentose phosphate cycle are precursors for the shikimic pathway. This metabolic pathway, which starts with shikimic acid, produces aromatic amino acids, while aliphatic amino acids are derived from intermediates of the citric acid cycle. Both types of amino acids are precursors of alkaloids. In addition, the amino acids tyrosine and phenylalanine are precursors for cumarins, lignans, flavonoids, and proanthocyanidins. Acetyl CoA, which is a metabolite of the citric acid cycle, is the direct precursor of the polyketides, terpenes, and terpenoids. Secondary products are commonly found in specific tissues or organs of the plant and are stored intracellularly in vacuoles, cell walls, and glandular hairs (1,2).

Plant secondary products have a specific (ecological) function as pollinator attractants, for chemical adaptations to environmental stress, and as defensive, protective, or offensive chemicals against microorganisms, insects, and higher herbivorous predators. Based on these functions, secondary products can be considered as biologically active compounds. Secondary products are used as dyes, pesticides, flavorings, and fragrances. But even more important, a significant number of secondary products exert pharmacological activities and can basically be applied as drugs. Since ancient times medicinal plants have been used to treat all kinds of diseases. Traditionally, extracts from naturally occurring whole plants or parts have been used. Nowadays isolated secondary products are used for medicinal purposes. The first isolated secondary product was an alkaloid, the narcotic analgesic morphine from *Papaver somniferum* (poppy) in 1806 [Fig. 1(a)]. The isolated products as such can be applied as drugs. Chemical modification may yield semisynthetic compounds with an improved, more specific action and/or fewer side effects. For example, from the novel antimalarial artemisinin [a sesquiterpene lactone, Fig. 1(b)] several derivatives with improved antimalarial activity have been prepared (3). Furthermore, secondary products, especially alkaloids, have served as model compounds ("leads") for the development of chemically prepared classes of drugs; for example, muscle relaxants used during operations are derived from tubocurarine [Fig. 1(c)].

In the plant (cell), secondary products are biosynthesized by the action of highly specific enzymes. For this reason, these compounds often have very complex chemical structures with many chiral centers that may be essential for the biological activity. For a number of secondary products total chemical syntheses has been described, but the large number of necessary reaction steps, together with the low yields, makes chemical synthesis unsuitable for production on a large scale. For a number of pharmaceutically important compounds the plant still remains the only economically efficient source, of, for example, the

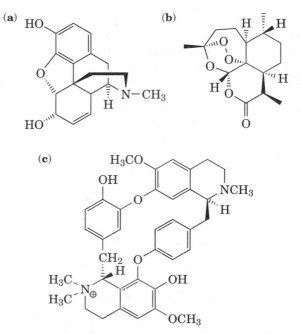

Figure 1. Chemical structures of morphine from *Papaver somniferum*, (**a**), artemisinin from *Artemisia annua* (**b**), and tubocurarine from *Chondrodendron* species (**c**).

already-mentioned morphine and artemisinin, the alkaloids scopolamine (an anticholinergic), vinblastine, and vincristine (cytostatics), and digoxin (a cardiac glycoside). In these cases commercial production is effected by cultivation of the plant species involved, including the selection of high-producing plants, followed by extraction of the secondary product and finally purification. The same procedure is applied for other valuable compounds like dyes, fragrances, insecticides, and flavorings.

Plant cell culture, the in vitro cultivation of plant cells, may offer an alternative for the production of secondary products under certain conditions: if the source plant is difficult to cultivate, if it has a long cultivation period or a low yield of secondary product, or if chemical synthesis is unachievable or inefficient. Basically, the plant biosynthetic potential can be exploited in vitro, as has already been successfully performed during decennia for secondary products of microbial origin, such as for the production of antibiotics by *Penicillium* species.

The first example of in vitro cultivation of plant cells dates from 1902 (4). Haberlandt described the cultivation of mesophyll cells of *Lamium purpureum* and *Eichhornia crassipes*, of epidermis cells of *Ornithogalum* species, and of hair cells of *Pulmonaria* species. Although he was not able to induce cell division, the prediction was that this should be possible and that each individual plant cell is basically omnipotent. More than 30 years later these predictions were proven by Nobécourt (5), White (6), and Gautheret (7). In 1952 Routien and Nickel applied for a U.S. patent on cultivation of plant tissue, which claimed that it was possible to grow plant cells under submerged conditions and that these cells could be used to produce useful materials (8). Since the late 1960s the development of plant cell culture accelerated. An increasing number of researchers started the in vitro cultivation of plant cells with the aim of investigating the biosynthesis of secondary products. For this purpose undifferentiated callus and cell suspension cultures, as well as differentiated cultures like root and shoot cultures, have been used. By using this technology, the secondary product can be produced under controlled and reproducible conditions, independently of various environmental factors such as climate, pests, and geographical and seasonal constraints. In this way a more consistent product quality and yield can be obtained. Moreover, a system consisting of freely suspended (or immobilized) cells may offer advantages in downstream recovery and efficiency of product purification. In the present time of endangered ecosystems plant cell cultures can serve as a means of maintaining rare and distinguishing plants of commercial significance by cryopreservation of cells and/or regeneration of cells.

The omnipotency of the plant cell implies that the complete genetic information as present in the plant is principally available. On the condition that genes encoding biosynthetic enzymes indeed come to an expression under in vitro circumstances, it should be feasible to produce most, if not all, secondary products using in vitro grown cultures. A limited number of plant cell culture systems are able to produce secondary products at a gram per liter concentration, some examples of which are given in Table 1 (9–14). In many cases, however, plant cell cultures accumulate low quantities of secondary product or there is no production at all. The secondary products that have been isolated from plant cell cultures belong to the groups of the phenylpropanoids, alkaloids, terpenoids, and quinones. Until 1992, over 140 novel secondary products that which are not synthesized by the whole plant have been found in plant cell culture (15), but they are of limited importance so far.

In the following sections the strategies that are used to realize a significant secondary product yield are discussed. Mainly empirical approaches, such as manipulation of culture conditions, cell selection, induction of differentiated cultures, and precursor feeding to cells (leading to bioconversion), have been used to achieve this goal. Fundamental, genetic approaches are increasingly applied to improve secondary product formation; attention will be paid to biosynthetic pathway engineering and heterologous expression of plant genes.

MANIPULATION OF CULTURE CONDITIONS

The medium composition is of utmost importance for the growth of cells and accumulation of secondary products. Ideally, a good production medium, which can be defined as the medium with a certain composition resulting in an optimal product yield, should give both optimal growth and productivity. In practice this results in a species dependent optimal composition where a balance between growth and product accumulation will lead to a maximal product yield. Product accumulation and growth do not always occur at the same time in the growth cycle. In such cases the accumulation of secondary products is highest when the growth ceases, in the stationary phase. At this stage, the cells should then be transferred to a production medium where induction of product formation takes place under

Table 1. Plant Cell Culture Systems that are able to Accumulate Secondary Products at a Gram per Liter Concentration

Secondary product	Biogenetic group	Cell culture	Product yield (g/L)	Ref.
Berberine	Alkaloid	*Coptis japonica*	7.0	9
Rosmarinic acid	Phenylpropanoid	*Coleus blumei*	5.6	10
Shikonin	Naphthoquinone	*Lithospermum erythrorhizon*	3.5	11
Ajmaline	Alkaloid	*Rauvolfia serpentina*	2.0	12
Coniferin	Phenylpropanoid	*Linum flavum*	2.0	13
L-DOPA	Amino acid	*Mucuna pruriens*	1.2	14

controlled conditions as has been successfully performed for shikonin (11).

Most of the constituents of plant cell culture media have been subjected to manipulation in attempts to enhance culture productivity, and many of these components have proven to be important for product accumulation (16–18). The results obtained suggest that this empirical approach only stands a good chance for success when reasonable levels of secondary product (1–2% on a dry weight basis) are already present. The most useful changes of medium constituents are discussed in the following on the guidance of randomly selected examples.

Optimization of the hormone concentration and combinations can be effective. High auxin concentrations, although favorable for cell growth, are often deleterious to secondary product accumulation (19). Indole alkaloid accumulation in cell cultures of *Catharanthus roseus* was generally depressed by the addition of 2,4-dichlorophenoxy acetic acid (2,4-D) to media (20). The manipulation of the amount and source of sugar in cell culture media was studied as a factor for enhanced growth and cantharanthine and ajmalicine synthesis in *C. roseus* hairy root cultures (21). Elevated sucrose levels were favorable for anthocyanin production by *Perilla frutescens* cells (22) and for steroidal alkaloid production by *Solanum aviculare* hairy roots (23). The addition of fructose promoted paclitaxel [Fig. 2(a)] production in *Taxus* cell cultures (24). The overall mineral salt concentration may be an important factor. It was found that half-strength B_5 salts were optimal for both biomass and verbascoside production in cell cultures of *Leucosceptrum japonicum* over a range of one-twentieth to twice the normal salts concentration (25). Nitrogen sources may also play an important role in secondary product accumulation in plant cells. For example, in *Lithospermum erythrorhizon* shikonin synthesis was inhibited by ammonium ions, but cell growth was promoted. To achieve production it was necessary to switch at the end of the growth phase to a medium containing nitrate ions (26). It has often been found that higher levels of phosphate promote cell growth, but negatively influence secondary product accumulation. In cell cultures of *Nicotiana tabacum*, *C. roseus*, and *Peganum harmala* the alkaloid biosynthesis decreased upon the addition of phosphate (27). Physical culture conditions such as light, temperature, agitation, medium pH, and aeration have been investigated for their effect upon secondary product accumulation in several types of cultures (28,29). The importance of light for an increased secondary product accumulation has been demonstrated, for example, for cardenolides in cell cultures of *Digitalis lanata* (30) and for betacyanins in cell cultures of *Chenopodium rubrum* (31). Aeration and agitation of cell cultures grown in bioreactors (and less in shake flasks) has been studied (29). The combination of oxygen tension, carbon dioxide, and irradiation influenced growth and cardenolide formation in somatic embryo cultures of *D. lanata*, which were grown in gaslift fermentors (32). Another example deals with the ajmalicine production by *C. roseus* cultures. In shake flasks and bioreactors growth was comparable, but in the bioreactors the ajmalicine production ceased. The production could be restarted with the recirculation of the ventilation gas (33).

Upon microbial invasion, many plants respond by producing antimicrobial secondary products, called phytoalexins. This plant defense strategy is called elicitation, and the molecules that stimulate secondary metabolism are called elicitors. "Artificial" elicitation, the addition of elicitors to the medium, has been widely explored in plant cell cultures. The biosynthesis of secondary products belonging to several chemical classes can be triggered this way. In fact, the expression of genes encoding the enzymes that are responsible for the synthesis of these metabolites is induced. Jasmonates, jasmonic acid, and its methyl ester, are thought to be the general signal transducing compounds in the elicitation process (34) that induce de novo gene transcription. When plant cell cultures of *Rauvolfia canescens* and *Eschscholzia californica* were treated with a yeast elicitor, the jasmonates were rapidly, but transiently, accumulated. Exogenously added methyl jasmonate was able to induce secondary product accumulation in 36 different plant cell cultures. Recently, the highest production rate ever reported for paclitaxel could be achieved by the addition of methyl jasmonate to *T. media* cultures. Paclitaxel was produced at an average rate of 7.9 mg/L/day during two weeks (35).

Biotic elicitors such as fungal extracts/homogenates and abiotic elicitors such as inorganic salts have been shown to induce a range of plant secondary products, but in many cases the yields were rather disappointing. Furthermore, a wide range of unrelated substances have been found somehow to induce secondary metabolism in cultured plant cells. These include inorganic compounds such as vanadyl sulfate, colchicine, and herbicides, and also unfavorable physical conditions such as osmotic stress. The choice of a certain elicitor for a plant cell culture system is mostly by a random process, and therefore elicitation will not occur in many cases. A number of selected elicitation results are summarized in Table 2 (36–41).

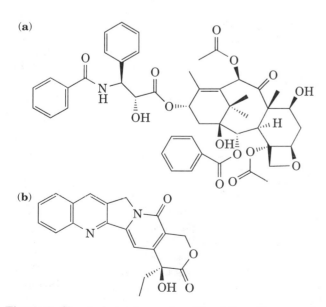

(a)

(b)

Figure 2. Chemical structures of paclitaxel from *Taxus* species (a) and camptothecine from *Campthoteca acuminata* (b).

Table 2. Increase in Secondary Product Accumulation in Plant Cell Cultures by Elicitation

Cell culture	Elicitor	Secondary product	Induced increase (fold/level)	Ref.
Gossypium arboreum	*Verticillium dahliae* (conidia)	Gossypol	50/500 mg/L	36
Papaver somniferum	*Botrytis* species	Sanguinarine	30/2.9% (DW)	37
Cinchona ledgeriana	*Phytophthora cinnamomii*	Anthraquinones	7.5/11.0% (DW)	38
Morinda citrifolia	Cell wall pectins	Anthraquinones	5.6/0.001% (DW)	39
Artemisia annua	*Aspergillus oryzae*	Artemisinin	2/550 mg/L	40
Valeriana wallichii	Colchicine	Valepotriates	70/0.83% (DW)	41

Another application of elicitation is to find the regulatory enzymes in biosynthetic pathways of secondary products. In this way the rate-limiting enzymatic steps can be identified, and this allows genetic intervention to increase secondary product accumulation (see section on genetic approaches).

Despite these results, no general rules can be deduced from all experiments performed so far. It can be concluded that manipulation of culture conditions may lead to an increase of secondary product accumulation, but to what extent is dependent on which factor(s) and the cell culture species involved. In other words, the effects to be expected are unpredictable.

CELL SELECTION

Plant cell cultures cannot be considered as cloned cells because they do not come from a single parent cell. They represent mixed cell populations consisting of cells with differences in morphology and productivity. Genetic instability often occurs, which results in a decrease or even loss of productivity. In the most ideal case, a secondary product is accumulated in large quantities in a genetically stable cell line or strain. This should be the goal of strain improvement.

The approach of screening and selection for high accumulating strains or cell lines has been applied successfully for industrial microorganisms. For plant cells the procedure starts with the choice of a parent plant with a high content of the desired secondary product with the aim to induce callus cultures. The basic idea is that high-producing plants should give high-producing cell lines. After optimization of the culture conditions, the next step is the analytical screening of the callus cultures for the desired secondary product, and sometimes protoplasts are used for this purpose. For this screening a reliable marker for the secondary product is needed. When colored secondary products are accumulated, the most intensively colored cells can easily be isolated and cultivated separately. Highly fluorescent products can be detected under UV light. Specific color reactions of squashed cells or immunological assays can be applied to detect colorless products. By means of screening only a small number of high-producing cell lines have been isolated. Some selected examples will be discussed in the following.

For the alkaloid berberine there was no direct relation between the production in the plants and the derived cell cultures of *Coptis japonica*. By performing five subsequent selection steps, a stable high-producing cell line (7 g/L)

was obtained (9). Screening of *C. roseus* cells for ajmalicine and serpentine yielded lines with tenfold increased levels of alkaloids, but with great instability (42). Light-exposed callus cultures of *Mucuna pruriens* were screened for high L-DOPA content using the green color as a marker. After six months photomixotrophic callus cultures with a rapid growth and a high, stable L-DOPA content of 0.9% (DW) were obtained. The cell suspensions derived from these calli accumulated up to 6% (DW) L-DOPA, and a yield of 1.2 g/L was calculated after 6 days of growth (14).

Shikonin is a red dye with antiseptic properties. After repeated analytical screening of callus cell lines of *Lithospermum erythrorhizon* with a shikonin content of 1.7% (DW) a high-producing line with a content of 15.3% (DW) was obtained (43). The shikonin accumulation of a high-producing parent cell line of *L. erythrorhizon* was improved further by screening of protoplast derived cultures, where the content increased from 17.6 to 23.2% (DW). Shikonin is now produced commercially by a two-step process: First the cells of *L. erythrorhizon* are grown in a fermentor with growth medium, then the cells are filtered and transferred to a second fermentor with a production medium in which the cells synthesize shikonin (11).

As an alternative for the selection of high-producing cells using the secondary product itself or a product-related marker, biochemical selection can be considered. This implies the choice of culture conditions under which certain cells survive while others are killed. The selection criterion is an expression of the biosynthetic pathway; certain enzymes will metabolize an added toxic compound, thus enabling the cell to survive. For example, by the addition of p-fluorophenylalanine (PFP) resistant *N. tabacum* cell lines could be selected. These cells accumulated six to ten times more cinnamoyl putrescines than wild-type cells (44). The activity of phenylalanine ammonia lyase (PAL), which decomposes PFP, was enhanced and also the activities of other enzymes belonging to the putrescine pathway should have been elevated as a result of the PFP addition. Unfortunately, the effect of an added toxic compound on the activity of enzymes other than the detoxifying enzyme is not predictable. *Peganum* cells tolerant to 4-fluorotryptophan (4-FT) did not accumulate higher quantities of ß-carbolines, although the tryptophan decarboxylase activity was strongly enhanced. A fluoro-DL-tyrosine resistant callus line of *M. pruriens* had a much lower phenoloxidase activity accompanied by a lower L-DOPA content in comparison with the parent callus line (N. Pras unpublished results, 1990). Principally, cell lines obtained by biochemical selection are stable and can be maintained under selective conditions. With respect to increased secondary product accumulation biochemical selection has had limited success so far.

It can be concluded that screening for cell lines with increased productivity has been disappointing up to now and only parent cell cultures that accumulate significant levels of secondary product stand a chance for the selection of a high-producing cell line.

INDUCTION OF DIFFERENTIATION IN PLANT CELL CULTURES

Often a degree of tissue differentiation or organ development has to be present before synthesis of secondary metabolites occurs (17). This is not surprising, since many secondary products are known to be found in specific tissues of the plant (1,2). Secondary products are often stored at the site of biosynthesis. Monoterpenes like menthol are accumulated in epidermal oil glands of the leaves of *Mentha* plants, while lignans occur in the rhizomes of *Podophyllum* plants. In some cases, it has been shown that undifferentiated cell cultures may accumulate higher secondary product levels than the intact plant, but mostly the biosynthesis of secondary products is lower or even absent. Generally, such cultures do not have specialized accumulation sites. It has been observed that when low- or nonproducing plant cell cultures are allowed to differentiate into shoots, roots, or embryos, secondary product formation indeed occurs. A logical approach seems to be the induction of differentiation in cell cultures, where levels of secondary products comparable to or even higher than in vivo circumstances should be achievable.

In general, there are two methods of inducing differentiation in plant cell cultures. First, under suitable conditions, mainly by variation of the combinations and concentrations of phytohormones, different types of cultures can be induced. These may be differentiated roots, shoots, or somatic embryos, which are a kind of "in between" state of tissue. Second, shoot and root cultures can be induced by genetic transformation with *Agrobacterium tumefaciens* and *A. rhizogenes*, respectively. On the basis of hormone autotrophy, these roots or hairy roots and shoots or shooty teratomas can be cultured in hormone-free media. As with undifferentiated callus and cell suspension cultures, the culture conditions, including "artificial" elicitation, can be manipulated in order to optimize secondary product accumulation. Organ cultures of many plant species have been initiated, and some characteristic examples will now be discussed.

The accumulation of monoterpenes in shooty cultures of *Mentha* species transformed by *A. tumefaciens* (T 37) has been studied. Oil glands on the leaves of the transformed cultures were observed. The terpene profile analyzed in extracts of the cultures was identical to that in extracts of the parent plant, but the overall oil yields were lower (45). The production of the novel antimalarial artemisinin [Fig. 1(b)] by plant cell cultures has been the target of many studies, including the use of differentiated cultures. Transformed shoot cultures have been established by infection with *A. tumefaciens* (T 37) and *A. rhizogenes*

(LBA 9402). The cultures were able to grow in hormone-free medium and produced artemisinin during prolonged subcultures (46). Several clones of transformed shoots were obtained, and the average artemisinin content was 0.0018% (DW). This content was lower than those found in wild intact plants and nontransformed cultures. In the first case, the artemisinin content during the blooming period was ca. 0.1% (DW), whereas for the nontransformed shoot cultures contents of 0.16% (DW) were reported (47).

Since many commercially interesting secondary products are synthesized in the roots of the plant, more attention has been given to the potential of transformed roots, hairy roots, as producers of secondary products. For example, tropane alkaloids are synthesized in the roots of plant species belonging to the Solanaceae (night shade) family. Plants like *Datura stramonium* and *Atropa belladonna*, which accumulate hyoscyamine and atropine, easily produce rapidly growing transformed roots after infection with *A. rhizogenes*. Several studies have confirmed that root morphology is demanded for the in vitro biosynthesis of tropane alkaloids. Levels of hyoscyamine comparable to those in the whole plant have been found in hairy roots of *A. belladonna* (48,49). Untransformed and hairy roots of *Duboisia* species produced significant quantities of both hyoscyamine and scopolamine (50,51). The ratio between scopolamine and hyoscyamine seems to be strongly dependent on the expression of the hyoscyamine 6ß-hydroxylase (H6H) gene in the roots, a higher expression yields more scopolamine. The introduction and expression of the H6H gene from *Hyoscyamus niger* in *A. belladonna* hairy roots resulted in a fivefold increase of the scopolamine level (52). Recently, a combination of shooty teratomas and hairy roots of *A. belladonna* was investigated as a production system for tropane alkaloids. Both culture types were co-cultured in the same hormone-free medium. Hyoscyamine produced by the roots was bioconverted by the shoots resulting in a high scopolamine–hyoscyamine ratio of 0.07–1.9. Up to 0.084% (DW) scopolamine was accumulated; this corresponded with 3–11 times the average concentration found in the leaves of the whole plant (53).

For the production of the already-mentioned artemisinin hairy root cultures have been initiated with variable succes. The effect of the phytohormone gibberellic acid on artemisin accumulation in hairy root cultures of *Artemisia annua* has been studied (54). At a gibberellic acid concentration of 0.01 mg/L the highest artemisinin yield of 80 mg/L was found. A much higher production of 550 mg/L artemisinin was achieved by elicited hairy roots of *A. annua* (40).

As with undifferentiated plant cell cultures, new secondary products are sometimes found to be produced by organ cultures. A recent example is the isolation of two new prenylated flavonoids, licoagrochalcon A and licoagrocarpin, from hairy root cultures of *Glycyrrhiza glabra* along with eight known flavonoids (55).

Somatic embryos may also form a good source of secondary products. A change in phytohormone composition may trigger embryogenesis in an undifferentiated cell culture. One of the scarce examples is the biosynthesis of cardenolides by somatic embryos of *D. lanata* (32).

In summary, it can be concluded that organ cultures are able to reach secondary product levels sometimes comparable to those of the parent whole plant, but often this not the case. Some examples of pharmaceutically important secondary products produced by organ cultures are shown in Table 3 (56–59). Large-scale cultivation using organ cultures, however, is difficult to perform, certainly in comparison with undifferentiated cell suspension cultures, which are easy to handle from a process technological point of view (28). At present, differentiated cells are not suitable for commercial production purposes. To increase the large-scale production possibilities by plant cell cultures a method should be found to identify the complex (genetic) mechanisms linking cell differentiation with secondary product synthesis. This will open new ways for commercial production of secondary products in simple cell culture systems. For the study of the regulation of secondary metabolism organ cultures may be attractive experimental systems. Furthermore, organ cultures offer excellent possibilities for regeneration and multiplication of selected high-producing clones.

BIOCONVERSION

The feeding of biosynthetic precursors to plant cell cultures with the aim to increase the secondary product yield has been frequently performed with variable success. For the formation of most secondary products cascades of enzymatic conversions in the cell are required. In a biosynthetic pathway limiting enzymatic steps and/or one or more side branches may be present. Therefore, precursor feeding, certainly of early biosynthetic precursors, will not always result in an increase of the desired secondary product. Genetic approaches, which will be discussed later, can be applied to relieve the bottlenecks in a biosynthetic pathway.

Still, plant cell cultures are an excellent source of enzymes (15,60). Enzymes belonging to a biosynthetic pathway can be explored for specific bioconversions to produce a secondary product or related compound. Not only can secondary product accumulating cell cultures be used, but nonproducing cell cultures have also been proven to bioconvert precursors with high efficiency (61). Bioconversion can be defined as the enzyme-catalyzed modification of added precursors (substrates) into more valuable products, using plant cells, either freely suspended or in an immobilized state, or enzyme preparations. Bioconversions by plant cells may involve the action of a single enzyme or several enzymes.

Transgenic cells may be used for bioconversion purposes; by means of recombinant DNA technology genes encoding for relevant plant enzymes can be introduced in suitable host cells, possibly leading to an improved biocatalyst based on a high production of the desired enzyme (see the section on genetic approaches).

Plant enzymes are able to perform stereo- and regiospecific reactions on a sometimes surprisingly broad range of substrates including plant-foreign, synthetic compounds (60). A number of these reactions cannot be carried out by organic synthesis or by the application of microorganisms. Two selected examples of stereospecific bioconversion are depicted in Figure 3 (62,63). The combination of plant cell culture with synthetic chemistry may be an attractive route to the synthesis of chirally pure secondary products or related compounds (64). Two types of enzymes are of importance for organic synthesis, hydrolase enzymes on the one hand and oxidoreductase enzymes on the other. These types can also be found in plant cells, such as in cells of *Papaver somniferum* and *Nicotiana tabacum*, respectively (65). Cultured cells of *N. tabacum* and *C. roseus* were found to have the ability to introduce stereo- and enantioselectively oxygenated functional groups such as epoxy and hydroxy groups into 3-carene and 2-pinene (66). This type of oxygen introduction is one of the most important reactions in organic chemistry.

The stereocontrolled formation of carbon–carbon bonds is the heart of organic synthesis, and this is performed by aldolase enzymes. The search for and the employment of lipases, esterases, and amidases for the preparation of chiral compounds of high optical purity is continued (67).

Regiospecific plant enzymes can convert one specific functional group to another [Fig. 4(a)] (68) or introduce, selectively, a functional group into a new position in the substrate molecule [Fig. 4(b)] (69). The general reaction types are oxidation, reduction, hydroxylation, methylation, demethylation, acetylation, isomerization, glycosylation, esterification, epoxidation, and saponification (15,60,70). The compounds that can undergo bioconversion are diverse and include aromatics, steroids, alkaloids, coumarins, terpenoids, and lignans. Chemically prepared compounds like some currently used drugs can be modified by the action of plant enzymes.

Freely suspended cells form the most simple biocatalytic system. Precursors can be supplied directly to the cultures, and mass-transfer limitations are less likely to occur in comparison with immobilized cells or enzymes. Several reports dealing with the production of valuable compounds by adding precursors to various culture

Table 3. Selected Examples of Pharmaceutically Important Products Produced by Organ Cultures

Secondary product	Bioactivity	Species	Culture type	Content (%, DW)	Ref.
Hyoscyamine	Anticholinergic	*Duboisia leichhardtii*	Root	0.5	56
Quinine	Antimalarial	*Cinchona ledgeriana*	Root	0.01	57
Artemisinin	Antimalarial	*Artemisia annua*	Shoot	0.16	47
5-Methoxy-podophyllotoxin	Antitumour	*Linum flavum*	Root-like	1.01	58
Valepotriates	Mild sedative	*Valeriana officinalis*	Hairy root	11	59
Atropine	Anticholinergic	*Atropa belladonna*	Hairy root	0.4	48

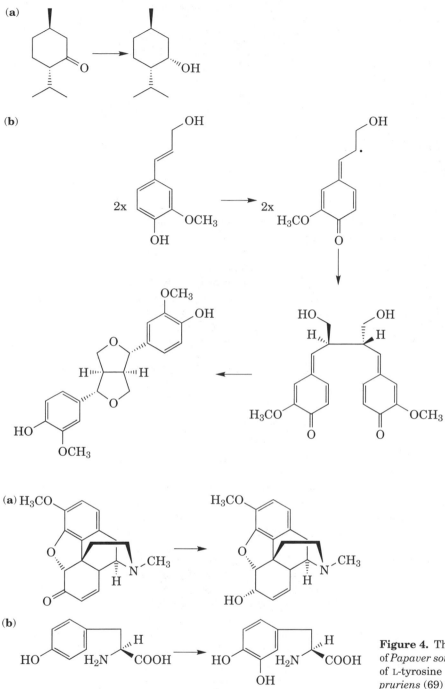

Figure 3. The stereospecific reduction of (−) menthone into (+) neomenthol by entrapped *Mentha* cells (62) (**a**) and the stereospecific bioconversion of coniferyl alcohol into pinoresinol by an enzyme preparation of *Forsythia suspensa* (adapted from Ref. 63) (**b**).

Figure 4. The reduction of codeinone into codeine by cells of *Papaver somniferum* (68) (**a**) and the ortho-hydroxylation of L-tyrosine into L-DOPA by entrapped cells of *Mucuna pruriens* (69) (**b**).

species have been published. As can be expected, the precursor often undergoes more than one bioconversion. This either results in complex mixtures of (unknown) secondary products, or the precursor is metabolized via unknown routes (71–74).

A small number of one-step bioconversions by freely suspended cells have been described and some characteristic examples are summarized in Table 4 (75–80). For example, cell suspensions of *Linum flavum* were able to convert the cytotoxic lignan podophyllotoxin into its ß-D-glucoside at the high bioconversion rate of 294 mg/L/day (70).

At present glycosylation seems one of the most interesting bioconversions. Glycosylation, particularly glucosylation, occurs readily in plant cells, but only with difficulty in microorganisms, and the organic chemist has problems with sugar coupling as well. The improvement of the action of certain currently applied drugs by glucosylation is very attractive because their solubility in aqueous solutions can be enhanced and the bioavailability may be improved. Glucosyl transferases with different substrate specificities for several hydroxyl moiety containing compounds have been investigated. Examples are glucosylations by cells of *Duboisia myoporoides, Solanum aviculare*, and

Table 4. Selected Examples of One-Step Bioconversions by Freely Suspended Cells (CS), Immobilized Plant Cells (IC), and Enzyme Preparations (EP)

Bioconversion	Cell culture	Precursor	Product	System	Ref.
Hydroxylation	*Digitalis lanata*	β-Methyldigitoxin	β-Methyldigitoxin	IC	75
	Mucuna pruriens	L-Tyrosine	L-DOPA	IC	76
	Mucuna pruriens	Monophenols	Catechols	EP	77
Glucosylation	*Linum flavum*	Podophyllotoxin (PT)	PT-β-glucoside	CS	70
	Rauvolfia serpentina	Hydroquinone	Arbutin	CS	78
Reduction	*Papaver somniferum*	Codeinone	Codeine	IC	68
Demethylation	*Nicotiana tabacum*	Nicotine	Nornicotine	CS	79
Esterification	*Coleus blumei*	Dihydroxyphenyl lactate	Rosmarinic acid	EP	80

Papaver somniferum (81) and glucosylations by cells of *Glycyrrhiza echinata, Aconitum japonicum, Coffea arabica, Dioscoreophyllum cumminsii,* and *N. tabacum* (82) have been studied as well.

Examples of other glycosylation reactions are the fructosylation of ergot alkaloids by cells of *Claviceps purpurea* (83) and the rhamnosylation by cells of *Eucalyptus perriniana* (84). Even glucuronylation of compounds, which is also a general metabolization reaction in the liver, has been reported to occur in plant cells of *Glycyrrhiza glabra* (85).

Sakui et al. described a typical bioconversion by suspension-cultured cells (86). Of a 10-membered ring sesquiterpene, germacrone, the 4,5- and 1,10-epoxides were formed by cells of *Curcuma zedoaria.* Epoxidation can be a very useful reaction for the modification of cytotoxic sesquiterpenes.

In most reports the state of differentiation of the plant cell cultures, proven to be linked with secondary metabolite formation, is not clearly indicated. From a practical point of view, however, undifferentiated cells are frequently used, but sometimes root cultures have also been tested in bioconversion experiments. It has been demonstrated that root cultures of *Panax ginseng* could perform several glycosylation reactions on taxicatigenin (84). Recently, the bioconversion of hydroquinone into arbutin by hairy roots of *Brugmansia candida* was described (87).

In particular cases new bioconversion products are found; cell suspension cultures of *P. ginseng* bioconverted digitoxigenine into nine compounds including a new compound, digitoxigenin ß-D-glucoside malonyl ester (88).

The measure of bioconversion may be dependent on the solubility of precursors in aqueous media, the amounts of enzyme activity that are intracellularly present, and the localization of the enzymes. As already stated, the precursors can also be metabolized by other (unknown) reactions and even (a)specific transport systems may be involved.

Several precursors are either not soluble or very poorly soluble in aqueous media, and because of this limitation bioconversion rates are very low. Partially water-soluble precursors have been applied in nonaqueous two-phase systems. Many plant cell species slowly convert precursors in the presence of organic phases, often as a result of a dramatic decrease of cell viability and enzyme activity (89). A novel solution to the problem of the bioconversion of water-insoluble precursors is the application of clathrating agents such as cylodextrins. The cyclodextrin-complexed precursors can then be used in sufficient concentrations to allow bioconversion in a cell-friendly, aqueous environment (90). Cyclodextrins are cyclic oligosaccharides that are able to form inclusion complexes with a variety of apolar ligands. Through complexation, the physical–chemical properties of the ligands are changed, including their solubility in aqueous media (91). The complexes are easily to prepare by autoclaving the suspension of the ligand in a medium together with the cyclodextrin or by simply shaking the whole mixture at room temperature in cases where the substrate is thermolabile.

Possibilities for cyclodextrin-facilitated bioconversions by plant cells or plant enzymes have been described by researchers from our group over the past years: the *ortho*-hydroxylation of 17β-estradiol, complexed with β-cyclodextrin, into 2- and 4-hydroxyestradiol by cells of *Mucuna pruriens* (89), the bioconversion of β-cyclodextrin-complexed coniferyl alcohol into podophyllotoxin by cells of *Podophyllum hexandrum* (92), the glucosylation of dimethyl-β-cyclodextrin-complexed podophyllotoxin into its β-D-glucoside (70), of dimethyl-β-cyclodextrin-complexed coniferyl alcohol into coniferin using cells of *Linum flavum* (Van Uden, unpublished results), and the bioconversion of dimethyl-β-cyclodextrin-complexed desoxypodophyllotoxin into podophyllotoxin and 5-methoxypodophyllotoxin by cells of *P. hexandrum* and *L. flavum*, respectively (61). The total bioconversion rates for podophyllotoxin and for 5-methoxypodophyllotoxin were 21.2 and 35.7 mg/L/day, respectively. These rates can be considered as high, taking the structural complexity of these secondary products into account. The examples show that cyclodextrins can be applied successfully to improve the bioconversion of water-insoluble precursors. Several other methods have been used with limited success to influence bioconversion capacities of cells, for example, elicitation (93), permeabilization (94), irradiation (62), or other forms of stress, such as pH and osmotic shock. For permeabilization organic alcohols or dimethylsulfoxide have been often used in order to enhance the accessability of enzymes or to provoke release of an intracellularly stored product (95,96). It can be concluded that feeding precursors to freely suspended cells has been employed with variable success for the production of one desired compound.

Immobilization may have advantageous physiological effects with respect to the production of secondary metabolites. The cells become resistant to shear damage in bioreactors by immobilization, the immobilized cells can be used over a prolonged period, high concentrations of biomass are possible, principally giving high bioconversions of substrate, and the method facilitates recovery of the cell mass and products. Product release may occur, which simplifies product isolation, and reuse of biocatalysts is possible (97,98). De novo synthesis by immobilized cells, meaning the formation of secondary metabolites by the cells when no precursor is added and only medium components are consumed, sometimes occurs.

Any immobilization method selected for plant cells should be harmless to the cells, easy to carry out under aseptic conditions, capable of operating for long periods, and particularly for large-scale applications, low in cost (99). General methods for immobilization of plant cells are entrapment in polymeric matrices and immobilization in insoluble supports like nylon mesh, polyurethane foam, hollow fibers, and cross-linking onto glutaraldehyde preactivated particles (100,101). Gel entrapment is the most popular method, since it is a simple and reproducible technique, which can be performed under cell-friendly conditions. It has been observed that immobilized plant cells may have higher production rates as compared with the freely suspended cells under the same bioconversion conditions (102).

Entrapment of cells may result in a kind of microenvironment, resembling that of the organized tissue in the intact plant. In addition, many polymers used in immobilization procedures contain charged groups that may lead to the concentration of certain ions within the microenvironment of the cells and create favorable nutritional gradients. Another explanation may be found in the growth phase of plant cells. Most freely suspended cells form their secondary metabolites in the stationary phase when their growth in terms of biomass stops. Entrapment of plant cells is one of the means to create nongrowth conditions under which the production of secondary metabolites may be improved (103). Other authors stressed the importance of physical contact, which can establish intercellular communication. This should enhance the biosynthetic capacity of plant cells; large aggregates or callus cultures might therefore have similar capacities to immobilized cells (104).

Some examples of one-step bioconversions by immobilized plant cells are shown in Table 4. For example, alginate-entrapped cells of *Digitalis lanata* can hydroxylate the cardiac glycoside ß-methyldigitoxin into ß-methyldigitoxin at a rate of 9 mg/L/day for a long period of 60 days (75).

As already mentioned, bioconversions by plant enzymes can be of help in organic chemistry. A nice example is the ortho-hydroxylation of several mono-, bi-, and tricyclic monophenols, including a series of chemically prepared aminotetralins, which are dopaminergic compounds, into catechols by calcium alginate-entrapped cells of *M. pruriens* (69,77).

Empirical attempts have been made to entrap cells in order to enhance the biosynthetic capacity or to induce

product release, permeation of cells has been a popular method (105,106). However, successful results were rather scarce because of the toxic effects of many permeabilizing agents on cells, where the viability and enzyme activities are often negatively influenced.

It can be concluded that immobilized plant cells can perform interesting bioconversions, even at relatively high rates for long periods. The effect of immobilization on cell behavior is not a general one: It is unpredictable whether release will occur; the bioconversion capacity is not generally improved in comparison with the freely suspended cells (107) or the regiospecificity of the bioconversion may even be changed (108). The bioconversion capacity may be matrix dependent, as has been shown for the immobilization of cells of *P. somniferum* and *M. pruriens* (109,110).

Since limitations in the transport of substrates, products, and/or other essential components are likely to occur in immobilized cell systems, kinetic studies are of importance (109,111). Determination of kinetic parameters such as diffusional coefficients of substrate(s) and product(s), apparent affinity constants, and apparent maximal bioconversion rates can quantify the suboptimal functioning of a system. Based on these parameters, the bioconversion conditions can be optimized.

The employment of more or less purified, isolated plant enzymes is an attractive approach if one wants to produce an individual compound by bioconversion. The bioconversion possibilities are extended, because precursors that cannot enter living cells or are metabolized by cells can be tested. When enzyme preparations are chosen for bioconversion purposes, some criteria have to be met. It is necessary that sufficient amounts of enzyme can be isolated easily from cell cultures and that their properties remain unchanged. The next step is the characterization of the enzyme involved; on the basis of knowledge of substrate specificity, temperature and pH optimum, and the cofactors (enzymes) required in the reaction, bioconversions can be carried out under optimal conditions. Furthermore, prolonged stability of activity during the bioconversion process as well as reusability are preferable. Isolated enzymes can be applied in solution, in an adsorbed or entrapped state (112,113).

The small number of isolated plant enzymes that have been described in the literature usually catalyze one-step reactions. Some examples are summarized in Table 4. The enzyme strictosidine synthase can convert the precursors tryptamine and secologanine into strictosidine, a key biosynthetic precursor in the biosynthesis of *Catharanthus* alkaloids, which are antitumor compounds, at the very high rate of 666 µkat/kg protein (114), where 1 µkat = 1 µmol/s of product formed. Using a phenoloxidase isolated from cell cultures of *M. pruriens*, a new pharmaceutical, the dopaminergic agent 7,8-dihydroxy N-di-*n*-propyl 2-aminotetralin, could be produced by regiospecific hydroxylation of its synthetically prepared 7-hydroxy precursor at a rate of 95 µkat/kg protein (77). This is a good example of how a plant enzyme can play a role in pharmaceutical chemistry. A crude enzyme preparation obtained from a *Catharanthus roseus* cell culture could bioconvert a complex synthetic substrate, a dibenzylbutanolide (115). By peroxidase-catalyzed cyclization a podophyllotoxin analogue was produced. This type of ring closure is very difficult to perform chemically in a stereospecifically controlled way, and therefore this bioconversion may be of help for the pharmacochemist in synthesis of novel, cytotoxic lignans. Recently, an UDP-glucosyltransferase fraction isolated from cultured cells of *Eucalyptus perriniana* was applied in an enzyme membrane reactor equipped with an ultrafiltration membrane (116). The enzyme catalyzed the regioselective glucosylation of salicyl alcohol to salicin, various polyphenols, and flavonoids.

As is demonstrated for these in vitro bioconversions, although small in number, enzyme preparations can serve as biocatalytic systems in order to produce valuable compounds of high purity. The applicability depends on the balance between the activity losses introduced by the enzyme isolation (the O-glucosyltransferases are problematic due to instability), the purification procedure, and the higher product yield obtained by the resulting preparation compared with the (entrapped) cell system.

From these examples, it can be concluded that, except for the bioconversion carried out by the phenoloxidase, synthetic substrates may have low affinity for plant enzymes, and low product yields are to be expected. At present, plant enzymes cannot play a prominent role as useful biocatalysts in pharmacy and organic chemistry. From a pharmaceutical point of view, it is still worthwhile considering and further exploring the use of enzyme preparations as a means of making modified synthetic (novel) compounds to be screened for pharmacological activities, since often only small amounts of compound are needed for preliminary testing. To have a real chance of synthesizing a number of compounds, enzymes need to have a broad specificity; these can be found in the large group of hydroxylating enzymes, but the very interesting glycosyltransferases can be regarded as rather specific but difficult to isolate.

GENETIC APPROACHES

In none of the strategies discussed so far, to improve product yields are the effects on the molecular level in the cell understood. During the past decade genetic strategies have been increasingly applied to achieve a controlled accumulation of secondary metabolites in plant cell cultures. For most secondary products the biosynthesis is rather complex, and the product yields are low. This can be caused by rate-limiting enzymatic steps in a biosynthetic pathway, precursor limitation, or a combination of both. Precursor limitations can be traced by bioconversion experiments; feeding of a limited precursor should give a higher secondary product yield. For example, by adding the terpenoid indole alkaloid precursor loganin to a low accumulating cell line of *Tabernaemontana divaricata*, a 100-fold increase in alkaloid levels was measured, but no enhanced enzyme activities were detected (117). Rate-limiting enzymatic steps and/or side branches are present in most biosynthetic pathways, and for their identification a pathway has to be investigated step by step. Theoretically, when a biosynthetic pathway has been

completely elucidated, secondary product accumulation can be increased by overexpression of genes encoding the limiting enzymes and/or by blocking undesired side branches. Another possibility is to use the plant enzymes for bioconversion purposes. The transfer of genes encoding interesting plant enzymes into suitable host cells like yeast or bacteria may yield biocatalysts of superior quality for the production of secondary products or related compounds. In the following examples the problems and possibilities of genetic strategies will be illustrated by recent investigations.

The enzymes involved in the complex biosynthesis of the *Rauvolfia* alkaloids, especially the antiarrhythmic ajmaline, have been extensively investigated (15). The enzymology of the biosynthesis was studied by precursor feeding to cell suspensions of *R. serpentina*. At least eleven enzymes with a high substrate specificity are involved. In addition to the main metabolic pathway leading to ajmaline, several side products and enzymes of side branches were detected, and further research is still in progress. The final goal is to block a major side branch that leads to the formation of raucaffricine to increase the ajmaline synthesis. This is basically possible by application of the antisense technique. An undesired side branch of a biosynthetic pathway may be blocked by introducing antisense genes in plant cells that switch off genes encoding the first enzymatic step of that branch. A nice example is the antisense repression of chalcone synthase, the key enzyme of flavonoid biosynthesis (118).

There have been many investigations on the improvement of paclitaxel (Taxol) production by plant cell cultures. Paclitaxel is a anticancer agent occurring in *Taxus* species and has recently been introduced in chemotherapy. The early enzymes in the paclitaxel biosynthesis have been identified (119–121). The initial conversion of geranylgeranyldiphosphate, the common precursor of diterpenoids, into 2-taxa-4(5), 11 (12)-diene, is catalyzed by taxadiene synthase. This diene product is hydroxylated to taxa-4(20), 11 (12)-diene-5a-ol by taxadiene-5-hydroxylase, a cytochrome P450–dependent enzyme. It is supposed that further oxygenation steps are also catalyzed by enzymes belonging to this class. Because the two initial steps are rather slow, the genetic strategy is to engineer cells that overproduce these two enzymes.

Elicitation as a method to increase secondary product accumulation has already been discussed. When plant cells indeed respond to an elicitor by increased biosynthetic enzyme activities, it is possible to determine the key enzymes or rate-limiting steps. After fungal elicitation of cell cultures of *Ruta graveolens* it was shown that chorismate mutase is not a key enzyme in the induction of furanocoumarin synthesis, but anthranilate synthase does play a key role in the regulation of acridone epoxide production (122).

Unfortunately, the genetic strategy of overexpression of genes encoding key enzymes will not automatically result in an increased secondary product formation. This can be illustrated by the enzyme tryptophan decarboxylase, a key enzyme in the biosynthesis of terpenoid indole alkaloids in *C. roseus*, which converts tryptophan into tryptamine. The enzyme is present at low levels in plant cell cultures and may thus be a rate-limiting step. By transformation and overexpression the tryptophan decarboxylase levels were increased together with an increase in tryptamine, but the alkaloid accumulation remained unchanged. Therefore, this enzyme should be considered as rate controlling for tryptamine formation but not for the final secondary products.

Plant cells often synthesize low quantities of the desired enzyme, resulting in low bioconversion rates. A solution to this problem may be found in heterologous expression. This implies the transfer of plant genes, which encode the enzymes into a bacterial or fungal cells (yeasts) and, more recently, in insect cells. The idea is to bring the gene to overexpression in a rapidly growing host cell resulting in a high production of the desired enzyme. The expression of genes encoding plant enzymes in a nonplant host cell is called heterologous expression: A gene is transferred from one cell species, a plant cell, to another cell species, the host cell. Recombinant DNA technology is applied for this purpose.

A number of genes encoding enzymes with a key regulatory role in biosynthetic pathways have now been individually cloned and characterized. These include genes encoding phenylalanine ammonia lyase (123,124), strictosidine synthase (125,126), berberine bridge enzyme (126,127), the hyoscyamine 6β-hydroxylase enzyme (52), and two tyrosine/DOPA decarboxylases (128).

In recombinant DNA technology vectors are used for the transfer of genetic material, and a vector or plasmid consists of circular bacterial DNA. Nowadays, different kinds of vectors are commercially available. The gene to be cloned is inserted into a chosen vector by the action of ligating enzymes, together with a marker gene (inducing resistance for a certain antibiotic) and promotors (a promotor is a DNA fragment responsible for the transcription of the gene, the result is expression; the gene switches on). This construct is introduced into the host cell, often a bacterium, under special conditions. In this way the vector uptake by the bacterium can be controlled; bacteria containing the vector will grow on medium supplemented with the antibiotic for which they now have acquired resistance. The DNA has to be stable inherited, and preferably many copies of the vector should be made in the host bacterium. The bacterium *Escherichia*

coli is most frequently used, and several strains of this bacterium species for this purpose are available. *E. coli* grows rapidly, is easily cultivated, and makes many copies of an introduced vector. Each copy contains the expressed plant gene and will produce the desired enzyme. As a consequence the enzyme will be produced in high amounts and is often released into the medium. Unfortunately, in a number of cases inactive enzyme will be produced, because this bacterium is not always able to glycosylate foreign proteins (in many cases glycosylation of protein is a prerequisite for activity). Sometimes, when overproduction of enzyme (protein) occurs, inclusion bodies are formed and the enzyme will also be inactive due to incorrect folding.

Yeasts are inexpensive microorganisms that are easy to cultivate at high densities on a large scale. Mostly *Saccharomyces cerevisiae* is used. For the expression of plant genes in yeasts different vectors have to be used. In contrast to bacteria, yeasts are able to glycosylate enzymes and can excrete the enzyme in the active form. For the expression in insect cells the gene to be cloned is inserted into in a special vector followed by recombination with viral DNA, in this case a baculovirus. The insect cell culture is infected with this recombinant virus, and this will lead to a rapid intracellular multiplication of the virus. The plant gene is strongly expressed, because the baculovirus has a powerful promotor; high amounts of enzyme will be produced. Cells of *Spodoptera frugiperda* (fall army worm) have proven to be extremely suitable for this goal. Disadvantages are the sensitivity of the cells to temperature changes, osmotic stress, and unwanted infections.

A number of plant enzymes produced by heterologous expression are listed in Table 5 (129,130). Two tyrosine/DOPA decarboxylases from *Papaver somniferum* were produced by genetically engineered *E. coli* cells (128). These enzymes act in the early stage of the benzylisochinolin alkaloid biosynthesis (morphine-like alkaloids). The enzymes were isolated from the medium, and both had decarboxylating activity, particularly towards L-DOPA. Strictosidine synthase stereospecifically condensates tryptamine and secologanine into strictosidine, the central intermediate of the indole alkaloid biosynthesis. Berberine bridge enzyme is able to form a methylene bridge in (S)-reticuline, an intermediate in the same

Table 5. Selected Examples of Heterologously Expressed Plant Enzymes; Details are Discussed in the Text

Plant species	Enzyme	Host cell	Remarks	Ref.
Rauvolfia serpentina	Strictosidine synthase	*E. coli*	Enzyme production	125
		S. frugiperda	Highly active enzyme	126
Eschscholzia californica	Berberine bridge enzyme	*S. frugiperda*	Highly active enzyme	126
		S. cerevisiae	Active enzyme	127
Papaver somniferum	Tyrosine/DOPA decarboxylases	*E. coli*	Active enzymes	128
Populus trichocarpa x deltoides	Phenylalanine ammonia lyase	*S. frugiperda*	Active enzyme	124
Rhodosporidium toruloides	Phenylalanine ammonia lyase	*S. cerevisiae*	Enzyme production	123
		E. coli	Enzyme production	123
Hyoscyamus niger	Hyoscyamine 6β-hydroxylase	*E. coli*	Active enzyme	52
Catharanthus roseus	Cinnamate 4-hydroxylase	*E. coli*	Active enzyme, fusion with reductase	129
Forsythia intermedia	Pinoresinol reductase	*E. coli*	Active enzyme	130

biosynthesis route. Genes encoding strictosidine synthase from *Rauvolfia serpentina* and berberine bridge enzyme from *Eschscholzia californica* were expressed in *S. frugiperda* insect cells (126). Both enzymes were excreted into the medium, and 4 mg per liter of each highly active enzyme could be isolated. In an earlier stage, cDNA encoding strictosidine synthase was successfully expressed in *E. coli* (125). The production of this enzyme was proven by immunodetection (using antibodies). The berberine bridge enzyme was also produced in *S. cerevisiae* (127); the enzyme was released into the medium in an active form. Phenylalanine ammonia lyase (PAL) is a key enzyme in the phenylpropanoid route, leading to the formation of cytostatic lignans, flavonoids, and coumarins. The enzyme deaminates phenylalanine into cinnamic acid. The PAL gene from *Populus trichocarpa x deltoides* was expressed in *S. frugiperda* insect cells (124) and the PAL gene from *Rhodosporidium toruloides* in *S. cerevisiae* and *E. coli* (123). The insect cells produced active PAL. Hyoscyamine 6β-hydroxylase is a key enzyme in the biosynthesis of scopolamine. Hashimoto et al. succeeded in the successful cloning of the gene encoding this enzyme from *Hyoscyamus niger* in *E. coli* (52). The enzyme could not be isolated without significant activity losses. Precursor feeding to the transgenic bacterium culture showed hydroxylating as well as epoxylating activities to be present. The culture was able to convert hyoscyamine into scopolamine at a moderate bioconversion rate of 5.5 mg/L/day.

The heterologous expression of plant genes has made considerable progress during recent years. A number of plant genes was successfully cloned in the bacterium *E. coli*, in the yeast *S. cerevisiae*, and in cells of the insect *S. frugiperda*. Recombinant DNA technology has not yet reached the stage at which large numbers of foreign genes can be transferred to and coordinately expressed in any host cell (or organism, e.g., a plant). This means that the problems regarding the expression of more complex pathways under in vitro circumstances are not likely to be solved in the near future. On the other hand, it should be emphasized that our general knowledge of plant biosynthetic pathways and its regulation is still poor. Only a few secondary product pathways have received in-depth attention during the past decade, for example, the tropane alkaloid route (scopolamine), the indole alkaloid route (strictosidine, vinblastine, vincristine), and the paclitaxel route. It can be concluded that the commercial application of genetically engineered cells for one-step bioconversions is not possible as yet, nor is the formation of plant cells with a stable, increased secondary product accumulation based on the overexpression of parts of a biosynthetic route.

CONCLUSIONS

The use of plant cell cultures for the accumulation of secondary products has made considerable progress for the past decades. To optimize the biosynthesis of secondary products several approaches have been used. Manipulation of culture conditions including elicitation, cell selection, induction of differentiation, and precursor feeding have led to improvement of secondary product accumulation in a number of cases, but in an unpredictable way and mostly species dependent. Despite the increased use of genetic tools, a controlled accumulation of secondary products has not been achieved. Briefly, the productivity of plant cell cultures is the main problem. Generally the productivity of plant cell cultures lie in the range of 10–100 mg/L/day (29). For this reason only a very limited number of secondary products can now be produced commercially by plant cells on a larger scale in bioreactors. These include shikonin from *Lithospermum erythrorhizon*, berberine from *Coptis japonica*, and ginsenosides from *Panax ginseng*.

At present, a number of interesting secondary products are receiving much attention with respect to their commercialization. These compounds are of structural complexity and so are their biosynthetic pathways; the chemical structures of the cytostatics paclitaxel and camptothecine are shown in Figure 2. The productivity of the plant cell cultures involved could be improved significantly by using one or a combination of the discussed approaches. The production of paclitaxel by cell cultures of *Taxus* species, for example, has been increased to 153 mg/L by using a wide variety of enhancement strategies, and the procedure has been patented (131). The production of the cytotoxic lignans podophyllotoxin and 5-methoxypodophyllotoxin was greatly improved by precursor feeding. By bioconversion of the late biosynthetic precursor deoxypodophyllotoxin cell cultures of *Podophyllum hexandrum* and *Linum flavum* produced 192 mg/L podophyllotoxin and 249 mg/L 5-methoxypodophyllotoxin, respectively (61). By using differentiated hairy root cultures of *Duboisia leichthardtii*, a relatively high scopolamine production of 80 mg/L was reached (132).

Large-scale cultivation of plant cells, especially of cell suspension cultures, does not give rise to large difficulties anymore. Process modeling has been successfully used as a tool for the design, analysis, and optimization of plant cell suspension cultures (133). The operating strategies, such as batch or two-stage systems, depend on the kinetics of secondary product synthesis. The induction of product release, of advantage for product isolation, and the use of two-phase systems may facilitate continuous processing (134).

The main problem to be solved remains the productivity of plant cell cultures. A solution may be found in the development of genetically stable, high-producing cell lines (135) in combination with optimal culture conditions. This goal can only be achieved when biosynthetic pathways of important secondary products are extensively analyzed with the aim to identify rate-limiting steps and key enzymes. By genetic engineering plant cells with a stable, increased secondary product accumulation can then be obtained.

In the first decennium of the twenty-first century it should become possible to reach the goal of genetically engineered synthesis of secondary products. As soon as the production of large quantities of a secondary product by genetically engineered plant cells, for example, paclitaxel is achieved, one can speak of a breakthrough in plant (cell) biotechnology.

BIBLIOGRAPHY

1. J.E. Robbers, M.K. Speedie, and V.E. Tyler, *Pharmacognosy and Pharmacobiotechnology*, Williams & Wilkins, Baltimore, Md., 1996.

2. W.C. Evans, *'Trease and Evans' Pharmacognosy*, 14th ed., Saunders, London, 1996.

3. H.J. Woerdenbag et al., *Pharm. World Sci.* **16**, 169–181 (1994).

4. G. Haberlandt, *Sitzungsber. Akad. Wiss. Wien, Math. Naturwiss. Kl., Abt. 3*, pp. 69–92 (1902).

5. P. Nobécourt, *C.R. Seances Soc. Biol.* **205**, 521–523 (1937).

6. P.R. White, *Am. J. Bot.* **26**, 59–64 (1939).

7. R.J. Gautheret, *C.R. Seances Soc. Biol.* **135**, 875–878 (1941).

8. U.S. Pat. 2,747,334 (1952), J.B. Routien and L.G. Nickel.

9. Y. Fujita and M. Tabata, in C.E. Green, D.A. Somers, W.P. Hackett, and D.D. Biesboer, eds., Liss, New York, 1987, pp. 169–185.

10. K. Kesselring, *Pflanzenzellkulturen (PZK) zur Auffindung neuer, therapeutisch relevanter Naturstoffe und deren Gewinnung durch Fermentationsprozesse*, BMFT, Bonn, 1985, pp. 111–129.

11. Y. Fujita, M. Tabata, A. Nishi, and Y. Yamada, in *Proceedings of the fifth International Congress on Plant Tissue and Cell Culture*, Fujiwara, ed., Maruzen, Tokyo, 1982, pp. 399–400.

12. A.G. Vollosovitch, in *Proceedings of the 14th V. Paces, ed., International Congress of Biochemistry*, Academia Prague, 1988, pp. 24–25.

13. W. van Uden et al., *Proceedings of the 40th Congress on Medicinal Plant Research, Planta Medica*, Thieme, Stuttgart and New York, 1992, p. A619.

14. N. Pras et al., *Pharm. World Sci.* **15**, 263–268 (1993).

15. J. Stöckigt et al., *Plant Cell, Tissue Organ Cult.* **43**, 97–109 (1995).

16. S.H. Mantell and H. Smith, *Plant Biotechnology*, Cambridge University Press, Cambridge, U.K., 1983, pp. 75–108.

17. M. Misawa, *Adv. Biochem. Eng. Biotechnol.* **31**, 59–88 (1985).

18. A. Stafford, P. Morris, and M.W. Fowler, *Enzyme Microb. Technol.* **8**, 577–587 (1986).

19. M.H. Zenk, H. El-Shagi, and U. Schulte, *Planta Med., Suppl.*, pp. 79–101 (1975).

20. M.H. Zenk et al., in W. Barz, E. Reinhard, and M.H. Zenk, eds., *Plant Tissue Culture and its Biotechnological Application*, Springer Verlag, Berlin and New York, 1977, pp. 27–43.

21. F. Vazquez-Flota, et al., *Plant Cell, Tissue Organ Cult.* **38**, 273–279 (1994).

22. J.-J. Zhong and T. Yoshida, *Enzyme Microb. Technol.* **17**, 1073–1079 (1995).

23. S. Yu, K.H. Kwok, and P.M. Doran, *Enzyme Microb. Technol.* **18**, 238–243 (1996).

24. J.-H. Kim et al., *Biotechnol. Lett.* **17**, 101–106 (1995).

25. N. Inagaki, M. Nashimura, M. Okada, and H. Mitsuhashi, *Plant Cell Rep.* **9**, 484–487 (1991).

26. M. Tabata and T. Fujita, in M. Zaitlin, P. Day, and A. Hollaender, eds., *Biotechnology in Plant Science: Relevance to Agriculture in the Eighties* Academic Press, New York, 1985, pp. 207–218.

27. F. Sasse, U. Heckenberg, and J. Berlin, *Plant Physiol.* **69**, 400–404 (1982).

28. P.M. Kieran, P.F. MacLoughlin, and D.M. Malone, *J. Biotechnol.* **59**, 39–52 (1997).

29. A.H. Scragg, *Plant Cell, Tissue Organ Cult.* **43**, 163–170 (1995).

30. A.B. Ohlsson, L. Björk, and S. Gatenbeck, *Phytochemistry* **22**, 2447–2450 (1983).

31. J. Berlin, S. Sieg, D. Strack, and M. Bokern, *Plant Cell, Tissue Organ Cult.* **5**, 163–174 (1986).

32. N. Greidziak, B. Diettrich, and M. Luckner, *Planta Med.* **56**, 175–178 (1990).

33. H.J.G. Ten Hoopen et al., *Plant Cell, Tissue Organ Cult.* **38**, 85–91 (1994).

34. H. Gundlach, M.J. Mueller, T.M. Kutchan, and M.H. Zenk, *Proc. Natl. Acad. Sci. U.S.A.* **89**, 2389–2393 (1992).

35. Y. Yukimune, H. Tabata, Y. Higashi, and Y. Hara, *Nat. Biotechnol.* **14**, 1129–1132 (1996).

36. P.F. Heinstein, *J. Nat. Prod.* **48**, 1–9 (1985).

37. U. Eilert, W.G.W. Kurz, and F. Constabel, *J. Plant Physiol.* **119**, 65–76 (1985).

38. R. Wijnsma et al., *Plant Cell Rep.* **4**, 241–244 (1985).

39. H. Dörnenburg and D. Knorr, *Enzyme Microb. Technol.* **17**, 674–684 (1995).

40. C.Z. Liu et al., *Biotechnol. Lett.* **19**, 927–929 (1997).

41. H. Becker and S. Chavadej, in Y.P.S. Bajaj, ed., *Biotechnology in Agriculture and Forestry*, Vol. 4, Springer-Verlag, Berlin and New York, 1988, pp. 294–309.

42. B. Deus-Neumann and M.H. Zenk, *Planta Med.* **50**, 427–431 (1984).

43. Y. Fujita, S. Takahashi, and Y. Yamada, *Agric. Biol. Chem.* **49**, 1755–1759 (1985).

44. O. Schiel et al., *Plant Cell Rep.* **3**, 18–20 (1984).

45. A. Spencer, J.D. Hamill, J. Reynolds, and M.J.C. Rhodes, in H.J.J. Nijkamp, L.H.W. van der Plas, and J. van Aartrijk, eds., *Progress in Plant Cellular and Molecular Biology*, Kluwer Academic Publishers, Dordrecht, The Netherlands, 1990, pp. 619–624.

46. N.B. Paniego and A.M. Giulietti, *Enzyme Microb. Technol.* **18**, 526–530 (1996).

47. H.J. Woerdenbag et al., *Plant Cell, Tissue Organ Cult.* **32**, 247–257 (1993).

48. H. Kamada et al., *Plant Cell Rep.* **5**, 239–242 (1986).

49. J.M. Sharp and P.M. Doran, *J. Biotechnol.* **16**, 171–186 (1990).

50. H. Deno et al., *J. Plant Physiol.* **131**, 315–323 (1987).

51. Y. Mano, in Y.P.S. Bajaj, ed., *Biotechnology in Agriculture and Forestry*, Vol. 22, Springer-Verlag, Berlin, 1993, pp. 190–201.

52. T. Hashimoto, J. Matsuda, and Y. Yamada, *FEBS Lett.* **329**, 35–39 (1993).

53. M.A. Subroto, K.H. Kwok, J.D. Hamill, and P.M. Doran, *Biotechnol. Bioeng.* **49**, 481–494 (1996).

54. T.C. Smith, P.J. Weathers, and R.D. Cheetham, *In Vitro Cell Dev. Biol.* **33**, 75–79 (1997).

55. Y. Asada, W. Li, and T. Yoshikawa, *Phytochemistry* **47**, 389–392 (1998).

56. T. Endo and Y. Yamada, *Phytochemistry* **24**, 1233–1236 (1985).

57. L.A. Anderson, A.T. Keene, and J.D. Philipson, *Planta Med.* **46**, 25–27 (1982).

58. W. van Uden, N. Pras, B. Homan, and Th.M. Malingré, *Plant Cell, Tissue Organ Cult.* **27**, 115–121 (1991).

59. F. Gränicher and P. Christen, in Y.P.S. Bajaj, ed., *Biotechnology in Agriculture and Forestry*; Springer-Verlag, Berlin, 1995, pp. 442–458.

60. N. Pras, *J. Biotechnol.* **26**, 29–62 (1992).

61. W. van Uden et al., *Plant Cell, Tissue Organ Cult.* **42**, 73–79 (1995).

62. E. Galun, D. Aviv, A. Dantes and A. Freeman, *Planta Med.* **10**, 511–514 (1985).

63. L.B. Davin, D.L. Bedgar, T. Katayama, and N.G. Lewis, *Phytochemistry* **31**, 3869–3874 (1992).

64. J.P. Kutney, *Pure Appl. Chem.* **69**, 431–436 (1997).

65. T. Suga and T. Hirata, *Phytochemistry* **29**, 2393–2406 (1990).

66. T. Hirata et al., *Phytochemistry* **37**, 401–403 (1994).

67. S.M. Roberts and N.J. Turner, *J. Biotechnol.* **22**, 227–244 (1992).

68. T. Furuya, T. Yoshikawa, and M. Taira, *Phytochemistry* **23**, 999–1001 (1984).

69. N. Pras, H.J. Wichers, A.P. Bruins, and Th.M. Malingré, *Plant Cell, Tissue Organ Cult.* **13**, 15–26 (1988).

70. W. van Uden, II. Oeij, II.J. Woerdenbag, and N. Pras, *Plant Cell, Tissue Organ Cult.* **34**, 169–175 (1993).

71. K. Kawaguchi, M. Hirotani, and T. Furuya, *Phytochemistry* **27**, 3475–3479 (1988).

72. F. Carrière, G. Gil, P. Tapie, and P. Chagvardieff, *Phytochemistry* **28**, 1087–1090 (1989).

73. Y. Naoshima and Y. Akakabe, *J. Org. Chem.* **54**, 4237–4239 (1989).

74. M.W. Fowler and A.M. Stafford, in M.W. Fowler, G.S. Warren, and M. Moo-Young, eds., *Plant Biotechnology*, Pergamon, Oxford, 1992, pp. 79–98.

75. A.W. Alfermann, J. Schuller, and E. Reinhard, *Planta Med.* **40**, 218–223 (1980).

76. H.J. Wichers, Th.M. Malingré, and H.J. Huizing, *Planta* **158**, 482–486 (1983).

77. N. Pras et al., *Plant Cell, Tissue Organ Cult.* **21**, 9–15 (1990).

78. R. Lutterbach and J. Stöckigt, *Helv. Chim. Acta* **75**, 2009–2011 (1992).

79. M.C. Hobbs and M.M. Yeoman, *New Phytol.* **119**, 477–482 (1991).

80. M. Petersen and A.W. Alfermann, *Z. Naturforsch. C* **43C**, 501–504 (1988).

81. M.A. Fliniaux et al., *Plant Sci.* **123**, 205–210 (1997).

82. M. Ushiyama and T. Furuya, *Phytochemistry* **28**, 3009–3013 (1989).

83. V. Kren, M. Flieger, and R. Sajdl, *Appl. Microbiol. Biotechnol.* **32**, 645–650 (1990).

84. Y. Orihara et al., *Phytochemistry* **31**, 827–831 (1992).

85. H. Hayashi, H. Fukui, and M. Tabata, *Phytochemistry* **29**, 2149–2152 (1990).

86. N. Sakui et al., *Phytochemistry* **31**, 143–147 (1992).

87. D.A. Casas, S.I. Pitta-Alvarez, and A.M. Giulietti, *Appl. Biochem. Biotechnol.* **69**, 127–136 (1998).

88. K. Kawaguchi, T. Watanabe, M. Hirotani, and T. Furuya, *Phytochemistry* **42**, 667–669 (1996).

89. H.J. Woerdenbag et al., *Phytochemistry* **29**, 1551–1554 (1990).

90. W. van Uden, H.J. Woerdenbag, and N. Pras, *Plant Cell, Tissue Organ Cult.* **38**, 103–113 (1994).

91. J. Szejtli, *Carbohydr. Polym.* **12**, 375–392 (1990).

92. H.J. Woerdenbag et al., *Plant Cell Rep.* **9**, 97–100 (1990).

93. W.G.W. Kurz, F. Constabel, U. Eilert, and R.T. Tyler, in D.D. Breimer and P. Speiser, eds., *Topics in Pharmaceutical Sciences*, Elsevier, Amsterdam, 1987, pp. 413–416.

94. H.R. Felix, *Anal. Biochem.* **120**, 211–234 (1982).

95. A.J. Parr, R.J. Robins, and J.C. Rhodes, *Plant Cell Rep.* **3**, 262–265 (1984).

96. J. Berlin et al., *Z. Naturforsch. C.* **44C**, 249–254 (1989).

97. A.K. Panda, S. Mishra, V.S. Bisaria, and S.S. Bhojwani, *Enzyme Microb. Technol.* **11**, 386–397 (1989).

98. P.D. Williams and F. Mavituna, in M.W. Fowler and G.S. Warren, eds., *Plant Biotechnology*, Pergamon, Oxford, 1992, pp. 63–78.

99. F. Mavituna, J. Park, P. Williams, and A. Wilkinson, in C. Webb and F. Mavituna, eds., *Plant and Animal Cells: Process Possibilities*, Harwood, Academic Publishers, Chichester, 1987, pp. 92–115.

100. P. Morris, A.H. Scragg, N.J. Smart, and A. Stafford, in R.A. Dixon, ed., *Plant Cell Culture: A Practical Approach*, IRL Press, Oxford and Washington, D.C., 1985, pp. 127–167.

101. J. Novais, in M. Pais, F. Mavituna, and J. Novais, eds., *Plant Cell Biotechnology*, NATO ASI Ser. Plenum, New York, 1988, pp. 353–363.

102. P. Brodelius and K.J. Mosbach, in W.W. Umberit, ed., *Advances in Applied Microbiology*, Academic Press, London and New York, 1982, pp. 1–26.

103. A.W. Rosevear and C.A. Lambe, *Adv. Biochem. Eng. Biotechnol.* **31**, 39–43 (1985).

104. A.L. Dainty et al., *Trends Biotechnol.* **8**, 59–60 (1985).

105. H.R. Felix and K. Mosbach, *Biotechnol. Lett.* **4**, 181–186 (1982).

106. P. Brodelius and K. Nilsson, *Eur. J. Appl. Microbiol. Biotechnol.* **17**, 275–280 (1983).

107. M. Seki, C. Ohzora, M. Takeda, and S. Furusaki, *Biotechnol. Bioeng.* **53**, 214–219 (1997).

108. T. Vanek, T. Macek, K. Stransky, and K. Ubik, *Biotechnol. Tech.* **3**, 411–414 (1989).

109. N. Pras, P.G.M. Hesselink, J. ten Tusscher, and Th.M. Malingré, *Biotechnol. Bioeng.* **34**, 214–222 (1989).

110. P. Corchete and M.M. Yeoman, *Plant Cell Rep.* **8**, 128–131 (1989).

111. A.C. Hulst and J. Tramper, *Enzyme Microb. Technol.* **11**, 546–558 (1989).

112. M.P.J. Kierstan and M.P. Coughlan, in J. Woodward, ed., *Immobilised Cells and Enzymes*, IRL Press, Oxford, 1985, pp. 39–48.

113. J. Woodward, ed., *Immobilised Cells and Enzymes*, IRL Press, Oxford, 1985, pp. 3–18.

114. U. Pfitzner and M.H. Zenk, *Planta Med.* **46**, 10–14 (1982).

115. J.P. Kutney, *Acc. Chem. Res.* **26**, 559–566 (1993).

116. N. Nakajima et al., *Ferment. Bioeng.* **84**, 455–460 (1997).

117. D. Dagnino, J. Schripsema, and R. Verpoorte, *Phytochemistry* **39**, 341–349 (1995).

118. J.N.M. Mol, P. de Lange, A. Oostdam, and L.H.W. van der Plas, in H.J.J. Nijkamp, L.H.W. van der Plas, and J. van Aartrijk, eds., *Progress in Plant Cellular and Molecular Biology*, Kluwer Academic Publishers, Dordrecht, The Netherlands, 1990, pp. 712–716.

119. A.E. Koepp et al., *J. Biol. Chem.* **270**, 8686–8690 (1995).

120. M. Hezari, N.G. Lewis, and R. Croteau, *Arch. Biochem. Biophys.* **322**, 437–444 (1995).

121. J. Hefner et al., *Chem. Biol.* **3**, 479–489 (1996).

122. J. Bohlmann and U. Eilert, *Plant Cell, Tissue Organ Cult.* **38**, 189–198 (1994).

123. J.D.B. Faulkner, J.G. Anson, M.F. Tuite, and N.P. Minton, *Gene* **143**, 13–20 (1994).

124. G.R. MacKegney, S.L. Butland, D. Theiman, and B.E. Ellis, *Phytochemistry* **41**, 1259–1263 (1996).

125. T.M. Kutchan, *Planta Med.* **55**, 593–594 (1989).

126. T.M. Kutchan, A. Bock, and H. Dittrich, *Phytochemistry* **35**, 353–360 (1993).

127. H. Dittrich and T.M. Kutchan, *Proc. Natl. Acad. Sci. USA.* **88**, 9969–9973 (1991).

128. P.J. Facchini and V. De Luca, *Phytochemistry* **38**, 1119–1126 (1995).

129. M. Hotze, G. Schröder, and J. Schröder, *FEBS Lett.* **374**, 345–350 (1995).

130. A.T. Dinkova-Kostova et al., *J. Biol. Chem.* **271**, 29473–29482 (1996).

131. U.S. Pat. 5,407,816 (1995), V. Bringi et al.

132. Murinaka, *Biosci. Biotech. Biochem.* **57**, 1398–1399 (1993).

133. W.M. van Gulik, H.J.G. ten Hoopen, and J.J. Heijnen, *Biotechnol. Bioeng.* **41**, 771–780 (1993).

134. R.M. Buitelaar and J. Tramper, *J. Biotechnol.* **23**, 111–141 (1992).

135. J. Berlin, in Y.P.S. Bajaj, ed., *Biotechnology in Agriculture and Forestry*; Springer-Verlag, Berlin, 1988, pp. 37–59.

See also Bryophyte in vitro cultures, secondary products; Plant cell culture, effect on growth and secondary product accumulation of organic compounds and surfactants; Plant cell cultures, selection and screening for secondary product accumulation.

PLANT CELL CULTURES, SELECTION AND SCREENING FOR SECONDARY PRODUCT ACCUMULATION

Alan Scragg
University of the West of England
Frenchay, Bristol
United Kingdom

OUTLINE

INTRODUCTION

In microbial systems screening and selection have been used successfully to increase the yields of antibiotics considerably, and these combined with mutation have seen penicillin yields increase over a thousand fold in 30 years. The development of screening and selection techniques in plant cell cultures has been carried out not only in order to increase yields of secondary metabolites, but also to select for resistance to pests and herbicides, tolerances to drought, salt, and cold, and as part of the genetic manipulation of plants involving the selection of transformed cells.

Screening and selection are not the same techniques. Screening is the analysis of a large number of cells, shoots, or plants in order to find the best cell line in a large population. Selection, as the name implies, involves some form of selection by the manipulation of conditions so that a negative or positive effect is applied to a population, thus selecting those with the desired properties.

In the case of microorganisms some form of mutation is often carried out before either screening or selection in order to increase the number of mutations, as the natural mutation rate can be very low. Mutation has been used in plant cell and tissue cultures, but in most cases the variation induced by the process of culturing is sufficient to give a high percentage of variants. The variation is known as *somaclonal variation* and can be as high as 20% compared with the natural mutation rate of 1×10^6. The disadvantage of somaclonal variation is that it can be unpredictable. The more dedifferentiated the plant culture has become, the higher the potential somaclonal variation, so that the highest levels are found with protoplasts, followed by cell suspensions, callus, organogenic cultures, and variation is at a minimum in meristem cultures. The high degree of variation should be avoided in micropropagation, whereas in screening and selection it is welcome. Another restriction with screening and selection using plant cultures is that this can only be carried out with traits that are expressed in the dedifferentiated cells, rather than just in the whole plant. Many traits are only expressed in the differentiated plant so that many changes like morphological variations cannot be selected in tissue culture. In addition, some of the traits selected or screened in the undifferentiated state may not be expressed in the whole plant, and some selected traits may be the result of the isolation of altered physiological states rather than permanent heritable changes.

SCREENING

Screening involves the analysis of a large population of cells or isolates. In order to be able to find cultures with the desired characteristic such as high yields of secondary products, a number of conditions need to be satisfied. The main condition is for sufficient variation in the population to find the desired cells. Mutation can be applied but, as has been explained, somaclonal variation is often sufficient without the need for mutation. Somaclonal variation can be affected by a number of factors but is highest in the most undifferentiated cultures such a protoplasts (1). It has been suggested that not only plant cultures but whole plants could be screened for high yield and the highest yielding plants used as a source of explants for the development of cell cultures (2). Subsequently the resulting cultures could also be screened. Figure 1 shows an outline of how such a process has been carried out to find cultures of *Catharanthus roseus* producing high yields of ajmalicine. The final cultures yielded both unstable and stable high yielding lines of *C. roseus* (3). The unstable high-yielding lines may have been due to epigenetic somaclonal variations. This approach can be extended to screening not only the plants but screening cell lines derived from:

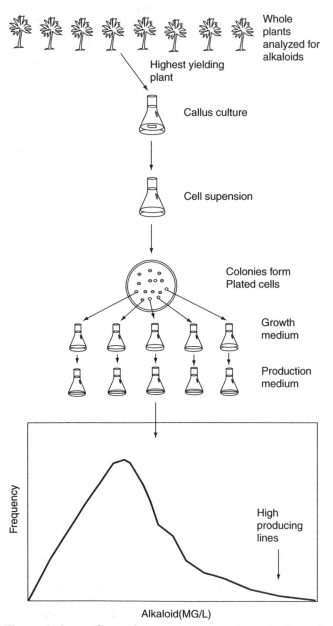

Figure 1. An outline of a process for the selection of high-ajmalicine-yielding culture of *Catharanthus roseus* starting from whole plants. *Source*: Adapted from Ref. 2.

- Different parts of one plant
- Different plants
- Different cultivars
- Different plant species

However, it must be appreciated that the source of the explant has only a limited effect on the yield of secondary products in many cases.

The screening with plant cultures can be on two levels, at the level of the individual cell as in most microbial systems or at the colony (callus) or aggregate level. The screening of individual cells would avoid screening mixtures of cells, and as plant cells are regarded as totipotent, whole plants can be regenerated from single cells. However, individual plant cells do not grow well in isolation, as they require the presence of a critical number of other cells for growth. In some cases the medium that plant cells have been growing in, known as *conditioned medium*, can replace the presence of a mass of cell enabling individual cells to grow. The exact nature of conditioned medium is unclear. In plant cell suspensions individual cells do not occur often, as plant cell suspensions are normally made up of aggregates of various sizes that can contain up to 1,000 cells. Therefore, if single cells are required for screening, the cell aggregates have to be disrupted and single cells isolated. Physical methods have been used to disrupt the cell aggregates. Disruption of the cell aggregates by blending and the use of a micropipette to collect individual cells have been used to isolate single cells. A growth system pulsed with air has been used to disrupt aggregates of a culture of *Glycine max* (4). One of the most common methods of single-cell or small-aggregate isolation is to use filters of various sizes to separate single cells from aggregates after disruption. Filters of 75 μm in mesh size have been used to separate individual cells from a mixture of aggregates and cells. Plant cells can be from 20 to 100 μm in length and 10–30 μm in width and are often irregular in shape, ranging from spherical to rodlike. Therefore, it can be difficult to filter in the preparation of individual cells. There has been one report of the use of immobilized plant cells for the production of single cells where a culture of *C. roseus* was immobilized in alginate beads and encouraged to grow. Eventually the beads became full of cells and single cells began to be released from the surface of the bead. The single cells remained viable, as the mass of immobilized cells had conditioned the medium.

Chemical methods have been used to produce single cells such as the addition of colichine to soybean culture (5), but perhaps the best method for the production of single cells is the formation of protoplasts. Protoplasts can be produced from plant material such as leaf tissue or tissue cultures such as callus and cell suspensions by the application of cell-wall-degrading enzymes. Provided the correct osmotic pressure is maintained in the medium, the protoplasts will survive and can be manipulated so that they regenerate their cell walls and divide to form minicalluses. The calluses formed can be regenerated into plants. However, not all plants or plant material will protoplast easily, and the growth and regeneration from protoplasts is far from easy.

Screening aggregates or callus material is considerably easier than single cells, but the aggregate may contain a mixture of cells. Regeneration from such a mixture is problematic, as the cells that grow may not be those that should have been selected. Mixed populations may require more than one cycle of screening.

ANALYSIS

The screening of cells or colonies for increased secondary product accumulation requires some form of analysis to detect the compound or measure the levels of the compound of interest. The methods used for analysis need to be rapid and cheap if large numbers of isolates are to screened. The methods also need to be accurate and sensitive, as they may be required to detect the compounds at very low levels if individual cells are to be analyzed. Ideally the method should be nondestructive, so that when analyzing single cells the isolates are not lost. The methods of analysis can be divided into two types, direct and indirect.

Direct

The simplest direct method of analysis is visual examination for colored secondary products such anthrocyanins (Fig. 2). The simplicity of the method is probably the reason that, of those plant cell culture selected for high yields, colored products dominate. Products that fluoresce can be detected by the use of microscopes with the ability to follow fluorescence. In one case a secondary product, rosmarinic acid, was detected in cultures of *Anchusa offinalis* by using microspectrophotometry (6). The selection of cells that contain secondary product that exhibits fluorescence can also be followed by flow cytometry (7) and in some cases the method used to separate high-yielding lines (8). Some examples of direct screening using visual methods are shown in Table 1 (9–14).

Indirect

Indirect methods can be simple, such as a small extraction or squash technique that can be linked to a chemical reaction such as color change. Tobacco calluses were screened for nicotine content by squeezing a portion of the callus onto filter paper and spraying the paper with Dragendorff's reagent, which will stain for nicotine (15). Other indirect techniques are more elaborate and include

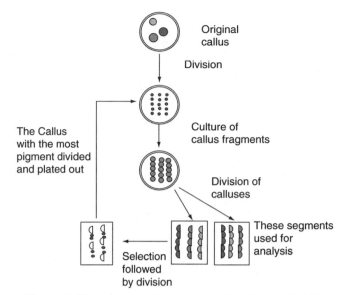

Figure 2. The selection of pigmented callus. *Source*: Ref. 10.

radioimmune assay (RIA) (2,16), which has been used for indole alkaloids, enzyme-linked immunosorbent assay (ELISA) (17,18), HPLC (19), and flow cytometry (13). The biological activity of the extracted compounds can also be tested if sufficiently active (20), and an example is shown in Figure 3, where berberine accumulation was detected by it activity on *Bacillus cereus*.

In general the indirect methods can only be used for colony screening, as they are destructive, but direct methods can be used for both types of culture. Examples of screening for high-producing lines are shown in Table 2.

METHODS OF CULTURING SINGLE CELLS

The ability to grow individual plant cells would allow both screening and selection to be used at the cell level. Some of the earliest techniques for the growth of single cells involved the separation of the single cells form other plant cells by a filter or membrane. Examples of this technique are shown in Figure 4. The first was perhaps the raft technique, where a callus was used to provide the conditioning that individual plant cells require for growth, and this was separated from the cells by filter

Table 1. Examples of Screening by Direct Methods

Compound	Plant and culture type	Screen method	Ref.
Anthocyanin	*Daucus carota*, cell aggregates	visible	9
	Euphorbia millii, callus	visible	10
Shikonin	*Lithospermum erythrorizon* cell aggregates and suspension	visible	11
Ubiquinone	*Nicotiana tabacum*, cell aggregates	visible HPLC	12
Berberine	*Coptis japonica*, cell aggregates	visible	13
β-Carbolines	*Peganum harmala*, cell aggregates	fluor.	14
Serpentine	*Catharanthus roseus*, cell aggregates	fluor.	3

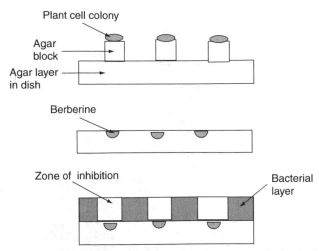

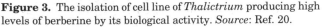

Figure 3. The isolation of cell line of *Thalictrium* producing high levels of berberine by its biological activity. *Source*: Ref. 20.

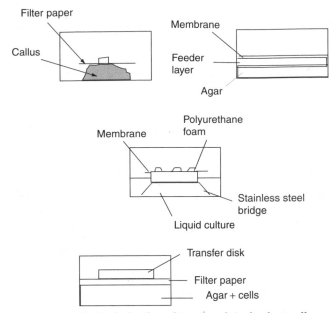

Figure 4. Methods for the cultivation of single plant cells.

paper and the whole thing incubated in a sealed Petri dish to avoid drying out. This was improved by growing or spreading a thick layer of cells on agar-solidified medium, known as the feeder layer and using a membrane filter to separate the single cells from this layer. A modification of this technique was to mix the feeder cells with molten agar and pour as a single layer. The single cells are grown on a disk that is sufficiently rigid to be able to be transferred from one Petri dish to another. The disk is separated from the agar/cell mix by a membrane filter. The feeder layer cells can come from the same species of plant as the single cells, or in some cases a different plant culture can be used. A liquid version of the feeder layer technique can be used if the cell and membrane are held above the liquid by a stainless steel bridge. A supply of medium is provided by placing the membrane on porous material such as polyurethane foam.

Other methods of growing single cells are to provide the cells with conditioned medium. Conditioned medium can be prepared by removing the cells after 1–2 weeks of growth, replacing some of the depleted medium components such as phosphate and nitrates and using this either in solidified form or as liquid. Single cells can be grown in microdroplets. Microdroplets rely on the single cell's being able to condition such a small volume. Microdroplets can be suspended on the bottom of a microscope slide and the whole slide incubated in a Petri dish to avoid drying out.

SELECTION

Selection is the application of some form of pressure, which can be either positive where all the cells die other than those with the desired characteristics or negative where the required cells fail to grow. Most positive selections are for resistance to a variety of agents as follows:

Table 2. The Increase in Secondary Product Produced by Screening

Product	Plant species and culture	Initial yield %[a]	Screened yield %[a]	Method used
Berberine	*Coptis japonica* plated clones	5	8.2[b]	visual
Anthocyanin	*Euphorbia millii* callus	1	7[b]	visual
Nicotine	*Nicotiana tabacum* plated clones	0.7	2.5[b]	squash and spray
Ubiquinone	*Nicotiana tabacum* plated clones	0.05	0.5[b]	visual and HPLC
Shikonin	*Lithospermum erythrorhizon* callus	1.7	15[b]	visual
Serpentine	*Catharanthus roseus* callus	0.1	0.5–1	fluor. and RIA

[a] Percentage of dry weight.
[b] Repeated screening.

- Environmental
  Salt tolerance
  IIeavy metal tolerance
  Cold tolerance
  Drought tolerance
- Disease resistance
- Herbicide resistance
- Amino acid overproduction
- Antibiotic resistance

Examples of the types of cells selected and the techniques involved can be found in a number of articles (21–26).

Positive selection for the overproduction of secondary products is more difficult, but there are a few examples.

One example of positive selection was to supply pimelic acid to cultures of *Lavandula vera* (27). Pimelic acid is toxic so that the cell will die unless pimelic acid is converted to another less toxic compound, and in this case pimelic acid is a precursor of biotin. In this way high-biotin-accumulating cultures were selected. In a similar way resistance to 5-methyltryptophan (5-MT) was used to select for *C. roseus* cells, which overproduce tryptophan, thus diluting the toxic effects. Tryptophan is a precursor of the indole alkaloids (28) so that cells that overproduce tryptophan should produce more indole alkaloids. Similarly resistance to 4-methyl tryptophan was also used to increase indole alkaloid accumulation in *C. roseus*. Resistance to para-fluorophenylalanine, an analogue of l-phenylalanine, was used to increase the accumulation of phenols in *Nicotiana tabacum* (29). These methods had only a limited success with a few lines. This is probably a refection of the complex nature of the pathways involved, where the lack of precursors is only one factor in the control a secondary product accumulation.

MUTATION

The degree of genetic variability can be increased in populations of plants by exposing suspension cells, callus, or even plants before culturing to physical or chemical mutagenesis. Ultraviolet light and x-rays have been used to mutate cell suspensions (30). The chemical mutagens are more predictable, and the most commonly used are ethyl or methyl methanesulfonate (EMS and MMS), alkylating agents, and base analogues such as 5-bromodeoxyuridine (BudR) and 5-bromouracil (BU). The alkylating agents are n-methyl-N′-N-nitrosquanidine (MNNG), EMS, N-ethyl-N-nitrosurea (ENU) and MMS. Some of the first mutations to be isolated were auxotrophic cell lines (31), aminoacid overproduction (32), and BudR resistance (33).

BIBLIOGRAPHY

1. O.P. Damasco et al., *Plant Cell Rep.* **16**, 118–123 (1996).
2. M.H. Zenk et al., in W. Barz, E. Reinhard, and M.H. Zenk, eds., *Plant Tissue Culture and Its Biotechnological Application*, Springer-Verlag, Berlin, 1977, pp. 27–43.
3. B. Deus-Neumann and M.H. Zenk, *Planta Med.* **50**, 427–431 (1984).
4. W.G.W. Kurz, *Exp. Cell Res.* **64**, 476–479 (1971).
5. N. Umetsu, K. Ojima, and K. Matsuda, *Planta* **125**, 197–200 (1975).
6. B.E. Ellis, in A. Fujiara, ed., *Plant Tissue Culture*, Maruzen, Tokyo, 1982, pp. 395–396.
7. S. Brown, *Physiol. Veg.* **22**, 341–349 (1984).
8. P. Adamse, in N.J.J. Nijkamp, L.H.W. Van der Plas, and J. Van Aartijk, eds., *Progress in Plant Cellular and Molecular Biology*, Kluwer Academic Publishers, Dordrecht, The Netherlands, 1990, pp. 726–731.
9. D.K. Dougall, J.M. Johnson, and G.M. Whitten, *Planta* **50**, 292–297 (1980).
10. Y. Yamamoto, R. Mizuguchi, and Y. Yamada, *Theor. Appl. Genet.* **61**, 113–116 (1982).
11. Y. Fujita, S. Takahashi, and Y. Yamada, *Agric. Biol. Chem.* **49**, 1755–1759 (1985).
12. T. Matsumoto et al., *Agric. Biol. Chem.* **44**, 967–969 (1980).
13. Y. Hara et al., *Planta Med.* **55**, 151–154 (1989).
14. F. Sasse, U. Heckenberg, and J. Berlin, *Plant Physiol.* **69**, 400–412 (1982).
15. T. Ogino, N. Hiraoka, and M. Tabata, *Phytochemistry* **17**, 1907–1911 (1978).
16. H. Arens, J. Stockigt, E.W. Weiler, and M.H. Zenk, *Planta Med.* **34**, 37–46 (1978).
17. S.P. Lapinjoki et al., *J. Immunoassay* **7**, 113–128 (1986).
18. R.J. Robins and M.J.C. Rhodes, *J. Chromatogr.* **283**, 436–440 (1984).
19. W. Kohl, B. Witte, and G. Hofle, *Planta Med.* **47**, 177–182 (1983).
20. T. Suzuki et al., *Plant Cell Rcp.* **6**, 194–196 (1987).
21. D.R. Duncan and J.M. Widholm, in J.W. Pollard, and J.M. Walker, eds., *Plant Cell and Tissue Culture*, Humana Press, Clifton, 1990, pp. 443–453.
22. J. Berlin and F. Sasse, *Adv. Biochem. Eng.* **31**, 99–132 (1985).
23. P.J. Dix, *Plant Cell Line Selection*, VCH, Weinheim, 1990.
24. P.J. Dix, in R.D. Hall, ed., *Plant Cell Culture Protocols*, Humana Press, Clifton, N.J., 1999, pp. 309–318.
25. R.A. Gonzales, in R.A. Dixon, and R.A. Gonzales, eds., *Plant Cell Culture, A Practical Approach*, IRL Press, Oxford, U.K., 1994, pp. 67–72.
26. W.H.-T. Loh, in M.W. Fowler, and G.S. Warren, eds., *Plant Biotechnology*, Pergamon, Oxford, U.K., 1992, pp. 33–45.
27. K. Watanabe, S.I. Yano, and Y. Yamada, *Phytochemistry* **21**, 513–517 (1982).
28. F. Sasse, M. Buchholz, and J. Berlin, *Z. Naturforsch, C* **38C**, 916–922 (1983).
29. J. Berlin, K.G. Kukoschke, and K.H. Knobloch, *Planta Med.* **42**, 173–175 (1981).
30. P.J. Dix, in M.M. Yeoman, ed., *Plant Cell Culture Technology*, Blackwell, Oxford, U.K., 1986, pp. 143–201.
31. J.M. Widholm, *Biochim. Biophys. Acta* **261**, 52–58 (1972).
32. P.S. Carlson, *Science* **168**, 47–489 (1970).
33. P. Maliga, in I.K. Vasil, ed., *Cell Culture and Somatic Cell Genetics of Plants*, Vol. 1, Academic Press, New York, 1984, pp. 552–556.

See also Bryophyte in vitro cultures, secondary products; Plant cell culture, effect on growth and secondary product accumulation of organic compounds and surfactants; Plant cell cultures, secondary product accumulation.

PLANT PROTOPLASTS

M.R. DAVEY
J.B. POWER
K.C. LOWE
University of Nottingham
Nottingham, United Kingdom

OUTLINE

INTRODUCTION

A unique feature of plant cells is their totipotency. Each cell carries the genetic information that, theoretically, enables that cell to develop into one or more intact, fertile plants under the correct culture conditions. The competence of cells to realize their totipotency is governed by several factors, such as the plant genotype, the ontogenetic state of the source tissues, and the culture conditions. The latter include the chemical composition of the culture medium and physical parameters, particularly the photoperiod, quality, and intensity of illumination and the temperature.

While the totipotency of plant cells was hypothesized as long ago as the early 1900s by the plant physiologist Gottlieb Haberlandt, approximately fifty years elapsed before this was confirmed. Likewise, the totipotency of isolated protoplasts was not demonstrated until the early 1970s, when plants were regenerated from leaf protoplasts of tobacco (1). Currently, the isolation of protoplasts from cells of many species is now routine, followed by their culture to produce tissues from which intact fertile plants can be regenerated.

WHAT ARE PLANT PROTOPLASTS?

Cells of primary plant tissues are surrounded by a cellulosic wall enclosing the living contents. A pectin-rich matrix, the middle lamella, joins the walls of adjacent cells. The living contents of each cell are bounded by the plasma membrane, and collectively, the plasma membrane and the living contents constitute the protoplast. Normally, the plasma membrane and the enveloping wall are in intimate contact, since the plasma membrane is involved in wall synthesis. However, under conditions of osmotic stress, the plasma membrane may contract away from the surrounding wall. Experimental removal of the cellulosic walls enveloping recently plasmolyzed protoplasts releases the latter as a population of single, free-floating, osmotically fragile "naked" cells in which the plasma membrane is the only barrier between the living interior of the cell and the surrounding environment. Large populations, often consisting of many millions of isolated protoplasts, provide the starting material for plant genetic manipulation techniques, particularly somatic hybridization involving protoplast fusion, exploitation of somaclonal (protoclonal variation), and aspects of transformation. Protoplasts are also unique material for physiological investigations and the isolation of organelles.

ISOLATION OF PLANT PROTOPLASTS

Mechanical and Enzymatic Isolation Procedures

Protoplasts can be isolated both mechanically and enzymatically from source tissues, the latter procedure being the most convenient and reliable method. The mechanical isolation of plant protoplasts dates back to the 1880s, when Klercker demonstrated that protoplasts were released from the cut ends of plasmolyzed cells following slicing of tissues in a hypertonic solution. The demonstration that the walls of bacteria and fungi could be degraded to release protoplasts and the realization that protoplasts are released by natural enzyme digestion of cell walls during fruit ripening, as in the case of tomato fruit locule tissue, prompted concerted efforts during the early 1960s to isolate protoplasts from root tips of tomato seedlings using cellulase from the fungus *Myrothecium verrucaria* (2). These experiments were followed by the exploitation of commercially produced cellulases, hemi-cellulases, and pectinases, once these became available, to isolate protoplasts from a range of source tissues. Pectinases digest the middle lamella, resulting in cell separation, while cellulases and hemi-cellulases remove the cellulosic wall components. Currently, a range of wall-degrading enzymes can be purchased, many of which are mixtures of several enzymes, although one component generally predominates. Additionally, such enzymes used for protoplast isolation often contain proteins and low-molecular-weight impurities. The passage of enzymes prior to use through Sephadex G-25 or G-75 resins or Biogel P-6 columns reduces contaminants and often improves enzyme activity with concomitant increase in protoplast yield and viability.

Cell wall composition influences the enzyme mixture required, particularly in relation to tissues of dicotyledons and monocotyledons (3). Consequently, the enzyme concentrations and the conditions for protoplast isolation from any particular plant must be determined empirically. However, there is an extensive literature on this subject, as many protocols have been reported for a range of genera and species. Typical enzyme mixtures for the isolation of protoplasts from leaves, petals, cell suspensions, and seedling tissues have been summarized recently (4,5), together with protocols for protoplast isolation from model dicotyledons and monocotyledons.

The time of enzyme digestion, usually at 25–28 °C, may be of short duration (usually up to 6 h) or, for convenience, overnight (12–20 h). The time of incubation determines the enzyme composition and combination. Removal of the lower epidemis of leaves with fine forceps, or dissection of leaves into thin strips coupled with vacuum infiltration of the enzyme solution, facilitate wall digestion and maximize protoplast release. It is well established that protoplasts undergo stress during tissue digestion, often accompanied by ethylene synthesis and the production of polyphenols, phytoalexins, and superoxide radicals. Changes in plasma membrane lipids and proteins also occur; some of the proteins synthesized during protoplast isolation may be similar to pathogenesis-related proteins. Indeed, several of these responses mimic those displayed by injured or pathogen-attacked cells (5). The preconditioning of donor plants or explants by exposure to low light intensity, dark or reduced photoperiods, or the preculture on suitable media of donor explants, sometimes associated with cold/dark pretreatments, may increase protoplast yield and viability. Preplasmolysis of source tissue in a suitable salts solution (6) containing the same osmoticum as the enzyme mixture [e.g., 13% (w/v) mannitol] assists in maintaining protoplast viability. This procedure also seals plasmodesmata between adjacent cells and reduces the enzyme uptake by endocytosis, which occurs when cells are immersed directly in the enzyme mixture. Generally, sugar alcohols such as mannitol or sorbitol are used as osmotica in the enzyme mixtures, rather than carbohydrates such as sucrose and glucose, since the latter are taken up and metabolized during enzyme incubation, resulting in starch accumulation and protoplast instability.

Enzymatically released protoplasts are normally contaminated by undigested cells and cellular debris. Passage of the enzyme–protoplast mixture through nylon or metal sieves of suitable pore size removes the larger contaminants. Subsequently, gentle centrifugation (e.g., $100 \times g$; 10 min) through a solution containing the same concentration of osmoticum as the enzyme mixture will pellet the protoplasts, leaving the finer debris in suspension. A flotation step may be beneficial; gently mixing the protoplasts with 21% (w/v) sucrose in a simple salts solution (6), or with a solution of Percoll or Ficoll, followed by centrifugation, causes leaf mesophyll protoplasts to band at the top of the sucrose solution from which they can be removed with a Pasteur pipette. The presence of Ca^{2+} ions in the washing solution is usually beneficial for plasma membrane stability.

Source Material for Protoplast Isolation

The nature of the source tissues are important for the routine and reliable isolation of viable protoplasts. Leaves of glasshouse-grown plants may be a suitable source of protoplasts, as in the case of *Passiflora* (7), although plant age is important and seasonal variation in light intensity, temperature, and humidity may necessitate the growth of plants in controlled-environment cabinets. Variation in the physical and chemical parameters experienced by the source material can be eliminated by the use of cultured shoots and *in vitro* grown seedlings, although ethylene accumulation *in vitro* may have a detrimental effect on protoplast yield and viability (8). The advantage of *in vitro* grown seedlings is that protoplasts can be isolated from radicles, hypocotyls, and cotyledons within a few days of seed germination. Protoplasts can be released from these organs of both light- and dark-grown seedlings. The viability and mitotic division frequency of protoplasts during subsequent culture may be influenced by the source tissue and plant variety. Interestingly, even root hairs will release totipotent protoplasts (9). Protoplasts from root tips are cytoplasmically dense; those from more differentiated regions are generally vacuolate. Protoplasts with a haploid genome can be isolated from pollen tetrads and, with more difficulty, from mature pollen (10). Cell suspensions are a useful source of large populations of protoplasts, although embryogenic suspensions must be employed, as in the case of cereals, if the released protoplasts are required to express their totipotency.

Isolated protoplasts should be assessed for their viability and for the removal of their cell walls immediately following isolation and prior to experimentation. A spherical shape and the absence of birefringence generally indicate complete cell wall digestion. Any wall material that may remain can be visualized following staining with Calcofluor White (11) or the fluorescent brightener, Tinopal (12). Wall material stained with Tinopal fluoresces yellow; that stained with Calcofluor White has a blue fluorescence under UV illumination. Fluorescein diacetate (FDA) is used to monitor protoplast viability. FDA molecules pass across the protoplast plasma membrane. Cleavage of the molecule by esterases within the cytoplasm of living cells releases fluorescein, which is unable to pass out through the plasma membrane and which fluoresces yellow-green under UV illumination. The number of protoplasts released is normally estimated by suspending the protoplasts in a known volume of osmoticum, removing an aliquot, and counting the protoplasts using a haemocytometer.

CULTURE OF ISOLATED PLANT PROTOPLASTS

Nutritional Requirements of Protoplasts and Culture Media

Over the years, more effort has been invested in attempts to develop protoplast-to-plant systems than in any other protoplast-based technology. Isolated protoplasts and cultured cells, especially cells in suspension, often have similar nutrient requirements, except that during the early stages of culture, protoplasts require osmotic protection until they have regenerated a new primary wall of sufficient strength to counteract the turgor pressure exerted by the protoplast itself. Protoplasts normally commence cell wall regeneration within minutes of being introduced into culture. Gradual reduction of the osmotic pressure, by dilution of the culture medium with medium of similar composition, but with a reduced concentration of osmotic stabilizer, is essential to sustain mitotic division and daughter cell formation, leading to tissue production. If the osmotic pressure is not reduced progressively, protoplast-derived cells undergo secondary plasmolysis, often with associated necrosis. Conversely, rapid reduction of the osmotic pressure results in the extrusion of cytoplasm through weak regions of the developing cell wall, often accompanied by cell lysis.

An infinite range of media are available for culturing isolated protoplasts. Such media are often based on the well-tested MS (13) and B5 (14) formulations, with the undefined but more nutrient-rich KM-type media (15) being beneficial for culturing protoplasts at low densities. Media are often modified from the original formulations to suit the requirements of protoplasts from specific species. Alteration of key media components may be essential, as in the case of ammonium ions, which are detrimental to some protoplasts, particularly those of woody species. Sucrose is the most common carbon source, although glucose may act as both a carbon source and osmotic stabilizer. Sugar alcohols, particularly mannitol, are normally employed as nonmetabolizable osmotica. Maltose as a carbon source may be beneficial in stimulating shoot regeneration during the latter stages of culture of protoplast-derived cells, as in the case of cereals (16).

Most protoplasts require one or more auxins or cytokinins as growth regulators in the culture medium, to sustain mitotic division. Again, an extensive range of growth regulators combinations and concentrations have been reported in the literature. A possible exception involves protoplasts isolated from crown gall tissues, although even these may require growth regulators at the begining of their culture period. The different growth requirements of freshly isolated protoplasts and protoplast-derived cells may necessitate changes in growth regulators as culture proceeds.

Experimental Systems for Protoplast Culture

Several procedures have been reported for culturing isolated protoplasts. Culture in thin layers of liquid medium in suitable containers (e.g., Petri dishes) is a simple technique, which is easily modified for culture of protoplasts in droplets (each usually less than 150 µL in size) hanging from the lids of Petri dishes (hanging drop culture). Culturing protoplasts in a shallow layer of liquid over the same medium semisolidified with a gelling agent, such as agar or agarose, may be beneficial in some cases. The inclusion of a filter paper at the interface between the liquid and semisolid phases may stimulate cell colony formation from isolated protoplasts, as in *Medicago* (17).

It is noteworthy that even freshly isolated protoplasts will withstand the rigors of embedding in semisolid culture medium, the protoplasts being mixed with the molten medium and plated at about 40 °C immediately prior to gelling of the medium. A range of gelling agents is available, with the more purified agaroses often enhancing protoplast plating efficiencies (calculated as the percentage of the protoplasts orginally plated that develop into cell colonies), probably by affording support and preventing loss from the surface of the plasma membrane of newly synthesized wall components. The medium containing the protoplasts may be dispensed as layers or droplets (usually up to 250 µL in size) in Petri dishes. Cutting of the semisolid layers of medium into sections and bathing the sections or droplets in liquid medium of the same composition generally stimulates the growth of embedded protoplasts. The osmotic pressure of the semisolid phase containing the embedded protoplasts can be reduced by changing the bathing medium. Cell colonies that develop from embedded protoplasts often become free-floating in the medium as culture proceeds.

Alginate is a useful alternative to agar or agarose as a gelling agent, particularly with protoplasts that are heat sensitive, since the alginate is gelled into thin layers by pouring the warm alginate-containing medium in which the protoplasts are suspended over an agar layer containing Ca^{2+} ions, or by gently dropping the molten medium into a solution containing Ca^{2+} ions. Subsequently, the release of protoplast-derived colonies is readily effected by depolymerizing the alginate by exposure to sodium citrate to remove the Ca^{2+} ions. Studies with flax protoplasts have compared the influence of agarose and calcium alginate matrices on protoplast viability and mitotic activity (18).

Plating Density and the Use of Nurse Cells

The density at which protoplasts are plated in the medium (the plating density) is crucial in sustaining mitotic division and cell colony formation. Generally, the optimum plating density is $5 \times 10^2 - 1.0 \times 10^6$ ml^{-1}. When the protoplast density is too high, the protoplasts initially enter division, but this soon ceases because of rapid depletion of nutrients from the medium. Protoplasts also fail to grow if they are plated below a minumum inoculum density. It is know that dividing cells stimulate division of neighboring cells, probably as a result of the release of growth factors, particularly amino acids into the surrounding medium. Presumably, this is less effective below the minimum cell density. Medium previously "conditioned" by the presence of actively dividing cells in that medium for a limited period of time has been used to stimulate the growth of freshly isolated protoplasts. Similarly, "nurse" cells or tissues are often employed to promote division in cultured protoplasts. In this respect, it is not essential for the nurse cells to be from the same species as the isolated protoplasts. For example, the growth of protoplasts isolated from embryogenic cell suspensions of Japonica and Indica rice varieties was stimulated by fast-growing nurse cells of the wild rice *Oryza ridleyi* and by cells of Italian ryegrass (*Lolium multiflorum*), used either alone or in combination (16). When using this procedure, the nurse cells are harvested from suspension cultures and spread in semisolidified medium in Petri dishes several hours prior to protoplast isolation. Subsequently, the isolated protoplasts can be cultured in a liquid layer, embedded in semisolidified medium, or spread in a liquid layer on a cellulose nitrate membrane overlaying the semisolid layer of nurse cells (16).

INNOVATIVE APPROACHES TO PROTOPLAST CULTURE

In the development of any protoplast-to-plant system, the prime objective is to maximize plant regeneration, particularly when experiments are designed to generate unique plants, as in the case of genetic manipulation through somatic hybridization and transformation.

Significant advances have been made in protoplast and cell culture technology during the past two decades, particularly in terms of refining media and optimizing the physical parameters for protoplasts of a range of dicotyledons and monocotyledons. While the overall aim has been to keep the medium composition simple with respect to inorganic salts, vitamins, carbohydrates, and growth regulators, complex nutrient media, sometimes supplemented with coconut milk of undefined composition, have been essential to stimulate protoplast division in some plant species, particularly at low cell densities. Although useful guidelines can be obtained from the literature, a universal formulation does not exist with respect to media composition and associated physical parameters. However, several innovative approaches have been evaluated recently, that address both chemical and physical parameters, often in combination. Some of these approaches have been developed earlier to maximize the growth of animal cells in culture.

Chemical Supplements for Protoplast Culture Media: Surfactants and Antibiotics

The nonionic surfactant *Pluronic*® F-68 (poloxamer 188), a long-chain block polymer (mol. wt. 8350) of polyoxyethylene and polyoxypropylene, is often added to cultured animal cells to reduce membrane damage during culture under forced aeration. In plant protoplast systems, *Pluronic*® F-68 increased the plating efficiency of protoplasts of *Solanum dulcamara* when added to the culture medium at 0.01, 0.1, and 1.0% (w/v), with maximum protoplast plating efficiency at 0.1% (w/v). The precise mode of action of surfactants, such as *Pluronic*® F-68, is still not clear, although they may increase the permeability of plasma membranes to growth regulators from the culture medium (19). In the future, a range of surfactants are worthy of assessment as medium supplements, although the optimum growth conditions at which they exert their physiological effect may be influenced by their hydrophilic–lipophilic balance, (HLB) numbers, which are indicators of their membrane-permeabilizing properties.

Certain antibiotics also stimulate protoplast division. For example, the cephalosporin antibiotic cefotaxime stimulated mitotic division and cell colony formation from protoplasts isolated from seedling leaves of the woody plant, passionfruit (7), when added to the culture medium at 250 µg ml^{-1}. Cefotaxime may be metabolized to a growth regulator-like compound(s) (20), although again the way in which it exerts its effect on cultured plant cells is unclear.

Manipulation of Respiratory Gases

An adequate and sustainable gaseous exchange is essential to maximize protoplast development. Gasing of culture vessels with oxygen soon after plating of the protoplasts has been demonstrated to increase the plating efficiency of protoplasts of jute and rice (21), the oxygen concentration in the culture dishes gradually reverting to the normal atmospheric concentration after the first few days of growth. Similarly, perfluorocarbon (PFC) liquids have been evaluated in higher plant protoplast systems, following their use in animal cells (22). Such inert, linear, cyclic, or polycyclic organic compounds are capable of dissolving large volumes of respiratory gases. For example, perfluorodecalin ($C_{10}F_{18}$; Flutec® PP6; BNFL Fluorochemicals, Preston, UK) dissolves approximately 40% by volume of oxygen when gassed with 100% oxygen at 10 mbar pressure for 15 min and more than 200 vol % of carbon dioxide. PFC liquids, typically being about twice as dense as water, form a layer beneath aqueous media, permitting the culture of protoplasts at the interface between the lower PFC layer and the overlying liquid medium. Oxygen-gassed perfluorodecalin significantly stimulated mitotic division in protoplasts of *Petunia hybrida* when used in this way. Several other PFCs, such as perfluoro-octyl bromide ($C_8F_{17}Br$; perflubron), are also worthy of investigation in protoplast culture systems. There is also evidence that surfactants and PFCs act synergistically, with 0.1% (w/v) *Pluronic*® F-68 supplementation of the culture medium overlying oxygenated PFC, further increasing the plating efficiency of *P. hybrida* suspension cell protoplasts (23).

Studies with animals and isolated perfused organs (24) have stimulated experimentation involving supplementation of protoplast culture media with commercial bovine haemoglobin solution (Erythrogen™; Biorelease Corporation, Salem, MA). In recent experiments, the mean initial protoplast plating efficiency with 1:50 (v:v) Erythrogen™ was significantly greater than with controls lacking haemoglobin (25). Again, *Pluronic*® F-68 at 0.01% (w/v) exerted a synergistic effect when added to the culture medium containing Erythrogen™.

Physical Procedures to Stimulate Protoplast Growth in Culture

Physical parameters have been investigated to stimulate protoplast development in culture. Mention has already been made of the culture of protoplasts in microliter volumes of liquid medium on the surface of cellulose nitrate filters (0.2 µm pore size) overlaying semisolidified culture medium, often in conjunction with nurse cells in the underlying semisolidified layer. Another simple experimental system, which probably acts by increasing aeration, involves the insertion of glass rods (each 6.0 mm in diameter and 8.0 mm in length) into a layer of agarose-solidified culture medium in Petri dishes. Isolated protoplasts are plated in a layer of liquid medium over the semisolid phase. This system stimulated mitotic division and cell colony formation from leaf protoplasts of cassava (*Manihot esculenta*), the protoplasts aggregating in the menisci formed around the glass rods and at the sides of the dishes (26).

The division of protoplasts in culture is stimulated by electrical currents (27). For example, prolonged, low-voltage currents induced division in protoplasts of *Trifolium* (28) and stimulated the development of protoplasts directly into somatic embryos in *Medicago* species (29). However, it is high-voltage (about 1250 V), short-duration (10–15 μsec) electrical pulses that have had the most dramatic effect in stimulating division of protoplasts of several genera, including those of *Prunus*, *Pyrus*, *Solanum* and *Glycine*, to enter division earlier than untreated protoplasts. High-voltage pulses were correlated with increased DNA synthesis in the protoplasts. Cell colony formation and shoot regeneration were also promoted, with shoots from electropulsed protoplasts of *Prunus* and *Solanum* developing more vigorous and more extensive root systems than shoots from tissues derived from untreated protoplasts. There is evidence that these effects of electrostimulation of protoplasts are long term, since they can be recognized after many cell generations. Clearly, considerable scope still exists for assessing the application of both chemical and physical parameters to those protoplast systems that are still recalcitrant in culture.

PROTOPLAST-TO-PLANT SYSTEMS

As already emphasized, the crucial stages occur during early culture in the development of protoplast-to-plant systems. Consequently, most attention has focused on these stages of culture. As in the case of explant-derived tissues, the induction of morphogenesis in protoplast-derived tissues depends upon the balance of growth regulators in the culture medium. Thus procedures already established for plant regeneration, through shoot regeneration and/or somatic embryogenesis, from explant-derived tissues can usually be applied to protoplast-derived tissues. In a limited number of genera, protoplasts may develop directly into somatic embryos through polar growth of the protoplast-derived cells, as in *Medicago* species (30), *Brassica juncea* (31), and *Citrus* species (32). Overall, the literature relating to plant regeneration from protoplasts is now extensive; some of the most significant publications relating to cereals, grasses, vegetables, tuber and root crops, legumes, woody plants, and ornamentals have been reviewed (5). Similarly, the general progress in relation to plant regeneration from protoplasts of woody species has been summarized (33,34). Details of the procedures for culture and plant recovery from protoplasts isolated from specific plants, including asparagus, barley, coffee, cotton, grasses, onion, peanut,

peppermint, sunflower, ornamentals, and trees, have also been collected into review volumes (35,36). While considerable progress has been made in regenerating plants from protoplast-derived tissues of a range of genera and species, several still remain recalcitrant in culture and protoplast-to-plant systems have yet to be established. In this respect, application of some of the more innovative culture approaches, including supplementation of the shoot regeneration medium with surfactants, PFCs, and electrostimulation, as already summarized for the early stages of protoplast culture, may be beneficial in maximizing plant regeneration from protoplast-derived tissues.

EXPLOITATION OF PROTOPLAST-TO-PLANT SYSTEMS: SOMATIC AND GAMETOSOMATIC HYBRIDIZATION

The ability to regenerate plants routinely from protoplast-derived cells and tissues is fundamental to genetic manipulation involving somatic hybridization and, to a lesser extent, transformation. As reviewed in detail elsewhere in this volume, the fusion of protoplasts isolated from different plant genera, species, and varieties presents few difficulties. Isolated protoplasts can be fused chemically, electrically, or by a combination of these procedures to generate heterokaryons from which somatic hybrid cells, tissues, and eventually, hybrid plants can be regenerated. The novelty of somatic hybridization is that it circumvents complex pre- and postzygotic sexual hybridization incompatibility barriers, enabling the nuclear genomes of parental protoplasts to be combined, initially in a mixed cytoplasm. The hybrid cells that result may produce plants with balanced or asymmetric nuclear genomes. Superimposed on the events at the nuclear level are complex interactions involving cytoplasmic organelles within the mixed cytoplasm. Such interactions may result in chloroplast segregation, or more rarely, the retention of a mixed plastid population. Occasionally, recombination of chloroplast DNAs occurs. Mitochondrial DNAs frequently undergo recombination in hybrid cells. The elimination of a nuclear genome of one protoplast parent may result in the production of cytoplasmic hybrids (cybrids). Indeed, effort is often made experimentally to generate asymmetric nuclear hybrids in order to introgress specific traits from a donor plant into a recipient genus or species, without dramatically affecting major characteristics, such as stature and fertility, of the recipient parent. Normally, this is achieved by the "donor–recipient" procedure, involving irradiation of donor protoplasts to fragment their nuclear DNA prior to fusion (37). Similarly, the generation of cybrids to transfer organelle-encoded traits, such as mitochondrially encoded cytoplasmic male sterility (CMS) or chloroplast DNA-encoded herbicide (e.g., atrazine) resistance, generally necessitates elimination of the nuclear genome of the donor by irradiation treatment of protoplasts prior to fusion.

Fusion is not restricted to diploid protoplasts; the latter can be fused with protoplasts isolated from cells of haploid plants, or with protoplasts isolated from pollen at the tetrad or mature stages. Fusion of diploid with haploid protoplasts generates fertile triploid plants through gametosomatic hybridization (38). Collectively, somatic and gametosomatic hybridization provide the opportunities to create novel nuclear and cytoplasmic combinations, increasing the genetic diversity available to plant breeders. Thus, somatic hybridization must not be utilized as a technique in isolation from conventional sexual hybridization. The incorporation of somatic hybrid plants into conventional breeding programs is generally essential in order to restore characteristics typical, for example, of one of the parents, especially if the latter is a cultivated crop. An excellent example is provided in the somatic hybridization of *Lycopersicon esculentum* with the wild tomato *L. peruvianum*, the small green fruit characteristic of the wild parent and of the somatic hybrid attaining the color and size of the fruit of the cultivated tomato by back cross-generation three (39).

TRANSFORMATION BY DNA UPTAKE INTO ISOLATED PROTOPLASTS

The fluid mosaic nature of the plasma membrane permits the nondestructive induction of transient pores in the membrane through which macromolecules, such as DNA, can be introduced by chemical and/or physical procedures. Since the earlier literature relating to the transformation of isolated protoplasts by DNA uptake has been collated in extensive reviews (5,40), only the relevant features of this process are summarized here.

Transformation of Protoplasts by Isolated DNA

Reports during the 1970s that cultured animal cells were capable of taking up and expressing cloned genes or isolated genomic DNA provided the impetus for assessing the feasibility of adopting this approach for isolated plant protoplasts. Such studies with protoplasts were also stimulated by major advances in knowledge of the molecular biology of crown gall disease of higher plants, particularly the fact that tumorigenesis was associated with transfer of part of the large tumor-inducing (Ti) plasmid, the T-DNA, from the Gram-negative soil bacterium *Agrobacterium tumefaciens* into the plant genome. Thus, by isolating Ti plasmid, it was feasible to mimic the DNA transformation experiments performed with animal cells. Interaction of supercoiled Ti plasmid from an octopine strain of *A. tumefaciens* with protoplasts from cell suspensions of *Petunia hybrida* in the presence of the membrane-active compound poly-L-ornithine resulted in protoplast-derived colonies that expressed crown gall characteristics, particularly the ability to grow on medium lacking growth regulators and the synthesis of octopine, both traits being encoded by bacterial genes on the T-DNA of the Ti plasmid. Other studies confirmed polyethylene glycol (PEG)-induced transformation of tobacco leaf protoplasts, with the regeneration of fertile, transgenic plants. An interesting and significant observation in such studies was that the T-DNA border sequences, normally involved in the integration of T-DNA into the plant genome during cell transformation by intact *Agrobacteria* (41), were not recognized during DNA uptake and integration into isolated protoplasts. The T-DNA was often truncated and fragmented following its introduction into the genome of recipient protoplasts. However, such experiments provided "proof of concept" that isolated DNA could transform freshly isolated protoplasts.

The most significant advance in protoplast transformation technology followed the demonstration that T-DNA borders were not essential for DNA integration into the plant genome. Moreover, the ready availability of chimaeric genes on small cloning vectors, which could be amplified in *Escherichia coli*, giving milligram quantities of isolated plasmid, circumvented problems associated with attempts to isolate the single copy Ti plasmid in similar amounts from *Agrobacterium*. Consequently, the natural progression in this technology was to clone genes on small plasmids in *E. coli*, to isolate the plasmids, and to use this DNA in protoplast transformation experiments. Both supercoiled (intact) plasmids and those linearized by restriction enzyme digestion were employed in such experiments.

Induction of DNA Uptake into Protoplasts

Several agents have been evaluated to induce DNA uptake into protoplasts. These include salt solutions with calcium ions at high pH, treatment of protoplast–plasmid mixtures with polyvinyl alcohol (PVA), and more extensively, exposure to PEG as employed in protoplast fusion. Other approaches have involved the formation of calcium phosphate–DNA precipitates combined with PVA treatment at high pH. Electroporation, involving short-duration, high-voltage electrical pulses, is employed routinely to induce DNA uptake, often in combination with PEG treatment. DNA has been microinjected into protoplasts, but this approach is labor intensive and normally demands the use of a costly, high-quality inverted microscope with micromanipulators. Cationic agents such as polybrene or lipofectin, as used for the transformation of animal cells, have also been exploited for plant protoplasts, together with encapsulation of DNA into cationic liposomes, followed by liposome fusion/uptake with protoplasts. Liposomes may see more widespread use in plant transformation in the future, following the demonstration that a yeast artificial chromosome (YAC) vector carrying the *npt*II and *uidA* genes, encoding neomycin phosphotransferase and β-glucuronidase, respectively, have been used to transform tobacco leaf protoplasts following treatment with PEG (42). YACs have already been introduced into several mammalian systems including cultured cells of mouse, monkey, and hamster. The advantage of YACs, in terms of transformation, is that they can carry stretches of DNA that are 10–50 times larger than the pieces of DNA carried by conventional vectors.

PEG treatment and electroporation remain the most successful and exploited procedures, although even with these approaches the frequency of transformation is still low and, at maximum only about 1 in 10^4 protoplasts give stably transformed tissues. Consequently, as emphasised earlier, reproducible protoplast culture combined with the expression of efficient selectable marker genes are essential to recover transformed protoplast-derived cells and tissues. Examples of the commonly used genes for selection include the *npt*II gene conferring resistance on plant cells to the antibiotics kanamycin sulfate, paromomycin, and Geneticin (G418), the hygromycin phosphotransferase (*hpt; hph*) gene giving resistance to hygromycin, and the phosphinothricin acetyltransferase (*bar*) gene resulting in resistance to the herbicide bialaphos, containing the active ingredient phosphinothricin.

An important observation in protoplast transformation technology was that it was possible to co-transform protoplasts simultaneously with more than one gene, the genes being carried either on the same or on separate vectors. In the latter case, the plasmids are mixed prior to the DNA uptake treatment. The relevance of this approach is that it eliminates many of the time-consuming molecular steps necessary to introduce more than one gene of interest into the same plasmid. Usually, 20–50% of protoplast-derived cells express both genes following co-transformation.

Factors Influencing Protoplast Transformation

Several parameters have been identified that influence the transformation of protoplasts by isolated DNA. The stage in the cell cycle of the recipient protoplasts is important, transformation being higher when protoplasts are in the S or M phases. Thus, it is beneficial to attempt to synchronize cells of the same tissue prior to protoplast isolation. Heat shock treatment and irradiation of recipient protoplasts prior to DNA uptake also stimulate transformation, irradiation probably increasing the recombination of genomic DNA with incoming DNA, or initiating repair mechanisms that favor DNA integration. Both single- and double-stranded DNA can effect transformation. Some workers have claimed 3–10-fold higher transformation rates using single-stranded DNA, although the latter may become double stranded following uptake and prior to integration into the nuclear genome of recipient protoplasts. The plant genotype itself probably also influences transformation. Carrier DNA, in the form of sheared salmon sperm or calf thymus DNA, is sometimes mixed in excess with the plasmid before uptake, with the aim of providing a substrate for nuclease activity and, hence, protecting the DNA of interest during the uptake process. However, it is recognized that unwanted carrier DNA sequences may also be integrated, in addition to the DNA of interest, into the genome of recipient protoplasts during transformation.

As in the early experiments involving the transformation of protoplasts by isolated Ti plasmid, the integration into the host genome of genes carried on small cloning vectors is probably random, although, in rare cases, homologous recombination has been demonstrated. More complex integration patterns have been observed with linear than with supercoiled plasmids; concatermerization and truncation of introduced DNA is common.

Application of DNA Uptake into Protoplasts: Stable and Transient Gene Expression Studies

Undoubtedly, the most important application of the uptake of DNA into isolated protoplasts has been in the transformation of those plants that are not readily amenable to transformation by other methods of DNA delivery, particularly *Agrobacterium*-mediated gene transfer. Primarily, studies have been directed to the transformation of cereals and grasses, particularly the major cereals such as rice (43), once protoplast-to-plant systems became available for these target crops. However, it seems likely following the recent success in the transformation of cereals such as rice (44), maize (45), and wheat (46) with *A. tumefaciens*, that DNA uptake into isolated protoplasts will assume less relevance in the context of cereal transformation. However, this may not be the case in certain crop plants, where the uptake of DNA into isolated protoplasts will continue to provide an approach for generating transgenic plants. An excellent example is provided by sugarbeet, in which DNA uptake into guard cell protoplasts currently provides a reproducible transformation system for this important root crop (47).

Although the generation of stably transformed tissues and plants has, and will remain, the main objective of most research programs, optimization of DNA uptake conditions and the rapid monitoring of gene expression are important in the development of constructs prior to their use in longer-term transformation experiments. Isolated protoplasts provide systems for evaluating gene expression within hours of DNA uptake (transient expression). In early transient expression studies, the chloramphenicol acetyltransferase (*cat*) gene was employed extensively in such investigations, but since monitoring of the expression of this gene involves the use of radioactive substrates, the *cat* gene has been superseded by the use of the *gus* gene (48). The latter can be assayed rapidly by histochemical or fluorometric procedures. Thus, isolated protoplasts will still have an important role in the evaluation of gene constructs, particularly in assessing the activity of gene regulatory elements, such as promoters and intron or intron/exon sequences. Moreover, since tissue specificity is often retained at the protoplast level, this permits gene constructs to be assessed in both homologous and heterologous cell systems.

In addition to the introduction of foreign DNA into the nuclear genome of recipient protoplasts, the targeting of genes to organelles has also been demonstrated by the simple process of PEG-mediated DNA uptake into isolated protoplasts. This approach was first demonstrated in tobacco, plant clones with transformed plastid genomes being selected by their spectinomycin resistance encoded by a mutant 16S ribosomal RNA gene carried on the plasmid used for transformation. A novel restriction site flanking the spectinomycin resistance mutation was used to confirm the incorporation of the antibiotic resistance marker into the plastid DNA (49). It is likely that plastome engineering will assume considerable importance in the future as the procedure is applied to major crop plants.

SOMACLONAL VARIATION: A SIMPLE FORM OF GENETIC ENGINEERING?

Since 1981, when a landmark paper was published in which the term *somaclonal variation* was adopted to describe variation in plants regenerated from cultured cells (50), it is now established that such variation may affect a range of traits, including those for plant morphology and vigor, flower color, yield, nutritional value, the production of secondary products, tolerance to environmental conditions, and resistance to pathogens. The variation may be transient and therefore not heritable sexually, but retained if plants are propagated vegetatively (epigenetic variation). Additionally, variation may be stable or unstable, but heritable. Clearly, stable, heritable variation is of most relevance to crop improvement, since it has potential in extending the genetic divesity available to breeders, particularly in plants in which this phenomenon has been studied extensively, including potato, rice, wheat, barley, pea, celery, oilseed rape, and sugarcane (51).

The precise genetic basis for somaclonal variation is still not understood, but several possible mechanisms have been proposed. It may relate to alteration in ploidy (although somaclonal variation is rarely associated with a readily visible cytological change in chromosome number), chromosome breakage with daughter cells failing to receive their full complement during mitotic division, or chromosomal aberrations related to mitotic recombination or the production of unusual genetic material resulting from deficiencies in the nucleotide pool available from the culture medium. Variation may also arise through insertion of active transposable elements into the plant DNA, or the activation of elements in the genomic DNA, which, normally, are silent. DNA methylation may also play a role in the expression of somaclonal variation. Other DNA aberrations that may occur at a higher rate when cells are in culture include changes in DNA bases, gene copy number, gene rearrangements, and variation in the DNA structure of mitochondria and chloroplasts (52).

There appears to be a relationship between the time during which cells are in culture and the extent of somaclonal variation. DNA changes may increase with time, and different changes may act synergistically. Subsequently, the culture medium may favor the growth of variant cells. The combination and concentration of growth regulators may affect DNA structure and expression, while imbalances in the nucleotide pool in the medium may affect DNA base structure. In general, the longer cells are in culture, particularly at the callus stage, the greater the variation that is to be expected. This applies to both explant-derived tissues and to protoplast-derived cells. Consequently, unless a conscious effort is made to induce and to identify somaclonal variation, the culture period from the isolation of source explant or protoplast population to plant regeneration should be kept to a minimum. In contrast, where genetic variation is required, somaclonal variation has several important attributes. For example, unlike transformation, it requires no knowledge of the genetic basis of the trait(s) and does not necessitate gene isolation and cloning. It negates the use of mutagenic agents, specialized apparatus, or containment procedures and is inexpensive. Exposure of somaclonal variation has the potential to increase genetic diversity, and it bypasses the sexual cycle. It may be considered as a simple, or probably the most simple, form of genetic manipulation and, as such, is a useful adjunct to conventional plant breeding alongside somatic hybridization and transformation.

MISCELLANEOUS STUDIES WITH PLANT PROTOPLASTS

Undoubtedly, while the main use of isolated protoplasts has been in plant genetic manipulation, large populations of single naked cells have provided ideal experimental material for physiological, ultrastructural, and genetical studies for nearly four decades. The fact that isolated protoplasts develop, in culture, into colonies of single cell origin has been exploited to isolate clonal lines of cells and plants, such as those for increased secondary product synthesis. Similarly, exposure of large populations of isolated protoplasts to mutagenic agents or irradiation permits the induction and selection during subsequent culture of mutant cells and plants (53). Protoplasts take up macromolecules other than DNA. This has been exploited primarily in studies of endocytosis at the plasma membrane, using compounds such as ferritin as molecular markers, which can be visualized by electron microscopy. Similarly, protoplasts have featured as experimental systems to study virus uptake and replication in plant cells (54). The osmotic fragility of isolated protoplasts permits their controlled lysis for the isolation of cellular fractions, including membranes, intact vacuoles, chloroplasts, mitochondria, and nuclei. In physiological studies, isolated vacuoles have been used to study the accumulation of compounds, such as sugars. Recently, protoplasts from barley aleurone cells have been shown to contain two distinct types of vacuole, namely, protein storage vacuoles and a lysosome-like organelle, designated the secondary vacuole (55). Protoplasts have provided ideal systems for studies of ion transport through the plasma membrane and regulation of the osmotic balance of cells, enabling patch-clamp studies to be performed (56), comparable to those with animal cells. Light-induced proton pumping has been investigated in guard cell protoplasts (57). Other notable investigations include studies of cell fusion and metabolism in microgravity (58), the detection of elicitor binding sites, and the binding of fungal phytotoxins to the plasma membrane (59), together with auxin accumulation and metabolism (60). Protoplasts have also provided unique material for studying the early stages of cell wall synthesis. Interestingly, some of the early studies of the role of the plasma membrane and cellular organelles in this process, as revealed by thin sectioning and freeze fracture for transmission electron microscopy, remain classic ultrastructural studies in the literature (61). More recently, some ultrastructural studies have focused attention upon the role of microtubules during cell development from isolated protoplasts (62). Protoplasts from fern prothalli have also been used to study the influence of gravity and light in the development of cell polarity (63). Generally, there have been relatively few investigations with protoplasts of lower plants, although those of mosses have been exploited in genetical studies, including investigations of the fate of mutant macrochloroplasts following somatic hybridization (64).

Currently, there is interest in exploiting simple, plant-based systems for toxicological assays, including the screening of pharmaceuticals, food additives, cosmetics, and agrochemicals, as well as radiation-related interactions. Isolated protoplasts, especially if totipotent, are useful for assessing both short-term and, more important, long-term effects of such agents on cells (65). The effects of chemical and environmental factors on plant cells may be apparent only after several seed generations. Consequently, rapid cycling *Arabidopsis thaliana* and *Brassica napus*, are particularly useful systems for generating several seed generations in a relatively short period (e.g., twelve months). Similar studies of the long-term effects of chemical and environmental factors are not possible with animal cells, since the latter do not express the unique feature of totipotency characteristic of cultured plant cells.

CONCLUDING REMARKS

The ever-increasing literature reflects the continuing interest in protoplasts as experimental single-cell systems for studying many aspects of plant physiology and development, together with genetic manipulation involving the simple exposure of genetic variation, to more complex cell fusion and molecular technologies. Coupled with these developments has been the progressive introduction of sophisticated molecular assays to assess gene transfer and expression in plants arising from the genetic manipulation of isolated protoplasts. Fundamental to many of the investigations involving the use of isolated protoplasts is the need to improve the culture of protoplasts of many species and to develop protoplast-to-plant procedures for those species that, to date, remain recalcitrant in culture. Several of the recent culture approaches applied to isolated protoplasts were, in fact, developed for the culture of animal cells. Similarly, procedures such as the uptake of isolated DNA were developed and evaluated in animal cells before being assessed in plant protoplasts. Such observations provide the clear message that plant and animal cells have certain similarities, emphasizing the fact that plant biologists should be aware of, and should exploit, advances reported in the animal cell literature.

BIBLIOGRAPHY

1. I. Takebe, G. Labib, and G. Melchers, *Naturwissenschaften* **58**, 318–320 (1971).
2. E.C. Cocking, *Nature (London)* **187**, 927–929 (1960).
3. S. Ishii and Y.P.S. Bajaj, ed., in *Biotechnology in Agriculture and Forestry*, Vol. 39, Part VIII, Springer-Verlag, Berlin, 1997, pp. 23–33.
4. N.W. Blackhall, M.R. Davey, and J.B. Power, in R.A. Dixon and R.A. Gonzales, eds., *Plant Cell Culture: A Practical Approach*, 2nd ed., IRL Press at Oxford University Press, New York, 1994, pp. 27–39.
5. A. Fehér and D. Dudits, in I.K. Vasil and T.A. Thorpe, eds., *Plant Cell and Tissue Culture*, Kluwer Academic Publishers, Dordrecht, The Netherlands, 1994, pp. 71–118.
6. E.M. Frearson, J.B. Power, and E.C. Cocking, *Dev. Biol.* **33**, 130–137 (1973).
7. F.B. d'Utra Vaz et al., *Plant Cell Rep.* **12**, 220–225 (1993).
8. N.O.M. Rethmeier et al., *Plant Cell Rep.* **9**, 539–543 (1991).
9. J.H. Raseed, M.K. Al-Mallah, E.C. Cocking, and M.R. Davey, *Plant Cell Rep.* **8**, 565–569 (1990).
10. B. Desprez et al., *Plant Cell Rep.* **14**, 204–209 (1995).
11. D.W. Galbraith, *Physiol. Plant.* **53**, 111–116 (1981).
12. E.C. Cocking, *Bio/Technology* **3**, 1104–1106 (1985).
13. T. Murashige and F. Skoog, *Physiol. Plant.* **15**, 473–497 (1962).
14. O.L. Gamborg, R.A. Miller, and K. Ojima, *Exp. Cell Res.* **50**, 151–158 (1968).
15. K.N. Kao and M.R. Michayluk, *Planta* **126**, 105–110 (1975).
16. R.K. Jain et al., *Plant Cell Rep.* **14**, 515–519 (1995).
17. A.V.P. dos Santos, D.E. Outka, E.C. Cocking, and M.R. Davey, *Z. Pflanzenphysiol.* **99**, 261–270 (1986).
18. H. David et al., *Protoplasma* **179**, 111–120 (1994).
19. K.C. Lowe, M.R. Davey, and J.B. Power, *Plant Tissue Cult. Biotechnol.* **2**, 175–186 (1996).
20. R.J. Mathias and L.A. Boyd, *Plant Sci.* **46**, 217–223 (1986).
21. F.B. d'Utra Vaz et al., *Plant Cell Rep.* **11**, 416–418 (1992).
22. K.C. Lowe, M.R. Davey, and J.B. Power, *Trends Biotechnol.* **16**, 272–277 (1998).
23. K.C. Lowe et al., *Blood Substitutes Immobil. Biotechnol.* **23**, 417–422 (1995).
24. R.M. Winslow, K.D. Vandegriff, and M. Intaglietta, eds., *Blood Substitutes: Physiological Basis of Efficiency*, Birkhäuser, Boston, 1995.
25. P. Anthony, K.C. Lowe, M.R. Davey, and J.B. Power, *Plant Cell Rep.* **17**, 13–16 (1997).
26. P. Anthony, M.R. Davey, J.B. Power, and K.C. Lowe, *Plant Cell Tissue Organ Cult.* **42**, 299–302 (1995).
27. M.R. Davey, N.W. Blackhall, K.C. Lowe, and J.B. Power, in P.T. Lynch and M.R. Davey, eds., *Electrical Manipulation of Cells*, Chapman & Hall, New York, 1996, pp. 273–286.
28. L. Zhongyi, G.J. Tanner, and P.J. Larkin, *Plant Cell Tissue Organ Cult.* **26**, 67–73 (1990).
29. M. Dijak, D.L. Smith, T.J. Wilson, and D.C.W. Brown, *Plant Cell Rep.* **5**, 468–470 (1986).
30. J. Song, E.L. Sorensen, and G.H. Liang, *Plant Cell Rep.* **9**, 21–25 (1990).
31. P.B. Kirti and V.L. Chopra, *Plant Cell Tissue Organ Cult.* **20**, 65–67 (1990).
32. G.E. Sim, C.S. Loh, and C.J. Goh, *Plant Cell Rep.* **7**, 418–420 (1988).
33. F. Bekkaoui, T.E. Tautorus, and D.I. Dunstan, in S. Mohan Jain, P.K. Gupta, and R.J. Newton, eds., *Somatic Embryogenesis in Woody Plants*, Vol. 1, Kluwer Academic Publishers, Dordrecht, The Netherlands, 1995, pp. 167–191.
34. A. Tibok, J.B. Power, and M.R. Davey, in S. Mohan Jain, P.K. Gupta, and R.J. Newton, eds., *Somatic Embryogenesis in Woody Plants*, Vol. 1, Kluwer Academic Publishers, Dordrecht, The Netherlands, 1995, pp. 143–166.
35. Y.P.S. Bajaj, ed., *Biotechnology in Agriculture and Forestry*, Vol. 34, Part VI, Springer-Verlag, Berlin, 1995.
36. Y.S. Bajaj, ed., *Biotechnology in Agriculture and Forestry*, Vol. 38, Part VII, Springer-Verlag, Berlin, 1996.
37. E. Galun and D. Aviv, *Methods Enzymol.* **118**, 595–611 (1986).
38. M.R. Davey, N.W. Blackhall, K.C. Lowe, and J.B. Power, in S. Mohan Jain, S.K. Sopory, and R.E. Vielleux, eds., *In Vitro Haploid Production in Higher Plants*, Vol. 2, Kluwer Academic Publishers, Dordrecht, The Netherlands, 1996, pp. 309–320.

39. R.S. Patil et al., *Plant Breed.* **111**, 273–282 (1993).

40. M.R. Davey, E.L. Rech, and B.J. Mulligan, *Plant Mol. Biol.* **13**, 273–285 (1989).

41. B. Tinland, *Trends Plant Sci.* **1**, 178–184 (1996).

42. M. van Wordragen et al., *Plant Mol. Biol. Rep.* **15**, 170–178 (1997).

43. K. Shimamoto, R.T. Terada, T. Izawa, and H. Fujimoto, *Nature (London)* **238**, 274–276 (1989).

44. X. Cheng, R. Sardana, H. Kaplan, and I. Altosaar, *Proc. Natl. Acad. Sci. U.S.A.* **95**, 2767–2772 (1998).

45. Y. Ishida et al., *Nat. Biotechnol.* **14**, 745–750 (1996).

46. M. Cheng et al., *Plant Physiol.* **115**, 971–980 (1997).

47. R.D. Hall et al., *Nat. Biotechnol.* **14**, 1133–1138 (1996).

48. S.K. Dhir, J. Oglesby, and A.S. Bhagsari, *Plant Cell Rep.* **17**, 665–669 (1998).

49. T.J. Golds, P. Maliga, and H.-U. Koop, *Bio/Technology* **11**, 95–97 (1993).

50. W.R. Scowcroft and P.J. Larkin, *Theor. Appl. Genet.* **60**, 179–184 (1981).

51. M.R. Leal et al., *Plant Breed.* **115**, 37–42 (1996).

52. V.M. Peschke and R.L. Phillips, *Adv. Genet.* **30**, 41–75 (1992).

53. P.J. Dix, in I.K. Vasil and T.A. Thorpe, eds., *Plant Cell and Tissue Culture*, Kluwer Academic Publishers, Dordrecht, The Netherlands, 1994, pp. 119–138.

54. W.L. Steinhart and T.T. Renvyle, *Virus Res.* **30**, 205–213 (1993).

55. S.J. Swanson, P.C. Bethke, and R.L. Jones, *Plant Cell* **10**, 685–698 (1998).

56. J.G. Barbara, H. Stoeckel, and K. Takeda, *Protoplasma* **180**, 136–144 (1994).

57. C.H. Goh, T. Oku, and K. Shizazaki, *Plant Physiol.* **109**, 187–194 (1995).

58. R. Hampp et al., *Planta* **203**, No.SS S42–S53 (1997).

59. I.A. Duberg and R. Meyer, *Plant Cell Rep.* **15**, 777–780 (1996).

60. A. Delbarre et al., *Planta* **195**, 159–167 (1994).

61. L.C. Fowke, L.R. Griffing, B.G. Mersey, and P. Van der Valk, *Experientia Supple.* **46**, 101–110 (1983).

62. I. Staxen, K. Klimaszeuska, and C.H. Bornman, *Physiol. Plant.* **91**, 680–686 (1994).

63. E.S. Edwards and S.J. Roux, *Plant Cell Rep.* **17**, 711–716 (1998).

64. S. Rother et al., *J. Plant Physiol.* **143**, 72–77 (1994).

65. K.C. Lowe, M.R. Davey, J.B. Power, and R.H. Clothier, *Pharm. News* **2**, 17–22 (1995).

See also CELL FUSION; MICROPROPAGATION OF PLANTS, PRINCIPLES AND PRACTICES; PROTOPLAST FUSION FOR THE GENERATION OF UNIQUE PLANTS.

PRODUCT DEVELOPMENT, QUALITY AND REGULATORY ISSUES

DAVID B. CLARK
Plasma Services
American Red Cross
Shawnee, Colorado

OUTLINE

To the R&D scientist or engineer the discovery of a potentially therapeutic protein and the development of a production method appear to be the major challenges in bringing a new biotechnology product to market. However, the subsequent task of gaining regulatory approval to market the product can be equally challenging and also require a great deal of technical input. These two areas are intimately linked. Satisfying the quality and regulatory requirements essentially involves proving that the scientific work is valid and comprehensive and can, in fact, produce a product that is safe and effective. This article is intended to provide the development scientist or engineer with the general concepts and with sources for further information concerning the quality and regulatory requirements for licensing a new product. Although the final judgments and interpretations should come from the organization's quality and regulatory professionals, understanding the general requirements and the approach can be a great help to the technical staff in streamlining product development. Following a typical project sequence, the activities and data required at various stages of development will be described. The focus will be mainly on the regulatory process in the United States for therapeutic biological products for human use. However, many other countries have similar requirements and procedures.

THE REGULATORY PROCESS

In the United States biological products are regulated by the Center for Biologics Evaluation and Review

(CBER), and other drugs are regulated by the Center for Drug Evaluation and Review (CDER), both divisions of the Food and Drug Administration (FDA). The FDA regulations for drugs and biologics are listed in Parts 1 to 680 of Title 21 of the Code of Federal Regulations (1), and specific regulations for biological products are given in Subchapter F (Parts 600 to 680). Today the terms "biologic" and "biological" are used interchangeably. The drug regulations generally also apply to biologics unless superseded by regulations in Subchapter F (2). The regulations are the working interpretation of the laws that govern the FDA, mainly; (1) the Federal Food Drug and Cosmetic Act for FDA in general and (2) the Public Health Service Act for biologics. The regulations have the force of law and must be followed. In addition, the FDA publishes various guidance documents including Guidelines and Points to Consider to assist organizations in understanding the FDA's views on various topics and in complying with the regulations.

Guidelines are legal documents in which the FDA describes one or more ways of meeting requirements. A company may choose to follow the guidance explicitly with the assurance that the procedure will be acceptable to the FDA (3). Alternatively, the company may propose a scientifically justifiable alternate method and negotiate its acceptance with the FDA. Many of the guidance documents will be found in draft form, open to comment by interested parties. However, although not yet finalized, such draft guidelines are still instructive as to the FDA's approach to the specific topic. Points to Consider are for information only and describe the FDA's current thinking and suggested approaches on various subjects. Points to Consider are often used in areas of rapidly developing technology such as recombinant protein production. In addition, the International Conference on Harmonisation (ICH) has been working toward unifying regulations among the United States the European Community, and Japan. The ICH has published a number of guidelines which are in various stages of development and many of which have been accepted by the member states. All of these documents are easily obtained from a number of sources including the FDA's Internet web site (4).

As informative as the FDA and ICH guidances are, they cannot cover all potential situations. Therefore, the FDA has always emphasized its willingness to meet with manufacturers to consider projects on a case-by-case basis. For unconventional products with potentially unique regulatory aspects, it can be beneficial to introduce the FDA to the new product early in the development project. The FDA has recently published a guidance document describing new policies that limit formal FDA meetings (5). However, informal phone conversations, teleconferences, and other meetings can often be arranged.

The groups overseeing drugs and biologics developed distinct regulations because the agencies were established by separate federal laws. A major difference between the two is that biological products have been licensed on the basis of both their specific production process and their final product characteristics. Drug products on the other hand are licensed mainly on their final product characteristics. The reason for this is historical. Traditionally, most biologics were complex mixtures produced from natural sources. Because these complex mixtures, such as human plasma fractions or vaccines from animal sera, could not be analyzed completely enough to give a precise description of their purity and composition, the manufacturing process was seen as equally important in producing a consistent product. The theory is that even though a product cannot be characterized completely, if the process is well-defined and run consistently, a consistent product, will be produced each time. A license for a biological product specifies both the precise process used to manufacture the product, as well as the final characteristics that the product must meet to be released for sale.

This view of biologics is changing due to improvements in process technology that can now produce products with extremely high purities and to advances in analytical technology that can more exactly define the product composition. As a first step, the FDA defined a new class of products known as Well-Characterized Biologics. These are high-purity products that can be well characterized analytically and are therefore less dependent on the process to define the final product. More recently the FDA has dropped the term "well-characterized" in favor of listing the specific product classes. The currently specified product classes include therapeutic DNA plasmid products, therapeutic synthetic peptide products with less than forty amino acids, monoclonal antibody products for *in vivo* use, and therapeutic recombinant DNA-derived products (6,7). Other distinctions between drugs and biologics are also disappearing (8). Biologics that were generally derived in the past from natural sources are now often made synthetically by recombinant DNA methods or other technology. Many novel new products cannot be clearly characterized as drugs or biologics, and some are combinations of both.

In response to these and other factors, the FDA is currently working toward unifying the regulation of drugs and biologics. They have issued inter-Center agreements to manage the licensing process for various types of products and provide for representation on the review team by staffs from more than one center. Inspections of biological production facilities are now conducted by Team Biologics which includes both CBER scientists and FDA field personnel. CBER is also changing its format for license applications. Until recently, licensure of any biological product required both a Product License Application (PLA) which mainly described the product and process and the clinical evidence for the safety and efficacy of the product, and an Establishment License Application (ELA) which described in great detail the methods and controls for manufacturing the product. Now CBER has established a unified Biological License Application (BLA) that is required for the specified (formerly "well-characterized") product classes listed before (6). Transition of all other biological products to the BLA format is currently in progress. The BLA contains some establishment information, but now the focus is on using the preapproval inspection to review manufacturing procedures and regulatory compliance. In this article, "BLA" will be used to refer to either type of application.

Concurrent with the changing FDA is the increasing emphasis on quality concepts and Total Quality Management in many organizations. Today, the in-house quality unit often has stricter requirements than the FDA, and satisfying those often ensures the satisfaction of most outside regulatory bodies. This article will describe specific regulatory requirements, as well as other information that is not required, but is highly recommended for use in establishing and maintaining the quality of the product and its manufacture. Such additional information can help in identifying and correcting potential problems and can be invaluable in providing timely responses to the FDA when problems arise.

Probably the most important regulations are the current Good Manufacturing Practices (cGMPs) listed in 21 CFR Parts 210 and 211. The cGMPs are generic to cover most aspects of pharmaceutical manufacturing, but they list essentially everything necessary to ensure production of quality products. The basic principles of the cGMPs are simple: control and documentation. They establish a control system comprised of product specifications, product characterization during development, process validation, raw material testing, in-process testing, stability testing, and other items, all defined by detailed documentation (9). The product and its entire manufacturing process are defined and controlled by one set of documentation. Another set of documentation is then used to record the complete details of the operation to determine whether the controls operated as planned. When basic quality/regulatory questions arise during a development project, the cGMPs are the first place to look for an answer or, at least, a governing approach. The specific implementation of the cGMPs is left up to the pharmaceutical manufacturer to adapt to his particular situation. The FDA has issued a guideline describing its recommended implementation of the cGMPs for manufacturing active pharmaceutical ingredients including biologics (10).

THE DEVELOPMENT PROCESS

Although most organizations have their own systems for new product development, a project usually proceeds through stages analogous to those shown in Table 1. The names of the stages may vary, but the tasks included in each stage are fairly consistent because they are defined by practical technological and regulatory constraints. Traditionally, a project would proceed through the stages sequentially, but recently strategies have been developed for shortening development times by proceeding with several stages concurrently (11,12). In any case, there is usually significant overlap among the various stages. The remainder of this article is arranged according to these stages and will describe the development activities and the quality and regulatory tasks involved in each.

INVENTION OR DISCOVERY

This initial stage of the project involves identifying or synthesizing the active ingredient along with basic laboratory methods for its production, purification, and

Table 1. Typical Stages in Product Development

Stage	Description
Invention or discovery	Identification of the protein or other compound that will comprise the active ingredient of the new product
Product design/Process development	Development of a process for manufacturing the active ingredient and placing it in an appropriate format for use by the consumer
Preclinical studies	Studies in support of an IND application to characterize the product and provide confidence that it will be safe for use in humans
IND/Clinical studies	Assembling and submitting an IND application for permission to perform studies in humans; the subsequent studies demonstrate that the product is safe and effective in its indicated use
CMC studies	Studies to implement and demonstrate full cGMP compliance in the manufacture of the product
License application and review	Compilation and submission of the BLA and response to subsequent FDA issues and questions
Licensure	Approval to market the product
Routine production	Ongoing cGMP compliance activities ensure that the product and process continue to meet their licensed attributes

characterization. For biologics purified from natural sources, the focus quickly moves to purification and characterization. For synthetic products, however, a large amount of time is usually spent selecting and fine-tuning gene constructs and expression systems. Although this work per se is not a regulated activity, the information gathered during this part of the project will be extremely useful in supporting future licensing activities. The FDA recommends that information regarding the characterization of the expression construct be collected during the development and validation of the cell expression clone (13). Accurate work carefully documented at this stage may save costly later replication of studies needed to support FDA submissions. A good example of this is a monoclonal antibody (MAb) that was being used by my organization to purify a specific clotting factor from plasma. The MAb had excellent properties for use in a large-scale process but had been obtained from one of our basic research labs which had no intention of using it in a new product. Because very limited information was available on the cloning and characterization, essentially our lab had to "rediscover" the MAb to obtain and document the necessary information. Learning from this, our current projects aimed at producing plasma proteins in the milk of transgenic animals include good characterization and documentation of constructs, transfection procedures, and breeding methods from the beginning.

For synthetic products made in cells or transgenic animals, it is not too early to begin studies toward validation of the synthetic process. Early awareness of the regulatory considerations can help greatly in making the best choice among and collecting the necessary data on gene constructs, cell lines or animals, and production methods. A number of guidelines have been published covering these areas. They include ICH guidelines on expression constructs (14) and cell substrates (15), as well as several FDA Points to Consider documents (16–19). In addition, another ICH guideline covers viral safety concerns for products made in cell lines (20), and two FDA guidelines cover considerations for the production process (10,21). Because all of these documents involve production of proteins in cells, much of the guidance overlaps, but it is instructive to consult all of them. Guidance documents are periodically updated, but at varying times, so although the most recent guidance may not specifically cover the product of interest, the guidance is usually generically valid for most cell-produced products. Note that the guidance on monoclonal antibodies also applies to non-MAb-based products that use MAbs for immunoaffinity purification or other process steps. Table 2 lists the general types of information requested for products produced in cells. Similar concepts are involved for proteins produced in transgenic animals, in addition to other aspects unique to that production system (18).

Development Reports

Although not required, development reports are becoming an expectation of the FDA (22,23). Development Reports should be written at the completion of each development study to document the results. Centralizing this information in a common format can be very beneficial in supporting both regulatory and product development activities. Although similar information has traditionally been kept in laboratory notebooks, locating and interpreting it often becomes difficult as a project evolves, especially because the people involved often change. Just the act of analyzing and summarizing the findings can often help identify inconsistencies and discrepancies that may be more easily addressed at the time the studies are done, rather than years later when trying to assemble an application. Development reports also often become the foundation for later validation protocols and can be invaluable in addressing FDA questions during BLA review and prelicensure inspections (10,22,24,25).

Good Laboratory Practices

Comparable to the cGMPs for manufacturing, the FDA has also developed a set of Good Laboratory Practice (GLP) regulations for nonclinical laboratory studies intended to support products regulated by the FDA (26). Compliance with GLPs is intended to ensure the quality and integrity of the data generated. In general, the GLPs describe procedures, documentation, and reporting requirements. As with the cGMPs, the primary focus of the GLPs is documentation and control to produce accurate, consistent results. Sound documentation cannot be emphasized too strongly; it is the key to acceptance of any data by the FDA. In the regulator's view, if something is not documented, it has not been done.

Table 2. Recommendations for Characterization of Constructs, Cell Lines, and Production Methods for Cell-Based Processing

Topic	Reference
Clones/Constructs	
Detailed method used to prepare the construct, its source, nucleotide sequence, and other characterization	13,14,16,21
Detailed method used to prepare the expression vector, its components and their sources, and other characterization	14,16,21
Detailed description of cloning process	14,21
Cells/Cell Banks	
Complete characterization of cell line including source, relevent phenotype, genotype, and cultivation history	13–17,19,21
For MAbs, a complete description of the methods used to develop the hybridoma or other MAb-producing cells	15,19,21
Expression construct method of transfection, amplification, copy number, etc.	13–15
Genetic stability of host cell and expression vector and description of markers used to ensure stability	13,15,16,21
Method of constructing of master cell bank (MCB), including cell cloning history and verification of fidelity of coding sequence	13–17,19,21
Characterization of MCB for adventitious agents	13,15,17,19–21
Steps taken to prevent or control contamination by adventitious agents including prions	15,19–21
Production, characterization, storage, and use of working cell bank (WCB)	13,15,17,19,21
Analysis of "end of production" cells; limit for *in vitro* cell age	13–15
Expressed Active Substance	
Extensive characterization	13,16,19,21
Production Method	
Methods of quality control for production runs including routine monitoring for adventitious agents and nucleic acid	17,20
Analysis of cells for relevant phenotypic or genotypic markers and for contamination by adventitious agents at the end of each run	13,20
Procedures and materials used for cell growth and expression	16
Methods to prevent cross-contamination with other cell lines	15,21
Detailed description of cell growth stages	21
Freedom of media components from contamination by adventitious agents	17,20
Consistency of yield	16
Method of harvesting, product isolation, and product storage/stability	16,21
Method for inactivating cells at end of run	21
Validation studies for process, sterilization, cell inactivation, etc.	21
Description of reference standards	21
Validation of elimination of adventitious agents and nucleic acids by downstream processing method	17,19,20

PRODUCT DESIGN/PROCESS DEVELOPMENT

This is the phase during which the final product and its manufacturing process are actually created. It is one of the most extensive phases and lays the groundwork for everything that is to come. This phase bridges the gap between experimental work on the lab bench and consistent, controlled production of the product in clinically useful quantities. It is important that the work be done carefully and accurately and be well documented, preferably in Development Reports as described before. A list of the major activities that usually occur in this phase is shown in Table 3.

Project Team Organization and Planning

Based on a promising outcome from the discovery phase, this is usually the stage at which an organization decides to start seriously pursuing development of a commercial product. Generally, a multidisciplinary project team is formed, and a project management system is employed to move the project forward in an organized manner. At this point the work leaves the purely technical realm to be governed by requirements from Marketing, Quality Assurance, Clinical Affairs, Regulatory Affairs, Manufacturing, and many other departments, all of which should be represented on the project team. However, the technical aspects usually continue to dominate to support the needs of these other groups. Good, detailed planning at this stage can be very beneficial in keeping a large team with diverse interests on track toward the project goals. It also provides management with information to determine resource requirements, as well as future operational and business requirements associated with the availability of the new product. Decision points or milestones are often set up at which progress to date is evaluated to determine whether to move the project forward to the next phase. My organization has learned the importance of good planning the hard way. Early development projects were done using a "seat-of-the-pants" approach, making up the plan as we went along. This very often resulted in overlooking important issues until the last minute and then wasting time waiting for those items to be completed. We are currently developing a generic development plan that can be adapted to any project. The generic plan lists all of the technical, regulatory, marketing, and business tasks that need to be considered for any product and gives their relative timing. Even using early versions as a simple check list has been extremely helpful.

Companies have evolved a large number of project management systems, but the usual goal is to bring a product to market in the shortest time possible. Whatever the system, two items are very important in keeping a project focused, a project objective and a product definition. These are generally developed by the project team and approved by company management. In later stages of the project when things tend to get complex, reference to these statements is often invaluable in keeping the project on track. The project objective is the overall goal of the project team. It is usually a simple statement such as, "To bring Product X to market by the first quarter of Year Y for the treatment of Disease Z." As simple as it seems, it is important to have such a statement to make sure that all of the team members understand and share the same common goal. The product definition is equally important. An initial definition might be something like, "Product X is a sterile liquid concentrate for intravenous administration that is supplied in glass vials of 1,000 activity units which can be stored for two years at room temperature." Both the objective and definition may be revised as the project proceeds. It might be determined, for instance, that a liquid formulation is not possible or that the market actually prefers that the product be supplied in plastic bags.

Product Design

This is the process of placing the active ingredient in a form that satisfies the product definition. It may include determining the required product purity, finding a formulation both to stabilize the active ingredient and to provide the necessary clinical utility, developing the proper delivery mechanism whether it is syringe injection or a more complex aerosol or controlled release method, and developing the packaging.

Formulation Studies. The goals of the formulation studies are (1) to find a method to stabilize the active ingredient to give it an acceptable shelf life and (2) depending on the particular product, to introduce additional components to modify the performance of the product. Such components could be, for instance, adjuvants to increase the effectiveness of vaccines or permeation enhancers to increase the absorption of a product through the skin. Various excipients such as salts, amino acids, pH buffers, other small molecules, polymers, or proteins are selected which can be mixed with the active ingredient to help preserve its activity or give the mixture other desired properties. These excipients must also be compatible with the intended clinical use of the product. For instance, they cannot be toxic, should not cause discomfort during product administration, and should not introduce any undesirable side effects of their own. On the practical side, they should be cost-effective and easily available in purified form from qualifiable vendors.

The form of the product, for instance, whether it is a liquid or a lyophilized cake, goes hand in hand with the formulation. A formulation that is good for a liquid product might be a disaster for freeze-drying. Although lyophilization methods are also part of process

---

Table 3. Product Design/Process Development Activities

Project team organization and planning
Product design
    Formulation studies
    Container/Closure/Delivery system
    Stability studies
Product specification development
Assay development
Process development
    Documentation
    Viral issues

development activities, the initial method is usually developed during formulation studies because different formulations require different cycles. Stability studies which will be discussed in more detail later, also play a major role here and are one of the primary tools used to determine the viability of a given formulation.

The formulation studies generate data that is important in supporting the license application. This starts with the formula or list of ingredients in the final product. Although this sounds simple, it actually leads to an extensive range of activities to comply with cGMP requirements. The required grade of each excipient, for instance, USP, ACS, or a manufacturer's "Analytical Reagent" grade, must be specified and justified. For United States Pharmacopoeia (USP) or National Formulary (NF) grade reagents, this is usually simple because such reagents are already qualified generically for pharmaceutical use. For other grades of reagents, analysis of the purity, impurities, stability, physical form, and other salient characteristics and their consistency from lot to lot are needed. Vendors must be identified, audited, and qualified. Many companies prefer to qualify more than one vendor to have a backup supplier in case of availability problems.

Regulatory authorities also want to know the purpose and necessity for each excipient. For instance, sodium chloride may be added to give correct ionic strength, citrate or phosphate may be added as a pH buffer, and PEG or albumin may be added to enhance the stability of the active ingredient. Although some of this may seem trivial, there can be hidden dangers. For instance, sucrose that was added as a stabilizer to the formulation of several immunoglobulin products has been implicated in kidney damage in some patients (27). Other biological products such as albumin or protease inhibitors that might be added to a formulation may receive even more scrutiny. Human albumin is a common stabilizer, but it can bring with it other contaminating proteins including active enzymes, and it also can introduce human viruses.

Container/Closure/Delivery System. Selecting the container and closure, as well as any associated delivery system, is also an important aspect of product design from both a marketing and a product quality perspective. The product container is what the consumer actually sees as the physical manifestation of the product. The container's appearance, storage convenience, and ease of use can be extremely important in differentiating a product from its competitors. Important practical considerations for manufacturing include the suitability of the container for cleaning, sterilizing, filling, sealing, final product inspection, packaging, and storage. Many of these operations utilize automated equipment, several may be performed in aseptic or sterile environments, and all must be performed under cGMP. The container/closure system also plays a role in formulation development in its potential effects on product stability, as well as its possible role as part of a delivery system.

From a quality/regulatory perspective, the product container is the main defense against contamination of the product in the field. The product developer must show that the chosen container/closure system adequately protects the product against contamination, loss of sterility for sterile products, degradation due to moisture, oxygen, light, and other factors, and any other outside influences. It also must be shown that the container/closure system does not interact detrimentally with the product. For instance, a current issue is leaching of aluminum from glass vials into liquid products (28). Container/closure requirements and qualification methods are given in the United States Pharmacopeia (29) and in an FDA guideline (30). In addition to these generic methods, specific product contact qualification is recommended. This is usually a short-term extractables study using the actual product but can also require a stability study depending on the issues being investigated. Additional parameters must be considered for multiple-use containers such as vials from which more than one dose may be drawn. Not only must such containers use a stopper that can be pierced more than once without losing the integrity of its seal, but the product may also include a preservative that must be stable and effective over multiple uses.

Stability Studies. Stability studies are one of the most valuable parts of a product development effort. Although R&D often sees stability testing as a nuisance that requires too many valuable vials of product, the results from a well-conducted stability study often give the earliest indication of problems with the product, assays, lot-to-lot variation, the container/closure system, or numerous other factors. In addition, continually accumulating stability data starting early in the project can provide a baseline for evaluating the effects of later process changes, as well as for presenting a good case for stability of the product in an IND or BLA application. In our experience with plasma products, stability studies and pharmacokinetic studies in animals have sometimes revealed subtle product changes due to process modifications that were not seen with other characterization methods. Because stability data inherently take time to collect, planning ahead is important, Organizations with limited development experience often scramble to assemble huge amounts of data from elaborate, complex studies only to realize at the last minute that they need to wait a few more months to obtain enough stability data for their IND. Although the FDA is often very reasonable in accommodating companies in this situation, they understand the importance and a priori unpredictability of stability testing and will usually allow only limited extrapolation from limited data (31).

Stability testing is a complex technology, but numerous guidelines have been issued to help simplify the task for the product developer. Stability testing is being harmonized under ICH which has issued several guidelines (32–35). In addition, an FDA guideline incorporates much of the ICH guidance in summarizing FDA expectations (31). An older FDA guideline also gives an excellent description of the principles and statistical considerations behind stability testing (36). The number of guidelines is an indication of the complexity and importance of stability testing.

Stability information is required on both the final product, as well as on process intermediates, if they are held for any appreciable time. It is also required for raw materials, process reagents and excipients, assay reagents, and assay standards, some of which may be available from vendors. For the final product, the relevant parameter is the stability of the complete final package, that is, the active ingredient in its chosen formulation and container/closure system. The stability of the finished product can be quite different than that of the active ingredient by itself. At the final stage of development, the complete product package, including the box or other outer wrapping, should be tested under the proposed storage conditions. My organization once discovered, for instance, that the humidity and condensation associated with refrigerated storage caused the product carton to soften to the extent that it no longer protected the product from damage during shipping. This is a good illustration of the reason that such attention to details is important. The miracle drug that will cure the world of all its ills is useless if the consumer cannot obtain it in an intact, usable condition.

The two major aspects of a stability study are storage and testing. Real-time studies store the product at its intended storage temperature, whereas accelerated and stress studies use higher temperatures to obtain data in a shorter period of time. Control samples may also be stored at lower temperatures at which it is assumed that product characteristics do not change. Depending on the product and its packaging, certain other environmental conditions such as exposure to light and humidity should also be explored (32,33). The product should be placed in the stability study as soon as possible after manufacture. Product storage should be continued for a period longer than that requested for product dating to give more credibility to the results at the time that corresponds to the desired product dating. For instance, a study designed to demonstrate stability for 24 months is usually carried out for at least 30 months. The crucial 24-month point is then bracketed by results at 18 and 30 months which can help to validate the results at the 24-month point. Some companies carry out studies for even longer periods in case they might want to extend the dating of the product at a later time.

The accuracy and predictivness of accelerated and stress studies can vary significantly from product to product. Theoretically, accelerated studies view product degradation as a chemical reaction that obeys the time–temperature relationship of the Arrhenius equation. Thus, results from higher temperature storage can be used to predict longer time results at lower temperatures. Stress testing is performed at even higher temperatures, often to provide data on degradation products and mechanisms. The FDA requires information on degradation mechanisms and the activity and toxicity of the degradation products. However, especially with biological products, additional degradation mechanisms which might be insignificant at lower temperatures can become important at higher temperatures, thus interfering with the predictability of the accelerated studies. However, for many products, an accelerated storage temperature can be found and enough experience can be obtained to demonstrate predictability and thus provide a valuable tool for providing more rapid results. Accelerated and stress testing can also provide information on the effects of short-term temperature excursions that might occur during shipping or as a result of equipment malfunctions. Although regulatory agencies rely mainly on real-time data, they will sometimes accept accelerated data on an interim basis if good correlation can be shown with real-time results.

Normally, samples of the stored product are withdrawn at regular, prespecified intervals and tested to determine the effect on various product characteristics. Lyophilized products are also usually tested at the beginning and end of the study for their short-term stability after reconstitution. Containers of the product are generally used whole, not sampled and returned to storage. All containers of product from the same lot are assumed to be identical, as they should be from a cGMP operation. Stability studies often give an early indication of problems with intralot, as well as lot-to-lot variation.

There is no specific list of product attributes that should be tested in a stability study. The guidelines recommend only that the study should examine those features susceptible to change that are likely to affect quality, safety, and/or efficacy (31). It is up to the manufacturer to propose a program that provides assurance that any significant changes are detected. For biological products, potency, purity, identity, appearance, moisture content for dried products, and solution characteristics such as pH for both liquid and reconstituted products are usually tested. As defined by the FDA, the analysis of purity includes examination of degradation products. As mentioned before, data on extractables from the container/closure system and evaluation of delivery system performance, for instance, for controlled release formulations, may also be subjects of stability testing. General safety and pyrogenicity are also generally included. A good place to begin choosing attributes is with the product specifications, as well as with other attributes that were included in the product characterization study. Confirmation of continuing sterility is also required. However, sterility testing is controversial because of the large number of samples that need to be tested for a statistically meaningful evaluation. In response to this the FDA allows substituting of container/closure integrity testing in lieu of sterility testing (37). At the end of the study companies often test the complete list of attributes listed in the product specifications.

Stability studies generally continue throughout the development project and on into regular commercial production. They start with samples from formulation studies and process development runs. That is followed by lots used in preclinical and clinical studies, conformance lots, and the first three production lots. Finally, companies are required by the cGMPs (38) to have an ongoing program to assess stability of at least one lot per year from regular production. Stability data must be submitted in support of both the IND and the BLA. For submission, real-time testing should cover at least twelve months on three batches, at least two of which should be manufactured at pilot scale or larger (31). Data are required on all product sizes, potencies, and packaging configurations that will be used in the clinical studies or that will be marketed under a BLA. Bracketing and matrixing methods that can minimize the number of lots needed to provide such data in some cases are described in the guidelines (31).

Product Specifications

Product specifications set requirements for the identity, strength, purity, and quality of a product by listing tests and acceptable ranges for various product attributes. Indirectly, they can also provide information about the process by showing whether it can consistently produce a product that meets the criteria. The specifications comprise a major part of the control strategy that ensures product quality and consistency. Satisfaction of the product specifications is one of the major criteria for release of lots (39). The product specifications may also list other important product information such as the definition of a lot, the definition of the date of manufacture, the expiry dating, and other special requirements. In the United States, only one set of acceptance limits is generally used to cover the product over its entire shelf life. However, in Europe and some other countries, two sets are used, one to be met for release of the product and the second to be met at the end of the product's shelf life. An ICH guideline (9) and other articles (40,41) give good recommendations for developing specifications.

The attributes included in the product specifications should be chosen carefully to adequately confirm the quality of the product. The specifications are not intended to be a full product characterization, only a check on product quality (9). The specifications and the other controls required by the cGMPs ensure that the commercially distributed product is comparable to the product that was shown to be safe and efficacious in the clinical studies. General requirements for biologics include potency, general safety, sterility, purity, and identity (42). The specifications should also include testing for all added excipients and process reagents and for any contaminants that must be removed during processing. This includes, for instance, any unwanted enzymatic activity that might be present in the starting materials or is generated during the process. Measurement of total protein is required (9), as is measurement of residual moisture for dried products (43). Solution characteristics such as pH, osmolality, and appearance are usually included. Pyrogenicity must be tested by infusion into rabbits or, if justifiable, by LAL testing (43). Demonstration of sterility requires testing twenty containers or 10% of the lot, whichever is smaller (44). Although that is not enough units in itself to statistically ensure sterility of the lot, this testing is only a final check on the validated processes that, operated under cGMP, provide the real assurance of product sterility. For products made in cells, testing for viruses and viral markers may also be required (19,20). The FDA also requires a final package identity test to verify that the labeling correctly indicates the content of the package (45). This involves selecting one or more tests that can definitively discern the product in question from any other product or material produced or used by the manufacturer.

Purity testing for synthetic products includes information about the structural heterogeneity of the active ingredients which is often inherent in the biosynthetic pathways used to produce them (9,31). For instance, post-translationally modified proteins may exist in various isoforms and glycoforms. Heterogeneity can also be created by reaction, rearrangement, and degradation during processing and storage. If the pattern of this heterogeneity is shown to be constant and comparable to that of the lots used in the clinical studies, that pattern can be used to define the acceptance criteria for that attribute (9). However, if the pattern is not constant or cannot be made constant by process modifications, an evaluation of the activity, efficacy, and safety of the various isoforms may be required (9). Purity also includes testing for potential contaminants such as inducers, antibiotics, media components, bacterial proteases, and nucleic acids derived from cell culture. A list of attributes for a typical biological product specification is shown in Table 4.

It is important to establish product specifications early in the development process even though they are expected

Table 4. Typical Biological Product Specification Attributes

Potency (biological activity) of active ingredient
Mass of active ingredient[a]
    Isoform/Glycoform pattern
    Degradation products
Mass of total protein in product
Specific activity
    Potency/(Mass of total protein)
    Potency/(Mass of active ingredient[a])
HPLC, SDS-PAGE, and/or other product characterization
Fill volume
Residual moisture of dried products
Appearance
Solubility of dried products
pH
Osmolality or conductivity
Mass of all formulation excipients
Mass of all potential process contaminants
    Process reagents intended to be removed
    MAbs if used
    Contaminants from cell culture
    Inactive products
    Media components
    Other cell products
    Nucleic acids
Protein identity
General safety
Pyrogenicity
Sterility
    Bioburden of presterile bulk
    Sterile bulk prior to filling
    Final container
Viral testing if required
Final package label identity
Additional Information Often Included:
Expiration dating
    Definition of date of manufacture
    Storage conditions
Definition of a lot
Number of retention samples
Specific gravity
Additional requirements for starting material
    Viral testing
    Lot size — amount of starting material
Revision history
References

[a]"Active ingredient" here refers to the total amount of the protein of interest whether or not it retains its biological activity.

to change as the project proceeds. Other than those required, the choice of the important attributes and acceptable ranges should be based on sound scientific and medical judgment coupled with experience from lab- and pilot-scale runs, product characterization studies, product testing, and stability studies. Acceptable ranges generally start out wide and are narrowed later as more experience with the product is obtained. Some attributes may be found unnecessary whereas others may need to be added. The FDA expects such changes and has spelled out its expectations for specifications at the various IND stages (46,47).

Regulatory agencies often request that acceptance criteria be given as two-sided ranges rather than as one-sided limits. This is not mentioned in the guideline (9) but is based more on quality management principles. Although one-sided limits such as "not more than 0.02 unit/mL of contaminant X" may seem adequate for the quality and safety of the product, they tell nothing about consistency of the process. Lot-to lot uniformity of residual levels of contaminants removed by the process, reagents used in the process, or by-products created during the process can give a good indication of process consistency. For instance, if one lot contains 0.01 unit/mL of contaminant X and the next lot contains 0.001 unit/mL, both would pass the specification, but the possible inconsistency of the process would be hidden. Of course, this has to be balanced against the sensitivity of the assay which might have a limit of detection of 0.01 unit/mL and thus would not be able to quantify the difference between the two lots.

Assay Development

All of product development involves measuring significant attributes of a product and process and then evaluating the results in light of scientific, medical, and regulatory requirements. Without accurate, precise assays for these measurements, the subsequent evaluations are problematic. Early development of reliable assays, especially for the active ingredient and its biological activity, are crucial to the timely success of a project. A large number of additional assays are usually needed in the product development process, some of which will be used only a few times and some of which will be used every time the product is manufactured. Table 5 lists many of the types of assays that are usually needed. What are not included are assays used in animal toxicological studies and viral validation studies because many of these studies are done by outside contractors or in-house service labs which have developed their own assays.

Assay methods must be documented and validated, instruments must be calibrated, specifications and stability data must be developed for assay reagents, and standards and controls must be produced and maintained (26,48–50). An assay can be thought of as a miniature process that, like the operations it supports, should be carried out under cGMP and GLP. All of the assays need to be validated for all of various milieus that will contain the test material because the milieu or matrix can often influence the outcome of an assay. For instance, the concentration of the active ingredient may have to be determined in a cell culture supernatant, in various in-process samples each at

Table 5. Typical Assays Used for Product Development

Biological activity of active ingredient
Mass of active ingredient
Other assays unique to the biological function, of the active substance
Total protein
Assays for process contaminants
Assays for process reagents
Assays for formulation excipients
pH
Osmolality
Conductivity
Residual moisture
Solubility
Appearance
Protein identity
Viral assays if required
Bioburden
Pyrogenicity
General safety
Sterility
Final package label identity
Assays for process components
    Raw materials
    Media, reagents
    Chromatographic media
    Filters/Filter aids
    Process water quality
    Process utilities
    Process intermediate storage containers
    Container/Closure
Filter integrity
Environmental monitoring
Assays for measuring clinical study parameters

different strengths in different buffers, in the final product, in clinical patient samples, and in samples from various preclinical studies. All of these should be validated. This is a major undertaking that companies have approached in various ways. There is currently much instructional and guidance information on assay validation by the FDA, ICH, and USP (52–55).

Process Development. When the active molecule was first identified in the laboratory, a process was used to produce and purify it. However, that laboratory process is usually not directly applicable to large-scale manufacture. The process development phase involves devising a production process that can be run on a large scale in a cost-effective, well-controlled manner to produce a consistent product. Broadly defined, the "process" spans everything from the raw materials coming in the door to the final product being delivered to the distributor or customer. This section will focus on what could be considered the core manufacturing process from the input of the starting materials into a manufacturing process to the packaging of the final product. The other aspects of the broader process will be covered below in the CMC section. These other aspects are somewhat generic and may already have well-established procedures in many companies.

Processes for producing biological products generally involve either isolation and purification from a natural source such as human plasma, or synthesis of an active ingredient, for instance, from cell culture or in transgenic animals, followed by isolation and purification. The basic manufacturing method is generally devised in the laboratory and then scaled up through one or more stages to a pilot plant scale suitable for producing preclinical and clinical material and finally to a full manufacturing scale. In addition to the practical considerations of efficiency, yield, safety, and ease of use, the process developer must consider the quality and regulatory aspects of the process (56). For cell-produced products, the process also has to be able to remove contaminants derived from cell culture such as cellular proteases and exogenous DNA (57). The process must be validatable, that is, well-controlled and able to produce a consistent product (58). Quality should be built in to a process; it is impossible to validate a poorly designed process (59). Steps should be chosen that are robust and easily controlled.

Building on the process work done during the Invention/Discovery phase, once a manufacturing-style process is defined, it must be characterized to identify important operating parameters. Then controls and limits must be established for those parameters. Thoughtful well-planned performance of these studies backed by good documentation of procedures and results can save a great deal of time later in the project. Because process development involves determining the optimum ranges for parameters such as pH, temperature, flow rates, and reagent concentrations, that work can significantly support later validation activities. A major part of validation is demonstrating that variations in process parameters within acceptable ranges still produce an acceptable product. Companies often define several types of operating ranges nested one inside the other (60). The maximum validated ranges will usually become the licensed limits whereas a narrower normal operating range may be specified in the run sheets. Other in-house alert or control ranges may be located between the licensed and normal ranges.

A list of desirable process characteristics is shown in Table 6. Modifying the process to optimize all of these items is an ongoing project that often continues until the final phase of clinical studies. Thus the product made, for instance, for early preclinical studies may be produced by a somewhat different process than that used later in the Phase 1 clinical study. One of the real challenges in product development is balancing the desire to move the project along as quickly as possible while minimizing the need to repeat studies due to product or process changes. Because all of the studies from early development through BLA submission build on each other to demonstrate the safety and efficacy of the product, it is important to be able to show that the later product is comparable to that used in the earlier studies. As the process evolves, this connectivity is facilitated by a good documented change-control process in which process modifications are recorded, justified, and approved (61). Although minor changes may be justified by scientific reasoning and simple testing, more extensive changes could require additional studies. If the product from a modified process cannot be shown to be comparable to that from the earlier process, some studies, including possibly even clinicals, may have to be repeated with the new version of the product. However, the FDA does expect changes during a project and has published a guideline for demonstrating comparability of products (62).

Documentation. As soon as the process has been devised, even on a bench scale, documentation should be developed to describe and control its use (63). This includes Manufacturing Records (run sheets), Standard Operating Procedures (SOPs), and specifications for raw materials, reagents, chromatographic media, filters, process equipment, packaging componentry, and other materials used in the process. Such documentation will be essential for future operation under cGMP, but developing it early has the added benefits of (1) maintaining a good record of process modifications through the company's change-control system and (2) minimizing mistakes and deviations in producing product for development studies.

Viral Issues. One of the main arguments for increased safety of recombinant-DNA derived products is that they are free from contamination with the pathological human viruses that often are present in natural sources such as human plasma. However, this is probably an oversimplification (20,64). Recombinant products, whether made in cells or transgenic animals, are still subject to contamination by viruses and other adventitious agents, including transmissible spongiform encephalopathy (TSE) agents. Many of these agents are unknown as are their effects on humans, especially when administered intravenously to patients with serious medical conditions. Therefore, viral contamination issues are important for all therapeutic biological products. Minimization of viral contamination of the active ingredient and provision of viral inactivation and/or removal steps in the purification process should be a major focus of the process development efforts (15–20). It is highly recommended that purification processes incorporate at least two robust viral inactivation/removal methods that target all viruses and operate by different mechanisms (19). These methods must be carefully validated as will be described in the following preclinical section.

PRECLINICAL STUDIES

To obtain permission to test a new product in human subjects, companies submit an Investigational New Drug (IND) application to FDA. An important part of the

Table 6. Desirable Process Characteristics

High yield	Cleanability/Reliability of equipment
High recovery	Personnel and product safety
High purity	Ease of use
Retention of biological activity	Sterile, pyrogen-free product
Cost-effective	Robust
Well-controlled	No patent infringement issues

IND application is a series of studies conducted to demonstrate a high degree of probability that the product will be safe for human use. According to the ICH guidelines (65), the primary goals of preclinical evaluation are (1) to identify an initial safe dose, (2) to identify potential target organs for toxicity, and (3) to identify safety parameters for clinical monitoring. Both *in vitro* and *in vivo* studies are generally conducted, including extensive product characterization. Processes utilizing cell lines or transgenic animals must also include extensive characterization of the constructs, cell lines, or animals employed, as described previously. The studies to be performed are selected on the basis of good scientific rationale in evaluating potential undesirable effects of the product and considering its intended usage. Several guidelines give a good general approach to selecting appropriate studies (16,21,65,66). The studies are expected to be performed under GLP although it is recognized that some studies needed for evaluating biologics may not be able to comply fully. To help ensure that the product used in the preclinical studies accurately reflects that being developed, some companies also have an internal policy that the test lots must be made under cGMP. Toxicity studies must be carefully designed to involve biologically relevant species and pathways in both short- and long-term evaluation. Many human biological products are immunogenic in animals, an important limitation that must be considered in designing the study. Pharmacokinetic studies in animals can also provide valuable information, although again, species variations have to be considered carefully. A good pharmacokinetic model can be a useful tool in evaluating the effects of process changes on products because recovery and clearance can be markedly affected, for instance, by minor changes in post-translational modifications or protein structure. All studies must be supported by testing to demonstrate the stability of the product over the time span of the studies.

Viral Validation

Validation of the viral safety of a new product is essential to support both IND and BLA submissions. This includes testing production cell lines and animals for the presence of various adventitious agents plus validation of process steps that are intended for viral inactivation or removal. ICH guidelines (20) and Points to Consider documents (17,21) give recommendations for such testing and validation. The European guidance document on viral validation studies (67) is also highly recommended for its description of the current state of the art in viral safety validation. Additional information is available in the literature (64,68). Complete viral validation studies, including a number of viruses and process robustness studies, are required for submission with the BLA. More abbreviated studies are often performed to support the IND. However, because the FDA's primary concern is the safety of the patients, these studies must be well thought out and well justified. For instance, abbreviated studies may include fewer viruses studied under typical rather than extreme process conditions. However, this limited data must be backed up by adequate scientific

justification that the process will eliminate any potential infectivity from the product. Previous experience with the chosen viral elimination methods under similar process conditions for other products can also help to justify the probable viral safety of an investigational product. It is recommended that the manufacturer consult the FDA to determine the extent of studies needed to support the IND.

In addition to viruses, manufacturers and regulators are becoming concerned with transmissible spongiform encephalopathy (TSE) agents such as BSE which causes mad cow disease or the agent that causes Creutzfeldt–Jacob disease (CJD) in humans. Techniques have been developed for assessing the risk, for instance, of BSE contamination in products made with bovine-source components (69,70). Lack of basic knowledge about the infectious agent and its mechanism of action coupled with the absence of simple assays for infectivity make TSE clearance studies extremely difficult. However, several organizations have attempted studies with reasonable success (71–73).

IND/CLINICAL STUDIES

The requirements for an Investigational New Drug application are given in 21 CFR Part 312 and in additional guidance documents (46,47). Clinical studies are generally divided into phases. Phase 1 studies are designed to determine the pharmacological actions of the product, as well as any adverse effects, and if possible, to provide preliminary evidence of effectiveness. Sometimes pharmacokinetic data is obtained to help design the subsequent Phase 2 studies. Depending on the nature of the product and the clinical indication, Phase 1 studies may be performed in healthy volunteers. Phase 2 studies begin to evaluate the clinical efficacy of the drug, including dose determination, as well as continuing to evaluate adverse effects. Phase 3 studies are the full-blown evaluation of safety and efficacy which will be used to support licensure of the product. Phase 1 and 2 studies lay the foundation for developing good Phase 3 studies. Phase 4 studies may be conducted after product licensure at FDA's request, for instance, to better define the longer term safety of a product. The FDA's primary objectives in approving an IND are to ensure the safety and rights of the study's subjects, plus for Phase 3 studies, to ensure that the data collected will be those needed to justify licensure. An IND may be submitted for one or several phases at a time.

An IND application includes a clinical plan, as well as product and process information. The clinical plan includes a protocol for the proposed study, an investigator's brochure giving details of the product including the results of preclinical safety studies, and examples of case report and informed consent forms. It also includes information about the clinical investigators and approvals of the study from their Institutional Review Boards (IRBs). A Chemistry, Manufacturing, and Controls (CMC) section describes the manufacturing process that will be used, including packaging and labeling procedures. The remainder of the IND describes the preclinical safety studies and other important information about the product. Companies are encouraged to arrange a pre-IND meeting with the FDA to discuss their clinical plans and any available preclinical data. Meetings with the FDA are also often held at the end of Phase 2 to help ensure the adequacy of the proposed Phase 3 pivotal study in the light of the data from the first two phases. Upon submission of the IND, the FDA has 30 days to review it and voice any objections. If the company has not had a response in 30 days, it may go ahead with the study. However, even after that implicit approval, it is wise to communicate with the FDA to see if it has any questions or concerns. For instance, although the FDA may have no serious safety objections that would cause it to place a "clinical hold" on the study, it could have concerns about whether the proposed study will provide adequate data to support licensure of the product. It is important for the manufacturer to be aware of such concerns before investing time and money in a study.

For the development scientist and engineer, the clinical study phase mainly involves supplying product to support the clinical studies, plus troubleshooting and resolving product issues identified during the studies. Because clinical research depends on the preclinical safety data, it is important that the clinical material be as comparable as possible to that used in the preclinical studies. In addition, all product for use in humans must be produced under cGMP. This includes manufacturing in a qualified facility using qualified production and analytical equipment with validated processes. However, FDA understands that product specifications, production methods, assay methods, and other aspects may change as the product moves through the various stages of clinical study. The FDA (74) and others (75) have published guidelines and strategies for coping with such changes while still maintaining the required cGMP controls.

CMC (CHEMISTRY, MANUFACTURING, AND CONTROLS) STUDIES

The CMC phase of the project usually overlaps one or more of the previous sections. It is a catch-all involving activities to assure complete compliance with cGMP and to develop information for the CMC section of the BLA and the subsequent preapproval inspection. Many of the CMC activities involve ancillary processes that support the basic manufacturing process, such as qualification of process ingredients and equipment, validation of product finishing operations, and validation of equipment cleaning. Because a clinical product must be manufactured under cGMP, a number of CMC activities must be completed before clinical production. Many of the activities in this phase fall into the categories of qualification and validation. The CMC studies also involve producing a series of conformance lots at full production scale to demonstrate the viability of the process.

Facility/Equipment Issues

One of the major decisions in these projects is the choice of facilities for producing the clinical material and for regular commercial production. Clinical production is often done in a pilot plant if it can be operated under cGMP conditions and if it has the facilities needed for any specialized processing such as for isolating the product after it has been treated for viral inactivation. The FDA recognizes that a company may be reluctant to invest in a commercial-scale production facility without knowing whether the new product will ultimately be approved and what its potential market will be. Therefore, it has developed guidelines that permit a company to license a product for commercial production in a pilot facility providing that facility can be operated in full compliance with cGMPs, as well as all other laws and regulations (76). The guideline also describes procedures for changing the site and scale of manufacture at a later time.

Facility and equipment requirements are given in the cGMPs (50), in a guideline on plasma-derived products (66), and in the literature (40,77,78). The requirements include suitable size and construction, flows of people, product, and materials designed to prevent product contamination, cleanability of the equipment and facility, and proper lighting and environmental controls. Conformance with the requirements is ensured by qualification and validation of the facility (48). For new or remodeled facilities, it is highly recommended that facility validation be considered early during the design of the facility (79,80). Many companies today are constructing facilities to produce more than one product. Such multiuse facilities are permitted by FDA but require careful design and validation to prevent cross-contamination from one product to the next (79,81,82). Adequate cleaning validation for both the facility and the process equipment is essential in multiuse facilities (79,81,82). However, even single-product facilities require controls and cleanability to prevent cross-contamination between lots.

Qualification and Validation

Qualification and validation are key activities of this project phase. Process validation is a cGMP requirement defined by the FDA as "... establishing documented evidence which provides a high degree of assurance that a specific process will consistently produce a product meeting its pre-defined specifications and quality characteristics" (83). Qualification is a similar concept that is usually applied to objects such as equipment or packaging componentry whereas validation applies to processes. Qualification is often divided into three phases: Installation Qualification (IQ) ensures that the equipment is received as designed and specified and that it is installed correctly; Operational Qualification (OQ) ensures that the equipment operates as specified and designed; and Performance Qualification (PQ) ensures that the equipment performs the job it was designed to do within the design specifications. Equipment and instruments must also be calibrated (49,78,84). Once everything is qualified and calibrated, process validation demonstrates that it all works together with the documented process to produce a consistently acceptable product. Validation is a constantly changing methodology for which there is a great deal of published literature (58,85–89).

Validation can seem like an overwhelming proposition because essentially everything involved in manufacturing the product must be qualified and validated. It spans the operation from receipt of raw materials through processing, facilities, utilities, cleaning procedures, sterility assurance, and finishing activities to the final shipping of the product to distributors or customers. Automated systems such as process control systems and facility environmental control systems have specialized validation requirements (90), as do cell culture (40) and chromatographic processes (91). It is highly recommended that organizations develop a Validation Master Plan to help plan and keep track of all of the validation activities (88). Although it is not a requirement, FDA inspectors often request the Validation Master Plan as a first step in reviewing the company's validation activities.

One of the major aspects of process validation is demonstrating that the process performs adequately at the extremes of the acceptable ranges of significant process parameters (92). This establishes the validity of the chosen ranges and demonstrates the robustness of the process (93). As described before in the process development section, information gained from early studies on acceptable ranges can be very beneficial in designing and simplifying such studies. Design of Experiments (DOE) methods can be very useful in validation studies (94). Several advantages include the ability to gain more information from fewer runs, the ability to screen parameters to identify those that have the greatest impact on product performance, and the ability to identify interactions between parameters. This last is important because process parameters often interact with each other and such interactions cannot be observed in traditional studies that vary one parameter at a time.

Product for clinical studies must also be made using a validated process, and the guidelines (74,83) provide suggestions for dealing with the limitations inherent at that early stage. The final, full process validation is generally not undertaken until the process is no longer expected to change. The final process is often validated in conjunction with conformance lot production or with Phase 3 clinical lot production. Process validation is actually an ongoing activity over the life span of the product. Even after licensure, validations should be checked periodically or after process modifications. A popular concept is the "life-cycle" approach to process validation (95).

Other Requirements

The ultimate goal of the CMC phase is to establish, document, and maintain a system for producing the new product that is in full compliance with the cGMPs. The cGMP regulations for finished pharmaceuticals given in 21 CFR Part 211 provide an excellent checklist of the necessary items. In addition, the guidelines on CMC information for recombinant and monoclonal antibody products (21), plasma-derived products (66) and on manufacturing active pharmaceutical ingredients (10) are excellent references.

Conformance Lots

Conformance lot production is usually one of the last steps in product development before BLA submission. The conformance lots (also termed submission lots or biobatches) are produced at full scale by the exact process and in the same facility that will be used for commercial production. Documentation and samples of these lots must be submitted to the FDA in support of the BLA (96–98). The lots are also generally placed in a stability study and may be sold if the product license is approved before the expiration of the lots. These lots are also often used as part of the final process validation which usually requires that three consecutive successful lots be produced as evidence that a quality product can be consistently produced.

LICENSE APPLICATION AND REVIEW

Once all of the development activities and all of the clinical studies have been completed, the next step is to assemble the resulting information into a license application. As mentioned before, this will be either a BLA or a PLA/ELA. Although in the past CBER would often accept PLAs and ELAs at different times, now they must be submitted simultaneously (97). The FDA has also implemented a system now for electronic filing of applications which is described in several guidelines (99–102). Companies are encouraged to arrange a pre-BLA meeting with the FDA to acquaint it with the information to be submitted and to receive feedback on any potential issues.

Receipt of the application and the required user fee by the FDA starts a review clock and a definite sequence of events. The review clock is a provision of the Food and Drug Administration Modernization Act of 1997, supported by the Prescription Drug User Fee Act of 1992. The fairly substantial user fees are intended to provide additional FDA resources to expedite the review of applications. The review period goals vary by year and are described in a guideline (103). In general, the FDA now targets about twelve months or less from the receipt of an application to completion of its review. Procedures also exist for accelerated approvals of products for serious or life-threatening illnesses (104). The first communication from the FDA is usually a reference number for the filing. This indicates only that the FDA has received the application. Next, within six weeks to two months CBER will decide whether to "file" the application, that is, administratively, whether the application contains all of the required documentation. At that point, the company will receive a letter stating whether the application is "fileable." Then the wait begins while the FDA takes about six months from the date of submission to review the application.

Within a few months after the application is filed, the FDA will perform a preapproval inspection of the production facility and possibly also other facilities such as R&D labs, QC labs, and pilot plants. The FDA may also inspect any contract manufacturers involved in any part of the product's production. The main purpose for this inspection is to determine whether the product has been and will be manufactured under full cGMP compliance and in conformance with commitments made in the BLA. During the inspection, the company should have available all qualification and validation information, all pertinent documentation, and any other information collected during product development and testing (105,106). The FDA may be especially interested in documentation for clinical trial batches and for changes made during the development process from lab to clinical to full-scale manufacturing (23). Many companies perform their own internal cGMP audit to prepare for the FDA inspection.

After about six months, the company may receive an "approvable" letter or a "not approvable" letter. An initial "approvable" letter is rare as is a "not approvable ever" letter (107). Normally a company will receive a "not approvable" letter listing deficiencies in and questions about various aspects of the application (107). Questions in a "not approvable" letter may also result from the preapproval inspection findings. At that point, the review clock stops while the company assembles a response. This is the point where good documentation of development data, validation information, and other activities really pays off. If the company has carried out a complete, comprehensive development project, the information requested by the FDA is often contained in that documentation and can be readily assembled into a response. In other cases, additional studies may be needed, sometimes even clinical studies. That can cost the company significant amounts of time and money. In one of our first development projects, PLA questions required us to perform several new studies which delayed our response for more than a year. More recently, because of good planning and documentation, responses can often be generated in a matter of days.

Once the FDA is satisfied that all of the necessary data has been submitted, an advisory review panel will be convened to review the application and provide its recommendations concerning licensure of the product (28). Finally, when all requirements have been satisfied, the company will usually receive an "approvable" letter. This is not the actual license approval but rather a statement that the product is approvable pending completion of certain tasks such as final labeling approval and review of the company's proposed promotional literature. Product labeling is usually left until last because it depends on information from many parts of the application, some of which may not be finalized until all questions have been resolved. Labeling refers to the container and carton labels (108) and also to the Package Insert which contains a great deal of information about the composition, indications, dosage, and precautions for use of the product (109). The final approval letter will include the Summary Basis of Approval which briefly describes clinical and compositional information on which license approval was based. The Summary Basis of Approval is the only information available to the public; the remainder of the license file is kept confidential to protect the manufacturer's proprietary information (110).

ROUTINE PRODUCTION

Once license approval has been granted, the company may routinely manufacture and release the product for sale. However, the company is obligated to maintain compliance with cGMPs and any additional provisions of the product license. The company must report to the FDA any errors associated with manufacture and release of the product (111), as well as adverse reactions reported to it by users of the product (112). Any changes in the product

or its manufacturing process must also be reported in either an annual report, a 30-day notification, or a preapproval supplement depending on the type of modifications (113,114). Many biological products are also subject to individual release of each lot by CBER (115). However, the specified product classes listed earlier are exempt from that requirement (7). Finally, the FDA will perform periodic, generally yearly, inspections of the manufacturing facility to examine cGMP compliance (116).

CONCLUSION

The road to a new product is long and complex, both from a technical and a quality/regulatory view point. Engineers or scientists navigating that path have to contend with both the laws of nature in which they are well trained and also the laws and regulations of the FDA about which they are often quite naïve. The regulations exist to ensure that the public has access to safe, effective medicines. This article has been written as an overview of the regulatory process and its requirements to assist technical professionals in devising the safest, most effective biological products. The most important points are (1) considering regulatory requirements early in the development project, (2) maintaining good documentation throughout the project, (3) careful planning to reduce project delays, and (4) taking advantage of the extensive written and verbal guidance available from the FDA. Following these recommendations should help technical professionals interact more productively with the company's quality and regulatory staff to find the quickest and easiest way to bring new products to market.

BIBLIOGRAPHY

1. *Code of Federal Regulations, Title 21 Food and Drugs*, U.S. Government Printing Office, Washington, D.C., 1999. Also available on the World Wide Web at *http://www.access.gpo.gov/nara/cfr/*

2. 21 CFR 601.25.

3. 21 CFR 10.90.

4. FDA Guidance documents and other information are available from 1) the FDA World Wide Web site at *http://www.fda.gov*; 2) from the CBER FAX Information System at 1-888-223-7329; 3) from the CBER e-mail system at *CBER_INFO@CBER.FDA.GOV*; or 4) as printed copies from CBER, FDA, 1401 Rockville Pike, Rockville, Md. 20852, or CDER, Drug Information Branch, 5600 Fishers Lane, Rockville, Md. 20858.

5. *Draft Guidance for Industry*: *Formal Meetings with Sponsors and Applicants for PDUFA Products*, U.S. Food and Drug Administration, Washington, D.C., 1999.

6. 21 CFR 601.2.

7. Interim Definition and Elimination of Lot-by-Lot Release for Well-Characterized Therapeutic Recombinant DNA-Derived and Monoclonal Antibody Biotechnology Products, *Fed. Regist.* **60**, 63048–63049 (1995).

8. J. Wechsler, *BioPharm* **11**(10), 16–19 (1998).

9. *ICH Draft Guidance Q6B on Specifications*: *Test Procedures and Acceptance Criteria for Biotechnological/Biological Products*, U.S. Food and Drug Administration, Washington, D.C., 1998.

10. *Draft Guidance for Industry; Manufacture, Processing, or Holding Active Pharmaceutical Ingredients*, U.S. Food and Drug Administration, Washington, D.C., 1998.

11. R. Fahrner, *BioPharm* **6**(3), 34–37 (1993).

12. R. Fahrner, *BioPharm* **6**(9), 18–22 (1993).

13. *Supplement to the Points to Consider in the Production and Testing of New Drugs and Biologicals Produced by Recombinant DNA Technology: Nucleic Acid Characterization and Genetic Stability*, U.S. Food and Drug Administration, Washington, D.C., 1992.

14. *ICH Final Guideline Q5B on Quality of Biotechnical Products: Analysis of the Expression Construct in Cells Used for the Production of r-DNA Derived Protein Products*, U.S. Food and Drug Administration, Washington, D.C., 1996.

15. *ICH Guidance Q5D on Quality of Biotechnological/Biological Products: Derivation and Characterization of Cell Substrates Used for Production of Biotechnological/Biological Products*, U.S. Food and Drug Administration, Washington, D.C., 1998.

16. *Points to Consider in the Production and Testing of New Drugs and Biologicals Produced by Recombinant DNA Technology*, U.S. Food and Drug Administration, Washington, D.C., 1985.

17. *Points to Consider in the Characterization of Cell Lines Used to Produce Biologicals*, U.S. Food and Drug Administration, Washington, D.C., 1993.

18. *Points to Consider in the Manufacturing and Testing of Therapeutic Products for Human Use Derived from Transgenic Animals*, U.S. Food and Drug Administration, Washington, D.C., 1995.

19. *Points to Consider in the Manufacturing and Testing of Monoclonal Antibody Products for Human Use*, U.S. Food and Drug Administration, Washington, D.C., 1997.

20. *ICH Guidance Q5A on Viral Safety Evaluation of Biotechnology Products Derived from Cell Lines of Human or Animal Origin*, U.S. Food and Drug Administration, Washington, D.C., 1998.

21. *Guidance for Industry for the Submission of Chemistry, Manufacturing, and Controls Information for a Therapeutic Recombinant DNA-Derived Product or a Monoclonal Antibody Product for in Vivo Use*, U.S. Food and Drug Administration, Washington, D.C., 1996.

22. R. Kaplan, *BioPharm* **8**(1), 26–30 (1995).

23. R.F. Tetzlaff, *Pharm. Technol.*, January, 46–60 (1998).

24. R.F. Tetzlaff, *Pharm. Technol.*, September, 44–56 (1992).

25. R.F. Tetzlaff, *Pharm. Technol.*, October, 84–94 (1992).

26. 21 CFR Part 58.

27. N. Ahsan, L.A. Wiegand, C.S. Abendroth, and E.C. Manning, *Am. J. Nephrol.* **16**, 532–536 (1996).

28. M. Inoue et al., *Vox Sang.* **66**, 249–252 (1994).

29. *United States Pharmacopeia XXIII/National Formulary XVIII*, U.S. Pharmacopeial Convention, Rockville, Md., 1995.

30. *Draft Guidance for Industry: Submission of Documentation in Drug Applications for Container Closure Systems Used for the Packaging of Human Drugs and Biologics*, U.S. Food and Drug Administration, Washington, D.C., 1997.

31. *Draft Guidance for Industry: Stability Testing of Drug Substances and Drug Products*, U.S. Food and Drug Administration, Washington, D.C., 1998.

32. *ICH Guidance Q1A Stability Testing of New Drug Substances and Products*, U.S. Food and Drug Administration, Washington, D.C., 1994.

33. *ICH Guidance Q1B Photostability Testing of New Drug Substances and Products*, U.S. Food and Drug Administration, Washington, D.C., 1996.

34. *ICH Guidance Q1C Stability Testing for New Dosage Forms*, U.S. Food and Drug Administration, Washington, D.C., 1996.

35. *ICH Guidance Q5C Quality of Biotechnological Products: Stability Testing of Biotechnological/Biological Products*, U.S. Food and Drug Administration, Washington, D.C., 1996.

36. *Guideline for Submitting Documentation for the Stability of Human Drugs and Biologics*, U.S. Food and Drug Administration, Washington, D.C., (1987).

37. *Draft Guidance for Industry: Container and Closure Integrity Testing in lieu of Sterility Testing as a Component of the Stability Protocol for Sterile Products*, U.S. Food and Drug Administration, Washington, D.C., 1998.

38. 21 CFR 211.166.

39. 21 CFR 610.1.

40. R. Kaplan, *BioPharm* **8**(2), 26–30 (1995).

41. J. Cohen and M. Busch, *BioPharm* **11**(8), 38–42 (1998).

42. 21 CFR Part 610.

43. 21 CFR 610.13.

44. 21 CFR 610.12.

45. 21 CFR 610.14.

46. *Content and Format of Investigational New Drug Applications (INDs) for Phase 1 Studies of Drugs, Including Well-Characterized, Therapeutic, Biotechnology-derived Products*, U.S. Food and Drug Administration, Washington, D.C., 1995.

47. *Draft Guidance for Industry: INDs for Phase 2 and 3 Studies of Drugs, Including Specified Therapeutic Biotechnology-Derived Products, Chemistry Manufacturing and Controls Content and Format*, U.S. Food and Drug Administration, Washington, D.C., 1999.

48. C. DeSain and C. Sutton, *BioPharm* **11**(1), 38–41 (1998).

49. 21 CFR Part 211.

50. S. Kuwahara, *BioPharm* **11**(4), 57–58 (1998).

51. *Guideline for Submitting Samples and Analytical Data for Methods Validation*, U.S. Food and Drug Administration, Washington, D.C., 1987.

52. *ICH Guideline Q2A: Text on Validation of Analytical Procedures*, U.S. Food and Drug Administration, Washington, D.C., 1995.

53. *United States Pharmacopeia XXIII/National Formulary XVIII*, Section 1225, U.S. Pharmacopeial Convention, Rockville, Md., 1995.

54. *ICH Guidance for Industry Q2B: Validation of Analytical Procedures: Methodology*, U.S. Food and Drug Administration, Washington, D.C., 1996.

55. *Guidance for Industry: Bioanalytical Methods Validation for Human Studies*, U.S. Food and Drug Administration, Washington, D.C., 1998.

56. C. DeSain and C.V. Sutton, *Pharm. Technol.*, October, 130–136 (1995).

57. A. Riggin, G.C. Davis, and T.L. Copmann, *BioPharm* **9**(9), 36–41 (1996).

58. N.M. Lugo, *BioPharm* **11**(6), 18–26 (1998).

59. J. Nally and R. Kieffer, *Pharm. Technol.*, October, 106–116 (1993).

60. K.G. Chapman, *Pharm. Technol.*, December, 22–36 (1984).

61. B. Immel, *BioPharm* **10**(GMP Suppl.), 14–15,22 (1997).

62. *FDA Guidance Concerning Demonstration of Comparability of Human Biological Products, Including Therapeutic Biotechnology-derived Products*, U.S. Food and Drug Administration, Washington, D.C., 1996.

63. B. Immel, *BioPharm* **10**(GMP Suppl.), 8–12 (1997).

64. E.M. White, J.B. Grun, C.-S. Sun, and A.F. Sito, *BioPharm* **4**(5), 34–39 (1991).

65. *ICH Guidance for Industry: S6 Preclinical Safety Evaluation of Biotechnology-Derived Pharmaceuticals*, U.S. Food and Drug Administration, Washington, D.C., 1997.

66. *Guidance for Industry: For the Submission of Chemistry, Manufacturing and Controls and Establishment Description Information for Human Plasma-Derived Biological Products, Animal Plasma or Serum-Derived Products*, U.S. Food and Drug Administration, Washington, D.C., 1997.

67. *Note for Guidance on Virus Validation Studies: The Design, Contribution and Interpretation of Studies Validating the Inactivation and Removal of Viruses*, CPMP/BWP/268/95, Final version 2, European Agency for the Evaluation of Medicinal Products, London, 1996.

68. A.J. Darling and J.J. Spaltro, *BioPharm* **9**(9), 42–50 (1996).

69. PhRMA BSE Committee, *BioPharm* **11**(1), 20–31 (1998).

70. PhRMA BSE Committee, *BioPharm* **11**(3), 18–30 (1998).

71. M. Blum et al., *BioPharm* **11**(4), 28–34 (1998).

72. C.F. Gölker et al., *Biologicals* **24**, 103–111 (1996).

73. S.R. Petteway, Jr., *Cambridge Healthtech Institute, 4th Annu. Conf. Blood Saf. Screen.*, McLean, Va., 1998.

74. *Guideline on the Preparation of Investigational New Drug Products (Human and Animal)*, U.S. Food and Drug Administration, Washington, D.C., 1991.

75. D. Bernstein, *BioPharm* **8**(1), 20–25 (1995).

76. *FDA Guidance Document Concerning the Use of Pilot Manufacturing Facilities for the Development and Manufacture of Biological Products*, U.S. Food and Drug Administration, Washington, D.C., 1995.

77. N.A. Roscioli et al., *BioPharm* **9**(8), 32–40 (1996).

78. J. Barta, *BioPharm* **11**(5), 84–89 (1998).

79. A.J. Shahidi, R. Torregrossa, and Y. Zelmanovich, *Pharm. Eng.*, September/October, 72–83 (1995).

80. J.N. Odum, *BioPharm* **11**(11), 36–41 (1998).

81. F.G. Bader et al., *BioPharm* **5**(7), 32–40 (1992).

82. J. Odum, *Pharm. Eng.*, September/October, 8–20 (1995).

83. *Guideline on General Principles of Process Validation*, U.S. Food and Drug Administration, Washington, D.C., 1987.

84. D.M. Evans and J. Erickson, *BioPharm* **11**(6), 73–74 (1998).

85. J. Agalloco, *PDA J. Pharm. Sci. Technol.* **49**, 175–179 (1995).

86. S. Buchholz, *BioPharm* **10**(1), 50–53 (1997).

87. ISPE San Francisco/Bay Area Chapter, *Pharm. Eng.*, January/February, pp. 8–24 1998.

88. P. James, *Pharm. Eng.*, January/February, pp. 72–82 (1998).

89. G.S. Hodgson, *BioPharm* **12**(3), 30–32 (1999).

90. J. Gottfried, *BioPharm* **11**(10), 40–43 (1998).

91. *Reviewer Guidance on Validation of Chromatographic Methods*, U.S. Food and Drug Administration, Washington, D.C., 1994.

92. R.J. Seely et al., *BioPharm* **12**(4), 33–36 (1999).

93. B.D. Kelley, P. Jennings, R. Wright, and C. Briasco, *BioPharm* **10**(10), 36–47 (1997).

94. L.D. Torbeck and R.C. Branning, *Pharm. Technol.*, June, 108–113 (1996).

95. J. Agalloco, *J. Parenter. Sci. Technol.* **47**, 142–147 (1993).

96. 21 CFR 601.2(c)(1)(vi).

97. 21 CFR 601.10(b).

98. 21 CFR 601.10(b), 601.20(a).

99. *Draft Guidance for Industry: Electronic Submissions of a Biologics License Application (BLA) or Product License Application (PLA) / Establishment License Application (ELA) to the Center for Biologics Evaluation and Research*, U.S. Food and Drug Administration, Washington, D.C., 1998.

100. *Draft Guidance for Industry: Electronic Submissions of Case Report Forms (CRFs), Case Report Tabulations (CRTs) and Data to the Center for Biologics Evaluation and Research*, U.S. Food and Drug Administration, Washington, D.C., 1998.

101. *Draft Guidance for Industry: Pilot Program for Electronic Investigational New Drug (eIND) Applications for Biological Products*, U.S. Food and Drug Administration, Washington, D.C., 1998.

102. *Guidance for Industry: Providing Regulatory Submissions in Electronic Format-General Considerations*, U.S. Food and Drug Administration, Washington, D.C., 1999.

103. *Guidance for Industry: Standards for the Prompt Review of Efficacy Supplements, Including Priority Efficacy Supplements*, U.S. Food and Drug Administration, Washington, D.C., 1999.

104. 21 CFR 601.40.

105. R.F. Tetzlaff, *BioPharm* **11**(8), 18–28 (1998).

106. J.R. Christensen, *BioPharm* **11**(8), 44–46 (1998).

107. N.J. Chew, *BioPharm* **7**(2), 20–24 (1994).

108. 21 CFR 610.60.

109. 21 CFR 201.56.

110. 21 CFR 314.430 and 601.51.

111. 21 CFR 600.14.

112. 21 CFR 314.80 and 600.80.

113. *Guidance for Industry: Changes to an Approved Application for Specified Biotechnology and Specified Synthetic Biological Products*, U.S. Food and Drug Administration, Washington, D.C., 1997.

114. Guidance for Industry: Changes to an Approved Application: Biological Products, U.S. Food and Drug Administration, Washington, D.C., 1997.

115. 21 CFR 610.2.

116. 21 CFR 312.58 and 600.21

See also cGMP COMPLIANCE FOR PRODUCTION ROOMS IN BIOTECHNOLOGY: A CASE STUDY; ETHICAL ISSUES IN ANIMAL AND PLANT CELL TECHNOLOGY; ICH GCP GUIDELINES: PREPARATION, CONDUCT AND REPORTING OF CLINICAL TRIALS; VIRAL INACTIVATION, EMERGING TECHNOLOGIES FOR HUMAN BLOOD PRODUCTS; VIRUS REMOVAL FROM PLANTS.

PROGRAMMED CELL DEATH (APOPTOSIS) IN CULTURE, IMPACT AND MODULATION

R.J. CARMODY
T.G. COTTER
S.L. MCKENNA
University College, Lee Maltings
Cork, Ireland

OUTLINE

ACKNOWLEDGMENTS

We would like to acknowledge the EU Biotech programme, Irish Cancer Society, and RP Ireland Fighting Blindness for their generous financial support.

INTRODUCTION

It is now apparent that physiological signals and mild cytotoxic insults do not directly kill their target cell, but rather they invite the cell to kill itself. This phenomenon of cell suicide is referred to as *programmed cell death* (PCD) or *apoptosis*. The biological significance of apoptosis has only been realized in the past decade, during which time many novel genes have been identified and many previously known proteins have been ascribed additional functions as apoptotic mediators. Moreover, researchers have demonstrated an ability to modulate the cellular response to death-inducing stimuli by equipping the cell with additional antiapoptotic genes, or by including specific survival factors in the culture environment. This advance has recently captured the attention of biotechnologists. The productivity of cell lines employed as "factories" for protein production is often limited by loss of viability in large-scale cultures. The recently established fact that cell death in such cultures is predominantly apoptotic suggests that the viability of such cultures may be amenable to manipulation with apoptotic mediators. In this article we introduce apoptosis to less familiar readers by giving a brief historical summary of its rise to prominence and subsequently detailing advances to date with respect to the morphological, biochemical, genetic, and environmental aspects of apoptosis regulation. We also surmise the evidence for apoptosis in large-scale cultures and the strategies biotechnologists are now employing in their attempts to generate more robust and productive "designer" cell lines for the bioprocessing industries.

A BRIEF HISTORY OF PCD/APOPTOSIS

The physiological induction of cell death was first recognized by embryologists in the nineteenth century who observed definitive cellular destruction during developmental limb formation and sexual differentiation. This physiological cell death was further described in subsequent studies on insect and amphibian metamorphosis as well as the formation of wood in plants. The term *programmed cell death* did not appear until 1964 and was used to describe cellular destruction following a predetermined sequence of events during development (1). In 1972, in what is now regarded as a landmark paper, Kerr and collegues described a morphologically distinct form of PCD, which they termed *apoptosis* (2). They noted in particular that most physiological cell deaths share a common set of morphological features, with the obvious implication that they also share a common mechanism. Despite the assumption that a predictable developmental event implies genetic regulation and previous reports of protein synthesis requirements, evidence for the genetic regulation of cell death was not revealed until the 1980s following studies on developmental mutants of *Caerorhabditis elegans* by Ellis and Horvitz (3). These studies identified two genes, *CED-3* and *CED-4*, which were required for normal developmental cell death, and a third, *CED-9*, which appeared to act as a negative regulator of cell death. The discovery of mammalian homologues of these genes initiated an intense search for other regulators of cell death, which were often found to have been previously described as oncogenes. This, coupled with reports of deregulated apoptosis in malignant disease and also in several forms of neurodegeneration (4), has propelled the study of apoptotic cell death to the forefront of modern-day biomedical research.

At this point it may be useful to comment on a matter of terminology. While programmed cell death was initially used to describe developmental cell death, it is now commonly used by many pioneers in the field to describe cell death which is directed by an internal program regardless of the initiating stimulus. Apoptosis is a descriptive term for cell death, which is characterized by certain morphological and biochemical features (to be discussed in the following). While the majority of PCDs reported thus far resemble apoptosis (particularly in mammalian cells), there are incidences that do not, particularly in invertebrates. In addition, PCD in plants exhibits unique features primarily due to the constitution of the plant cell wall. It remains to be established whether these differences in morphology represent different types of cell death or are merely different manifestations of a similar internal program.

Several hypotheses exist for the evolution and conservation of programmed cell death (5). Included in these is the function of PCD as an important defense mechanism against viral infection, a view supported by the hypersensitivity response of plants to bacterial infection and the observation that many successful viruses carry antiapoptotic genes. The importance of developmentally regulated cell death also suggests the evolution of apoptosis for developmental and morphogenetic purposes. An extension of this view is the regulation of tissue homeostasis and cell turnover by apoptosis, which will be discussed in the following.

It had been assumed that regulated cell suicide would be confined to multicellular organisms, since unicellular organisms with the ability to undergo PCD might be negatively selected through evolution. However, recent evidence suggests that PCD with characteristics similar to apoptosis also exists in single-celled eukaryotes (6) and that some bacteria may also undergo a primitive form of PCD (7). The advantages of unicellular PCD are unclear, but it has been proposed that (in addition to an antiviral defense) it may contribute to the selection of the fittest

cell in a colony as well as the establishment of a stable host–parasite ratio. These findings imply that the origin of PCD is much older than once assumed, with some researchers proposing that the process of cell suicide is as old as the cell itself.

BIOLOGICAL FEATURES OF APOPTOSIS

Apoptosis, as a biological phenomenon, is readily identifiable by several characteristic features. These include chromatin condensation, nuclear fragmentation, cell shrinkage, membrane blebbing, and the formation of membrane-bound vesicles termed *apoptotic bodies* (see Fig. 1). The regulated manner in which a cell actively coordinates its own destruction during apoptosis is in stark contrast to necrosis, the pathological form of cell death. Necrosis typically occurs under conditions of extreme cellular injury and involves cell swelling, organelle disruption, membrane rupture, and subsequent cell lysis (8). The lysis of a necrotic cell can result in the triggering of an associated inflammatory response with the potential to cause further damage to surrounding cells. The ordered disassembly of a cell into apoptotic bodies that are rapidly phagocytosed by neighboring cells or resident macrophage removes any risk of an inflammatory response.

Nuclear Events

Apoptotic cells display dramatic changes in the nucleus, including nuclear shrinkage, chromatin condensation, and the formation of crescent-shaped deposits along the nuclear envelope. A further nuclear-associated event

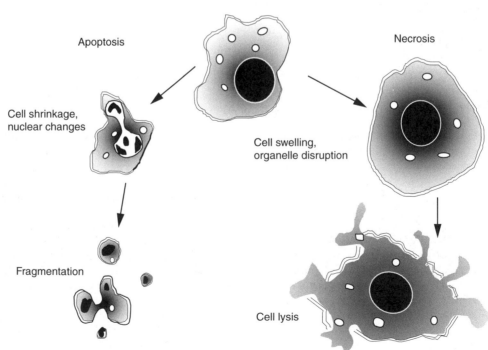

Figure 1. Apoptosis is morphologically distinct from necrosis. Apoptosis involves cell shrinkage, nuclear condensation, and fragmentation, followed by membrane blebbing and the formation of apoptotic bodies. In contrast, necrosis entails cell swelling, organelle disruption, and eventual cell lysis.

during apoptosis is the degradation of DNA into nucleosomal-sized fragments of approximately 180–200 bp in size, which form a ladder-type pattern when subjected to gel electrophoresis, a feature that is now one of the biochemical hallmarks of apoptosis (9). However, it should be noted that apoptotic internucleosomal DNA fragmentation is not universal, although high-molecular-weight fragmentation in the absence of low-molecular-weight fragmentation has been reported in certain cell types (10). The observation of varying degrees of DNA fragmentation in different cell types may be a consequence of the activation of one or more endonucleases that may be dependent on the inducing stimulus and/or differentiation status of the cell.

Much research has focused on the identification of the apoptotic endonuclease(s), which has resulted in the proposal of several putative enzymes, including DNAse I and DNAse II as well as other novel endonucleases (10). These enzymes have been put forward as apoptotic endonucleases on the basis of their ionic properties and expression patterns. The most recently described apoptotic endonuclease is the caspase-activated DNAse (CAD) (11). It appears that this enzyme is present in normal cells in association with an inhibitor termed ICAD. The specific proteolytic cleavage of ICAD during apoptosis appears to allow the activation of CAD and subsequent DNA fragmentation. Although CAD represents the most promising candidate to date for the apoptotic endonuclease, its existence does not exclude the possible participation of other enzymes in the degradation of DNA during apoptosis.

Cytoskeletal and Membrane Lipid Alterations

Cell shrinkage and apoptotic body formation requires significant changes in both the cytoskeleton and plasma membrane. The proteolytic degradation of cytoskeletal components such as actin, fodrin (12), and Gas2 during apoptosis appear to facilitate cytoplasmic collapse, membrane blebbing, and apoptotic body formation, processes that may also involve an elevation and redistribution of intracellular calcium (13).

Activation and accumulation of tissue-type transglutaminase, which catalyses $\varepsilon(\gamma$-glutamyl) lysine cross-linkages between protein substrates, may play a role in the maintenance of plasma membrane integrity in apoptoticcells (14). Several other alterations in plasma membrane composition are believed to play a role in the recognition and eventual phagocytosis of apoptotic cells. Redistribution of phosphatidylserine from its normal location on the inner leaf of the plasma membrane lipid bilayer to the outer leaf is believed to represent one such signal for apoptotic cell recognition (13). Indeed the translocation of phosphatidylserine in the plasma membrane is the basis for several currently available apoptosis assays. Other signaling molecules that appear to be involved in apoptotic cell recognition and phagocytosis include $\alpha_v\beta_3$ vitronectin, CD36, CD14, and the recently identified ced-5 protein product cloned from C. elegans, which shares homology to the human DOCK180 protein (15,16).

Cell Shrinkage

Changes in cell volume and granularity appear to be universal characteristics of apoptosis. The shrinkage of cells during apoptosis has been proposed to occur as a result of a net movement of fluid out of the cell. The exact mechanism by which this fluid movement occurs is currently unclear, but it has been suggested to involve the fusion of golgi and endoplasmic recticulum membranes with the plasma membrane (17). More recent data implicate a role for the active efflux of sodium and potassium ions through the Na^+, K^+-ATPase pump and the Ca^{2+}-dependent channel (18). This active ion efflux appears to be necessary for cell shrinkage and subsequent apoptotic body formation and is preceded by the exposition of phosphatidylserine on the outer leaf of the plasma membrane.

GENETIC REGULATION OF APOPTOSIS

bcl-2 Family

bcl-2 was the first oncogene shown to mediate its effects by an inhibition of apoptosis as opposed to the promotion of cell proliferation (19). It is the mammalian homologue of the *CED-9* gene in *C. elegans* and is now but one member of a growing family of related genes that encode both positive (Bax, Bak, Bcl-x$_S$, Bad, Bik) and negative (Bcl-2, Bcl-x$_L$, A1) regulators of apoptosis (see Table 1). Members of the Bcl-2 family are localized at the mitochondrial, endoplasmic, and nuclear membranes, where they interact to form hetero- and homodimers. It now appears that the relative ratio of these pro- and antiapoptotic members is of greater significance in the regulation of apoptosis than the expression of any single member in particular (20).

The exact mechanism by which the Bcl-2 family of proteins regulates apoptosis remains elusive. It has been suggested that Bcl-2 and the other antiapoptotic members of the family such as Bcl-x$_L$ act by sequestering target proteins to the nuclear, mitochondrial, and endoplasmic membranes, thereby inactivating them or allowing them to interact with other membrane-associated proteins. This hypothesis proposes that the formation of heterodimers with the proapoptotic members of the Bcl-2 family, such as Bax, prevents the docking/adaptor function of Bcl-2 or Bcl-x$_L$, thus thwarting their antiapoptotic effects (21).

Recent structural studies carried out on Bcl-x$_L$ suggest homology with the pore-forming domain of the diphtheria

Table 1. Genetic Regulators of Apoptosis

Positive regulators	Negative regulators
Bax	Bcl-2
Bcl-X$_s$	Bcl-X$_L$
Bad	A1
Bak	Mcl-1
Bik	BHRF-1
Caspases	CrmA
	p35
	IAP
Fas/FasL	soluble survival factors

toxin (22). Reports on the ability of Bcl-2 to affect calcium fluxes across the mitochondrial, endoplasmic, and nuclear membranes implies that Bcl-2 proteins might also serve a membrane transport function (23). In vitro studies demonstrate that Bcl-2 and Bcl-x$_L$ can form discrete ion channels, further supporting the notion that membrane transport may play a role in the modus operandi of this family of proteins (24). The ability of the proapoptotic Bax homologue to heterodimerize with Bcl-2 and Bcl-x$_L$ raises the possibility that Bax may prevent Bcl-2 or Bcl-x$_L$ from forming ion channels that may be central to their antiapoptotic function. It is also possible that heterodimeric channels may have different ion specificities and thereby different effects on cell viability.

Caspases (ICE-like Proteases)

A large body of evidence now supports a role for a family of aspartate specific cysteine proteases (caspases) in the effector phase of apoptosis (25). The initial link between apoptosis and the caspases followed the cloning and characterization of the *CED-3* death-promoting gene from *C. elegans*, which revealed significant homology to the mammalian interleukin-1β-converting enzyme (ICE) (26). Since then at least fourteen caspases have been identified, all of which are cysteine proteases requiring aspartate residues at the cleavage site.

Evidence for the role of caspases in apoptosis comes primarily from the ability of selective inhibitors to prevent apoptosis. Viral inhibitors of apoptosis such as CrmA and p35 have been demonstrated to interact directly with several caspases and are effective in protecting against apoptosis induced by many stimuli, including Fas/Apo-1, and serum and growth factor deprivation (27). Indeed it is worth noting that there are no documented cases of apoptosis that are p35 resistant. Artificial inhibitors of the caspases, designed on the basis of caspase cleavage sites, have also proven to be effective blockers of apoptosis and have been used to define the sequence of caspase activation in several models of apoptotic cell death. However, conflicting evidence is now emerging that suggests that while caspase inhibitors may prevent certain features of apoptosis, cells that have sustained a cytotoxic insult and have been treated with caspase inhibitors are nonetheless destined to die, albeit by a mechanism not readily identifiable as classical apoptosis (28).

Caspase-dependent cleavage of poly-adenyl-ribose polymerase (PARP) is now recognized as one of the hallmarks of apoptotic cell death (29). Other substrates of caspase activity include the nuclear proteins U1, small ribonucleoprotein, DNA-dependent protein kinase, sterol regulatory element binding proteins 1 and 2, and the nuclear lamins A, C, and B1. Cleavage of the cytoskeletal components actin, fodrin, and Gas2 by caspases are likely to facilitate cytosolic collapse and membrane blebbing. Cytoplasmic caspase substrates include protein kinase C δ, D4-GDI, and PITSLRE kinases. Other substrates include the retinoblastoma gene product product and ICAD, a recently described inhibitor of a caspase-activated DNAse (11). In addition to these substrates, several caspases appear to have autocatalyic activity as well as activity on other caspases, thus enabling the amplification of proteolytic activity during apoptosis.

Fas/Apo-1(CD95)

The Fas/Apo-1(CD95) receptor is a member of the TNF superfamily and represents a type 1 transmembrane protein. The primary function of the Fas receptor appears to be the induction of apoptosis following cross-linking by its ligand or agonistic antibody binding. *lpr* (reduced *fas* expression), *lpr^{cg}* (mutated Fas receptor), and *gld* (mutated Fas ligand) mice phenotypically exhibit lymphadenopathy and splenomegaly and generate large quantities of autoreactive antibodies (30). These mutants, and a recently identified human homologue of the *lpr* condition, strongly imply a role for Fas signaling in the deletion of peripheral autoreactive lymphocytes. More recent evidence also suggests a role for Fas signaling in the maintenance of the immunoprivilege status in the eye and testis (31), as well as the induction of apoptosis induced by chemotherapeutic drugs (32).

The Fas receptor signaling pathway now represents the archetype for a growing number of related death receptors. Cross-linking of the Fas receptor recruits FADD to the receptor complex through a specific amino acid sequence termed the *death domain* (33). Binding of FADD allows the subsequent recruitment of caspase 8 to form the death-inducing signal complex (DISC) (34). Caspase 8 becomes proteolytically active on DISC formation, an event negatively regulated by FLIP proteins (35), and is subsequently released and thereby free to initiate a cascade of proteolytic events, including the activation of other caspases.

The activation of phosphatidylcholine specific phospholipase C and the production of ceramides by an acidic sphingomyelinase are associated events of Fas signaling (36). However, reduced levels of acidic sphingomyelinase in humans and the deletion of the sphingomyelinase gene in mice does not result in an *lpr/gld* phenotype. Subsequently the exact role of ceramide signaling in Fas-mediated cell death remains unclear.

p53

p53 protein is a transcription factor whose activation may be induced under certain cellular conditions, including various types of DNA damage, hypoxia, and depletion of ribonucleoside triphosphate pools (37). p53 has been shown directly to transcribe at least six known genes, including the proapoptotic *bax* and a regulator of IGF signalling, *IGF-BP3* (38). Circumstantial evidence also exists for the upregulation of Fas receptor by p53. The cellular response to p53 activation depends on the level of the inducing signal. Following a mild cytotoxic insult p53 will mediate cell cycle arrest. It is believed that p53-mediated cell cycle arrest presents the cell with an opportunity to repair DNA damage (39). However, if the damage is extensive, apoptosis follows cell cycle arrest.

The exact mechanism by which p53 induces apoptosis remains unclear. While the upregulation of genes such as *bax* and *fas* would be expected to facilitate apoptosis, p53-mediated apoptosis has been demonstrated in the absence of transcriptional activity (40). Furthermore, the separation of p53's apoptotic function from its transcriptionally dependent cell cycle activity suggests separate regulatory mechanisms. The possibility, therefore, exists that p53 may mediate apoptosis by direct interaction with proteins such as c-Abl, whose overexpression has been reported to induce cell cycle arrest in a p53-dependent manner (41).

Experimental evidence from p53 null mice indicates that p53 is not required for developmental cell death (42), suggesting that p53's main role may be in the detection of DNA damage and the mediation of the appropriate response.

Mitochondria

It is now becoming apparent that the mitochondria play a central role in the execution of the apoptotic program. Reports on the use of cell-free systems to study apoptosis have described the requirement of a mitochondrial fraction in order for caspase activation and DNA fragmentation to occur (43). Subsequent fractionation and purification of the mitochondrial fraction has revealed cytochrome-c as necessary for caspase activation (44). Indeed the release of cytochrome-c from the mitochondria has been reported to occur during apoptosis, while microinjection of cytochrome-c into the cytosol appears to be sufficient to induce apoptosis (45). A second protein necessary for the activation of the caspases downstream of the mitochondria is Apaf-1, the mammalian homologue of the *C. elegans* death gene *CED-4* (46). Interaction between ced-4, cytochrome-c, and ced-9 (the nematode homologue of Bcl-2) has also recently been demonstrated, offering a possible mechanism for caspase activation by cytochrome-c (47) (see Fig. 2).

The release of cytochrome-c seems to occur prior to any other changes in the mitochondria, such as loss of transmembrane potential ($\Delta\psi_m$). Alterations in $\Delta\psi_m$ have been reported during apoptosis induced by a diverse range of stimuli (48). It is believed that this loss of $\Delta\psi_m$ occurs via the permeability transition (PT) pore, which allows the movement of solutes 1.5 kD and smaller out of the mitochondria. Inhibitors of PT, which include Bcl-2 and Bcl-x_L, have also been demonstrated as efficient inhibitors of apoptosis. The interaction between cytochrome-c, *ced-9*, and *ced-4*, as well as the ability of Bcl-2 and Bcl-x_L to inhibit cytochrome-c release and PT, has led to the proposition that the mitochondria represent the site of regulatory action for the Bcl-2 family. This view is supported by the observation that Bax is capable of inducing cytochrome-c release and loss of $\Delta\psi_m$ (49). The exact mechanisms by which the Bcl-2 family control cytochrome-c release and PT, however, remain to be elucidated.

SURVIVAL FACTORS

Several studies have established that many soluble factors previously referred to as growth factors are capable of maintaining viability in the absence of proliferation. Such factors are now referred to as survival factors. Survival factors play a major role in the homeostatic maintenance

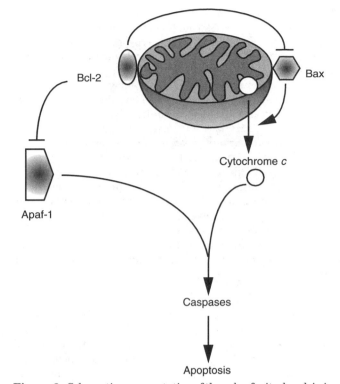

Figure 2. Schematic representation of the role of mitochondria in apoptosis. Cellular insult causes the release of cytochrome-c from the mitochondria facilitated by Bax. The release of cytochrome-c may be inhibited by the heterodimerization of Bcl-2 with Bax. Cytosolic cytochrome-c interacts with the mammalian homologue of CED 4, Apaf-1, allowing subsequent caspase activation. Proteolytic activity of caspases on specific substrates completes the apoptotic program.

of cell populations in the adult, and also in the formation of embryonic structures during development.

Survival factors (e.g., insulin-like growth factors and platelet-derived growth factor) have been shown to prevent apoptosis induced by activation of the *myc* proto-oncogene (50). In the absence of a survival signal, activation of *myc* results in concomitant proliferation and apoptosis and thus no net gain in population size. This mechanism, whereby proliferation is inherently linked to apoptosis, results in the restriction of population size according to the availability of survival factors.

These and other studies support the view initially proposed by Raff in 1992 that all cells (with the exception perhaps of the zygote) express a default program for cell death and will undergo apoptosis unless they are rescued by the presence of survival factors (51). Thus specific cell types would be localized to the tissues producing their survival factor, and population size would be limited by its availability. Evidence for this hypothesis has since been accumulating. For example, vertebrate neurons are dependent upon neurotrophins secreted by target cells, ventral prostate epithelial cells rely upon testosterone secreted by the testes, and the adrenal cortex depends upon adreno-corticotropic hormone produced by the pituitary. Endothelial cells rely upon several survival factors including fibroblast growth factor for their viability (50). Subsets of haematopoietic cells have also been shown to be dependent on specific survival factors (e.g., IL-3, GM-CSF, erythropoietin) (52). In all these instances, withdrawal of the relevant survival factor induces apoptosis.

Survival signals have also been shown to play a major role in the control of cell numbers during embryonic development in higher animals. Excess numbers of sympathetic neurons are formed during the development of the central nervous system. These cells compete for survival signals produced by target cells, a process that automatically balances the number of innervating neurons to target cells. A similar process appears to operate in the matching of presynaptic and postsynaptic neurons during the development of both the peripheral and central nervous systems. Thus excessive cellular production and apoptosis appear to be normal features of both development and homeostasis in multicellular organisms.

APOPTOSIS IN CELL CULTURE: SMALL TO LARGE SCALE

The emergence of apoptosis as a genetically regulated homeostatic mechanism has extended the boundaries of current medical research into both malignant and degenerative disorders. In addition, it has offered a new parameter for consideration in the long-term culture of animal cell lines. A better understanding of the factors that influence viability in laboratory cultures may assist in the generation of novel cell lines, particularly from tissues that are difficult to propagate and are currently studied in short-term primary cultures. Apoptosis research may also provide insights into the extension of cell viability in large-scale cultures and contribute to significant productivity improvements in bioprocessing industries.

Apoptosis in Small-Scale Cultures

Synthetic media for long-term cell culture have been optimized to sustain a high proliferative capacity. Heat-inactivated serum (usually foetal bovine) is an essential media supplement for growing cells. Cell death was initially of little regard in preliminary studies for medium design. Provided cells had an energy source (e.g., glucose) to sustain their metabolism, building blocks (e.g., amino acids, nucleic acids) for daughter cells, and serum-derived growth factors, proliferation could be achieved. It is now apparent, however, that resistance to apoptosis has already played a significant role in the development of long-term cell cultures. Many cell lines have attained antiapoptotic properties. Indeed most have been derived from tumor cells, which by their very nature are resistant to the normal physiological mechanisms that induce apoptosis in abnormal or excessive cells. Such cells have frequently gained expression of antiapoptotic genes (e.g., Bcl-2 or Bcr-Ab1) and/or lost expression of proapoptotic genes such as p53. In addition, serum is now known to contain factors distinct from growth factors, which provide survival signals for cells in culture (see section on survival factors). Cell lines that are not malignant in origin often require extra supplementation with specific survival factors (e.g., IL-3 is an important survival factor for several nontumorigenic haematopoietic cell lines). Thus factors (genetic or environmental) that promote viability and reduce apoptosis are important for the long-term propagation of cells.

Apoptosis can be induced in cell cultures by a variety of stimuli, including those that resemble physiological signals (serum starvation, depletion of survival factors) and also nonphysiological signals (cytotoxic drugs, ultraviolet irradiation). In addition, it has been noted that in most cell cultures background levels (~5%) of apoptosis are apparent in the absence of inducing stimuli. This perhaps questions the idea that cell lines are immortal; rather it should be considered that growing cultures rely upon the proliferative rate exceeding that of apoptosis.

The artificial nature of cell cultures enables apoptotic cells to progress to the later stages of cell disintegration. Under physiological circumstances apoptotic cells are rapidly recognized and ingested by phagocytic cells, and thus the latter stages of apoptosis are contained within the phagocytic cell. In cell cultures apoptosis proceeds to a late stage referred to as secondary necrosis. At this stage, the apoptotic cell loses membrane integrity and can therefore take up certain dyes that are usually indicative of necrosis (primary necrosis). Methodology for the detection of cell death has therefore progressed to include characteristics of apoptosis (e.g., chromatin condensation/DNA fragmentation), in addition to traditional assessments of membrane integrity.

Apoptosis in Large-Scale Cultures

Large-scale animal cell cultures are employed in the biotechnology and pharmaceutical industries for the production of biologically active proteins such as cytokines, vaccines, and antibodies. Such proteins are becoming increasingly important for therapeutic, diagnostic, and analytical purposes. Cell lines are most frequently cultivated in industrial bioreactors in batch mode. The producing cell line is initially seeded into a nutrient-rich medium. The culture proceeds through a logarithmic growth phase to a stationary phase, followed by death due to nutrient depletion and/or the accumulation of toxic metabolites. Viable cells in the late logarithmic growth phase and the subsequent stationary (non-growth-viable) phase are the major contributors to productivity. Other types of cultivation procedure being developed include "fed batch," in which the feeding of essential nutrients may prolong viability at the stationary phase of a culture, or "perfusion" cultures, in which depleted medium is continuously removed and the culture is replenished with fresh medium. Such cultivation strategies are aimed at prolonging viability in high-density cultures (53).

In all types of culture the induction of cell death limits productivity. Even in perfusion cultures when the population is at a stationary phase for an extended period, the culture has reached an equilibrium between proliferation and death (54). Thus dead and fragmented cells can accumulate in the bioreactor and present problems in downstream processing, such as fouling of filtration devices. In addition, the release of cellular contents from dead cells liberates various proteases and glycosidases, which can damage the protein product. Although the factors that contribute to cell death in large-scale cultures have been known for many years, it is only recently that investigators have begun to ask which type of cell death is prevalent. Apoptosis has been reported to be the predominant method of cell death at the late exponential and stationary phases of batch culture (55–57). Depletion of amino acids (58), glucose and glutamine (57), serum components (56), and mechanical agitation (59) have all been reported to induce apoptosis in commercially important cell lines.

Thus cell death in bioreactors is not a purely passive process as has been previously thought. Cells respond to adverse culture conditions in a manner resembling their normal response to physiological signals. Cell death is not directly caused by serum starvation or presence of a toxin, but rather by the cell itself in a measured response to the inducing signal. This knowledge presents a new parameter for manipulation in the optimization of large-scale culture conditions.

STRATEGIES FOR MANIPULATION

Strategies for enhancing cell productivity are being extensively studied. Of particular interest is the development of cell cultures with reduced dependence upon serum. Serum can be an extremely expensive component of culture media, and it can often complicate downstream purification and recovery of protein product. In addition, the poorly defined nature and consistency of properties of animal serum may be an obstacle for regulatory approval when the protein product is intended for therapeutic use.

Previous efforts to improve viability and productivity have largely focused on feeding strategies and media designed to promote proliferation. It has, however, been established that high proliferation rates facilitated by excessive levels of glucose or glutamine result in high levels of cell death due to byproduct (lactate or ammonia) formation (53). Moreover, it has also been reported that cells are most productive in the G0/G1 phase of the cell cycle (60), and that slower growth rates can improve product yield (61). Complete cell cycle arrest will, however, eventually lead to apoptosis. Given the fact that cells are more productive when they are not dividing, it is reasonable to expect that once a population has achieved maximum density, productivity could be significantly improved by conditions that reduce cell death. The knowledge that apoptosis is initially the predominant form of cell death in bioreactor cell populations, coupled with the recent expansion in information regarding control mechanisms in apoptosis, has provided an opportunity to manipulate a previously unconsidered parameter.

Genetic Optimization of Cell Lines

Many new genes and large gene families have recently been discovered which are involved in the regulation of cell death (see section on genetic regulation and Table 1). It is now evident that tumor cells have been availing themselves of antiapoptotic mechanisms to promote their viability and progression, and also in the attainment of resistance to chemotherapeutic drugs (52). Many viruses have also exploited antiapoptotic genes, including *bcl-2* family members and caspase inhibitors, to prevent apoptosis in their host cells. In effect, biological manipulators of apoptosis have been around for many thousands of years. This realization further substantiates the idea that more "genetically fit" cell lines for industrial purposes could be generated by manipulating viability with antiapoptotic genes or surival factors (see Fig. 3).

The first mammalian antiapoptotic gene to be discovered was *bcl-2*. This gene has already been shown to confer resistance to apoptosis induced by a variety of stimuli in small-scale cultures. Several investigators have therefore assessed the ability of Bcl-2 constructs to generate more robust and productive commercially important cell lines. Burkitts lymphoma cells transfected with Bcl-2 and subjected to batch culture conditions were found to be more resistant to the induction of apoptosis following glutamine deprivation, serum depletion, and growth arrest (56). TB/C3 hybridoma cells expressing exogenous Bcl-2 were also found to have extended viability in conditions of hypoxia, hyperoxia, glutamine and glucose deprivation, and serum limitation. Monoclonal antibody production in batch culture was increased by approximately 40% compared to control cell cultures (62). In another mouse hybridoma cell line, expression of high levels of exogenous Bcl-2 raised the maximum viable cell density by 45%

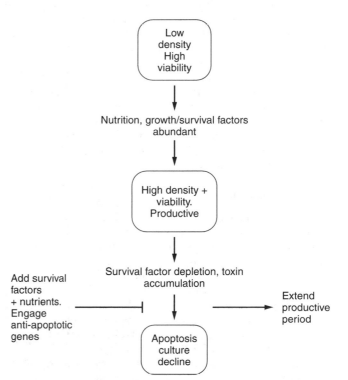

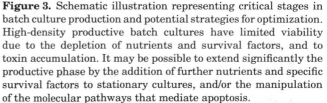

Figure 3. Schematic illustration representing critical stages in batch culture production and potential strategies for optimization. High-density productive batch cultures have limited viability due to the depletion of nutrients and survival factors, and to toxin accumulation. It may be possible to extend significantly the productive phase by the addition of further nutrients and specific survival factors to stationary cultures, and/or the manipulation of the molecular pathways that mediate apoptosis.

and delayed the initiation of apoptosis in batch culture by 2 days. The specific productivity of Bcl-2 transfectants was more than twice that of control transfected cell lines (63). COS cells stably expressing Bcl-2 showed markedly improved survival when cultured in low serum, and their productivity was also increased twofold (64). A recent study has suggested that the protection levels afforded by Bcl-2 are dependent upon the apoptosis-inducing stimuli. Transfection of the CRL-1606 hybridoma cell line with Bcl-2 provided marginal, if any, protection from nutrient depletion, but significantly reduced apoptosis induced by serum starvation (65). These authors suggest that Bcl-2 functionally compensates for the absence of survival factors. They further suggest that the massive cell death exhibited by cultures of CRL-1606 during fed-batch fermentation (66) is likely to be a consequence of inappropriate cell cycle entry in a survival-factor-limited environment.

Other studies suggest that exogenous expression of Bcl-2 may be of little consequence in certain cell lines. Bcl-2 was found to extend viability of High Five™ but not Sf-9 insect cell lines (67). In NSO myeloma cells, expression of Bcl-2 failed to influence serum dependence or the decline phase characteristics of a batch culture (68). Further analysis of this cell line revealed high expression levels of Bcl-X_L, a functional homologue of Bcl-2. Thus high endogenous expression of another antiapoptotic Bcl-2 family member may render exogenous expression of Bcl-2 functionally redundant.

Decreased expression of proapoptotic genes may also prove to be a useful tool for modifying cell viability. *c-jun* is an immediate early gene that plays a critical role in the commitment of a cell to proliferate, but (analogous to *myc*) it can also promote apoptosis (69). F-Mel cells transfected with an inducable *c-jun* antisense gene were found to maintain a constant cell density (after antisense induction) and a high viability above 80% for 8 days under serum starvation. In contrast, control cell lines died by apoptosis within 3 days (70). Productivity was not assessed in this preliminary study.

Media Formulation

In addition to genetically optimizing cell lines, media formulations could be tailored to extend cell viability. This may involve the inclusion of specific survival factors provided the productivity improvement could justify the additional expense. Interleukin-6 (IL-6) was found to extend significantly the viability of Sp2/0 hybridoma cells in low serum (71). As cytokines are expensive, it is at present impractical to consider their inclusion in media formulations. Consequently these investigators transfected the cDNA for the IL-6 gene into the hybridoma cell line. The transfected cultures, however, exhibited growth inhibitory properties compared to control cultures and a decrease in batch culture yield. It is possible that this problem could be overcome by using an inducable promoter (as used for *c-jun* in the preceding discussion) and limiting IL-6 expression until after an optimal cell density has been achieved.

Other less expensive media additives may include nonessential amino acids (NEAAs), peptide inhibitors of caspases, or antioxidant molecules. The addition of NEAAs was found to prolong membrane stability during the death phase of batch cultures and to increase antibody productivity (72). Short peptides (~4 amino acids) that interfere with the catalytic site of caspases have been shown to protect small-scale cultures from apoptosis induced by a variety of stimuli (25). Although such peptides are expensive to purchase at present, their simplicity suggests that their production could be achieved relatively inexpensively by biotechnology companies if so required. Antioxidant molecules such as zinc and pyrrolidine dithiocarbamate have been shown to protect small-scale cultures from apoptosis induced by a variety of stimuli. These compounds exert their effects by neutralizing reactive oxygen species that are thought to be important signalling molecules in apoptotic pathways (73). The effects of anti-oxidants on batch culture apoptosis and productivity has not been established.

There are undoubtedly many mediators of apoptosis (in particular, *bcl-2* family members and caspase inhibitors) which remain untested with respect to their potential modulatory effects on the viability and productivity of commercially important cell lines.

CONCLUSIONS AND FUTURE PERSPECTIVES

Since the acceptance of apoptosis as a genetically regulated physiological phenomenon, the level of interest and information on the subject has expanded exponentially. Cell death resembling apoptosis has been identified in a range of organisms, and can be induced by diverse stimuli. New highly conserved gene families have been identified, and many genes previously associated with cell cycle or proliferation (e.g., *p53*, *myc*, *jun*) have now also been shown to influence apoptosis.

Much recent research has focused on key cytoplasmic components of apoptotic pathways and the possible links between them. Significant progress has been made in identifying important mediators of apoptosis, yet the biochemical functions of many (e.g., *bcl-2* family members) are poorly understood. In addition, while considerable effort has been focused on the cytoplasmic execution pathways, upstream signalling pathways involved in life and death decision making remain elusive. The current pace of research suggests that many gaps in present knowledge will be filled in the very near future. Progress in apoptosis research will undoubtedly expedite medical research, particularly into degenerative diseases that are characterized by excessive cell death, and malignant diseases that are characterized by insufficient cell death. It is also anticipated that a better understanding of apoptosis will deliver significant productivity improvements in the biotechnology industry.

Cell lines currently in use in industrial bioreactors have already been partially selected for their antiapoptotic nature. In particular, if the cell line has been established from a malignant disease, it will undoubtedly have gained antiapoptotic lesions during the course of its development. Recent research, however, suggests that, providing the same pathway has not already been fully exploited by a cell line, the expression of additional antiapoptotic genes (or downregulation of proapoptotic genes) can significantly extend viability and enhance productivity in adverse conditions. Genetic optimization of cell lines may therefore require an initial assessment of important survival pathways already present.

Optimization of serum-free media also requires a better knowledge of survival factors and the internal pathways they activate. While progress has been made in identifying some important survival factors (e.g., IGF-1), the growth and survival components of serum are undefined and must be better elucidated. Given the rapidly expanding families of cell death mediators, it seems likely that there are numerous pathways that lead to apoptosis and possibly many opposing survival pathways that could be activated. It is likely that the generation of "designer" cell cultures may require the manipulation of more than one relevant gene, coupled with a carefully considered media formulation for a given cell type.

Many cellular-derived proteins are of significant therapeutic potential, but their expense often restricts initial availability. The value of such products justifies the continuous quest for productivity improvements.

BIBLIOGRAPHY

1. R.A. Lockshin and C.M. Williams, *J. Insect Physiol.* **10**, 643–649 (1994).

2. J.F.R. Kerr, A.H. Wyllie, and A.R. Currie, *Br J. Cancer* **26**, 239–245 (1972).

3. H.M. Ellis and H.R. Horvitz, *Cell (Cambridge, Mass.)* **44**, 817–829 (1986).

4. A.M. Gorman, A. McGowan, C. O'Neill, and T. Cotter, *J. Neurol. Sci.* **139**, 45–52 (1996).

5. D.L. Vaux, G. Haecker, and A. Strasser, *Cell (Cambridge, Mass.)* **76**, 777–779 (1994).

6. J.C. Ameisen, *Science* **272**, 1278–1279 (1996).

7. M.B. Yarmolinsky, *Science* **267**, 836–836 (1995).

8. A.H. Wyllie, J.F.R. Kerr, and A.R. Currie, *Int. Rev. Cytol.* **68**, 251–306 (1980).

9. J.J. Cohen and R.C. Duke, *J.Immunol.* **132**, 38–42 (1984).

10. P.R. Walker, S. Pandey, and M. Sikorska, *Cell Death Differ.* **2**, 97–104 (1995).

11. M. Enari et al., *Nature (London)* **391**, 43–50 (1998).

12. S.J. Martin et al., *J. Biol. Chem.* **270**, 6425–6428 (1995).

13. S.J. Martin et al., *J. Exp. Med.* **182**, 1545–1556 (1995).

14. L. Fesus, V. Thomazy, and A. Falus, *FEBS Lett.* **224**, 104–108 (1987).

15. Y.-C. Wu and H.R. Horvitz, *Nature (London)* **392**, 501–504 (1998).

16. A. Devitt et al., *Nature (London)* **392**, 505–509 (1998).

17. D.G. Morris, E. Duvall, A.D. Hargreaves, and A.H. Wyllie, *Am. J. Pathol.* **115**, 426–436 (1984).

18. J.V. McCarthy and T.G. Cotter, *Cell Death. Differ.* **4**, 756–770 (1997).

19. P. Vaux, S. Cory, and J.M. Adams, *Nature (London)* **335**, 440–442 (1988).

20. Z.N. Oltvai, C.L. Milliman, and S. Korsmeyer, *Cell (Cambridge, Mass.)* **74**, 609–619 (1993).

21. J.C. Reed, *Nature (London)* **387**, 773–776 (1997).

22. S.W. Muchmore et al., *Nature (London)* **381**, 335–341 (1996).

23. M. Lam et al., *Proc. Natl. Acad. Sci. U.S.A.* **91**, 6569–6573 (1994).

24. A.J. Minn et al., *Nature (London)* **385**, 353–357 (1997).

25. P. Villa, S. Kaufmann, and W.C. Earnshaw, *Trends Biochem. Sci.* **22**, 388–393 (1997).

26. J. Yuan et al., *Cell (Cambridge, Mass.)* **75**, 641–652 (1993).

27. N.J. McCarthy, M.K.B. Whyte, C.S. Gilbert, and G.I. Evans, *J. Cell Biol.* **136**, 215–227 (1997).

28. S.H. Kaufmann et al., *Cancer Res.* **53**, 3976–3985 (1993).

29. M. Tewari and V.M. Dixit, *J. Biol. Chem.* **270**, 3255–3260 (1995).

30. K.-M. Debatin, *Cell Death Differ.* **3**, 185–189 (1996).

31. T.S. Griffith et al., *Science* **270**, 1189–1192 (1995).

32. C. Friesen, I. Herr, P.H. Krammer, and K.-M. Debatin, *Nat. Med.* **2**, 574–577 (1996).

33. F.C. Kischkel et al., *EMBO J.* **14**, 5579–5588 (1995).

34. M. Muzio et al., *Cell (Cambridge, Mass.)* **85**, 817–827 (1996).

35. M. Thome et al., *Nature (London)* **386**, 517–521 (1997).

36. E.W. Skowronski, R.N. Kolesnick, and D.R. Green, *Cell Death Differ.* **3**, 171–176 (1996).

37. A.J. Levine, *Cell (Cambridge, Mass.)* **88**, 323–331 (1997).

38. E. Yonish-Rouach, *Experientia* **52**, 1001–1007 (1996).

39. S.E. Morgan and M.B. Kastan, *Adv. Cancer Res.* **71**, 1–25 (1997).

40. C. Caelles, A. Helmberg, and M. Karin, *Nature (London)* **370**, 220–223 (1994).

41. A. Goga et al., *Oncogene* **11**, 791–799 (1995).

42. C. Deng et al., *Cell (Cambridge, Mass.)* **82**, 675–684 (1995).

43. D.D. Newmeyer, D.M. Farschan, and J.C. Reed, *Cell (Cambridge, Mass.)* **79**, 353–364 (1994).

44. K. Liu et al., *Cell (Cambridge, Mass.)* **86**, 147–157 (1996).

45. B. Zhivotovsky, S. Orrenius, O.T. Brustugun and S.O. Doskeland, *Nature (London)* **391**, 449–450 (1998).

46. H. Zou et al., *Cell (Cambridge, Mass.)* **90**, 405–413 (1997).

47. A.M. Chinnaiyan, K. O'Rourke, B.R. Lane, and V.M. Dixit, *Science* **275**, 1122–1126 (1997).

48. G. Kroemer, *Cell Death Differ.* **4**, 443–456 (1997).

49. R.M. Kluck, E. Bossy-Wetzel, D.R. Green, and D.D. Newmeyer, *Science* **275**, 1132–1136 (1997).

50. E.A. Harrington, M.R. Bennett, A. Fanidi, and G.I. Evan, *EMBO J.* **13**, 3286–3295 (1994).

51. M.C. Raff, *Nature (London)* **356**, 397–400 (1992).

52. S.L. McKenna and T.G. Cotter, *Adv. Cancer Res.* **71**, 121–164 (1997).

53. L. Xie and D.I.C. Wang, *Trends Biotechnol.* **15**, 109–113 (1997).

54. S. Terada, H. Morita, F. Makishima, and E. Suzuki, *Kagaku Kogaku Ronbunshu* **19**, 207–213 (1993).

55. T. Vomastek and F. Franek, *Immunol. Lett.* **35**, 19–24 (1993).

56. R.P. Singh, A.N. Emery, and M. Al-Rubeai, *Biotechnol. Bioeng.* **52**, 166–175 (1996).

57. S. Mercille and B. Massie, *Biotechnol. Bioeng.* **44**, 1140–1154 (1994).

58. F. Franek and K. Chladkova-Sramkova, *Cytotechnology* **18**, 113–117 (1995).

59. M. Al-Rubeai, R.P. Singh, M.H. Goldman, and A.N. Emery, *Biotechnol. Bioeng.* **45**, 463–472 (1995).

60. M. Al-Rubeai and A.N. Emery, *J. Biotechnol.* **16**, 67–86 (1990).

61. E. Suzuki and D.F. Ollis, *Biotechnol. Prog.* **6**, 231–236 (1990).

62. N.H. Simpson, A.E. Milner, and M. Al-Rubeai, *Biotechnol. Bioeng.* **54**, 1–16 (1997).

63. Y. Itoh, H. Ueda, and E. Suzuki, *Biotechnol. Bioeng.* **48**, 118–122 (1995).

64. T. Fujita, S. Terada, H. Ueda, and E. Suzuki, *J. Ferment. Bioeng.* **82**, 589–591 (1996).

65. J.D. Chung, A.J. Sinskey, and G. Stephanopoulos *Biotechnol. Bioeng.* **57**, 164–171 (1998).

66. L. Xie and D.I.C. Wang, *Cytotechnology* **15**, 17–29 (1994).

67. C. Mitchell-Logean and D.W. Murhammer, *Biotechnol. Bioeng.* **56**, 380–390 (1997).

68. K. Murry et al., *Biotechnol. Bioeng.* **51**, 298–304 (1996).

69. H. Sawai et al., *J. Biol. Chem.* **270**, 27326–27331 (1995).

70. Y.H. Kim et al., *Biotechnol. Bioeng.* **58**, 65–72 (1998).

71. J.D. Chung, C. Zabel, A.J. Sinskey, and G. Stephanopoulos, *Biotechnol. Bioeng.* **55**, 439–446 (1997).

72. D. Fassnacht, S. Rossing, N. Ghaussy, and R. Portner, *Biotechnol. Lett.* **19**, 35–38 (1997).

73. A.F.G. Slater et al., *Cell Death Differ.* **3**, 57–62 (1996).

See also Cell cycle events and cell cycle-dependent processes; Cell cycle in suspension cultured plant cells; Characterization and determination of cell death by apoptosis.

PROTEIN PROCESSING, ENDOCYTOSIS AND INTRACELLULAR SORTING OF GROWTH FACTORS

Alexander Sorkin
University of Colorado Health Sciences Center
Denver, Colorado

OUTLINE

Introduction

Endocytosis of Growth Factor Receptors

Receptor Recruitment into Clathrin-Coated Pits

Molecular Mechanisms of Internalization

Pathway Through Endosomal Compartments

Kinetics of Intracellular Trafficking: Recycling Versus Degradation

Mechanism of Receptor Sorting in Endosomes

Other Types of Signaling Receptors

Perspectives

Acknowledgments

Bibliography

INTRODUCTION

Receptor-mediated endocytosis is the main gate for the entry of many macromolecules into the cell (1). The ligand—receptor complexes formed on the cell surface can be clustered in small areas of the plasma membrane covered with a protein coat from the inside of the membrane. The coated areas of the plasma membrane pouch inward and pinch off vesicles. These endocytic vesicles fuse with specialized membrane organelles known as endosomes, which deliver the receptors and their ligands to various intracellular compartments. Receptors can recycle back to the cell surface and participate in several rounds of endocytosis, or are delivered to lysosomes for degradation. Endocytosis, recycling, and therefore surface expression of many receptors is not affected by ligand binding. However, for receptors that transduce signals across the membrane, such as receptors for polypeptide growth factors (GFs) or G protein-coupled receptors, endocytosis and subsequent sorting of the internalized receptors to the lysosome-degradation pathway are dramatically accelerated by the ligand. As a result, the surface and total cellular receptor pool is substantially reduced, a phenomenon called ligand-induced "down-regulation" of the receptors.

ENDOCYTOSIS OF GROWTH FACTOR RECEPTORS

The endocytosis of GF receptors that possess intrinsic tyrosine kinase activity remains to be a classical model system to study down-regulation. The specificity of down-regulation for the signaling receptors suggests that GF-induced endocytosis may play an important role in the control of the signal transduction process. However, neither the molecular mechanisms by which ligand triggers receptor down-regulation nor the biological role of this phenomenon are fully understood. In this article, the general pathways of receptor-mediated endocytosis will be described with the focus on the mechanisms that are unique for GF receptors. We will build our discussion around endocytosis of the epidermal growth factor (EGF) receptor since studies of this receptor have produced most of the original data on which the current model of GF receptor endocytosis is based. In light of very recent findings obtained in studies of the cytokine and G-coupled receptors, we will discuss some novel mechanisms of endocytosis of these receptors.

RECEPTOR RECRUITMENT INTO CLATHRIN-COATED PITS

The process of constitutive formation of endocytic vesicles from the plasma membrane is a part of the recycling of cellular membranes. However, vesicle budding is significantly accelerated in specialized regions termed *clathrin-coated pits* (reviewed in Ref. 2). These organelles contain two major structural components: clathrin itself and adaptor—protein complexes (APs). Clathrin consists of three copies each of heavy chain (~190 kD) and light chain (~23–27 kD), forming a three-legged structure called a triskelion. Clathrin triskelions are the assembly units of the polygonal lattice. Clathrin assembles into coats on the cytoplasmic side of the plasma membrane by interacting with its adaptor complex AP-2. AP-2 is heterotetramer consisting of two large (~100 kD) α and $\beta 2$, one medium $\mu 2$ (50 kD), and one small $\sigma 2$ subunit (17 kD). In addition, several other proteins that play a regulatory role are found in coated pits.

One group of receptors (class I) is clustered in coated pits and rapidly internalized even when no ligand has bound. The well-known examples of this type are the receptors for transferrin, mannose-6-phosphate, and low-density lipoprotein. Signaling receptors, for example, EGF receptors, are the class II receptors that are efficiently concentrated in coated pits and internalized only when occupied with the specific ligand (3). In the absence of EGF, EGF receptors are diffusely distributed at the cell surface (4,5). A small pool of unoccupied receptors can be detected in coated pits (5,6). The relative size of this pool appears to be dependent on cell type and level of receptor expression (4,6,7). Although quantitative studies of the distribution of EGF receptors in coated and uncoated regions of the plasma membrane are limited, several reports clearly demonstrated rapid aggregation and accumulation of EGF receptors in coated pits upon EGF binding (4,5,7–9) (Fig. 1).

An individual coated pit can package and internalize more than one type of receptor (10). Conformational rearrangements of the clathrin lattice result in deep invagination of the coated pit and fission of the coated endocytic vesicle containing cargo proteins. Clathrin and associated proteins must then return back to the plasma membrane to reassemble coated pits (Fig. 1). Several stages of the coated pit cycle require energy and physiological temperature, and are regulated by GTP-binding proteins. Importantly, whereas late steps of internalization appear to be common for all types of receptors, receptor recruitment into coated pits is the rate-limiting and ligand-dependent step of the internalization of GF receptors (9,11).

MOLECULAR MECHANISMS OF INTERNALIZATION

Although endocytosis of some receptors can occur in the absence of functional coated pits, clathrin-dependent endocytosis is the most efficient and fastest pathway. Coated pits recruit receptors with high efficiency and selectivity because they can recognize "endocytic codes" or "internalization signals," sequence motifs in the cytoplasmic domains of the receptors (12). There are several such signals; the motifs based on the tyrosine residue and a hydrophobic residue in +3 position (YxxΘ) are most well characterized (12). The receptor-recognition protein in coated pits is the $\mu2$ subunit of AP-2 (13), although β-arrestin proteins are also implicated in the recruitment of the G protein-coupled receptors (see the following).

The EGF receptor (EGFR) interaction with AP-2 has been demonstrated in in vivo and in vitro experiments (14,15). However, it is not formally proven whether this interaction is important and sufficient for EGF-induced recruitment of receptors into coated pits. In fact, the dogma did not survive functional testing in vivo: EGFRs lacking the high-affinity AP-2 binding site can be internalized via a clathrin-dependent mechanism (16,17). Moreover, coimmunoprecipitation with AP-2 has been reported for the EGF receptor family only (18,19). The interactions of other GF receptors with AP-2 have not been shown in any type of experimental assays.

Analysis of EGF endocytosis revealed that, besides characteristics common for endocytosis of class I and II receptors (for instance, temperature and ATP dependence), the specific internalization rate of EGF was several fold higher at low than at high EGF concentrations (20). Mathematical modeling of these data led to the proposal that there are two pathways of internalization of EGF receptors: a rapid saturable pathway used by a limited number of EGF-activated receptors, and a five to ten times slower nonsaturable endocytosis that is employed by the unoccupied or EGF-occupied receptors when the rapid pathway is saturated (11). It has been postulated that whereas the saturable pathway involves clathrin-coated pits, the slow pathway is clathrin-independent (11).

The low capacity of high-affinity EGF-induced receptor internalization suggested that unique mechanisms may regulate this pathway. It has been hypothesized that proteins other than AP-2, expressed in limited amounts in the cell, control the rapid pathway (9,11,21,22). These proteins are not yet identified. A study on MDCK cells demonstrated that the microinjection of src-homology 2 (SH2) domains of GRB2 adapter protein blocks endocytosis of the EGF receptor (23). However, because removal of all phosphorylation sites of the EGF receptor, including GRB2 binding, did not affect EGF endocytosis (24,25), it is difficult to reconcile this observation with the previous results of kinetics analysis of receptor mutants (24–27) (see also the following). An EGF receptor phosphorylation substrate, eps15, has been also implicated in EGF receptor endocytosis (28). However, eps15 appears to play an essential role in general endocytic machinery and is not specific for growth factor internalization (29).

Intensive studies were directed to determine which regions of the receptor molecule are critical for internalization. The EGF receptor is a glycoprotein (170 kD) of which approximately 40 kD is N-linked carbohydrate. The mature EGF receptor is composed of three major regions: an extracellular ligand binding domain containing two high-cysteine-content regions, a hydrophobic transmembrane region, and a cytoplasmic domain. The cytoplasmic domain consists of a conserved kinase domain located between two regulatory regions: juxtamembrane and carboxyl-terminal domains. The carboxyl-terminus contains at least five tyrosine and several serine residues that can be phosphorylated, whereas the juxtamembrane domain has two threonine phosphorylation sites (Fig. 2). Phosphorylated residues are involved in regulation of the receptor kinase activity and receptor interaction with other proteins. Since the intracellular domain of the EGF receptor is essential for endocytosis, the importance of the kinase activity and various regions of the carboxyl terminus were examined using receptor mutagenesis (Fig. 2). Mutational inactivation of the receptor kinase resulted in significant reduction of the internalization rate (30–34). Kinase-negative receptors were capable of internalization with a moderate speed that did not depend on EGF concentration (nonsaturable pathway), suggesting that kinase activity controls the specific saturable internalization. Kinase activity is also necessary for the maximum rapid internalization of the platelet-derived growth factor (PDGF) (35), macrophage colony-stimulating factor

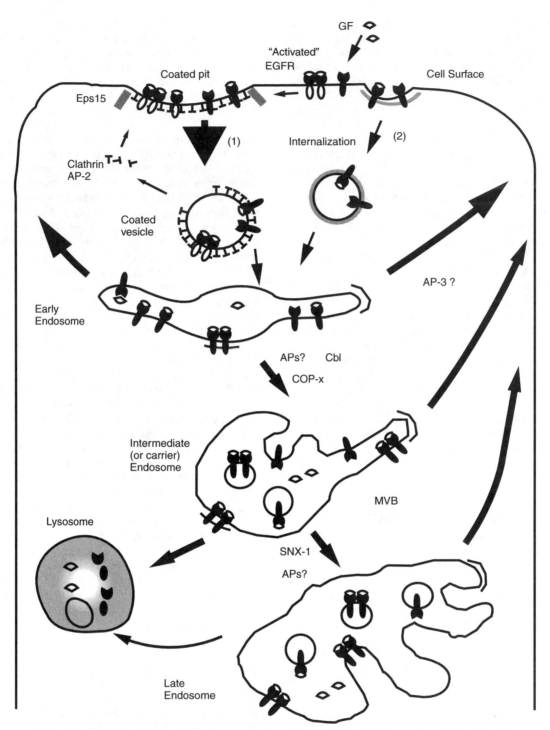

Figure 1. Pathways of internalization and intracellular sorting of GF receptors. Two pathways of endocytosis of EGF receptors are indicated: (1) high-affinity saturable pathway via coated pits (internalization rate constant $k_e = 0.2-0.4$, capacity is typically less than 50,000 receptors), which is utilized by EGF-activated receptors (EGFR); (2) nonsaturable clathrin-independent pathway with slow kinetics ($k_e = 0.02-0.10$) used by unoccupied and occupied EGF receptors when the first pathway is overwhelmed. Clathrin, AP-2, and eps15 are indicated as components of the clathrin coat. The coats involved in the second pathway are not known. Both clathrin-dependent and -independent internalization pathways lead receptors to the early endosomal compartments. Black arrows show recycling of occupied and unoccupied receptors from endosomes. The relative width of arrows indicates that the recycling is much slower from intermediate and late endosomes than from the early compartment. Putative endosomal sorting and coat proteins are indicated as APs (known or unidentified clathrin–adaptor complexes), SNX-1 (sorting nexin-1), COP-X [coatomer (COP-I)-like proteins].

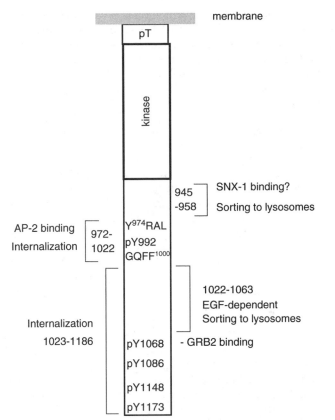

Figure 2. Intracellular domain of the EGF receptor. Depicted are the regions of the EGF receptor that have been implicated in the regulation of internalization and lysosomal targeting. Major tyrosine phosphorylation sites are indicated as pY, whereas serine and threonine phosphorylation is indicated as pS and pT. Two putative internalization motifs are Y^{974}RAL and GGQFF^{1000}. The first sequence has been also shown to serve as the major AP-2 binding site in the EGF receptor

(m-CSF) (c-Fms receptor) (36), fibroblast growth factor (FGF) (37), and *c-kit* receptors (38). Receptor tyrosine kinases are known to be autophosphorylated, but it is unlikely that kinase activity is required only for receptor autophosphorylation. For instance, rapid endocytosis of the EGF receptor mutant lacking the entire C-terminal tail and all autophosphorylation sites preserved kinase dependency (24,25). It is possible that tyrosine phosphorylation of an unidentified substrate of the receptor kinase is necessary for the receptor internalization through the rapid saturable pathway.

Rapid internalization of EGF also requires multiple tyrosine phosphorylation of the receptor (26,34), although the role of autophosphorylation is not clear. The experiments with partially truncated receptor mutants (25) suggested that tyrosine phosphorylation is not essential for the internalization of EGF receptors. This means that neither phosphorylated tyrosine residues nor proteins that contain SH2 domains and interact with phosphotyrosines directly mediate the association of EGF receptors with coated pits. However, tyrosine phosphorylation of the full-length receptor may be needed to support conformational changes that expose endocytic codes. In PDGF receptor β, tyrosine 579 was found to be involved in

the control of internalization (39). Phosphorylation of the c-Fms and c-*kit* receptors is not important for internalization (36,38,40), whereas the phosphorylation site of FGF receptor is crucial for its endocytosis (37). It is possible that observed effects of mutations of autophosphorylation sites of FGF and PDGF receptors on endocytosis reflect the necessity of phosphorylation-dependent conformational changes rather than the direct involvement of SH2-containing proteins.

Besides kinase activity and tyrosine phosphorylation, several peptide sequences of the carboxyl terminus of EGF receptor were found to be necessary for both saturable and nonsaturable internalization (25,27). These sequences are analogous to the coated pit localization motifs found in class I receptors and contain tyrosine residues (Fig. 2). It is not clear, however, which of these endocytic codes function in native, full-length EGF receptor, which of them are cryptic and exposed only in truncated receptor mutants, and whether different motifs can be involved in distinct pathways of internalization. Interestingly, the tyrosine-containing motif that is essential for internalization of c-Fms receptor was found in its juxtamembrane region (36). In PDGF receptor β, the hydrophobic region downstream of the kinase domain has been implicated in the control of internalization (41). However, the kinase activity of the receptor mutants lacking this region is also severely impaired, and therefore, the direct involvement of the region in the interaction with the endocytic machinery is unlikely.

In summary, the rapid saturable pathway of GF endocytosis is controlled by endocytic codes, receptor kinase activity and in some cases by receptor phosphorylation. The endocytic codes presumably interact with AP-2, although other mechanisms might be involved. Receptors that lack endocytic codes, for instance, EGF receptors in which the whole C-terminal domain was truncated, do not interact with AP-2 (42) and undergo internalization through the slow and nonsaturable pathway of constitutive clathrin-independent endocytosis (Fig. 1).

PATHWAY THROUGH ENDOSOMAL COMPARTMENTS

After internalization, receptors and ligands begin their passage through the endosomal compartments (Fig. 1). Internalized molecules can be recycled back from endosomes to the plasma membrane, sequestered in endosomes for a long time, or transported to lysosomes or other organelles. Classification of endosomes is based on their biogenesis and currently is the subject of debate. Here, for simplicity, we will use the terminology of early, intermediate, and late endosomes according to the time of appearance of the endocytic markers in these compartments after internalization.

Endocytosed molecules are first delivered to early endosomes after uncoating of the coated vesicle and its fusion with the endosomal membranes. Early endosomes are the tubular and vesicular membrane structures often connected into networks and located close to the plasma membrane. EGF and EGF receptors can be detected in this compartment within 2–5 min of EGF-induced internalization at 37 °C (4,5,43,44). After 10–15 min, receptors begin to accumulate in large tubular–vesicular endosomes located mainly in perinuclear area, often close to the centriole (4,5,8,44). In electron microscopic sections, these endosomes frequently appear as multivesicular bodies (MVBs) because they contain internal vesicles (4,5,8,44). In our classification, MVBs are likely to correspond to the intermediate (or "carrier" from early to late endosomes) and late endosomes. Since the delivery of receptors from intermediate to late endosomes is highly temperature dependent, these two populations of organelles can be distinguished by lowering the temperature to 16–18 °C (44–46). The late endosomal compartment serves as the last destination of molecules sorted to the lysosomal pathway; it is also referred to as a prelysosomal compartment (47). Although the appearance of EGF receptors in late endosomes can be detected by subcellular fractionation, the colocalization of the EGF and mannose-6-phosphate receptors (markers of late endosomes) has not been shown morphologically. Moreover, the direct fusion of MVB-containing EGF receptors with lysosomes has been recently demonstrated (45).

EGF and EGF receptors become detectable in lysosomes after 30–60 min of internalization, but in some cells can be seen in MVBs for several hours (44). Degradation of EGF and other GFs, as well as their receptors, can be detected 20–30 min after initiation of endocytosis (3,35,48), suggesting that the degradation begins in MVB/late endosomes that contain functionally active proteolytic enzymes. However, the complete degradation of EGF and its receptors is thought to occur in mature lysosomes. Both EGF and EGF receptors, as well as the intermediate products of their proteolysis, are difficult to detect in lysosomes, presumably because they are very rapidly degraded to low-molecular-weight peptides (49,50).

The intravesicular pH drops along the endocytic pathway, from 6.0–6.5 in early endosomes to 4.5–5.5 in late endosomes and lysosomes, which causes dissociation of many ligand–receptor complexes (51). However, several lines of evidence indicate that the release of EGF from the receptor is insignificant until the late stages of endocytosis, and that there is a large pool of endosomal EGF–receptor complexes (52–54). This is in agreement with the common localization of EGF and EGF receptor throughout the endocytic pathway (44,55) (Fig. 1). Similarly, a pool of intact PDGF–receptor complexes can be detected in endosomes (56). Thus internalized GF receptors maintain their ligand-dependent dimerization and phosphorylation status during trafficking through the endosomal compartments.

KINETICS OF INTRACELLULAR TRAFFICKING: RECYCLING VERSUS DEGRADATION

The relative values of trafficking rate parameters of occupied and unoccupied EGF receptors are compared in Figure 3 (57–59). In the absence of EGF, the endosomal pool of EGF receptors is small compared to the surface pool, suggesting that unoccupied EGF receptors must recycle very rapidly after internalization (22). Because EGF-accelerated receptor down-regulation is very rapid, it was assumed in early studies that recycling of internalized EGF-occupied receptors did not occur or was insignificant (4,30). In later studies, however, rapid recycling of EGF–receptor complexes was demonstrated first in human carcinoma A-431 cells and then in all types of cells tested (33,46,57). These observations showed that GF receptor sorting is not a simple, one-directional process of lysosomal targeting. In fact, after each round of endocytosis as much as 70–80% of EGF–receptor complexes can be recycled and then reinternalized, while only 20–30% are degraded.

Unoccupied receptors recycle two to three times faster than receptors in the presence of EGF (57,60), indicating that only 5–10% of unoccupied receptors are degraded after each round of internalization. Given the low internalization rate and the small pool of endocytosed receptors, the apparent degradation rate of unoccupied receptors is very low, and the loss of receptors is compensated for by biosynthesis. This allows the maintenance of a stable level of receptor expression. EGF binding decreases the recycling rate and, therefore, increases the degradation/recycling ratio that determines the fate of receptors after endocytosis. This effect of EGF, together with EGF-accelerated internalization, results in the dramatic elevation of the overall degradation of receptors, which causes receptor down-regulation.

The importance of ligand binding for the lysosomal targeting and down-regulation of internalized receptors can be illustrated by the example of the differential trafficking of EGF and transforming growth factor α (TGFα), which both bind to the EGF receptor. The complex of TGFα and the EGF receptor is much more sensitive to low pH than the EGF–EGF receptor complex, and probably, most of TGFα dissociates from the receptor at pH 5.5–6.0 early in the endosomal pathway (61,62). This dissociation allows rapid recycling of unoccupied receptors and reduces receptor degradation. As a consequence, TGFα causes a much weaker down-regulating effect on EGF receptors compared to that effect of EGF (61,62).

MECHANISM OF RECEPTOR SORTING IN ENDOSOMES

Recycling of EGF–receptor complexes is partially inhibited at 18 °C, suggesting that some recycling does occur from the late endosomes (46). This recycling is, however, much slower than recycling from early endosomes. Therefore, relocating receptors from early to late compartments can reduce the overall rate and extent of receptor recycling.

The details of morphological pathways of intracellular sorting of EGF receptors have been compared with those of transferrin receptors, which are targeted to lysosomes very insignificantly (8,43). In early endosomes, EGF receptors tend to accumulate in vesicular parts of the compartments (Fig. 1), whereas transferrin receptors are mostly located in tubular parts (8). It has been also noticed that in MVB-like endosomes, EGF receptors are preferentially associated with the internal vesicular structures, whereas transferrin receptors are distributed mainly in the outer membrane and tubular parts of endosomes. On the basis of these observations, the following model of intracellular sorting has been proposed (8,63). Receptors located in

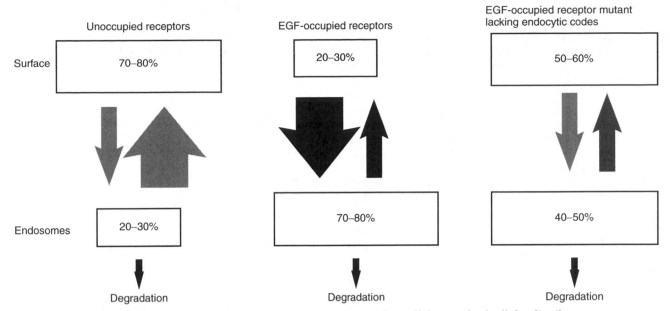

Figure 3. GF-induced changes in the rate parameters of the trafficking and subcellular distribution of the receptors. The relative values of the specific rate constants of internalization, recycling, and degradation were averaged from several studies of EGF receptor endocytosis (22,26,34,57–59) and expressed as the widths of arrows. The model is applicable to cells expressing a moderate physiological amount of EGF receptors (not more than 100,000 per cell) and assumes no saturation of internalization and degradation systems. In this model we propose that EGF binding accelerates receptor internalization by activating the rapid pathway and reduces recycling of the receptors by retaining occupied receptors in endosomes and preventing them from recycling. The resulting accumulation of 70–80% of occupied receptors in endosomes after 20–30 min of continuous ligand-induced endocytosis leads to the increased apparent degradation rate and down-regulation of receptors without any change in the specific rate constant of degradation. Receptor mutants that are incapable of internalization via the clathrin-dependent pathway but that preserve EGF-dependent retention in nonrecycling compartments (for instance, kinase-negative mutant) display an intermediate behavior, resulting in partial down-regulation

the tubular portions of endosomes are constitutively recycled. In contrast, a pool of EGF receptors are trapped (retained) in the vesicular parts and subsequently become incorporated into internal vesicles of MVBs. According to this model, sorting to the internal vesicles prevents recycling of EGF receptors, and leads to their retention in MVB/late endosomes and subsequent exposure to proteolytic enzymes after endosome–lysosome fusion.

The molecular mechanisms of the EGF receptor retention in the vesicular compartments of endosomes are unclear. It has been hypothesized that EGF-induced activation of receptor kinase and tyrosine phosphorylation of annexin I in MVBs is important for inclusion of EGF receptors in internal vesicles of MVBs (64,65). However, the data that receptor mutants lacking an ATP-binding site or the entire kinase domain are degraded as fast as wild-type receptors have questioned the direct involvement of tyrosine kinase activity in the intracellular sorting of EGF receptors (22,27,57,58). Recent reports (27,66) suggested that carboxyl-terminal regions of the receptor between residues 945–958 and 1022–1063 (Fig. 2) distinct from its internalization codes are necessary for the receptor degradation. Interestingly, kinetic studies revealed that the lysosomal sorting (or

retention) pathway of EGF receptors is also saturable (58), indicating that either the proteins responsible for sorting or the pool of EGF receptors competent for lysosomal sorting are limited. This saturable pathway is controlled by the receptor kinase activity (66).

The protein coats and adaptor molecules involved in endosomal sorting of GF receptors are unknown. PDGF-dependent activation of phosphatidylinositol-3-kinase has been implicated in regulation of the endosomal sorting of the PDGF receptor (67). However, this kinase appears to play a role in some universal steps of endosomal sorting and is not specific for GF endocytosis. An endosomal protein called sorting nexin, SNX-1, has been recently discovered based on its ability to interact with the cytoplasmic domain of the EGF receptor in a yeast two-hybrid system (68). Overexpression of SNX-1 leads to down-regulation of the EGF receptor but not other GF receptors, suggesting that SNX-1 plays an important role in the specific targeting of EGF receptors to the degradation pathway.

OTHER TYPES OF SIGNALING RECEPTORS

Multimeric receptors for cytokines, which become assembled from several subunits and then associate with the cytoplasmic tyrosine kinases after ligand binding, are also rapidly down-regulated in the presence of the ligand (69). It has been demonstrated that the internalization of IL-2 receptor is clathrinindependent (70). Interestingly, the subunits of IL-2 receptors are sorted in endosomes to distinct pathways: The α subunit is recycled between plasma membrane and early endosomes, while the β and γ subunits are rapidly sorted to late endosomes and lysosomes (71). The role of the sorting sequence motifs of the cytoplasmic tail of the receptor in intracellular targeting is under investigation.

The mechanism of down-regulation of G protein-coupled receptors has been the focus of research of many laboratories. Recently, a new internalization mechanism has emerged from studies of the β_2-adrenergic receptor. It has been found that β-arrestins play an essential role in the agonist-induced internalization of these receptors (72). Upon agonist binding to the receptor, the cytoplasmic tail of the receptor interacts with β-arrestins (72). β-arrestins are capable of direct binding to clathrin, which allows recruitment of the receptors in coated pits (73). Thus, aside from the classical mechanism of receptor recognition by clathrin adaptors, alternative mechanisms specific to diverse types of membrane receptors exist in mammalian cells.

PERSPECTIVES

We have discussed morphology, kinetics, and possible molecular mechanisms of receptor-mediated endocytosis of GFs. Two GF effects on receptor trafficking that cause down-regulation of receptors have been identified: (1) acceleration of internalization via coated pits, and (2) reduction of recycling of internalized receptors through their retention in endosomes. Although mutagenesis of GF receptors revealed several putative internalization and endosome retention domains, further studies are required to determine which of these domains function in native forms of the receptors. The proteins that interact with these domains and are essential for the receptor trafficking, as well as the role of receptor kinase activity and phosphorylation in these interactions, remain unknown. Because GF-dependent internalization and lysosomal targeting are saturable pathways, they are probably regulated by specific sorting machineries. Elucidation of the mechanisms and identification of the principal players involved in GF receptor trafficking may provide new insights into general mechanisms of endocytosis and may unveil the possibility to control the expression of GF receptors and, therefore, the cellular responses to GFs.

ACKNOWLEDGMENTS

Supported by NIH grant DK46817.

BIBLIOGRAPHY

1. J.L. Goldstein et al., *Annu. Rev. Cell Biol.* **1**, 1–19 (1985).
2. S. Schmid, *Annu. Rev. Biochem.* **66**, 511–548 (1997).
3. G. Carpenter and S. Cohen, *J. Cell Biol.* **71**, 159–171 (1976).
4. L. Beguinot, R.M. Lyall, M.C. Willingham, and I. Pastan, *Proc. Natl. Acad. Sci. U.S.A.* **81**, 2384–2388 (1984).
5. H.T. Haigler, J.A. McKanna, and S. Cohen, *J. Cell Biol.* **81**, 382–395 (1979).
6. P. Gorden, J.-L. Carpentier, S. Cohen, and L. Orci, *Proc. Nat. Acad. Sci. U.S.A.* **75**, 5025–5029 (1978).
7. J.A. Hanover, M.C. Willingham, and I. Pastan, *Cell* **39**, 283–293 (1984).
8. C.R. Hopkins and I.S. Trowbridge, *J. Cell Biol.* **97**, 508–521 (1983).
9. C. Lamaze, T. Baba, T.E. Redelmeier, and S.L. Schmid, *Mol. Biol. Cell* **4**, 715–727 (1993).
10. J.-L. Carpentier et al., *J. Cell Biol.* **95**, 73–77 (1982).
11. K.A. Lund et al., *J. Biol. Chem.* **265**, 15713–15723 (1990).
12. T. Kirchhausen, J.S. Bonifacino, and H. Riezman, *Curr. Opin. Cell Biol.* **9**, 488–495 (1997).
13. H. Ohno et al., *Science* **269**, 1872–1875 (1995).
14. A. Sorkin and G. Carpenter, *Science* **261**, 612–615 (1993).
15. A. Nesterov, R.C. Kurten, and G.N. Gill, *J. Biol. Chem.* **270**, 6320–6327 (1995).
16. A. Nesterov, H.S. Wiley, and G.N. Gill, *Proc. Natl. Acad. Sci. U.S.A.* **92**, 8719–8723 (1995).
17. A. Sorkin et al., *J. Biol. Chem.* **271**, 13377–13384 (1996).
18. L. Gilboa, R. Ben-Levy, Y. Yarden, and Y.I. Henis, *J. Biol. Chem.* **270**, 7061–7067 (1995).
19. J. Baulida et al., *J. Biol. Chem.* **271**, 5251–5257 (1996).
20. H.S. Wiley, *J. Cell Biol.* **107**, 801–810 (1988).
21. C. Lamaze and S.L. Schmid, *J. Cell Biol.* **129**, 47–54 (1995).
22. H.S. Wiley et al., *J. Biol. Chem.* **266**, 11083–11094 (1991).
23. Z. Wong and M.F. Moran, *Science* **272**, 1935–1939 (1996).
24. C.-P. Chang et al., *J. Biol. Chem.* **266**, 23467–23470 (1991).
25. C.-P. Chang et al., *J. Biol. Chem.* **268**, 19312–19320 (1993).
26. A. Sorkin et al., *J. Biol. Chem.* **267**, 8672–8678 (1992).
27. L.K. Opresko et al., *J. Biol. Chem.* **270**, 4325–4333 (1995).
28. S. van Delft et al., *J. Cell Biol.* **136**, 811–821 (1997).
29. P.P. Di Fiore, P.G. Pelicci, and A. Sorkin, *Trends Biochem. Sci.* **22**, 411–413 (1997).
30. J.R. Glenney, Jr. et al., *Cell* **52**, 675–684 (1988).
31. W.S. Chen et al., *Cell* **59**, 33–43 (1989).
32. J.L. Countaway, A.C. Nairn, and R.J. Davis, *J. Biol. Chem.* **267**, 1129–1140 (1992).
33. S. Felder, J. LaVin, A. Ullrich, and J. Schlessinger, *J. Cell Biol.* **117**, 203–212 (1992).
34. A. Sorkin, C.M. Waters, K.A. Overholser, and G. Carpenter, *J. Biol. Chem.* **266**, 8355–8362 (1991).
35. A. Sorkin, B. Westermark, C.-H. Heldin, and L. Claesson-Welsh, *J. Cell Biol.* **112**, 469–478 (1991).
36. G.M. Myles, C.S. Brandt, K. Carlberg, and L.R. Rohrschneider, *Mol. Cell. Biol.* **14**, 4843–4854 (1994).
37. A. Sorokin, M. Mohammadi, J. Huang, and J. Schlessinger, *J. Biol. Chem.* **269**, 17056–17061 (1994).
38. N.S. Yee et al., *J. Biol. Chem.* **269**, 31991–31998 (1994).
39. S. Mori, L. Ronnstrand, L. Claesson-Welsh, and C.-H. Heldin, *J. Biol. Chem.* **269**, 4917–4921 (1994).
40. K. Carlberg, P. Tapley, C. Haystead, and L. Rohrschneider, *EMBO J.* **4**, 877–883 (1991).

41. S. Mori, L. Claesson-Welsh, and C.-H. Heldin, *J. Biol. Chem.* **266**, 21158–21164 (1991).

42. A. Sorkin et al., *J. Biol. Chem.* **270**, 619–625 (1995).

43. C.R. Hopkins, A. Gibson, M. Shipman, and K. Miller, *Nature (London)* **346**, 335–339 (1990).

44. K. Miller et al., *J. Cell Biol.* **102**, 500–509 (1986).

45. C.E. Futter, A. Pearse, L.J. Hewlett, and C.R. Hopkins, *J. Cell Biol.* **132**, 1011–1024 (1996).

46. A. Sorkin et al., *J. Cell Biol.* **112**, 55–63 (1991).

47. G. Griffiths and J. Gruenberg, *Trends Cell Biol.* **1**, 5–9 (1991).

48. C.-H. Heldin, A. Wasteson, and B. Westermark, *J. Biol. Chem.* **257**, 4216–4221 (1982).

49. C.M. Stoscheck and G. Carpenter, *J. Cell Physiol.* **120**, 296–302 (1984).

50. C.M. Stoscheck and G. Carpenter, *J. Cell Biol.* **98**, 1048–1053 (1984).

51. J. Gruenberg and F. Maxfield, *Curr. Opin. Cell Biol.* **7**, 552–563 (1995).

52. A. Sorkin, L. Teslenko, and N. Nikolsky, *Exp. Cell Res.* **175**, 192–205 (1988).

53. A. Sorkin and G. Carpenter, *J. Biol. Chem.* **266**, 23453–23460 (1991).

54. W.H. Lai et al., *J. Cell Biol.* **109**, 2751–2750 (1989).

55. J.L. Carpentier, M.F. White, L. Orci, and C.R. Kahn, *J. Cell Biol.* **105**, 2751–2762 (1987).

56. A. Sorkin et al., *J. Cell. Physiol.* **156**, 373–382 (1993).

57. J.J. Herbst et al., *J. Biol. Chem.* **269**, 12865–12873 (1994).

58. A.R. French, G.P. Sudlow, H.S. Wiley, and D.A. Lauffenberger, *J. Biol. Chem.* **269**, 15749–15755 (1994).

59. K.A. Lund et al., *J. Biol. Chem.* **265**, 20517–20523 (1990).

60. A. Sorkin and C.M. Waters, *Bio Essays* **15**, 375–382 (1993).

61. R. Ebner and R. Derynck, *Cell Regul.* **2**, 599–612 (1991).

62. A.R. French, D.K. Tadaki, N.S.K., and D.A. Lauffenberger, *J. Biol. Chem.* **270**, 4334–4340 (1995).

63. C.R. Hopkins, *Trends Biochem. Sci.* **17**, 27–32 (1992).

64. S. Felder et al., *Cell* **61**, 623–634 (1990).

65. C.E. Futter et al., *J. Cell Biol.* **120**, 77–83 (1993).

66. E. Kornilova, T. Sorkina, L. Beguinot, and A. Sorkin, *J. Biol. Chem.* **271**, 30340–30346 (1996).

67. M. Joly, A. Kazlauskas, F.S. Fay, and S. Corvera, *Science* **263**, 684–687 (1994).

68. R.C. Kurten, D.L. Cadena, and G.N. Gill, *Science* **272**, 1008–1010 (1996).

69. V. Duprez, V. Cornet, and A. Dautry-Varsat, *J. Biol. Chem.* **263**, 12860–12865 (1988).

70. A. Subtil, A. Hemar, and A. Dautry-Varsat, *J. Cell Sci.* **107**, 3461–3468 (1994).

71. A. Hemar et al., *J. Cell Biol.* **129**, 55–64 (1995).

72. S.S.G. Ferguson et al., *Science* **271**, 363–366 (1996).

73. O.B.J. Goodman et al., *Nature (London)* **383**, 447–450 (1996).

See also Animal cell products, overview; Cell metabolism, animal; Genetic engineering: animal cell technology; Protein processing, processing in the endoplasmic reticulum and golgi network; Receptors and cell signaling, intracellular receptors — steroid hormones and no; Transcription, translation and the control of gene expression.

PROTEIN PROCESSING, PROCESSING IN THE ENDOPLASMIC RETICULUM AND GOLGI NETWORK

Erik M. Whiteley*
Michael J. Betenbaugh
The Johns Hopkins University
Baltimore, Maryland

OUTLINE

INTRODUCTION

The processing of secreted and membrane proteins takes place within the secretion pathway. The secretion pathway consists of a complex array of organelles and proteins involved in the production and processing of proteins destined for a number of possible locations: intracellular organelles, the plasma membrane, or the extracellular medium. It is now recognized that production of secreted and membrane proteins involves far more than generating the correct sequence of amino acids. Within the secretory compartments, proteins fold, associate into multimers, and are co-translationally modified. In addition, the proteins must be transported through the compartments to arrive at their final destination. To accomplish these secretion processes, the cell possesses a number of ancillary proteins, including chaperones, folding enzymes, glycosylation enzymes, and transport factors. This article provides an overview of the processing steps and cellular

* Current Address:
    Fermentation & Cell Culture Development
    Berlex Biosciences
    Richmond, CA

proteins dedicated to ensuring processing and movement of secretory proteins to their final destinations.

THE PROTEIN PROCESSING ASSEMBLY LINE

There are a myriad of functions that a single cell must perform either as a unicellular entity or as a subunit of a larger multicellular organism. Mammalian cells contain almost 10 billion protein molecules of 10,000 types (1). How can a cell perform all its functions amid this seemingly chaotic environment? The cell subdivides its functions into specialized compartments dedicated to various cellular operations. Several of these compartments are involved in the secretory pathway (Fig. 1), which is essential to the production of proteins destined for localization in other compartments, secretion into the extracellular environment, or display at the membrane surface.

The secretory pathway begins with the translation of messenger RNA (mRNA) on ribosomes within the cytosol. The ribosome facilitates translation of the mRNA blueprint into a nascent precursor polypeptide. Structural features intrinsic to newly made and maturing secreted and membrane proteins direct the sorting decisions that target these proteins for entry into the ER and subsequently for retention within, or export from, the various compartments of the cell (2–4).

If a newly synthesized polypeptide is destined to be secreted, a set of cellular proteins is responsible for movement of the polypeptide from the cytosol to the endoplasmic reticulum (ER) lumen in a process called *translocation* [Fig. 2(a)]. A number of cytosolic proteins operate in order to direct the nascent polypeptide and attached ribosome to the ER membrane. Once attached to the ER, the ribosome synthesis of the nascent polypeptide continues as the polypeptide is co-translationally transported into the ER lumen. After passing through the membrane, the signal sequence of the secreted protein is removed by the signal peptidase enzyme.

Concurrent with the translation and translocation process the polypeptide will begin to fold, perhaps oligomerize, and have N-linked oligosaccharides added. While the amino acid sequence of a protein does include all the information necessary to assume its final conformation, the folding and assembly process in procaryotes and eucaryotes is assisted by chaperones and folding enzymes [Fig. 2(b)]. It is now known that these molecular chaperones and folding enzymes do not function independently, but act in concert with a number of other co-chaperones, foldases, and assistance factors to facilitate processing in the secretory pathway. After traveling from the rough ER through the smooth ER, proteins destined for export from the cell or presentation on a membrane next move into the Golgi apparatus. The Golgi apparatus consists of organized stacks of disc-like compartments called the Golgi cisternae. The Golgi is a directional compartment, receiving lipids and proteins from the smooth ER in the *cis* Golgi network (CGN) and modifying them en route through the *trans* Golgi before dispatching them to their destinations such as the extracellular environment of the cell or the surface of the plasma membrane.

Webster's Dictionary defines a factory or assembly line as:

> A *line of factory workers and equipment on which the product being assembled passes consecutively from operation to operation until completed.*

With this definition in mind, a cell's secretory pathway may be metaphorically viewed as a protein assembly and processing line. A polypeptide product traverses a series of compartments wherein numerous operations and processes take place in order to generate the final functional protein product.

The following sections examine the key steps and compartments, as well as some of the many proteins, involved in the production and processing of proteins in the secretory pathway. Although the proteins described are critical to the processing of secreted and membrane proteins, not all of them are involved in all secretory events. The secretory pathway is extremely versatile and dynamic; it must continually adapt its processing apparatus depending on the processing requirements of the different secretory proteins.

POLYPEPTIDE PRODUCTION

The synthesis of all proteins begins with the translation of an mRNA sequence to the amino acid sequence of the polypeptide by the ribosome machinery. The ribosome is a complex of more than 50 proteins and several structural RNA molecules (rRNAs). Each ribosome is a large protein-synthesizing machine on which transfer RNA (tRNA) molecules translate the nucleotide sequence into the amino acid sequence.

Nascent polypeptides destined for the ER contain a hydrophobic secretion signal sequence. The co-translational targeting of a nascent secretory polypeptide to the ER is initiated by the high-affinity binding of the signal sequence to the signal recognition particle (SRP), which cycles between the ER membrane and the cytosol [Fig. 2(a)]. The SRP, a particle composed of one molecule of RNA and six distinct polypeptides organized into four SRP proteins (5), binds not only to the signal sequence, but

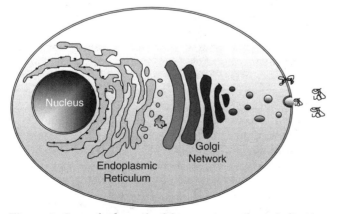

Figure 1. General schematic of the secretion pathway indicating the endoplasmic reticulum, the Golgi network, and the transport of secreted or membrane proteins to the cell surface.

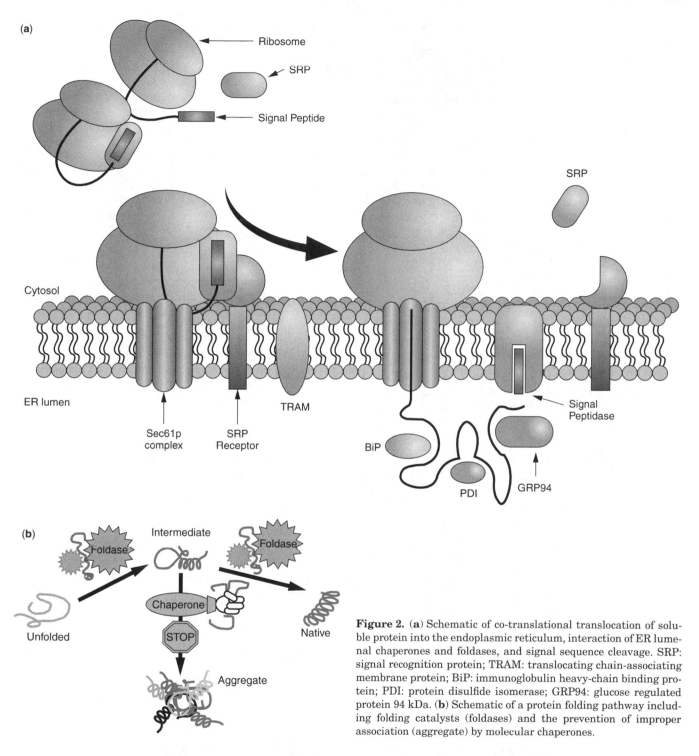

Figure 2. (a) Schematic of co-translational translocation of soluble protein into the endoplasmic reticulum, interaction of ER lumenal chaperones and foldases, and signal sequence cleavage. SRP: signal recognition protein; TRAM: translocating chain-associating membrane protein; BiP: immunoglobulin heavy-chain binding protein; PDI: protein disulfide isomerase; GRP94: glucose regulated protein 94 kDa. **(b)** Schematic of a protein folding pathway including folding catalysts (foldases) and the prevention of improper association (aggregate) by molecular chaperones.

also to the ribosome and the ER-specific docking protein, or SRP receptor. SRP binding to the polypeptide causes a pause in protein synthesis to occur prior to its interaction with the SRP receptor. The SRP receptor, which is composed of a 60-kDa α-subunit and a 30-kDa β-subunit, is a complex of two membrane proteins located in the rough ER. The pause in synthesis also allows sufficient time for the ribosome to form the essential interaction with the ribosome receptor, which may include a 180-kDa membrane protein called ribosome receptor protein and other

membrane proteins such as sec61P (5a), and initiate the release of the nascent polypeptide from SRP.

Polypeptide release from SRP is instrumental to the vital insertion of the signal sequence into the ER membrane. Transmembrane proteins, in contrast to secreted proteins, do not proceed into the lumen, but move laterally into the polylipid ER bilayer to attain their correct position. For these membrane-bound proteins, the signal sequence is usually located within an internal segment of the polypeptide sequence and is not cleaved off after the protein is inserted into the membrane (6). Internal hydrophobic regions are usually buried within the bilayer, while lumenal regions are translocated normally. Aside from a small group of proteins, protein translocation in mammalian cells occurs concurrent to translation or co-translationally (7). Post-translational translocation, common in yeast, may also occur following the termination of polypeptide translation.

The polypeptide chains being transferred across the ER membrane pass through a protein translocator channel. Ribosome interaction with the translocation complex or translocon may play a role in the gating of the channel during co-translational protein translocation (8). Several proteins have been identified as components of the protein conducting channel [Fig. 2(a)]. These include Sec61-α, the 40-kDa integral membrane mammalian homologue of yeast Sec61p and *Escherichia coli* SecY, as well as the smaller proteins Sec61-β and Sec61-γ (9). The translocating chain-associating membrane protein (TRAM) is a 36-kDa integral membrane protein that is stimulatory or required for the translocation of different secretory proteins (10), though its exact function is still unknown.

The role of ER lumenal proteins, such as BiP and the yeast ER homologue of hsp40, Sec63p, in co-translational translocation across mammalian ER membranes remains unsettled (7), even though the Kar2 protein, a BiP homologue in yeast, has been clearly implicated in translocation within yeast. In addition, there is growing evidence in mammalian cells of BiP's involvement in the co-translational translocation (7).

As secretory polypeptides co-translationally pass through the ER membrane, the amino-terminal signal peptide sequence is removed by the enzymatic signal peptidase complex (SPC) on the luminal side of the ER membrane. Mammalian signal peptidase is a complex of five polypeptides, SPC12, SPC18, SPC21, glycosylated SPC22/23, and SPC25 (11). However, studies suggest that only a subset of the signal peptidase complex, including SPC22/23, is required for proteolytic processing (12). Beyond the necessity of phosphatidylcholine, the SPC does not require other co-factors for its proteolytic activity (12). Also, the insensitivity of signal peptidase to protease inhibitors for all common active sites suggests that SPC may represent a novel proteolytic enzyme complex (12).

THE ENDOPLASMIC RETICULUM: POLYPEPTIDE FOLDING AND MODIFICATION

Overview of the ER Lumen

The ER is the organelle dedicated to the synthesis of secretory and membrane proteins, protein folding and oligomerization, disulfide bond formation, and the initial steps in N-glycosylation. The ER also produces lipids for the cell and acts as a reservoir for Ca^{2+}. In order to perform these functions, the lumen of the ER contains a high concentration of both transient and resident polypeptides. The protein concentration of the ER has been estimated at 30–100 mg/mL for one mammalian cell line (13). With a reduced to oxidized glutathione ratio of 10:1, the ER is also a highly oxidizing environment relative to the cytosol, which has a much higher ratio of 100:1.

Many of the proteins that reside either within the ER lumen or its polylipid membrane assist in folding, assembly, processing, or transport. These ER resident proteins often contain the four-amino-acid (–KDEL or –Lys–Asp–Glu–Leu) ER retention signal at the C-terminus, preventing these proteins from escaping the ER. Some of these proteins are involved in translocation across the ER membrane, and others act as chaperones or catalysts to aid in polypeptide folding, proper assembly, and quality control. Still other ER-resident enzymes are responsible for the addition and processing of the oligosaccharide side chains during N-linked glycosylation.

Folding in the ER

Chaperones.

BiP (Immunoglobulin Heavy-Chain Binding Protein), GRP78. One category of ER resident proteins is the chaperones, including the 78-kDa immunoglobulin heavy-chain binding protein (BiP) (14), also known as glucose-regulated protein 78 (GRP78). BiP, a member of the HSP70 heat stress protein family (15), will associate with numerous incompletely folded and unassembled proteins. The role of BiP is to bind newly synthesized secretory proteins as they are translocated into the ER. BiP binding is transient for many secreted or membrane bound proteins, while the association can be more stable for proteins that are misfolded, improperly glycosylated, or otherwise incompetent for secretion (15). As with HSP70, BiP has a strong ATP affinity and displays weak ATPase activity (16,17) that is stimulated by the binding of unfolded proteins (18). BiP will bind linear peptides of about 7 amino acids that include hydrophobic and aromatic residues that are likely to be buried in the interior of the folded protein (17,19). By binding the nascent polypeptides, BiP prevents nonproductive aggregation (20,21) and maintains the polypeptides in a state competent for subsequent folding and oligomerization. Cycles of BiP binding to and release of nascent polypeptides may be optimized in the presence of other co-chaperones, including ER homologues of DnaJ and GrpE. In addition, BiP may act in conjunction with other ER chaperones, such as calnexin or GRP94, in order to facilitate folding and assembly in the ER (22–24).

GRP94. GRP94 (glucose regulated stress protein 94), also known as endoplasmin, ERp99, and HSP 108 (25), is a 94-kDa member of the 90-kDa heat stress protein family (HSP90) found in the ER lumen. GRP94 has been shown to be a major Ca^{2+} and ATP binding component of the ER (13,26) and has been found in cells as both a monomer and as a disulfide-bonded homodimer (25). GRP94 has been seen in association with unassembled immunoglobulin (26), unassembled major histocompatibility complex (MHC) class II polypeptides (27), and with a mutant herpes glycoprotein (28).

Recent findings indicate that GRP94 could act as a chaperone for some polypeptides. GRP94, ERp72, and another unidentified protein have been shown to form a specific complex with the heterodimer formed by α- and β-chains of HLA-DR molecules when these proteins are expressed in the absence of the invariant chain (27). GRP94, as well as BiP, has also been found in association with unassembled immunoglobulin chains in cross-linking experiments. GRP94 binds strongly to mutated immunoglobulin subunits that cannot fold in the ER, but only transiently to wild-type secretable molecules, much like BiP does (29). Experimental evidence demonstrates that GRP94 acts subsequently to BiP, binding to more mature proteins, and remains bound for longer periods (29). Melnik et al., (29) go on to suggest that BiP and GRP94 may work together on overlapping populations of folding intermediates.

Calnexin and Calreticulin. Calnexin, a transmembrane protein also identified as p88 and IP90, is one of the major Ca^{2+} binding proteins of the ER membrane (30). Calnexin is a type I membrane protein with a mobility of approximately 90 kDa, even though it has a calculated molecular mass of 65 kD. This discrepancy may be due to a highly acidic cluster at the C-terminus (30). Calnexin can be modified through phosphorylation (30), and it has been proposed that this modification, as well as its calcium binding ability, may be essential to the chaperoning activity of the protein (31). Calnexin has been found in association with several proteins, including MHC class I molecules (32), T-cell receptor subunits, membrane-bound immunoglobulin (33), and serotonin receptor (SERT) (33a). Calreticulin, a major luminal ER resident protein, is the 55-kDa soluble homologue of calnexin in mammalian cells (34). One of the most acidic proteins in mammalian cells, calreticulin, is glycosylated and binds concanavilin A (35). Due to its single, high-capacity, low-affinity Ca^{2+} binding site, it has been suggested that calreticulin has a role in calcium storage within the ER (34).

The type I membrane-protein calnexin and its soluble, lumenal homologue calreticulin both display lectin-like binding activity. These two proteins are believed to serve both as chaperones and as part of the quality control system in the ER, preventing incorrectly folded proteins from proceeding along the secretion pathway.

Calreticulin and calnexin bind transiently to a wide variety of membrane and secreted glycosylated proteins primarily through lectin-like binding to an early N-linked oligosaccharide intermediate, $Glc_1Man_9GlcNAc_2$, but also through secondary peptide binding (36). Most interactions with calnexin or calreticulin are prevented when target glycoproteins are subjected to tunicamycin treatment (preventing formation of $Glc_3Man_9GlcNAc_2$) or to castanospermine or 1-deoxynojirimycin (glucosidase inhibitors that prevent conversion of $Glc_3Man_9GlcNAc_2$ to $Glc_1Man_9GlcNAc_2$). Evidence for calnexin's role as a molecular chaperone was indicated by a delay or impairment in the maturation and assembly of vesicular stomatitis virus G protein glycoprotein (VSV G), and the heavy chain of both the human and murine class I histocompatibility molecules, in the absence of calnexin (37–39). Furthermore, inhibition of calreticulin and calnexin binding also decreases the efficiency of influenza hemagglutinin maturation. In addition, many nascent glycoproteins have been shown to be protected from intracellular degradation in the presence of calnexin.

The role of calnexin and calreticulin in the quality control mechanism for preventing secretion of improperly folded proteins is regulated through the action of glucosidase II and UDP-glucose:glycoprotein glucosyltransferase. After glucosidase I has removed the terminal glucose from $Glc_3Man_9GlcNAc_2$-Asn, glucosidase II removes a single glucose residue from $Glc_2Man_9GlcNAc_2$-Asn on the target glycoprotein to allow binding of calnexin/calreticulin. The glycoprotein is eventually released by calnexin/calreticulin and the innermost glucose of $Glc_1Man_9GlcNAc_2$-Asn is removed by glucosidase II. However, if the protein is not yet folded, UDP-glucose:glycoprotein glucosyltransferase attaches a new glucose residue to the $Man_9GlcNAc_2$-Asn to recycle the glycoprotein until proper folding occurs and the glycoprotein is competent for transport into the Golgi (Fig. 3). Recent studies have revealed that not only is the terminal glucose essential for calnexin/calreticulin binding, but the entire α-3-linked branch of the oligosaccharide, $Glc\alpha1$-3$Man\alpha1$-2$Man\alpha1$-2Man (see Fig. 4 and the section on glycosylation), is recognized by both proteins (36). NMR analysis has shown that the oligosaccharide structure is highly extended from the terminal glucose to the Asn-linked N-acetylglucosamine so that the glucosylated $\alpha3$-linked branch is relatively easily accessible (40). Using deletion analysis, oligosaccharide binding has been traced to two tandem repeat motifs within calnexin and calreticulin (30,41). These repeat motifs are also the site of calcium binding for both calnexin and calreticulin.

Even with all the similarities between calnexin and calreticulin and the existence of numerous common substrates (42–46), there is an ever increasing list of examples in which the binding of some substrates is exclusive to one chaperone or the other (39,42,45–48). Studies with various target proteins suggest that lectin binding specificity may not account for the variable substrate specificity. Polypeptide geometry and oligosaccharide orientation could be key factors. Another possibility is that calnexin and calreticulin differ in their affinity for polypeptide segments of unfolded glycopolypeptides (45,49–51). Calnexin and calreticulin may first recognize the N-glycans on substrate proteins as a primary mode of association and then bind to a peptide determinant, which is eliminated upon completion of folding.

Foldases. There are numerous other folding processes within the ER, and many are catalyzed by enzymatic processing proteins. Folding events include formation, reduction, and isomerization of disulfide bonds as well as isomerization of proline bonds, accelerated by the ER proteins protein disulfide isomerase (PDI) and peptyl prolyl isomerase (PPI), respectively.

Protein Disulfide Isomerase. Protein disulfide isomerase is a 58-kDa, multifunctional protein containing multiple structural and functional domains. PDI, also called Erp59, cellular thyroid hormone (T3) binding protein, glycosylation site binding protein, and iodothyronine monodeiodinase (55), has been identified as the ß subunit of prolyl-4-hydroxylase (52,53) and the microsomal triglyceride transfer protein 58-kDa subunit.

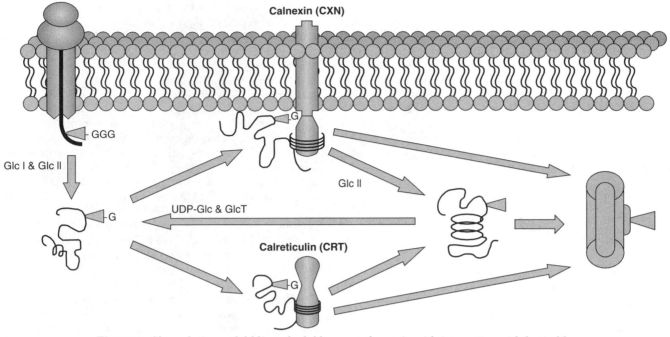

Figure 3. Glycosylation and folding of soluble secreted protein with interaction with lectin-like chaperones calnexin (CXN) and calreticulin (CRT). Calnexin/calreticulin along with the glucosidases and glucosyltransferase provide quality control for proper folding of glycoproteins prior to their exit from the ER. G: glucose residues; Glc I: glucosidase I; Glc II: glucosidase II; Glc T: glucosyltransferase (transfers glucose from UDP-Glc); ◁: GlcNAc$_2$ Man$_9$GlcNAc$_2$.

PDI contains amino acid regions that are highly homologous to the small bacterial protein thioredoxin (trx), another protein having thiol:disulfide oxidoreductase activity. These thioredoxin-like domains, one near the amino terminus and the other near the carboxyl terminus of the protein, contain the highly conserved active site sequence, –CGHC–. This sequence is important in catalyzing thio–disulfide interchange reactions in vitro leading to oxidation, reduction, or isomerization of protein disulfide bonds (56,57). Mutations of the first, upstream, cysteine of the active site in either the amino- or carboxyl-terminal thioredoxin domain inhibits the capacity of PDI to catalyze thiol–disulfide exchange reactions in vitro (58,59), while mutations at both initial cysteines reduce enzymatic activity to negligible levels (59,60).

The crystal structure of PDI has not yet been elucidated, but sequence and intron–exon analysis have indicated that the domain grouping for the structure of PDI is as follows (56):

$$a - e - b - b' - a' - c$$

The a and a' domains, containing the –CGHC–active-site sequences, are similar to each other, thioredoxin, and bacterial protein DsbA. Other regions, such as the peptide binding domain in c, are likely to be involved in activities such as assembly of prolyl-4-hydroxylase, triglyceride transferase, and calcium binding (56).

PDI has been observed to prevent aggregation of other proteins in vitro in a role comparable to chaperones (61,62). Conversely, PDI and PDI varinants have also been implicated in the in vitro and in vivo aggregation of substrate proteins in an antichaperoning role (63,64). The active sites' cysteines do not appear to be required for the antichaperoning function of PDI (65).

Peptidyl Prolyl Isomerase. Peptidyl prolyl *cis–trans* isomerase, a ubiquitously expressed enzyme in many organisms and subcellular compartments, was first identified by its catalysis of the *cis–trans* isomerization of the short peptide succinyl–Ala–Ala–Pro–Phe–4-nitroanilide (66). Whereas the peptide Xaa–Xaa bond (where Xaa represents any amino acid) between two amino acids is generally planar and in the *trans* isomeric state, the Xaa–Pro peptide bond can exist in either the *cis* or *trans* conformation with about 7% of these peptide bonds in the *cis* conformation in native proteins. The proline hypothesis states that many slow transitions in protein folding are the result of slow *trans*-to-*cis* or *cis*-to-*trans* isomerizations of one or more Xaa–Pro bonds (67) due to the high energy of activation (E_A approx. 20 kcal/mol) required for rotations about the partial double bond of Xaa–Pro peptide bonds. Time constants from 10 to 100 seconds have been reported for this reaction in vitro (68,69).

Following the discovery of PPI, a number of investigators evaluated PPI as a catalyst for slow folding phases of proteins. Folding-rate enhancement by prolyl isomerization in vitro has been demonstrated for the slow folding phases of mouse IgG light chain, porcine RNase (70), RNase T1 (71), mouse antibody fragment MAK 33 Fab (72), human carbonic anhydrase II (HCA II) (73,74), and collagen (75).

The effect of PPI on in vivo protein folding is much less well understood. Indirect evidence of PPI involvement is suggested by the retardation of in vivo maturation of

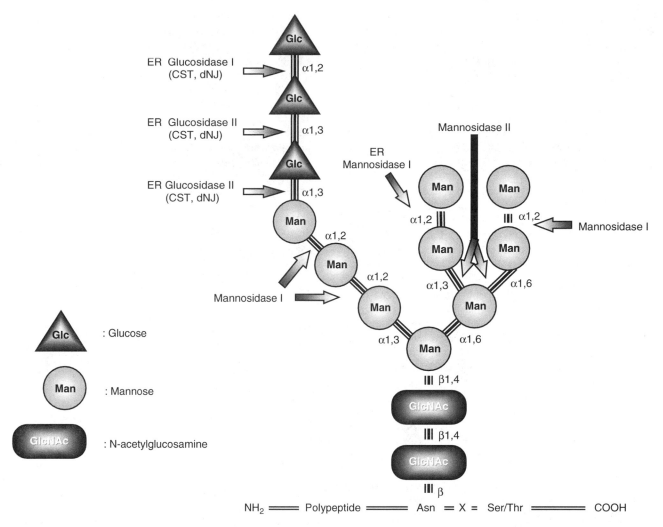

Figure 4. The N-linked core oligosaccharide is transferred en bloc from the dolichol carrier to the asparagine (Asn) residue in the consensus sequence Asn–X–Ser/Thr (serine/threonine), where X denotes any amino acid other than proline. Castanospermine (CST) and deoxynojirimycin (dNJ) inhibit glucosidases I and II.

two proteins, procollagen (76) and transferrin (77), in the presence of the PPI inhibitor cyclosporin A. Also, correct processing of rhodopsin has been attributed to the presence of the PPIase NinaA in *Drosophila* (78,79).

Glycosylation in the ER

Proteins designated for secretion from the cell, insertion into membranes, or localization within other organelles often include carbohydrate side units. These proteins are termed glycoproteins, and the attachment and subsequent processing of these oligosaccharides is glycosylation. Glycosylation and oligosaccharide processing play a vital role in the sorting and distribution of glycoproteins to their proper cellular destinations, glycoprotein solubility, receptor–ligand binding, and in vivo circulatory half-lives. Nonetheless, the exact role of glycosylation remains unknown for many glycoproteins.

The glycosylation process in mammalian cells can be generally classified as either N-linked or O-linked. N-linked oligosaccharides are attached to polypeptides

through a β-N-glycosidic bond between a N-acetylglucosamine residue of the oligosaccharide and an asparagine (Asn) residue in the recognition sequence Asn-X-Ser/Thr, where X is any amino acid except proline. O-linked glycosylation occurs within the Golgi and will be discussed in a subsequent section. This section will focus on the steps involved in N-linked glycosylation of glycoproteins in the ER and the processing enzymes involved.

N-linked glycosylation in mammalian cells begins with the generation of a common oligosaccharide core,[1] $Glc_3Man_9GlcNAc_2$, attached to a lipid carrier, dolichol, followed by the co-translational transfer onto an asparagine residue on the nascent peptide (80,81). Synthesis of

---

[1] The following monosaccharides are most often associated with the oligosaccharide glycosylation of glycoproteins: D-galactose (Gal or Ga), D-glucose (Glc or G), L-fucose (Fuc or F), D-mannose (Man or M), N-acetyl-D-glucosamine (GlcNAc or GN), N-acetyl-D-galactosamine (GalNAc or GaN), and sialic acids, including N-acetylneuramic acid (usually NANA or NeuAc).

dolichyl phosphate, assembly of the $Glc_3Man_9GlcNAc_2$ on dolichol, and the subsequent transfer of the oligosaccharide precursor to the protein involves over sixty enzymatic steps in three intracellular compartments (82).

Oligosaccharyltransferase Complex. The lipid-linked oligosaccharide is transferred en bloc by the oligosaccharyltransferase (OST) complex, which specifically recognizes the Asn–X–Ser/Thr consesus sequence. However, only one-third of these consensus sites are actually N-glycosylated. The heterooligomeric OST complex is composed of four subunits having molecular masses of 66 kDa (ribophorin I), 64 kDa (ribophorin II), 48 kDa (OST48), and 12 kDa (DAD1). The glycoprotein ribophorin I, which has also been implicated in the translocation of polypeptides (83), possesses a membrane-spanning segment containing a sequence matching a proposed dolichol recognition consensus sequence (83). Ribophorin I and the 64-kDa glycosylated ribophorin II, both type I transmembrane proteins, are also thought to be involved in preventing translocation sites from diffusing from the rough ER to the smooth ER. The 48-kDa subunit in the OST complex is an unglycosylated type I membrane protein known as OST48. The final subunit, DAD1, originally identified as an inhibitor of apoptosis, was linked to the OST complex based on homology with a conserved OST2 protein from yeast (83a,83b).

ER Glycosyl-Trimming Enzymes. Subsequent to the transfer of the oligosaccharide precursor to the nascent polypeptide, the processing of the N-linked glycosylation side chain begins with the removal of three glucose residues followed by the removal of an initial mannose residue (Fig. 4).

The trimming phase of the glycosylation pathway in mammalian cells begins with the enzyme α-glucosidase I. This enzyme, a tetramer of 85-kDa subunits, removes the terminal glucose residue from $Glc_3Man_9GlcNAc_2$ linked to the nascent polypeptide's Asn residue to form $Glc_2Man_9GlcNAc_2$-Asn. This processing step is inhibited by 1-deoxynojirimycin (dNJ), N-methyl-dNJ (N-Me-dNJ), N-butyl-dNJ, castanospermine, and australine (84). Prevention of this initial step is known to interfere with the secretion and cellular localization of affected glycoproteins (85).

The glucose trimming initiated by α-glucosidase I is continued by α-glucosidase II through the removal of both remaining glucose residues from the $Glc_2Man_9GlcNAc_2$ oligosaccharide structure. Along with calnexin, calreticulin, UDP-glucose, and glucosyltransferase, this 123-kDa membrane glycoprotein is an integral part of the quality control mechanism within the ER. It has been demonstrated that removal of the innermost glucose residue is much slower than that of the terminal glucose and, furthermore, that the mannose residues on the upper α-1,6-linked Man branch are required for glucosidase II activity (84). It is likely that these two properties are essential to the quality control activity; with the slower removal of the second glucose, either calnexin/calreticulin or glucosyltransferase will have an opportunity to reassociate with an aberrant glycoprotein to prevent further processing. Also, the necessity of the upper α-1,6-linked Man branch may prevent divergent, nonconsecutive processing

of the oligosaccharide branches. As noted for glucosidase I, mammalian α-glucosidase II is also inhibited by 1-deoxynojirimycin (dNJ), castanospermine, and related compounds (84).

Succeeding the activity of glucosidases I and II, the 65-kDa Ca^{2+}-dependent membrane-bound enzyme α-1,2-mannosidase removes the α-1,2-mannose residue of the $Man\alpha1–3Man\alpha1–6Man$ branch from glycoprotein substrates (Fig. 4). This enzyme activity is calcium activated and can be inhibited by 1-deoxymannojirimycin (dMNJ). The enzyme has been localized to the rough ER (RER), the smooth ER (SER), in transitional elements of the RER, and in smooth-surfaced membranes corresponding to transport vesicles between the ER and the Golgi (84).

Glycosylphosphatidylinositol-Linked Proteins

Glycosylphosphatidylinositol (GPI) groups function to anchor a wide variety of proteins to the exterior surface of the eukaryotic plasma membrane, providing an alternative to integral transmembrane polypeptide domains. The anchoring of these polypeptides to a preformed GPI glycolipid occurs rapidly following synthesis and transfer of a target protein into the ER. The core GPI structure is constructed on the lumenal side of the ER membrane from phosphatidyllinositol, UDP-N-acetylglucosamine, dolichol-P-mannose, and phosphatidylethanolamine. The core may be modified by a variety of additional sugar residues, depending on the species and protein to which it is attached. Target proteins become anchored to the membrane surface following the nucleophilic attack of a specific C-terminal amino acid residue by the amino group of the GPI phosphoethanolamine, resulting in the release of a hydrophobic C-terminal peptide (86). Since GPI groups are added on the lumenal surface of the rough ER, GPI-anchored proteins are transported to the exterior surface of the plasma membrane and in principle can be released from cells in a soluble form in response to signals that activate a specific phospholipase in the plasma membrane (1).

Membrane Traffic: ER to Golgi and Beyond

Mammalian cells require a number of membrane-delimited organelles to compartmentalize biochemical reactions and to regulate not only secretion but the localization of intracellular proteins. Although the ER and Golgi (and all the other organelles) maintain unique molecular compositions, membranes and proteins are continuously shuttled between the compartments. This operation is mediated by transport vesicles that bud from the membranes of donor compartments and then fuse to target membranes of other organelles. Fusion of intracellular membranes is not only required in the transport of proteins from the ER to the Golgi complex, but at other steps along the secretion pathway including secretion to the extracellular environment, presentation of membrane proteins, formation of endosomes, and retrieval of lumenal ER proteins (87).

Following the ER-specific folding, oligomerization, and processing, secreted proteins are exported from the ER through the sequential formation, or budding, of carrier vesicles followed by the targeting and fusion of these vesicles to the *cis* Golgi network, the first compartment of the Golgi apparatus. Most of the protein components in vesicle transport are highly specific in order to maintain organelle distinction, yet the same general steps are thought to be involved in many of the vesicle transport processes throughout the secretory pathway. Transport from the ER to the Golgi network, therefore, is most often used as the typical transport model. Two general categories of transport proteins have been identified: proteins required for export (budding) from the ER (or other membrane of origin), which leads to the formation of carrier vesicles, and proteins involved in either vesicle targeting or fusion to the CGN (or other target vesicle or membrane).

The first step in ER to Golgi transport involves the recruitment and potential concentration of proteins at the site of export. Some system must be in place to segregate lipids and proteins at the export site from the bulk of the ER. It is probable that this mechanism is also intrinsically involved with the quality control machinery, ensuring that incorrectly folded or oligomerized proteins or inproperly glycosylated glycoproteins do not exit the ER (88).

ERGIC53. The type I transmembrane, nonglycosylated, 53-kDa protein ERGIC-53 (endoplasmic reticulum–Golgi intermediate compartment-53) (89) may be involved not only in the sorting of secreted proteins but also in the quality control mechanism within the ER. ERGIC-53 has been shown to cycle between the ER and the intermediate compartment (90) and has also been localized in the *cis* Golgi cisterna (89). In addition, recent studies have found that ERGIC-53 contains constituents for ER retention, ER exit (anterograde transport), and ER retrieval (retrograde transport) (91). Interestingly, ERGIC-53 also displays lectin-like mannose-specific binding (92). In light of these results, ERGIC-53 may play a pivotal role in the segregation and sorting of glycosylated proteins in preparation for transport from the ER to the Golgi apparatus (93).

COP I and II and ARF. To be transported from one secretory compartment to another, protein products must be packaged into transport vesicles. Transport vesicles arise from specialized coated regions of membranes within the secretory apparatus. These membranes are surrounded by a cage of proteins covering the cytosolic face so that these membranes eventually bud off as coated vesicles. Prior to fusing with the target membrane, this protein coat is discarded to allow the membranes to fuse directly. There are two types of well-characterized coated vesicles: clatherin-coated and coatomer-coated. The structurally best-characterized coat protein is clatherin, which is involved primarily with endocytosis and in the transport of lysosomal or vacuolar proteins from the *trans* Golgi network (94).

The formation of vesicular buds in the secretory pathway is propelled by the recruitment of cytosolic coat proteins to the membrane of origin. There are two different cytosolic protein complexes, COP I and COP II, involved in the formation of at least two types of transport vesicles in the secretory pathway (95). COP II is involved in vesicle budding from the ER for the anterograde transport of secretory proteins (91). The COP I complex, or coatomer, encompasses seven polypeptide subunits: α-COP (160 kD), β-COP (110 kD), β'-COP (102 kD), γ-COP (98 kD), δ-COP (61 kD), ε-COP (31 kD), and ξ-COP (20 kD). The exact nature of the COP I complex's role in a number of transport pathways is not well established, but it has been implicated in many different traffic pathways, including exit from the ER (96), transport from ERGIC to the *cis* Golgi (97), movement through the Golgi cisternae (98), early to late endosome transport (99), and Golgi to ER retrograde transport (95).

Found in association with coatomer is ADP-ribosylation factor or ARF, a GTP-binding protein. Prior to COP I/coatomer assembly and binding to the Golgi membranes to form vesicles, the GTP-bound form of ARF must bind to its membrane receptor subsequent to a brefeldin A-sensitive nucleotide exchange step (100). Disassembly of the coat complex prior to fusion with the target membrane occurs following the hydrolysis of bound GTP by ARF (100). In vitro studies have shown that in ARF- or coatomer-depleted systems there is inhibition of vesicle formation, yet there is no inhibition of the fusenogenic vesicular stomatitis virus G protein (VSV G) transport (101). Interestingly, it would, therefore, appear that protein transport is uncoupled from vesicle formation in vitro. One hypothesis states that during the biosynthesis of the vesicle fusion machinery, fusogenic proteins must remain concealed by coat proteins in order to prevent immature fusion between membranes (102). In the absence of either coat proteins or ARF, the apparent protein transport mechanism may actually be due to the fusion of donor and acceptor compartment without the formation of an intermediate vesicle (95).

NSF, SNAPS, Rab, and v- and t-SNAREs. Amidst the anterograde and retrograde transport among the ER and the Golgi cisternae, these organelles must maintain their unique identities. Vesicle targeting and fusion is an area under intense study, and considerable progress has been made in elucidating the complex machinery involved. Numerous protein families have been implicated in transport and fusion along the secretion pathway, including Rabs, NSF (N-ethylmaleimide sensitive factor), SNAPs (soluble NSF attachment proteins), SNAREs (soluble NSF attachment proteins receptors or SNAP receptors), and others. Proper vesicle fusion is facilitated by vesicle targeting molecules, v-SNAREs (vesicle SNAREs), which interact with the analogous t-SNAREs (target-SNAREs) on the target membranes of the CGN or other target membrane.

The exact mechanism involved in the fusion of vesicle and target membranes is still not completely characterized. Many of the proteins involved have been elucidated, yet the precise manner and sequence in which they interact is still obscure. However, a number of recent studies have begun to shed some light on the nature of membrane docking and fusion. To understand the process of transport, one must first examine vesicle budding to determine the nature of the vesicles themselves and the targeting proteins they possess.

One interesting fact in protein transport is that proteins do not leave the ER only near the Golgi membranes. They may also emerge at seemingly random sites marked by small groups of vesicles and tubules (vesicular–tubular clusters or VTCs) (103). A recent study (104) used VSV G tagged with green fluorescent protein (GFP) to visualize ER-to-Golgi transport. The transport of proteins was observed directly and relatively unobtrusively in vivo. Over short distances, secreted proteins bud off in vesicles that dock with the CGN. However, proteins can also be transported from the ER to the Golgi over longer distances. In a process similar to the formation of early endosomes, the vesicles bud and then fuse into the VTC, sort out and recycle ER proteins, and move along microtubules to merge with the CGN (104,105). This indicates that carrier vesicles from the same organelle source are fusing prior to fusion with the target membrane, implying that these carrier vesicles contain both v- and t-SNAREs.

In contrast to the previously held theory that vesicles contain only v-SNAREs and the target membranes contain the t-SNAREs, the initial step in transfer from ER to Golgi may be between similar carrier vesicles containing both v-SNAREs and t-SNAREs. A recent study in yeast fusion supporting this model has demonstrated that the fusion of vacuoles containing both v-SNAREs and t-SNAREs is more efficient than fusion of two vesicles that exclusively contain only a v-SNARE or a t-SNARE (87). The fusion model (Fig. 5) still suggests that the individual SNAREs are activated through ATP hydrolysis by the soluble ATPase, NSF, by way of the α-SNAP (87). Then through the Rab-mediated catalytic targeting and the other cytosolic factors, such as syntaxin and Rab, the SNARE complex is formed and membrane fusion occurs. Following fusion, the very stable SNARE complex may be broken apart to be recycled for another round of vesicle transport by repeated cycles of NSF–SNAP catalysis (106).

Rab proteins, involved in vesicle transport all along the secretion pathway, represent a large family of low-molecular-weight GTPases (107). These proteins act to facilitate v- and t-SNARE complex formation, without being a core component of the complex itself (108,109). One current model suggests that Rabs, in the GTP-bound state, recruit specific docking factors from the cytosol (109). These factors are predicted to catalyze v-SNARE and t-SNARE binding through the removal of SNARE protectors, such as mammalian syntaxin-1A or yeast Sec1p (109). With the evidence that Sec1p binding inhibits v-SNARE to t-SNARE binding (110), it appears that SNARE protectors are required to prevent inadvertent binding of whole organelles. In this sense

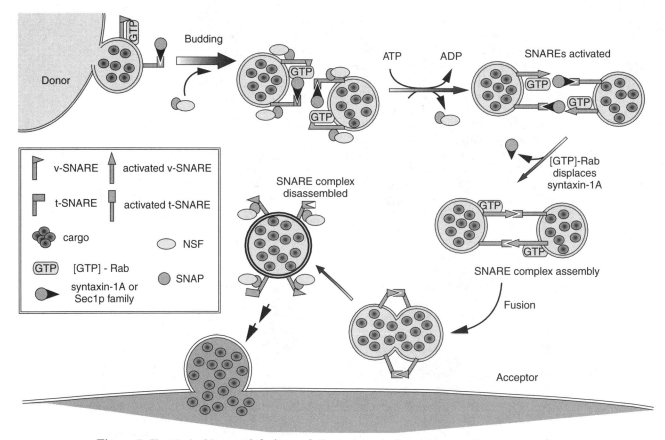

Figure 5. Vesicle budding and fusion and the transport of protein cargo between membrane compartments. A donor membrane buds a cargo-containing vesicle. Two cargo-containing transport vesicles interact and fuse via specialized vesicle and target receptors controlled by transport regulating proteins. The process may then repeat so that the larger "fusion product" vesicle can dock with the acceptor membrane.

the Rab–GTP complex can be viewed as the rate contol or "throttle" in membrane fusion, and the t-SNARE protectors act as the brakes or "dampers" of membrane fusion (111).

THE GOLGI APPARATUS

Overview of the Golgi Complex

The Golgi apparatus was originally identified in eukaryotic cells as four to eight membrane-enclosed flattened cisternae held together as parallel stacks (112). Two tubular networks of membranes have also been identified at either end of the Golgi compartment (the *cis*-Golgi and *trans*-Golgi networks). The *cis*-Golgi network, which may be synonymous with the ER–Golgi intermediate compartment, acts as the receptor site for newly synthesized and processed proteins from the ER. However, the exact borders of the Golgi apparatus are rather enigmatic. It has been difficult to define the boundaries between the transitional elements involved in ER to Golgi transport and the ER–Golgi intermediate compartment (ERGIC) (113) located between the ER and the Golgi apparatus. There has been no clear consensus on whether the ERGIC is a distinct organelle. However, this is the first compartment to which budded vesicles from the ER fuse; so there is little difference between this "organelle" and the traditional start of the Golgi apparatus, the *cis* cisternae of the Golgi apparatus, at least in terms of function. Passage through the Golgi involves a variety of post-translational processing steps, including the synthesis of O-linked glycans (114), processing of the N-linked oligosaccharides (80), and cleavage of select polypeptides.

Golgi Targeting and Protein Trafficking

The nature by which proteins are targeted to and moved through the Golgi complex has yet to be clearly defined. Recent studies have found that the length of the hydrophobic transmembrane region in Golgi membrane proteins is crucial to retaining the proteins in the Golgi membrane (115). Work in the area of Golgi protein traffic has also begun to discern the process by which proteins travel between cisternae. There has been renewed support for a model that states that Golgi cisternae form at the *cis* face of the stack and then progressively mature into the *trans*-cisternae. Morphological data support this model of protein transport through the Golgi, but other studies indicate that COP I vesicles are responsible for transporting material between Golgi cisternae. The maturation model of protein trafficking through the Golgi combines these findings by assuming that cisternae carry secretory cargo through the apparatus in the anterograde (forward) direction, while COP I vesicles transport Golgi enzymes in the retrograde (reverse) direction (116,117).

Oligosaccharide Processing in the Golgi

N-linked oligosaccharide processing continues throughout the Golgi network and O-linked glycosylation is initiated within the *cis*-Golgi cisternae. O-linked glycosylation involves an α-O-glycosidic bond between the oligosaccharide unit and a serine or threonine in the polypeptide's sequence, except in collagens, where this covalent linkage occurs between the oligosaccharide side chain and the polypeptide's 5-hydroxylysine residues. While N-linked oligosaccharides usually have a distinctive core unit of oligosaccharides, the same generalization cannot be made for O-linked glycosylation. In O-linked glycosylation the oligosaccharide modifications can vary from a single galactose in collagen to chains of up to 1000 disaccharide units in proteoglycans (118).

O-linked oligosaccharides are synthesized in the Golgi apparatus by serial addition of monosaccharide subunits to a completed polypeptide chain. Synthesis usually starts with the addition of N-acetylgalactosamine (GalNAc) to a Ser or Thr residue by GalNac transferase. Unlike N-linked glycosylation, the Ser and Thr residues involved in O-linked glycosylation are not part of a consensus sequence. It appears that the location of O-linked glycosylation sites is dictated by the secondary or tertiary structure of the protein. O-linked glycosylation continues in a stepwise manner through the addition of other monosaccharides (such as galactose and fucose) by the appropriate glycosyltransferases.

Processing of N-linked carbohydrates occurs in a sequential manner defined by the exposure of N-glycans to processing enzymes located at different sites within the Golgi apparatus. Each cisternae, beginning with the *cis* compartment and ending with the *trans* compartment, contains its own set of processing enzymes. Passing through a multistage processing line, glycoproteins are modified in successive stages as they move through the cisternae.

Golgi α-Mannosidase. Upon entrance into the *cis* cisternae, the first glycosylation enzyme to act on N-glycans is Golgi α-1,2-mannosidase (α-1,2-Man), a glycoprotein tetramer consisting of 57–58-kDa subunits. Golgi α-mannosidase (mannosidase I) removes the final three α-1,2-linked mannoses from $Man_8GlcNAc_2$ to form the $Man_5GlcNAc_2$ (Figs. 4 and 6). Unlike ER α-mannosidase I, it is not clear whether the Golgi mannosidase I is Ca^{2+} dependent. However, it is still inhibited by 1-deoxymannojirimycin (dMNJ) (84).

Endo-α-Mannosidase. Processing of N-linked oligosaccharides typically occurs in a sequential manner due the high specificity of the glycosylation enzymes. However, an alternative pathway has been identified. The divergent pathway involves the processing enzyme, endo-α-mannosidase (Endo α-Man, which is capable of cleaving $Glc_{3-1}Man$ from $Glc_{3-1}Man_9GlcNAc_2$ to produce $Man_8GlcNAc_2$ (84). In contrast to α-glucosidase II, endo-α-mannosidase shows preferential activity toward oligosaccharides with truncated mannose branches ($GlcMan_{8-4}GlcNAc_2$) (84). The enzyme has been localized in the Golgi and acts on glycoproteins that have escaped the ER with a remaining terminal glucose because of incomplete processing by glucosidase II or protein reglucosylation in the ER (119). The activity of endo-α-mannosidase has been shown to account for the inability of glucosidase inhibitors to completely block

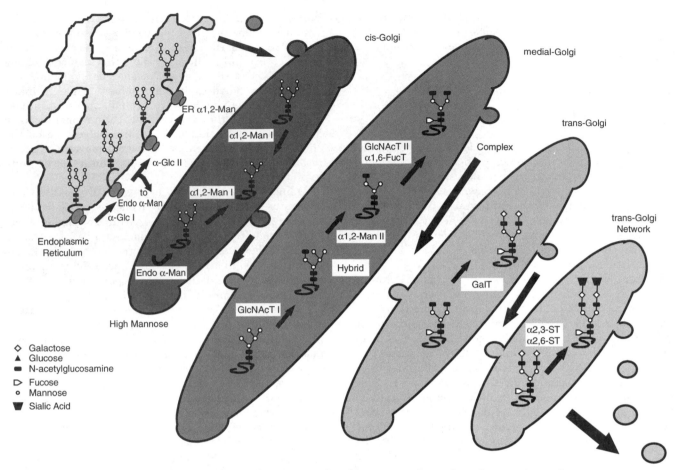

Figure 6. N-linked oligosaccharide processing for a biantennary glycan along the secretion pathway.

processing to complex oligosaccharides (120). Although this α-mannosidase is considered to work primarily in the *cis* cisternae, it has been localized in both the *cis* and *medial* cisternae.

N-Acetylglucoaminyltransferase I (GlcNAc TI or GnTI). After the oligosaccharide chain has been trimmed down to the Man₅GlcNAc₂-Asn, the glycan is passed on to the *medial* cisternae, where the renewed synthesis and maturation of N-linked carbohydrates continues with the 51-kDa enzyme N-acetylglucosaminyltransferase I (GlcNAc TI or GnTI). GlcNAc TI adds a β-1,2-linked N-acetylglucosamine residue to the α-1,3-Man branch to form GlcNAcMan₅GlcNAc₂-Asn (Fig. 6). As with all Golgi glycosyltransferases sequenced to date, GlcNAc TI is a type II transmembrane protein.

α-Mannosidase II (Man II). Following the addition of GlcNAc, α-mannosidase II (Man II), a type II transmembrane glycoprotein 124-kDa dimer, removes both the α-1,3- and α-1,6-linked mannose residues attached to the α-1,6-linked mannose branch to generate the oligosaccharide stucture GlcNAcMan₃GlcNac₂-Asn (Fig. 6). Subsequent to these enzymatic cleavages, the oligosaccharide structure is endoglycosidase H (endo H) resistant. Mannosidase II has been found to be strongly inhibited by the indolizine alkaloid, swainsonine, and the non-alkaloid inhibitor mannostatin (84).

N-Acetylglucosaminyltransferase II (GlcNAc TII or GnTII) and α-1,6-Fucosyltransferase (FucT). Succeeding the removal of the terminal mannosidase residues, N-acetylglucosaminyltransferase II (GlcNAc TII or GnTII) will adjoin a GlcNAc residue to the α-1,6-linked mannose branch to form the complex structure, GlcNAc₂Man₃GlcNac₂-Asn (Fig. 6). This is followed by the addition of an α-1,6-linked fucose onto the Asn-linked GlcNAc by α-1,6-fucosyltransferase (FucT) prior to transport to the *trans* Golgi and the *trans* Golgi network.

Galactosyltransferase and Sialyltransferase (ST). Within the *trans* Golgi cisternae, galactose is added to the terminal N-acetylglucosamine residues to form Gal₂GlcNAc₂Man₃GlcNac₂-Asn by the 44-kDa β-1,4-galactosyltransferase (GalT) (Fig. 6). The final step in the generation of complex mammalian N-glycans is the attachment of the negatively charged N-acetylneuraminic acid (NANA), a form of sialic acid, by either the α-2,6-N-acetylneuraminic acid transferase (α-2,6-NANAT or α-2,6-ST) or α-2,3-N-acetylneuraminic acid transferase (α-2,3-NANAT or α-2,3-ST).

The level of oligosaccharide processing in the Golgi is dependent on particular cell types, as well as the locations of the specific asparagine residues in the glycoprotein (121). Sometimes N-linked oligosaccharides may remain high mannose due to the inaccessibility of

N-glycans to processing enzymes following folding. For those glycoproteins that are modified, the processing of N-linked oligosaccharides appears to be identical through the addition of a GlcNAc residue by N-acetylglucoaminyltransferase I (Fig. 6). At this point, however, considerable divergence in processing is possible. N-glycans can, in fact, contain numerous configurations incuding a bisecting β-1,4 GlcNAc unit on the core β-1,4 Man or a triantennary structure with two GlcNAc units joined to the α-1,6-Man branch of the core (Fig. 4).

Other Post-Translational Processing Events

Fatty Acylation. There are a number of membrane proteins, including transferrin receptor, viral envelope glycoproteins, viral oncogene products, and other proteolipids, that are modified with long-chain fatty acid addition. The exact signal sequences that specify fatty acid addition have not yet been determined, nor have the functions of the added fatty acid residues been elucidated beyond membrane anchoring. It has been suggested that these additional hydrophobic groups may be essential for protein targeting within the cell (122). Two common examples of fatty acylation are palmitylation and myristylation.

Analysis of the acylated viral glycoproteins E1 and E2 of the small-enveloped Sindbis virus revealed that a palmitic acid was attached to the proteins' serine residues embedded within the membrane bilayer. This palmitylation also appears in vesicular stomatitis virus G protein (VSV G), influenza hemagglutinin, and p15E of murine leukemia virus (122). The attachment of palmitic acid residues appears to be at internal amino acids such as cysteine and serine that are found within the lipid bilayer.

There have also been a number of reports of proteins containing myristic acid residues at or near the amino terminus of proteins, including viral transforming protein pp60^{src} and the catalytic subunit of cAMP-dependent ATPase of bovine cardiac muscle (122). Unlike palmitylation, myristylation appears to occur at amino-terminal glycine residues, presumably after cleavage of the initial methionine group.

The location within the secretory pathway for the addition of these fatty acid residues varies with the type of fatty acid added. For instance, VSV G palmitylation occurs during post-translational processing in the Golgi apparatus, while myristylation of other proteins appears to occur during protein synthesis (122).

Sulfation, Glycosaminoglycans, and Proteglycans. Glycosaminoglycans (GAGs) are composed of repeating, unbranched disaccharide units in which one of the two sugar residues is an amino sugar such as N-acetylglucosamine or N-acetylgalactosamine. In most cases these amino sugar groups are sulfated and the second sugar residue is usually a uronic acid (glucuronic or iduronic). Typically, GAGs are highly negatively charged due to the presence of sulfate or carboxyl groups on the sugar residues. Since these oligosaccharide chains are too inflexible to fold up into compact structures like polypeptides chains, these hydrophillic GAGs will adopt highly extended conformations that occupy huge volumes compared to their mass (123). GAGs are characterized by their sugar residues, the type of linkage between residues, and the number and location of sulfate groups.

Except for the simplest GAG, hyaluronan, all GAGs are found covalently attached to protein to form proteoglycans, which are made by most mammalian cells. Most proteoglycans are secreted and become components of the extracellular matrix, while others remain anchored to the plasma membrane. Proteoglycans are distinguished from other glycoproteins by the nature, quantity, and arrangement of their sugar chains. Most glycoproteins contain from 1 to 60% carbohydrate by weight in the form of the relatively short, branched oligosaccharide chains described previously. In contrast, proteoglycans can contain up to 95% carbohydrate by weight primarily in the form of long unbranched GAG chains, typically 80 sugar residues long. Due to the large degree of heterogeneity among the core proteins and the number and types of attached GAG chains, it is difficult to categorize the proteoglycans beyond a diverse group of heavily glycosylated proteins whose function can be mediated both by the core protein and its attached GAG chains (1,124).

As with other glycoproteins, the core protein is translated on a membrane-bound ribosome and translocated into the ER lumen. The polysaccharide chains are primarily assembled on the protein core within the Golgi apparatus. The first processing step is the addition of a special link tetrasaccharide to a serine residue on the core protein. Then, specific glycosyltransferases sequentially add one sugar residue at a time to the tetrasaccharide primer. In most cases it is not evident as to how the serine residue is selected, but specific local polypeptide conformations seem to be recognized rather than specific linear amino acid sequences. While in the Golgi, many of the polymerized sugar residues are modified through sulfation and epimerization reactions. Epimerizations alter the configuration of the substituents around individual carbon atoms in the sugar molecules, while the sulfations increase the negative charge of the proteoglycans (124). In some instances tyrosine residues in proteins can also become sulfated within the *trans* Golgi network. In both cases, sulfation depends on the presence of the sulfate donor, 3'-phosphoadenosine-5'-phosphosulfate or PAPS (1).

Phosphorylation. The phosphorylation of oligosaccharides is important in the recognition and selection of glycoproteins destined for the lysosomal pathway. Lysosomal enzymes carry a unique marker in the form of phosphorylated mannose groups, specifically mannose 6-phosphate (M6P) groups. These are added in the lumen of the *cis* Golgi network to the N-linked oligosaccharides of soluble lysosomal enzymes. These M6P groups are recognized by M6P receptor transmembrane proteins found in the *trans* Golgi network. These receptors help package these enzymes into specific transport vesicles that ultimately fuse with late endosomes (125).

Endoproteases: The Proprotein Convertase Family

This specific family of endoproteases is a growing family of highly specific mammalian Ca^{2+}-dependent proteases that cleave protein precursors typically at Arg–Xaa–(Lys/Arg)–Arg recognition sites (126). This family of proprotein convertases, which is related to the yeast Kex2p and the bacterial subtilisins, includes seven distinct enzymes: furin, PC2, PC1/PC3, PC4, PACE4, PC5/PC6, and LPC/PC7/PC8/SPC7. Furin, PACE4, PC5/PC6, and LPC/PC7/PC8/SPC7 are expressed in a wide variety of tissues and cell lines, while PC2 and PC1/PC3 are found only in neuroendocrine tissues, such as pancreatic islets (126). Expression of PC4 is found only in testicular spermatogenic cells.

Furin. Furin, the first proprotein convertase discovered and the most extensively studied, has been localized within the *trans* Golgi network. However, indirect evidence has suggested that some furin may also be present on the cell surface (126). Furin is a glycosylated type I membrane protein that has been shown to cleave a wide variety of protein precursors, including numerous growth factors, receptors, plasma proteins, and viral envelope proteins such as HIV gp 160, in order to produce the active proteins. The insulin receptor, for example, is synthesized as a single nonfunctional polypeptide that requires cleavage of both the signal peptide and the $-R-K-R-R-$(Arg–Lys–Arg–Arg–) sequence to generate the disulfide-linked α and β subunits that form the active receptor (127).

TRANSPORT TO THE CELL SURFACE

There are essentially two types of secretion within mammalian cells: constitutive and regulated secretion. Constitutive secretion refers to export of proteins and other cargo without the need for an external stimulus or the accumulation of a large intracellular reservoir. In contrast, regulated secretion requires external stimuli to trigger the release of stored secretory proteins. While all cells possess a constitutive secretory pathway, only specialized cells contain both a regulated and constitutive pathway. Upon reaching the "end" of the *trans* Golgi network, constitutive secretory and membrane proteins become packaged into vesicles destined for their designated location—which can be within another cellular organelle (including the lysosomes), the plasma membrane, or the extracellular environment. Once again, specific transport proteins are present to facilitate the budding, transport, and fusion of the secretory vesicles to the plasma membrane (or another intracellular membrane destination). For those proteins destined for the plasma membrane, the secretory vesicles fuse to the cellular membrane, releasing the contents of the lumen into the extracellular environment. For membrane proteins, the protein becomes integrated into the plasma membrane surface as cell surface proteins. Following vesicle fusion, many of the cellular components responsible for transport and fusion are then recycled back to the Golgi for another round of protein transport and release of the proteins into the extracellular environment.

CONCLUDING REMARKS

Completing the secretory process involves an assembly line of proteins that act in concert to produce a diverse collection of proteins for the cellular compartments, the extracellular environment, and cell surface display. The wide range of secretory functions include folding, assembly, post-translational modification, transport, and distribution into other cellular compartments and the extracellular environment. In this way the secretory apparatus is similar to a complex, dynamic manufacturing operation possessing multiple options for processing and distribution. As research continues on all aspects of the secretory pathway, we will be able to utilize our knowledge of this ubiquitous and invaluable processing system for bioprocessing, biotechnological, and biomedical applications.

BIBLIOGRAPHY

1. B. Alberts et al., *Molecular Biology of the Cell*, Garland Publishing, New York, 1994.
2. W.T. Wickner and H.F. Lodish, *Science* **230**, 400–407 (1985).
3. J.K. Rose and R.W. Doms, *Annu. Rev. Cell Biol.* **4**, 257–288 (1988).
4. H.R.B. Pelham, *Annu. Rev. Cell Biol.* **5**, 1–23 (1989).
5. D.L. Zimmerman and P. Walter, in J. Rothblatt, P. Novick, and T. Stevens, eds., *Guidebook to the Secretory Pathway*, Oxford University Press, Oxford, 1994, pp. 68–70.
5a. S.L. Saunder and R. Schekman, *J. Biol. Chem.* **267**, 13791–13794 (1992).
6. S.K. Lyman and R. Schekman, in M.J. Gething, ed., *Guidebook Molecular Chaperones and Protein-Folding Catalysts*, Oxford University Press, Oxford, 1997, pp. 506–514.
7. B.M. Wilkinson, C.J. Regnacq, and C.J. Stirling, *J. Membr. Biol.* **155**, 189–197 (1997).
8. S.M. Simon and G. Blobel, *Cell* **65**, 371–380 (1991).
9. E. Hartmann et al., *Nature (London)* **367**, 654–659 (1994).
10. D. Gorlich and T.A. Rapoport, *Cell* **75**, 615–630 (1993).
11. E.A. Evans, R. Gilmore, and G. Blobel, *Proc. Natl. Acad. Sci. U.S.A.* **83**, 581–585 (1986).
12. G. Shelness in J. Rothblatt, P. Novick, and T. Stevens, eds., *Guidebook to the Secretory Pathway*, Oxford University Press, 1994, pp. 88–89.
13. C. Booth and G.L.E. Koch, *Cell* **59**, 729–737 (1989).
14. I.G. Haas and M. Wabl, *Nature (London)* **306**, 387–389 (1983).
15. M.J. Gething and J.F. Sambrook, *Nature (London)* **355**, 33–45 (1992).
16. C.K. Kassenbrock and R.B. Kelly, *EMBO J.* **8**, 1461–1467 (1989).
17. G.C. Flynn, T.G. Chappell, and J.E. Rothman, *Science* **245**, 385–390 (1989).
18. M.J. Gething, S. Blond-Elguindi, K. Mori, and J.F. Sambrook, in R.I. Morimoto, A. Tissieres, and C. Georgopoulos, eds., *The Biology of Heat Shock Proteins and Molecular Chaperones*, Cold Spring Harbor Lab. Press, Cold Spring Harbary, 1994, pp. 111–135.
19. S. Blonde-Elguindi et al., *Cell* **75**, 717–728 (1993).
20. T.-A. Hsu et al., *Protein Express. Purif.* **5**, 595–603 (1994).
21. T.-A. Hsu and M.J. Betenbaugh, *Biotechnol. Prog.* **13**, 96–104 (1997).
22. D.M. Cyr, T. Langer, and M.G. Douglas, *Trends Biochem. Sci.* **19**, 176–181 (1994).
23. C. Georgopoulos, K. Liberek, M. Zylick, and D. Ang, in R.I. Morimoto, A. Tissières, and C. Georgopoulos, eds., *The Biology of Heat Shock Proteins and Molecular Chaperones*, Cold Spring Harbor Lab. Press, Cold Spring Harbor, N.Y., 1994, p. 209–249.

24. X. Zhu et al., *Science* **272**, 1606–1614 (1996).

25. M. Green, in J. Rothblatt, P. Novick, and T. Stevens, eds., *Guidebook to the Secretory Pathway*, Oxford University Press, Oxford, 1994, pp. 80–81.

26. J. Melnick, S. Aviel, and Y. Argon, *J. Biol. Chem.* **267**, 21303–21306 (1992).

27. W.T. Schaiff et al., *J. Exp. Med.* **176**, 657–666 (1992).

28. D. Navarro, I. Qadri, and L. Pereira, *Virology* **184**, 253–264 (1991).

29. J. Melnik, J.L. Dul, and Y. Argon, *Nature (London)* **370**, 373–375 (1994).

30. I. Wada et al., *J. Biol. Chem.* **266**, 19599–19610 (1991).

31. S. Pind and D.B. Williams, in M.J. Gething, ed., *Guidebook Molecular Chaperones and Protein-Folding Catalysts*, Oxford University Press, Oxford, 1997, pp. 299–304.

32. E. Degen and D.B. Williams, *J. Cell Biol.* **112**, 1099–1115 (1991).

33. F. Hochstenbach, V. David, S. Watkins, and M.B. Brenner, *Proc. Natl. Acad. U.S.A.* **89**, 4734–4738 (1992).

33a. C.G. Tate, E.W. Whiteley, and M.J. Betenbaugh, *J. Biol. Chem.* **274**, 17551–17558 (1999).

34. D.R.J. Macer and G.L.E. Koch, *J. Cell. Sci.* **92**, 61–70 (1988).

35. D.H. MacLennan and P.T.S. Wong, *Proc. Natl. Acad. U.S.A.* **68**, 1231–1235 (1971).

36. A. Vassilakos, M. Michalak, M.A. Lehrman, and D.B. Williams, *Biochemistry* **37**, 3480–3490 (1998).

37. C. Hammond and A. Helenius, *Science* **266**, 456–458 (1994).

38. M. Tector and R.D. Salter, *J. Biol. Chem.* **270**, 19638–19642 (1995).

39. A. Vassilakos et al., *EMBO J.* **15**, 1495–1506 (1996).

40. A.J. Petrescu et al., *EMBO J.* **16**, 4302–4310 (1997).

41. M. Michalak, R.E. Milner, K. Burns, and M. Opas, *Biochem. J.* **285**, 681–692 (1992).

42. J.R. Peterson, A. Ora, P.N. Van, and A. Helenius, *Mol. Biol. Cell* **6**, 1173–1184 (1995).

43. A. Otteken and B. Moss, *J. Biol. Chem.* **271**, 97–103 (1996).

44. J.D. Oliver, R.C. Hresko, M. Mueckler, and S. High, *J. Biol. Chem.* **271**, 13691–13696 (1996).

45. J.E.M. van Leeuwen and K.P. Kearse, *J. Biol. Chem.* **271**, 25345–25349 (1996).

46. A. Helenius, E.S. Trombetta, D.N. Hebert, and J.F. Simons, *Trends Cell Biol.* **7**, 193–200 (1997).

47. I. Wada et al., *J. Biol. Chem.* **270**, 20298–20304 (1995).

48. B. Sadasivan et al., *Immunity* **5**, 103–114 (1996).

49. F. Ware et al., *J. Biol. Chem.* **270**, 4697–4704 (1995).

50. Q. Zhang, M. Tector, and R.D. Salter, *J. Biol. Chem.* **270**, 3944–3948 (1995).

51. B. Arunachalam and P. Cresswell, *J. Biol. Chem.* **270**, 2784–2790 (1995).

52. T. Pihlajaniemi et al., *EMBO J.* **6**, 643–649 (1987).

53. J. Koivu et al., *J. Biol. Chem.* **262**, 6447–6449 (1987).

54. J.R. Wetterau, K.A. Combs, S.N. Spinner, and B.J. Joiner, *J. Biol. Chem.* **265**, 9801–9807 (1990).

55. R.B. Freedman, in M.J. Gething, ed., *Guidebook Molecular Chaperones and Protein-Folding Catalysts*, Oxford University Press, Oxford, 1997, pp. 348–351.

56. R.B. Freedman, T.R. Hirst, and M.F. Tuite, *Trends Prochem. Sci.* **19**, 331–336 (1994).

57. K.D. Wittrup, *Curr. Opin. Biotechnol.* **6**, 203–208 (1995).

58. K. Vouri, R. Myllylä, T. Pihlajaniemi, and K.I. Kivirikko, *J. Biol. Chem.* **267**, 7211–7217 (1992).

59. M.M. Lyles and H.F. Gilbert, *J. Biol. Chem.* **269**, 30946–30952 (1994).

60. M.C.A. Laboissière, S.L. Sturley, and R.T. Raines, *J. Biol. Chem.* **270**, 28006–28009 (1995).

61. H. Cai, C.-C. Wang, and C.-L. Tsou, *J. Biol. Chem.* **269**, 24550–24552 (1994).

62. H. Quan, G. Fan, and C.-C. Wang, *J. Biol. Chem.* **270**, 17078–17080 (1995).

63. A. Puig and H.F. Gilbert, *J. Biol. Chem.* **269**, 7764–7771 (1994).

64. E.M. Whiteley, T.-A. Hsu, and M.J. Betenbaugh, *J. Biol. Chem.* **272**, 22556–22563 (1997).

65. A. Puig, M.M. Lyles, R. Noiva, and H.F. Gilbert, *J. Biol. Chem.* **269**, 19128–19135 (1994).

66. G. Fischer, H. Bang, and C. Mech, *Biomed. Biochim. Acta* **43**, 1101–1111 (1984).

67. J.F. Brandts, H. Halvorson, and M. Brennan, *Biochemistry* **14**, 4953–4963 (1975).

68. H.N. Cheng and F.A. Bovey, *Biopolymers* **16**, 1465–1472 (1977).

69. C. Grathwohl and K. Wuthrich, *Biopolymers* **20**, 2623–2633 (1981).

70. K. Lang, F. Schmid, and G. Fischer, *Nature (London)* **329**, 268–270 (1987).

71. F. Schmid, *Annu. Rev. Biophys. Biomol. Struct.* **22**, 123–143 (1993).

72. H. Lilie, K. Lang, R. Rudolph, and J. Buchner, *Protein Sci.* **2**, 1490–1496 (1993).

73. C. Fransson, P.O. Freskgard, H. Herbertsson, and A. Johansson, *FEBS Lett.* **296**, 90–94 (1992).

74. P.O. Freskgard et al., *Science* **258**, 466–468 (1992).

75. H.P. Bachinger, *J. Biol. Chem.* **262**, 17144–17148 (1987).

76. B. Steinmann, P. Bruckner, and A. Superti-furga, *J. Biol. Chem.* **266**, 1299–1303 (1991).

77. H.F. Lodish and N. Kong, *J. Biol. Chem.* **266**, 14835–14838 (1991).

78. N.J. Colley, E.K. Baker, M.A. Stamnes, and C.S. Zuker, *Cell* **6**, 255–263 (1991).

79. M.A. Stamnes, B.H. Shieh, L. Chuman, and C.S. Zuker, *Cell* **65**, 219–227 (1991).

80. R. Kornfeld and S. Kornfeld, *Annu. Rev. Biochem.* **54**, 631–664 (1985).

81. K.W. Moremen and O. Touster, in R.C. Das and P.W. Robbins, eds., *Protein Transferase and Organelle Biogenesis*, Academic Press, San Diego, Calif., 1988, pp. 209–240.

82. S.S. Krag, in J. Rothblatt, P. Novick, and T. Stevens, eds., *Guidebook to the Secretory Pathway*, Oxford University Press, Oxford, 1994, pp. 92–93.

83. G. Kreibich, in J. Rothblatt, P. Novick, and T. Stevens eds., *Guidebook to the Secretory Pathway*, Oxford University Press, Oxford, 1994, pp. 97–98.

83a. T. Nakashima, et al., *Mol. Cell. Biol.* **13**, 6367–6374 (1993).

83b. D.J. Kelleher and R. Gilmore, *Proc. Natl. Acad. Sci. U.S.A.* **94**, 4994–4999 (1997).

84. K.W. Moremen, R.B. Trimble, and A. Herscovics, *Glycobiology* **4**, 113–125 (1994).

85. A.D. Elbein, *FASEB J.* **5**, 3055–3063 (1991).

86. P.T. Englund, *Annu. Rev. Biochem.* **62**, 65–100 (1993).

87. B.J. Nichols et al., *Nature (London)* **387**, 199–202 (1997).

88. B.E. Balch, in J. Rothblatt, P. Novick, and T. Stevens, eds., *Guidebook to the Secretory Pathway*, Oxford University Press, 1994, pp. 107–109.

89. H.-P. Hauri, in J. Rothblatt, P. Novick and T. Stevens, eds., *Guidebook to the Secretory Pathway*, Oxford University Press, Oxford, 1994, p. 141.

90. R. Schindler et al., *Eur. J. Cell Biol.* **61**, 1–9 (1993).

91. F. Kappeler et al., *J. Biol. Chem.* **272**, 31801–31808 (1997).

92. C. Arar et al., *J. Biol. Chem.* **270**, 3551–3553 (1995).

93. C. Hammond and A. Helenius, *Curr. Opin. Cell Biol.* **7**, 523–529 (1995).

94. B. Pearse and M. Robinson, *Annu. Rev. Cell Biol.* **6**, 151–171 (1990).

95. R. Schekman and L. Orci, *Science* **271**, 1526–1533 (1996).

96. S.Y. Bednarek et al., *Cell* **83**, 1183–1196 (1995).

97. R. Pepperkok et al., *Cell* **74**, 71–82 (1993).

98. J.E. Rothman and L. Orci, *Nature (London)* **355**, 409–415 (1992).

99. F. Aniento, G. Feng, R.G. Parton, and J. Gruenberg, *J. Cell Biol.* **133**, 29–41 (1996).

100. R. Kahn, in J. Rothblatt, P. Novick, and T. Stevens, eds., *Guidebook to the Secretory Pathway*, Oxford University Press, Oxford, 1994, pp. 181–182.

101. T. Taylor, P. Kanstein, P. Weidman, and P. Melacon, *Mol. Biol. Cell* **5**, 237–252 (1994).

102. Z. Elazar et al., *J. Cell Biol.* **124**, 415–424 (1994).

103. S.L. Bannykh and W.E. Balch, *J. Cell Biol.* **138**, 1–4 (1997).

104. J.F. Presley et al., *Nature (London)* **389**, 81–85 (1997).

105. H.R.B. Pelham, *Nature (London)* **389**, 17–19 (1997).

106. J.B. Bock and R.H. Scheller, *Nature (London)* **386**, 133–135 (1997).

107. M. Zerial et al., in J. Rothblatt, P. Novick, and T. Stevens, eds., *Guidebook to the Secretory Pathway*, Oxford University Press, Oxford, 1994, pp. 202–204.

108. V.V. Lupashin and M.G. Waters, *Science* **276**, 1255–1258 (1997).

109. F. Schimmöller, I. Simon, and S.R. Pfeffer, *J. Biol. Chem.* **273**, 22161–22164 (1998).

110. J. Pevsner et al., *Neuron* **13**, 353–361 (1994).

111. J.E. Rothman and T.H. Söllner, *Science* **276**, 1212–1213 (1997).

112. R.D. Teasdale and M.R. Jackson, *Annu. Rev. Cell Dev. Biol.* **12**, 27–54 (1996).

113. J. Saraste and E. Kuismanen, *Cell* **38**, 535–549 (1983).

114. S.A. Tooze, J. Tooze, and G. Warren, *J.Cell Biol.* **106**, 1475–1487 (1988).

115. S. Munro, *Trends Cell. Biol.* **8**, 11–15 (1998).

116. B.S. Glick, T. Elston, and G. Oster, *FEBS Lett.* **414**, 177–181 (1997).

117. S. Wooding and H.R.B. Pelham, *Mol. Biol. Cell* **9**, 2667–2680 (1998).

118. L. Stryer, *Biochemistry*, Freeman, New York, 1988.

119. S.E. Trombetta, S.A. Ganan, and A.J. Parodi, *Glycobiology* **1**, 155–161 (1991).

120. S. Hiraizumi, U. Spohr, and R.G. Spiro, *J. Biol. Chem.* **268**, 9927–9935 (1993).

121. C.F. Goochee et al., *Bio/Technology* **9**, 1347–1357 (1991).

122. M.R. Rosner, in W.G. Thilly, ed., *Mammalian Cell Technology*, Boston, 1986, pp. 63–89.

123. R.L. Jackson, S.J. Busch, and A.D. Cardin, *Physiol. Rev.* **71**, 481–539 (1991).

124. T.E. Hardingham and A.J. Fosang, *FASEB J.* **6**, 861–870 (1992).

125. K. von Figura, *Curr. Opin. Cell Biol.* **3**, 642–646 (1991).

126. K. Nakayama, *Biochem. J.* **327**, 625–635 (1997).

127. R. Grisshammer and C.G. Tate, *Q. Rev. of Biophys.* **28**, 315–422 (1995).

See also GENETIC ENGINEERING: ANIMAL CELL TECHNOLOGY; PROTEIN PROCESSING, ENDOCYTOSIS AND INTRACELLULAR SORTING OF GROWTH FACTORS; RECEPTORS AND CELL SIGNALING, INTRACELLULAR RECEPTORS—STEROID HORMONES AND NO; TRANSCRIPTION, TRANSLATION AND THE CONTROL OF GENE EXPRESSION.

PROTOPLAST FUSION FOR THE GENERATION OF UNIQUE PLANTS

M.R. DAVEY
K.C. LOWE
J.B. POWER
University of Nottingham
Nottingham, United Kingdom

OUTLINE

Introduction

Why Fuse Isolated Plant Protoplasts?

Procedures for Protoplast Fusion

  Chemical Fusion of Protoplasts

  Electrical Fusion of Protoplasts

Products of Protoplast Fusion and the Selection of Somatic Hybrid Tissues and Plants

  Homokaryons and Heterokaryons

  Procedures for Selecting Hybrid Cells and Plants

Characterization of Somatic Hybrid Plants

Generation of Asymmetrical Hybrids and Cybrids by Protoplast Fusion

Gametosomatic Hybridization

Transfer of Unique Traits by Protoplast Fusion

Concluding Remarks

Bibliography

INTRODUCTION

The totipotency of isolated protoplasts enables exploiting these naked cells in plant genetic manipulation. Plant protoplasts from which the enveloping cell wall has been removed by enzymatic digestion will fuse when exposed to the correct chemical and/or electrical stimuli. The fusion of isolated protoplasts enables generating unique plants through somatic hybridization.

WHY FUSE ISOLATED PLANT PROTOPLASTS?

Plant breeders rely on sexual hybridization to combine useful genetic traits from different species or genera, but naturally occurring, complex sexual incompatibility barriers often act at the prezygotic or postzygotic stages of embryonic development (1). Even when prezygotic barriers are absent and when pollination and fertilization result in zygote formation, postzygotic barriers may still prevent embryonic development. The fusion of protoplasts isolated from somatic cells circumvents such sexually incompatible barriers at the intergeneric and interspecific levels.

During protoplast fusion, there is no strict maternal inheritance of organelles, as is usually the case in sexual hybridization. Additionally, the combinations of nuclear and organellar genomes that result from protoplast fusion are complex. Consequently, the fusion of somatic cells can generate unique germplasm. Indeed, wide hybridization at the intergeneric level creates new evolutionary opportunities that would be difficult or impossible to achieve by conventional hybridization. Even in those genera or species where sexual hybridization is possible, the production of somatic hybrid plants between the same parental combinations produces novel germplasm for comparison with the sexual counterpart.

PROCEDURES FOR PROTOPLAST FUSION

Protoplast fusion can be induced by chemical or electrical methods and by a combination of these two techniques. Detailed protocols for both small-scale and large-scale chemical and electrical fusion have been published (2), although protocols may require modification for any specific combination of protoplast partners. The optimum protocol for fusion is influenced by the parental protoplasts. Protoplast size and the source of the protoplasts affect protoplast stability and fusion frequency. Irrespective of the procedure, the naked plasma membranes of the parental protoplasts are destabilized for a short period, resulting in establishing cytoplasmic continuity between tightly adhering protoplasts.

Chemical Fusion of Protoplasts

Chemical fusogens, such as solutions of sodium nitrate, calcium nitrate, polyvinyl alcohol (PVA), dextran sulfate, and polycations, including poly-L-lysine, have been exploited to fuse protoplasts, although some fusogens may be more detrimental to protoplast viability than others. Polyethylene glycol (PEG) is most commonly used, sometimes combined with high pH and calcium ions. High pH/Ca^{2+} solutions are also employed in their own right. Even with PEG, the source and purity of the compound is important. PEG of low carbonyl content is essential to maximize fusion and protoplast viability (3). Recently, PEG solutions have been supplemented with dimethyl sulfoxide (DMSO) to fuse protoplasts from cell suspensions of *Lycopersicon esculentum* x *pennellii* with mesophyll protoplasts of *Solanum melongena* (4). In other studies, the addition of the nonionic, polyoxyethylene-polyoxypropylene surfactant, Pluronic F-68 (poloxamer 188), commonly used as an antifoaming agent and cytoprotectant in fermentation vessels, increased the fusion of leaf protoplasts of *Petunia parodii* with suspension cell protoplasts of *P. hybrida* twofold when added at 0.01% (w/v) to the PEG solution (5).

Copolymers, such as Pluronic F-68, may act more as membrane stabilizers than as fusogens *per se*. Their effects on cell membranes have been studied more extensively in animal cells than in plant cells, highlighting the importance for workers interested in plant systems to be aware of developments pertaining to animal cells. Chemical fusion is simple and inexpensive.

Electrical Fusion of Protoplasts

Electrical fusion of protoplasts is more reproducible than chemical fusion and generally is less damaging to the protoplasts. The frequency of electrical fusion of protoplasts may be higher than chemical fusion. However, the procedure necessitates relatively sophisticated instrumentation to ensure safety. Equipment is available commercially, although more versatile instruments can be constructed in a laboratory workshop (6). Electrodes in the form of parallel wires and parallel or concentric plates have been used which are often designed to fit the wells of standard commercially available laboratory plasticware. Small-scale electrofusion enables fusing limited numbers of parental protoplasts (e.g., one protoplast of each parent) in liquid droplets using platinum wire electrodes. This approach has also been exploited to introduce organelles within subprotoplasts (miniprotoplasts) into recipient protoplasts.

Immediately before electrofusion, isolated protoplasts are suspended in a medium of low conductivity, such as 6 to 13% w/v mannitol, usually with a small quantity of calcium ions (e.g., 1.0 M $CaCl_2$) to stabilize the plasma membranes. During fusion, the protoplasts are exposed to an alternating current (ac) of 0.5 to 2.0 MHz at 100 to 400 V cm^{-1}. The protoplasts become differentially charged and align into chains ("pearl chains") perpendicular to the electrodes. Increasing the field strength induces close membrane-to-membrane contact. A subsequent square-wave direct-current (dc) pulse 10 to 200 microseconds long and 500 to 2000 V cm^{-1} results in breaking down the plasma membranes (pore formation) at the poles of the protoplasts where they are in contact.

Chemical treatment of protoplasts with polyamines, cytochalasins B and D, and calcium ions before electrofusion reduces protoplast lysis during the fusion process. Such treatments of mesophyll protoplasts of *Nicotiana tabacum* increased electrofusion more than 1.5 times than with 11% w/v mannitol solution alone. A substantial increase in the plating efficiency of electrofusion-treated protoplasts was also obtained following exposure of the protoplasts to prostaglandin F-2a, lecithin, and $CaCl_2 \cdot 2H_2O$ (7). Protease treatment, PEG agglutination and Ca^{2+} also increase electrofusion. The fusion of protoplasts normally occurs over a period of approximately 10 min after application of the dc pulse.

PRODUCTS OF PROTOPLAST FUSION AND THE SELECTION OF SOMATIC HYBRID TISSUES AND PLANTS

Homokaryons and Heterokaryons

Protoplast fusion is a random process. Homokaryons result from fusing protoplasts of the same genetic composition and are of little interest in plant genetic manipulation because they merely increase the ploidy of plants regenerated from such fusion products. Heterokaryons are of interest to genetic improvement programs because they contain the nuclei of the two parental genera or species, initially in a mixed cytoplasm. Heterokaryons may develop into hybrid cells; the latter may be induced, under the correct culture conditions, to express their totipotency via organogenesis or somatic embryogenesis.

Procedures for Selecting Hybrid Cells and Plants

Instigating procedures that encourage the development of heterokaryons, heterokaryon-derived tissues, and somatic hybrid plants remains the most difficult aspect of somatic hybridization. In some protoplast combinations, it is possible to rely upon heterosis (hybrid vigor) and to select manually those protoplast-derived cell colonies that first develop in the culture vessels. Some of these colonies may be somatic hybrid. An excellent example follows the electrofusion of leaf mesophyll protoplasts of *Petunia hybrida* ($2n = 14$), with a wild sexually incompatible species, *P. variabilis* ($2n = 18$), hybrids ($2n = 32$) being selected by the vigorous growth of tissues and regenerated shoots (8). The main disadvantage of a selection system based upon heterosis is that, eventually, unfused parental protoplasts and homokaryons may overgrow somatic hybrid cells. Culture media have been developed that encourage the growth of hybrid cells, while limiting the growth of protoplast-derived cells of one, or preferably both fusion partners. Hormone autotrophism, which is relatively common in intergeneric and interspecific hybrids in the Solanaceae, has been exploited in selection. The classic example is the recovery of the first somatic hybrid plants ever reported between *Nicotiana glauca* and *N. langsdorffii*, using a growth-regulator-free medium (9).

Manual selection, with a simple laboratory-constructed micromanipulator utilizing glass micropipettes (10), is useful when the parental protoplasts are morphologically distinct and enables visualizing heterokaryons for several hours after fusion, before complete mixing of the two parental cytoplasms. Heterokaryons from the fusion of chloroplast-containing leaf protoplasts with suspension cell protoplasts can be identified initially by the chloroplasts in one-half of their cytoplasm and colorless plastids in the other half. Subsequently, selected heterokaryons can be cultured at low densities in the presence of nurse cells or protoplasts, in specially constructed small-volume chambers. Although micromanipulation is time-consuming, the development of selected heterokaryons can be observed in the culture vessels, giving confidence in the origin of potentially somatic hybrid tissues. Fluorochromes can be used to assist heterokaryon identification before selection. For example, the red chlorophyll autofluorescence of leaf protoplasts can be combined with the pale green fluorescence following fluorescein diacetate (FDA) staining of suspension cell protoplasts.

Flow cytometry is a high-technology procedure that exploits fluorescence to select heterokaryons from homokaryons and unfused parental protoplasts. As many as 2000 protoplasts are processed per second by the instrument. The approach was first used to recover somatic hybrids in *Nicotiana* (11). The dual fluorescence of heterokaryons is recognized by the computer of the cytometer, and the droplets containing the heterokaryons are deflected into a receiving vessel. Flow cytometry is useful following the fusion of large populations of parental protoplasts, but the instrumentation is costly, and some protoplasts fail to survive the physical stresses of passing through the machine.

Several complementation systems have been devised, the simplest of which involves albino mutants. Thus, fusion of nonallelic protoplasts from albino mutants results in hybrid cells that complement to synthesize chlorophyll. Similarly, complementation to chlorophyll proficiency is achieved by fusing albino mutant protoplasts with wild-type protoplasts, as in fusing chlorophyll deficient *Senecio jacobaea* with wild-type *S. fuchsii* (12). Hybrid tissues are identified by their chlorophyll production on transfer of the cultures from the dark to the light. Subsequently, green somatic hybrid tissues are isolated manually using forceps.

Of the auxotrophic mutants used in selection, those exhibiting nitrate reductase deficiency are the best known. For example, the nitrate reductase deficiency of the *nia-63* mutant of *Nicotiana tabacum* can be complemented by the chlorate-resistant line (*cnx-68*) of *N. tabacum*. Although the mutants cannot utilize nitrate and fail to grow on nitrate-supplemented medium, somatic hybrid cells undergo complementation and can be selected on nitrate-containing medium (13). The natural dominant or semidominant resistance of some cells to amino acid analogs, such as 5-methyltryptophan and *S*-2-aminotheylcysteine, has also been exploited. The most clear-cut selection system is that where somatic hybrid cells acquire resistance from both parents and can grow in the presence of two aminoacid analogs, as in carrot (14).

Antibiotic resistant cells are also useful in selection, but such cells, like mutants, are naturally uncommon. However, dominant genetic markers, such as antibiotic resistance, can be introduced through transformation by *Agrobacterium* or other gene delivery techniques into cells used as a source of protoplasts. The disadvantaage of this approach is that it increases the timescale of experiments because detailed molecular characterization of the presence and expression of transgenes in parental cells is essential before protoplast isolation. Nevertheless, in a simple demonstration of this approach, resistance to the two antibiotics, kanamycin sulfate and methotrexate, was used to select rare symmetrical and asymmetrical somatic hybrids between transgenic *Nicotiana megalosiphon* (kanamycin-resistant) and *N. tabacum* (15). Genetically marked parental protoplasts act as "universal hybridizers," as in *Lactuca sativa* (16).

Comparatively rarely, selection is based solely on characteristics, such as albinism, auxotrophy, or antibiotic resistance. Commonly, two approaches are combined. Antimetabolites that inhibit cell division and development, rather than killing cells, are useful in this respect. In the hybridization of cultivated lettuce (*Lactuca sativa*) with the wild species *L. virosa*, hybrid selection was based on inactivating protoplasts of *L. sativa* with 20 mM iodoacetamide for 15 min, combined with the inability of *L. virosa* protoplasts to divide under the culture conditions employed (17). Inhibition by the metabolic inhibitor was complemented by the *L. virosa* parent. In other examples, transformation to kanamycin resistance has been combined with the use of a metabolic inhibitor (18).

An interesting recent development has been the application to plant protoplasts of a physicochemical magnetic cell sorter (MACS) technique originally designed for animal cells. This approach has been applied to the somatic hybridization of potato. Selected biotinylated lectins were used to mediate, via streptavidin, the binding of superparamagnetic microbeads to protoplasts of one fusion partner. The other protoplast partner was marked genetically with the neomycin phosphotransferase II (*npt*II) gene, conferring kanamycin resistance. Following fusion, the protoplasts were sorted by MACS, which retained the protoplasts labeled with the magnetic microbeads. Only somatic hybrid cells continued to grow following culture of such labeled protoplasts in kanamycin-supplemented medium. Interestingly, MACS treatment increased the percentage of somatic hybrid plants between two clones of *Solanum tuberosum* from 8 to 36%, and in the interspecific combination *S. tuberosum* (+) *S. bulbocastanum*, the increase was more dramatic, from 28 to 82% (19). Again, these observations highlight the need to follow the animal cell literature and to exploit this technology for plant systems. It is likely that MACS will have considerable potential in plant cell fusion in the future.

Attempts have been made to exploit differences in the density of vacuolate and cytoplasmically dense protoplasts to enrich populations of heterokaryons and hybrid cells by density gradient centrifugation, using solutions of Percoll or Ficoll. Although success has been limited, this approach has been applied to *Nicotiana*. Thus, following the fusion of vacuolate protoplasts of *N. tabacum* cv. Xanthi with cytoplasmically dense, streptomycin-resistant protoplasts of *N. tabacum* cv. Petit Havana SR1, fused and unfused protoplasts of the Petit Havana parent were removed by flotation on an iso-osmolar sucrose-containing medium. Subsequently, hybrid cells were selected on the basis of their streptomycin resistance. Homokaryons and unfused vacuolated protoplasts of the Xanthi parent died in the presence of the antibiotic (20).

CHARACTERIZATION OF SOMATIC HYBRID PLANTS

Complex nuclear-cytoplasmic interactions follow protoplast fusion. Consequently, characterizing plants generated in protoplast fusion experiments necessitates an integrated approach, based on morphological, cytological, and molecular analyses. In some cases, traits characteristic of both parents are readily visualized in somatic hybrid plants. For example, leaf shape, floral form, and pigmentation may be intermediate between those of both parents. In other cases, characteristics from one parent may dominate in somatic hybrids.

Plants regenerated from fusing two diploid somatic cell protoplasts should be tetraploid. In somatic hybrids between *Diplotaxis catholica* ($2n = 18$) and *Brassica juncea* ($2n = 36$) symmetric hybrids did, in fact, predominate, and each of the hybrids had 54 chromosomes (21). However, it is generally rare to find plants whose chromosome complements represent the summation of those of the parents. More frequently, hybrids possess an asymmetrical combination of parental chromosomes, and parts of one or both genomes are eliminated during culture (22). The reason for chromosome elimination is still not understood, although it is probably influenced by several factors. For example, the parental protoplasts may be at different stages of the cell cycle immediately before fusion, and mixing of the chromosomes may be incomplete on a common metaphase plate. Therefore, daughter cells may receive different numbers of chromosomes with additional loss during subsequent mitotic divisions. Nuclei in heterokaryons may fuse before mitosis, but subsequent mitotic events in such cells are unknown. Recently, the molecular technique of genomic *in situ* hybridization (GISH) has been used to characterize parental chromosomes in somatic hybrids. Interestingly, this "chromosome painting" approach has provided evidence for chromosomal translocations which are not visible by standard cytological procedures (23). Undoubtedly, further refinement of the technique and its application to fusion products will provide additional information concerning the behavior of parental chromosomes in somatic hybrids.

Both sterile and fertile plants result from protoplast fusion. In the somatic hybridization of *Brassica napus* with *B. tournefortii*, five plants were fertile, ten were male sterile, and four were completely sterile (24). Genetic analysis is possible when somatic hybrids are fertile, coupled with backcrossing to one or both of the parents. Detailed molecular cytological analysis of backcross progeny provides evidence of parental chromosomal behavior during mitiosis and meiosis following introduction of somatic hybrids into breeding programs.

Analysis of isozymes, such as esterases and peroxidases, has been a routine biochemical procedure used for many years to confirm the hybridity of plants arising from fused protoplasts. Generally, hybrids exhibit isozyme fingerprints characteristic of their parents, often with additional hybrid-specific bands. Again, attention has focused recently on molecular techniques. For example, flow cytometric analysis of DNA in isolated nuclei is a rapid procedure for estimating the ploidy of plants generated by somatic hybridization; it also provides a baseline for more detailed cytological analyses. DNA fingerprinting techniques, including restriction fragment length polymorphism (RFLP), random amplified polymorphic DNA (RAPD), and amplified fragment length polymorphism (AFLP) analyses, together with the use of microsatellites (25), are receiving considerable attention because they permit detailed characterization of nuclear and organellar genomes of parental plants and their somatic hybrids.

Events at the organellar level in somatic hybrids are complex. Initially, heterokaryons contain a mixed population of plastids and mitochondria. Subsequently, plastids usually segregate, and those of one partner become dominant (24); in rare cases the plastids of both partners persist in somatic hybrids, or recombination of plastid DNA may occur. Analysis of fraction 1 protein (ribulose bisphosphate carboxylase-oxygenase), linked to the chloroplast DNA restriction enzyme profile, confirms the parental origin of chloroplasts in somatic hybrids. The large enzyme subunits are encoded by chloroplast DNA. Recombination of mitochondrial DNA is common, and "new" organelles are generated, as evidenced by the restriction enzyme digestion pattern of mitochondrial DNA (24). Such DNA recombination in cytoplasmic organelles also increases the genetic diversity that arises from protoplast fusion.

GENERATION OF ASYMMETRICAL HYBRIDS AND CYBRIDS BY PROTOPLAST FUSION

Symmetrical nuclear hybrids that arise from protoplast fusion are generally rare; most populations of somatic hybrid plants are predominantly asymmetrical hybrids. Frequently, breeders require the introgression of a limited number of chromosomes, parts of chromosomes, or only organelles, such as chloroplasts, from one species into another. As a result of this, conscious effort has been made to generate asymmetrical nuclear hybrids and cytoplasmic hybrids (cybrids). Cybrid cells have a nuclear genome of a given genus or species (the recipient) which contains an alien plastid genome (plastome) or plastids from both the recipient and a donor. Cybrids also harbor a mitochondrial genome (chondriome), derived partly or totally from the recipient or the donor, or novel mitochondria with unique DNA following recombination between mitochondrial DNA of the recipient and donor.

Treatment of protoplasts of one partner with X- or gamma-irradiation and treatment of the protoplasts of the other parent with a metabolic inhibitor before fusion encourage asymmetrical hybrid production. Irradiation promotes partial genomic transfer, and the irradiated and nondividing but metabolically active protoplasts overcome the inability of the inhibitor-treated protoplasts to undergo mitosis. Somatic hybrid plants frequently resemble the partner used as the source of the inhibitor-treated protoplasts. In the somatic hybridization of *Medicago sativa* (alfalfa) with *Onobrychis viciifolia* (26), the hybrids resembled the *Medicago* parent. Cytogenetic studies confirmed the existence of euploid ($2n = 32$), as well as aneuploid ($2n = 30, 33-78$) individuals in the regenerated plants. Other procedures have also been evaluated to promote partial genomic transfer. The phosphoric amide herbicide, Cremart, which acts on the mitotic spindle to induce micronuclei, has been assessed in potato and tobacco (27). Clearly, this procedure merits more extensive investigation in the future.

Although cybrid plants appear spontaneously following protoplast fusion, two main approaches are used to induce cybrid cells and plants. One involves enucleated protoplasts as organelle donors (28) fused with either protoplasts or miniprotoplasts. The other approach, the so-called "donor-recipient protoplast fusion," is similar to that used to generate asymmetrical hybrids and uses X- or gamma-irradiated protoplasts as organelle

donors fused with recipient protoplasts treated with an antimetabolite, such as iodoacetamide (29). Presumably, the doses of irradiation and metabolic inhibitor influence the generation of asymmetrical nuclear hybrids or cybrids. Examples of cybridization in the literature include transfer of mitochrondrially encoded cytoplasmic male sterility (CMS) in carrot (30) and of CMS linked to choloroplast-encoded cold tolerance in *Brassica* (31).

GAMETOSOMATIC HYBRIDIZATION

The transfer of genetic information from wild germplasm to cultivated plants can be achieved by producing alien addition or substitution lines through the generation of triploids by sexual crossing. Triploids arise infrequently during the fusion of diploid protoplasts, as in *Citrus* (32). However, they can also be generated by fusing diploid with haploid protoplasts. Haploid protoplasts can be isolated directly from tissues of anther-derived haploid plants or from cell suspensions initiated from tissues of such plants. Additionally, microspores at the tetrad stage release protoplasts with a haploid genome. Gametosomatic protoplast fusion has generated triploid plants between *Nicotiana* species (33). Haploid protoplasts for gametosomatic hybridization have also been isolated from mature pollen, the fusion of pollen-derived protoplasts of *N. tabacum* with diploid leaf mesophyll protoplasts of *N. plumbaginifolia* resulting in gametosomatic hybrid and also cybrid plants. The range of gametosomatic hybrid plants generated is limited, which is probably related to the general difficulty of isolating haploid protoplasts from microspores or mature pollen in plants outside the Solanaceae.

TRANSFER OF UNIQUE TRAITS BY PROTOPLAST FUSION

Several examples exist now of the transfer of agronomically useful traits through protoplast fusion. Some of these are summarized in Table 1 (34–46). Generally, effort has focused on members of the Solanaceae, such as potato and tobacco, together with representatives in the Brassicaceae. It is noteworthy that the woody plant *Citrus* (Rutaceae) is very amenable to protoplast-based manipulations, and examples exist of interspecific and intergeneric hybrids between both sexually compatible and sexually incompatible partners (47). Currently, somatic hybrids and cybrids of *Citrus* are probably more advanced in their commercial exploitation than somatic hybrids or cybrids in other crops.

CONCLUDING REMARKS

Since 1993, there has been a resurgence of interest in protoplast fusion because this technique effectively mobilizes large amounts of genetic material, often polygenic traits, between genera and species. Indeed, somatic hybridization provides a relatively simple approach to extending genetic variation, as proposed for improving the agronomic characteristics of tomato by fusing protoplasts with those of other members of the Solanaceae, including *Nicotiana*

Table 1. Examples of the Transfer of Agronomically Useful Traits by Protoplast Fusion

Genus/Species Combination	Trait Transferred	Reference
Brassica juncea (+) *B. juncea* cv."RLM 198"	Cessation of chlorosis, increased female fertility, improved pod quality	34
B. napus (+) *B. nigra*	*B. napus* cybrids resistant to *Phoma lingam*	35
B. napus (+) *B. tournefortii*	CMS into *B. napus*	36
B. oleracea (+) *B. rapa*	Rapid cycling *B. napus* with novel fatty acids and rapid flowering	37
B. oleracea ssp. Botrytis (+) *B. oleracea*	Cauliflower with cytoplasmic male sterility and cold tolerance	31
B. oleracea var. Botrytis (+) *B. rapa* va.oleifera	*B. napus* with increased seed size, lodging resistance, non shatter pods combined with high erucic acid	38
B. oleracea (+) *B. napus*	*B. oleracea* resistant to *Xanthomonas campestris* pv. campestris	39
B. oleracea (+) *Sinapsis alba*	*B. oleracea* resistant to *Alternaria brassicae*	40
Solanum tuberosum PDH40 (+) *S. tuberosum* PDH417	Potato resistant to cyst nematode	41
S. tuberosum (+) *S. bulbocastanum*	Potato resistant to *Meliodogyne chitwoodi*	42
S. tuberosum (+) *S. chacoense*	Potato resistant to Colorado beetle	43
S. tuberosum (+) *S. torvum*	Potato resistant to *Verticillium dahliae*	44
S. tuberosum (+) *Lycopersicon pennellii*	Saline-tolerant potato	45
Citrus aurantium (+) *C. limonia* (*C. jambhiri* × *C. sinensis*) (+) *C. reticulata* *C. aurantium* (+) *Poncirus trifoliata* *C. reticulata* (+) *Poncirus trifoliata* *C. sinensis* (+) *P. trifoliata*	Cold hardiness, disease resistance, nematode resistance	46

and *Solanum* (48). Now, molecular techniques permit the detailed genetic mapping of somatic hybrids and cybrids. Such methods reveal that many plants that arise from fusion although morphologically similar, are, in fact, genetically extremely diverse, a feature which provides unique germplasm for direct exploitation or incorporation into breeding programs. It is likely that somatic hybridization and cybridization will see increasing application in plant genetic manipulation because this relatively simple approach circumvents sophisticated recombinant DNA technology required to isolate, clone, and reintroduce complex genes into target plants.

BIBLIOGRAPHY

1. D. de Nettencourt, *Sex. Plant Reprod.* **10**, 185–199 (1997).

2. N.W. Blackhall, M.R. Davey, and J.B. Power, in R.A. Dixon and R.A. Gonzales, eds., *Plant Cell Culture: A Practical Approach*, 2nd ed., IRL Press at Oxford University Press, New York, 1994, pp. 41–48.

3. P.K. Chand, M.R. Davey, J.B. Power, and E.C. Cocking, *J. Plant Physiol.* **133**, 480–485 (1988).

4. K.B. Liu, Y.M. Li, and K.C. Sink, *Plant Cell Rep.* **14**, 652–656 (1995).

5. T.K. Hill et al., *Euphytica* **85**, 269–273 (1995).

6. B. Jones et al., *BioTechniques* **6**, 312–321 (1994).

7. E.A. Matibiri and S.H. Mantell, *Plant Cell Tissue Organ Cult.* **40**, 125–131 (1995).

8. T. Taguchi, K. Sakamoto, and M. Terada, *Theor. Appl. Genet.* **87**, 75–80 (1993).

9. P.S. Carlson, H.H. Smith, and R.D. Dearing, *Proc. Natl. Acad. Sci. U.S.A.* **69**, 2292–2294 (1972).

10. D.M. Gilmour, M.R. Davey, and E.C. Cocking, *Plant Sci.* **53**, 267–270 (1987).

11. C.L. Afonso et al., *Bio/Technology* **3**, 811–816 (1985).

12. G.R. Wang and H. Binding, *Theor. Appl. Genet.* **87**, 561–567 (1993).

13. K. Glimelius, T. Eriksson, R. Grafe, and A.J. Müller, *Physiol. Plant.* **44**, 273–277 (1978).

14. C.T. Harms, I. Potrykus, and J.M. Widholm, *Z. Pflanzenphysiol.* **101**, 377–390 (1981).

15. P.A. Donaldson, E. Bevis, R. Pandeya, and S. Gleddie, *Theor. Appl. Genet.* **91**, 747–755 (1995).

16. T. Ishige, *Plant Sci.* **112**, 231–238 (1995).

17. E. Matsumoto, *Plant Cell Rep.* **9**, 531–534 (1991).

18. M.A. Aziz, P.K. Chand, J.B. Power, and M.R. Davey, *J. Exp. Bot.* **41**, 471–479 (1990).

19. I. Dorr, S. Mitenyi, F. Salamini, and H. Uhrig, *Bio/Technology* **12**, 511–515 (1994).

20. E. Pfister, G. Klock, and U. Zimmermann, *Biochim. Biophys. Acta* **1062**, 13–18 (1991).

21. P.B. Kirti et al., *Plant Cell Rep.* **14**, 593–597 (1995).

22. J. Imamura, M.W. Saul, and I. Potrykus, *Theor. Appl. Genet.* **74**, 445–450 (1987).

23. A.S. Parokonny et al., *Theor. Appl. Genet.* **94**, 713–723 (1997).

24. J.H. Liu, C. Dixelius, I. Eriksson, and K. Glimelius, *Plant Sci.* **109**, 75–86 (1995).

25. B. Oberwalder et al., *Theor. Appl. Genet.* **94**, 1104–1112 (1997).

26. Y.G. Li, G.J. Tanner, A.C. Delves, and P.J. Larkin, *Theor. Appl. Genet.* **87**, 455–463 (1993).

27. K.S. Ramulu et al., *Plant Cell Rep.* **13**, 687–691 (1994).

28. H. Lörz, I. Paszkowshy, C. Dierks-Ventling, and I. Potrykus, *Physiol. Plan* **53**, 385–391 (1981).

29. E. Galun and D. Aviv, *Methods Enzymol.* **118**, 595–611 (1986).

30. M. Kihara et al., *Jpn. J. Breed.* **42**, 55–64 (1992).

31. T.W. Walters, M.A. Mutschler, and E.D. Earle, *Plant Cell Rep.* **10**, 624–628 (1992).

32. S. Kobayashi et al., *J. Jpn. Soc. Hortic. Sci.* **66**, 453–458 (1997).

33. M.R. Davey, N.W. Blackhall, K.C. Lowe, and J.B. Power, in S. Mohan Jain, S.K. Sopory, and R.E. Vielleux, eds., *In Vitro Haploid Production in Higher Plants, Vol. 2*, Kluwer Academic Publishers, Dordrecht, The Netherlands, 1996, pp. 309–320.

34. P.B. Kirti, S.S. Banga, S. Prakash, and V.L. Chopra, *Theor. Appl. Genet.* **91**, 517–521 (1995).

35. M. Gerdemannknorck, M.D. Sacristan, C. Braatz, and O. Schieder, *Z. Pflanzenzuecht.* **113**, 106–113 (1994).

36. G. Stiewe and G. Robbelen, *Z. Pflanzenzuecht.* **113**, 294–304 (1994).

37. L.N. Hansen and E.D. Earle, *Plant Cell Rep.* **14**, 151–156 (1994).

38. D.W. Heath and E.D. Earle, *Theor. Appl. Genet.* **91**, 1129–1136 (1995).

39. L.N. Hansen and E.D. Earle, *Theor. Appl. Genet.* **91**, 1293–1300 (1995).

40. L.N. Hansen and E.D. Earle, *Theor. Appl. Genet.* **94**, 1078–1085 (1997).

41. S. Cooper-Bland et al., *J. Exp. Bot.* **45**, 1319–1325 (1994).

42. H. Mojtahedi, C.R. Brown, and G.S. Santo, *J. Nematol.* **27**, 86–93 (1995).

43. J.P. Cheng, J.A. Saunders, and S.L. Sinden, *In Vitro Cell Dev. Biol.-Plant* **31**, 90–95 (1995).

44. R. Jadari, D. Sihachakr, L. Rossignol, and G. Ducreux, *Euphytica* **64**, 39–47 (1992).

45. I. Sherraf et al., *Plant Cell Tissue Organ Cult.* **37**, 137–144 (1994).

46. J.W. Grosser, E.S. Louzada, F.G. Gmitter, and J.L. Chandler, *Hort Science* **29**, 812–81 (1994).

47. J.W. Grosser, E.S. Louzada, F.G. Gmitter, and J.L. Chandler, *Hort Science* **29**, 812–813 (1994).

48. A.M. Wolters et al., *Euphytica* **79**, 265–277 (1994).

See also Cell fusion; Micropropagation of plants, principles and practices; Plant protoplasts.

R

RECEPTORS AND CELL SIGNALING, INTRACELLULAR RECEPTORS — STEROID HORMONES AND NO

Scott L. Diamond
Institute for Medicine and Engineering
Philadelphia, Pennsylvania

OUTLINE

Introduction
Steroids and their Biosynthesis
Steroid Receptors and Gene Regulation
Nitric Oxide and Nitric Oxide Synthase
Nitric Oxide: cGMP-Dependent Signaling
Nitric Oxide: cGMP-Independent Signaling
Nitric Oxide, Peroxynitrite, and Nitrotyrosine
Crosstalk between Nitric Oxide and Steroid Signaling
Summary: Relevance to Biotechnology
Acknowledgments
Bibliography

INTRODUCTION

Soluble extracellular molecules that cross the cell membrane, bind an intracellular receptor, and alter cellular function are essential regulators of mammalian endocrine biology. This article reviews two of the most well-studied and prototypical intracellular receptors: steroid hormone receptors, which are transcriptional regulators, and the nitric oxide receptor, which is soluble guanylate cyclase. These two systems are quite different and represent the diverse mechanisms by which animal cells respond to diffusible mediators that cross the plasmalemma. While steroids alter gene and cell regulation on a time scale of minutes to days, nitric oxide (NO) has diverse effects (on a time scale of seconds to hours) such as vasodilation, inhibition of platelet activation, neurotransmission, and cytotoxicity. In some instances, crosstalk exists between NO and steroid receptor pathways. The biochemistry and molecular biology of steroids and NO can impact numerous biotechnological applications such as gene therapy, tissue engineering, and bioreactor dynamics, particularly in relation to the external control of cellular metabolism and gene expression.

STEROIDS AND THEIR BIOSYNTHESIS

Steroid hormones are small hydrophobic metabolites of cholesterol (C_{27}), and are broadly divided into five classes (Table 1): *progestagens, glucocorticoids, mineralocorticoids, androgens,* and *estrogens.* Cleavage of the C_6 unit from cholesterol involves the hydroxylation of C-20 and C-22 followed by cleavage by desmolase to produce pregnenolone (C_{21}). Conversion of pregnenolone to progesterone requires oxidation of the 3-hydroxyl group to a 3-keto group and isomerization of the C-5–C-6 double bond to the C-4–C-5 position. Progesterone can be metabolized to the major glucocorticoid, cortisol (by multiple hydroxylations), or to the major mineralocorticoid, aldosterone (by multiple hydroxylations and oxidation of the C-18 methyl group to an aldehyde). Alternatively, progesterone can be modified to androgens and estrogens via specific hydroxylation, chain cleavage, and reduction reactions. Thyroid hormones, retinoids, and vitamin D are not derived from cholesterol and are unrelated in structure to steroid hormones, but also diffuse across the cell membrane to bind their intracellular receptor in target tissues.

STEROID RECEPTORS AND GENE REGULATION

Steroid regulation of gene expression involves steroid molecules crossing the plasmalemma via passive transport (Fig. 1). Once in the cytoplasm, the steroid binds its receptor with high affinity ($K_d \sim 1$ nM), which causes the release of chaperones [including heat shock proteins hsp70 and hsp90, p23, and various peptidylprolyl isomerase (PPIase)-active immunophilins/cyclophilins (CyP) such as FKBP52 (hsp56), CyP18, and CyP40] from the receptor, and consequent exposure of nuclear localization sequences and phosphorylation sites in the steroid receptor (1,2). The chaperones maintain the receptor in a conformation that is competent for steroid binding but lacks DNA regulatory activity. The receptor with bound steroid (termed the steroid receptor complex or liganded steroid receptor) undergoes nuclear import, after which the liganded steroid receptor dimerizes. The dimer binds its specific hormone response element (HRE or SRE for steroid response element) to activate or repress within 30 min about 50 to 100 *primary response* genes via its interactions with numerous other transcriptional factors and consequent changes in chromatin structure. Other *secondary response genes* can then be regulated over the course of hours or days through mechanisms requiring expression of the primary response genes. The ability of a liganded steroid receptor to find the handful of promoters containing HRE among the $\sim$100,000 genes in the mammalian genome represents an extraordinary diffusional search process. The dimer may undergo one-dimensional diffusion along DNA segments or DNA–intersegment transfer facilitated by the bivalent interactions made possible with a dimer complex (3).

The steroid receptor has three functional domains: the N-terminal domain (site of transcriptional activation and binding of transcriptional factors; A/B domain in Table 1), a DNA binding domain (which also confers dimerization; C/D domain in Table 1), and a hormone binding domain at the C-terminus of the protein which also participates in transcriptional activation (E domain in Table 1) (4).

Table 1. Steroids and their receptors

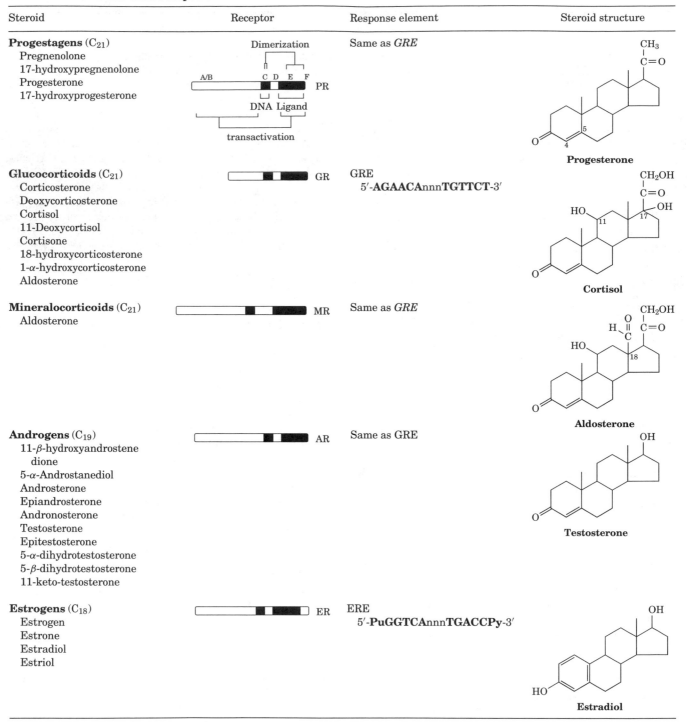

Steroid	Receptor	Response element	Steroid structure
Progestagens (C_{21}) Pregnenolone 17-hydroxypregnenolone Progesterone 17-hydroxyprogesterone	PR	Same as *GRE*	**Progesterone**
Glucocorticoids (C_{21}) Corticosterone Deoxycorticosterone Cortisol 11-Deoxycortisol Cortisone 18-hydroxycorticosterone 1-α-hydroxycorticosterone Aldosterone	GR	GRE 5′-**AGAACA**nnn**TGTTCT**-3′	**Cortisol**
Mineralocorticoids (C_{21}) Aldosterone	MR	Same as *GRE*	**Aldosterone**
Androgens (C_{19}) 11-β-hydroxyandrostene dione 5-α-Androstanediol Androsterone Epiandrosterone Andronosterone Testosterone Epitestosterone 5-α-dihydrotestosterone 5-β-dihydrotestosterone 11-keto-testosterone	AR	Same as GRE	**Testosterone**
Estrogens (C_{18}) Estrogen Estrone Estradiol Estriol	ER	ERE 5′-**PuGGTCA**nnn**TGACCPy**-3′	**Estradiol**

The DNA binding domain and hormone binding domain are highly conserved across the steroid receptor family, while the N-terminus, which controls transcriptional regulatory activity, is not. Crystal structures are widely available for many mammalian steroid receptors (see *http://nrr.georgetown.edu/NRR/NRR.html*).

The liganded steroid receptor dimer bound to its HRE has an extremely complicated and not fully characterized set of interactions with other proteins. Once in the nucleus, steroid hormone receptors can interact in three-dimensional assemblies with general transcription factors (TBP, $TAF_{II}30$, $dTAF_{II}110$, TFIIB), coactivators (ARA_{70}, RIP140, ERAP, TIF-2, SRC-1, RSP5, TIF1, SUG1, GRIP170), sequence-specific transcription factors (fos/jun, GATA-1, RelA, PML, OTF-1), and chromatin regulators (hBrm, BRG1, Spt6, and HMG1) (5–11). Coactivators can bridge the dimer with other DNA binding proteins of the transcriptional initation complex that assemble on the TATA box of the promoter (Fig. 1). In contrast to activation, gene repression is commonly

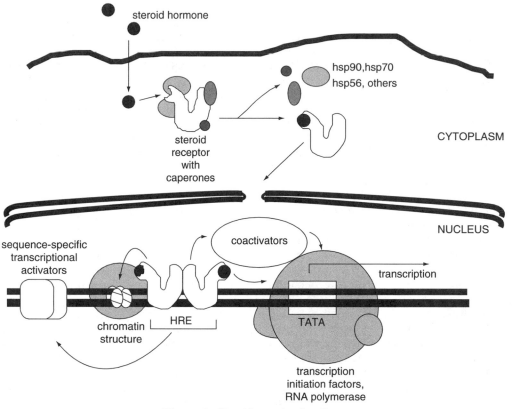

Figure 1. Steroid receptor function.

viewed as an action of the steroid hormone dimer that: (1) sterically blocks DNA binding sites used by other factors, such as fos/jun (AP1 complex); (2) inactivates normally competent transcription factors; or (3) serves as a binding sink for factors needed for transcription (4). In addition to these issues of assembly on the promoter, steroid receptors may function by altering the structure of the chromatin via its effects on hBrm and BRG1 (5–7). hBrm is the human homolog of *Drosophila Brama* (*brm*) and yeast SWI/SNF complex and is a 180-kDa nuclear protein that mediates ATP-dependent nucleosome disruption. BRG1 (205 kDa) is a second human homolog of yeast SWI/SNF that binds the retinoblastoma gene product Rb, on which assembly processes occur. Interestingly, hBrm is not expressed in all cells.

The human progesterone receptor (PR) can bind steroid receptor coactivator 1 (SRC-1A) for up-regulation of transcription. Interestingly, SRC-1A has histone acetyltransferase activity. Histone acetylation opens up the chromatin structure for transactivating factors. Human PR can also bind p300/CREB-binding protein (CBP)-associated factor, which has histone acetyltransferase activity. The localization of histone acetyltransferase activity by PR suggests an important role in chromatin reorganization since histone deacylase activity can repress the PR activation of gene expression (12). Similar interactions are found for the human estrogen receptor (13).

The HRE are typically palindromes containing two 6-base consensus half-site sequences separated by a spacer region (Table 1), although direct repeats of the consensus sequence are possible. A promoter may contain several HREs. Receptors for glucocorticoids, mineralocorticoids, progesterone, and androgens utilize the same 6-base DNA sequence 5'-AGAACA-3' (4). The estrogen receptor utilizes the sequence 5'-AGGTCA-3', which is also the sequence used by nonsteroid nuclear receptors. The DNA binding domain of the steroid receptor contains two zinc binding motifs—the *P Box* binds the HRE half-site and the *D Box* facilitates dimerization. Liganded steroid receptors predominantly form homodimers on the HRE in vivo. The nonsteroidal thyroid hormone response elements contain copies of a core consensus motif: 5'-AGGTCA-3' commonly in a head-to-tail repeat separated by four base or inverted tail-to-tail repeats. Numerous variations exist naturally or have been constructed artificially. The response elements for one or more hormone receptors may exist on a single promoter to cause synergistic activation of the gene. In promoter construct experiments, a single glucocorticoid response element (GRE) (or estrogen response element, ERE) upstream of a TATA box confers a steroid responsive promoter, with two GRE (or two ERE) elements resulting in synergistic gene activation. Such experiments indicate that the steroid hormone receptor dimer can interact directly with TATA binding factors to cause gene activation, independent of other transcriptional factors. Mutations in steroid receptors and their associated proteins are implicated in a variety of developmental, inflammatory, and carcinogenic processes. For example, the androgen receptor has a critical role in male sexual differentiation, and its mutations may play a role in prostate cancer (10).

NITRIC OXIDE AND NITRIC OXIDE SYNTHASE

The pioneering discovery by R. Furchgott in 1980 (14) that acetylcholine-induced vasodilation was endothelial-dependent set the stage for the identification of endothelial-derived relaxing factor (EDRF) as nitric oxide. By 1998, over 22,000 publications have defined in great detail the biochemistry, molecular biology, and physiology of the nitric oxide pathway. In mammalian cells, L-arginine is cleaved by nitric oxide synthase (NOS) to NO and citrulline (Fig. 2). Three isoforms of NOS have been cloned and their gene products fully characterized: neuronal NOS (nNOS, Type I isoform, 155 kDa); inducible NOS (iNOS, Type II isoform, 130 kDa); and endothelial NOS (eNOS, Type III isoform, 140 kDa). The genes are highly homologous across species, and the three isoforms are about 50% homologous with each other (15). For full NO synthesis activity, the eNOS enzyme requires three co-substrates, L-arginine, O_2, and NADPH, along with several cofactors, FMN, FAD, tetrahydrobiopterin (BH_4), calmodulin and a heme group, as well as, superoxide dismutase and glutathione. Distinct from iNOS, the isoforms eNOS and nNOS are activated when intracellular calcium is elevated above resting levels. The eNOS gene does not contain a TATA box, which is not uncommon for constitutive genes. The eNOS promoter contains two AP-1 sites, five SP1 (GC-rich) sites, and SSRE and NF1 sites. The SP-1 sites in the eNOS promoter have been shown to be functional by gel shift assays (16). The iNOS gene is dramatically induced in macrophages, smooth muscle cells, and other cell types by cytokines (IFN-γ, TNF-α, and IL-1) as well as bacterial endotoxin. The transcription factor NF-κB is critical for the induction of iNOS.

In several bioprocess or biomedical environments, the cellular response to mechanical forces can regulate cellular function. Nitric oxide can play an important role in the response of mammalian cells to fluid mechanical forces. The eNOS mRNA and protein levels can be elevated several fold in endothelial cells when the cells are exposed to laminar shear stress (15 or 25 dyn/cm^2) (17,18). The eNOS enzyme can be activated by fluid shear stress via a tyrosine kinase–dependent mechanism that is largely independent of elevation of intracellular calcium (19) or binding of hsp90 (20). During chemical activation of endothelium, eNOS can be phosphorylated, palmitoylated, and myristoylated at specific sites on the enzyme. In light of eNOS activation by shear stress, several changes in the post-translational state of eNOS are expected. (see

Whiteley et al.—Protein Processing, Processing in the Endoplasmic Reticulum and Golgi Network).

NITRIC OXIDE: cGMP-DEPENDENT SIGNALING

Nitric oxide rapidly diffuses through cellular membranes to bind its intracellular receptor, soluble guanylate cyclase, leading to the production of cGMP. Guanylate cyclase is a heme-containing protein. Nitric oxide is a highly reactive species that exerts autocrine and paracrine action over very short distances of a few hundred micrometers due to its short half-life in biological fluids. However, recent evidence has raised the possibility that NO can bind to oxyhemoglobin in an S-nitrosothiol complex (21).

Endothelial-produced NO, elicited by shear stress, can act as an autocrine factor to elevate cGMP levels (22). NO released by endothelium can diffuse through the internal elastic lamina to reach smooth muscle cells in the media of the vessel. In smooth muscle cells, the elevated levels of cGMP caused by NO binding and activating soluble guanylate cyclase results in a potent smooth muscle cell relaxation and consequent vasodilation. The signaling pathway downstream of guanylate cyclase activation includes the activation of cGMP-dependent protein kinases and subsequent phosphorylation of several targets such as calcium-sensitive potassium channels (K_{Ca}). Additionally, there exist cGMP-gated ion channels and cGMP-regulated cyclic nucleotide phosphodiesterases.

NITRIC OXIDE: cGMP-INDEPENDENT SIGNALING

During the bioreactor cultivation of animal cells, sublytic fluid shear forces may have significant effects on cellular metabolism. Hydrodynamic shear stress elevates the release of NO and prostacyclin (PGI_2) from endothelial cells in culture (23,24). Recent reports have suggested that elevated levels of NO can lead to the activation of constitutive cyclooxygenase (COX1, also named constitutive PGH synthase 1) (25–27). Davidge et al. (25) tested whether NO-activated PGI_2 production required cGMP using several different approaches. Their work indicated that NO stimulation of PGI_2 production is most likely independent of cGMP levels. This is consistent with earlier reports that elevated levels of cGMP do not enhance PGI_2 production in bovine endothelial cells (28). Treatment of bovine aortic endothelial cells in culture

Figure 2. The NO pathway. Activation of nitric oxide synthase (NOS) results in the production of nitric oxide (NO), which can bind and activate soluble guanylate cyclase (GC), resulting in the production of cyclic GMP (cGMP). The activation of cGMP-dependent protein kinase leads to phosphorylation events that alter cellular function. Through nonenzymatic routes, NO rapidly reacts with superoxide anion (O_2^-) to form peroxynitrite ($ONOO^-$), which can react with tyrosine residues to form nitrotyrosine.

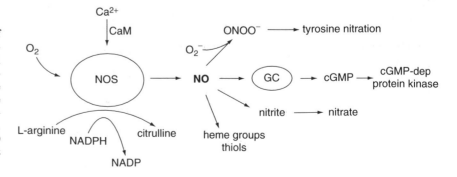

(BAEC) with glyceryl trinitrate, sodium nitroprusside, or 3′-morpholinosydnonimine (SIN-1, a donor of NO and O_2^-, and consequently peroxynitrite) dramatically enhanced by four- to six fold the release of PGI_2 from arachidonic acid–stimulated BAEC via cGMP-independent pathways (27). In calcium ionophore A23187-treated bovine microvessel endothelial cells, both NO and PGI_2 production were increased several fold in a cGMP-independent manner, but inhibition of NO production with N^G-nitro-L-arginine methyl ester (LNAME) attenuated the PGI_2 release by half (25). Recently, peroxynitrite generated from the reaction of NO with O_2^- was shown to activate purified ram seminal vesicle COX1 and recombinant human COX2 by serving as a substrate for the peroxidase activity of the enzymes (29). While BAEC posseses a soluble guanylate cyclase that can be activated by nitric oxide to elevate intracellular cGMP levels (22), there is some uncertainty if human umbilical endothelial cells or BAEC possess cGMP-dependent protein kinases (30). However, a more recent report has demonstrated cGMP-dependent protein kinase type I in BAEC (31). In light of the above observations, Wang and Diamond (32) tested the hypothesis that shear induced nitric oxide was responsible for the elevated release of PGI_2 when endothelial cells were exposed to arterial levels of shear stress. They found that blocking shear-induced NO production caused ~50% decrease in shear-induced production of PGI_2.

While the COX enzymes are potential targets for NO activation because they contain an iron-heme center at their active site, Tsai et al. (33) found no activation of cyclooxygenase activity at NO concentrations ranging from micromolar to millimolar added to purified ovine seminal vesicle COX1 enzyme. This is in contrast to a report of heme-independent S-nitrosation of cysteines in the active site of COX1 (34). Furthermore, in the mouse macrophage cell line RAW264.7, lipophilic superoxide dismutase–mimetic agents decreased the prostaglandin production without affecting the level of NOS or COX or by inhibiting the release of arachidonic acid (29). Clearly, nitric oxide has diverse effects as an intracellular signaling molecule, many of which are independent of soluble guanylate cyclase.

NITRIC OXIDE, PEROXYNITRITE, AND NITROTYROSINE

Excessive production of nitric oxide has also been associated with cellular injury (35). Nitric oxide–related tissue injury may be at least partially due to peroxynitrite ($ONOO^-$), a relatively long-lived, strong cytotoxic oxidant that is generated by the diffusion-limited reaction between nitric oxide (NO) and superoxide anion (O_2^-) with a second-order rate constant of 6×10^9 M^{-1} sec^{-1} (36). High levels of NO production can result in the formation of significant amounts of $ONOO^-$, because nitric oxide is capable of outcompeting superoxide dismutase for the metabolism of cellular superoxide.

Oxidative stress and reactive oxygen species (ROS) may contribute to the response of mammalian cells to various environmental stimuli, either chemical or mechanical. The antioxidant N-acetyl cysteine (NAC) has been shown to impair the induction of endothelial intracellular adhesion molecule (ICAM-1) by shear stress (37) via elevated production of ROS. Similarly, NAC impairs the induction of ICAM-1, monocyte chemotactic protein-1 (MCP-1), and plasminogen activator inhibitor-1 (PAI-1) in endothelium exposed to cyclic stretch (38–40). It is unclear why ROS generated by stretch (but not shear stress) can induce the PAI-1 gene. Interestingly, the MCP-1 gene, which is induced by shear stress via AP-1 elements in the promoter (41) by mechanisms that likely involve ROS (38), is also induced by NO (42). The activation by shear stress of AP-1 activity, and shear stress mediated induction of ICAM-1, MCP-1, and PAI-1 through ROS pathways, may involve NO and peroxynitrite.

Protein nitration by peroxynitrite has been hypothesized to be a major mechanism of oxidative modification of proteins associated with atherosclerosis (43). Peroxynitrite nitrates the aromatic ring of free tyrosine to produce a stable product, 3′-nitrotyrosine, which accumulates in proteins and acts as a cumulative index of peroxynitrite production. This reaction occurs spontaneously but is also catalyzed by low-molecular-mass transition metals as well as superoxide dismutase. This aberrant addition of a nitrate group to the *ortho* position of the hydroxyl group of tyrosine represents one outcome of cellular oxidative stress, rendering nitrated proteins dysfunctional and disrupting the phosphorylation of tyrosine residues in proteins involved in cell signaling networks. More specifically, peroxynitrite was recently reported to have vasoregulatory significance by relaxing vascular tissue through nitrosylation of tissue glutathione (or other thiols), subsequently releasing NO over prolonged time periods (44,45).

CROSSTALK BETWEEN NITRIC OXIDE AND STEROID SIGNALING

The nuclear factor NF-κB exists as an inactive cytoplasmic heterotrimer of p50 and p65 complex bound by the inhibitor IκB. Upon phosphorylation of IκB by tyrosine kinases or IκB kinase [potentially activated by protein kinase C isoforms that are activated by shear stress (46)], the heterodimer p50,p65 is released as an active DNA binding complex, which rapidly translocates to the nucleus. NF-κB activity is inhibited by dexamethasone, sodium salicylate, and aspirin via distinct mechanisms (47). The expression of the iNOS gene is dramatically elevated by cytokines and endotoxin through a NF-κB pathway. The induction of iNOS is markedly blocked by the steroid dexamethasone (48). Thus NF-κB and IκB regulation represents an important point of crosstalk between NO/NOS and steroid pathways. Furthermore, it has been shown that nitric oxide donors such as S-nitroso-glutathione decrease cytokine induction of endothelial vascular cell adhesion molecule (VCAM-1) and endothelial-leucocyte adhesion molecule (ELAM) (49). Promoter construct experiments and gel shift assays indicated that NO partially inhibited the activation of NF-κB. This is consistent with the role of NO as an anti-inflammatory and antiatherosclerotic agent (50) similar in function to steroids such as estrogen. While NF-κB activity is induced at early times of shear stress exposure (51), probably through PKC and mitogen activated protein (MAP) kinase signaling, NF-κB may eventually be downregulated through the continued elevated production of NO by shear-stressed endothelium. There have been several reports of endothelial genes (for example, PAI-1) being less inducible by cytokines after shear stress exposure (52). It is attractive to speculate that the lack of cytokine inducibility in sheared cells is NO dependent. This scenario, however, is in contrast to NO causing MAP kinase and p21ras activation, and NF-κB induction in Jurkat cells, as well as activation of G proteins (53–55). Also, NO increases the amount of GTP-bound p21ras in human T cells, likely through S-nitrosylation of a critical cysteine in p21ras that enhances guanine nucleotide exchange (53–55). Finally, an important example of NO-steroid crosstalk is the antiatherosclerotic effects of estrogen. This activity of estrogen is ascribed to the enhanced production by endothelial cells of NO through estrogen-dependent inhibition of superoxide anion production (56).

SUMMARY: RELEVANCE TO BIOTECHNOLOGY

Numerous expression vectors utilize hormone response elements to confer external regulation of the gene of interest. These vectors are used in bioprocessing applications to time the induction of protein expression, independent of other growth-dependent phases of the bioreactor dynamics. In biotechnology applications where expression of a gene is linked to the cell cycle, it is difficult to optimize simultaneously the cell growth rate, protein expression per cell, and overall reactor productivity. For example, expression of the heavy- and light-chain mRNA by hybridomas may display cell-cycle dependency, with high expression during stationary phase. The use of an HRE-rich promoter for these genes would allow a precisely timed induction of the genes or utilization of a continous process for protein expression, thus avoiding batch configurations typical of hybridoma technology. Furthermore, recent evidence of growth factor activation of kinases that phosphorylate steroid receptors suggests important crosstalk between steroids and growth factors that may be exploited to improve bioreactor operation.

In gene therapy, retroviral and adenoviral vectors can contain hormone response elements to help control the tissue distribution, timing, and level of expression of the therapeutic gene (57). Steroid-regulated promoters can be constructed with as little as 300 bp of DNA and thus can meet the packing constraints imposed by viral-based gene transfer. Additionally, the level of expression can be controlled by the level of the administered hormone and/or the number of repeats of the response element in the promoter. A limitation of this approach is that wild-type genes would also be susceptible to the hormonal induction during the clinical implementation. Important goals include the design of: (1) synthetic steroid ligands that are neither agonists nor antagonists of endogenous receptors; (2) novel HREs; and (3) novel ligand and DNA binding specificities of engineered hormone receptors. An extremely specific genetic switch would then be possible by co-expressing the modified receptor with a gene construct containing a modified HRE. Addition of the steroid analog (that has no activity for or against the endogenous receptor) would activate the modified receptor that would then bind the novel HRE of the transgene of interest. While chimeras utilizing the human steroid binding domain and yeast transactivator GAL4 are useful tools of study, the expression of a yeast protein in humans would present likely immunological complications. Thus the human steroid receptor gene requires mutation to confer novel ligand and DNA binding properties. Both rational design and combinatorial/screening strategies may produce optimal steroid analog/receptor constructs that meet these goals.

The biology of nitric oxide may impact gene therapy, tissue engineering, and biocultivation dynamics of human cells. Nitric oxide synthase has been an important target for gene therapy of blood vessels to prevent restenosis after balloon angioplasty. Nitric oxide is widely viewed as an inhibitor of smooth muscle cell division (a major source of wall thickening) and an inhibitor of platelet and neutrophil activation and adhesion. The diffusible nature of nitric oxide in conjunction with its short half-life and local zone of action makes the eNOS gene an attractive candidate for gene therapy. Furthermore, a major challenge in tissue engineering an artificial blood vessel requires the creation of a nonthrombogenic lining. The antiplatelet activity of nitric oxide is a primary motivation for seeding tissue constructs with endothelium or engineered smooth muscle cells expressing nitric oxide synthase. Thus nitric oxide, when locally produced at the correct level, may prevent intimal hyperplasia, accelerated atherosclerosis, and thrombosis that would reduce the patency of implanted grafts. Finally, in the biocultivation of complex human cells such as endothelium, stem cells, or neurons, the intracellular signaling generated through nitric oxide pathways may be an important consideration. This is especially true in cellular systems where the NO pathways are highly sensitive to chemical perturbations in oxygen or glucose or to mechanical pertubations common to bioreactors.

ACKNOWLEDGMENTS

The work was supported by NIH Grant HL47486. The author is the recipient of the National Foundation National Young Investigator Award no. BES9358236.

BIBLIOGRAPHY

1. W.B. Pratt and D.O. Toft, *Endocr. Rev.* **18**, 306–360 (1997).
2. B.C. Freeman, D.O. Toft, and R.I. Morimoto, *Science* **274**, 1718–1720 (1996).
3. B.A. Lieberman and S.R. Nordeen, *J. Biol. Chem.* **272**, 1061–1068 (1997).
4. M. Beato, P. Herrlich, and G. Schütz, *Cell* **83**, 851–857 (1995).
5. M. Beato and A. Sánchez-Pacheco, *Endocr. Rev.* **17**, 587–609 (1996).
6. M. Beato, S. Chávez, and M. Truss, *Steroids* **61**, 240–251 (1996).

7. M.F. Ruh, R. Dunn, II, and T.S. Ruh, *Crit. Rev. Eukaryotic Gene Expression* **6**(2/3), 271–283 (1996).

8. S.A. Oñate, S.Y. Tsai, M.-J. Tsai, and B.W. O'Mally, *Science* **270**, 1354–1357 (1995).

9. S.L. Anzick et al., *Science* **277**, 965–968 (1997).

10. S. Yeh and C. Chang, *Proc. Natl. Acad. Sci. U.S.A.* **93**, 5517–5521 (1996).

11. H. Hong et al., *Proc. Natl. Acad. Sci. U.S.A.* **93**, 4948–4952 (1996).

12. G. Jenster et al., *Proc. Natl. Acad. Sci. U.S.A.* **94**, 7879–7884 (1997).

13. C.L. Smith, S.A. Oñate, M.-J. Tsai, and B.W. O'Mally, *Proc. Natl. Acad. Sci. U.S.A.* **7**, 8884–8888 (1996).

14. R.F. Furchgott and J.V. Zawadzki, *Nature (London)* **288**, 373–376 (1980).

15. R.G. Knowles and S. Moncada, *Biochem. J.* **298**, 249–258 (1994).

16. S. Wariishi et al., *Biochem. Biophys. Res. Commun.* **216**, 729–735 (1995).

17. V. Ranjan, Z. Xiao, and S.L. Diamond, *Am. J. Physiol.* **268**, H550–H555 (1995).

18. K. Nishida et al., *J. Clin. Invest.* **90**, 2092–2096 (1992).

19. K. Ayajiki et al., *Circ. Res.* **78**, 750–758 (1996).

20. G. Garcia-Cardena et al., *Nature (London)* **392**, 821–824 (1998).

21. L. Jia, C. Bonaventura, J. Bonaventura, and J.S. Stamler, *Nature (London)* **380**, 221–226 (1996).

22. M.J. Kuchan and J.A. Frangos, *Am. J. Physiol.* **264**, H150–H156 (1993).

23. E.F. Grabowski, E.A. Jaffe, and B.B. Weksler, *J. Lab. Clin. Med.* **105**, 36–43 (1985).

24. J.A. Frangos, S.G. Eskin, L.V. McIntire, and C.L. Ives, *Science* **227**, 1477–1479 (1985).

25. S.T. Davidge, N.B. Philip, M.K. McLaughlin, and J.M. Roberts, *Circ. Res.* **77**, 274–283 (1995).

26. D. Salvemini et al., *Proc. Natl. Acad. Sci. U.S.A.* **90**, 7240–7244 (1993).

27. D. Salvemini, M.G. Currie, and V. Mollace, *J. Clin. Invest* **97**, 2562–2568 (1996).

28. A.F. Adams Brotherton, *J. Clin. Invest.* **78**, 1253–1260 (1986).

29. L.M. Landino et al., *Proc. Natl. Acad. Sci. U.S.A.* **93**, 15069–15074 (1996).

30. R. Draijer et al., *Circ. Res.* **77**, 897–905 (1995).

31. L.A. MacMillan-Crow, J.E. Murphy-Ullich, and T.M. Lincoln, *Biochem. Biophys. Res. Commun.* **201**, 531–537 (1994).

32. W. Wang and S.L. Diamond, *Biochem. Biophys. Res. Commun.* **233**, 748–751 (1997).

33. A. Tsai, C. Wei, and R.J. Kulmacz, *Arch. Biochem. Biophys.* **313**, 367–372 (1994).

34. D.P. Hajjar et al., *J. Am. Chem. Soc.* **117**, 3340–3346 (1995).

35. J.S. Beckman et al., *Proc. Natl. Acad. Sci. U.S.A.* **87**, 1620–1624 (1990).

36. R.E. Huie and S. Padmaja, *Free Radical Biol. Med.* **18**, 195–199 (1993).

37. J.J. Chiu et al., *Arterioscler. Thromb. Vasc. Biol.* **17**, 3570–3477 (1997).

38. B.S. Wung et al., *Circ. Res.* **81**, 1–7 (1997).

39. J.J. Cheng, Y.J. Chao, B.S. Wung, and D.L. Wang, *Biochem. Biophys. Res. Commun.* **225**, 100–105 (1996).

40. J.J. Cheng, B.S. Wung, Y.J. Chao, and D.L. Wang, *Hypertension* **31**, 125–130 (1998).

41. J.Y. Shyy et al., *Proc. Natl. Acad. Sci. U.S.A.* **93**, 8069–8073 (1995).

42. P.S. Tsao et al., *Circulation* **96**(3), 934–940 (1997).

43. J.S. Beckman et al., *Biol. Chem. Hoppe-Seyler* **375**, 81–88 (1994).

44. M. Wu et al., *Am. J. Physiol.* **266**, H2108–H2113 (1994).

45. B. Mayer et al., *J. Biol. Chem.* **270**, 17355–17360 (1995).

46. H. Tseng, T.E. Peterson, and B. Berk, *Circ. Res.* **77**, 869–878 (1995).

47. E. Kopp and S. Ghosh, *Science* **265**, 956–959 (1994).

48. M.W. Radomski, R.M.J. Palmer, and S. Moncada, *Proc. Natl. Acad. Sci. U.S.A.* **87**, 10043–10047 (1990).

49. R. De Caterina et al., *J. Clin. Invest.* **96**, 60–68 (1995).

50. J.P. Cooke and P.S. Tsao, *Arterioscler. Thromb.* **14**, 653–655 (1994).

51. Q. Lan, K.O. Mercurius, and P.F. Davies, *Biochem. Biophys. Res. Commun.* **201**(2), 950–956 (1994).

52. Y. Kawai et al., *Blood* **87**(6), 2314–2321 (1996).

53. H.M. Lander, P.K. Sehajpal, and A. Novogrodsky, *J. Immunol.* **151**, 7182–7187 (1993).

54. H.M. Lander et al., *J. Biol. Chem.* **270**, 7017–7020 (1995).

55. H.M. Lander, J.S. Ogiste, K.K. Teng, and A. Novogrodsky, *J. Biol. Chem.* **270**, 21195–21198 (1995).

56. J.F. Arnal et al., *Proc. Natl. Acad. Sci. U.S.A.* **93**, 4108–4113 (1996).

57. J.H. White, *Adv. Pharmacol.* **40**, 339–367 (1997).

See also CELL STRUCTURE AND MOTION, EXTRACELLULAR MATRIX AND CELL ADHESION; CELL-SURFACE RECEPTORS: STRUCTURE, ACTIVATION, AND SIGNALING; CELLULAR TRANSFORMATION, CHARACTERISTICS; TRANSCRIPTION, TRANSLATION AND THE CONTROL OF GENE EXPRESSION.

S

SEAWEEDS: CELL AND TISSUE SUSPENSION CULTURES

GREGORY L. RORRER
Oregon State University
Corvallis, Oregon

OUTLINE

INTRODUCTION

Macrophytic marine algae, commonly known as seaweeds, are nonvascular, photosynthetic marine organisms that inhabit the coastal regions of temperate and tropical ocean waters, commonly within rocky intertidal or completely submerged reef-like habitats. Unlike microscopic algae (microalgae), seaweeds generally live attached to the ocean bottom and can assume considerable anatomical complexity and intricate life histories. The three major phyla of marine macroalgae include Phaeophyta (brown algae), Rhodophyta (red algae), and Chlorophyta (green algae), which together encompass over 7000 species.

Marine macroalgae are currently a source of food. For example, nori from the red seaweed *Porphyra* spp. has a $1.8 billion per year market. Red and brown marine macroalgae are also the primary source of alginates, carrageenans, and agars, which have a $0.5 billion per year market, predominantly as food ingredients (1). Red and brown macroalgae are also a rich and diverse source of unique, pharmacologically active compounds, including

partially oxidized fatty acids deriving from arachidonic acid metabolism and halogenated monoterpenes (2). Many of these unique compounds cannot be duplicated by chemical synthesis due to their complex stereochemistry. In the future, these pharmaceutical compounds may be the most valued natural products obtained from marine plants, considering that 25% of all pharmaceutical sales are compounds derived from natural products of land plant origin (3).

Cell or tissue suspension cultures derived from anatomically complex marine seaweeds have the potential to make bioactive natural compounds in the controlled quantities required for further product development or commercial production. Unfortunately, techniques for cell and tissue culture of marine plants are vastly underdeveloped relative to those for land plants (4,5). Furthermore, the traditional rationale for establishing cell and tissue cultures from marine seaweeds has been strain improvement or micropropagation for mariculture and not the development of axenic liquid suspension cultures suitable for cultivation in agitated biological reactor systems.

In this article, reliable techniques are presented for establishing phototrophic liquid cell or tissue suspension cultures from marine seaweeds. The common characteristics of phototrophic macroalgal suspension culture systems, including culture morphology, environmental requirements for culture growth, and typical growth rates are illustrated through representative culture systems developed in the author's laboratory for each of the three major phyla of marine macroalgae. To date, no heterotrophic suspension cultures capable of growth on an externally supplied organic carbon source have been established from macrophytic marine algae, and so this article will focus solely on phototrophic suspension cultures that assimilate carbon through photosynthesis.

COMMON CHARACTERISTICS OF MACROALGAL SUSPENSION CULTURES

The taxonomy of the three major phyla of macrophytic marine algae is extremely diverse, and the interested reader is referred to the appropriate introductory texts (6,7). Despite this taxonomic diversity, the phototrophic suspension cultures established from macrophytic marine algae share common characteristics with respect to culture morphology and environmental conditions for growth.

Morphology

The characteristics of three macroalgal suspension culture systems developed in the author's laboratory that illustrate each of the major three phyla of macrophytic marine algae are summarized in Table 1. Illustrations of the parent plants found in the intertidal marine habitat for each of the culture systems described in Table 1 are

Table 1. Cell and Tissue Suspension Cultures Representing all Three Major Phyla of Macrophytic Marine Algae

Culture and classification	Culture development strategy	Culture morphology and color
Laminaria saccharina gametophyte cell clumps (Phaeophyta)	isolation of microscopic gametophytic life phase	Uniseriate, branched filaments packed into clumps of 0.5–2 mm diameter (brown)
Agardhiella subulata filamentous cell clumps (Rhodophyta)	induction of undifferentiated filaments from thallus explant	Undifferentiated filamentous clumps, 2–8 mm diameter; rounded cells and uniseriate filaments (clear, light red)
Agardhiella subulata microplantlets (Rhodophyta)	microplantlets regenerated from filament clumps	Multiple thallus shoots from a common branch point, 2–10 mm shoot length (dark red)
Acrosiphonia coalita tissue filaments (Chlorophyta)	induction of linear filaments from apical meristem tips	Uniseriate, linear or lightly branched filaments, 2–10 mm length (green)

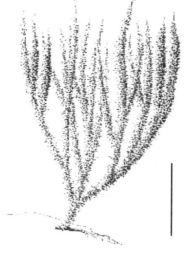

(a)

Laminaria saccharina
(brown alga)

(b)

Agardhiella subulata
(red alga)

(c)

Acrosiphonia coalita
(green alga)

Figure 1. Appearance of representative marine seaweeds selected for suspension culture development. (**a**) *Laminaria saccharina* (scale bar = 15 cm); (**b**) *Agardhiella subulata* (scale bar = 5 cm); (**c**) *Acrosiphonia coalita* (scale bar = 5 cm).

presented in Figure 1. The morphology of the cultured cell mass derived from macrophytic marine algae is generally filamentous and multicellular despite the appearance of the parent plant. However, the cultured cell mass retains the accessory photosynthetic pigments found in the parent plant which render their distinct color, such as fucoxanthin in brown algae and various phycobilins in red algae.

Suspension cultures established by isolation of microscopic gametophytes from the macrophytic brown alga

Laminaria saccharina (Laminariales, Phaeophyta) consist of branched, uniseriate filaments of 5–20 µm diameter and 10–30 µm length packed together into brown clumps ranging from 0.5 to 2 mm in diameter (Fig. 2).

Undifferentiated, filamentous cell clumps established from the macrophytic red alga *Agardhiella subulata* (Giginarales, Rhodophyta) by a callus induction technique range from 2 to 8 mm in diameter. The clumps consist of round, dark red cells at the center with clear or lightly pigmented uniseriate filaments emanating from the center as a thick bushy mass [Fig. 3(a)]. Microplantlets of *A. subulata* established by partial regeneration of the filament clumps consist of dark red, multicellular shoot tissues with cortical and medullary cells [Fig. 3(c,d)]. The tissue does not fully regenerate into the intact plant with highly branched thallus and holdfast structures, and individual shoots do not exceed 2 cm in length.

Tissue suspension cultures of the macrophytic green alga *Acrosiphonia coalita* (Acrosiphoniales, Chlorophyta) consist of dark green, linear, or lightly branched linear uniseriate filaments of 10–50 µm diameter and 2–10 mm length which branch out from a common center (Fig. 4).

Partial reduction in the anatomical complexity of the marine plant is sufficient for the development of a liquid suspension culture system. None of the culture systems described has been fully reduced to the friable, single cells typical of many land plant cell culture systems. Consequently, the cell mass of the macroalgal suspension is mechanically dissociated prior to subculture.

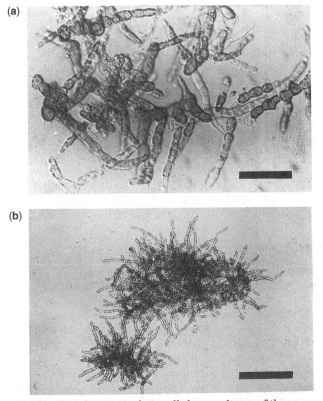

Figure 2. Female gametophyte cell clump cultures of the macrophytic brown alga *Laminaria saccharina*. (**a**) Branched filaments (scale bar = 50 µm); (**b**) filament clumps (scale bar = 200 µm).

Physical reduction of the multicellular mass is a critical step for maintaining the macroalgal suspension cultures. *L. saccharina* and *A. coalita* suspensions are blended at high speeds and short times, typically under 15 sec. This process reduces the size of the filament clumps but does not seriously compromise culture viability, except for the cells at the cut face. The blended suspension culture is filtered and then resuspended in fresh medium. *A. subulata* filament clumps were very sensitive to even short-term shear forces. Therefore, each clump is carefully cut into four to six sections. Each section must contain both the rounded center cells and the outer filamentous cells in order to sustain culture growth. Microplantlets of *A. subulata* are also cut into four to six sections through the center of common branch point for the shoot tissue.

Special efforts must also be made to maintain the suspension culture morphology. Gameotophyte suspension cultures of *L. saccharina* are prone to gametogenesis, and filament clump cultures of *A. subulata* are prone to regeneration. Strategies for avoiding these morphological changes are described later.

Environmental Conditions for Culture Growth

The cultivation environment for macroalgal suspension cultures reflects the environment of the parent seaweed in its marine habitat. Cultures developed from macroalgae endogenous to temperate marine waters, for example, the Atlantic Northeast or the Pacific Northwest, typically grow best at 12–18 °C and sometimes higher, whereas macroalgae from tropical marine waters grow best at 24–28 °C.

All formulated media used for macroalgal cultures have an artificial seawater base that reflects the type and level of the salts found in seawater. To promote growth, these media also contain elevated levels of nitrate and phosphate as well as trace levels of vitamins and essential metals required for primary metabolism (7). Artificial seawater-based medium formulations adopted by the author's laboratory include modified GP2 (8), PES (9), ASP12 (9), and ESS (10). Exogenously supplied plant growth regulators such as auxins and cytokinins do not have a clearly demonstrated effect on growth and development of macrophytic marine algae (11), and so are usually not present in these media. Macroalgal suspension cultures grow best at relatively high pH, typically within the 7.5–8.5 range, consistent with the nominal seawater pH of 8.

Macroalgal cell cultures are phototrophic, requiring light and an externally supplied, dissolved inorganic carbon source for growth. Heterotrophic growth in the dark on an externally supplied organic carbon source in the liquid medium has never been demonstrated in marine macroalgae. One reason may be that nitrogen assimilation is strongly coupled to photosynthesis in the metabolism of macrophytic marine algae (12). Even mixotrophic growth with an organic carbon source in the presence of light has not been conclusively demonstrated (13).

In phototrophic cultures, the inorganic carbon source is supplied by aerating the culture with air containing ambient or elevated levels of carbon dioxide (CO_2).

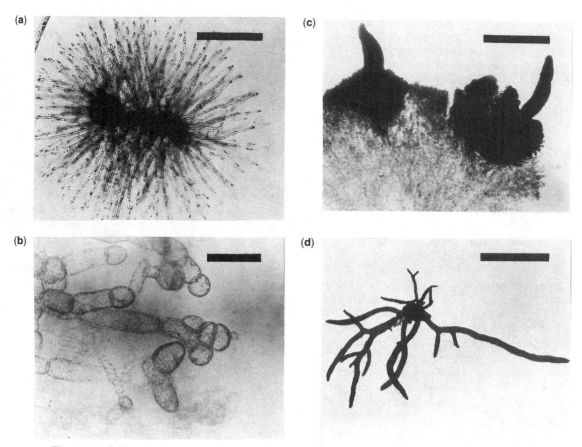

Figure 3. Cell and tissue culture development for the macrophytic red alga *Agardhiella subulata*. (**a**) Single undifferentiated filament clump (scale bar = 500 μm); (**b**) filament tips, showing microscopic onset of regeneration (scale bar = 20 μm); (**c**) formation of two shoot tissues regenerating filament clump (scale bar = 200 μm); (**d**) single microplantlet (scale bar = 2000 μm).

The dissolved CO_2 is speciated primarily as bicarbonate (HCO_3^-) and carbonate (CO_3^{2-})

$$CO_2(g) \longleftrightarrow CO_2(aq)$$

$$CO_2(aq) + H_2O \longleftrightarrow HCO_3^- + H^+$$

$$HCO_3^- \longleftrightarrow CO_3^{2-} + H^+$$

The pK_a values for HCO_3^- and CO_3^{2-} dissociation are 6.05 and 9.23, respectively, in seawater of 35 ppt salinity at 15 °C, and the Henry's law constant for CO_2 is 0.0257 atm mmol^{-1} L at the same conditions (14). For example, if ambient air containing 350 ppm CO_2 is bubbled into seawater medium at pH 8.5 and 15 °C, the equilibrium bicarbonate (HCO_3^-) and carbonate (CO_3^{2-}) concentrations are 3.84 and 0.71 mM, respectively. This bicarbonate reservoir supplies the inorganic carbon needs for culture growth. Bicarbonate (as sodium bicarbonate, $NaHCO_3$) cannot be added directly to the culture without concurrent CO_2 addition to maintain the pH at a constant value. Assuming Calvin photosynthesis stoichiometry, oxygen (O_2) is produced in a one-to-one stoichiometric ratio with CO_2 consumption. Therefore, the liquid suspension culture must provide an opportunity for gas exchange through surface or bubble aeration to prevent buildup of dissolved O_2 in the liquid medium, as high concentrations of dissolved O_2 may be inhibitory to growth.

In the marine environment, macrophytic marine algae grow submerged at depths that can range from 1 m to more than 10 m. Since ambient light at these depths is attenuated, macrophytic marine algae have adapted to fairly low light levels relative to surface-dwelling microalgae. Similarly, macroalgal suspension cultures grow optimally at relatively low light intensities. The irradiance for light-saturated growth ranges from less than 20 to 100 μE m^{-2} s^{-1}, depending on the species.

Growth Kinetics

Generally, macroalgal suspension cultures are slow growing, with specific growth rates ranging from 3% to 15% per day depending on the species of the parent plant, the type of culture system, and the environmental conditions. Representative growth rates and environmental conditions, including nutrient medium, temperature, and light for each culture system described in Table 1 are presented in Table 2. All culture systems were either bubble aerated or surface aerated with ambient air nominally containing 350 ppm CO_2. Details of growth rate experiments are provided in several recent papers from the author's laboratory (15–18).

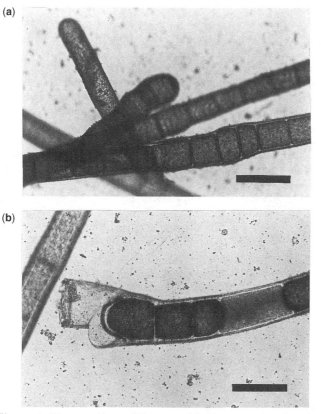

Figure 4. Tissue culture of the macrophytic green alga *Acrosiphonia coalita*. (**a**) Linear filaments (scale bar = 200 μm); (**b**) cut face of filament after blending procedure used for subculture (scale bar = 100 μm).

SUSPENSION CULTURE DEVELOPMENT TECHNIQUES

Techniques successfully used in the author's laboratory to develop phototrophic suspension cultures of macrophytic marine algae include:

1. Isolation and culture of microscopic gametophyte life phase of the macrophytic brown *L. saccharina*
2. callus-like tissue initiation and culture of the macrophytic red alga *A. subulata*
3. partial regeneration of freely suspended microplantlets from callus-like tissue of *A. subulata*
4. isolation and suspension culture of apical meristems from the macrophytic green alga *A. coalita*

Techniques for establishing suspension cultures of two representative macrophytic marine algae, *L. saccharina* and *A. subulata*, are described in the following to illustrate the basic procedures and approaches for culture development. Techniques for establishing tissue suspension cultures of the green alga *A. coalita* will not be described here, but the interested reader is referred to Rorrer et al. (17). Protoplast isolation techniques for establishing cell suspension cultures, developed specifically for the macrophytic red algal genus *Porphyra* as described by Chen (19) and Tait et al. (13), will not be described here as well. Finally, cultivation of macroalgal suspensions within engineered biological reactor systems (bioreactors) is briefly overviewed.

Laminaria Saccharina Female Gametophyte Cell Suspension Cultures (Macrophytic Brown Algae)

The life cycle of many macroalgae involve alternating, heteromorphic gametophyte and sporophyte stages. For brown algae within the order Laminariales, the gametophyte life phase exists as microscopic, undifferentiated filaments, whereas the sporophyte life phase is morphologically complex with blade, stipe, and holdfast structures. A representative life cycle of *Laminaria* species is shown in Figure 5. A reliable technique for establishing a liquid suspension culture involves the isolation and culture of microscopic gametophyte cells, as schematically outlined in Figure 6. A representative species for culture development is *L. saccharina*, found naturally in the lower

Table 2. Typical Growth Rates and Environmental Conditions for the Macroalgal Cell and Tissue Culture Systems Summarized in Table 1

	Culture system			
	Laminaria saccharina	*Acrosiphonia coalita*	*Agardhiella subulata*	
Process condition	gametophyte cells	tissue filaments	filament clumps	micro plantets
Seawater medium	GP2	PES	ASP12	ASP12
Medium exchange (% per day)	0	0	25	25
pH	8.5	8.0	8.8	8.8
Temperature (°C)	12	12	24	24
Saturation light intensity ($\mu E\ m^{-2}\ s^{-1}$)	20	80	40	40
Photoperiod (h on: h off)	16:8	16:8	10:14	10:14
Initial cell density (mg DCW L^{-1} or g FW L^{-1})	150 (DCW)	150 (DCW)	5.0 (FW)	1.0 (FW)
Final cell density (mg DCW L^{-1} or g FW L^{-1})	1000 (DCW)	1000 (DCW)	15 (FW)	5.0 (FW)
Specific growth rate (% per day)	10	15	3.0	6.0

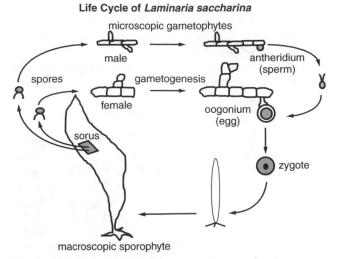

Figure 5. Life cycle of *Laminaria saccharina*, showing macroscopic sporophyte and microscopic gametophyte life phases.

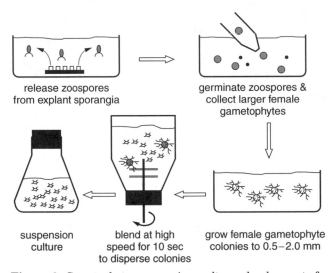

Figure 6. Gametophyte suspension culture development for *Laminaria saccharina*.

intertidal zone of temperate coastal waters, most typically in the Pacific northwest or Atlantic northeast of the United States. Both field-collected sporophytes and cell-cultured female gametophytes of *L. saccharina*, are a rich source of bioactive hydroxy fatty acids produced through 15-lipoxygenase metabolism of arachidonic and linoleic acids (20,21).

Isolation of Microscopic Gametophytes from *L. saccharina*. The isolation of gametophytes from *Laminaria* species originally described by Lüning and Neushul (22) and Lüning (23) require the in vitro release of zoospores from sporangia of blade sections of sporophytic plants followed by microscopic separation of large-cell female gametophytes from small-cell male gametophytes.

Basic techniques for *L. saccharina* are described in the following. All procedures were carried out using sterile technique in a laminar flow hood. Intact sporophytes

of *L. saccharina* were collected from the intertidal zone at −0.5 m tide near Shannon Point, Washington. Blade tissue with visible reproductive structures bearing spores (sporangia) on the blade surface were cut into 1-cm-square explants. Each explant section was immersed in 1% v/v of the surface sterilization agent betadine and then rinsed with autoclaved distilled water to remove epiphytes (small marine animals), marine microalgae, and marine bacteria attached to the explant surface. The surface-sterilized explants were placed on filter paper moistened with sterile distilled water and then allowed to sit for 12 hours in a sealed petri dish in the dark at 12 °C. Filter-sterilized seawater was added to the petri dish, and the sporangia released zoospores (motile spores) giving a light orange tint to the solution. One-mL aliquots of the solution containing the zoospores were diluted at 10x, 100x, 1000x in filter-sterilized seawater, and the diluted zoospore cultures were transferred to petri dishes. The filter-sterilized seawater contained germanium dioxide (0.5 mg GeO_2 L^{-1}) to kill off marine diatoms that survived the initial sterilization treatment.

Each diluted zoospore culture was incubated at 12 °C and 20 μE m^{-2} s^{-1} cool white fluorescent light (16 h light, 8 h dark photoperiod) for three to four weeks. During this time, zoospores germinated into male gametophytes and female gametophytes, which grew as loosely packed colonies of branched filaments. Single colonies of female gametophytes were three to five times larger than the male gametophytes (20 to 30 μm length for females versus 5 to 10 μm for males). These were removed one colony at a time with a pipet under an inverted microscope at 100x, and then transferred to fresh GP2 medium. The isolated colonies were cultured at 12 °C and 20 μE m^{-2} s^{-1} cool white fluorescent light (16 h light, 8 h dark photoperiod) for an additional three to four weeks in petri dish culture. This process was repeated for each dilution, and the best growing colonies, now 0.5 to 2 mm in diameter after about six to eight weeks in culture, were selected for subculture and maintenance.

Maintenance of *Laminaria Saccharina* Gametophyte Suspension Cultures. Female gametophytes of *L. saccharina* must not undergo gametogenesis, a process where the female gametophyte produces an egg within a sac-like structure called an oogonium and awaits fertilization from the sperm-bearing antheridium of the male gametophyte. In culture, fertilization is prevented because the female gametophytes have been isolated from the male gametophytes. But under low levels of blue light (24) and lack of iron in the liquid medium (25) gametogenesis of female gametophytes is also suppressed. When gametogenesis is suppressed, gametophytes undergo phototrophic, vegetative growth as undifferentiated, uniseriate filaments in liquid suspension culture.

The phototrophic female gametophyte suspension cultures were maintained on GP2 artificial seawater medium at pH 8.5 as modified by Steele and Thursby (8). Iron was removed from the medium to suppress gametogenesis. Suspension cultures were contained within foam-stoppered 250-mL Erlenmeyer flasks (100 mL culture per flask). The culture flasks were incubated at 12 °C under

20 µE m^{-2} s^{-1} cool white fluorescent light (16 h light, 8 h dark photoperiod) within an illuminated low-temperature incubator. For cold-water species of *Laminaria*, suitable cultivation temperatures ranged from 5 to 18 °C (22). The cultures flasks were swirled for 10 sec once per day to disperse the culture and to re-equilibrate the concentrations of CO_2 and O_2 dissolved in the liquid medium.

Subculture was performed every four weeks. All procedures were carried out using sterile technique in a laminar flow hood. In flask culture, the gametophytes grew as branched uniseriate filaments loosely packed into clumps of 0.5 to 2 mm in diameter, and individual cells within the uniseriate filament ranged from 10 to 30 µm in length (Fig. 2). These clumps could not be dispersed by vigorously shaking the liquid suspension. Therefore, the size of the gametophyte clumps was reduced mechanically by blending the liquid suspension. Specifically, four heathy flasks of the gametophyte suspension culture (400 mL) were poured into an autoclaved, 500-mL glass blending jar. A sealed stainless-steel shaft assembly fitted with two removable double-edged razor blades was mounted on the lid of the blending jar. The shaft assembly was also fitted with a coupling compatible with an Osterizer blender. The liquid suspension culture was blended within the sealed glass jar on an Osterizer blender for 10 sec at "liquefy" speed. The blending procedure dispersed the filamentous cell mass to uniform clumps between 300 and 400 µm in diameter (as determined by wet sieving) but did not compromise cell viability. The blended suspension culture was sterile filtered on 60-µm autoclaved nylon mesh, rinsed with 400 mL of autoclaved GP2 medium, and then resuspended into 400 mL of GP2 medium. The resuspended culture was subcultured at 25% v/v with respect to the parent flask culture. After approximately ten subculture passages, gametogenesis of female gametophytes could not be induced, even when iron was replaced in the medium. At this point, a truly vegetative suspension culture was established.

Decontamination. The cultures were unialgal but not truly axenic. In a few flask cultures, latent microscopic contaminants carried in with the original explant tissue would occasionally bloom, primarily marine cyanobacteria, green microalgae, and protozoans. Cultures were decontaminated by washing the blended cell mass three times with autoclaved distilled water on a 60-µm nylon mesh filter followed by a final rinse with GP2 medium. The distilled water lysed the marine contaminants by osmotic shock but did not significantly lyse the shear-tolerant gametophyte cells. The decontaminated gametophyte clumps retained on the nylon mesh were then resuspended in GP2 medium.

Agardhiella Subulata Filament Clump and Microplantlet Suspension Cultures (Macrophytic Red Algae)

Callus induction and microplantlet regeneration techniques can be used to establish liquid suspension cultures from macrophytic red algae, which possess terete thallus morphology and apical meristems. The temperate macrophytic red alga *A. subulata* is an ideal model candidate for cell and tissue culture development (26). *Agardhiella* species contain a diverse array

of potentially valuable natural products, including iota-carrageenan (26), sulfonated galactans with strong activity against the human immunodeficiency virus (27), and potentially bioactive secondary metabolites deriving from arachidonic acid metabolism, including the eicosanoids 8S-hydroxy-5,11,13,15-eicosatetraenoic acid (8-HETE) and agardhilactone (28).

The culture development scheme for the *A. subulata* is summarized in Figure 7. Two liquid suspension cultures can be established. The first culture consists of undifferentiated filament clumps established by induction of callus-like tissue from thallus explant sections. The second culture consists of microplantlets established by partial regeneration of the filament clumps. Both cultures are freely suspended in liquid medium and can be maintained indefinitely with periodic subculture. Specific techniques for establishing and maintaining the two culture systems illustrated in Figure 7 are detailed in the following. All procedures were carried out using sterile technique in a laminar flow hood.

Explant Preparation, Sterilization, and Induction of Callus-Like Tissue. Mature plants of *A. subulata* (29) were collected near Waterford, Connecticut, at 1 m depth. Thalli were shaken with 0.5-mm glass beads to remove epiphytes, surface sterilized with 1% v/v betadine in filter-sterilized seawater, and then allowed to recover in sterile-filtered seawater supplemented with ESS nutrients (10) for three days. Primary thalli near the tip or branch points were cut into 96 segments of 1–2 mm length and 0.5–1.0 mm diameter and placed in 24-well culture plates at only 2 segments per well to isolate contamination. Each culture well contained 2 mL of filter-sterilized ASP12 medium supplemented with 12 mM nitrate, 0.01 mg L^{-1} zeatin, and 0.01 mg L^{-1} phenylacetic acid, prepared according to Bradley and Cheney (30). The explants were incubated in the culture wells without agitation at 24 °C under 10 µE m^{-2} s^{-1} cool white fluorescent light (10 h light, 14 h dark photoperiod) within an illuminated incubator.

After 1 week, elongated, clear, uniseriate filaments appeared on the cut faces of the explant, presumably as a wound response. After formation of filaments, ASP12 medium was completely replaced once per week. After four weeks, about three-quarters of the explants possessed a thick bushy mass of proliferating filaments at the cut face of the explant. Explant sections bearing the most extensive filamentous growth were selected for culture development. The filamentous mass was cut from the explant near the origin, carrying over a small portion of the explant. After three weeks, each section was divided in half and placed in new culture wells with 2 mL new medium, 2 sections per well. After 3 weeks, each section was divided in half again and placed in new medium. After three more subcultures, the parent explant was completely removed. The final cell mass was undifferentiated, consisting of tightly meshed filaments and some round cells at the core of the clump with uniseriate filaments emanating from the core cell mass as a thick bushy mass [Fig. 3(a)]. The overall diameter of the cell clump ranged from 2 to 8 mm. The uniseriate filaments were about 10 µm in diameter and

filament induction

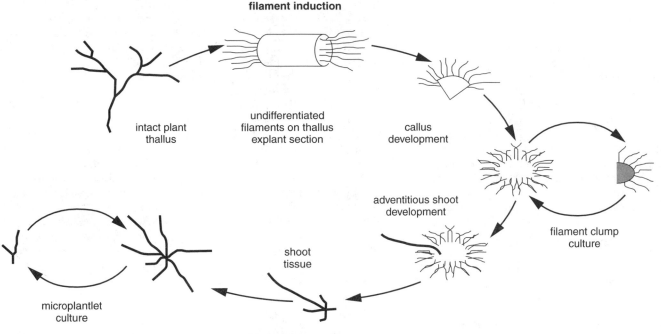

plantlet regeneration

Figure 7. Simplified schematic of cell and tissue culture development for *Agardhiella subulata*.

10 to 30 µm in length. The filaments were clear or lightly pigmented, whereas the cells near the core of the clump were darkly pigmented. The filamentous mass could not be dispersed by agitating the liquid; that is, the cell mass was not friable.

Maintenance of Undifferentiated Filament Clump Culture. Subculture was performed every 6 weeks. Healthy filament clumps were cut into four to six pieces with a razor blade. Each piece contained a portion of the compact core cells and lightly packed, uniseriate filaments. New growth continued from the uncut filaments after the first week and then from the cut face after the second week. If the subcultured filament clump did not contain a portion of the compact core cells, it usually died within 2 weeks. Filament clumps were best maintained in culture well plates with 8 to 10 clumps per 8 mL medium in each well. Filter-sterilized ASP12 medium supplemented with 12 mM sodium nitrate without plant growth regulators served as the culture growth medium. The medium was buffered with 10 mM sodium bicarbonate and sodium HEPE to pH 8. The culture well plates were not agitated. The filament clump culture was maintained at 24 °C under $8 \, \mu E \, m^{-2} \, s^{-1}$ cool white fluorescent light (10 h light, 14 h dark photoperiod) within an illuminated incubator. The medium volume was completely replaced every 4 days (replacement rate of 25% per day) to prevent nutrient starvation and wash away waste products.

The undifferentiated filament clumps were fragile and susceptible to regeneration. The filament clumps could only be maintained under the narrow set of culture conditions described to promote proliferation of undifferentiated cell mass but not regeneration. Adventitious shoots developed from the filament clumps

by imposing stress conditions on the culture, such as continuous agitation or reducing the nutrient medium replacement rate. Agitation was a particularly sensitive factor. When flasks containing a liquid suspension of the filament clumps were mixed on an orbital shaker or bubble-aerated, adventitious shoots formed from the filament clumps. Higher levels of agitation intensity, such as mixing a liquid suspension of filament clumps with a magnetic stir bar, killed the cells. The medium also had to be completely replaced at least every 7 days. The filament clumps generally died within 14 days without medium replacement.

Regeneration and Maintenance of Microplantlets from Filament Clumps. As described, filament clumps of *A. subulata* were fragile and prone to regeneration. Regeneration was gently and reliably initiated at 24 °C by continuously mixing a liquid suspension of 3-week-old filament clumps in well-plate culture on an orbital shaker at $100 \, \text{rev} \, \text{min}^{-1}$ under $24 \, \mu E \, m^{-2} \, s^{-1}$ incident light intensity (10 h light, 14 h dark photoperiod). Medium replacement was performed every 10 days. The continuous mixing put a sublethal stress on the culture. Adventitious protoshoot formation marking the initiation of the regeneration process was observed microscopically by a change in the plane of division of the uniseriate filaments [Fig. 3(b)]. One or more shoots ultimately formed from each filament clump undergoing regeneration [Fig. 3(c)]. Unlike the filament clumps, the shoots were not uniseriate and the cells were highly pigmented. Many, but not all, of the shoots formed branches. As the microplantlet developed, the inner core of compact cells turned white, died off, and disintegrated away from the microplantlet. The shoots elongated and formed new branches but did not fully regenerate to intact plants with highly branched thallus and holdfast structures [Fig. 3(d)]. Typically, 40–70% of the filament clumps consistently regenerated after 30 days. The remainder of the filament clumps either died or remained undifferentiated.

Typically, about 50 microplantlets were cultured in 75 mL of filter-sterilized ASP12 medium within a 250-mL foam-stoppered Erlenmeyer flask. The ASP12 medium was supplemented with 12 mM sodium nitrate, 10 mM sodium bicarbonate, and no plant growth regulators. The regenerated microplantlet culture was maintained at 24 °C under 24 $\mu E \, m^{-2} \, s^{-1}$ cool white fluorescent light (10 h light, 14 h dark photoperiod) within an illuminated incubator. Unlike the filament clump cultures, microplantlets were stable when the suspension culture was mixed, and flask cultures could be continuously bubble aerated. For routine maintenance, the medium was completely replaced every 14 days, and the tissues were subcultured every 4 weeks. The microplantlet shoots formed branches from a common center. During subculture a given microplantlet was cut through the center into two to four pieces, and the shoots were trimmed to 2 to 5 mm length from the tip. Microplantlets of 2 to 10 mm length could be readily suspended in liquid culture. The cut microplantlets were then inoculated into fresh medium.

BIOREACTOR CULTIVATION OF MACROALGAL SUSPENSION CULTURES

The controlled cultivation of macroalgal suspensions must be carried out in engineered biological reactor systems (bioreactors) that provide light and CO_2 to the culture. Bioreactors that provide light to the liquid suspension culture are called photobioreactors.

Common Photobioreactor Configurations

All photobioreactors for macroalgal suspension culture must provide four basic process requirements: illumination, mixing, gas exchange, and temperature control. Each one of these process parameters must be tightly controlled. Bioreactor configurations suitable for macroalgal suspension culture include externally illuminated bubble-column or airlift photobioreactors, stirred-tank photobioreactors, and tubular recycle photobioreactors, as shown in Figure 8. The bubble column photobioreactor is the best configuration to initiate cultivation studies with, as it is simple in design and provides adequate mixing, gas exchange, and light delivery. A more detailed schematic of a bench-scale bubble-column photobioreactor is presented in Figure 9.

In our laboratory, the cultivation of macroalgal suspensions has been studied in each of the photobioreactor configurations shown in Figure 8. For example, gametophyte cell suspensions of *L. saccharina* were successfully cultivated in several bench-scale bioreactor systems, including stirred-tank photobioreactors (15), bubble-column photobioreactors (16), and tubular recycle photobioreactors (31). *A. coalita* tissue suspensions were cultivated in bubble-column and stirred-tank photobioreactor configurations, but only the stirred tank provided sufficient agitation to suspend the culture and promote optimal growth (17). Microplantlet suspension cultures of *A. subulata* can be cultivated in bubble-column photobioreactors (18).

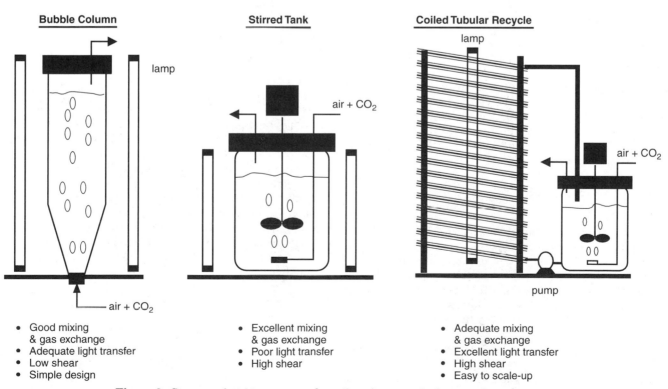

Figure 8. Common photobioreactor configurations for macroalgal suspension cultures.

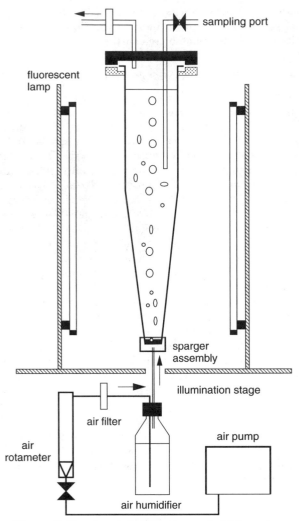

Figure 9. Bench-scale bubble column photobioreactor.

Photobioreactor Illumination

Light delivery to the culture is an important photo-bioreactor design variable for cultivation of macroalgal suspension cultures. In a nutrient-rich environment, the specific growth rate of the macroalgal suspension culture (μ) exhibits saturation growth kinetics with respect to the light intensity incident to the cell

$$\mu = \frac{\mu_{max}I}{I_k + I} \qquad (1)$$

where I is the light intensity incident to the cell ($\mu E\ m^{-2}\ s^{-1}$), μ_{max} is the maximum specific growth rate at light saturation (day^{-1}), and I_k is the light intensity at $\mu = 0.5\ \mu_{max}$. Values of I_k for macroalgal suspension cultures can range from 5 to 50 $\mu E\ m^{-2}\ s^{-1}$. As light penetrates the suspension culture, the light intensity decreases. The attenuation of light is described by the Beer–Lambert law

$$I(z) = I_o e^{-k_c X_z} \qquad (2)$$

where k_c is the specific light attenuation constant, I_o is the light intensity incident to the surface of the culture

vessel, X is the dry cell concentration (g DCW L^{-1}), and z is the position within the suspension culture. Values for the attenuation constant (k_c) of macroalgal suspension cultures range from 0.1 to 0.2 L cm^{-1} g DCW^{-1}. Light attenuation increases as the path length for light transfer increases and the cell concentration increases. If the suspension culture is well mixed, the mean light intensity (I_m) experienced by the culture is estimated by

$$I_m = \frac{1}{d}\int_0^d \alpha I(z)\,dz = \frac{1}{d}\int_0^d \alpha I_o e^{-k_c X_z}\,dz = \frac{\alpha I_o}{k_c X d}(1 - e^{-k_c X d}) \qquad (3)$$

where d is the path length for light transfer and α is the view factor. Usually, d is the width of the vessel, or the vessel dimension that is normal to the plane of light delivery. The view factor α is 1 if the vessel is illuminated from one side, or α is 2 if the vessel is illuminated from two opposing sides. To estimate the specific growth rate of the macroalgal suspension culture within the photobioreactor, the light intensity I in Eq. (1) is replaced by the mean light intensity I_m.

Mixing and CO$_2$ Transfer

Macroalgal suspension cultures sediment easily due to their large clump size and so must be well agitated to maintain the suspension. Agitation is provided by aeration alone using bubble-column or airlift photobioreactors, or in combination with impellers using stirred-tank photobioreactors.

Photobioreactors for macroalgal suspension cultures must be continuously aerated to provide CO$_2$ for phototrophic growth and to remove O$_2$ produced by photosynthesis. Carbon dioxide is supplied to the culture in accordance with the gas-liquid interphase mass transfer principles. The volumetric CO$_2$ transfer rate is defined as

$$R_{CO_2} = k_L a(C_A^* - C_A) = k_L a\left(\frac{P_A}{H} - C_A\right) \qquad (4)$$

where C_A is the dissolved CO$_2$ concentration (mmol L^{-1}) in the liquid medium, C_A^* is the dissolved CO$_2$ concentration in the liquid medium in equilibrium with the CO$_2$ partial pressure of the aeration gas (P_A), H is the Henry's law constant for CO$_2$ dissolved in seawater (atm mmol^{-1} L), and $k_L a$ is the volumetric mass transfer coefficient for CO$_2$ transfer (h^{-1}).

The phototrophic culture consumes dissolved CO$_2$ for photosynthetic growth. The volumetric CO$_2$ consumption rate follows zero-order kinetics with respect to dissolved CO$_2$ concentration and is estimated by the specific growth rate (μ) and dry cell concentration (X) through the equation

$$q_{CO_2} = \frac{\mu X}{Y_{X/CO_2}} \qquad (5)$$

where Y_{X/CO_2} is the biomass yield coefficient for CO$_2$ consumption. If the biomass production is described by Calvin photosynthesis stoichiometry, given by

$$CO_2 + H_2O \longrightarrow CH_2O + O_2 \qquad (6)$$

then Y_{X/CO_2} is 30 g DCW produced per mol CO_2 consumed. To avoid CO_2 mass-transfer-limited growth, R_{CO_2} must be greater than q_{CO_2}.

Problem Example

A problem example illustrating the use of Eqs. (1)–(5) is provided in the following. Consider that a macroalgal suspension is being cultivated in an aerated bubble-column bioreactor at 15 °C. Ambient air at 1.0 atm total system pressure containing 350 ppm air serves as the aeration gas, and the Henry's law constant for the dissolution of CO_2 gas in seawater at 15 °C is 0.0257 atm mmol^{-1} L. The vessel width is 15 cm, and the vessel is uniformly illuminated from both sides to provide an incident light intensity of 30 µE m^{-2} s^{-1}. Intrinsic suspension culture parameters include $I_k = 10$ µE m^{-2} s^{-1}, $\mu_{max} = 0.15$ day^{-1}, and $k_c = 0.2$ L cm^{-1} g DCW^{-1}. If the cell concentration within the photobioreactor is 1.2 g DCW L^{-1}, answer the following questions.

What is the mean light intensity within the photobioreactor? Use Eq. (3) with $k_c = 0.2$ L cm^{-1} g DCW^{-1}, $d = 15$ cm, $I_o = 30$ µE m^{-2} s^{-1}, $X = 1.2$ g DCW L^{-1}, and $\alpha = 2$:

$$k_c X d = \frac{0.2\ \text{L}}{\text{g DCW cm}} \frac{1.2\ \text{g DCW}}{\text{L}} 15\ \text{cm} = 3.6$$

$$I_m = \frac{\alpha I_o}{k_c X d}(1 - e^{-k_c X d}) = \frac{2 \times 30\ \text{µE m}^2\ \text{s}^{-1}}{3.6}(1 - e^{-3.6})$$

$$= 16.2\ \text{µE m}^2\ \text{s}^{-1}$$

What is the specific growth rate within the photobioreactor? Use Eq. (1) with $I_m = 16.2$ µE m^{-2} s^{-1}, $I_k = 10$ µE m^{-2} s^{-1}, and $\mu_{max} = 0.15$ day^{-1}:

$$\mu = \frac{\mu_{max} I_m}{I_k + I_m}$$

$$= \frac{0.15\ \text{day}^{-1} \times 16.2\ \text{µE m}^{-2}\ \text{s}^{-1}}{(10.0 + 16.2)\ \text{µE m}^{-2}\ \text{s}^{-1}} = 0.093\ \text{day}^{-1}$$

What is the CO_2 demand? Use Eq. (5) with $\mu = 0.093$ day^{-1}, $X = 1.2$ g DCW L^{-1}, and $Y_{X/CO_2} = 30$ g DCW/mol CO_2:

$$q_{CO_2} = \frac{\mu X}{Y_{x/CO_2}}$$

$$= \frac{0.093\ \text{day}^{-1} \times 1.2\ \text{g DCW L}^{-1}}{30\ \text{g DCW mol}^{-1}\text{CO}_2} \frac{1000\ \text{mmol}}{1\ \text{mol}} \frac{1\ \text{day}}{24\ \text{h}}$$

$$= 0.155\ \text{mmol CO}_2\ \text{L}^{-1}\ \text{h}^{-1}$$

What is the $k_L a$ value for CO_2 transfer necessary to avoid CO_2-limited growth in the photobioreactor? First, set R_{CO_2} equal to q_{CO_2} so that $R_{CO_2} = 0.155$ mmol CO_2 L^{-1} h^{-1}. Now, from Eq. (4), back out $k_L a$ at $C_A = 0$ (the point of CO_2 limitation) with $P_A = 0.00035$ atm (350 ppm CO_2 in the aeration gas) and $H = 0.0257$ atm mmol^{-1} L at 15 °C:

$$k_L a = \frac{R_{CO_2}}{P_A} H = \frac{0.155\ \text{mmol L}^{-1}\ \text{h}^{-1}}{0.00035\ \text{atm}} 0.0257\ \text{atm mmol}^{-1}\ \text{L}$$

$$= 11.4\ \text{h}^{-1}$$

Therefore, the photobioreactor aeration system must be designed to achieve a $k_L a$ value of 11.4 h^{-1} to avoid CO_2-limited growth. Values less than $k_L a$ of 11.4 h^{-1} will result in the biomass production rate being limited by the rate of CO_2 interphase mass transfer. In a bubble column bioreactor, the volumetric mass transfer coefficient $k_L a$ increases with increasing aeration rate and decreasing bubble size. Bubble size is most easily set by specifying the aeration sparger design. Values for $k_L a$ can be measured directly in the bioreactor at different aeration rates and sparger types using the techniques described by Van't Riet (32) so that the proper aeration rate and bubble size necessary to achieve the design value for $k_L a$ can be specified.

CONCLUDING REMARKS

Macrophytic marine algae, commonly known as seaweeds, are a major source of food and a rich source of natural compounds, including specialty polysaccharides and bioactive compounds that have potential as future drugs. Cell or tissue suspension cultures derived from marine seaweeds offer a platform for the controlled production of biomass and these natural compounds, ultimately in bioreactor systems. Unfortunately, cell and tissue suspension culture development techniques for anatomically complex marine plants are not well developed relative to those for land plants. However, a few reliable techniques are now available. For macrophytic brown algae, which have a heteromorphic life cycle, the isolation and vegetative propagation of the microscopic gametophytic life phase can establish an undifferentiated, clumped-filamentous suspension culture. For macrophytic red algae of terete thallus morphology, induction of callus-like filaments from explant tissue can be used to establish an undifferentiated filament clump culture, which grows as a free liquid suspension. However, the filament clumps are fragile and prone to regeneration. Partial regeneration of filament clumps results in freely suspended microplantlets, which can be maintained indefinitely with periodic subculture following mechanical size reduction of the tissue.

Cell or tissue suspension cultures derived from macrophytic marine algae by these techniques are phototrophic and require light, dissolved carbon dioxide, and a seawater-based nutrient medium for growth. These macroalgal suspension culture systems can be cultivated in bench-scale illuminated bioreactors of various configurations, and the results appear promising for future bioprocess development.

ACKNOWLEDGMENTS

Procedures described in this article were developed under grant no. NA36RG0451 (project no. R/BT-8) from the National Oceanic and Atmospheric Administration to the Oregon State University Sea Grant College Program, under the National Sea Grant Program Marine Biotechnology Initiative. The author also kindly acknowledges a long-standing and fruitful collaboration with Donald

P. Cheney of Northeastern University, who worked closely with the author to develop suspension culture systems for red algae.

BIBLIOGRAPHY

1. R.J. Radmer, *BioScience* **46**, 263–270 (1996).

2. B.K. Carte, *BioScience* **46**, 271–286 (1996).

3. S. Joffe and R. Thomas, *AgBiotech. News Inf.* **1**, 697–700 (1989).

4. D.M. Butler and L.V. Evans, in I. Akatsuka, ed., *Introduction to Applied Phycology*, SPB Academic Publishing, The Hague, The Netherlands, 1990, pp. 629–645.

5. M. Aguirre-Lipperheide, F.J. Estrada-Rodriguez, and L.V. Evans, *J. Phycol.* **31**, 677–688 (1995).

6. H.C. Bold and M.J. Wynne, *Introduction to the Algae*, Prentice Hall, Englewood cliffs, N.J., 1978.

7. G.R. South and A. Whittick, *Introduction to Phycology*, Blackwell, Oxford, 1987.

8. R.L. Steele and G.B. Thursby, *Environ. Toxicol. Chemi.* **7**, 997–1002 (1988).

9. L. Provasoli, *Proc. Int. Seaweed Symp.* **4**, 9–17 (1963).

10. N. Saga, in Y. Yamada and Y. Okada, eds., *Plant Biotechnology*, Tokyo Kaaymkes, Dojin, 1986, pp. 55–69.

11. L.V. Evans and A.J. Trawavas, *J. Phycol.* **27**, 322–326 (1991).

12. D.H. Turpin, *J. Phycol.* **27**, 14–20 (1991).

13. M.I. Tait et al., *J. Appl. Phycol.* **2**, 63–70 (1990).

14. J.A. Raven, *Energetics and Transport in Aquatic Plants*, Alan R. Liss, New York, 1984, pp. 189–194.

15. H. Qi and G.L. Rorrer, *Biotechnol. Bioeng.* **45**, 251–260 (1995).

16. C. Zhi and G.L. Rorrer, *Enzyme Microb. Technol.* **18**, 291–299 (1996).

17. G.L. Rorrer, M. Polne-Fuller, and C. Zhi, *Biotechnol. Bioeng.* **49**, 559–567 (1996).

18. G.L. Rorrer et al., in T.-J. Fu, G. Singh, and W.R. Curtis, eds., *Plant Cell and Tissue Culture for Food Ingredient Production*, Kluwer Scientific/Plenum, New York, 1998, pp. 165–184.

19. L.C.M. Chen, *J. App. Phycol.* **1**, 153–159 (1989).

20. P.J. Proteau and W.H. Gerwick, *Lipids* **28**, 783–787 (1993).

21. G.L. Rorrer et al., *Phytochemistry* **46**, 871–877 (1997).

22. K. Lüning and M. Neushul, *Mar. Biol.* **45**, 297–309 (1978).

23. K. Lüning, *J. Phycol.* **16**, 1–15 (1980).

24. K. Lüning and M.J. Dring, *Planta* **104**, 252–256 (1972).

25. T. Montomura and Y. Sakai, *Jp. J. Phycol.* **32**, 209–215 (1984).

26. D.P. Cheney, A.H. Luistro, and P.M. Bradley, *Hydrobiologia* **151/152**, 161–166 (1987).

27. M. Witrvouw et al., *Antiviral Chem. Chemother.* **5**, 297–303 (1994).

28. M.A. Graber, D.P. Cheney, and W.H. Gerwick, *Tetrahedron Lett.* **37**, 4635–4638 (1996).

29. P.W. Gabrielson and M.H. Hommersand, *J. Phycol.* **18**, 46–58 (1982).

30. P.M. Bradley and D.P. Cheney, *Hydrobiologia* **204/205**, 353–360 (1990).

31. R.K. Mullikin and G.L. Rorrer, in O.R. Zaborsky, ed., *Bio-Hydrogen*, Plenum, New York, 1998, pp. 403–414.

32. K. Van't Riet, *Ind. Eng. Chem. Process Res. Dev.* **18**, 357–364 (1979).

See also Culture establishment, plant cell culture; Equipment and laboratory design for cell culture; Micropropagation of plants, principles and practices; Plant cell culture, laboratory techniques.

SOMACLONAL VARIATION

Alan Scragg
University of the West of England
Frenchay, Bristol
United Kingdom

OUTLINE

INTRODUCTION

It was observed some years ago that plants regenerated using plant cell and tissue culture techniques were not phenotypically uniform but displayed considerable variation in their characteristics. The term somaclonal variation was adopted to described this variation (1). Somaclonal variation is found in regenerants from callus, cell suspension, and protoplasts and has a number of the following characteristics:

- It is widespread.
- It occurs at high frequency.
- It can affect both qualitative and quantitative traits.
- It occurs in homozygous cultures.
- The variation is not always stable.
- It can involve a range of genetic changes.

The types of variation found are similar to those from normal mutation, but the frequency associated with plant tissue culture is much greater, although it can show a different spectrum from *in vivo* mutations. For example, variation has been detected at a level of 15% in regenerated tomato whereas the normal mutation rate was 1 in 10^6 (2). The degree of variation found in tissue culture is greatest with protoplasts, less so with cell suspension and callus, and shoot culture has the least variation (3).

There are two possible sources for the variation observed. First, the variation is an expression of the variation already present, and second, the tissue culture process induces the variation. Investigators have found that both sources are present (4). Table 1 lists some of the crops that show somaclonal variation and the

Table 1. Some Examples of Somaclonal Variation

Plant Species	Characteristic
Alfalfa	Leaf color
Onion	Bulb size and shape
Pelargonium	Flower and leaf morphology
Potato	Ribosomal DNA copy number
Potato	Tuber morphology
Rapeseed	Seed color
Sugarcane	Viral resistance
Tobacco	Alkaloid levels
Tobacco	Leaf color
Tomato	Fruit color
Wheat	Adh isozyme[a]

[a] Adh: alcohol dehydrogenase.

characteristics involved. Somaclonal variation has been found in all plants investigated, although the degree of variation can vary considerable. In sugar beet, the frequency of variation was 0.05% (5), but variation in garlic was 16% (6). The variation in phenotype is not welcome in micropropagated plants where uniformity is required or in seed propagated crops where the mode of inheritance is important. However, when variation is required, for example, when the aim is to select new lines, this type of variation has some advantages. The variation is higher than normal mutation, the plants are regenerated from single cells or small groups so that the development of mosaics will be reduced, and the process of regeneration will introduce some form of selection.

SOURCES OF VARIATION

Somaclonal variation could result from a number of causes, and the mixture of stable and unstable regenerants indicates that the variation is both genetic and epigenetic. Genetic variation is transmitted sexually, whereas epigenetic changes cannot be transmitted and can be lost over time. The following are possible sources of variation:

Epigenetic Changes
- Gene amplification
- Gene methylation
- Controlling elements

Genetic Changes
- Changes in ploidy
- Changes in chromosomal number
- Chromosomal aberrations such as translocation, inversions, deletions, duplications, somatic crossing-over
- Changes in the cytoplasmic genome
- Single gene mutation

Epigenetic Changes

Epigenetic changes have been used to describe changes in gene expression that do not arise from permanent alterations in the cell genome. These are characterized by highly variable, stable changes but with a high reversal rate and no transmission into the progeny. A number of unstable and nontransmissible changes have been observed in regenerants, which indicate that some epigenetic change has occurred. It has been demonstrated that the tissue culture process can cause amplification of certain gene sequences (7), and this has been shown to be responsible for increased enzyme levels in some cultures (8). Methylation of DNA has been shown to control gene expression (9), and in plant cells 25% of the cytosine residues can be methylated (7). In animal cells, DNA methylation is developmentally regulated and can only be reversed by passage through the germ line. In plant cell cultures, alterations in DNA methylation have been detected in carrot, soybean, and maize after regeneration and therefore could affect gene expression in regenerants.

Transposable elements were first detected by McClintock (10) in maize and these were responsible for the instability of the maize phenotype. Since then a number of controlling elements have been detected in regenerants (11). There is some evidence that the tissue culture process can affect the mobility of these elements.

Genetic Changes

Chromosomes can easily be visualized and counted in tissue cultured cells, and because of this there are many examples of the alteration in the chromosomal number in regenerants (Table 2). Changes in the number of chromosomes or ploidy can occur naturally *in vivo*, but the frequency of polyploidy is considerably higher in tissue culture (12). Polyploidy is the most frequently detected abnormality, and the mechanisms involved have been reviewed (13). A number of mechanisms could account for the formation of polyploids in culture, including fusion of the spindle during the division of binucleate cells and the arrest of chromatid separation by the spindle. Aneuploids are cells that have a chromosomal number, which is not a multiple of the normal chromosomal number. Aneuploidy is also frequently detected in cell culture and regenerants and appears to be derived from aberrant mitotic events, including nondisjunction where both chromatids pass to one pole during mitosis.

Chromosomal aberrations can consist of deletions, translocations, inversions, and duplications and have been studied in maize and oat regenerants (4,14). One explanation for these aberrations is disruption of normal cell controls during tissue culture that allows cell division before DNA replication is complete. Another possibility is that chromosomal breakage could result from altered levels of DNA methylation (13).

Table 2. Frequency of Chromosomal Variation in Three Regenerated Garlic Lines[a]

Variety	Diploid	Tetraploid	Aneuploid	Nondiploids
California Late	87.8%	6%	3%	12.1%
Chinese	82.6%	13%	4.3%	17.4%
Solent White	78.9%	10%	5.2%	21.1%
Total	84%	9.3%	4%	16%

[a] From Ref. 6.

Mitotic or somatic crossing-over could also account for some of the variation that could involve symmetrical and asymmetrical recombination and may be the reason that homozygous recessive genes are found in regenerated plants.

Cytoplasmic genetic changes have also been detected in regenerants. Mitochondrial DNA changes have been found in maize (14) and potato regenerants (15).

Somaclonal variation has been responsible for single gene and organelle mutations. Brettell et al. (16) showed a change in the alcohol dehydrogenase (Adh), and cloned fragments were used to show changes in potato clones (17).

FACTORS AFFECTING VARIATION

The extent of somaclonal variation can be influenced by a number of factors associated with the plant material and conditions of culture. It is clear that the source plant's genotype and species, the explant source, will have an influence because it is likely to be heterogeneous in its stage of differentiation, age, and ploidy status. It has been found that plants regenerated from different types of tissue show variation in somaclonal variation. For example, *Chrysanthemum morifolium* stem segments give more flower color variations than those from the capitula (18). The conditions during the culture of the plant tissue also influence somaclonal variation. The length of time in culture has been shown to reduce the ability to regenerate in a number of species, and in strawberry callus culture this loss after 24 weeks was caused by the formation of abnormal DNA (7,19). Changes have been shown in cultures of *Begonia* and *Pelargonium*. The components of the culture medium, in particular the growth regulators, have also been implicated. The concentrations of growth regulators have influenced cultures of strawberry, *Begonia* and *Saintpaulia* (20).

DETECTION OF SOMACLONAL VARIATION

Somaclonal variation was initially observed as phenotypic changes such as flower color or leaf shape, but to use this in breeding programes, changes at the molecular levels need to be detected (20). Isozyme and cytological analysis have been carried out with many species, but changes in these parameters do not always mirror phenotypic changes (21). The detailed study of chromosomes is difficult and time-consuming. However, techniques based on recombinant technology have been used with some success to monitor variation. Restriction fragment length polymorphism (RFLP) analysis can reveal point or structural mutations and in some case changes in methylation (5,22). Random amplified polymorphic DNA (RAPD) analysis has been used in a number of cases to follow somaclonal variation (5,23,24). RAPD is a PCR-based technique where arbitrary 10-base primers are used to generate fragments that can be used as genetic markers.

USE IN PLANT BREEDING

Plant tissue cultures techniques have a number of applications in plant breeding. Micropropagation can be

Table 3. The Use of Somaclonal Variation for the Production of Variants

Plant Species	Variant Produced
Disease resistance	
Celery	Resistant to *Fusarium oxysporum*
Sugarcane	Resistant to Fiji disease
Tomato	Resistant to Fusarium wilt
Herbicide resistance	
Alfalfa	Resistant to glyphosate
Barley	Resistant to chlorosulfuran
Carrot	Resistant to chlorosulfuran
Carrot	Resistant to glyphosate
Maize	Resistant to glyphosate
Maize	Resistant to imidazoline
Maize	Resistant to sethoxydim
Tobacco	Resistant to chlorosulfuran
Tobacco	Resistant to glyphosate

used to multiply elite lines and those in short supply, those plants that are difficult to cultivate. Embryo rescue can allow crosses for some plants, and meristem culture can be used to produce virus-free plants (8). In all of these cases, variation needs to be kept to a minimum, and if the process does not involve regeneration via callus, variation can be small. Somaclonal variation can produce high levels of variation, higher than normal mutations, that can be used in selecting of new lines. One disadvantage is that the variation is unpredictable and in some cases not heritable. Somaclonal variations have been used in breeding programs to produce a number of different types such as disease resistance, and herbicide resistance. Examples of these are shown in Table 3. Other characteristics such as salt tolerance, metal tolerance, chill tolerance, and pest resistance can also be isolated (25). Selection can be at the callus by growing the callus in the presence of a herbicide, and those calluses that survive can be regenerated into plants. In many cases, the regenerated plant retains the resistance characteristic. In other cases, plants are regenerated first, and then selection or screening is applied.

BIBLIOGRAPHY

1. P.J. Larkin and W.R. Scowcroft, *Theor. Appl. Genet.* **60**, 197–214 (1981).

2. D.A. Evans and W.R. Sharp, *Science* **221**, 949–951 (1983).

3. O.P. Damasco et al., *Plant Cell Rep.* **16**, 118–123 (1996).

4. D.A. Evans and W.R. Sharp, *Bio/Technology* **4**, 528–532 (1986).

5. M.T. Munthali, H.J. Newbury, and B.V. Ford-Lloyd, *Plant Cell Rep.* **15**, 474–478 (1996).

6. M.A. Al-Zahim, B.V. Ford-Lloyd, and H.J. Newbury, *Plant Cell Rep.* **18**, 473–477 (1999).

7. H. Yang et al., *Plant Cell Rep.* **18**, 520–526 (1999).

8. A. Stafford and G. Warren, *Plant Cell and Tissue Culture*, Open University Press, Milton Keynes, U.K., 1991, pp. 25–46.

9. P.A. Jones, *Trends Genet.* **15**, 34–37 (1999).

10. B. McClintock, *Science* **226**, 792–801 (1984).

11. V.M. Peschke and R.L. Phillips, *Theor. Appl. Genet.* **81**, 90–97 (1991).

12. F. D'Amato, in T.A. Thorpe, ed., *Frontiers of Plant Tissue Culture*, IAPTC/University of Calgary, Calgary, 1978, pp. 287–295.

13. R.L. Phillips, S.M. Kaeppler, and P. Olhoft, *Proc. Natl. Acad. Sci. U.S.A.* **91**, 5222–5226 (1994).

14. T.J. McCoy, R.L. Phillips, and H.W. Rines, *Can. J. Genet. Cytol.* **24**, 37–50 (1982).

15. B.G. Gengenbach, C.E. Green, and C.M. Donovan, *Proc. Natl. Acad. Sci. U.S.A.* **74**, 5113–5117 (1977).

16. R.I.S. Brettell, E.S. Dennis, W.R. Scowcroft, and W.J. Peacock, *Mol. Gen. Genet.* **202**, 235–239 (1986).

17. J. Landsmann and H. Uhrig, *Theor. Appl. Genet.* **71**, 500–505 (1985).

18. S.R. Bush, E.D. Earle, and R.W. Langhans, *Am. J. Bot.* **63**, 729–737 (1976).

19. N.S. Nehra, K.K. Kartha, C. Stusnoff, and K. Giles, *Plant Cell, Tissue Organ Cult.* **29**, 257–268 (1992)

20. S.M. Jain and G.-J. DeKlerk, *Plant Tissue Cult. Biotechnol.* **4**, 63–75 (1998)

21. S. Goto, R.C. Thakur, and K. Ishii, *Plant Cell Rep.* **18**, 193–197 (1998).

22. K.K. Kidwell and T.C. Osborne, *Genome* **36**, 906–912 (1993).

23. J.G.K. Williams et al., *Nucleic Acids Res.* **18**, 6531–6535 (1990).

24. G. Hashmi et al., *Plant Cell Rep.* **16**, 624–627 (1997).

25. M.Z. Hadi and M.P. Bridgen, *Plant Cell, Tissue Organ Cult.* **46**, 43–50 (1996).

See also ENRICHMENT AND ISOLATION TECHNIQUES FOR ANIMAL CELL TYPES; PLANT CELL CULTURES, SELECTION AND SCREENING FOR SECONDARY PRODUCT ACCUMULATION; TRANSFORMATION OF PLANTS.

STERILIZATION AND DECONTAMINATION

P.L. ROBERTS
Bio Products Laboratory, Elstree
Herts, United Kingdom

OUTLINE

INTRODUCTION

During the culture of animal or plant cells, it is essential to exclude microbiological agents such as bacteria, mycoplasmas, fungi, and viruses by using sterile techniques to ensure that exogenous microorganisms are not introduced into the cultures. All components added to the culture, that is, the growth medium, and all items of equipment to which the cells come into contact must be sterile. The methods used to maintain sterility are often called "aseptic technique." Sterilization is defined as a process that kills all living organisms. The classical sterilization methods used in hospitals and the pharmaceutical industry, autoclaving and sterile filtration, can inactivate or remove microorganisms by an order of $>1 \times 10^{10}$. However, in some cases, such a high assurance of sterility is difficult to reach, and therefore it is necessary to ensure that the level of sterility is sufficient for the specific situation and application intended.

The impact of a breakdown in aseptic technique and sterilization could range from the gross and obvious destruction of a critical cell line to difficulties in culturing cells, although contamination may not be obvious or easily detectable. Sterile operations have an additional significance in the cell culture laboratory. Increasingly, cells have been recognized as a potential source of infectious agents, for example, persistent/latent viruses, such as retroviruses or herpesviruses. In addition, microorganisms, particularly viruses, are commonly grown in cell culture rather than in animals or eggs. Moreover, viruses may be used to immortalize primary cell lines and to engineer cells to produce biological products by using recombinant DNA technology. Thus cell cultures pose a threat to the recipient of any bioproduct that they may be used to produce, as well as to all those that handle the cells, whether in a laboratory or in industry. Therefore, those who work in the cell culture laboratory or manufacturing facility must be protected. In addition, consideration must be given to the disposal of potentially contaminated waste materials. These safety aspects are becoming increasingly subject to governmental legislation.

The range of microbial agents that may contaminate a cell culture include protozoa, fungi, bacteria, mycoplasma, and viruses. The range is further extended by the so-called unconventional agents that cause prion-associated diseases in animals and man, including bovine spongiform encephalitis (BSE), Creutzfeldt–Jakob disease (CJD) and scrapie, the spongiform encephalopathies. The exact nature of these agents is still far from clear; no viral agent or nucleic acid has been detected, and they are currently considered infectious proteins (1,2). The sensitivity to inactivation of these microbiological agents varies widely, although generally all are inactivated by heat treatment using a standard autoclave or dry heat oven, or they can be removed by filter sterilization. Exceptions to this include highly resistant prions (3) and bacterial endospores, for example, *Bacillus* and *Clostridium* species. Smaller microorganisms, such as mycoplasma and viruses, can also pass thorough conventional bacteria-retentive filters. Because of the fundamental nature of the subject of sterilization and decontamination, there are many publications on this topic. Consult Ref. 4–9 for further background or supplementary information.

STERILIZATION BY HEAT

Heat treatment by either dry heat in an oven at about 160 °C or with steam at about 121 °C, autoclaving, are two of the most commonly used methods of sterilization (10,11). In general, autoclaving is the more severe of the two methods but to be done successfully requires an efficient, well-maintained, and validated machine. It may not be possible to use these standard sterilization methods for some materials because of their heat sensitivity. Less effective conditions may be acceptable, such as treatment with boiling water or steam at about 100 °C. For instance, cell culture incubators can commonly be heated at about 80 °C for decontamination. The recommended procedure in this case is to repeat

the heat treatment on several successive occasions. It is preferable to keep the incubator in a humid state to maximize the sterilizing effect. Heat treatments such as these can be very effective but fall short of conditions that are accepted as true sterilization. In particular, agents such as bacterial endospores or even standard vegetative bacteria may not be inactivated at these temperatures.

Autoclaves

Almost all microorganisms, apart from some bacterial endospores and prions, are readily inactivated by moist heat at about 121 °C, such as that generated in an autoclave (Fig. 1–3). Various standard cycle conditions may be used, for example, 115 °C for 30 minutes, 121 °C for 15 minutes, 126 °C for 10 minutes, or 134 °C for 3 minutes. These conditions should actually be found in the load during the sterilization phase and exclude the machine and load warm-up phase. These standard cycles are not strictly equivalent. That at 115 °C is the least effective, and that at 134 °C is the most effective. The efficiency of these cycles is tested by determining the survival of highly heat-resistant endospores of *Bacillus stearothermophilus* at a given temperature after various time intervals. The cycle of 121 °C for 15 minutes is most commonly used and can inactivate 1×10^8 of *B. stearothermophilus*. Although it is possible to use other cycles with a similar sterilizing capability, these would be either excessively long, for example, 115 °C for 60 minutes, or excessively short, for example 126 °C for 5 minutes or 134 °C for 1 minute. In practice cycles of 115 °C for 30 minutes, 121 °C for 15 minutes, 126 °C for 10 minutes and 134 °C for 3 minutes have become the accepted standards. These cycles can kill in the order of 1×10^4, 1×10^8, 1×10^{17} or 1×10^{32} of *B. stearothermophilus*, respectively. For routine cell

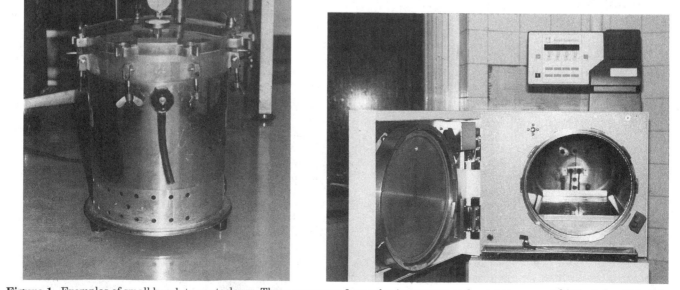

(a)   **(b)**

Figure 1. Examples of small bench top autoclaves. These can range from a basic pressure cooker (**a**) to more sophisticated models (**b**).

Figure 2. The large multipurpose laboratory autoclave. An example of a large capacity autoclave with a loading trolley is shown.

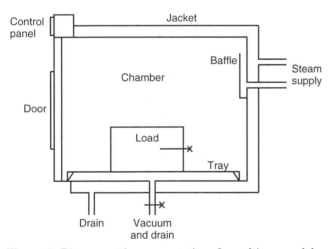

Figure 3. Diagrammatic representation of a multipurpose laboratory autoclave. The sterilization phase of the cycle is controlled by thermocouple probes placed in the chamber drain or in the load. The control panel contains temperature and pressure and cycle stage indicators, as well as various recording instruments, such as a chart recorder or printer. A filter is usually placed on the vacuum line to prevent any microorganisms from leaving the chamber.

culture applications, the cycle at 121 °C for 15 minutes is commonly used.

A more severe cycle is currently recommended to inactivate prions, 132 °C for 1 hour or 134 °C to 138 °C for 18 minutes (12). This latter cycle is applicable only if an adequate porous load cycle can be used. Even these extreme cycles may not be fully effective for certain strains/types of agent. To operate the autoclave, steam must be generated in the equipment itself, as in a small bench top model, or from an external boiler for a large capacity machine used in industry, hospitals, or microbiology departments. It is critical to operate these machines correctly to ensure that a sterile load is produced. In addition, the use of high pressure and high temperatures in the equipment requires that appropriate safety precautions be followed, as directed by the manufacturers.

Bench Top Autoclaves. At their most basic, bench top autoclaves are simply small domestic pressure cookers with a volume of about 0.01 m³ (Fig. 1a). To operate such a machine, open the lid and fill to the required depth with water. Then, the items to be sterilized are placed in the machine on shelves or in a basket as appropriate. The lid is closed and tightly sealed. The water is heated to boiling point, and the steam generated is allowed to purge the chamber for several minutes before the pressure valve is closed. The pressure valve may close automatically in some models. The timer is started when the required pressure/temperature is reached. At the end of the cycle, the heater is turned off, and the pressure allowed to fall. When a temperature of about 80 °C and atmospheric pressure is reached, the door is opened and the sterilized items are removed. Horizontal models (Fig. 1b) of portable bench top autoclaves are often more sophisticated and have additional controls and safety features. They may have more than one cycle, for example, 121 °C and 134 °C, a drying option at the end of the sterilization process, and safety features, such as a temperature lock, to prevent access during the process. In addition, a unit may have an automatic timer and various cycle stage indicators.

There are various limitations in using such small bench top machines. Generally, they lack adequate air removal methods and therefore are not suitable for porous loads, such as wrapped items or laboratory discards. If they do not have an adequate drying stage after sterilization, items may be wet. Because the temperature and pressure in the load are not monitored and there is no printed cycle record, documentation and assurance of sterility may be difficult to demonstrate. In addition, because of the absence of a cooling phase, the load may cool slowly and the cycle may take excessively long to complete. There may also be concerns about operator safety using the more basic models. Their use in the cell culture laboratory is limited to small unwrapped items and bottled fluids. They should not be used for very critical applications, for wrapped or difficult items, or for contaminated laboratory discards.

Large Capacity Autoclaves. Larger autoclaves have a chamber of at least 1 m³ and use an external steam supply (Figs. 2 and 3). In a single cycle gravity displacement autoclave, air is displaced from the bottom of the chamber by steam of lower density entering at the top. A system for cooling the load at the end of the cycle via a jacket or spray cooling system is included. There is often a drying stage, using vacuum and heat, at the end of the run. This type of autoclave is useful for items which are easily exposed to steam, those not wrapped and bottled fluids. However, they are not really suitable for porous loads and wrapped items because air removal is probably not adequate to ensure complete steam penetration and thus sterilization.

To overcome these limitations and to ensure maximum flexibility in use, a multicycle porous load autoclave is preferable in a cell culture laboratory. It is essential that such a machine includes a porous load cycle, in which air is removed from the load and the chamber by vacuum and pressure pulsing stages. The basic steps in such a cycle generally include air removal, sterilization, and cooling and drying using heat and vacuum. The precise details of the stages involved depend on the exact type of cycle and machine because each is dedicated to a specific type of load. A standard gravity displacement cycle is also included for bottled fluids.

Examples of various cycles are given in Figure 4. In contrast to the standard gravity displacement cycle (Fig. 4d), the use of a vacuum pump and steam pressure to produce pulses of pressure in the chamber is more effective for removing air from difficult loads and wrapped items. A wide range of cycles are specifically dedicated to this purpose, and examples are given in Figure 4a–c. Including a single high vacuum step at the start of the cycle (Fig. 4a) is the simplest approach. However other methods are generally more effective. A cycle that includes a number of pulses at negative and/or positive pressure is preferable (Fig. 4b–c) to ensure effective air removal. Such cycles should be used for sterilizing/decontaminating critical loads, such as contaminated laboratory discards and well-wrapped items. Relevant aspects of each cycle program are generally predetermined by the manufacturer. Dials and/or digital meters on the equipment indicate the cycle stage and the current operating pressure and temperature. This information is also recorded via a printer or chart recorder. An air detector is usually used to monitor the efficiency of air removal from the load and chamber. The cycle will not start unless air removal is adequate.

There are many advantages in using a multi-cycle autoclave with a porous load cycle. For instance,

- there is good steam penetration into wrapped items, thus ensuring sterility;
- several cycles available allow flexibility of use;
- the equipment has a large capacity;
- items are free of moisture at the end of the cycle.

In general, large capacity/industrial scale autoclaves are tailored to the customer's specific requirements. They are used in hospitals and the pharmaceutical industry and are preferable for cell culture and microbiology.

After the machine has been installed and initial tests carried out, it may be necessary to conduct further tests to validate critical loads. The heat sensitivity of items should be considered and tested if necessary. Most plastics can withstand the standard 121 °C cycle, although polystyrene does not. Only a relatively few cell culture media or supplements can be autoclaved. Autoclavable formulations of some media do exist, and these omit glutamine because is heat sensitive. The suppliers of cell culture reagents should be consulted for further information.

It is best to add temperature indicators to every item in the load. It is essential to locate such indicators in

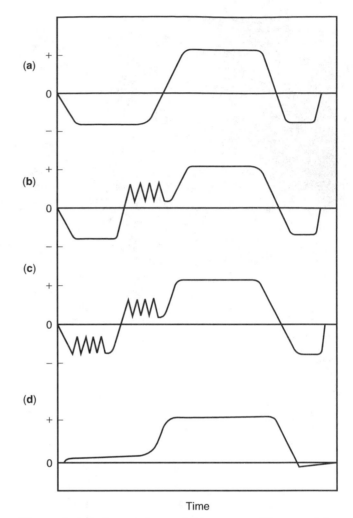

Time

Figure 4. Autoclave cycles available on a multipurpose laboratory autoclave. For difficult porous loads, wrapped items, or laboratory discards, a cycle using air removal must be used. Different methods are available to achieve this and some are illustrated. Positive (+) and negative (−) pressure are indicated. In the simplest approach a single initial vacuum pulse is used at the start of the cycle (**a**). However, cycles with a combination of negative and positive pressure pulsing stages, as shown in (**b**) and (**c**), are generally more effective for air removal. A combination of both negative and positive pulsing stages, as shown in (**c**), is particularly effective. A cycle in which the air is simply removed by gravity displacement and steam flow is shown in (**d**). This type of cycle is suitable only for bottled fluids and unwrapped items. At the end of the sterilizing phase, a vacuum is created while the load is still warm to dry porous loads. The exact details of pressures, times, and resulting temperatures depend on the specific nature of the cycle.

the center of the load to be sterilized when an autoclave does not have a temperature recorder. Autoclave-sensitive tape, autoclave tubes (Browne's tubes), or indicator strips can be used. Such indicators provide only an approximate indication that sterilization conditions have been met. Items of equipment to be sterilized are usually placed in paper sterilization bags or are wrapped in aluminum foil or paper sealed by folding and taping. However, care must be taken not to seal the package completely so that air is removed and steam can penetrate. In the case of empty bottles and containers with caps, the caps should be loosened. Although some autoclave bag manufacturers claim that steam can penetrate directly into discard bags, it is best to open the neck completely before autoclaving to ensure adequate air removal and effective steam penetration. Bottled fluids are best autoclaved with the lids tightly closed to prevent any possibility that the fluid boils over. Suitable bottles should be used that can withstand the autoclave cycle when used in this way; alternatively, the lids can be loosened. The ability of the container or bottle/cap combination to withstand autoclaving should also be checked. The manufacturer's or sterilization engineer's instructions and Standard Operating Procedures should always be followed. These are different for each autoclave. Logbooks on servicing, testing, and use of the machines must be maintained.

Testing. Although in theory it may be possible to directly confirm the sterility of every autoclave load, for example, by incubating the complete batch of product or by inoculating suitable culture media in the case of critical therapeutic products, this is rarely done in practice. Instead, the performance of the autoclave is confirmed by a comprehensive program of routine testing and validation by autoclave engineers. Testing should be carried out regularly, and records should be kept to ensure efficient and safe operation of the machine and to meet regulatory requirements, such as Health & Safety; Good Manufacturing Practice (GMP); and Good Laboratory Practice (GLP) guidelines. The user should record details of all runs in a logbook, and a leak rate test should be carried out at least weekly. At the end of every run, the autoclave recorder should be checked to ensure a satisfactory cycle, as indicated by pulsing profiles, temperature, and time. A steam penetration test into a standardized load of towels or cotton sheets, the Bowie-Dick Test, is usually done daily or weekly (13).

Servicing must be carried out at regular and agreed intervals, for example, every three to six months. Before the machine is first used, the testing of critical worst case loads should be validated by thermocouple studies. The types of load to be tested might include a mixed load of typical laboratory discards. To ensure that the worst case is tested, the autoclave should be filled to capacity and thermocouple probes placed in those items into which steam will have difficulty penetrating. When carrying out a testing program, a standard test pack of towels, as used in the Bowie Dick Test, should be monitored with a thermocouple placed in the center of the test pack. The temperature should be maintained at an acceptable limit, for example, 0 to 2 degrees above the target temperature, throughout the cycle. The temperature indicated on charts and displays should correspond with this limit. Important critical loads are best tested using the worst case situation and critical or difficult items, such as filters used in sterilization, must also be specifically validated. The operation of the door lock, which prevents entry into the machine until the load has cooled to a safe 80 °C level, should be checked. A similar testing procedure is used for liquids, and the temperature of all bottles within the load should agree to within set limits, for example 1 °C. Full details of the current operating requirements for sterilizers are given in various published standards and guidelines (9,14,15).

Hot Air Ovens and Incineration

Heating in the dry state by incineration or treatment in a hot air oven is an alternative method of sterilization (10,11,14). Generally, higher temperatures and longer times than autoclaving must be used. Incineration may be used during routine aseptic techniques, for example, the mouths and lids of bottles may be briefly flamed directly in a Bunsen burner. Metal items and scissors, used during the preparation of primary tissue cultures, can be sterilized in ethanol and subsequently flamed. Waste contaminated with microorganisms is considered clinical waste. This is also true for biological materials that include cell cultures. Various guidelines control the safe disposal of such waste (12,16). Incineration of microbiologically contaminated material is best carried out after the material has been made safe by autoclaving or chemical treatment directly in the laboratory. Then, the waste material can be sent for incineration. Where incineration is the only means of decontamination and is outside the user's control, health and safety issues in the use of contractors must be considered. Incineration is effective when a temperature of about 350 °C is reached, and thus the operation and type of incinerator is important. The incinerator used must be effective and must ensure that no unburned material remains or escapes in the smoke.

Ovens are simple and cheap alternatives to autoclaves. They are routinely used to sterilize glassware and metal objects, but they are generally unsuitable for plastic items. Heat in an oven, may be distributed by convection or more effectively by a fan. A filter must be fitted to the air vent to prevent any recontamination of the load by air that gains access to the chamber during the cooling process. The actual time in the load at sterilizing conditions is the critical factor for ensuring effective sterilization. The timer fitted to the oven may either start when the machine is switched on or when the interior of the chamber reaches a predetermined temperature. In more sophisticated cases, thermocoupled probes placed in the load provide the control for the sterilizing phase. Where this is not the case, an estimate for the load warm-up period must be included when setting the timer. The treatment process can be monitored by chart or digital recorders. In the pharmaceutical industry, tunnel sterilizers may be used to increase capacity. Items of equipment, for example, bottles, are continuously fed through the oven on a conveyor system. This type of equipment requires extensive validation to ensure effective sterilization.

The most common heat treatment cycle is 170 °C for 1 hour. However alternative combinations are 160 °C for 2 hours or 180 °C for 0.5 hour. In all cases, this represents the actual temperature at the center of the load during the sterilization phase. Other cycles exist, for example, 150 °C for 2.5 hours, 140 °C for 3 hours, and 120 °C for 18 hours. These cycles are less effective and are much less commonly used but may be suitable for less critical applications or where the material is heat-sensitive, such as plasticware.

The basic steps involved in using an oven for sterilization are relatively straightforward and much simpler than for an autoclave. Care must be taken not to overfill the oven, so as to ensure good air circulation. As with autoclaves, suitable indicators can be included to confirm that items have been heat treated. Heat-sensitive tape is available which changes color at 160 °C to reveal dark stripes. Other strip indicators are available which indicate that other temperatures have been reached.

Because of their simplicity, the need for extensive engineering maintenance and validation is reduced. However it is wise to test the performance of the instrument as part of the commissioning process. Further ongoing testing on a routine basis is required for critical use in pharmaceutical and hospital applications. Testing may include the use of thermocouples placed in the oven, next to the oven temperature probe, to confirm that the warm-up phase and any temperature overshoot is not excessive, for example, warm up <135 min, overshoot <2 °C. Slight fluctuations during the sterilization phase and the general drift in temperature must also be within acceptable limits, 1 and 2 °C, respectively. Thermocouples placed around and within the load should confirm that the load temperature agrees with the oven temperature indicator, for example, within 5 °C. The appropriate guidelines for sterilizers should be checked for details of the exact current requirements (14,17).

FILTRATION

Filtration is used in the cell culture laboratory to remove microbial agents from liquids and gases (18–20). It is commonly used to sterilize cell culture media and additives because of the heat sensitivity of these items. Filtration has the added risk of recontamination between the actual filter sterilization step and dispensing the sterile material into the sterile final container. Because of the critical nature of this process, commercial sterile filtration/final filling operations need to be closely monitored and controlled, and extensive regulatory and GMP requirements must be complied with. In practice, many of the commonly used materials in cell culture are filter-sterilized. Standard filtration processes commonly use filters with a pore size of 0.2 μm which are suitable for removing bacteria, yeast, and fungi. There are essentially two types of filter; membrane filters which trap microorganisms on their surface and depth filters with a less defined pore size which trap microorganisms in the depth of the matrix. Both types are considered in more detail later.

Membrane filters are preferred for critical sterilizing applications because they have a defined pore size and mode of action. They trap bacteria on the surface. However, depth filters are often very useful for prefiltering a product and thus reducing the bio-burden of microorganisms present before the final sterile filtration step. Recently, filters with a small enough pore size (about 15 nm), to remove viruses have become available (21–26). However, this is a relatively new area, and thus far its application in cell culture and bioproducts has been limited. This technology is being used by some

manufacturers of calf-serum based products, as well as for treating bioproducts for therapeutic use. Recently, plasma-derived products that use this technology have become available (26). In addition to removing conventional microbial agents, filtration may be a useful method for removing prions (27) because these agents normally exist in a highly aggregated state and even the minimal infectious unit comprises a large number of individual prion protein units. The range of filters and filtration equipment available is very large. However, the manufacturers produce technical literature and are happy to provide technical advice. In some cases they are willing to optimize/filtration systems for a specific user's application in their own testing laboratory.

Depth Filters

This type of filter is often made of glass fiber but other materials may be used. Depth filters operate by trapping microorganisms in the depth of the filter matrix. This may involve physical trapping or may result from electrostatic or other interactions. It is possible, at least in theory, to saturate the microbial binding capacity of this type of filter. For this reason, membrane filters are normally used for operations where the absolute sterilization of liquids is critical. However with extensive validation, it may be possible to justify the use of specific depth filters/product combinations. Depth filters are more commonly used to reduce the microbial content/bio-burden, at various stages in a manufacturing process, for example, before specific purification stages, and immediately before the final sterile filtration step. Thus, the efficiency of the purification process and the capacity of the final sterile filtration step can be enhanced.

Depth filters are commonly used for filtering gases (28). The simplest example of the use of this type of filter is the cotton wool used for plugging pipettes used in liquid transfer. In addition, micropipette tips, tubes, and flasks are available with integral depth filters. One type of depth filter extensively used in cell culture operations is the so-called high-efficiency particulate air HEPA filter. This is used to filter air in laminar air flow or microbiological safety cabinets, as well as in sterile rooms. In addition, it can be used as a vent filter on cell culture fermentation equipment or to filter gases supplied to cell cultures. The filter removes particles 0.3 μm or larger at >9.97% efficiency. HEPA is effective for all types of microorganisms, including viruses, even though these agents are much smaller than the nominal filter pore size. The effectiveness results from the fact that these agents exist in the atmosphere attached to liquid droplets in aerosols or attached to dust particles. For pharmaceutical use, there are standards for the quality of air permitted for any particular class of clean room or cabinet. For filter sterilization and aseptic filling, there should be no more than 3500 particles per cubic meter (29). Relevant standards and classifications should be consulted for the current requirements. Various types of cabinet can be used for handling cell cultures and these are reviewed in Chapter X.

Depth filters such as the Planova filter manufactured by Asahi are also available for virus removal (23,26). This particular type of filter uses hollow fibers assembled into cartridges. It may be operated in a tangential or dead-end mode. It is available in a range of nominal pore sizes, ranging from 15 to 75 nm. The 15 nm filter can remove very small viruses, such as polio, hepatitis A, and parvovirus. A 35 nm filter is not suitable for these very small viruses but nevertheless can remove larger viruses, such as herpesvirus, retroviruses, and Hepatitis B and C.

Membrane Filters

Where possible, membrane filters are preferable to depth filters for critical sterilization applications where a high level of assurance for sterility is required. Membrane filters are made from a range of materials, including cellulose (acetate, nitrate, or a mixture), nylon, polysulfone, polyvinylidene fluoride, and polycarbonate. Filters made with low protein binding properties, such as polyvinylidene fluoride, may also be useful in some circumstances. The pores of polycarbonate filters are of a particularly discrete size because they are produced by radiation etching. Because membrane filters act exclusively by retaining microorganisms on their surface by pores of a defined size, there is theoretically no risk of exceeding the capacity of the filter and allowing microorganisms to pass through.

Filters with a nominal pore size of 0.2 µm are the current standard for sterilizing liquids and removing cellular microorganisms. If the effective removal of mycoplasmas is essential, membrane filters with a pore size of 0.1 µm should be considered. These are now commonly used by most manufacturers of serum-based additives for cell culture. Such filters may also help by removing any large animal viruses present. Low residual levels of the chemicals used during the filter manufacturing process, such as detergent and ethylene oxide if used as the sterilizing agent, can affect cell growth (30,31). Filter manufacturers can usually provide data on the levels of extractable chemicals determined by using standard solutions/solvents. Such data may not be sufficient for pharmaceutical products, and product-specific testing may be required by the regulatory agencies. For cell culture applications, it is preferable to use filters with low extractable levels which have been sterilized by gamma irradiation or autoclaving rather than by ethylene oxide. In critical applications, the first volume of liquid through the filter can be discarded. Membrane filters can also be used for filtering the gases, such as CO_2 or air, that may be used in cell culture. Cell culture flasks are available with integral membranes which allow gaseous exchange without having to leave the cap partially open. To sterilize gases, it is possible to use a filter with a pore size of 0.02 µm (32) which is small enough to remove viruses. Membrane filters may also be used to protect pipette handling devices from contamination.

Many types of filters are available. In the simplest systems, a filter of 11 or 25 mm diameter can be attached to a syringe. On a larger scale, cartridges of various sizes which may be pleated to maximize area are used for filtering large volumes of at least several liters. Filter units, comprising the filter membrane in a plastic housing, often come presterilised or may be autoclavable.

The unit is designed for single use. In some cases the filter cartridge must be inserted into a metal housing to produce the complete unit. Filter discs need to be assembled in metal or plastic holders prior to sterilization. Complete preassembled and presterilized filter units have the advantage that they are convenient and pretested by the filter manufacturer, whereas filters that require assembly in housings, particularly filter discs, are more prone to failure.

Membrane filters can also be used for removing viruses. In the Millipore Viresolve system (24,25), a membrane filter with a small and tightly controlled pore size is used. This system is operated in a tangential flow method for virus removal. These filters are available with nominal molecular weight cutoff values of 70 or 180 kDa and remove a range of viruses in a size-dependent manner. The filter with the smaller pore size, Viresolve 70, removes viruses as small as 30 nm, for example, picornaviruses, such as polio and hepatitis A, and parvoviruses. Larger viruses of about 50 nm, such as hepatitis B and C, herpesviruses, and retroviruses, are also removed. However, such filters only allow the passage of products with a molecular weight of less than about 100,000. The type of filter with a larger pore size, Viresolve 180, allows the passage of larger products but has only a limited capacity for removing small viruses. An alternative membrane filtration system for removing viruses is the Pall Ultipor VF DV-50 filter (22). The nominal pore size for this filter is about 50 nm, although filters with a smaller pore size (20 nm), have recently become available. These filters operate in a simple dead-end mode and are available both as filter discs for small-scale testing and as filter cartridges for large-scale pharmaceutical operations. The 50 nm filter allows the passage of larger products and is effective at removing viruses of 50 nm or larger from protein solutions and cell culture media. Smaller viruses, such as polio, are not effectively removed.

Using Filters

Although filtration can be carried out using positive or negative pressure, it is best carried out using positive pressure because in some situations, for example, when filtering buffers/medium with bicarbonate, the pH may rise during filtration. In addition, frothing and protein denaturation may occur if protein solutions are filtered under negative pressure. On a small scale, the apparatus may simply involve using a syringe, but on a larger scale air or nitrogen at positive pressure can be used. An alternative approach is using a peristaltic pump (Fig. 5). Metal vessels dedicated for filter applications, which can be pressurized, are commercially available.

The exact details for using filters vary widely and depend on the type of filtration system used. For commonly used stainless steel filter housings and filter discs (Fig. 6), the method is as follows:

Disassemble the unit and place the filter on top of the metal grid. Care must be taken to ensure that the filter is used in the correct orientation. To increase the capacity of the filtration system, appropriate prefilters (depth or membrane) can be included with the use of

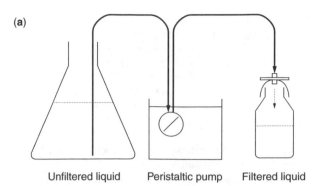

(a)

Unfiltered liquid   Peristaltic pump   Filtered liquid

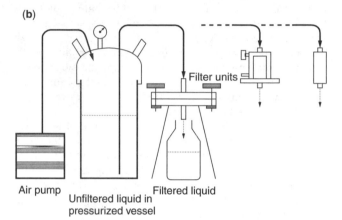

(b)

Filter units

Air pump   Unfiltered liquid in   Filtered liquid
pressurized vessel

Figure 5. Methods used for sterilizing liquids by filtration. The systems shown are designed for minimum filter volumes of 1 liter but are usually used for volumes of 5 liters or more. In system (**a**) a peristaltic pump forces the liquid through a disposable sterile disc filter. In system (**b**) a pump pressurizes the vessel holding the liquid to be sterilized. Then this liquid can be filtered in one of several ways, for example, by a disc filter, a cartridge filter in a stainless steel metal housing that has been autoclaved by the user. Alternatively a presterilized cartridge filter or disc filter that requires no special housing can be used.

appropriate separators between the layers. The assembly of the unit is a critical process, and the manufacturer's instructions must be carefully followed to avoid damaging the filter. Then the assembled unit, along with any associated plastic tubing, is autoclaved. The standard conditions for autoclaving are 121 °C for 15 minutes, although some types of filter can withstand higher temperatures. The manufacturer's instructions must be consulted. The filtration process itself is carried out in a laminar air flow cabinet or sterile room using appropriate aseptic procedures. The liquid to be filtered may be placed in a pressure vessel, or alternatively a peristaltic pump may be used. An air vent may be present on the housing to allow the bleeding off of any air bubbles in the system at the start of the filtration process.

In the Millipore Viresolve system for virus removal, the manufacturer's instructions must be followed precisely (Fig. 7). For this system, it is important to optimize conditions carefully for the recirculation rate, as well as the cross-membrane flow rate to ensure optimum performance and high product throughput and recovery. A postfiltration

Figure 6. Example of a filtration system that uses filter discs. The disc filter is placed within a stainless steel filter holder which is carefully tightened by four retaining nuts. Then, the unit is wrapped and sterilized by autoclaving. An example of a small cartridge filter is also shown which requires the use of an appropriate housing. The filter is connected to suitable plastic tubing via the ridged hose connectors for in-line filtration.

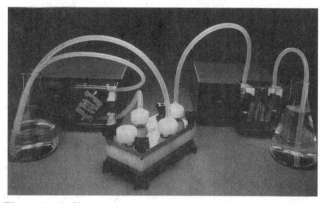

Figure 7. A filtration system used for removing viruses. The system shown uses the Millipore Viresolve filter. The tangential membrane filter is retained in a stainless steel housing. The liquid to be filtered is circulated through the filter by the pump shown on the left. The rate of filtration across the membrane is optimized and controlled by the pump on the right.

washing step is usually required at the end of the process. Allowance for this diluting effect may be required to ensure that the final target concentration/potency is reached. The exact instructions given for the other virus removal filtration systems, Asahi Planova and Pall Ultipor VF, must also be carefully followed to ensure optimal performance and effective virus removal.

Integrity Testing

The manufacturer of the filter will confirm its integrity before release. In addition, the user can test the integrity of filters. This monitoring is essential in the pharmaceutical industry for sterile filling operations. It must be carried out after using the filter, but may also be performed before use. Various methods are available, including the bubble point, diffusion air-flow (or forward flow), and pressure hold tests. The filter manufacturers have correlated these tests with filter performance for removing microbial agents and provide acceptance limits for the test. The industry standard is based on using a particularly small bacterium, for example, *Pseudomonas diminuta* for 0.2 μm filters, which provides a severe test of the filter's efficiency. The filter used should preferably confirm the integrity of the complete filter system, that is, with the housing where relevant. The different integrity test methods are:

1. Bubble point test: Relatively simple tests may be sufficient, for instance, testing the bubble point by trying to force air forward or backward through a wet filter unit attached to a syringe. If air passes through unhindered, then the filter is damaged. During the filtration operation itself, the presence of back pressure also provides some assurance of filter integrity. More sophisticated quantitative procedures can also be used. The manufacturers provide appropriate values for the pass/fail limit which depend on the exact filter type and size and the filter system in use.

2. Diffusion air-flow (forward-flow) test: An alternative approach is based on determining the air flow across the filter. This method is known as the diffusion air-flow or forward-flow method and involves testing the air flow across the wet filter at a specified pressure, usually at about 80% of the bubble point pressure.

3. Pressure hold test: A third method is the pressure hold test. For this, the filter is pressurized, and the pressure decay against time is measured.

In addition to all of these methods, the actual sterility of the final product can be tested directly, simply by incubating the final product at an appropriate temperature and inspecting for microbial growth. This may be carried out on the complete batch or samples can be taken and incubated in appropriate microbiological growth media. The sensitivity of such methods depends on the sample size and the use of suitable growth media. This approach is routinely carried out in critical applications, such as with therapeutic products because the sterilization step itself is not carried out on the product in its final container, as with autoclaving, and thus the risk of contamination exists during the final sterile filling operation itself. Testing for viruses is not generally carried out because of the wide range of virus types. Instead these agents are usually controlled by testing and controlling the starting materials, the cell cultures and growth media.

There are also specific integrity test procedures for virus-retentive filters. For instance in the Millipore Viresolve system (24,25), a water intrusion test is performed. Before this can be done, the filter must be wetted with a proprietary agent to reduce the pressure required for testing filter integrity. The test value has been correlated with the removal of model bacteriophage viruses, as well as a range of other viruses of various sizes. With this data, the user can define an acceptable pass limit based on the degree of virus removal required for a particular virus of known size. This is likely to be in the order of at least four orders of magnitude (10,000 = 4 log) for most applications. For the Pall Ultipor VF filter, a simple forward-flow integrity test is carried out after wetting the filter with isopropanol (33). Performance in this test has been correlated to removal of the bacteriophage PR772 (53 nm) and is used to demonstrate filter integrity.

Critical applications in the pharmaceutical industry may require testing the filter performance with the specific product in use. Although this may not be essential for filters that remove bacteria, product-specific testing is likely to be required to confirm the effectiveness of virus filters because virus removal systems have only recently been developed and experience in their use is limited. In contrast, bacterial filters have long been in use and so extensive knowledge of filter performance relative to a wide range of specific types of test products has been built up. This is sometimes called the matrix approach and may be used to justify the efficiency of a specific product/filter combination without recourse to specific bacterial challenge testing with a particular new product. Smoke challenge tests are used for HEPA filters in microbiological safety cabinets and filtered air in sterile rooms or containment rooms. Dioctyl phthalate particles about 0.3 μm in diameter are used for this test. Testing should be carried out approximately every year. (See Chapter X.)

FUMIGATION

An alternative sterilization method involves fumigation, using disinfectants in the gaseous state. Either formaldehyde gas or ethylene oxide are commonly used (5,9,34). They are, in general, effective against most types of microorganisms although bacterial endospores are somewhat more resistant. These agents are more effective at temperatures over 37 °C and high humidity levels of 75 to 100%. Fumigation is less effective if conditions reduce the accessibility of the microorganisms to the gas, for example, when dried in organic or inorganic material. Fumigation is not used for decontaminating general laboratory waste because of the difficulty in penetrating the load and the presence of organic materials.

Formaldehyde

Formaldehyde gas is commonly used to decontaminate or sterilize laminar airflow cabinets and rooms used for handling cell cultures (6,9). It can also be used for sterilizing equipment. Formaldehyde gas is toxic, and appropriate safety precautions must be observed including the use of breathing apparatus.

Before fumigating a sterile room, all unnecessary items must be removed, particularly those that would or might be harmed by exposure to the gas, for example, cell cultures and sensitive electrical or electronic equipment, such as computers. Then, the room must be cleaned to minimize the level of microbial contamination and to remove substances that may hinder penetration of the gas. There are various methods for generating the formaldehyde gas. In the pharmaceutical industry where regular fumigation is performed, equipment that generates a mist of formaldehyde in droplet form can be used, for example, the Phagojet system (Sterling Health Care). This has some advantage in that levels of deposits of paraformaldehyde are likely to be lower. The fumigation system may be an integral part of the building management system. In the laboratory a dedicated formaldehyde-generating kettle can be used.

Alternatively, a simple pan filled with formaldehyde can be placed on a hot plate connected to a timer. Formalin (40% formaldehyde) solution (20 mL per m^3 room volume) is placed in a suitable container and heated. Alternatively, paraformaldehyde (10 g per m^3 room volume) can be used. Formaldehyde gas can also be generated by mixing formalin solution, or paraformaldehyde and water, with potassium permanganate. However, caution must be exercised with this method because the reaction can be very rapid and may be violent. With the environmental air handling system for the room turned off, the formaldehyde generator is turned on, and the room is evacuated. Then, the door is locked and fully taped up and sealed and a safety warning notice is placed on the door. The room should remain unoccupied until the next day. Before entering the room, the total exhaust cabinet and/or air extracting system, operating in total exhaust mode, should be turned on remotely. If this is not possible, the room should be entered by someone wearing breathing apparatus who can turn on the cabinet air handling system or open the windows, as appropriate. The room should be left unoccupied until the formaldehyde reaches an acceptably safe level. Testing equipment can be used to monitor the formaldehyde level. It may be necessary to clean the room to remove deposits of paraformaldehyde which will emit formaldehyde gas. It may take several days to fully remove residues of the formaldehyde gas from the area. In view of the safety implications, fumigation is considered a fairly specialized procedure and a last resort, for example, for major spills of high-risk microbial agents and in sterile filling rooms in the pharmaceutical industry.

Microbiological laminar air-flow/safety cabinets used for handling cell cultures should be decontaminated regularly, or after contaminated cultures have been handled. Appropriate respiratory protective clothing is not necessary for this procedure. Only cabinets that can be sealed and which are ducted to the outside can be decontaminated using formaldehyde. First the cabinet must be thoroughly cleaned before fumigation, particularly if spills of cell culture media or reagents have occurred. This should include the area below the removable work surface. In some cases, the cabinets may have integral formaldehyde generators that can be filled from outside the cabinet. Otherwise, a small dedicated portable formaldehyde generator can be placed inside the cabinet. The generator should be filled with about 25 ml of Formalin solution. However, this will depend on the size of the cabinet. Where appropriate, follow the manufacturer's instructions. The cabinet door should be closed and sealed with masking tape. The generator should be turned on and a warning notice placed on the cabinet. The cabinet should be left overnight for the fumigant to act. The next day, the air-exhaust system should be switched on while gradually opening the door to the cabinet. The cabinet should be

left running for about half an hour to remove residues of formaldehyde gas. Deposits of paraformaldehyde should preferably be cleaned from the cabinet. However, the operator must take care to avoid exposure to formaldehyde when carrying out this task because residual levels remain high for a considerable period of time. Full cleaning of the cabinet, involving removal of the work surface and opening the glass front panel, are preferably carried out several hours later.

Items of equipment can be conveniently sterilized when the room or cabinet is fumigated by leaving them inside the room/cabinet. An alternative procedure is to place the items in a suitable plastic bag or box together with some formalin liquid. Items used routinely in cell culture procedures, such as pipette aids and micropipettors, should be treated regularly and before returning them to the equipment manufacturer for calibration or servicing.

Ethylene Oxide

Ethylene oxide is used for sterilizing items of clean equipment in so-called "cold-temperature" autoclaves or in combination with steam, particularly in hospitals (34). It is not commonly used in the laboratory. However, it is possible to buy some items of plasticware that have been presterilised with ethylene oxide, for example, syringes and filters. However, this method of sterilization can leave behind toxic residues, so items sterilized by alternative methods, such as gamma irradiation, may be preferable. As with formaldehyde, it is also important to remember that ethylene oxide gas is very toxic, and operator exposure must be controlled.

GAMMA IRRADIATION

Gamma irradiation is a very common method of sterilization (35). Most presterilized items of equipment are treated in this way, for example, tissue culture flasks, filters, plastic pipettes, pipette tips, and syringes. It is frequently used to sterilize items that cannot be heated. It has good penetrating powers and thus has the advantage that items can be completely sealed and packaged before being sterilized. Items are exposed to 2.5 mrad, the accepted standard dose in a ^{60}Co plant. Some chemicals, such as antibiotics can also be purchased that have been sterilized in this way. This level of exposure has been in industrial use for a considerable time and has been found acceptable as long as there are only low levels of contamination by microorganisms. Thus, it is suitable for items made in a factory that are essentially sterile before final irradiation. This method may not eradicate the more resistant bacterial spores and viruses. Both gamma and UV irradiation have almost no effect on prions (2,3), an observation suggesting that they have no nucleic acid or have a very small and highly resistant genome.

ULTRAVIOLET LIGHT

Ultraviolet (UV) light at a wavelength of about 260 nm inactivates microorganisms and viruses (35). However its usefulness as a method of sterilization is limited because of its poor penetrating power. UV light can be used to sterilize the air in cell culture cabinets and rooms and to sterilize surfaces once they have been cleaned. The power of UV lamps decreases with use so they must be checked regularly. Bacterial spores and prions are highly resistant and bacteria possess DNA repair mechanisms which can overcome limited damage. Irradiation with UV light is used in some high purity, pyrogen-free water systems to keep the level of viable microorganisms at a low level. This approach can also be combined with other chemical methods to decontaminate water, for example, in swimming pools. Recent developments with high-intensity visible and UV light sources have allowed the use of this method for sterilizing simple pharmaceutical products, such as water or saline solution. However, more complex bioproducts may be too sensitive for this method.

LIQUID DISINFECTANTS

Many types of liquid disinfectant are available and play a useful role in the cell culture laboratory (4,5,9). A summary of common disinfectants, their effectiveness, and use is given in Table 1. Disinfectants can be prepared using laboratory reagents or can be purchased as proprietary formulations. Various factors should be taken into account when using or selecting a suitable disinfectant. The use of disinfectants is not considered an absolute method of sterilization compared to such methods as autoclaving. They have limitations in their spectrum of antimicrobial activity (see Table 1). All disinfectants, some more than others, are less effective in the presence of organic matter. Although the concentrated stock disinfectant is stable, the stability of the working dilution varies with the type of disinfectant. Nevertheless, diluted disinfectants are used in the laboratory for routinely disinfecting equipment and surfaces in rooms and cabinets, for routine hygiene within the laboratory, for disinfecting cell culture items after use and before washing and resterilizing for recycling, for example, glassware, and for treating used or contaminated cell culture media before disposal. However, care must be taken to ensure that they are effectively used. For instance, when treating items by immersion, care must be taken to fully immerse the equipment and to prevent pockets of air being trapped which can prevent all surfaces from exposure to the disinfectant. For this reason and to ensure that all organic material is removed, exposing the item to the disinfectant in two separate steps is

preferable to ensure effective decontamination in more critical situations.

Disinfectants can be applied to surfaces on a cloth or by a handheld sprayer. Paper towels should be used to cover liquid spills, and then disinfectant is applied. This must be allowed to act for the recommended time before disposal, and then the surface must be re-treated with the disinfectant. Some disinfectants are available in powder form which can be directly applied to liquid spills so that they can be contained, absorbed, and treated in one step.

Disinfectants can be used to disinfect clean rooms routinely before fumigation with a "knapsack" or a large volume sprayer with a long lance. Appropriate safety precautions must be taken to avoid exposure of the face, eyes, and lungs to the disinfectant.

Formaldehyde and Glutaraldehyde

Formaldehyde and glutaraldehyde can both be used as liquid disinfectants, although glutaraldehyde is more commonly used and is probably more effective. Their advantage is that they are relatively insensitive to the presence of organic matter and both can inactivate bacterial endospores. However, there are health and safety problems related to their use. For glutaraldehyde, in particular, there is pressure to limit exposure. Formaldehyde is used at about 4%, and this is easily prepared by diluting the commercially available 40% formaldehyde solution (Formalin). Glutaraldehyde is used at 2%, and this is available as a component of many commercial formulations, including Cidex and Gigasept. The typical treatment time is at least 30 minutes, but longer times are advised to obtain full sporicidal activity. Proprietary glutaraldehyde-based disinfectants need the addition of an activator before use and then have a recommended life of about seven days. Aldehyde vapors are considered relatively toxic because they can sensitize and also have mutagenic and carcinogenic properties. Therefore, steps to limit exposure must be taken by using a fume cupboard or appropriate microbiological safety cabinet.

Hypochlorite

Hypochlorite has a relatively low cost and is readily available, for example, household bleach and Chloros. Its disadvantage is that it is not so effective in the presence of high levels of organic matter. It corrodes metals and therefore must not be used to sterilize centrifuge

Table 1. Use of Common Disinfectants

| Type | Recommended conditions[a] | | Effect[b] | | | |
	Concentration	Time (min)	Bacteria	Bacterial Endospores	Fungi	Viruses
Alcohol	70%	30[c]	+	−	−	+/−
Phenolics	2–5%	30	+	−	+	+/−
Hypochlorite	10,000 ppm	30		+	+	+
Aldehydes	2–4%	30	+	+	+	+

[a]For proprietary products, the specific manufacturer's recommendations should be followed.
[b]Agents that are inactivated at the recommended concentration are indicated by (+). In the case of viruses, the agent may be effective against enveloped viruses, but its effect on nonenveloped viruses may be more variable or only partial (+/−).
[c]In practice repeated applications are required to achieve a sufficient exposure time.

rotors or cell culture cabinets. Although the concentrate is stable, dilute hypochlorite is not and should be changed after 24 hours. The recommended concentration for high levels of organic matter or for critical situations when contamination is known to be present is 10,000 ppm available chlorine. Lower concentrations of 2,500 ppm are recommended for routine hygiene. The recommended exposure time is at least 30 minutes, although overnight exposure may be preferable. Extended exposure to hypochlorite at 20,000 ppm available chlorine is currently a recommended procedure for inactivating prions. Sodium dichloroisocyanurate powder can be used for treating spills by absorbing the liquid and rapidly releasing high levels of chlorine.

Phenolics

Clear phenolic disinfectants, such as Hycolin, used at a concentration of 2 to 5%, are effective against most standard microorganisms although they are less effective against bacterial endospores. Phenolics are largely unaffected by organic matter and are commonly used in bacteriology laboratories. One disadvantage is that they tend to leave sticky residues when used for cleaning surfaces.

Alcohol

Alcohol, usually in the form of ethanol, is frequently used for disinfecting surfaces, protective gloves, and hands. For optimal effect it should be used at a concentration of about 70%. It can be readily applied by a handheld sprayer. Surfaces must be fully saturated to ensure that exposure time is sufficient. Then, the 70% ethanol/water mixture is left to evaporate naturally. Its rapid rate of evaporation, enhanced in a cabinet due to the airflow, may make it difficult to ensure adequate exposure time. In such situations, more than one application of the alcohol may be preferable. Its advantages are that it has low toxicity, is convenient, easy to use, and leaves no residue. However, it is not very effective against fungi, bacterial endospores, or nonenveloped viruses. Care must also be taken when handling it because of its flammability. Therefore, alcohol is best used as a cleaning agent or disinfectant for less critical applications. In the cell culture procedures, it can be used as a precautionary measure for treating work surfaces and the exterior of cell culture flasks before and during work. For critical use or where contamination is suspected, it is best to decontaminate first with a more effective disinfectant and then to treat or spray surfaces with an alcohol solution as an additional precautionary measure.

OTHER DISINFECTANTS

Many other useful disinfectants can be prepared in the laboratory or purchased as commercial formulations. Some examples are hydrogen peroxide at 5 to 10%; acids or alkali; ethanol (70%) mixed with 4% formaldehyde or 2000 ppm hypochlorite; ethanol/propanol/aldehyde mixtures. The proprietary disinfectant Virkon which inactivates a wide range of viruses and other microorganisms, is made up of three components: an oxidizing agent (peroxide), acid at pH 2.6, and detergent. This is used as a 1% solution and requires an exposure time of at least 10 minutes.

In the pharmaceutical industry, chemical "clean in place" systems are used to clean and disinfect pipe systems and vessels. This procedure usually involves wash cycles with sodium hydroxide (0.5 M) followed by acid. Final sterilization is usually accomplished with steam.

VIRUS TESTING AND ELIMINATION

The risk that viruses are present in cell cultures is particularly great because some viruses can go largely undetected and have no obvious effect on the cells. Similar considerations may apply to other cellular microorganisms, in particular, mycoplasmas. (See Drexler & Liphoff, Chapter X.) Although these agents can be removed and inactivated during the purification and manufacturing of a bioproduct, the first line of defense is screening the cell line.

Procedures have become relatively standardised, and many contract laboratories offer services for testing cell lines for viral agents (36–38). They can provide advice on current regulatory requirements and carry out testing in accordance with GLP guidelines. In addition they have available the animal testing facilities needed for some aspects of this work. The standard approach involves testing the manufacturer's master cell bank/working cell banks for a wide range of viruses of human and/or animal origin. The details of the viruses to be tested depend on whether the cells are human or animal and on the type of animal involved. For this reason, it is relevant to ascertain the origins and history of the cells and details of any cell culture growth additives used. This information, together with further details on the donors, such as their health status, is also required by regulatory authorities when registering cell-derived bioproducts for human therapeutic use. The range of human viruses that may theoretically be present is extensive. Because they can form latent/persistent infections, the presence of retroviruses, such as the human immunodeficiency viruses (HIV-1 and -2) or the human T-cell lymphotropic viruses (HTLV-1 and -2) should be included in such tests. Similar considerations apply to herpesviruses, such as herpes simplex virus (HSV-1 and -2), Epstein–Barr virus, cytomegalovirus, varicella zoster, and human herpes virus 6 (HHV-6). The viruses that may be present in rodent cells, include rat rotavirus, reovirus type 3, Sendai virus, lymphocyte choriomeningitis virus, and hantavirus. Tests are commonly performed on bovine cells or those that have been grown with bovine serum for the following viruses: bovine viral diarrhoea, infectious bovine rhinotracheitis, parainfluenza, bovine parvovirus, and bovine adenovirus. Various strategies may be employed in virus testing, including the inoculation of animals or eggs. The induction of virus-specific antibodies in rodents or mice in the so-called mouse antibody production or rat antibody production tests is also commonly used and can detect about twenty different viruses. A range of indicator cell lines is used to detect viruses as revealed by the presence of a cytopathic effect or the ability to adsorb red blood cells.

Specific virus tests can involve molecular techniques, such as the polymerase chain reaction. However, such testing methods can be too specific, and some variants of the virus involved may be missed. To overcome this problem, primer pairs must be selected to detect as wide a range of variants/strains of a particular virus as possible. For this reason, the use of two or more pairs of primers may be the best approach for any given virus. Furthermore it may be possible to detect several viruses in one test, the so-called multiplex approach and thus reduce the workload. Extended cell banks produced at the end of the manufacturing run are tested. To assure testing the worst case situation, a passage number well in excess of that which is likely to be used in the final full-scale manufacturing process should be tested. The sensitivity of detecting certain latent viruses, such as herpesvirus and retroviruses, can be increased by including appropriate chemical agents that induce virus replication.

Viruses of particular concern in cell cultures are those that can be latent and/or persistent without any cytopathic effect on the cell line. Often these agents have oncogenic/cancer-causing potential. These viruses include mouse retroviruses, human retroviruses, for example, human immunodeficiency virus, human T-cell leukemia virus and herpesviruses, such as Epstein–Barr virus and human herpes virus type 6.

Because of the limitations of virus screening technology, in particular their limited sensitivity and the fact that virus detection methods are specific, methods for inactivating or removing viruses from cell-culture-derived products are also needed (39–41). These are incorporated at the time the bio-product is harvested from the cell culture or later in the downstream manufacturing process. The standard purification method developed for a product may in itself be effective for removing/inactivating viruses. Process steps, such as precipitation, chromatography, freeze-drying, low pH, ethanol treatment, and product storage may all make a contribution. Affinity chromatography using a metal chelate, monoclonal antibody, Protein A or G based ligands, or ion exchange chromatography have proved effective for virus removal.

The use of multiple washing steps, including the use of harsh conditions, such as high or low pH, and/or extended column washing, can enhance the effectiveness of these procedures for virus removal/inactivation. For example, during the purification of human monoclonal antibodies for human use, affinity chromatography on Protein-G Sepharose Fast Flow, involving acid elution, gave a virus reduction value of 6 to 7 log for herpes simplex virus (HSV) and 5 log for Sindbis virus (42). These viruses were used as models for relevant herpesviruses and retroviruses that might theoretically be present in such cell cultures. Virus reduction for the nonenveloped poliovirus was more limited, 3 log. This virus was resistant to the acid conditions used, in contrast to Sindbis and HSV which are relatively sensitive to acid conditions. This suggests that acid inactivation, combined with physical virus removal, contributed to the high level of virus reduction for HSV and Sindbis in this system. It may be possible to further optimize such standard protein purification

processes to enhance their ability to remove/inactivate viruses. The best virus reduction steps must be fully validated, controlled, and shown to be robust in their action with regard to process variability. In addition, they must be shown to be effective against the viruses of main concern and preferably against as wide a range of virus types as possible. Unfortunately this ideal may be difficult to achieve in practice. Any one particular virus reduction method can suffer from limitations/restrictions in the range of viruses affected. Thus the concept of using multiple virus inactivation steps in a manufacturing process is becoming increasingly important.

A wide range of specific methods are now available for inactivating and/or removing viruses from products derived from cell-culture harvests, as well as from other sources of potential therapeutic products, such as human plasma (39–41). Their use depends on the nature of the specific product involved and the viruses that may be present. However, some viruses are more difficult to control than others. For instance, nonenveloped viruses are generally more resistant to physical or chemical inactivation methods. In addition, by virtue of their small size, they are also more difficult to remove by using dedicated virus filters. For these reasons, viruses, such as hepatitis A and human parvovirus B19, and animal parvoviruses, such as minute virus of mice, can be a problem in certain situations. The use of heat treatments represents one of the earliest approaches to inactivating them. For instance, human albumin derived from human plasma is heated at 60 °C for 10 hours in a liquid state, pasteurization. This step was introduced in the 1950s to prevent the transmission of hepatitis. To prevent this step from affecting the protein, specific stabilizers may be needed, such as sodium octanoate for albumin, or general stabilizers, such as amino acids, salts, and sugars. Although this procedure is very effective for enveloped viruses, it is less effective for nonenveloped viruses, most of which tend to be heat-resistant. In most cases it may be necessary to remove the stabilizer after treatment. Where this is not required, for example, in albumin, pasteurization becomes a terminal step carried out on the product in its final container. In one variation of this approach, microwaves are used to expose products to high temperatures for very short periods of time, for example, 70° to 80 °C for 0.01 seconds.

An alternative is to heat treat the final freeze-dried product. For instance, heating coagulation factor concentrates at 80 °C for 72 hour has prevented the transmission of hepatitis viruses and HIV. This extreme treatment does not significantly affect the activity of the final product. More severe heat treatments, such as 100 °C for 24 hours, currently being tested, are more effective against the heat-resistant nonenveloped viruses, such as hepatitis A and parvovirus. In all cases, it must be confirmed that heat treatment does not affect the product in any way. Possible effects that may occur include denaturation of the protein, decreased storage stability, increased aggregation levels, and decreased activity or changes to antigenic properties. Less obvious effects may become apparent only from testing in animals or clinical trials in humans. For instance, subtle changes to the product may have a significant effect in vivo. In human coagulation factors, heat treatment may induce new antigenic determinants that can induce an immune response in humans. Consequently, the activity and effectiveness of the clotting factor may be severely inhibited. In Factor IX concentrates, the thrombogenic potential of the product may be increased.

The solvent/detergent procedure for inactivating enveloped viruses was originally developed for plasma products. However it is also increasingly used for products derived from cell cultures. This technique involves treating the product with tri-*n*-butyl phosphate, as the solvent, combined with a suitable nonionic detergent, such as sodium cholate, Tween 80 or Triton X-100. These chemicals must be removed from the product after being used. However, this can often be accomplished by the standard purification process itself, particularly if affinity chromatography is involved. However, dedicated methods for removing solvent by oil extraction or for removing the detergent by specific chromatographic resins can be used. There is some evidence that certain enveloped viruses of the poxvirus group are relatively resistant to this method.

Extreme pH is another approach to inactivating viruses. Extended incubation at the moderately low pH of 4.2 inactivates a wide range of enveloped viruses. However, extended incubation periods are necessary at temperatures of about 35 °C. In some cases it may be possible to do this on the product in its final container if it is stable under such conditions. However certain animal viruses are extremely acid resistant, for example, enteroviruses, such as Hepatitis A and poliovirus, and parvoviruses. High pH conditions of up to 1 M sodium hydroxide are commonly used as part of the sanitization/clean-in-place procedures for equipment used in large-scale manufacturing processes. This method removes protein contamination and also inactivate most viruses. Although β-propriolactone has been used in the past to inactivate viral vaccines, it has not always been effective and is rarely used now to treat bioproducts.

Photochemical methods may also be used to inactivate viruses and in some cases may be effective for cellular products. This approach involves adding a photosensitive agent or dye, which causes virus inactivation when exposed to UV or visible light. Some of these systems, used directly on cells, such as human red cells and platelets, inactivate both the extracellular as well as intracellular forms of some viruses.

Various other methods are under evaluation, such as the use of UV irradiation at a wavelength of 200 to 290 nm, UV-C. It has been reported that the inclusion of a quencher, such as rutin, is necessary to prevent damage to some products while allowing viruses to be effectively inactivated. The use of virus-retentive filters has been considered in the previous section.

Prions

Screening for prions is not routinely carried out presently. However, current concerns over prions and evidence that lymphocytes are involved in their spread and pathogenesis may lead to routine testing for such agents in the future. At present, the most sensitive detection methods for prions are based on infectivity; however, such testing may take at least one year to be completed and is very expensive to conduct. An alternative approach is to screen for the abnormal form of the prion protein which appears to coexist with infectivity. This can be done by Western blotting, but this is a relatively insensitive technique compared with the infectivity assay. However, rapid developments in this area are likely, given public and regulatory concerns over bovine spongiform encephalopathy and its possible human derivative, new variant Creutzfeldt–Jakob disease. Although it has proved possible to inactivate conventional viruses without significantly affecting the product, this has been difficult with prions. Prions are extremely stable to all physical and chemical inactivation procedures. However, because prions exist as highly aggregated sticky proteins, they are likely to be removed by many manufacturing processes including filtration, chemical precipitation, and chromatography. Presently, health screening and/or sourcing the biological starting material is the standard approach recommended for controlling such agents and preventing them from getting into therapeutic products. Where bovine-derived material is essential, such as in fetal calf serum, source material should not be used from countries where there is a high incidence of BSE. Instead, material should be used from countries where there have been no reported cases of BSE.

REGULATORY AND SAFETY ISSUES

Many aspects of the use of cell cultures, sterilization and decontamination procedures, and the use of cell-derived biopharmaceuticals are subject to regulations which may include government legislation. These are designed to protect those handling cell cultures or manufacturing products derived from cell cultures from risk. Such considerations also apply to patients who receive cell lines or their products for therapeutic purposes. Safety considerations are relevant to the cell culture and products themselves and also to many of the associated activities involving sterilization and decontamination. Various guidelines, codes of practice, standards, and other documents have been produced by government agencies and manufacturing organizations that address these issues by giving practical guidance and illustrating the best practice on these topics.

Safety Requirements

The safety of individuals involved in cell culture and associated procedures is controlled by the Control of Substances Hazardous to Health (COSHH) regulations in the United Kingdom. Codes of practice are published that provide practical guidance on how to meet such legal requirements, covering hazards from both chemical as well as biological agents which may pose a safety risk, for instance, chemical agents that are used as disinfectants, such as glutaraldehyde and formaldehyde, as well as microorganisms and viruses.

Microorganisms may be classified into one of several risk groups (12). Those in Group 1 are considered unlikely to cause human disease, whereas those in higher groups, Groups 2 and 3, can cause human disease. Agents in Group 3 represent a serious hazard to the individual and may spread in the community. Those in Group 4 represent a very serious hazard to the individual and the community and usually no effective prophylaxis or treatment is available. Detailed guidance on these aspects is given in such documents as the Categorisation of Biological Agents According to Hazard and Categories of Containment, which is regularly updated. More specific guidance may exist for specific groups of agents, such as HIV and prions. From a legal point of view, the COSHH regulations put the onus for safety on the employer. From a practical point of view this means that the manager of those individuals handling cell cultures and microorganisms is responsible for their safety. This involves assessing the associated risks, developing and implementing safe working practices, and ensuring that these are followed. In turn, the workers must ensure that such safe working procedures are followed and must also ensure the safety of other individuals.

Although the cell culture worker may not be intentionally involved in using microorganisms themselves, risks from such agents are nevertheless considered to exist. The current view is that cells should be treated as posing a potential risk and handled in the same way as an infectious agent (12). Thus, the recommended containment level is to use those required for Group 2 agents for standard/characterized cell lines. Where particular concerns exist, for example, with primary cell cultures from human or primate sources, or where specific viruses are known or suspected to be present, higher levels of containment may be required. Primary cell cultures derived from monkeys have transmitted highly pathogenic agents, such as simian herpes virus (herpes B virus) or Marburg virus, the agent of Green Monkey Disease. Human T lymphocytes can also pose an enhanced risk when derived from untested individuals, particularly when the cells are maintained in long-term culture.

In addition, it has been proposed that cell cultures be considered as infectious agents in their own right because cells may possess the capacity to colonize individuals after, for example accidental inoculation. This is significant in view of the fact that many cells have oncogenic potential. Appropriate guidelines for sterilizing and decontaminating equipment and contaminated waste materials must be followed to protect individuals and the environment. This also applies to the effective operation of autoclaves and ovens designed to sterilize and decontaminate. Such aspects are covered by documents including Health Technical Memorandum 2010 (14) and appropriate British Standards (15). The equipment used for sterilization poses potential hazards due to the high temperatures and pressures involved, and safe working practices must be adopted.

Good Manufacturing Practice

The manufacturers of sterile pharmaceutical products are required by regulatory authorities to follow Good Manufacturing Practice (GMP) guidelines (29). GMP is defined by regulatory bodies, such as the Medicines

Control Agency in the United Kingdom, the European Medicines Enforcement Agency in the European Union, the Federal Drug Administration in the Unites States, and equivalent bodies in other countries. These regulators are required to ensure that products are safe and effective for public use. Therefore products must be free of bacteria and other microorganisms and, in addition, the risks from viruses and prions must be reduced to an acceptable minimum. Guidelines have been issued and are regularly updated on the testing of cell lines for viruses and other infectious agents (36–38), methods for removing and inactivating viruses from cell culture and plasma-derived products, and validating such procedures (43).

Good Laboratory Practice

Using the principles of Good Laboratory Practice (GLP) may also be relevant in the cell culture laboratory. Their use may be mandatory in the safety studies required for new pharmaceutical products. Details of the procedures to be followed have been published (44–45). The use of the principles of GLP is designed to ensure the quality and integrity of scientific data generated in the laboratory. They are designed to ensure that all of the methods used are adequately described and that the results are accurately recorded and fully traceable. All aspects of the study are covered, including the planning, performance, recording and independent monitoring, and archiving of the data generated. Standard Operating Procedures (SOP) can be used for routine activities. In the context of sterilization, this may include sterile filtration, the use of disinfectants, and the operation of ovens/autoclaves.

There must also be an independent Quality Assurance program. A Study Director is required to take overall responsibility for any particular safety study. It is also a requirement that all of the equipment, such as autoclaves and ovens, must be well maintained, regularly serviced, and calibrated at suitable intervals and records kept. In addition to official documents on GLP, practical guidance on its interpretation in the context of the cell culture laboratory has been published (46). Although working to GLP is only essential in limited situations, such as studies designed to ensure the safety of therapeutic products, these include animal toxicity testing of cell lines and products, the screening of cell lines for viruses, and the evaluation of virus inactivation/removal methods used in biological products.

However, many or all of the principles involved may be usefully applied in the research or R & D laboratory. For instance, some studies carried out when developing a product, for example, on purity, characterization, and stability testing, ultimately impinge on the safety or efficacy of the resultant therapeutic product. The use of GLP may also have other advantages. For instance, it can help substantiate or justify ownership of any new products or inventions when patents are considered. Although such considerations may seen unnecessary when it comes to basic research, such work may lead to an important therapeutic cell line or product. The subsequent development of these may be severely hampered if adequate standards, such as those based on GLP or similar, have not been used at the research stage.

BIBLIOGRAPHY

1. S.B. Prusiner, *Dev. Biol. Stand.* **75**, 55–74 (1991).
2. R.H. Kimberlin, in L.H. Collier and M.C. Timbury, eds., *Topley and Wilson's Principles of Bacteriology, Virology and Immunity*, 8th ed., Edward Arnold, London, 1990, pp. 671–693.
3. D.M. Taylor, *Dev. Biol. Stand.* **75**, 97–102 (1991).
4. A.D. Russell, W.B. Hugo, and G.A.J. Ayliffe, *Principles and Practice of Disinfection, Preservation and Sterilization.* 2nd ed., Blackwell, Oxford, 1992.
5. S.S. Block, *Disinfection, Sterilization and Preservation*, 3rd ed., Lea & Febiger, Philadelphia, 1983.
6. A. Doyle, J.B. Griffiths, and D.G. Newell, *Cell and Tissue Culture: Laboratory Procedures*, Wiley, Chichester, England, 1996.
7. J.M. Davis, *Basic Cell Culture: A Practical Approach*, IRL Press, Oxford, 1994.
8. R.E. Spier and J.B. Griffiths, *Animal Cell Biotechnology* **1**, Academic Press, London, 1984.
9. C.H. Collins, P.M. Lyne, and J.M. Grange, *Collins and Lyne's Microbiological Methods*, 7th ed., Butterworth-Heinemann Oxford, 1995.
10. V.G. Alder and R.A. Simpson, in A.D. Russell, W.B. Hugo, and G.A.J. Ayliffe, eds., *Principles and Practice of Disinfection, Preservation and Sterilization*, Blackwell, Oxford, 1992, pp. 483–511.
11. L. Josyln, in S.S. Block, ed., *Disinfection, Sterilization and Preservation*, 3rd ed., Lea & Febiger, Philadelphia, 1983, pp. 3–46.
12. Advisory Committee on Dangerous Pathogens, *Categorisation of Biological Agents According to Hazard and Categories of Containment*, 4th ed., H.M. Stationery Office, London, 1995.
13. J.H. Bowie, J.C. Kelsey, and G.R. Thompson, *Lancet* **1**, 586 (1963).
14. Department of Health, *Sterilizers*, Health Tech. Memo. No. 2010, H.M. Stationery Office, London, 1994.
15. British Standards Institute, *Autoclaves for Sterilization in Laboratories*, BS2646, British Standards Institute, London, 1993.
16. Health Services Advisory Committee, *Safe Disposal of Clinical Waste*, H.M. Stationery Office, London, 1992.
17. British Standards Institute, *Specification for the Performance of Electrically Heated Sterilizing Ovens*, BS3421, British Standards Institute, London, 1961.
18. T.D. Brock, *Membrane Filtration*, Springer-Verlag, Berlin, 1983.
19. C.W. Fifield and T.J. Leahy, in S.S. Block, ed., *Disinfection, Sterilization and Preservation*, 3rd ed., Lea & Febiger, Philadelphia, 1983, pp. 125–153.
20. S.P. Denyer, in A.D. Russell, W.B. Hugo, and G.A.J. Ayliffe, eds., *Principles and Practice of Disinfection, Preservation and Sterilization*, 2nd ed., Blackwell, Oxford, 1992, pp. 573–603.
21. P.L. Roberts, *Vox Sang* **69**, 82–83 (1995).
22. P. Roberts, *J. Virol. Methods* **65**, 27–31 (1997).
23. M. Burnouf-Radosevich, P. Apourchaux, J.J. Huart, and T. Burnouf, *Vox Sang* **67**, 132–138 (1994).
24. A.J. DiLeo, A.E. Allegrezza, Jr., and S.E. Builder, *Bio Technology* **10**, 182–188 (1992).
25. A.J. DiLeo, D.A. Vacante, and E.F. Deane, *Biologicals* **21**, 287–293 (1993).
26. D. Crombie et al., *Thromb. Haemostasis* **73**, 1023 (1995).
27. J. Tateishi, T. Kitamoto, G. Ishikawa, and S.I. Manabe, *Membrane* **18**, 101–106 (1993).
28. G.J. Harper, in R.E. Spier and J.B. Griffiths, eds., *Animal Cell Biotechnology*, Vol. 1, Academic Press, London, 1985, pp. 141–164.
29. Medicines Control Agency, *Rules and Guidance for Pharmaceutical Manufacturers and Distributors*, H.M. Stationery Office, London, 1997.
30. K.L. Harrison et al., *J. in Vitro Fertil. Embryol. Transus.* **7**, 347–350 (1990).
31. D.E. Knight, *Nature (London)* **343**, 218 (1990).
32. Pall Process Filtration Ltd., *Retention of Viral Contaminants by 0.04 µm Nylon 66 Filters*, Pall Sci. Tech. Rep. STR 1358, Pall Process Filtration, Ltd., Portsmouth, UK.
33. Pall Ultrafine Filtration Company *Validation Guide for Pall Ultipor VF DV50 Ultipleat AB Style Virus Removal Cartridges*, Pall Ultrafine Filtration Company, New York.
34. E.A. Christensen and H. Kristenson, in A.D. Russell, W.B. Hugo, and G.A.J. Ayliffe, eds., *Principles and Practice of Disinfection, Preservation and Sterilization*, 2nd ed., Blackwell, Oxford, 1992, pp. 557–572.
35. E.A. Christensen, H. Kristenson, and A. Miller, in A.D. Russell, W.B. Hugo, and G.A.J. Ayliffe, eds., *Principles and Practice of Disinfection, Preservation and Sterilization*, 2nd ed., Blackwell, Oxford, 1992, pp. 528–556.
36. U.S. Food and Drug Administration, *Points to Consider in the Characterization of Cell Lines used to Produce Biologicals*, USFDA, Washington, D.C., 1987.
37. U.S. Food and Drug Administration, *Points to Consider in the Manufacture and Testing of Monoclonal Antibody Products for Human Use*, USFDA, Washington, D.C., 1987.
38. Committee for Proprietary Medicinal Products, European Medicines Evaluation Agency, *Note for Guidance on the Quality of Biotechnological Products: Viral Safety Evaluation of Biotechnology Products Derived from Cell Lines of Human or Animal Origin*, CPMP/ICH/295/95, CPMP, 1995.
39. P. Roberts, *Rev. Med. Virol.* **6**, 25–38 (1986).
40. T. Burnouf, *Biologicals* **20**, 91–100 (1992).
41. P.R. Foster and B. Cuthbertson, in R. Madhok, C.D. Forbes, and B.L. Evatt, eds., *Blood, Blood Products and HIV*, Chapman & Hall, London, 1994, pp. 207–248.
42. R.M. Baker et al., in D.L. Pyle, ed., *Separations for Biotechnology 3*, Royal Society of Chemistry, Cambridge, England, 1994, pp. 53–59.
43. Committee for Proprietary Medicinal Products, European Medicines Evaluation Agency, *Note for Guidance on Virus Validation Studies: The Design, Contribution and Interpretation of Studies Validating the Inactivation and Removal of Viruses*, CPMP/BWP/268/95, CPMP, 1996.
44. Department of Health, *Good Laboratory Practice: The United Kingdom Compliance Programme*, HM Stationery Office, London, 1989.
45. Organization for Economic Co-Operation and Development, *OECD Principles of Good Laboratory Practice*, OECD Publications, Paris, 1998.
46. S.J. Froud and J. Luker, in J.M. Davis, ed., *Basic Cell Culture: A Practical Approach*, IRL Press, Oxford, 1994, pp. 273–286.

See also Aseptic techniques in cell culture; Contamination detection and elimination in plant cell culture; Contamination detection in animal cell culture; Contamination of cell cultures, mycoplasma.

T

TOXIN RESISTANT PLANTS FROM PLANT CELL CULTURE AND TRANSFORMATION

JAN BRAZOLOT
K. PETER PAULS
University of Guelph
Guelph, Ontario
Canada

OUTLINE

Introduction
Toxins: Definition and Types
Toxin Modes of Action
    Host-Selective Toxins
    Nonhost-Selective Toxins
Approaches to Developing Toxin-Resistant Plants
    In Vitro Selection
    Plant Transformation
Bibliography

INTRODUCTION

Treatments of plant tissues with culture filtrates from fungal and bacterial plant pathogens show that some of these organisms produce low molecular weight toxins (pathotoxins) that have deleterious effects on the plants they invade. Knowledge of the roles that these compounds play in establishing disease and controlling its severity is being used to develop entirely new approaches for increasing the disease resistance of crops. In particular, *in vitro* selection with pathotoxins and plant transformation with genes that confer resistance to pathotoxins have been used to produce disease-resistant plants.

TOXINS: DEFINITION AND TYPES

The word toxin in plant pathology means a product of the pathogen, other than an enzyme, that causes damage to plant tissues and is involved in disease development. Two broad categories of pathotoxins exist: host-selective toxins (HSTs) and nonhost-selective toxins. A host-selective toxin causes damage only in those plant varieties that are susceptible to the pathogen, and typically the virulence of the pathogen is related to the amount of toxin it produces. In addition, the level of disease resistance in the plant depends on its ability to resist the effects of the toxin or its ability to degrade the toxin. Nonhost-selective toxins affect a wide variety of plants and other organisms. These compounds are not the primary determinants of pathogenicity, but their presence can increase the severity of the disease.

Approximately twenty HSTs have been identified. With one exception, they consist of low molecular weight secondary metabolites that have diverse chemical structures, including cyclic peptides, terpenoids, oligosaccharides, polyketides, and other compounds of unknown biochemical origin (Table 1, Fig. 1). All of the HSTs identified so far are produced by filamentous fungi, especially the genera *Alternaria* and *Helminthosporium*. Nonhost-specific toxins are produced by a variety of bacteria and fungi. These compounds include plant hormones (gibberellins, cytokinins, and auxins), fatty acid derivatives, modified amino acids, peptides, polyketides, and terpenoids (Table 1, Fig. 2). In addition to the well-documented cases of toxin production by pathogens, there are many reports in the literature of the possible involvements of toxins in disease states that have been difficult to prove for a variety of reasons (1–4).

TOXIN MODES OF ACTION

Toxins kill plant cells at concentrations ranging from approximately 10 pM to 1 μM. Because many of the toxins are small, diffusible molecules, they can cause symptoms like leaf chlorosis (yellowing) or necrosis (cell death) at a distance from the site of infection. In fact, this pattern of symptom development is often the first indication that a toxin is involved in pathogenesis. The cellular targets and the modes of action are known for some of the toxins. As expected for such a diverse group of compounds, the toxins have quite varied effects on plants (1–6).

Host-Selective Toxins

The specific targets or modes of action of the *Alternaria* HSTs are not known, but the cellular sites of action have been determined for some, and they can be classified into three groups on this basis. ACT-, AF-, and AK-toxins, which are produced by pathotypes that cause black or brown spot diseases on tangerines, strawberries and pears, respectively, share a common epoxy decatrienoic acid structure and exert their effects on the plasma membranes of susceptible cells thereby causing rapid electrolyte loss. The ACR-toxin from a pathotype that causes brown spot in rough lemon induces mitochondrial pathologies like swelling, vesiculation of the cristae, and inhibition of malate oxidation. The AM-toxin, produced by the apple blotch pathotype, causes vesiculation of grana lamellae of chloroplasts, inhibition of CO_2 fixation, and electrolyte loss from cells. In addition, the AAL-toxin produced by *A. alternata f.sp. lycopersici* causes Alternaria stem canker in tomato which induces apoptosis or programmed cell death symptoms in treated cells.

The fungus *Bipolaris* (formerly *Helminthosporium*) *maydis* race T produces a mixture of related toxic linear alkane chains that are 35–45 carbons long and contain several oxy–oxo groups. Corn (*Zea Mays* L.) plants that carry Texas male sterile cytoplasm are one thousandfold more sensitive to T-toxin than corn with normal cytoplasm and produce a unique 13-kDa protein (URF13) which has three membrane-spanning helices. T-toxin binds to the URF13 oligomer and causes rapid permeabilization of the mitochondrial membrane. The extreme sensitivity of the

Table 1. Main Phytopathogenic Toxins in Plant Diseases[a]

Pathogens	Toxins	Host Plants	Action or Target Sites
Host-specific toxins			
Fungi			
Alternaria alternata			
Apple pathotype	AM-toxin	Apple	Chloroplast
Japanese pear pathotype	AK-toxin	Japanese pear	Membrane
Strawberry pathotype	AF-toxin	Strawberry	Membrane
Tangerine pathotype	ACT-toxin	Tobacco	Membrane
Rough lemon pathotype	ACR-toxin	Citrus	Mitochondria
Tomato pathotype	AAL-toxin	Tomato	Cell death
Helminthosporium maydis	T-toxin	Maize	Mitochondria
H. carbonum	HC-toxin	Maize	Histone deacetylase
H. sacchari	HS-toxin	Sugarcane	Membrane
H. victoriae	Victorin	Oat	Photorespiration
Periconia circinata	PC-toxin	Sorghum	Membrane
Phyllostica maydis	PM-toxin	Maize	Mitochondria
Nonhost-specific toxins			
Bacteria			
Pseudomonas syringae pv. *tabaci*	Tabtoxin	Tobacco	Glutamine synthesis
P. syringae pv. *phaseolicola*	Phaseolotoxin	Bean	Arginine synthesis
P. syringae pv. *syringae*	Syringomycin	Peach	Membrane
Rhizobium japonicus	Rhizobitoxine	Soybean	Methionine metabolism
Agrobacterium tumefaciens	Indolacetic acid cis-Zeatin	Dicots	Plant hormone
Fungi			
Alternaria solani	Tentoxin	Potato	Chloroplasts
Fusarium oxysporum	Fusaric acid	Vegetables	Water permeability
Gibberella fujikuroi	Gibberellin	Rice	Plant hormone
Fusicoccum amygdali	Fusicoccin	Peach	H^+-ATPase

Source: [a]Adapted from Ref. 1.

Texas male sterile cytoplasm (cms) corn became an issue in agriculture. By the late 1960s approximately 85% of the corn hybrids grown in the U.S. were produced with this background because its use eliminated the need for hand or mechanical emasculation of the female parents used to produce hybrid seed. Unfortunately, the unique suscepti- bility of the Texas-cms background, the widespread use of this cytoplasm, and weather conditions favorable to corn blight combined in 1970 to produce a disease epidemic that devastated corn production in the southern U.S.

The HC-toxin produced by the fungus *Cochliobolus carbonum* race 1 is a cyclic tetrapeptide that is involved in leaf spot disease of maize. It inhibits the function of maize histone deacetylase. Because histone deacetylation is thought to be involved in expressing inducible genes, like many of those involved in plant disease defense responses, it has been postulated that it facilitates the disease by inhibiting maize defense gene expression but does not affect the housekeeping genes required for normal plant function.

Victorin is a pentpeptide produced by the fungus *Cochliobulus victoriae* that causes Victoria blight in oats that carry the dominant *Vb* gene which was introduced into oat varieties because it conferred resistance to crown rust caused by *Puccinia coronata*. *Victorin* binds to the pyridoxal phosphate-containing subunit of glycine decarboxylase, a nuclear-encoded, mitochondrial matrix enzyme complex involved in photorespiration in a genotype-specific manner.

Nonhost-Selective Toxins

Although the roles that nonhost-selective toxins play in disease are not as well understood as those of host- selective toxins, their impact on agriculture is undoubtedly serious because they have a broad spectrum of effects on many economically important crops. This category includes all of the known bacterial toxins and most of the fungal toxins. Interestingly, some specific nonhost- selective toxins are produced by several genera of bacteria suggesting that the genes for their synthesis are widespread. Information about some nonhost-selective toxins is given here.

Tabtoxin is a monocyclic β-lactam produced by *Pseu- domonas syringae* pv. *tabaci*, *P. syringae* pv. *coronafaciens*, and *P. syringae* pv. *garcae*. The active form of the toxin is tabtoxin-β-lactam (TβL), which is released after hydroly- sis of the peptide bond in the middle of the molecule by peptidases from the bacterium or the host plant. TβL irre- versably inhibits glutamine synthase which leads to toxic concentrations of ammonia in the plant. The production of phaseolotoxin is restricted only to one bacterial species (*P. syringae* pv. *phaseolicola*) that causes halo blight on a range of legumes. Phaseolotoxin is a tripeptide that

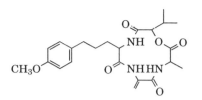

AM-toxin

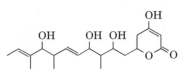

ACR-toxin

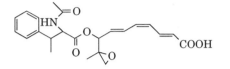

AK-toxin

T-toxin

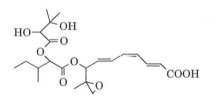

AF-toxin

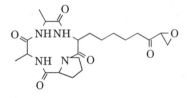

HC-toxin

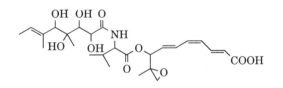

ACT-toxin

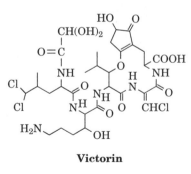

Victorin

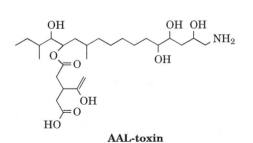

AAL-toxin

Figure 1. Structures of some host-specific toxins produced by plant pathogens.

is modified by peptidases of plant or bacterial origin to octicidin which binds to ornithine carbamyltransferase to inhibit the conversion of ornithine to citrulline, a precursor of arginine. Rhizobitoxine is produced by three genera of bacteria, *Bradyrhizobium, Pseudomonas,* and *Streptomyces*, and its phytotoxicity may be through

the inactivation of β-cystathionase-pyridoxal phosphate. *P. syringae* pv. *syringae* is considered the most widespread plant pathogen in nature because it occurs as an epiphyte on many plants and has little restriction in host range as a pathogen. Syringomycin toxins (like syringomycin) have been isolated from disparate hosts, including fruit

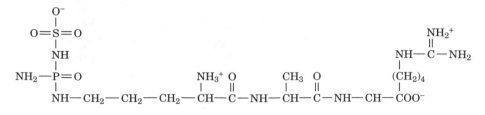

Phaseolotoxin

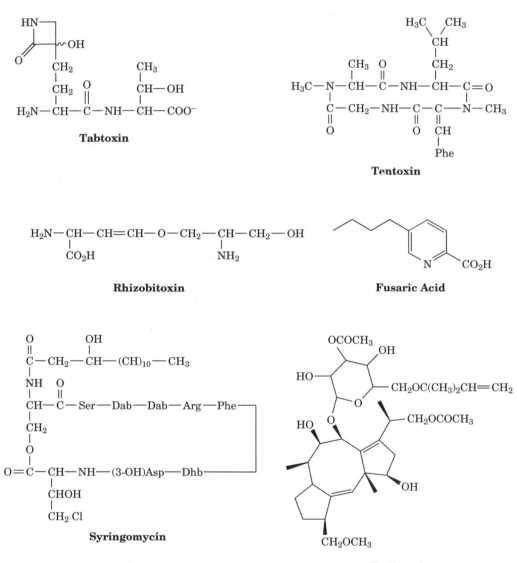

Figure 2. Structures of some nonhost-specific toxins produced by plant pathogens. Arg. Arginine; (3-OH)Asp, 3-hydroxyaspartic acid; (4-Cl)Thr, 4-chlorothreonine; Dab, 2,4-diaminobutyric acid; Dhb, 2,3-dehydro-2-aminobutyric acid; Gly, glycine; Hse, homoserine; Orn, ornithine; Phe, phenylalanine; Ser, serine, Thr, threonine.

trees and grasses. Their lipopeptide structures allow them to insert into membranes, disrupt ion equilibrium across membranes, and activate membrane proteins. Tentoxin is a cyclic tetrapeptide produced by a fungal pathogen of several higher plant seedlings (*Alternaria alternata*), and it inhibits the function of the chloroplast-coupling factor and causes chlorosis. Fusaric acid is produced by *Fusarium oxysporum* which causes wilt diseases in tomato, cotton, pea, banana and other plants. Fusicoccin is the major phytotoxic metabolite of *Fusicoccum amygdali*, the causative agent of peach and almond canker. It activates the plasma membrane H^+-ATPase and consequently influences a variety of metabolic and physiological processes, including stomatal opening and leaf wilt.

APPROACHES TO DEVELOPING TOXIN-RESISTANT PLANTS

In Vitro Selection

A correlation has been demonstrated for many host-selective and some nonhost-selective toxins between resistance to the pathogen at the plant level and insensitivity to the toxin at the cellular level. This phenomenon has led to the use of plant cell cultures and pathotoxin preparations to select disease-resistant plants. The rationale for this approach is that because most plant cells are totipotent (able to regenerate into a complete individual), it should be possible to expose cells in tissue culture to a toxin and regenerate plants from the mutant cells that survive because they have resistance to the toxin (and the disease). The major advantage of such an approach is its efficiency relative to whole plant screening. Whereas a typical breeding program may be able to screen only a few hundred to a few thousand seedlings for disease resistance in a year, several million cells can be screened in a single in vitro experiment lasting only a few weeks (7). The genetic variants that are selected in vitro can be created by a variety of physical or chemical mutagens, or they can arise spontaneously in tissue culture. Mutants from tissue culture are called somaclonal variants. The rate of somaclonal variation can be as high as 15–20% of the regenerants which is 10^6- to 10^7-fold higher than the spontaneous mutation rate in seed progeny at a given locus. In addition, the somaclonal variants that arise from plant cell cultures show a different mutational spectrum than that observed in vivo. Therefore, populations of plants from in vitro selection are a potential source of novel mutations for disease resistance breeding (8). However, both genetic and epigenetic somaclonal variation has been observed. Therefore, determination of the mode of inheritance of the somaclonal variant is important for seed propagated crops.

In vitro selection with a variety of plant species and different pathotoxins has been used to obtain disease-resistant plants (Table 2). The selective agents used for these studies include purified host-selective and nonhost-selective toxins, as well as crude filtrates obtained from pathogen cultures. The types of plant tissue cultures used include callus, suspension culture cells, protoplasts, and microspores (9,10).

For some of the studies, the genetic basis of the resistance in the selected somaclone was confirmed by testing progeny with the pathogen. For example, the host-selective T-toxin from H. maydis was used to select resistant maize callus lines from which plants were regenerated that were resistant to the fungus. The tolerance expressed in the cell cultures was correlated with tolerance of mitochondria isolated from the tissue to T-toxin, and the character was maternally inherited (11).

A few of the disease-resistant somaclonal variants produced have been incorporated into new varieties; for example, a new sugarcane cultivar that is resistant to Fiji disease was developed, a tomato variety (DNAP-17) with resistance to Fusarium wilt race 2 was released, and a celery line (UC-T3 Somaclone) with resistance to F. oxysporum f.sp. apii was released (9).

Plant Transformation

Plant transformation techniques can be used to insert foreign genes into plants. By moving a detoxifying gene or a gene resistant to the toxin from the pathogen into

Table 2. Disease-Resistant Plants Obtained by In Vitro Selection

Crop	Pathogen	Selective Agent	Selection Tissue	Resistance Observed	Inheritance
Alfalfa	Fusarium oxysporum	Culture filtrate	Callus	Increased resistance	Transmitted to progeny
Barley	Fusarium spp.	Fusaric acid	Callus	Increased resistance to fusaric acid	Not tested
Maize	Helminthosporium maydis	T-toxin	Callus	Resistance	Maternally inherited
Oats	Helminthosporium victoriae	Victorin	Callus	Resistance to victorin	Transmitted to progeny
Rape	Phoma lingam	Culture filtrate	Cell; embryo cultures	Increased resistance	Transmitted to progeny
Rice	Helminthosporium oryzae	Crude toxin	Callus	Increased resistance	Transmitted to progeny
Sugarcane	Helminthosporium sacchari	Toxin	Callus	Increased resistance	Transmitted vegetatively
Tobacco	Pseudomonas syringae pv. tabaci. Alternaria alternata	Crude toxin	Callus	Resistance	Transmitted to progeny
Wheat	Pseudomonas syringae pv. syringae	Syringomycin	Callus	Reduced bacterial multiplication	Not tested
Wheat	Helminthosporium sativum	Crude toxin	Callus	Resistance	Transmitted to progeny

plants, researchers have been able to increase their disease resistance.

Because nonhost-selective toxins have such a broad spectrum of toxicity it is common for these pathogens to have detoxification mechanisms. For example, a gene to detoxify tabtoxin was obtained from *Pseudomonas syringae* pv. *tabaci*, which causes wildfire disease on tobacco. To isolate the tabtoxin-detoxifying gene, the genomic DNA of a toxin-producing strain of *P. Syringae* pv. *tabaci* was cut with a restriction enzyme, the fragments were cloned into an *Escherichia coli* vector, and the resulting genomic library was used to transform an *E. coli* strain that was sensitive to tabtoxin. The transformants were cultured on a medium containing tabtoxin, and colonies that grew were found to contain a gene for an acetyltransferase enzyme that detoxified tabtoxin. To produce tabtoxin-resistant plants, the tabtoxin resistance (ttr) gene was fused with a constitutive promoter and cloned into an *Agrobacterium* vector that was used to transform tobacco plants. Transgenic plants expressing the *ttr* gene did not produce the chlorotic halos around sites of inoculation with *Pseudomonas syringae* pv. *tabaci* that are typical of wildfire-diseased plants. The introduction of a *ttr* gene might be a general approach for creating resistance to a variety of tabtoxin-secreting phytopathogenic *Pseudomonads* that affect corn, coffee, beans, and soybeans.

Another mechanism for self-protection in pathogens is for the organism to produce at least one form of the enzyme target for the toxin that is resistant to its effects. For example, a gene (*argK*) that encodes a phaseolotoxin-resistant ornithine carbamoyl transferase (OCTase) was isolated from *P. syringae* pv. *phaseolicola*. The *argK* gene occurs in the chromosomal DNA of *P. syringae* pv. *phaseolicola* adjacent to the tox gene cluster of genes required for phaseolotoxin synthesis. It encodes an OCTase that has several amino acid substitutions at the presumed binding sites for the phaseolotoxin. Two research groups used the resistant *argK* gene to produce phaseolotoxin-resistant plants (12,13). The *argK* gene was fused to a transit peptide sequence of a ribulose biphosphate carboxylase (rbcS) gene that targets its protein product to the chloroplast, which is where plant OCTases are located. Transgenic tobacco plants created by *Agrobacterium*-mediated transformation with the chimeric gene resulted in plants that had two- to ten fold increases in OCTase activity compared to control plants. The transgenics were resistant to the effects of the toxin applied to the leaves and were less susceptible to systemic infection by *P. syringae* pv. *phaseolicola* strain TEXCOCO (an unusual strain of *P. syringae* pv. *phaseolicola* that is pathogenic on tobacco).

BIBLIOGRAPHY

1. K. Yoneyama and H. Anzai, in I. Chet, ed., *Biotechnology in Plant Disease Control*, Wiley-Liss, New York, 1993, pp. 115–137.

2. J.D. Walton, *Plant Cell* **8**, 1723–1733 (1996).

3. H. Otani, K. Kohmoto, and M. Kodama, *Can. J. Bot.* **73** (Suppl. 1), S453–S458 (1995).

4. R.E. Mitchell, *Experientia* **47**, 791–803 (1991).

5. D.C. Gross, *Annu. Rev. Phytopathol* **29**, 247–278 (1991).

6. A. Ballio, *Experientia* **47**, 783–789 (1991).

7. J. Brazolot and K.P. Pauls, in R.A. Dixon and R.A. Gonzales, eds., *Plant Cell Culture: A Practical Approach*, Oxford University Press, Oxford, U.K., 1994, pp. 87–97.

8. D.A. Evans, *Trends Genet.* **5**, 46–50 (1989).

9. R.W. van den Bulk, *Euphytica* **56**, 269–285 (1991).

10. M. Buiatti and D.S. Ingram, *Experientia* **47**, 811–819 (1991).

11. B.C. Gengenbach, C.E. Green, and C.M. Donovan, *Proc. Natl. Acad. Sci. U.S.A.* **74**, 5113–5117 (1977).

12. J.M. de la Feunte-Martinez, G. Mosqueda-Cano, A. Alvarez-Morales, and L. Herrera-Estrella, *Bio/Technology* **10**, 905–909 (1992).

13. E. Hatziloukas and N.J. Panopoulos, *J. Bacteriol.* **174**, 5895–5909 (1992).

See also DISEASE RESISTANCE IN TRANSGENIC PLANTS; GENETIC ENGINEERING: ANIMAL CELL TECHNOLOGY; HERBICIDE-RESISTANT PLANTS, PRODUCTION OF; TRANSFORMATION OF PLANTS.

TRANSCRIPTION, TRANSLATION AND THE CONTROL OF GENE EXPRESSION

ALAKA MULLICK
BERNARD MASSIE
Institut de Recherche en Biotechnologie
Conseil National de Recherches du Canada
Montréal, Québec, Canada

OUTLINE

INTRODUCTION

Gene expression is controlled at three major levels: transcription, message processing and stability, and finally translation. The basic knowledge of all three steps can be exploited in the design of vectors to maximize heterologous gene expression in eukaryotic cells. Contained herein is a description of the numerous elements that have emerged as key in the process of gene expression, reviewed in the perspective of some of the factors to consider when using this information in a practical application.

STRUCTURE OF EUKARYOTIC PROMOTERS AND REGULATION OF TRANSCRIPTION

Transcription Initiation

Genes encoding messenger RNA are transcribed by RNA polymerase II (pol II), itself a multisubunit protein that requires a number of auxiliary proteins to recognize a promoter and initiate transcription. These auxiliary factors comprise the general transcription machinery and, with the polymerase, are able to carry out basal transcription. Such basal transcription has been described only on the basis of in vitro experiments and requires only a TATA box. Whether it occurs in vivo is doubtful since it is not clear whether such minimal promoters exist. Figure 1 is a schematic representation of the promoter region of a RNA polymerase II transcribed gene. Most promoters have a number of promoter-proximal regulatory elements, located within 50–100 bp upstream of the TATA box. In addition, distal enhancer elements, which are characterized by their ability to act at a distance and in either orientation, are found in many promoters. Although sometimes referred to as distal elements, there is a fair degree of flexibility in the location and arrangement of enhancers. They can be tightly clustered as in the simian virus (SV40) early promoter or the *fos* gene, or they can be spread over large distances, as in the globin promoters or the steroid-regulated *tyrosine aminotransferase* gene (1). The identification of these regulatory sequences has led to the isolation and characterization of *trans*-acting factors that either directly bind to them or modulate their activity by interacting with other DNA-binding factors. Such activator-modulated transcription cannot be supported by the general transcription machinery. Required in addition are a plethora of coactivators and TATA-activating factors (TAFs), which function as mediators.

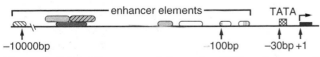

Figure 1. Schematic representation of a RNA polymerase II promoter. The transcription start site is represented by the bent arrow. Enhancer elements can be close to the start site (within the first 100 base pairs) or far from it (more than 10 kb). They can be spread out over large distances or be tightly clustered, even overlapping each other (see text for details).

RNA pol II and Basal Transcription Factors. The elements recognized by pol II and its associated factors are the core promoter elements, DNA sequences that direct where transcription should start and in what direction it should proceed. The best characterized of these elements is the TATA box, an adenine/thymine-rich sequence located 25–30 base pairs upstream of the start site, also known as the cap site (2). The other element, located at the start site, is the pyrimidine-rich initiator element (Inr) (3). These two elements can function independently or synergistically, and a given promoter may contain one or both of them (4–6).

For pol II–catalyzed transcription initiation, polymerase-associated factors (TFIIA, TFIIB, TFIID, TFIIE, TFIIF, and TFIIH), also known as general transcription factors (GTFs), must be part of the protein–DNA complex. Although somewhat of a simplification, transcription initiation can be viewed as a series of events, the first of which is the sequence-specific recognition of the TATA box or Inr by TFIID, followed by the accretion of the other factors by virtue of protein–protein interactions, since none of them bind DNA directly (reviewed in Refs. 7,8).

TFIID is composed of a number of polypeptides, one of which is the TATA-binding protein (TBP) (9). As the name suggests, this protein recognizes the TATA motif, and in fact it is the only protein in the complex that has DNA binding ability. The role of the other polypeptides that make up TFIID (TBP associated factors, or TAFs) is understood mainly in the context of activated transcription. TAFs do not appear to be required for initiation per se, but are required for stimulation of initiation by regulatory proteins. For strictly basal transcription initiation, TBP is capable of avid DNA binding and cooperation with pol II for accurate transcription initiation (10).

Genes encoding TBP have been cloned from organisms ranging from archaebacteria to humans. Sequence comparison indicates considerable conservation of structure, especially in the C-terminal portion of the protein. The three-dimensional structures of yeast and *Arabidopsis* TBP bound to the TATA box were determined by the groups of Burley and Sigler (11,12). They found that TBP assumes the conformation of a saddle on horseback when it is bound to the TATA box and that it bends the DNA in the process. The convex upper surface of the saddle is implicated in the interactions with other transcription factors such as TFIIA, TFIIB, the C-terminus of the large subunit of pol II, negative cofactors NC1 and NC2, and possibly TFII I (which recognizes the Inr element) in the case of certain TATA-less promoters. It is the highly conserved C-terminal domain that is involved in these interactions. Not much is known of the function of the less conserved N-terminal portion of the protein.

The TBP component of the TFIID–DNA complex is recognized by TFIIB, which is composed of a single polypeptide (13,14). TFIIB also interacts with TFIIF and pol II, and this interaction is instrumental in their recruitment to the complex. The TBP–pol II interaction seems to be critical in determining the transcription start site. This idea is supported by genetic experiments in yeast, wherein mutations in either gene (SUA7, the yeast homologue of TFIIB, or in the largest subunit of the yeast polymerase) affects the start site of several genes (15,16).

The assembly of the polymerase and the auxiliary transcription factors at the core promoter elements constitutes the formation of the preinitiation complex (PIC). This is followed by strand separation at the start site in the presence of nucleoside triphosphates, and finally by chain elongation. However, the polymerase is known to pause after the first few nucleotides. To render the polymerase processive, or competent for elongation, it is necessary that it undergoes a conformational change that is affected by hyperphosphorylation of its carboxy-terminal domain (CTD). The CTD is composed of a series of tandem repeats of the heptapeptide sequence YSPTSPS (17). The isoform of the enzyme that interacts with the GTFs and participates in the PIC is unphoshorylated (RNAP IIA) (18–20). Phosphorylation of the serine, threonine, and/or tyrosine residues of the CTD generates a hyperphosphorylated form of the enzyme (RNAP IIO) that is competent for chain elongation and escape of the polymerase from the promoter region (21–23). CTD is phosphorylated by a kinase activity (cyclin-dependent kinase MO15/cdk7) that is thought to be part of TFIIH (24,25). This kinase activity is in turn regulated by TFIIE (26–28). Thus initiation can take place without TFIIH and TFIIE, but it is not processive.

TATA-Less Promoters. The promoter regions of pol II transcribed genes can be classified as TATA+Inr+, TATA+Inr−, TATA−Inr−, and TATA−Inr+. In the last two cases the Inr element directs complex assembly since some Inr− promoters, as defined by the consensus sequence, can still recongnize Inr-binding proteins. Inr-binding proteins TFII-I (29,30) and YY1 (31) have been isolated, and these may drive PIC assembly in such TATA-less promoters. Both of these proteins interact with TBP, ensuring the recruitment of TFIID to the promoter region. There is also some evidence that certain TAFs may be able to interact with the Inr sequence (32), resulting in the recruitment of TFIID. Another model for initiation in the absence of a typical TATA box attributes an intrinsic ability of the polymerase to interact with the Inr motif (4,33).

Activator-Dependent Transcription

Higher eukaryotes have evolved a sophisticated circuitry to coordinate the expression of over 50,000 genes following precise spatio-temporal patterns. This complex process is controlled through the interaction of a limited repertoire of transcriptional activators that cooperate synergistically with the PIC to modulate the magnitude of gene expression. In turn, their expression and activity are regulated by signaling pathways, allowing for fine tuning of gene expression in response to the cell's environment. Through the years, a number of different classes of transcriptional activators have been identified, and many of them share a similar functional organization. Generally, they are composed of a DNA-binding domain, a transactivation domain, and possibly a dimerization domain. It has been found that most of these domains are modular structures that are interchangeable between

different molecules. In 1985 Brent and Ptashne (34) did a "domain swap" experiment, wherein the DNA binding domain of the LexA repressor was fused to the activation domain of GAL4; the resulting chimeric molecule bound DNA with the specificity of LexA but activated transcription like GAL4. Since then, a number of such chimeric molecules have been shown to be functional. The flexibility of the domain swap is evident from a number of different observations. First, the position of the different domains in the chimera is not restricting. Second, the modules do not even have to be covalently linked to each other as long as they can be brought together by an intermediary protein. Finally, molecules from different species can swap domains, indicating that the mechanism of action of the transcription machinery has been conserved through evolution (35–37).

DNA-Binding Domains. Deletion analysis has revealed that the DNA-binding ability of most of the transcriptional activators is restricted to a relatively small stretch of amino acids, and that this region is capable of DNA binding, but not transcriptional activation on its own. A number of different types of DNA-binding structures have been identified, and with them different types of DNA sequence motifs that they recognize.

Zn-finger DNA-binding domain: A zinc-finger DNA-binding domain was originally identified in 1985 (38,39). It gets its name from the fingerlike structures that result from the loops of amino acids between the two cysteines and two histidines that tetrahedrally coordinate a Zn ion. Such TFIIIA-like Zn fingers are found in a number of sequence-specific DNA binding proteins, all of which may contain a different number of zinc fingers ranging from 1 to 37 per molecule (40,41). For instance, TFIIIA contains nine such cysteine–histidine fingers (42), and Sp1, on the other hand, contains three at its carboxy-terminal end (43). Nuclear hormone receptors also contain zinc-finger DNA-binding domains (44–46). However, in contrast to the TFIIIA-like Zn finger, which has the cysteine–histidine pair, the steroid hormone receptors have Zn fingers where four molecules of cysteine coordinate the Zn ion. A third variation on the theme is found in some yeast activators, including GAL4, wherein two closely spaced Zn atoms share six cysteines. The distribution of zinc fingers within the protein is also highly variable. They may be localized as a single cluster, or groups of fingers may be organized as a hand. They may even be dispersed over the entire length of the protein (47). Furthermore, zinc-finger proteins may bind to their DNA recognition sequences as monomers or dimers. With all the variations, it is not surprising that there is no one consensus DNA-recognition site for all zinc-finger DNA-binding domains. Crystallographic and NMR studies on several zinc-finger protein–DNA complexes (48–51) have revealed that the zinc fingers are structurally quite distinct. For instance, TFIIIA fingers act as independent, conformationally stable structural units, each contributing to DNA binding. The two zinc fingers of the glucocorticoid receptor, on the other hand, bind DNA as one globular unit.

Helix–turn–helix DNA-binding domain: Another group of DNA-binding proteins includes the majority of prokaryotic regulatory proteins and the eukaryotic homeodomain. These proteins contain a helix–turn–helix (HTH) motif in their DNA-binding domain (52). In its simplest form the HTH motif consists of two helices separated by a turn, wherein the two helices cross each other at an angle approaching 120°. The second helix is known as the recognition helix, since it is the one embedded in the DNA major groove and makes several base-specific DNA contacts. The eukaryotic homeodomain shares the same basic structure except that at the level of the amino acid sequence there is not as much shared between the prokaryotic HTH motif and the eukaryotic homeodomain.

The homeodomain (HD) is encoded by a 180-bp sequence called the homeobox, after the homeotic genes of *Drosophila* where they were first described. The fly homeotic genes and their homologues in other species, collectively called *Hox* genes, encode transcriptional regulators that direct embryonic development along the anteroposterior axis (53–55). In addition to the *Hox* family, many other homeobox-containing genes have been identified. A striking number are likewise found to play key developmental roles. In yeast, homeoproteins are required to establish mating type. Overall, the evidence strongly suggests that homeoproteins are involved in both positive and negative transcriptional regulation of downstream target genes.

The structure of the HD has been examined in a number of studies employing both NMR and crystallography (54,56). The 60-amino-acid HD is a relatively simple DNA-binding domain. It is composed of three alpha helices and an N-terminal extension or "arm." The second and third helices form a helix–turn–helix motif, with the third helix making base-specific contact with the major groove of DNA. This is highly reminiscent of the DNA-binding helix–turn–helix motifs of a number of prokaryotic transcriptional regulators, and thus represents an ancient mechanism for protein–DNA interaction (54). The helix–turn–helix motif is also represented in other DNA-binding structures besides the HD. The POU domain of the POU family of transcription factors was defined by a region of homology shared by Pit-1, Oct-1, Oct-2 and Unc-86. It is comprised of two DNA-binding domains, an HD and a so called POU-specific domain. Although not an HD, the POU-specific domain contains a helix–turn–helix motif that contacts DNA in a manner very similar to bacterial repressors (57).

The first and second helices of the HD are arranged in antiparallel fashion and pack against the third helix through hydrophobic interactions involving conserved residues. In addition to base-specific contacts to the major groove, provided by the third helix, DNA-binding places the flexible N-terminal arm in the DNA minor groove, where it also participates in base recognition and interactions with the phosphate backbone. Additional contacts to the phosphate backbone by the loop separating helices one and two, and by the second and third helices, serve to stabilize DNA binding further (54, and references therein).

Despite major and minor groove contacts to DNA, the specificity of HD–DNA interaction is only moderately high (58). Increased specificity is achieved through cooperative interactions with another type of homeoprotein,

PBX in vertebrates, or extradenticle (EXD) in flies (59). The PBX HD is a variation on a theme, having three extra amino acids in the loop between helices one and two. PBX has extremely poor DNA-binding ability as a monomer. However, in conjunction with a HOX partner, the stability of the bound complex is greatly enhanced. Moreover, the extended site recognized by the PBX/HOX cooperative complex, 5'-TGATTGATGG-3' (and variations thereof), provides an increased measure of specificity. As seen for other HD-containing complexes, interaction with the protein partner can alter the site on DNA optimally recognized by the HD.

For other HD-containing proteins, a DNA-binding partner is provided within the same polypeptide. The POU and paired families of transcriptional regulators have a non-HD DNA-binding domain in addition to the HD. For at least some POU family members, concerted DNA binding by the two domains is cooperative (60). The fly I-POU homeoprotein lacks two amino acids normally found in the N-terminal arm and, as a consequence, is defective for DNA binding. Nonetheless, I-POU exerts a regulatory influence by physically interacting with the Cf1-a transcription factor to prevent Cf1-a–mediated activation of gene expression. Alternative splicing of the I-POU transcript yields a related product, twin of I-POU, in which these two amino acids are restored. The twin of I-POU is now competent for DNA binding, but is unable to bind and inactivate Cf1-a (61,62).

The post-translational control of HD function has been studied in some laboratories. DNA binding by Pit1, a POU protein implicated in pituitary-specific gene regulation, is modulated through phosphorylation of a threonine residue in the HD N-terminal arm (63). At another level, nuclear localization of *Drosophila* EXD is effected through interaction with homothorax (64). Moreover, while homeoproteins are typically considered to be transcriptional regulators, at least one of them, the product of the *Drosophila bicoid* gene, can also regulate translation through site-specific binding to RNA (65).

Although most HTH proteins need dimerization to bind DNA efficiently, a variation of this motif that allows high-affinity DNA binding of monomeric factors is the winged helix (66). In this case the DNA contacts made by one of the three α helices are stabilized by adjacent loop structures that also interact with DNA, hence the name winged helix (67). Such a DNA-binding domain was described by X-ray analysis for the liver-specific HNF-3γ, a member of the forkhead family of developmental regulatory proteins in *Drosophila*. Other members of the family include HNF-3α, HNF-3β, sloppy paired 1 and 2, interleukin binding factor, and human T-cell leukemia virus enhancer factor. Most of these factors are key players in tissue differentiation and organ development and thus show characteristic tissue- and developmental-stage-specific expression patterns.

Helix–loop–helix DNA-binding domains: Yet another group of sequence-specific DNA-binding proteins contain the helix–loop–helix (HLH) structure, which is composed of two short α-helices joined by a loop of nonhelical amino acids. Mutagenesis studies support the idea that these helices are required for dimerization. The HLH region is almost always preceded by a basic region of about fifteen residues (68). It is in fact the basic region that interacts with DNA, and only on binding DNA does it assume an α-helical structure (reviewed in Ref. 69). Examples of HLH proteins that lack the basic region have revealed a transcriptional control mechanism based on dimerization. Thus, for example, Id is an HLH protein that is competent to dimerize, but has no basic region and thus cannot interact with DNA. MyoD, a DNA-binding protein of the HLH type, is negatively regulated by Id, since MyoD-Id heterodimers are inactive (70). Similarly, the *D. melanogaster* gene *extramacrochaetae* (*emc*) is an HLH protein lacking DNA-binding properties and is thus able to inhibit the action of factors such as the genes products of the *achaete–scute* complex and *daughterless* that promote the development of cells that participate in the formation of sensory organs (71,72). What is also remarkable is that the dosage of the genes determines the final phenotype of the sensory organs (73).

bZIP DNA-binding domain: Also known as the leucine zipper coiled coil, this DNA-binding domain is easily recognized by the presence of leucine residues positioned at regular intervals (74,75). The leucine-rich segments of two proteins dimerize by forming an α-helical coiled coil reminiscent of the doing up of a zipper. The leucine residues appear to contribute both to dimerization and to DNA binding. A stretch of about 30 amino acids N-terminal to the leucine-rich region is comprised of a high proportion of basic residues, and this basic region is important only for DNA binding. When bound, this stretch of amino acids assumes an α-helical conformation. The bZIP type of DNA-binding domain was first reported for C/EBP, an enhancer binding protein. Since then, this motif has been recognized in a number of other transcriptional activators such as Jun, Fos, GCN4, and CREB. Jun and Fos belong to two different families of Jun-related (Jun, Jun-B, Jun-D) and Fos-related (Fos, Fra-1, Fra-2, Fos-B) factors, respectively. The specificity of interaction between different family members is provided by the leucine zipper sequence (76,77). The Jun family members can form homo- and heterodimers within the family, and heterodimers with the Fos family members. However, the leucine zippers of two Fos family members do not form stable dimers. It is only on heterodimer formation, in this case with Jun, that dimerization is stabilized (77–79).

HMG-box factors: The high-mobility group (HMG) proteins are DNA-binding chromatin components with a conserved DNA-binding structure. HMGs play roles in chromatin modeling and can contribute to enhancer activity by modulation of spatial relationships in the enhanceosome (80). A number of transcription factors have been shown to bear DNA-binding domains of the HMG type. An interesting example is lymphocyte enhancer factor 1 (LEF1), which modulates the activity of the enhancer for the T-cell receptor (TCR) gene (80,81). At least under some conditions, LEF1 has little intrinsic ability to activate transcription. However, it is nonetheless able to influence the activity of other factors bound to flanking sites. As has been noted for HMGs, LEF1 deforms DNA, introducing a sharp bend as a consequence of binding. This serves to appose transcription factors bound on either side of LEF1 in the TCR enhancer. This physical juxtaposition results in cooperative interactions and transcriptional activation.

Other studies have revealed that LEF1 and related proteins of the TCF family can activate transcription in a more direct manner, but still require the intervention of a partner, β-catenin (82). β-catenin was first described as a cytoplasmic component of the adherins junction involved in cell adhesion by cadherins. However, a free pool of β-catenin is available for an entirely different function. These proteins can physically associate with LEF1/TCF and end up in the nucleus at LEF1/TCF binding sites. Because β-catenin harbors a transcriptional activation domain, physical association with LEF1/TCF leads to increased transcription. The half-life of β-catenin is very short due to phosphorylation at sites in the N-terminus. However, upon activation of the cell surface receptor frizzled, which binds members of the Wnt family of extracellular ligands (83), phosphorylation is diminished. This leads to an increase in the levels of β-catenin, association with LEF1/TCF, and transcriptional activation. This mechanism appears to be conserved throughout the animal kingdom.

The REL family: REL is the transduced oncogene of the avian reticulendotheliosis virus. This large family named after it is typified by the vertebrate NFkappa-B transcription factor, which plays a pivotal role in the response to interleukin-1 (IL-1) and tumor necrosis factor (TNF) (84). Control by these pathways is at the level of nuclear translocation. In the absence of IL-1 or TNF signaling, NFkappa-B is retained in the cytoplasm by physical association with another protein, Ikappa-B. Upon signaling, however, Ikappa-B is phosphorylated, leading to its rapid destruction and the freeing of NFkappa-B to enter the nucleus and program gene expression. In *Drosophila*, the activity of the NFkappa-B homologue DORSAL is likewise controlled through subcellular localization. Maternally deposited components establish a dorsal–ventral gradient of nuclearly localized DORSAL protein that serves to establish different developmental compartments along this axis. The NFAT (nuclear factor of activated T cells) family is related to REL and is important as the target of cyclosporin and FK506 immunosuppressants (85).

The MADS family: This group derives its name from the four founding homologues, Mcm1, agamous (AG), deficiens (DEFA), and serum response factor (SRF) (86). A shared block of homology within the DNA-binding domain defines the so-called MADS box. The N-terminal portion of the MADS box contributes to site-specific DNA-binding, while the C-terminus provides a dimerization interface. MADS members have been shown to undergo important interactions with homeoprotein transcription factors: Mcm1 with Matα2 and SRF with Phox1. SRF plays a key role in the immediate early response to mitogens and growth factors. The signaling cascade results in the binding of SRF to one or more serum response elements (SREs) in a variety of genes including the c-*fos* protooncogene.

Additional transcription factors: In a number of instances, a class of transcriptional regulators is as yet represented by a single member. This includes Brachyury, important in the production of mesoderm during vertebrate gastrulation. As the human genome project progresses, there is no doubt that many more transcription factors will be discovered with new specificities and regulatory activities.

Activation Domains. Different classes of transcriptional activators can be identified on the basis of their primary sequence. The following classification is based on similarities in amino acid composition in the activation domains. It is also possible to classify transcriptional activators functionally on the basis of basal transcription factors or cofactors that they may interact with. For instance, two activators from the same group may interact with different TAFs, and we may have functionally different activators from the same group. Genetic evidence of differences in the mechanism of action of different acidic activators came from studies where deletion of ADA2 drastically affected the activation function of GCN4 and VP16, while having no effect on acidic activators HAP1 and HAP2 (87). Similarly, members of different activator families may act with the same coactivator, as is the case for PC4, a coactivator that can potentiate the activity of acidic, glutamine-rich, and proline-rich activators (88). Another functional classification of activation domains is based on their ability to transactivate from proximal or distal binding sites. Comparing the ability of different transactivation domains to function from proximal and more distal sites, Seipel et al. (89) found that the VP16 activation domain fused to a heterologous DNA-binding domain could function from both proximal and remote binding sites, whereas the glutamine-rich Sp1 activation domain functions only when the binding site is close to the TATA box. Interesting in this context is a study by Hagmann et al. (90). They show that, although the VP16 activation domain can act from a distance when linked to a heterologous DNA-binding domain, the intact VP16 molecule functions only when bound in a promoter-proximal position.

Acidic activation domain: The activation domain of a number of well-characterized transcriptional activators such as GAL4, VP16, steroid hormone receptors, etc. is characterized not so much by a specific sequence, but by the preponderance of negatively charged amino acids (91–94). Deletion of a 30-amino-acid region of GAL4 that has six acidic residues reduces its activity dramatically (95). GCN4 is another example of an activator with a preponderance of acidic amino acids in the activation domain whose deletion affects activity (96). In fact, when random bits of *E. coli* DNA were fused to the GAL4 DNA-binding domain, a number of sequences could act as activation domains (97). The only common feature of these fragments was the net negative charge. Although it is true that a comparison of the amino acid sequences of the different acidic activation domains does not reveal a shared sequence (only the presence of negative charges), mutagenesis analysis has revealed that the amino acid sequence may in fact be important (98). For instance, two mutants that had the same net negative charge, although with different sequences, differed in their ability to activate transcription. Similarly, mutations in

amino acids other than those contributing to the negative charge, in particular the hydrophobic amino acids, also affected the activity of the transactivating domain. In fact, Leuther et al. (99) have mutagenized a 21-amino-acid stretch within the acidic activation domain of GAL4, eliminating all negatively charged residues, but still have a transcriptionally active molecule. Thus, although the net negative charge plays a key role, it alone is not responsible for the entire effect.

Pro-rich activation domain: A stretch of prolines characterizes the activation domain of CTF1. As in the acidic activation domains, there seems to be no sequence conservation among different polyproline activation domains except for the preponderance of prolines (100). Proline is a helix-disrupter, and introduction of proline into a sequence results in the formation of kinks and turns in the structure. A proline-rich domain can then be expected to contain several such kinks and turns, possibly creating a structure that allows important residues to be positioned appropriately. Such positioning may be required for them to make functional contacts with the transcriptional machinery (101). Although the prolines play a key role in transcriptional activation, residues other than the prolines cannot be ignored. As in the case of the acidic activation domain, stretches of hydrophobic residues seem to be important (100).

Glutamine-rich activation domain: Homopolymeric glutamine repeats characterize another family of transcriptional activators. These were first identified in the *Drosophila* factor ANTP (102). Since then, other *Drosophila* factors such as NOTCH, BITHORAX, and ENGRAILED have been shown to contain similar repeats, which are now referred to as opa repeats (103). Apart from glutamine stretches, CUT and the *Drosophila* ZESTE have a preponderance of alanine residues in their activation domain (104,105). Sp1, another member of this family, has been the subject of numerous studies that have shed some light on the mechanism of action of such an activation domain. Deletion analysis allowed the identification of four regions that could act as activation domains (106). Two of these were rich in glutamine residues, and functional studies attributed all the activation potential to them.

Regulation of Transcriptional Activators

Most activator function can be modulated in the cell. The degree of modulation can vary from something quite subtle to a complete activation/inactivation. Several mechanisms of activation are called into play for different activators. Many enhancer factors are regulated by phosphorylation by specific kinases. Phosphorylation controls the subcellular localization and hence the activity of NF-κB, as well as members of the signal transducer and activator of transcription (STAT) family of enhancer factors, the DNA-binding affinity of c-jun, and the activity of the transactivating domain of the cyclic AMP–responsive element binding protein (CREB) (107). Ligand binding triggers the activation of steroid hormone receptors. In the absence of ligand binding, these receptors are sequestered in complexes with members of the family of heat shock proteins (108–110). On hormone binding the receptor undergoes a conformational change and dissociates from the heat shock proteins. It is then able to dimerize, translocate to the nucleus, and bind DNA. Other nuclear receptors are capable of DNA binding in the absence of hormone, but are transcriptionally inactive because of their interaction with repressors of transcription. Hormone binding is required to relieve this repression (111). The heat shock response is another example of inducible gene expression. The transcriptional activator in this case is the HSF. In fact, this factor is involved in most cases of stress response, including exposure to heavy metals, amino acid analogues, and oxidative stress. Under normal conditions, the HSF is present both in the cytoplasm and in the nucleus in a monomeric form. The monomer is sequestered in a non-DNA-binding form in a complex with hsp70. During heat shock or other stress, there is a large increase in the number of misfolded proteins, which compete with HSF for binding to hsp70. HSF monomers released as a consequence are thus free to trimerize and bind DNA (112).

In cases where an added stimulus is required to activate the molecule and thus induce transcription, there is an added level of control as compared to constitutively active molecules such as Sp1, GAL4, VP16, etc.

Mechanisms of Transcriptional Activation

The complexity of the pol II initiation pathway provides numerous points that can be targeted by activators of transcription, and this is shown schematically in Figure 2. Activators may act by directly facilitating PIC assembly or by overcoming forces that may repress the process. Recently it has become clear that nucleosome assembly blocks the access of the basal factors to DNA. The presence of some activators causes conformational changes in the nucleosomal structure that facilitates transcription factor entry and hence PIC assembly.

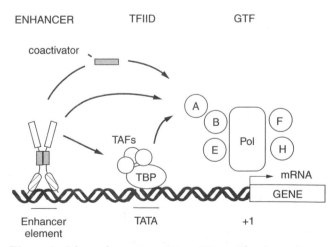

Figure 2. Schematic representation of the mechanisms of transcriptional activation. Transcriptional activators are composed of a DNA-binding domain, an activation domain and possibly a dimerization domain. They can mediate their effect via coactivators, TAFs, or direct interaction with the GTFs (see text for details).

The role of the chromatin structure in gene expression has been the subject of discussion for many years, and the level of histone acetylation has emerged as an important factor. Some regulators of transcription have been shown to mediate their effect by altering levels of histone acetylation. The retinoic acid receptor is a member of a family of sequence-specific DNA-binding proteins that mediate the effect of the retinoid hormones. In the absence of hormone, these receptors interact with factors (SMRT and N-Cor) that have a deacetylase activity (113,114). When recruited to the promoter, these factors will deactylate and hence render the chromatin conformation nonconducive to transcription initiation. On hormone binding, not only is the interaction of the receptor molecules with the deacetylases reduced, they now interact with coactivators that can increase the acetylation level and hence favor the recruitment of the transcription machinery (115). Thus the emerging view for the mechanism of transcriptional regulation by such activators would be by recruiting factors, both negative and positive, to the vicinity of the promoter. These would in turn alter the state of the chromatin to repress or facilitate transcription factor assembly (reviewed in Ref. 116).

Apart from negatively and positively acting cofactors that modify the chromatin accessibility of GTFs, there are others that interact directly with the GTFs. Negative cofactors such as DR1/NC2 (117) and NC1 (118) repress basal transcription. In the case of DR1, the basis of the repressor function is its ability to interact with TBP and inhibit the subsequent recruitment of TFIIB. Dr1 is thus a general repressor of transcription, in contrast to repressors that have specific targets based on their DNA-binding specificity [Kruppel (Kr), or, evenskipped (eve)] ability to interact with a specific transcription factor (IkB). Dr1 does, however, share some sequence homology in glutamine- and alanine-rich regions with these latter repressors. By deletion analysis, the alanine-rich region has been shown to mediate repression by Dr1 (119). This repression is overcome by transcriptional activators, such that the fold activation is higher than if the activation was over a nonrepressed state. Mediating the action of the activators are the positive cofactors. In contrast to TAFs that are also required for activator-mediated transcription, coactivators are not part of the TFIID complex. One of the better-characterized positive cofactors is PC4 (88). Its cDNA was cloned recently, and comparison of its amino acid sequence with known transcriptional activators revealed shared motifs between PC4 and herpes virus immediate early IE62 and ICP4 of herpes simplex type 1 virus (88,120). PC4 does not affect basal transcription but enhances the response to glutamine-rich, acidic, and proline-rich activators.

There are some activators that make direct contact with the components of the PIC, thereby facilitating their recruitment. The herpes simplex virus transcriptional activator VP16 does not bind DNA itself but carries a strong activation domain and thus potentiates transcription via interaction with DNA-binding proteins. The VP16 activation domain, rich in negatively charged amino acids, is of the acidic type. It is able to interact with TFIIB, one of the basal transcription factors that is instrumental in recruiting pol II to the PIC (121,122). Binding of VP16 to TFIIB is thought to alter TFIIB conformation, such that it is more conducive to pol II recruitment. The N- and C-terminal domains of TFIIB are folded together by intramolecular interactions. Binding of VP16 destroys this interaction, exposing binding sites for TFIIF, pol II and TBP, thus driving PIC assembly (123). Another GTF that is a direct target of several activators (Sp1, VP16, NTF1, and Zta) is TFIIA (124).

Activators such as VP16 affect not only PIC assembly but can also affect pol II processivity. As has been mentioned, TFIIE/TFIIH basal transcription factors control the phosphorylation state of the CTD. That in turn determines whether the pol II is capable of participating in PIC assembly or in chain elongation. Initiation of transcription can take place with complexes lacking TFIIE/TFIIH, but such initiation results in an increased rate of abortive RNA synthesis (125). By recruiting TFIIE/TFIIH to the initiation complex, activators ensure that the pol II is competent for complete elongation. Direct contact between TFIIH and activators such as VP16 has been demonstrated (126).

Another component of the basic transcriptional apparatus that is targeted by transcriptional activators is TFIID. TFIID is a multiprotein complex containing TBP and at least 12 TAF's. A number of TAF molecules have been cloned from yeast, Drosophila, and humans. The majority of these display a striking evolutionary conservation. Primary sequence analysis of the TAFs revealed the presence of a number of well-known sequence motifs such as Sp1-like glutamine-rich domains (hTAF135, dTAF110), WD40 repeats (hTAF95, dTAF80), and HMG domains (hTAF250, dTAF250) (reviewed in Ref. 9). Transcriptional activators recruit TFIID by interaction with TAFs. It is reasonable to think of TAFs as molecules that receive and integrate signals from a number of activators and coactivators and then convey this information to the rest of the GTFs in the PIC. This idea is based both on biochemical evidence demonstrating direct interactions of certain activators with TAFs and also on studies of the effect of disrupting these interactions on the ability of the activator to function. Another experimental approach that supports this idea is that of partial reconstitution of TFIID. The effect of the presence/absence of a certain TAF can be correlated with the ability of a particular activator to function (127). Different activators interact with different TAF's. Several activators interact with more than one TAF; for example, the glutamine-rich activation domain of Sp1 with dTAF110 and the DNA-binding domain with hTAF55 (128), the VP16 activation domain with dTAF42 and hTAF31 (129,130), and the isoleucine-rich activation domain of NTF1 with dTAF150 and dTAF62 (127), to name just a few. Biochemical interactions of certain TAFs with pol II have been demonstrated. It also appears that there are TAF–TAF interactions, for example, hTAF55–hTAF20/15 (131), hTAF250–hTAF80 (132), and hTAF250–hTAF30 (133). Thus there is a very intricate circuitry comprising many different kinds of intermolecular interactions. However, a lot of this circuitry has been established on the basis of biochemical experiments only and awaits confirmation by functional tests.

Locus Control Region: Globin Gene Expression

The transcriptional activation mechanisms discussed in the preceding section are operative over a few hundred base pairs at the maximum. There is an interesting example of the control of gene expression that is exerted over several kb. The human β-globin cluster contains five genes whose expression is both tissue and developmental-stage specific and is affected by an extended regulatory element termed the locus control region (LCR) located 6–21 kb 5' of the cluster (for reviews, see Refs. 134–136). The LCR has been proposed to modify chromatin structure over large distances. Each of the five genes has its own promoter and enhancer. Thus gene regulation in this case, involves a complex interaction between transcriptional activators, (both tissue specific and ubiquitous) and multiple promoters, all being influenced by changes in chromatin structure.

In the human globin locus the five genes ε, Gγ, Aγ, δ and β are arranged in a 5' to 3' order that reflects their developmental expression. The ε-globin gene is expressed in erythrocytes of the embryonic yolk sac. When the site of hematopoiesis switches to the fetal liver, the ε gene is silenced and the γ genes become active. Finally, in the late fetal period there is a switch to the δ and β genes, which stay active during adult life. All five genes are expressed only in erythroid cells, and the tissue specificity is controlled to a major extent by tissue-specific factors binding gene proximal elements. The importance of the LCR is evident in a naturally occurring deletion in the LCR region in patients suffering from $\beta\gamma\delta$-thalassemia, wherein the β-globin genes fail to be activated (137,138). Deletion of the LCR in transgenic experiments showed appropriate tissue-specific expression of the β gene, albeit at lower levels (139,140). Thus the LCR appears to facilitate transcription by keeping the chromatin in an open configuration. Also, Felsenfeld (141) reported that the LCR is only active when integrated into the genome and not when transiently transfected into cells, again implicating a role for chromatin remodeling. Furthermore, this effect on chromatin does not take place in the absence of a compatible promoter (142). The LCR can be thought of as being composed of four domains, each a few hundred base pairs in length spread out over about 10 kb of genomic DNA. Each of these domains represents an area of increased sensitivity to DNase1 digestion in erythroid cells, but not in nonerythroid cells. Within these regions of hypersensitivity lie binding sites for transcriptional activators (143). There are sites for ubiquitous factors such as AP-1 and GT-1, and others for erythroid-specific factors such as GATA-1 and NF-E2. In fact, the activity of NF-E2 results from the dimerization of two factors, a ubiquitously occurring 18K factor and an erythroid-specific 45K factor (144–146). Since both factors are required for activity it is functionally erythroid specific. Binding sites for these factors are also present in the gene proximal enhancer regions and can direct tissue-specific expression in the absence of the LCR, although for maximal expression the presence of the LCR is essential. Thus the LCR may enhance expression both because it has a high concentration of binding sites for transcription factors and because it can modify chromatin structure.

Another important aspect of globin gene expression concerns developmental regulation. As mentioned earlier, each of these genes is activated and silenced at precise moments during the course of erythroid development. Since each gene is activated by a different set of factors, one level of developmental regulation comes from changes in the subset of factors that are active at any given stage. In support of that idea, transgenic mice produced with constructs containing either the γ or β gene, but lacking the LCR, expressed these genes at the correct developmental stage (139,140). However, from experiments where transgenic mice were made containing either the γ or β gene linked to the LCR, it is clear that changes in the *trans*-acting environment do not totally account for developmental switching. In both cases developmental regulation was lost (147,148). Correct stage-specific expression was restored when both genes were linked to the LCR in the same construct (149). This observation suggests a competition between the two genes for interaction with the LCR. Which gene is favored for this interaction is determined by the set of *trans*-acting factors active at that stage. Thus, although the γ and β genes are present in the genome in a 5' to 3' direction that reflects the order of developmental expression, stage-specific switching is not dependent on this arrangement. Transgenic mice produced with constructs where the gene order was switched (LCR$\beta\gamma$) still exhibit correct developmental regulation (148). Where gene order and proximity to the LCR play a more important role is in the case of two identical genes linked to the LCR (LCR$\gamma\gamma$). Both genes are correctly expressed in the fetal stage; however, the proximal gene, or the gene closer to the LCR, has the higher level of expression (150).

POSTTRANSCRIPTIONAL REGULATION: mRNA STABILITY

In eukaryotic cells the abundance of a particular message can vary many-fold, and this change can take place very rapidly without a concomitant change in transcription levels. Thus changes in message stability offer another important form of regulation of gene expression (for a review, see Ref. 151). Relatively small changes in mRNA half-life can have quite dramatic effects on message and protein abundance. Furthermore, the half-life of an mRNA species will determine how fast its levels will change as a result of a change in the rate of transcription. Thus messages that code for regulatory molecules, whose levels must change rapidly in response to an external stimulus, have shorter half-lives than others that code for proteins whose levels stay relatively constant.

mRNA degradation can occur by several different pathways (for a review, see Ref. 152). In many cases, the signal for the onset of degradation can come from deadenylation, and degradation proceeds in a 3' to 5' direction. In other cases, deadenylation can trigger decapping, and degradation occurs in a 5' to 3' direction. Evidence for the latter mechanism comes from studies in yeast where the deletion of XRN1, the major nuclease responsible for 5' to 3' degradation, results in the accumulation of uncapped messages (153). The uncapped intermediate is normally not present, probably because it is so short-lived. Although there is no clear evidence for a direct interaction between the 5' and 3' ends, the number of circular polysomes seen in electron micrographs is suggestive of such an interaction (154). There are also cases of mRNA degradation by endonucleolytic cleavage that is initiated in the absence of deadenylation. Intermediates of such a degradative pathway, in other words capped 5' and adenylated 3' halves of messages, are detected in vivo (155–157).

Another deadenylation-independent pathway involves decapping followed by 5' to 3' exonucleolytic cleavage. Exonucleolytic cleavage of uncapped mRNA is part of a surveillance mechanism operative in the cells to ensure the removal of aberrant messages. How aberrant messages are recognized as such is unclear, but this is an important mechanism that increases fidelity of gene expression. Messages that contain nonsense codons, unspliced introns or 3'UTRs of abnormal length, can be eliminated by this mechanism (158–161). Most of the evidence for such a surveillance mechanism comes from studies in yeast and *C. elegans*. In fact, proteins have been identified in both species whose mutation results in a shutdown of this pathway (162–164). In mammalian cells the situation is a little less clear, and there is some evidence that at least some aberrant messages may be degraded in the nucleus. For example, in the case of the triosephosphate isomerase gene, the steady-state level of a message containing a missense mutation is about fivefold less than that of the wild type, even though no difference is seen in the cytoplasmic decay rates (165–167). In other cases degradation appears to be cytoplasmic (168,169). Thus in mammalian cells there are probably several mechanisms to get rid of aberrant messages.

Over the years, a number of studies have attempted to identify sequences in the message that affect its stability. Several sequences and the *trans*-acting factors that recognize them have been identified, and it is clear that there are two types: sequences that affect many different kinds of messages and others that are message specific. The majority of sequences identified are in the 3' untranslated region (UTR). However, there are examples of such sequences both in the coding region and in the 5' untranslated region of the message. The identification of sequences in the message that mediate the effect of stabilizing or destabilizing extra/intracellular signals have led to the identification of the proteins that bind to them, and in some cases the elucidation of the operative mechanisms.

3'UTR

PolyA. Most mRNAs in a mammalian cell have a polyadenylated (polyA) tail at their 3' end. This stretch of adenine residues appears to be implicated in a number of aspects of RNA metabolism, including nuclear processing of pre-mRNA, transport to the cytoplasm, translation, and message stability. The polyA tail is recognized by the polyA-binding protein, and removal of either the polyA sequence or the binding protein is known to destabilize many messages (170). However, it should be noted that deadenylation in itself is not necessarily a sufficient cue for the onset of 5′ to 3′ decay, since there exist in the cell examples of relatively stable messages essentially without a polyA tail (171–173).

AU-Rich Regions. Several relatively unstable RNAs, for example, those encoding some transcription factors or growth factors belonging to the group of early response genes (ergs), contain AU- or U-rich regions (AUREs) in their 3′UTRs. The first direct evidence that such regions could function as destabilizing sequences came from experiments where a 51-nucleotide fragment containing AUUUA motifs from the 3′UTR of the GM-CSF message was inserted into the 3′UTR of the normally stable β-globin message. The chimaeric message was clearly destabilized (174). Since then, AU-rich sequences have been found in several genes, and analysis of these sequences has revealed several important features of this element (175,176). First, the AUUUA motif is neither necessary nor sufficient to form a functional element. Several examples of destabilizing AUREs have been described (such as one from the 3′UTR of the c-*jun* and *zif* 268 mRNAs) that are functional but have no AUUUA sequence. Both of these AUREs are just U-rich domains. Other mRNAs, such as the c-*fos* mRNA, have, in addition to the AUUUA pentanucleotide, a UUAUUUA(U/A)(U/A) motif that appears to be functional as a destabilizing element. Thus the AURE is a composite element that can be composed of AUUUA motifs, U-rich domains, and/or the UUAUUUA(U/A)(U/A) motif, and it is the combination of the different elements that determines the destabilizing potential of any AURE.

AUREs are recognized by a family of proteins called AU-binding proteins (AUBP). Several of these have been identified and cloned. These include the heterogeneous nuclear ribonucleoprotein (hnRNP) A1 (177,178), hnRNP C (177) and hnRNP A0 (179), glyceraldehyde-3-phosphate dehydrogenase (180), Auf (181), and a 32-kDa protein (182). The ability of these proteins to interact with the AURE has been correlated with the destabilizing function. Since most of the genes that have AUREs in their 3′UTR are sensitive to external stimuli, it is reasonable to suppose that the activity of the proteins mediating the effect would also change in response to extracellular stimuli. There is evidence that some AUBPs are not constitutively active. For instance, the glucocorticoid -mediated destabilization of interferon mRNA is dependent on the presence of the AURE, and glucocorticoids regulate the activity of AUBPs that bind the AURE in the 3′UTR of interferon mRNA (183). It is clear that there is no single model that can describe all AURE-dependent destabilization; however, there are common features. In all cases the process starts with a deadenylation, albeit to different degrees and with different kinetics in different cases. This is followed by the degradation of the message, but it is not clear whether it is endo- or exonucleases that mediate this process or whether they are the same ones in all cases.

Ribonucleotide Reductase mRNA-Binding Protein. Ribonucleotide reductase is composed of two subunits, R1 and R2. The stability of the two messages R1 and R2 is controlled by proteins R1BP and R2BP, respectively. The binding of these two proteins destabilizes the mRNA. The two proteins recognize different sequences in the 3′UTRs of the two messages. R1BP recognizes then 8-nucleotide sequence CAAACUUC, whereas R2BP recognizes UCGUGUGCU. However, the binding activity of both R1BP and R2BP is altered by a protein-kinase-C-dependent mechanism. Agents that activate the protein kinase C pathway decrease the binding affinity of the two proteins for their respective binding sites, and this leads to a stabilization of the message (184–186). The situation for R2 is further complicated by the fact that a second protein recognizes a different region in the 3′UTR of the mRNA (187). This is a 75-kDa protein whose binding stabilizes the message, as opposed to R2BP binding that destabilizes it. Thus the stability of the R2 message at any given moment is the result of a balance between the opposing effects of R2BP and the 75-kDa protein.

Iron Homeostasis. Iron homeostasis is controlled by two proteins, the transferrin receptor, which imports iron into the cell, and ferritin, which is a major intracellular storage protein for iron. An iron-responsive sequence is present in both of these messages, but at different locations and with different effects on the metabolism of these two mRNAs (for reviews, see Refs. 188,189). The 3′UTR of the transferrin receptor mRNA contains five copies of the iron responsive element (IRE). The IRE is recognized by the iron-responsive protein (IRP), whose ability to recognize the IRE is regulated by the level of intracellular iron (190). When iron is abundant, the conformation of the protein is such that it has a low affinity for the IRE. In the absence of IRP binding, the transferrin receptor message is not very stable. In contrast, when intracellular iron is low, the IRP–IRE complex forms and the message is stabilized by 20- to 30-fold. A greater abundance of the receptor message would be expected to translate into higher levels of the protein, which in turn would enhance further iron uptake. The ferritin message, on the other hand, does not need to be present in great quantities when iron levels are low; so it is down-regulated. This down-regulation is mediated by the same element, except this time it is present in the 5′UTR and blocks translation of the ferritin mRNA.

Histone mRNA. Histone mRNA needs to be regulated in a cell-cycle-dependent manner (for reviews, see Refs. 191,192). It is only during the S phase that there is a lot of histone production. At the end of the S phase there is a rapid decrease in the half-life of the message. This destabilization is mediated by the last 30 nucleotides of the message, which, unlike most other messages, does not contain a polyA tail (193). This 30-nucleotide stretch can assume the conformation of a stem–loop structure. There are restrictions on the position of this structure. It has to be at or very close to the 3′ end of the message. Also, its distance from the termination codon cannot be varied. It is recognized by an ∼50-kDa protein, the binding of which renders the message more stable (194,195). Other proteins have also been reported to recognize the stem–loop structure and thus may also be involved in regulating the stability of the histone message (196,197). The situation is further complicated by the observation that histones themselves destabilize their own mRNA, and the effect seems to be mediated by the same terminal 30 bases (198). There is, however, no evidence that histones act by directly interacting with the stem–loop structure. Thus, they possibly act by altering the binding activity of one of the proteins that do recognize this structure.

Coding Region: c-fos Message

The c-fos message presents another example of an mRNA species that undergoes rapid changes in its level. When serum-deprived cells in tissue culture are exposed to serum or growth factors, c-fos is rapidly induced. As was discussed, the rapidity with which an mRNA species can change its levels is related to its half-life, and proteins whose level must fluctuate rapidly usually have very unstable messages. The instability determinant in the c-fos message is located in its coding region. It is contained in a stretch of 320 nucleotides that codes for the basic and leucine zipper regions of the protein (199,200). However, it does not appear to be the peptide that is coded by this stretch that is responsible for the effect, because even a frame-shifted message, where the protein produced is quite different, has the same kinetics of disappearance.

5′UTR

There are several examples in the literature that demonstrate the effect of the 5′UTR sequence on message stability. For instance, certain plasmacytoma cells contain chimaeric messages with a 5′UTR that is derived from the intron of the immunoglobulin gene and a coding region and 3′UTR from exons 2 and 3 of the c-myc gene. This fusion product is more stable than the wild-type c-myc mRNA, and the stability correlates with the length of the immunoglobulin intron sequence that forms the 5′UTR. Although there have been a number of studies to identify specific sequences and elucidate the mechanism of message stabilization/destabilization, it appears that no one rule applies to all messages. However, certain common themes are apparent. For instance, message stability does appear to be linked to translation. A stem–loop structure that interferes with translation can confer higher stability to a message. This is nicely illustrated in a study by Aharon and Schneider (201), wherein a chimaeric message containing the coding region of the hepatitis B virus surface antigen and a 3′UTR with the AURE from the GM-CSF mRNA has a short half-life of 18 min. The introduction of a stem–loop structure, in the 5′UTR, stabilizes it such that now the half-life is 7 hours. If, however, an IRES sequence is introduced downstream of the block, the stabilization effect is lost. In this case, it is clear that it is not the sequence per se, but its effect on translation, that conferred the stability. Consistent with this idea, inhibitors of translation stabilize messages several-fold (201). This is possibly related to the protection that polysome assembly might provide to the mRNA. There are, however, exceptions to the rule. For instance, a chimaeric message containing an IRE in the 5′UTR, the transferrin receptor coding region, and the c-fos AURE is

not stabilized if translation is inhibited (202). An added complication in the case of the c-myc message is that the C-terminal coding sequences have to be present for the message to be stabilized in the presence of translation inhibitors. Thus c-myc mRNA is stabilized four-fold in the presence of cycloheximide only if the C-terminal coding sequence is present (203–205). Another mechanism that may explain message stabilization by translational inhibitors is the depletion of short-lived RNAses as a consequence of inhibiting translation. Any RNA that was normally degraded by one of those RNAses would then be stabilized. For example, Eg2 is an oocyte RNA that is stabilized by cycloheximide, without having been associated with polysomes (206).

MECHANISM OF TRANSLATION INITIATION AND ITS REGULATION

Regulation of gene expression often involves control at the translational level, especially in cases when a very rapid response is required. Since translation is the last step before a protein is produced, if the cell can store inactive mRNA until the moment a particular protein is required, all the time required for transcription, processing, and transport can be saved, and protein production can start relatively rapidly. Most of the control of translation occurs at the initiation step, which is usually the rate-limiting step of translation (reviewed in Ref. 207).

Translation Initiation

For translation to begin, an mRNA molecule has to associate with the ribosome to form the polysome. It does so, not with the intact ribosome, but with the 40S subunit, and this mRNA–40S complex then associates with the larger 60S subunit. Thus, during the first step of translation initiation, the 80S ribosomes reversibly dissociate into 60S and 40S subunits. These subunits are composed of a number of proteins and RNA molecules, some of which have been shown to play crucial roles in the process of initiation. Two such ribosomal factors, eIF-3 and eIF-1A, are thought to shift the equilibrium towards dissociation. The intracellular conditions favor the association of the two subunits to form the 80S ribosome. eIF-3 and eIF-1A keep the subunits dissociated long enough to allow binding of a mRNA molecule. Sequence analysis of eIF-1A has shown that it has a basic N-terminus and an acidic C-terminus (208,209). Such a dipolar structure is consistent with its role as a molecular bridge between different factors.

After subunit dissociation, the following steps take place: (1) binding of Met-tRNAi (tRNA carrying the initiator methionine) to the 40S ribosomal subunit to form the 43S preinitiation complex, (2) the binding of this complex to mRNA to form the 48S intermediate, and (3) the assembly of the initiation complex as a result of association with the 60S subunit. During these steps some of the initiation factors that participated in the process are released so that they can be recycled for another round of initiation (Fig. 3).

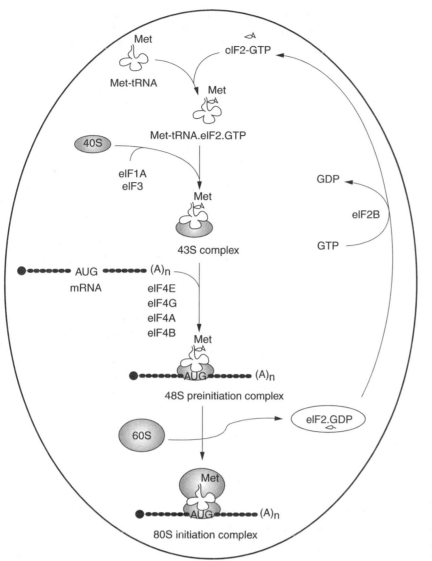

Figure 3. Schematic representation of the process of translation initiation. Binding of met-tRNAi to the 40S ribosomal subunit to form the 43S preinitiation complex; the binding of this complex to mRNA to form the 48S preinitiation intermediate; the assembly of the initiation complex as a result of the association of the 60S ribosomal subunit (see text for details).

Binding of Met-tRNAi to the 40S Ribosomal Subunit. For the binding of Met-tRNAi to the 40S ribosomal subunit, it has to be a part of a ternary complex with eIF-2 and GTP (210). Since all mRNAs need the initiator methionine, regulation at this step is very effective for global control over protein synthesis, and in fact the cell uses this step very efficiently to this end. Central to this control mechanism is eIF-2 phosphorylation. Highly phosphorylated eIF-2 is capable of forming a ternary complex with Met-tRNAi and GTP. However, it is not capable of efficient guanine nucleotide exchange at the end of the cycle, when it must exchange the bound GDP for GTP enabling it to be released and participate in a new cycle. The exchange reaction is normally catalyzed by eIF-2B, but in the situation where eIF-2 is phosphorylated, and hence unable to carry out this exchange, eIF-2B remains bound to the eIF-2–GDP complex, creating a short supply of eIF-2B molecules to catalyze the exchange for even the nonphosphorylated molecules (211,212). Thus not only do the hyperphosphorylated molecules of eIF-2 not get recirculated to complex with other Met-tRNAis, even the nonphosphorylated molecules cannot be recycled for another round of translation initiation because of the lack of free eIF-2B molecules. One level of control of the degree of phosphorylation of eIF-2 is affected by p67, inasmuch as when p67 is bound to eIF-2, the p67–eIF-2 complex resists phosphorylation (213,214). Thus variations in the level of p67 would be expected to affect the level of eIF-2 phosphorylation. In situations where the cell needs severely to reduce protein synthesis, for instance, during heat shock, amino acid starvation, exposure to heavy metals, or viral infection, eIF-2 phosphorylation provides a rapid and effective means of regulation.

mRNA Recruitment. Once the ribosome–Met-tRNAi complex has formed, the 40S subunit is ready to associate with an mRNA species to be translated. The efficiency of this step for a particular mRNA species can determine its rate of translation and thus provides a means of differentially regulating the translation levels of different mRNAs. This association can be via the 5′ end, the middle or the 3′ end of the message. Since it is the first of these possibilities that is most frequently observed and is best studied, we will start by discussing it.

At their 5′ ends all eukaryotic messages have a modification, the cap structure (^{7}mGpppN, 7-methyl guanosine triphosphate), and this is central to ribosomal recruitment. Although uncapped messages can be translated both in vitro and in vivo and thus the requirement for the cap structure does not appear to be absolute, it is clear that the presence of the cap structure greatly stimulates translation initiation. Apart from initiation, the cap has been implicated in RNA splicing, transport, and stability (215). The cap structure is recognized by the cap binding protein eIF-4E. eIF-4E associates with eIF-4G to form a larger complex, eIF-4F. eIF-4G's role is to make contact with the 40S ribosomal subunit, and it does so via the ribosomal factor eIF-3 (216,217). Also eIF-4G binds eIF-4A, an ATP-dependent RNA helicase whose activity is stimulated by eIF-4B (218). Thus the ribosomal subunit is recruited to the 5′ end of the message, and bridging this interaction are eIF-3, eIF-4G, and eIF-4E. All these interactions are also the target of strict control. For instance, cells express a family of proteins called the 4E-binding proteins (4E-BPs), which, as their name indicates, bind eIF-4E and in doing so inhibit its association with eIF-4G (219). This family of inhibitory proteins shares among its members and with eIF-4G an amino acid motif that is responsible for eIF-4E binding, resulting in competition for eIF-4E binding. The degree of binding is controlled by the level of phosphorylation of these factors. Dephosphorylation enhances their association with eIF-4E and consequently inhibits translation; conversely, phosphorylation reduces this interaction and stimulates translation. Growth factors have been shown to induce 4E-BP phosphorylation, and studies involving specific inhibitors for different pathways suggest a pathway involving phosphatidylinositol-3-kinase (PI3K) and the FRAP/RAFT1 family of kinases (220,221).

eIF-4E itself is phosphorylated, and this is another important method of regulating the initiation of translation. eIF-4E phosphorylation increases after a wide variety of growth-stimulatory stimuli that are associated with an increase in translation. The increased level of phosphorylation of eIF-4E enhances its binding to the cap structure and its interaction with eIF-4G (222,223). It is not clear what the physiological kinase is, since there is some evidence for the involvement of PKC (224) and other evidence for the involvement of an insulin-stimulated protamine kinase (225). Altering eIF-4E activity is a strategy employed by a number of viruses to reduce host cell protein synthesis. Adenoviruses (Ad) decrease the amount of phosphorylated eIF-4E in the cells they infect in order to slow down host cell protein synthesis (226). Thus a 10- to 20-fold reduction in the level of eIF-4E phosphorylation is observed, displaying kinetics that correlate with suppression of cellular protein synthesis. The adenoviral mRNAs, however, continue to be translated, since their tripartite leader (tpl) sequence makes them less dependent on phosphorylated eIF-4E. The Ad-tpl is a 200-bp stretch of 5′UTR that is remarkably low in secondary structure. This makes Ad mRNAs less dependent on a functional eIF-4F complex, which can melt secondary structure due to the association of eIF-4A and eIF-4B. The polio virus, on the other hand, targets the same factor but uses a different strategy to reduce the levels of active eIF-4E. It induces its degradation (227).

The Scanning Model: Kozak Consensus Sequence. Association of the 40S subunit is followed by migration in a 5′ to 3′ direction toward the initiator AUG. Any secondary structure that it may encounter en route is undone by the recruitment of additional eIF-4A and eIF-4B. The sequence around the initiator AUG is also thought to play an important role in ribosome recruitment. After analyzing numerous vertebrate mRNA sequences at their initiator methionine and studying the effect of manipulating sequences in the vicinity of the AUG on their relative translational efficiency, Kozak determined a consensus sequence around the initiation codon that favors binding (A/GCCAUGG) (228–230). These studies revealed that mutation of the purine at −3 or the G at +4 to a pyrimidine greatly reduced the chance of the AUG being recognized by the 43S complex. The context of the AUG becomes particularly important when additional AUGs are present in the 5′UTR. If the upstream AUG is in a good context, it can significantly affect translation initiation at the downstream AUG. That is, if the AUG is part of the Kozak consensus, this favors translation initiation. Thus if the are two AUGs on a message and the first one is in a favorable context, the scanning ribosome will use it to initiate translation. This might reduce the frequency with which the second AUG is used.

Structural Features in the mRNA that Influence Its Recruitment. In general, the efficiency of 40S recruitment to the mRNA is greatly influenced by the accessibility of the cap structure to eIF-4F, and thus lack of strong secondary structure, sufficient length, and lack of upstream AUGs or protein-binding sites in the 5′ untranslated leader all make for increased translated messages (231). The inhibitory effect of a highly structured 5′ UTR can be reduced under different physiological conditions, in selective tissues, or during different stages of development. For instance, a number of messages that code for proteins implicated in cell proliferation are encumbered by 5′ UTRs with a high potential to form secondary structure (232). Under conditions of cell proliferation, activation of factors such as eIF-4A and eIF-4B that would melt the secondary structure can be envisioned as a mechanism to augment translation of these messages. Furthermore, altered forms of the messages lacking the inhibitory motifs have been reported to be expressed by certain tumor cells (233,234). A 5′ terminal oligopyrimidine tract (about 5–14 nucleotides long) mediates the growth-dependent translational stimulation of a family of mRNAs encoding several ribosomal proteins, the translation elongation factors 1A and 2, and the polyA binding protein (235,236). This tract is predicted to assume a hairpin structure and results in the underutilization of RNAs that contain it in their 5′ ends. The translation of these messages may be dependent on the cell cycle and is selectively enhanced during growth stimulation (237). The identification of factors that bind this tract will be important in elucidating the mechanism of action. Another example of a message whose translation is selectively inhibited is the c-*myc* mRNA. Its 5'UTR can significantly inhibit translation in unstimulated *Xenopus* oocytes but is ineffective in mature fertilized eggs. There are other examples where the secondary structure is stabilized by protein binding. A widely studied mechanism is the one used by ferritin mRNA (238,239). A high concentration of iron specifically reduces translation of this message. This regulation is mediated by a cap-proximal sequence, the iron-responsive element (IRE). A complex of iron and iron-regulatory proteins (IRP1 and IRP2) can bind this sequence and block the recruitment of the 40S ribosomal subunit to the cap structure (240). Since the inhibition is based on steric hindrance, the position of the IRE with respect to the cap structure is crucial to the regulatory process (241).

Role of PolyA in Initiation. Finally it is important to discuss translation stimulated by the 3' end, in other words the polyA tail. Over the years, it has become clear that the presence of a polyA tail stimulated translation initiation, both from messages with a functional cap structure and from others without a cap structure. In messages with a cap structure, there appeared to be a synergy between cap- and polyA-stimulated initiation and thus to require the participation of eIF-4E. It was only after the identification of the polyA binding protein (Pab1p) that it became possible to gain an insight into the possible mechanism of this stimulation. Using GDP-affinity chromatography, it was discovered that there is a direct interaction between Pab1p and eIF-4G, and that this interaction required RNA. Furthermore, if the Pab1p binding site on eIF-4G was mutated, the polyA tract was no longer able to stimulate cap-dependent initiation (242)

Reinitiation: IRES Elements and 40S Recruitment

The presence of upstream AUGs may or may not present a serious problem for initiation at the authentic AUG depending on the context of the upstream AUGs. If it is present in a weak context, it will simply not be recognized efficiently by the 40S subunit, which will continue scanning the message until it finds the downstream initiation codon. There would thus be initiation at both AUGs and, depending on whether they were in frame or not, two peptides differing in their 5' ends or two different peptides would result. This would not constitute a case of true reinitiation, since it is just an extention of scanning. However, in cases where there is a termination codon between the two AUGs, the first open reading frame will be translated and then some of the 40S subunits will remain bound, continue scanning, and reinitiate at the downstream authentic initiation codon. The efficiency of the process is determined by factors such as the length of the first cistron. Reinitiation is favored when the length of the first cistron is not too great, perhaps because some essential factor remains associated for a relatively brief period. Also, the distance of the second AUG from the first mini cistron influences the probability of reinitiation.

Since the 40S subunit needs to reacquire Met-tRNA−eIF-2−GTP for reinitiation, a relatively large distance between the two cistrons is the preferred scenario.

Most eukaryotic messages use the cap-dependent initiation mechanism discussed. However, there are some examples of initiation within the message. This was first observed in positive-stranded picornaviral mRNAs where it was unclear how the ribosome was recruited to messages with extremely long (600−1500 bp) 5' untranslated regions. These are encumbered with a number of AUGs in a good context that would easily be recognized by a ribosome scanning the message and thus greatly reduce initiation at the true initiation codon. They also have regions of stable secondary structure that also greatly inhibit the scanning mechanism.

Experiments were conducted to explore the possibility that the 5'UTR has specific sequences capable of directing translation initiation involving an alternative initiation mechanism. Translation from dicistronic messages was studied where the sequence between the two coding regions was either the noncoding region (NCR) of polio virus or an unrelated sequence. It was seen that the first cistron was translated equally well in the two cases, but the second cistron was only well translated when preceded by the NCR of the polio virus (243). Analysis of the polio virus NCR sequence allowed the identification of the sequence that supported translation initiation, the internal ribosome entry segment (IRES).

Since their identification, IRES elements have been detected, not only in other viral mRNAs, but also in some eukaryotic messages (244−246). Among the viruses, the picornaviruses, are notable since all of them have been shown to contain IRES elements. Furthermore, on the basis of sequence comparison, they have been classified into three different groups (247). In fact, it is not so much the sequence itself but the resulting secondary structure that is shared among members of a group. The first group contains the type I IRES elements, which can be as far as 50−100 base pairs upstream of the initiator AUG; this group includes IRES elements from enterovirus and rhinovirus messages (e.g., poliovirus). The type II elements contain the initiation codon at their 3' boundary, and it is the cardiovirus and aphtovirus that fall into this category. The third type of IRES elements is that of the hepatitis A virus, and it too contains the initiation codon at its 3' end. Initiation from type II elements is more efficient, presumably because the proximity of the IRES element to the AUG precludes the need for ribosomal scanning of a long NCR sequence before binding at the initiation site. Strangely, the hepatitis A virus IRES is not efficient either in vitro or in vivo. Clearly, there are factors other than the proximity of the IRES to the AUG that determine efficiency (248).

Secondary structure, which is so well conserved among members of a group, appears to be important for the function of the IRES. There is evidence that the stems and loops that form distinct domains of secondary structure may serve as binding sites for RNA or protein factors that may directly or indirectly influence the recruitment of the 40S ribosomal subunit. There are some indications that a pyrimidine-rich tract found approximately 24 nucleotides upstream of the initiation codon plays an important role in the polio virus IRES, possibly because of its complementarity with the 18S rRNA. Much more effort has been focused on the factors that recognize the IRES (reviewed in Ref. 249), and it seems clear that the same set of factors that participate in cap-dependent initiation are also involved in IRES initiation. In recent studies, eIF-4F has been shown to bind directly to the IRES element, and this binding is due to the ability of one of its subunits, eIF-4G, to interact with RNA. eIF-4G also has the ability to interact with the ribosomal factor eIF-3. Thus it can make the bridge between the IRES and the ribosome and affect ribosomal recruitment at the IRES. This proposed mechanism does not involve eIF-4E, which normally makes contact with the RNA via the cap structure (250,251). This is important because this mechanism has been exploited by picornaviruses as an alternative initiation strategy.

Several picornavirus proteases are known to cleave eIF-4G into two fragments, one that contains the binding site for eIF-4E and the other that contains the binding sites for both the IRES and eIF-3 (252,253). The second fragment is thus competent for IRES-dependent initiation, whereas neither fragment is able to support cap-dependent initiation. Since most cellular RNAs rely on the latter mechanism, the virus can be assured of preferential translation of its messages. Furthermore, in the case of the picornaviruses, they can afford to have long 5′NCRs that are also involved in viral replication and yet have efficient translation of the open reading frame.

Regeneration of the 80S Ribosome

The last step involves the binding of the 60S subunit to regenerate the ribosome. Before this can take place, the GTP molecule in the Met-tRNAi−eIF-2−GTP complex is hydrolyzed in a reaction catalyzed by eIF-5. Finally, the initiation factors are released from the complex, leaving the met-tRNA bound to the initiator AUG. At this point the ribosome is ready to start translation of the coding sequence.

RECOMBINANT CISTRONS

In order to attain high-level expression of a protein in a heterologous system, a chimaeric molecule containing all the relevant information for efficient transcription and translation has to be constructed. A typical recombinant cistron for overexpression of proteins in mammalian cells includes a strong promoter/enhancer, splicing signals, an appropriate leader sequence at the 5′ end of the mRNA for efficient translation, and finally strong polyA/termination sequences (254). Any plasmid harboring such a recombinant cistron must contain sequences for its amplification in bacteria (bacterial replication origin and selection) and possibly a marker for selection in mammalian cells (such as the drug resistance genes *Neo, Phleo, Hyg,* etc.). For viral vectors other sequences, such as sequences for packaging, homologous recombination, etc. need to be included [Fig. 4(a)]. If two genes need to be expressed coordinately, they can be included on the same plasmid as two independent transcription units [Fig. 4(b)] or in a dicistronic configuration (with an IRES) [Fig. 4(c)]. As will be evident in the following discussion, there is no ideal vector that can perform in every situation. Different combinations of the various components have to be chosen to get the best results for a particular application. Although the selection of the right promoter/enhancer is paramount to ensure high-level expression, other components of the expression cassette, such as leader sequences, splice sites, and polyA sites, can also contribute to maximize gene expression (255). Furthermore, the assembly of the recombinant cistron must be optimized in the context of the host cell used for expression (255).

Constitutive and Inducible Promoters

The use of a number of constitutive promoters, derived both from cellular and viral genes, has been reported. In general it has been observed that the viral promoters are more powerful than the cellular ones. This stands to reason since the virus must maximize the synthesis of its own proteins. The cytomegalovirus immediate early (CMV-IE) promoter/enhancer is often used in the expression cassette since this promoter is one of the strongest in a wide range of cell types (256,257). Among the constitutive promoters, there are those that direct tissue-specific expression. In the tissue in question, then, this promoter may be very active, but in other tissues where tissue-specific transactivators are lacking, it may be less useful. Thus the strength of a promoter has to be considered in the context of the expressing cell type. A short list of tissue-specific promoters includes the: insulin promoter (β islet cells of the pancreas), elastase promoter (acinar cells of the pancreas), whey acidic promoter (breast), tyrosinase promoter (melanocytes), tyrosine hydroxylase promoter (sympathetic nervous system), neurofilament protein promoter (brain, neurons), glial fibrillary acidic protein promoter (brain, astrocytes), Ren-2 promoter (kidney), collagen promoter (connective tissue), α-actin promoter (muscle), von Willebrand factor promoter (endothelial cells), α-fetoprotein promoter (liver), albumin promoter (liver), surfactant promoter (lung), CEA promoter (gastrointestinal tract, breast, lung), T-cell receptor promoter (T lymphocytes), immunoglobulin heavy chain promoter (B lymphocytes), and muscle creatine kinase promoter (skeletal muscles) (258).

An elegant strategy for tumor-specific expression involves using E2F-1-responsive promoters. The rationale is that, since most tumors have lower amounts of the retinoblastoma gene product, the activity of E2F-1 in tumors is not repressed as much as in normal tissues. Thus an E2F-1-responsive promoter, which has a very low activity in normal cells, was shown to be as strong as the CMV-IE promoter in tumor cells (259).

Variability in promoter strengths is documented in a study by Cheng et al. (260), where the activity of several promoters was compared in different cell types in vivo using a transient transfection assay. Cellular promoters such as the mouse phosphoglycerate kinase (PGK) gene promoter, mouse phosphoenolpyruvate carboxykinase (PEP) gene promoter, mouse metallothionein (mMT) gene

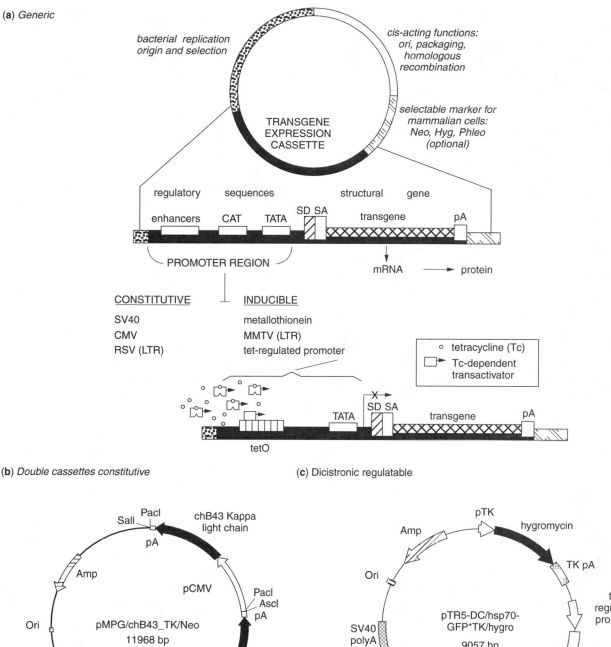

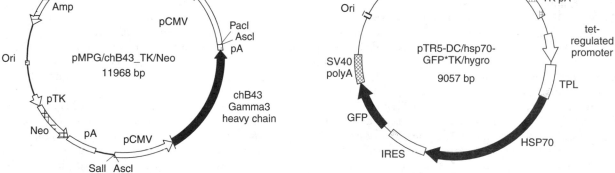

Figure 4. Vectors for expression in mammalian cells. (**a**) Components of a typical expression vector. The expression cassette is composed of the promoter sequences link to the transgene of interest and polyadenylation sequences (pA). There are also splice acceptor (SA) and donor sites (SD) since splicing may enhance the level of expression. An example of an inducible promoter is shown diagramatically: The tetracycline-dependent transactivator binds its cognate DNA- recognition sequence, the Tet operator sequence (tetO) in the absence of tetracycline and stimulates transcription from the base promoter downstream. (**b**) A schematic representation of an expression vector with two independent cassettes of expression, both being driven by the constitutive promoter of the CMV immediate early ganes (pCMV). (**c**) A schematic representation of an expression vector in a dicistronic configuration. Expression of two genes the HSP 70 and the reporter GFP are both controlled by the tetracyline-regulated promoter resulting in dicistronic message. The IRES sequence allows reinitiation at the second cistron.

promoter, bovine β-lactoglobulin (BLG) gene promoter, and bovine prolactin (PL) gene promoter were compared to viral promoters such as the Ad major late promoter (Ad-MLP), the CMV-IE, the Rous sarcoma virus long terminal repeat (RSV-LTR), and the simian virus 40 early promoter/enhancer (SV40-E). In most cases the viral promoters were stronger than the cellular ones. Exceptions were the PGK and PEP gene promoters that were very active in the dermis. Also, the mMT gene promoter was significantly active in epidermal cells. It is important to keep in mind that most promoter fragments tested contained more than just the minimal promoter. They all contained upstream enhancer elements that would augment transcriptional activation.

Of the cellular promoters used, both the mMT and the PEP gene promoters contain enhancer elements that can be induced by the addition of heavy metals or dibutyryl cAMP, respectively. Two injections of $ZnSO_4$ (20 mg/kg body weight) resulted in up to a 42-fold increase of luciferase activity driven by the mMT gene promoter in the livers of treated animals. Similarly, within 4 h of an injection of dibutyryl-cAMP there was a 20- to 30-fold increase in transcription driven by the PEP gene promoter. Thus these are both examples of inducible elements that allow precise control of the level of transcription that could be used in an expression vector.

Other examples of naturally occurring inducible elements are the hormone-responsive promoters. The GR has been widely used to drive heterologous gene expression. Bocquel et al. (261) studied transcriptional activation from a GR-responsive plasmid in two different cell lines, HeLa and CV-1. In this study, the transactivator, GR, was co-transfected with the reporter plasmid, and thus the effect being measured is over and above any endogenous GR that may be present in the cell lines in question. It was seen that the GR's ability to activate transcription from the same promoter construct was different in the two cell lines. In the case of HeLa cells, transcriptional activity increased in parallel with the increase in GR vector transfected. In the case of CV-1 cells, however, there was an increase when an expression vector containing the coding region of the GR was transfected into the cell lines, but only from 0.05 to 1 μg. Further increasing the amount of DNA transfected (up to 7.5 μg) had no effect on the level of transcription. Similar cell-specific variations were seen for other steroid hormone receptors and deletion mutants tested in this study. Variations in the levels of coactivators/corepressors or TAFs that are required for transactivator function likely account for these differences. Thus it is clear yet again that the choice of the promoter elements and the cells in which they are studied are very closely linked.

When using inducers such as glucocorticoids, heavy metals, or di-butyryl cAMP, it is important to keep in mind that they will induce more than just the reporter construct being studied. A number of cellular processes can also be affected. This may not always be desirable. To overcome this problem, prokaryotic and insect regulatory elements have been adapted to construct gene switches that function in mammalian cells. Since the inducer molecules are not expected to have targets in mammalian cells, the possibility of interference with cellular processes is reduced. For example, the tetracycline-regulatable genetic switch (Tet-switch) is one of the most widely used of these systems, as discussed in the following. Another example is the cre/lox-mediated recombination based on E. coli phage P1, which has been developed to activate genes in the tissue of interest. Anton and Graham (262) showed that the cre-recombinase could be used to excise a fragment of DNA between the CMV-IE promoter and the luciferase reporter that was blocking expression and thus induce expression in a regulated fashion.

The Tetracycline-Regulatable Genetic Switch. The bacterial tetracycline resistance operon has been exploited in the design of the Tet-switch (263). The transcription of resistance-mediating genes is negatively regulated by the tetracycline repressor (tetR) such that, in the absence of tetracycline, it binds operator sequences downstream of the start site and blocks transcription. Conversely, in the presence of the antibiotic, tetR cannot bind these sequences, and transcription is allowed to proceed.

The addition of a strong activation domain (activation domain of the herpes simplex virus protein VP16) on the tetR DNA-binding domain creates a hybrid molecule tTA that acts, not as a repressor, but as a transcriptional activator in the absence of antibiotic. tTA is tethered to DNA via the DNA-binding domain of the repressor, and the presence of an activation domain allows the hybrid molecule to function as an activator. Thus, in the presence of antibiotic, tTA will not bind the operator sequences, and there will be no activation of transcription [shown schematically in Fig. 4(a)]. Since in theory the cis-acting element targeted by the tetR DNA-binding site is not found in the mammalian cell genome, there is minimal interference with the expression of other genes. The tTA transactivator can stimulate transcription from a promoter containing the tet operator sequences (tetO) but is prevented from interacting with the tetO by tetracycline concentrations that are not toxic for eukaryotic cells (reviewed in Ref. 264). A modified tTA (rtTA) has also been developed that interacts with the tetO only when certain tetracycline analogs are present (265). The tet-controllable transactivator system has become the most widely used inducible expression system in mammalian cells in culture (263–269), in plants (270), and in transgenic mice (271–274). Schultze et al. (271) have generated a single plasmid Combi-tTA that combines activator expression and the reporter cassette. Another modification renders the system autoregulated (269). The minimal promoter driving the reporter expression was changed to give a lower basal activity and thus an enhanced induction level (275). These and other modifications have rendered the system moderately versatile. However, its efficacy is not the same in all cells. Specific modifications in certain components may be required to make it optimal for a given application.

The Ecdysone-Regulatable Genetic Switch. The Drosophila ecdysone inducible system has also been modified to be used in mammalian cells (276). Ecdysone is an insect molting hormone, and its action is mediated by the ecdysone receptor, which forms a functional complex with the product of the ultraspiracle gene. The strong activation domain of VP16 has replaced that of the ecdysone receptor, resulting in a more sensitive activator, VpEcR. This can heterodimerize with RXR, the mammalian homologue of the ultraspiracles gene product, such that hormone activation results in an ~200-fold activation. Since the natural responsive element of the EcR can be recognized by the farsenoid X receptor, the binding specificity of VpEcR has been modified to that of the glucocorticoid receptor. The modified receptor recognizes a binding site that is a hybrid between the glucocorticoid receptor binding site and the RXR receptor binding site, a site not expected to be found in the genome. The ligand does not have a mammalian receptor, and VpEcR bound to ecdysone cannot recognize DNA-binding sites in the mammalian genome. Thus with these modifications the interference with cellular transcription is expected to be minimal.

An important consideration when using inducible systems in cells in culture is the possible presence of substances in the culture medium that might influence transcriptional activity of the test construct. For instances, tetracycline levels in serum may not be negligible, and thus an artifactually high basal level of activity may be detected when using the tet-switch with the rtTA activator. Similarly, other small molecules that can readily enter the cells such as glucocorticoids, cAMP, metals, etc., if present in the medium, can complicate the interpretation of results. A recent report on the analysis of FBS for the presence of various transcription factors revealed that certain factors such as ATF-2, SRE-ZBP, GATA-2, TFIID, and Ets-1/Ets-2, E2F1, Oct-2, p53, and AP2 were in fact present in the serum (277). Whether or not these factors enter the cell is not clear, but the possibility that they might has serious implications for expression analysis. Internalization by receptor-mediated endocytosis or by a transport mechanism are reasonable possibilities. It is also possible that extracellular factors may affect cellular processes via extracellular receptor binding followed by signal transduction.

Other Components of Expression Vectors

Transcriptional Terminators. The choice of the 3′UTR and transcriptional terminator can also influence expression levels. In a study where plasmid DNA was injected into mouse muscle tissue and transcriptional activity was assessed with a reporter gene assay, three different sequences were linked to the coding region of the reporter gene: the 3′UTR sequences from SV40, which are 800 bases and include a small t intron; 117 bases of 3′UTR from BGH; and a minimal transcriptional terminator derived from the β-globin gene, which contains the polyA and termination signals, but no additional 3′UTR sequences (278). The β-globin termination sequence was found to give the highest results. It happens to be the one with the shortest 3′ sequence. Deleting any extra sequences from the gene under study might help if they contained message-destabilizing regions. However, that is not always the case. For example, a comparison of the BGH terminator comprising the entire 3′UTR or a deleted version with just the minimal requirements showed no

difference. The relative inefficacy of the SV40 element is possibly explained by the presence of a small intron that gives rise to aberrant splicing.

Intron Sequences. Addition of intron sequences in expression plasmids has been reported to increase expression, both in cells in culture and in transgenic animals. The effect can vary from being absent to 400-fold depending on the gene being studied (255,279). On the one hand, the expression of the tk gene is not affected at all by the presence of intervening sequences. In fact, in certain cases sequences from this gene can confer intron-independent expression to another gene, for instance, the β-globin gene, whose expression is highly intron dependent (279). A number of studies have investigated the mechanism of intron dependence. There does not seem to be a single mechanism that accounts for all the intronic sequences. Brinster et al. (280) have studied the effect of the growth hormone gene introns in transgenic mice and found an increase in the rate of transcription in the intron-containing constructs compared to the intronless ones. The first intron appears to account for most of the effect. Introns 2 and 3 have a minimal additional effect. Possibly there are enhancer sequences located in intron 1 of the growth hormone gene. In fact, there are known examples where enhancers naturally reside within introns (281,282). Interestingly, in Brinsters report, there was no effect when the constuct was transfected into cells in culture. Buchman and Berg (279), on the other hand, studied β-globin gene transcription in cells in culture. They reported an enhancement in message levels in intron-containing constructs in comparison to intron-less ones. They, however, do not believe that the effect is due to the presence of enhancers in the intron, but rather that the assembly of spliceosomes in intron-containing messages may protect them from degradation. Kurachi et al. (283), studying the effect of factor IX gene expression with and without its intron sequences, also favor the "protection from degradation" hypothesis.

Adenovirus Tripartite Leader Sequence. It is also possible to optimize the construct for translation efficiency. For example, the Ad-tpl binds translation-initiating proteins much more efficiently than most cellular messages. This is a strategy evolved by the virus for efficient translation of the late proteins, and it can be exploited in an expression vector with a variety of promoters. Sheay et al. (284) compared expression from constructs with and without the Ad-tpl and found up to an 18-fold increase in expression levels when it was present. It was not clear, however, from this study that the increased expression could be soley attributed to an increased translation efficiency. The tpl is composed of three segments, and all three are required for efficient translation (285–287). The presence of the entire tpl is, however, not the only requirement for maximal stimulation of translation. The distance between the tpl and the initiation codon must be kept to a minimum. For example, an Ad expression vector containing the Ad-tpl, where expression was driven by the Ad-MLP, did not result in expression of a foreign protein at levels comparable to those of the late proteins until 5′ noncoding sequences were deleted, reducing the distance between the tpl and the DHFR initiation codon (288).

The tpl sequences have been used in a number of different configurations (289). In one study where the tpl was embedded internally in an mRNA, it still had a stimulatory effect on translation. Similarly, in a polycistronic context the tpl facilitates translation of the cistron that is immediately downstream of it. Although in most cases the presence of the tpl is thought to facilitate translation, there is some evidence for its role in improving gene expression at the level of transcription (290) and message stability, both by increasing cytoplasmic mRNA half-life and by decreasing nuclear half-life (291), as well as mRNA export (292).

Plasmid Backbone. The recombinant cistron has to be incorporated into a plasmid containing prokaryotic elements for selection of the recombinant cistron and its production. Manthorpe's group has made alterations in the plasmid backbone that include changing the antibiotic resistance gene, reversing its orientation and removing certain superfluous sequences (278). They reported an amelioration in plasmid function. Again, the exact explanation for this observation is unclear, although several possibilities can be imagined. The unwitting creation of transcriptional enhancer elements or conversely the removal of repressor sequences during plasmid modification is an obvious scenario. The authors are investigating the possibility that the changes in plasmid backbone may change DNA structure in a manner that would favor transactivator recruitment. Clearly, the assembly of expression vectors through DNA recombinant technology is creating new DNA sequences at every junction, and this can result in the fortuitous generation of cis-acting elements with unexpected functions.

Reporter Genes. Especially in cases where there is not an easy detection system for a protein of interest, it is possible to incorporate into the plasmid a reporter gene that would facilitate both the screening of positively expressing cells and the quantification of expression. The reporter could be included in the plasmid as an independent transcription unit or be translated off a dicistronic message. It could also be fused to the protein of interest. In all cases the detection of the reporter would be indicative of protein production. Throughout the years, a number of reporter genes have been used to monitor expression in mammalian cells. These genes include bacterial chloramphenicol acetyl transferase (CAT) and β-galactosidase (β-gal), firefly luciferase (Luc), and sectreted alkanine phosphatase (SEAP), to name a few. Detection of the activity of these reporter proteins is based on an enzymatic reaction using radiolabeled (CAT), chromogenic (β-gal and SEAP), or luminescent (Luc) substrates. More recently, a new type of reporter gene encoding the green fluorescent protein (GFP) from the jelly fish *Aequora victoria*, was shown to be extremeley useful in mammalian cells, primarily because of the ease with which it can be detected (293). The fluorescent properties are inherent to the protein, so that the detection process can be totally noninvasive. For example, both β-gal and GFP

expression allow for the screening and selection of live cells by flow cytometry. However, expression of GFP has the advantage of being detectable in living cells without the need of loading the cells with substrates or cofactors. Its fluorescent properties are essentially the same as those of fluorescein, and thus a standard fluorescence microscope can be used. GFP has been expressed in a broad spectrum of cell types, including transgenic mice, without significant cytotoxic effects. It has been expressed as a fusion protein, using a wide variety of different proteins, either at the N- or C-terminal end. Interestingly enough, it retains its fluorescent properties and does not appear to alter the physiological properties of its fusion partner. In another application, GFP is expressed as part of a dicistronic message, facilitating the screening of positively expressing cells and retaining the protein of interest in its native state (268). The myriad of applications of GFP and its derivatives was recently reviewed by Tsien (294).

IRES. The EMCV and picornaviral IRES sequences are most commonly used since they are functional in a wide variety of cell lines. New IRES elements are continuously being studied, and it will be possible to combine IRES elements with host cell lines to obtain the desired expression levels. Using a dicistronic construct can ease the task of clone screening. Co-expressing a drug resistance marker in a dicistronic message will ensure that drug-resistant clones also express the gene of interest. Cells expressing high levels of a protein of interest can be selected on the basis of resistance to high levels of the drug. By introducing decrease-in-function mutations in the IRES, so that the second cistron encoding neo is translated less efficiently, Rees et al. (295) were able to obtain clones that produced higher amounts of a protein encoded by the first cistron. It is assumed that this results from insertion of the expression cassette in a chromosomal site with high transcriptional activity. Of course, the dicistronic drug resistance strategy would not be useful with inducible expression systems, since in this case drug selection could only be applied when the gene of interest is also being expressed. Alternatively, coexpressing a reporter gene can simplify the process of clone identification. This strategy has been successfully used with β-gal (296), SEAP (297), Luc (298), and GFP (268). Dicistronic expression of GFP can be used to select for high expressors by simply screening for brighter cells. The level of expression of a protein of interest will be proportional to the level of GFP fluorecsence. However, constructs containing different cDNAs encoded by the first cistron or lacking an insert in the position of the first cistron can give different GFP expression levels. This may be the result of differences in message stability. Furthermore, clones expressing different proteins and selected for identical GFP levels can have very different levels of protein expression (D.D. Mosser and B. Massie, unpublished results 1998).

Multicistronic vectors are also the solution for coordinate expression of two or more proteins, for example, two subunits of a protein or a cofactor required for stabilising or activating the protein of interest. Such multicistronic strategy has been elegantly exploited by Fussenegger et al. (299). By extending the dicistronic configuration

(SEAP–p21, where SEAP is used to monitor expression) to a tricistronic one, they have successfully generated CHO-derived cell lines that stably produce high levels of p21. In initial attempts to produce CHO cells overexpressing p21, it was not possible to isolate clones that expressed high enough levels to cause growth arrest. This was possible when a tricistronic approach was used and the differentiation factor CCAAT/enhancer binding protein was expressed coordinately as the third cistron (SEAP–p21–C/EBPa). C/EBPa is known to stabilize p21 at the protein level. Although it was shown in their study that multicistronic vectors can allow for the coexpression of several genes at similar levels, generalization of this observation awaits further analysis with various gene combinations.

Optimizing the Junction Between the Transcriptional Start Site and the Cloning Site(s). Examples of expression cassettes in Ad vectors that allow high-level constitutive or inducible expression of toxic proteins have been reported recently by our group (300–302). Similar expression cassettes were also shown to be very effective for the production of secreted proteins in recombinant NS/0 or 293 cells (255, and C. Gervais and B. Massie unpublished results). The constitutive expression is driven by either a modified Ad-MLP or the CMV-IE promoter, whereas regulated expression is dependent on the tetracycline-inducible system. All three promoters have been optimized using the same *cis*-acting elements. As shown in Figure 5, the expression cassettes include the Ad-tpl, which is expected to increase expression both at the level of mRNA

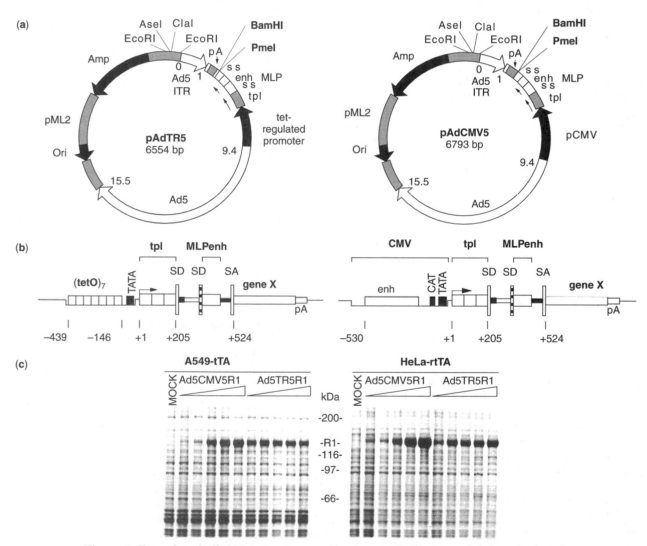

Figure 5. Examples of efficient expression cassettes for constitutive or regulated expression of HSV-2 R1. (**a**) Genetic maps of expression vectors. (**b**) Schematic representation of the expression cassettes: the two cassettes are identical from the TATA box to the polyA site (pA). The difference is upstream of the TATA box where the tetracycline operator binding sequences (tetO) replace the CAAT box and the enhancer of the CMV-IE promoter. (**c**) Coomassie blue stained gel of total cellular proteins of A549 or HeLa cells producing HSV-2 R1 following infection at increasing multiplicity of infection with the two different Ad vectors (for details, see Ref. 301). Symbols: (SS) splicing signal; (SD) splice donor; (SA) splice acceptor; (MLP) major late promoter; (tpl) tripartite leader.

and translation efficiency, as well as splicing signals, since there is plenty of evidence that the presence of an intron can increase expression levels for many genes. The polyA sequence is taken from the rabbit β-globin gene. For nontoxic or secreted proteins, these optimized expression cassettes allow protein production at 10 to 30 % of total cell protein, which is fairly close to the saturation level (255,300–302).

It is important to note that there is probably not a single component that is responsible for this success, since all the components have been widely used in other applications with less success. It is rather the combination that determines the efficiency. Furthermore, removing extraneous sequences between the start of transcription and the gene cloning site could be as important as adding effective *cis*-acting element such as the Ad-tpl. Indeed, as discussed, both 5′UTR and 3′UTR can significantly contribute to the post-transcriptional regulation of expression. It follows that to avoid any putative negative effects, extraneous sequences shoud be minimized as much as possible (288). For example, optimization of the CMV-IE promoter has improved the expression levels from 5- to 12-fold depending on the cell line (302). In the process of adding the Ad-tpl, the 5′ UTR was removed such that the +1 position of the start of transcription was the first nucleotide of the Ad-tpl. Also, the cloning site was positioned such that the Ad-tpl was spliced as closely as possible to the cloning site. In a typical construct, this would be followed immediately by a Kozak sequence before the AUG. We have recently shown that adding additional sequences such as multiple cloning sites (MCS) at that position can reduce gene expresion by as much as 20-fold when most of the MCS is 5′ to the gene, and about four-fold when most of the MCS is in the 3′ position. Interestingly, the reduction of expression is mainly at the level of mRNA, suggesting that reduction in translation efficiency is not involved (Mullick et al., manuscript in preparation). A similar observation was also reported by Luckow and Summers for baculovirus vectors (303).

CONCLUSION

There are a number of factors to consider in the design of expression vectors, and the requirements for different applications are emphasizing the need for an ever-expanding arsenal of vectors. Our understanding of the regulation of gene expression in mammalian cells is progressing at a rapid pace. Thus far, only a small proportion of this knowledge has been sucessfully applied in the design of expression vectors. Exciting developments in the field are making many new combinations possible. This will improve our ability to reprogram gene expression to better fit our needs for protein production, cell engineering, or gene therapy.

ACKNOWLEDGMENTS

We thank Dr. D.D. Mosser for critical reading of the manuscript, and Julie Dionne for art work. This is a NRC publication 42922.

BIBLIOGRAPHY

1. H.M. Jantzen et al., *Cell* **49**, 29–38 (1987).
2. R. Breathnach and P. Chambon, *Annu. Rev. Biochem.* **50**, 349–383 (1981).
3. S.T. Smale and D. Baltimore, *Cell* **57**, 103–113 (1989).
4. L. Weis and D. Reinberg, *FASEB J.* **6**, 3300–3309 (1992).
5. S.R. Wiley, R.J. Kraus, and J.E. Mertz, *Proc. Natl. Acad. Sci. U.S.A.* **89**, 5814–5818 (1992).
6. B. Zenzie-Gregory, A. Khachi, I.P. Garraway, and S.T. Smale, *Mol. Cell. Biol.* **13**, 3841–3849 (1993).
7. E. Maldonado and D. Reinberg, *Curr. Opin. Cell. Biol.* **7**, 352–361 (1995).
8. S.L. McKnight, *Genes Dev.* **10**, 367–381 (1996).
9. S.K. Burley and R.G. Roeder, *Annu. Rev. Biochem.* **65**, 769–799 (1996).
10. M.G. Peterson, N. Tanese, B.F. Pugh, and R. Tijan, *Science* **248**, 1625–1630 (1990).
11. Y. Kim, J. Geiger, S. Hahn, and P.B. Sigler, *Nature (London)* **365**, 512–520 (1993).
12. Y. Kim, D.B. Nikolov, and S.K. Burley, *Nature (London)* **365**, 520–527 (1993).
13. S. Buratowski, S. Hahn, L. Guarente, and P.A. Sharp, *Cell* **56**, 549–561 (1989).
14. E. Maldonado et al., *Mol. Cell. Biol.* **10**, 6335–6347 (1990).
15. R.W. Berroteran, D.E. Ware, and M. Hampsey, *Mol. Cell. Biol.* **14**, 226–237 (1994).
16. I. Pinto, D.E. Ware, and M. Hampsey, *Cell* **68**, 977–988 (1992).
17. M.E. Dahmus, *J. Biol. Chem.* **256**, 3332–3339 (1981).
18. H. Lu, O. Flores, R. Weinmann, and D. Reinberg, *Proc. Natl. Acad. Sci. U.S.A.* **88**, 10004–10008 (1991).
19. J.D. Chestnut, J.H. Stephens, and M.E. Dahmus, *J. Biol. Chem.* **267**, 10500–10506 (1992).
20. M.E. Kang and M.E. Dahmus, *J. Biol. Chem.* **268**, 25033–25040 (1993).
21. D.L. Cadena and M.E. Dahmus, *J. Biol. Chem.* **262**, 12468–12474 (1987).
22. B. Bartholomew, M.E. Dahmus, and C.F. Meares, *J. Biol. Chem.* **261**, 14226–14231 (1986).
23. J.R. Weeks et al., *Genes Dev.* **7**, 2329–2344 (1993).
24. H. Serizawa et al., *Nature (London)* **374**, 280–282 (1995).
25. R. Roy et al., *Cell* **79**, 1093–1101 (1994).
26. H. Serizawa, J.W. Conaway, and R.C. Conaway, *J. Biol. Chem.* **269**, 20750–20756 (1994).
27. Y. Ohkuma and R.G. Roeder, *Nature (London)* **368**, 160–163 (1994).
28. H. Lu et al., *Nature (London)* **358**, 641–645 (1992).
29. A.L. Roy, M. Meisterernst, P. Pognonec, and R.G. Roeder, *Nature (London)* **354**, 245–248 (1991).
30. A.L. Roy, S. Malik, M. Meisterernst, and R.G. Roeder, *Nature (London)* **365**, 355–359 (1993).
31. E. Seto, Y. Shi, and T. Shenk, *Nature (London)* **354**, 241–244 (1991).
32. C.P. Verrijzer, K. Yokomori, J.-L. Chen, and R. Tijan, *Science* **264**, 933–941 (1994).
33. J. Carcamo, L. Buckbinder, and D. Reinberg, *Proc. Natl. Acad. Sci. U.S.A.* **88**, 8052–8056 (1991).
34. R. Brent and M. Ptashne, *Cell* **43**, 729–736 (1985).
35. S.M. Hollenberg and R.M. Evans, *Cell* **55**, 899–906 (1988).

36. F. Liu and M.R. Green, *Cell* **61**, 1217–1224 (1990).

37. A.D. Frankel and P.S. Kim, *Cell* **65**, 717–719 (1991).

38. J. Miller, A.D. McLachlan, and A. Klug, *EMBO J.* **4**, 1609–1614 (1985).

39. R.S. Brown, C. Sander, and P. Argos, *FEBS Lett.* **186**, 271–274 (1985).

40. R.M. Baldarelli et al., *Dev. Biol.* **135**, 85–95 (1988).

41. A. Ruiz i Altaba, H. Perry-O'Keefe, and D.A. Melton, *EMBO J.* **6**, 3065–3070 (1987).

42. G.P. Diakun, L. Fairall, and A. Klug, *Nature (London)* **324**, 698–699 (1986).

43. J.T. Kadonga, K.R. Carner, F.R. Masiarz, and R. Tijan, *Cell* **51**, 1079–1090 (1987).

44. R.M. Evans, *Science* **240**, 889–895 (1988).

45. S. Green and P. Chambon, *Trends Genet.* **4**, 309–314 (1988).

46. M. Beato, *Cell* **56**, 335–344 (1989).

47. L. Fasano et al., *Cell* **64**, 63–79 (1990).

48. N.P. Pavletich and C.O. Pabo, *Science* **252**, 809–817 (1991).

49. B.F. Luisi et al., *Nature (London)* **352**, 497–505 (1991).

50. M.S. Lee et al., *Science* **260**, 1117–1121 (1993).

51. F. Rastinejad, T. Perlmann, R.M. Evans, and P.B. Sigler, *Nature (London)* **375**, 203–211 (1995).

52. C.O. Pabo and M. Lewis, *Nature (London)* **298**, 443–447 (1982).

53. D. Duboule, *Guidebook to Homeobox Genes*, Oxford University Press, Oxford, 1994.

54. W.J. Gehring et al., *Cell* **78**, 211–223 (1994).

55. R. Krumlauf, *Cell* **78**, 191–201 (1994).

56. T. Tullius, *Structure* **3**, 1143–1145 (1995).

57. J.D. Klemm et al., *Cell* **77**, 21–32 (1994).

58. M. Affolter et al., *Proc. Natl. Acad. Sci. U.S.A.* **87**, 4093–4097 (1990).

59. R.S. Mann and S.K. Chan, *Trends Genet.* **12**, 258–262 (1996).

60. J.D. Klemm and C.O. Pabo, *Genes Dev.* **10**, 27–36 (1996).

61. M.N. Treacy, X. He, and M.G. Rosenfeld, *Nature* **350**, 577–584 (1991).

62. M.N. Treacy et al., *Cell* **68**, 491–505 (1992).

63. M.S. Kapiloff, Y. Farkash, M. Wegner, and M.G. Rosenfeld, *Science* **253**, 786–789 (1991).

64. G.E. Rieckhof et al., *Cell* **91**, 171–183 (1997).

65. R. Rivera-Pomar et al., *Nature (London)* **379**, 746–749 (1996).

66. R.G. Brennan, *Cell* **74**, 773–776 (1993).

67. K.L. Clark, E.D. Halay, E. Lai, and S.K. Burley, *Nature (London)* **346**, 412–420 (1993).

68. C. Murre, P.S. McCaw, and D. Baltimore, *Cell* **56**, 777–783 (1989).

69. A.R. Ferre-D'Amare and S.K. Burley, *Nucleic Acids Mol. Biol.* **9**, 285–298 (1995).

70. R. Benezra et al., *Cell* **61**, 49–59 (1990).

71. H.M. Ellis, D.R. Span, and J.W. Posakony, *Cell* **61**, 27–38 (1990).

72. J. Garrell and J. Modolcll, *Cell* **61**, 39–48 (1990).

73. J. Mosoco del Prado and A. Garcia-Bellido, *Wilhelm Roux's Arch. Dev. Biol.* **193**, 242–245 (1984).

74. W.H. Landschulz et al., *Genes Dev.* **2**, 786–800 (1988).

75. W.H. Landschulz, P.F. Johnson, and S.L. McKnight, *Science* **240**, 1759–1764 (1988).

76. T. Kouzarides and E. Ziff, *Nature (London)* **336**, 646–651 (1988).

77. T. Kouzarides and E. Ziff, *Nature (London)* **340**, 568–571 (1989).

78. T.D. Halazonetis, K. Georgopoulos, M.E. Greenberg, and P. Leder, *Cell* **55**, 917–924 (1988).

79. Y. Nakabeppu, K. Ryder, and D. Nathans, *Cell* **55**, 907–915 (1988).

80. M. Carey, *Cell* **92**, 5–8 (1998).

81. R. Grosschedl, K. Giese, and J. Pagel, *Trends Genet.* **10**, 94–100 (1994).

82. R. Nusse, *Cell* **89**, 321–333 (1997).

83. K.M. Cadigan and R. Nusse, *Genes Dev.* **11**, 3286–3205 (1997).

84. I.M. Verma et al., *Genes Dev.* **9**, 2723–2735 (1995).

85. A. Rao, C. Luo, and P.G. Hogan, *Annu. Rev. Immunol.* **15**, 707–747 (1997).

86. P. Shore and A.D. Sharrocks, *Eur. J. Biochem.* **229**, 1–13 (1995).

87. S.L. Berger et al., *Cell* **70**, 251–265 (1992).

88. H. Ge and R.G. Roeder, *Cell* **78**, 513–523 (1994).

89. K. Seipel, O. Georgiev, and W. Schaffner, *EMBO J.* **11**, 4961–4968 (1992).

90. M. Hagmann, O. Georgiev, and W. Schaffner, *J. Virol.* **71**, 5952–5962 (1997).

91. I.A. Hope and K. Struhl, *Cell* **46**, 885–894 (1986).

92. J. Ma and M. Ptashne, *Cell* **48**, 847–853 (1987).

93. S.L. Forsburg and L. Guarente, *Genes Dev.* **3**, 1166–1178 (1989).

94. P.J. Godowski, D. Picard, and K.R. Yamamoto, *Science* **241**, 812–816 (1988).

95. J.C. Swaffield, J. Bromberg, and S.A. Johnston, *Nature (London)* **357**, 698–700 (1992).

96. I.A. Hope, S. Mahadevan, and K. Struhl, *Nature (London)* **333**, 635–640 (1988).

97. J. Ma and M. Ptashne, *Cell* **51**, 113–119 (1987).

98. W.D. Cress and S.J. Triezenberg, *Science* **251**, 87–90 (1991).

99. K.K. Leuther, J.M. Salmeron, and S.A. Johnston, *Cell* **72**, 575–585 (1993).

100. T.K. Kim and R.G. Roeder, *J. Biol. Chem.* **268**, 20866–20869 (1993).

101. J.F. Leszczynski and G.D. Rose, *Science* **234**, 849–855 (1986).

102. S. Schnewly, A. Kuroiwa, P. Baumgartener, and W. Gehring, *EMBO J.* **5**, 733–739 (1986).

103. K.A. Wharton, B. Yedvobnick, V.G. Finnerty, and S. Artavanis-Tsakonas, *Cell* **40**, 55–62 (1985).

104. K. Blochlinger et al., *Nature (London)* **333**, 629–635 (1988).

105. V. Pirrotta et al., *EMBO J.* **6**, 791–799 (1987).

106. A.J. Courey and R. Tijan, *Cell* **55**, 887–898 (1988).

107. T. Hunter and M. Karin, *Cell* **70**, 375–387 (1992).

108. K.R. Yamamoto, P.J. Godowski, and D. Picard, *Cold Spring Harbor Symp. Quant. Biol.* **53**, 803–811 (1988).

109. D. Smith and D. Toft, *Mol. Endocrinol.* **7**, 4–11 (1993).

110. C. Church-Landel, P.J. Cushner, and G. Greene, *Mol. Endocrinol.* **8**, 1407–1419 (1994).

111. T. Perlmann and R.M. Evans, *Cell* **90**, 391–397 (1997).

112. R.I. Morimoto, *Science* **259**, 1409–1411 (1993).

113. J.D. Chen and R.M. Evans, *Nature (London)* **377**, 454–457 (1995).

114. A.J. Horlein et al., *Nature (London)* **377**, 397–404 (1995).

115. L. Nagy et al., *Cell* **89**, 373–380 (1997).

116. L. Zawel and D. Reinberg, *Annu. Rev. Biochem.* **64**, 533–561 (1995).

117. J.A. Inostroza et al., *Cell* **70**, 477–489 (1992).

118. A. Merino et al., *Nature (London)* **365**, 227–232 (1993).

119. K.C. Yeung et al., *Genes Dev.* **8**, 2097–2109 (1994).

120. M. Kretzschmar, K. Kaiser, F. Lottspeich, and M. Meisterernst, *Cell* **78**, 525–534 (1994).

121. Y. Lin and M.R. Green, *Cell* **64**, 971–981 (1991).

122. S.G.E. Roberts et al., *Nature (London)* **363**, 741–744 (1993).

123. S. Roberts and M.R. Green, *Nature (London)* **371**, 717–720 (1994).

124. K. Yokomori et al., *Genes Dev.* **8**, 2313–2323 (1994).

125. J.A. Goodrich and R. Tijan, *Cell* **77**, 145–156 (1994).

126. H. Xiao et al., *Mol. Cell. Biol.* **14**, 7013–7024 (1994).

127. J.-L. Chen et al., *Cell* **79**, 93–105 (1994).

128. C.-M. Chiang and R.G. Roeder, *Science* **267**, 531–536 (1995).

129. R. Klemm, J. Goodrich, S. Zhou, and R. Tijan, *Proc. Natl. Acad. Sci. U.S.A.* **92**, 5788–5792 (1995).

130. J.A. Goodrich et al., *Cell* **75**, 519–530 (1993).

131. A. Hoffman et al., *Nature (London)* **380**, 356–359 (1996).

132. K. Hisatake et al., *Proc. Natl. Acad. Sci. U.S.A.* **92**, 8195–8199 (1995).

133. X. Jacq et al., *Cell* **79**, 107–117 (1994).

134. M. Crossley and S.H. Orkin, *Curr. Opin. Genet. Dev.* **3**, 232–237 (1993).

135. C. Andrin and C. Spencer, *Biochem. Cell. Biol.* **72**, 377–380 (1994).

136. D.I.K. Martin, S. Fiering, and M. Groudine, *Curr. Opin. Genes Dev.* **6**, 488–495 (1996).

137. M.C. Driscoll, C.S. Dobkin, and B.P. Alter, *Proc. Natl. Acad. Sci. U.S.A.* **86**, 7470–7474 (1989).

138. W.C. Forrester et al., *Genes Dev.* **4**, 1637–1649 (1990).

139. J. Magram, K. Chada, and F. Costantini, *Nature (London)* **315**, 338–340 (1985).

140. T.M. Townes et al., *EMBO J.* **4**, 1715–1723 (1985).

141. G. Felsenfeld, *Nature (London)* **355**, 219–223 (1992).

142. M. Reitman, E. Lee, H. Westphal, and G. Felsenfeld, *Mol. Cell. Biol.* **13**, 3990–3998 (1993).

143. J.J. Catarina et al., *Nucleic Acids Res.* **22**, 1006–1011 (1994).

144. N.C. Andrews et al., *Nature (London)* **362**, 722–728 (1993).

145. N.C. Andrews et al., *Proc. Natl. Acad. Sci. U.S.A.* **90**, 11488–11492 (1993).

146. P.A. Ney et al., *Mol. Cell. Biol.* **13**, 5604–5612 (1993).

147. T. Enver et al., *Nature (London)* **344**, 309–313 (1990).

148. R.R. Behringer et al., *Genes Dev.* **4**, 380–389 (1990).

149. J. Strouboulis, N. Dillon, and F. Grosveld, *Genes Dev.* **6**, 1857–1864 (1987).

150. K.R. Peterson and G. Stamatoyannopoulos, *Mol. Cell. Biol.* **13**, 4836–4843 (1993).

151. J. Ross, *Microbiol. Rev.* **59**, 423–450 (1995).

152. C.A. Beelman and R. Parker, *Cell* **81**, 179–183 (1995).

153. F.W. Larimer and A. Stevens, *Gene* **95**, 85–90 (1990).

154. A.K. Christensen, L.E. Kahn, and C.M. Bourne, *Am. J. Anat.* **178**, 1–10 (1987).

155. M.Y. Stoekle and H. Hanafusa, *Mol. Cell. Biol.* **9**, 4738–4745 (1989).

156. F.C. Nielson and J. Christensen, *J. Biol. Chem.* **267**, 19404–19411 (1992).

157. R. Binder et al., *EMBO J.* **13**, 1969–1980 (1994).

158. D. Muhlrad and R. Parker, *Nature (London)* **340**, 578–581 (1994).

159. K.W. Hagan, M.J. Ruiz-Echervarria, Y. Quan, and S.W. Peltz, *Mol. Cell. Biol.* **15**, 809–823 (1995).

160. F. He et al., *Proc. Natl. Acad. Sci. U.S.A.* **90**, 7034–7038 (1993).

161. R. Pulak and P. Anderson, *Genes Dev.* **7**, 1885–1897 (1993).

162. J. Hodgkin et al., *Genetics* **123**, 301–313 (1989).

163. P. Leeds, S.W. Peltz, A. Jacobson, and M.R. Culbertson, *Genes Dev.* **5**, 2303–2314 (1991).

164. P. Leeds, J.M. Wood, B.S. Lee, and M.R. Culbertson, *Mol. Cell. Biol.* **12**, 2165–2177 (1992).

165. J. Cheng, M. Fogel-Petrovic, and L.E. Maquat, *Mol. Cell. Biol.* **10**, 5215–5225 (1990).

166. J. Cheng and L.E. Maquat, *Mol. Cell. Biol.* **13**, 1892–1902 (1993).

167. I.O. Daar and L.E. Maquat, *Mol. Cell. Biol.* **8**, 802–813 (1988).

168. S.K. Lim and L.E. Maquat, *EMBO J.* **11**, 3271–3278 (1992).

169. S.K. Lim, C.D. Sigmund, K.W. Gross, and L.E. Maquat, *Mol. Cell. Biol.* **12**, 1149–1161 (1992).

170. P. Bernstein, S.W. Peltz, and J. Ross, *Mol. Cell. Biol.* **9**, 659–670 (1989).

171. Y. Kaufmann, C. Milcarek, H. Berissi, and S. Penman, *Proc. Natl. Acad. Sci. U.S.A.* **74**, 4801–4805 (1977).

172. T.E. Geoghegan and L. McCoy, *Exp. Cell Res.* **162**, 175–182 (1986).

173. A. Krowczynska, R. Yenofsky, and G. Brawerman, *J. Mol. Biol.* **181**, 213–239 (1985).

174. G. Shaw and R. Kamen, *Cell* **46**, 659–667 (1986).

175. C.A. Chen and A. Shyu, *Mol. Cell. Biol.* **14**, 8471–8482 (1994).

176. A. Chyi-Ying and A. Shyu, *Trends Biochem. Sci.* **20**, 465–470 (1995).

177. B.J. Hamilton et al., *J. Biol. Chem.* **268**, 8881–8887 (1993).

178. D.A. Katz et al., *Nucleic Acids Res.* **22**, 238–246 (1994).

179. V.E. Myer and J.A. Steitz, *RNA* **1**, 171–182 (1995).

180. E. Nagy and W.F.C. Rigby, *J. Biol. Chem.* **270**, 2755–2763 (1995).

181. W. Zhang et al., *Mol. Cell. Biol.* **13**, 7652–7665 (1993).

182. J. Nakagawa et al., *Proc. Natl. Acad. Sci. U.S.A.* **92**, 2051–2055 (1995).

183. K. Peppel, J.M. Vinci, and C. Baglioni, *J. Exp. Med.* **173**, 349–355 (1991).

184. F.M. Amara, F.Y. Chen, and J.A. Wright, *J. Biol. Chem.* **269**, 6709–6715 (1994).

185. F.Y. Chen, F.M. Amara, and J.A. Wright, *Nucleic Acids Res.* **22**, 4796–4797 (1994).

186. F.Y. Chen, F.M. Amara, and J.A. Wright, *Biochem. J.* **302**, 125–132 (1994).

187. F.M. Amara, F.Y. Chen, and J.A. Wright, *Nucleic Acids Res.* **21**, 4803–4809 (1993).

188. J.B. Harford, T.A. Rouault, and R.D. Klausner, in J.H. Brock, J.W. Halliday, M.J. Pippard, and L.W. Powell, eds., *Iron Metabolism in Health and Diseases*, Saunders, Philadelphia, 1994, pp. 123–149.

189. R.D. Klausner, T.A. Rouault, and J.B. Harford, *Cell* **72**, 19–28 (1993).

190. A. Constable, S. Quick, N.K. Gray, and M.W. Hentze, *Proc. Natl. Acad. Sci. U.S.A.* **89**, 4554–4558 (1992).

191. W.F. Marzluff and N.B. Pandey, *Trends Biochem. Sci.* **13**, 49–52 (1988).

192. D. Schumperli, *Trends Genet.* **4**, 187–191 (1988).

193. B. Luscher, C. Stauber, R. Schindler, and D. Schumperli, *Proc. natl. Acad. Sci. U.S.A.* **82**, 4389–4393 (1985).

194. N.B. Pandey, J.-H. Sun, and W.F. Marzluff, *Nucleic Acids Res.* **19**, 5653–5659 (1991).

195. N.B. Pandey et al., *Mol. Cell. Biol.* **14**, 1709–1720 (1994).

196. L. Melin et al., *EMBO J.* **11**, 691–697 (1992).

197. R. Eckner and M.L. Birnstiel, *Nucleic Acids Res.* **20**, 1023–1030 (1992).

198. M.A. McRae and H.R. Woodland, *Eur. J. Biochem.* **116**, 467–470 (1981).

199. A. Shyu, J.G. Belasco, and M.E. Greenberg, *Genes Dev.* **5**, 221–231 (1991).

200. A. Shyu, M.E. Greenberg, and J.G. Belasco, *Genes Dev.* **3**, 60–72 (1989).

201. T. Aharon and R.J. Schneider, *Mol. Cell. Biol.* **13**, 1971–1980 (1993).

202. D.M. Koeller et al., *Proc. Natl. Acad. Sci. U.S.A.* **88**, 7778–7782 (1991).

203. R. Wisdom and W. Lee, *Genes Dev.* **5**, 232–243 (1991).

204. P.L. Bernstein, D.J. Herrick, R.D. Prokipcak, and J. Ross, *Genes Dev.* **6**, 642–654 (1992).

205. D.J. Herrick and J. Ross, *Mol. Cell. Biol.* **14**, 2119–2128 (1994).

206. P. Bouvet, J. Paris, M. Philippe, and H.B. Osborne, *Mol. Cell. Biol.* **11**, 3115–3124 (1991).

207. A.B. Sachs, P. Sarnow, and M.W. Hentze, *Cell* **89**, 831–838 (1997).

208. T.E. Dever et al., *J. Biol. Chem.* **269**, 3215–3218 (1994).

209. C.-L. Wei, M. Kainuma, and J.W.B. Hershey, *J. Biol. Chem.* **270**, 22788–22794 (1995).

210. V.M. Pain, *Eur. J. Biochem.* **236**, 747–771 (1996).

211. M. Gross, M. Wing, C. Rundquist, and M.S. Rubino, *J. Biol. Chem.* **262**, 6899–6907 (1987).

212. J.W.B. Hershey, *Semin. Virol.* **4**, 201–207 (1993).

213. B. Datta, D. Chakrabarti, A.L. Roy, and N.K. Gupta, *Proc. Natl. Acad. Sci. U.S.A.* **85**, 3324–3328 (1988).

214. M.K. Ray et al., *Proc. Natl. Acad. Sci. U.S.A.* **89**, 539–543 (1992).

215. J.D. Lewis and E. Izaurralde, *Eur. J. Biochem.* **247**, 461–469 (1997).

216. B.J. Lamphear, R. Kirchweger, T. Skern, and R.E. Rhoads, *J. Biol. Chem.* **270**, 21975–21983 (1995).

217. S. Mader, H. Lee, A. Pause, and N. Sonenberg, *Mol. Cell. Biol.* **15**, 4990–4997 (1995).

218. F. Rozen et al., *Mol. Cell. Biol.* **10**, 1134–1144 (1990).

219. A. Pause et al., *Nature (London)* **371**, 762–767 (1994).

220. T.A. Lin et al., *J. Biol. Chem.* **270**, 18531–18538 (1995).

221. L. Beretta et al., *EMBO J.* **15**, 658–664 (1996).

222. S. Joshi-Barve, W. Rychlik, and R.E. Rhoads, *J. Biol. Chem.* **265**, 2979–2983 (1990).

223. S.J. Morley, M. Rau, J.E. Kay, and V.M. Pain, *Eur. J. Biochem.* **218**, 39–48 (1993).

224. S.J. Morley, *FEBS Lett.* **418**, 327–332 (1997).

225. A. Makkinje, H. Xiong, M. Li, and Z. Damuni, *J. Biol. Chem.* **270**, 14824–14828 (1995).

226. J. Huang and R.J. Schneider, *Cell* **65**, 271–280 (1991).

227. H.-G. Krausslich et al., *J. Virol.* **61**, 2711–2718 (1987).

228. M. Kozak, *Nucleic Acids Res.* **12**, 857–872 (1984).

229. M. Kozak, *Cell* **44**, 283–292 (1986).

230. M. Kozak, *J. Biol. Chem.* **266**, 19867–19870 (1991).

231. M. Kozak, *J. Mol. Biol.* **235**, 95–110 (1994).

232. M. Kozak, *J. Cell. Biol.* **115**, 887–903 (1991).

233. A. Darveau, J. Pelletier, and N. Sonenberg, *Proc. Natl. Acad. Sci. U.S.A.* **82**, 2315–2319 (1985).

234. B.A. Arrick, R.L. Grendell, and L.A. Griffin, *Mol. Cell. Biol.* **14**, 619–628 (1994).

235. D. Avni, S. Shama, F. Loreni, and O. Meyuhas, *Mol. Cell. Biol.* **14**, 3822–3833 (1994).

236. O. Meyuhas, D. Avni, and S. Shama, in J.W.B. Hershey, ed., *Translational Control*, Cold Spring Harbor Lab. Press, Cold Spring Harbour, N. Y., 1996, pp. 363–388.

237. H.B.J. Jefferies and G. Thomas, *J. Biol. Chem.* **269**, 4367–4372 (1994).

238. M.W. Hentze and L.C. Kuhn, *Proc. Natl. Acad. Sci. U.S.A.* **93**, 8175–8182 (1996).

239. T.A. Rouault, R.D. Klausner, and J.B. Harford, in J.W.B. Hershey, M.B. Mathews, and N. Sonenberg, eds., *Translational Control*, Cold Spring Harbor Lab. Press, Cold Spring Harbor, N. Y., 1996, pp. 335–362.

240. N.K. Gray and M.W. Hentze, *EMBO J.* **13**, 3882–3891 (1994).

241. B. Goossen and M.W. Hentze, *Mol. Cell. Biol.* **12**, 1959–1966 (1992).

242. S.Z. Tarun and A.B. Sachs, *EMBO J.* **15**, 7168–7177 (1996).

243. J. Pelletier and N. Sonenberg, *Nature (London)* **334**, 320–325 (1988).

244. D.G. Macajek and P. Sarnow, *Nature (London)* **353**, 90–94 (1991).

245. S.K. Oh, M.P. Scott, and P. Sarnow, *Genes Dev.* **6**, 1643–1653 (1992).

246. S. Vagner et al., *Mol. Cell. Biol.* **15**, 35–44 (1995).

247. R.J. Jackson and A. Kaminski, *RNA* **1**, 985–1000 (1995).

248. A.M. Borman, J.L. Bailly, M. Girard, and K.M. Kean, *Nucleic Acids Res.* **23**, 3656–3663 (1995).

249. G.J. Belsham and N. Sonenberg, *Microbiol. Rev.* **60**, 499–511 (1996).

250. D.D. Anthony and W.C. Merrick, *J. Biol. Chem.* **266**, 10218–10226 (1991).

251. A. Pause et al., *EMBO J.* **13**, 1205–1215 (1994).

252. E. Ziegler et al., *Virology* **213**, 549–557 (1995).

253. E. Ziegler et al., *J. Virol.* **69**, 3465–3474 (1995).

254. M. Kriegler, *Methods Enzymol.* **185**, 512–527 (1990).

255. C. Gervais et al., in K. Nagai and M. Wachi, eds., *Animal Cell Technology: Basic and Applied Aspects*, Vol. 9, Kluwer Academic Publishers, Dordrecht, The Netherlands, 1998, pp. 349–354.

256. G.W.G. Wilkinson and A. Akrigg, in P.J. Greenaway, ed., *Advances in Gene Technology*, JAI Press, London, 1991, pp. 287–310.

257. M. Manthorpe et al., *Hum. Gene Ther.* **4**, 419–421 (1993).

258. N. Miller and J. Whelan, *Hum. Gene Ther.* **8**, 803–815 (1997).

259. M.J. Parr et al., *Nat. Med.* **3**, 1145–1149 (1997).

260. L. Cheng, P. Ziegelhoffer, and N.-S. Yang, *Proc. Natl. Acad. Sci. U.S.A.* **90**, 4455–4459 (1993).

261. M.T. Bocquel et al., *Nucleic Acids Res.* **17**, 2581–2595 (1989).

262. M. Anton and F.L. Graham, *J. Virol.* **69**, 4600–4606 (1995).

263. M. Gossen and H. Bujard, *Proc. Natl. Acad. Sci. U.S.A.* **89**, 5547–5551 (1992).

264. M. Gossen, A.L. Bonin, S. Freundlieb, and H. Bujard, *Curr. Opin. Biotechnol.* **5**, 516–520 (1994).

265. D. Resnitzky, M. Gossen, H. Bujard, and S.I. Reed, *Mol. Cell. Biol.* **14**, 1669–1679 (1994).

266. M. Gossen et al., *Science* **268**, 1766–1769 (1995).

267. S.X. Hu et al., *Cancer Res.* **57**, 3339–3343 (1997).

268. D.D. Mosser et al., *Bio Techniques* **22**, 150–161 (1997).

269. P. Schockett, M. Difilippantonio, N. Hellman, and D.G. Schatz, *Proc. Natl. Acad. Sci. U.S.A.* **92**, 6522–6526 (1992).

270. P. Weinmann et al., *Plant J.* **5**, 559–569 (1994).

271. N. Schultze et al., *Nat. Biotechnol.* **14**, 499–503 (1996).

272. P.A. Furth et al., *Proc. Natl. Acad. Sci. U.S.A.* **91**, 9302–9306 (1994).

273. R.S. Passman and G.I. Fishman, *J. Clin. Invest.* **94**, 2421–2425 (1994).

274. S. Efrat et al., *Proc. Natl. Acad. Sci. U.S.A.* **92**, 3576–3580 (1995).

275. A. Hoffmann, M. Vilalba, L. Journot, and D. Spengler, *Nucleic Acids Res.* **25**, 1078–1079 (1997).

276. D. No, T. Yao, and R.M. Evans, *Proc. Natl. Acad. Sci. U.S.A.* **93**, 3346–3351 (1996).

277. P.A. Knepper et al., *In Vitro Cell Dev. Biol.—Anim.* **34**, 170–173 (1998).

278. J. Hartikka et al., *Hum. Gene Ther.* **7**, 1205–1217 (1996).

279. A.R. Buchman and P. Berg, *Mol. Cell. Biol.* **8**, 4395–4405 (1988).

280. R.L. Brinster et al., *Proc. Natl. Acad. Sci. U.S.A.* **85**, 836–840 (1988).

281. J. Banerji, L. Olson, and W. Schaffner, *Cell* **33**, 729–740 (1983).

282. S.D. Gillies, S.L. Morrison, V.T. Oi, and S. Tonegawa, *Cell* **33**, 717–728 (1983).

283. S. Kurachi, Y. Hitomi, M. Furukawa, and K. Kurachi, *J. Biol. Chem.* **270**, 5276–5281 (1995).

284. W. Sheay et al., *BioTechniques* **15**, 856–862 (1993).

285. K.L. Berkner and P.A. Sharp, *Nucleic Acids Res.* **12**, 1925–1941 (1984).

286. D. Solnick, *EMBO J.* **2**, 845–851 (1983).

287. C. Thummel, R. Tijan, and T. Grodzicker, *Cell* **23**, 825–836 (1981).

288. K.L. Berkner, B.S. Schauffhausen, T.M. Roberts, and P.A. Sharp, *J. Virol.* **61**, 1213–1220 (1987).

289. K.L. Berkner, E. Boel, and D. Prunkard, in Y. Gluzman, ed., *Viral vectors*, Cold Spring Harbor Lab., Cold Spring Harbor, N.Y., 1988, pp. 56–61.

290. F.V. Alonso-Caplen, M.G. Katze, and R.M. Krug, *J. Virol.* **62**, 1606–1616 (1988).

291. M.A. Moore and T. Shenk, *Nucleic Acids Res.* **16**, 2247–2262 (1988).

292. W. Huang and S.J. Flint, *J. Virol.* **72**, 225–235 (1998).

293. M. Chalfie et al., *Science* **263**, 802–805 (1994).

294. R.Y. Tsien, *Annu. Rev. Biochem.* **67**, 509–544 (1998).

295. S. Rees et al., *BioTechniques* **20**, 48–56 (1996).

296. K.M. Klucher, M.J. Gerlach, and G.Q. Daley, *Nucleic Acids Res.* **25**, 4858–4860.

297. S. Kirchhoff et al., *Trends Genet.* **11**, 219–220 (1995).

298. W. Dirks, M. Wirth, and H. Hauser, *Gene* **128**, 247–249 (1993).

299. M. Fussenegger, X. Mazur, and J.E. Bailey, *Biotechnol. Bioeng.* **57**, 1–10 (1998).

300. B. Massie et al., *BioTechnology* **13**, 602–608 (1995).

301. B. Massie et al., *J. Virol.* **72**, 2289–2296 (1998).

302. B. Massie et al., *Cytotechnology* **28**, 189–203 (1998).

303. V.A. Luckow and M.D. Summers, *Virology* **170**, 31–39 (1989).

See also Genetic engineering: animal cell technology;
Protein processing, endocytosis and intracellular sorting
of growth factors; Protein processing, processing in the
endoplasmic reticulum and golgi network; Transformation
of plants.

TRANSFORMATION OF PLANTS

Johannes Siemens
Thomas Pickardt
Institute of Applied Genetics
Berlin, Germany

OUTLINE

Introduction

Agrobacterium-Meditated Gene Transfer

Direct Gene Transfer into Protoplasts

Direct Gene Transfer — Biolistic Approach

Direct Gene Transfer Across the Cell Wall Without Carrier Particles

In Planta Transformation — Unusual Methods for a Tiny Plant

Viral Transformation Vectors

Conclusions and Remaining Problems

Acknowledgment

Bibliography

INTRODUCTION

The advances in recombinant DNA technology and the obvious impact on basic and applied plant science led to the first attempts to develop strategies for DNA delivery into plants three decades ago. Experimental approaches to accomplish the uptake of exogenous DNA into various plant tissues like shoots and shoot apical meristems (1,2), seeds (3), cultured cells and protoplasts (4,5), and pollen (6) were described (7). Due to the lack of appropriate marker genes and selection schemes, as well as to difficulties to achieve clear evidence for the uptake, integration and expression of foreign genes, the outcome of these approaches finally remained unclear. Nevertheless, these investigations were pioneer work, and at least the protoplast approach and (in *Arabidopsis thaliana*) the use of seeds as targets for gene delivery turned out to be feasible strategies (see the following).

A key discovery in another area of research, the mechanism underlying the process of crown gall formation initiated by the infection with *Agrobacterium tumefaciens*, was the finding that virulent strains of *A. tumefaciens* contain a plasmid of an exceptionally large size (more than 200 kb), containing genes involved in crown gall induction (8,9). The presence of a fragment (designated as T-DNA) of this plasmid in an aseptically growing crown gall line was first demonstrated by Chilton et al. (10). Four years later, the first tobacco plant that transmitted T-DNA-specific sequences through meiosis as a single dominant Mendelian factor was described (11). The rapid development in *Agrobacterium* research finally led to the most successful and the most widely used transformation system for the introduction of foreign genes into plants.

In addition, a wide range of methods and different approaches for gene transfer into plant cells has been explored (e.g., microlaser, macroinjection, direct DNA application) in numerous variations, often with limited success (12). However, the *Agrobacterium*-mediated gene transfer, the protoplast-based direct gene transfer, and the biolistic DNA transfer are the major techniques to date that have allowed the routine production of transgenic plants. Tissue electroporation (13), silicon carbide fiber-mediated transformation (14), and microinjection (15) are further techniques that have yielded transgenic plants but have not found widespread use up to now.

This article will refer to established techniques that allow DNA delivery into plant cells and the regeneration of transgenic plants (schematically summarized in Fig. 1). Studies on transient expression are not considered. The following methods will be assessed: (*1*) *Agrobacterium*-mediated gene transfer, (*2*) direct gene transfer into protoplasts, (*3*) biolistic gene transfer, (*4*) direct gene transfer across the cell wall without carrier particles, (*5*) in planta transformation, and (*6*) the use of viruses for transformation. In the last section we will briefly refer to certain problems that arise from the current situation of a more or less uncontrollable integration of foreign DNA sequences into the plant genome.

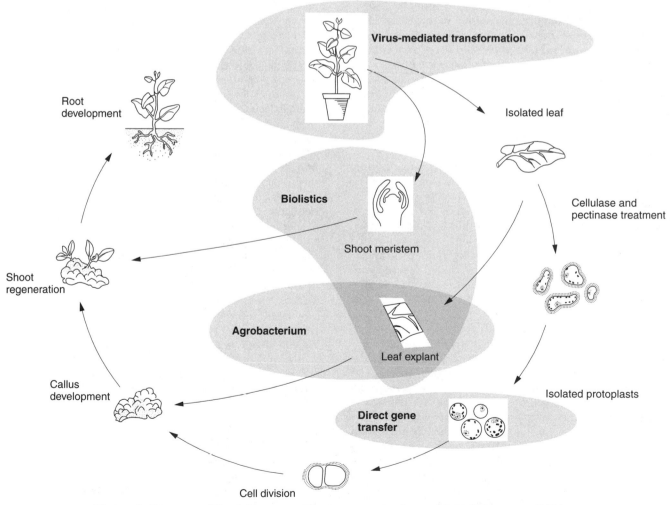

Figure 1. Summary of the main opportunities to regenerate plants and the different possibilities of transforming plants. The target cells or explants and the corresponding methods (*Agrobacterium*, biolistics, direct and virus-mediated gene transfer) are indicated by shaded areas.

AGROBACTERIUM-MEDITATED GENE TRANSFER

The gram-negative bacterium *A. tumefaciens* is the causative agent of crown galls, a neoplastic disease of many dicotyledonous plant species. The virulence determinants of *A. tumefaciens* are located on a so-called Ti (tumor-inducing) plasmid (8,9,16), which contains an insertion element transferred by *Agrobacterium* into plants cells (10). The transferred DNA (T-DNA), which is flanked by characteristic 24-bp repeats, is transported from the *Agrobacterium* to the nucleus of infected plant cells and integrated into the nuclear genome. T-DNA encoded genes that are subsequently expressed are *(1)* genes responsible for the synthesis of the basic plant growth regulators auxins and cytokinins (onc-genes), leading to the neoplastic growth of transformed cells, and *(2)* genes that code for enzymes involved in the synthesis of particular amino acid and sugar derivatives, called opines. Opines are excreted from the plant cell and are consumed by *A. tumefaciens* (see, e.g., Refs. 17,18). Many steps of this bacterium–plant interaction are still incompletely understood (19,20). The potential use of *A. tumefaciens* as a vector for the delivery of foreign DNA into plant cells was recognized when experiments revealed that a defined DNA segment (Tn7) artificially inserted into the T-DNA was co-transferred to, and maintained in, the plant DNA of the tumor tissue induced by this mutant strain (21). A further step towards the establishment of *A. tumefaciens* as a powerful transformation system was the observation that only the characteristic border sequences, but none of the T-DNA genes itself, are involved in the transfer process (22); thus all onc-genes responsible for tumorous growth could be deleted. So-called "disarmed" vectors were developed, that allowed the generation of normal plants from *Agrobacterium*-infected cells (23).

The *Agrobacterium*-mediated gene transfer rapidly became the method of choice due to the simplicity of the transformation procedure and is today the most widely and successfully applied technique. Many of the currently used protocols are modifications of the "leaf disk" method described by Horsch et al. (24). Explants are co-cultivated with *Agrobacterium*, followed by cultivation on an appropriate medium for shoot regeneration under selective conditions. An important prerequisite for the successful application of this technique, however, is the existence of cells sharing competence for regeneration and susceptibility to *Agrobacterium*. In so-called "recalcitrant" species, the competence for *Agrobacterium* infection may be absent or low in regenerable cells, as described, for example, for Kohleria (25) or shoot meristems of sunflower (26), at least under the conditions tested so far. Competence for *Agrobacterium* infection was also considered to be absent in species that lie outside the host range of *A. tumefaciens*, like many monocot species, including the agronomically important cereals (27). Only members of the monocot orders Liliales and Arales had originally been described as susceptible to *A. tumefaciens* (28). Recently, however, induction of tumors following inoculation of *A. tumefaciens* has been demonstrated in several other monocot species (see Refs. 29,30), including *Zea mays* (31). Grimsley et al. (32) have proven by agroinfection the ability of *Agrobacterium*

to transfer T-DNA sequences into maize cells. It was demonstrated that the efficiency of such T-DNA transfer is comparable to that of dicot species (33) and the importance of the *vir*A gene for interaction between the bacterium and moncot plants was demonstrated (34). Recently transgenic plants of rice (35,36), maize (37,38), and barley (39) were obtained by *Agrobacterium*-mediated gene transfer. In general, in spite of its simplicicity, the *Agrobacterium* approach finally depends on a reliable tissue culture system. *Agrobacterium*-mediated transformation systems that entirely circumvent tissue culture steps have been developed only for *Arabidopsis thaliana*, using seeds (40) or even whole plants for co-cultivation (41,42). Due to their unique methodical approach, these techniques are described in a separate section (see the following).

Until recently the size of the transferred T-DNA was assumed to be a limiting factor, since the introduction of DNA fragments larger than approximately 25 kb into the plant genome could not routinely be achieved. Hamilton et al. (43,44) developed a new binary vector that, in conjunction with *Agrobacterium* strains expressing enhanced levels of *vir*G and *vir*E proteins, was capable of transferring 150 kb of foreign DNA, which was stably inherited in subsequent generations of transgenic tobacco plants. This so-called bibac (binary BAC) vector is based on the bacterial artificial chromosome library vector and has been designed to introduce entire genomic libraries into plants, in order to identify desirable characteristics by complementation. Furthermore, this technique offers the possibility to introduce a series of foreign genes, coding, for example, for enzymes of a new metabolic pathway, into a single locus.

Agrobacterium-mediated insertion has been described as a precise event. DNA between two defined border sequences is almost completely and exclusively transferred into the plant nuclear genome. The *Agrobacterium*-mediated gene transfer was, therefore, generally supposed to possess more accuracy than direct DNA transformation methods (using "naked" plasmid DNA), which are suspected to generate plants containing more frequently fragmented, scrambled, or multiple DNA copies that may be prone to recombination, rearrangement, or silencing (17). Recently data are accumulating that demonstrate that DNA sequences residing outside the T-DNA borders can be transferred to the plant genome as well (45–48). The integration of so-called "backbone" sequences from binary vectors is reported to occur with a frequency of up to 75% (48). These findings will have practical implications, for example, regarding the regulatory guidelines for the release of transgenic plants, which may require a complete description of the transferred DNA sequences.

DIRECT GENE TRANSFER INTO PROTOPLASTS

The isolation of plant protoplasts was first described by Cocking in 1960 (49). Methods for protoplast isolation, sustained cultivation, and subsequent plant regeneration were subsequently developed for many plant species (see Refs. 50,51). Protoplasts became targets in studies of genetic manipulation in the early 1970s (e.g., Refs. 5,52). It was assumed that under certain conditions protoplasts are capable of DNA uptake, probably followed by a stable integration into the genome. The first clear evidence of the integration of foreign DNA and the recovery of transformed cells from protoplasts treated with "naked" plasmid DNA was reported by Davey et al. (53). The generation of transgenic plants using this method was published in 1984 (54,55). The experimental approaches to achieve DNA delivery into protoplasts involve treatment with polyethylene glycol (PEG; 56,57) or electroporation (58; see Refs. 59,60). The PEG-mediated transformation is generally favored and more widely used, due to the ease of the application, the possibility of handling larger numbers of protoplasts at the same time, and the higher survival rates of treated protoplasts.

While the delivery of DNA into protoplasts itself causes only minor problems, major problems arise from the difficulties in regeneration of plants from protoplasts in many species. Furthermore, plants regenerated from protoplasts are often sterile and phenotypically abnormal (61,62), probably related to the generally long culture periods. In addition, protoplast systems are time consuming and require a high level of experience. Another disadvantage of the method is the high probability of the integration of multiple or fragmented copies into the plant genome (63–65). Therefore, direct gene transfer into protoplasts is generally avoided, when an alternative approach is available, and its importance for the production of transgenic plants will probably decrease. However, the method is currently still relevant for the regeneration and transformation of mosses (66) and important cereal species, which had shown (or still show) a high level of recalcitrance towards the *Agrobacterium*-mediated gene transfer, for example, rice (67,68), wheat (69,70), and maize (71).

The PEG-mediated method has also been used for plastome transformation in *Nicotiana* species (72,73). Compared to the biolistic approach aiming at organelle transformation, the PEG method does not require specialized equipment and is therefore relatively inexpensive. It is, however, more tedious and relies on an efficient protoplast culture system, which limits the range of species to which it can be applied.

DIRECT GENE TRANSFER — BIOLISTIC APPROACH

In 1987 Sanford et al. (74) reported the construction of a device that accelerates small tungsten particles (0.5–2 µm) to velocities of approximately 400 m/sec. These particles, which could enter cells in a nonlethal manner, were used to carry bacterial genes on their surface that were expressed and integrated in penetrated cells (75,76). Whereas John Sanford's device used a gun-powder charge (later changed to a helium blast) for particle acceleration, a comparable system was presented by the company Agracetus using a high-voltage discharger to generate an explosive expansion of water vapor (77,78). Soon after the introduction of the method the so-called "particle" or "electric discharge gun" became a widely useful transformation method capable of circumventing host-range restrictions or lack of transformation competence

of cells in the *Agrobacterium* system, or the regeneration problems in protoplast transformation. The "biolistic" (i.e., biological ballistic) approach depends far less on sophisticated tissue culture procedures and competence. In principle, every plant tissue could be used as a target of the biolistic approach. Beside plasmids, RNA (79), YAC DNA clones (80), or even *E. coli* or *Agrobacterium* cells (81) have been successfully used for transformation. Sanford et al. (82) reviewed the factors that influence gene transfer by particle bombardment. Important physical variables are the acceleration system (e.g., gun powder, electric discharge, different gases), particle size, material (tungsten/gold), or the particles momentum. Tissue culture pretreatments (e.g., osmolarity of the medium) are also critical.

A certain disadvantage of the biolistic system are the relative high costs associated with leasing or purchase of the equipment. However, detailed instructions for making low-cost versions like, for example, the particle inflow gun, using flowing helium, have been published (83–85). A "ballistic microtargeting" transformation system has been developed by Sautter et al. (86,87), in which uniform-sized gold particles are accelerated by nitrogen under pressure. The device allows an improved control of microprojectile penetration and the delivery of 80% of the particles to an area as small as 150 µm in diameter, which corresponds to the size of a meristem (87).

The transformation of several recalcitrant species became feasible (see Ref. 88) due to the extended range of tissues, explants, and cell cultures that could be used for transformation, such as shoot meristems (78), zygotic embryos from cereal species (89,90), embryogenic suspension cultures (91), or microspores (92). Transgenic plants of soybean (89), rice (90,93), wheat (90,94,95), and maize (96,97) were obtained using particle bombardment.

Particle bombardment has also been applied for organelle transformation in *Chlamydomonas* (98) and tobacco (99,100; reviewed in Ref. 101). Efficient targeting of foreign genes into the tobacco plastid genome is possible (102). The plastid genome of higher plants is an attractive target for crop engineering due to the feasibility of expressing the transgenes at a high level (103,104). The biolistic transformation of mitochondria has so far been achieved only in yeast (e.g., Refs. 105,106).

DIRECT GENE TRANSFER ACROSS THE CELL WALL WITHOUT CARRIER PARTICLES

The cell wall has been considered as a barrier for large DNA molecules, which could only be overcome by quite forceful methods like microinjection or the particle gun (12).

Microinjection is a direct physical method for introducing any kind of molecule into a single plant cell under optical control (for a review, see Ref. 107). Although microinjection is one of the most difficult and laborious methods, it offers certain advantages: The number of transferred molecules can be controlled; cotransfer of DNA, RNA, proteins, or even mitochondria (108) is possible; transfer of molecules can be carried out into single cells even within whole plants; the specific individual recipient cell can be monitored before, during, and after transfer. In spite of these advantages microinjection will only be used in special situations (if alternative gene transfer protocols are not available), but remains a well-established technique for the functional analysis of molecules at the single cell level. From a genetic engineering perspective it might be significant that fertile plants can be regenerated after electrofusion of isolated gametes of maize (109) and from mechanically isolated fertilized eggs of barley (110). Microspores of *Brassica napus* could be also targeted by microinjection (111).

Recently, two more simple methods were established for transformation of intact (walled) cells in explants and embryos, namely, electroporation and silicon carbide whisker transformation. Multicellular explants of maize were transformed by electroporation combined with partial enzymatic maceration (13,112) or without maceration (113). Xu and Li (114) reported fertile transgenic plants of Indica rice by using electroporation to transfer DNA into cells of mature embryos. Subsequently transgenic calli were selected and transgenic fertile plants were regenerated within 3 months. Sugarcane (115) was also successfully transformed by electroporation. Jardinaud et al. (116) established electroporation of microspores from *B. napus,* but they have not regenerated transgenic plants. Electroporation has also been successfully used for transformation of pollen (117).

A direct delivery of plasmid DNA with silicone carbide whiskers offers an extremely simple and inexpensive option for the production of fertile transgenic plants (14,118). Embryogenic suspension culture cells are mixed with plasmid DNA and whiskers; the resulting collisions between cell clusters and the needle-like whiskers appear to result in cell penetration and DNA uptake (119). Up to now the method was only applied to maize, but Grayburn and Vick (120) used a similiar method for the transformation of sunflower.

IN PLANTA TRANSFORMATION — UNUSUAL METHODS FOR A TINY PLANT

Seed transformation, transformation by vacuum infiltration and in planta inoculation of *Arabidopsis thaliana* are *Agrobacterium*-mediated gene transfers. The separation in an extra topic is justified due to the avoidance of any tissue culture step. Therefore, the main advantage of these methods is the simplicity of the procedure: All steps could be performed in horticultural, nonsterile conditions. Until now the main disadvantage of these methods is the restriction to the single model plant *A. thaliana.* In principle, it should be possible to adapt this method for the transformation of other plant species. However, one should consider that certain features of *A. thaliana*, like the small size (fitting into a test tube), the rapid generation time (6 weeks), and the very high seed production (more than 10,000 per plant) are essential prerequisites for the applicability of this method, features that are not shared by any economically important plant species.

For seed transformation a large charge of *A. thaliana* seeds were briefly imbibed and afterwards cocultivated with *A. tumefaciens* for 1 day. The plants were grown up and the progeny were screened for T-DNA insertion (40,121). By this method a large set of transgenic plants were generated which were used for gene tagging by T-DNA insertion (40,121). But seed transformation turned out to be difficult to reproduce.

A second approach is based on the vacuum infiltration of a suspension of *Agrobacterium* cells containing a binary T-DNA vector into flowering *Arabidopsis* plants (41). On characterization, these plants were found to carry both transformed and nontransformed vegetative sectors. Up to 5 transformants per inoculated plant could be recovered from the progeny of infiltrated plants. Genetic and molecular analyses suggest that transformation occurred late during floral development because all transformants were hemizygous and contained different T-DNA inserts (41). Chang et al. (42) achieved stable genetic transformation of *A. thaliana* by simple in planta inoculation with *A. tumefaciens.* The transformation procedure involves severing of apical shoots at their bases, inoculation with *Agrobacterium* at the severed sites, and generation of shoots from the severed sites. On average, 5.5% of the newly formed shoots produced transformed progenies.

VIRAL TRANSFORMATION VECTORS

Viral vectors have not been shown to generate stable transformants due to the lack of nuclear integration and transmission through the generative cells of plants. However, virus vectors allow studies on expression of foreign genes without being integrated into the plant genome (see Ref. 122). The ability of viruses to spread systemically through the plant can result in very high expression levels of the target gene (123). This latter approach was used to develop autonomously replicating RNA viral vectors for the production of heterologous proteins in plants (for review, see Refs. 124,125). The vectors were derived from modified tobacco mosaic virus (126,127), potato virus X (128,129), or tomato bushy stunt virus (130), causing no disease symptoms but spreading systemically and containing a foreign gene. Mass production of viral inoculum for transfection can be achieved from cDNA clones through a transgenic plant, which is able to produce the appropriate capsid proteins constitutively (packaging host). High-level expression and accumulation of foreign proteins in plants 2 weeks post inoculation have been shown (127,129). Large-scale production of recombinant proteins as well as the manipulation of plant secondary metabolism has been demonstrated (127). By this approach of systemic transfection large numbers of plants could be transformed without any need of regeneration and with less genotype specificity. If expression cassettes of viral vectors become commercial available, the method might become more widely used due to its simplicity.

CONCLUSIONS AND REMAINING PROBLEMS

Transformation of plants has become an essential tool in plant biology, and its importance in supplementing conventional breeding methods is increasing. More than 3,000 field trials are in progress in at least 30 countries, involving over 40 plant species. Some genetically engineered crop species have already entered the market, such as glyphosate-resistant soybeans and (insect-resistant) BT-maize, which contributed about 15% and 12%, respectively, to the total U.S. production of these crops in 1997 (U.S. Department of Agriculture).

The establishment of transformation systems has improved for many important plant species during recent last years. In general, the generation of transgenic plants is no longer the factor limiting the application of transformation systems in basic and applied research in many plant species. There are, of course, still problems to be solved, but these problems are more related to biological or genetic phenomena than to the delivery of DNA into plants per se. By various methods DNA can be delivered into the cell, but the events within the cell and the nucleus (or organelle), as well as the integration process itself, are largely unexplored. Targeted transformation is still in its infancy (131,132). Gene silencing and interactions between different transgenes result in unexpected expression patterns of foreign genes (133–135). Several independent transformants with a specific gene construct are still necessary to find one transgenic plant with the proposed expression pattern. Position effects might be one but not the only explanation of this phenomenon. Transgene-mediated suppression of a gene by antisense constructs can be achieved, but the mechanism is still quite unclear (136,137). Until now, plant biotechnology has mainly focused on a single gene strategy. It is still cumbersome to change physiological traits that are determined by multiple genes and/or quantitatively inherited. If the relevant genes of such traits are dissected, it will be possible to deal with polygenic traits, such as drought tolerance. In principle this problem could be overcome by engineering several genes in a single step, or "pyramiding" by crossing individuals previously engineered to contain single genes. Whichever approach is used, transgene inactivation may cause problems (135).

ACKNOWLEDGMENT

We thank Bernd Plümper and Hubertus Kohn for carefully reading this manuscript.

BIBLIOGRAPHY

1. M. Stroun, P. Anker, P. Charles, and L. Ledoux, *Nature (London)* **121**, 397–398 (1966).

2. E.H. Coe and K.R. Sarkar, *Crop Sci.* **6**, 432–435 (1966).

3. L. Ledoux, R. Huart, and M. Jacobs, *Eur. J. Biochem.* **23**, 96–108 (1971).

4. A.J. Bendich and P. Filner, *Mutat. Res.* **13**, 199–214 (1971).

5. K. Ohyama, O.L. Gamborg, and R.A. Miller, *Can. J. Bot.* **50**, 2077–2080 (1972).

6. D. Hess, H. Lörz, and E.M. Weissert, *Z. Pflanzenphysiol* **74**, 52–63 (1974).

7. D. Hess, in J. Reinert and Y.P.S. Bajaj, eds., *Plant Cell, Tissue and Organ Culture*, Springer, Berlin, 1977, pp. 506–535.

8. I. Zaenen et al., *J. Mol. Biol.* **86**, 109–127 (1974).

9. N. Van Larebeke et al., *Nature, (London)* **252**, 9–170 (1974).

10. M.D. Chilton et al., *Cell* **11**, 263–271 (1977).

11. L. Otten et al., *Mol. Gen. Genet.* **183**, 209–213 (1981).

12. I. Potrykus, *Annu. Rev. Plant Physiol. Plant Mol. Biol.* **42**, 205–225 (1991).

13. K. D'Halluin, E. Bonne, M. DeBeukeleer, and J. Leemans, *Plant Cell* **4**, 1495–1505 (1992).

14. B.R. Frame et al., *Plant J.* **6**, 941–948 (1994).

15. G. Neuhaus et al., *Theor. Appl. Genet.* **75**, 30–36 (1987).

16. B. Watson et al., *J. Bacteriol.* **123**, 255–264 (1975).

17. P.J.J. Hooykaas and R.A. Schilperoort, *Plant Mol. Biol.* **19**, 15–38 (1992).

18. P.C. Zambryski, *Annu. Rev. Plant Physiol. Plant Mol. Biol.* **43**, 465–490 (1992).

19. J. Zupan and P. Zambryski, *Crit. Rev. Plant Sci.* **16**, 279–295 (1997).

20. J. Sheng and V. Citovsky, *Plant Cell* **8**, 1699–1710 (1996).

21. J. Hernalsteens et al., *Nature, (London)* **287**, 654–656 (1980).

22. J. Leemans et al., *EMBO J.* **1**, 147–152 (1982).

23. P. Zambryski et al., *EMBO J.* **2**, 2143–1250 (1983).

24. R. Horsch et al., *Science* **227**, 1229–1231 (1985).

25. T. Geier and R.S. Sangwan, *Plant Cell Rep.* **15**, 386–390 (1996).

26. B. Schrammeijer et al., *Plant Cell Rep.* **9**, 55–60 (1990).

27. I. Potrykus, in D.J. Chadwick and J. Marsh, eds., *Bioactive Compounds from Plants*, Wiley, Chichester; U.K., 1990, pp. 198–212.

28. M. DeCleene and J. DeLey, *Bot. Rev.* **42**, 389–466 (1976).

29. I.E. Godwin, B.V. Ford Lloyd, and H.J. Newbury, *Aust. J. Bot.* **40**, 751–763 (1992).

30. Y. Hiei, T. Komari, and T. Kubo, *Plant Mol. Biol.* **35**, 205–218 (1997).

31. A.C.F. Graves and S.L. Goldman, *Plant Mol. Biol.* **7**, 43–50 (1986).

32. N.H. Grimsley, T. Hohn, J. Davies, and B. Hohn, *Nature, (London)* **325**, 177–179 (1987).

33. N.H. Grimsley et al., *Mol. Gen. Genet.* **217**, 309–316 (1989).

34. D.M. Raineri, M.I. Boulton, J.W. Davies, and E.W. Nester, *Proc. Natl. Acad. Sci. U.S.A.* **90**, 3549–3553 (1993).

35. Y. Hiei, S. Ohta, T. Komari, and T. Kumashiro, *Plant J.* **6**, 271–282 (1994).

36. H. Rashid, S. Yokoi, K. Toriyama, and K. Hinata, *Plant Cell Rep.* **15**, 727–730 (1996).

37. S.W. Ritchie et al., *Transgenic Res.* **2**, 252–265 (1993).

38. Y. Ishida et al., *Nat. Biotechnol.* **14**, 745–750 (1996).

39. S. Tingay et al., *Plant J.* **11**, 1369–1376 (1997).

40. K.A. Feldman and M.D. Marks, *Mol. Gen. Genet.* **208**, 1–9 (1987).

41. N. Bechtold, J. Ellis, and G. Pelletier, *C. Re. Seances Acad. Sci. Ser. 3* **316**, 1194–1199 (1993).

42. S.S. Chang et al., *Plant J.* **5**, 551–558 (1994).

43. C.M. Hamilton, A. Frary, C. Lewis, and S.D. Tanksley, *Proc. Natl. Acad. Sci. U.S.A.* **93**, 9975–9979 (1996).

44. C.M. Hamilton, *Gene* **200**, 107–116 (1997).

45. B. Martineau, T.A. Voelker, and R.A. Sanders, *Plant Cell* **6**, 1032–1033 (1994).

46. V. Ramanathan and K. Veluthambi, *Plant Mol. Biol.* **28**, 1149–1154 (1995).

47. E. Van der Graaff, A. Den Dulk Ras, and P.J.J. Hooykaas, *Plant Mol. Biol.* **31**, 677–681 (1996).

48. M.E. Kononov, B. Bassuner, and S.B. Gelvin, *Plant J.* **11**, 945–957 (1997).

49. E.C. Cocking, *Nature, (London)* **187**, 962–963 (1960).

50. S. Roest and L.J.W. Gilissen, *Acta Bot. Neerl.* **38**, 1–24 (1989).

51. S. Roest and L.J.W. Gilissen, *Acta Bot. Neerl.* **42**, 1–23 (1993).

52. F. Hoffmann and D. Hess, *Z. Pflanzenphysiol.* **69**, 81–83 (1973).

53. M.R. Davey et al., *Plant Sci. Lett.* **18**, 307–313 (1980).

54. M. De Block et al., *EMBO J.* **3**, 1681–1689 (1984).

55. J. Paszkowski et al., *EMBO J.* **3**, 2717–2722 (1984).

56. I. Negrutiu et al., *Plant Mol. Biol.* **8**, 363–373 (1987).

57. S. Krüger-Lebus and I. Potrykus, *Plant Mol. Biol. Rep.* **5**, 289–294 (1987).

58. M. Fromm, L.P. Taylor, and V. Walbot, *Nature, (London)* **319**, 791–793 (1987).

59. X.Y. Zhu and I. Negrutiu, in I. Negrutiu and X. Gharti-Ghhetri, eds., *A Laboratory Guide for Cellular and Molecular Plant Biology*, Birkhäuser, Basel, 1991, pp. 18–27.

60. G.B. Ghartichhetri et al., *Physiol. Plant.* **85**, 345–351 (1992).

61. R. Abdullah et al., *Plant Sci.* **65**, 97–102 (1989).

62. S.K. Datta et al., *Plant Mol. Biol.* **20**, 619–629 (1992).

63. Y. Tada, M. Sakamoto, and T. Tujimura, *Theor. Appl. Genet.* **80**, 475–480 (1990).

64. A. Hayashimoto, Z. Li, and N. Murai, *Plant Physiol.* **93**, 857–863 (1990).

65. Y. Xu, W.G. Buchholz, R.T. Derose, and T.C. Hall, *Plant Mol. Biol.* **27**, 237–248 (1995).

66. M. Zeidler, C. Gatz, E. Hartmann, and J. Hughes, *Plant Mol. Biol.* **29**, 811–818 (1995).

67. K.S. Rathore, V.K. Chowdhury, and T.K. Hodges, *Plant Mol. Biol.* **21**, 871–884 (1993).

68. F.J. Wen, J.Y. Peng, R.M. Lister, and T.K. Hodges, *Chin. J. Bot.* **5**, 102–109 (1993).

69. P.A. Marsan et al., *Plant Sci.* **93**, 85–94 (1993).

70. D.G. He et al., *Plant Cell Rep.* **14**, 192–196 (1994).

71. M.V. Golovkin et al., *Plant Sci.* **90**, 41–52 (1993).

72. C. O'Neill et al., *Plant J.* **3**, 729–738 (1993).

73. T. Golds, M. Maliga, and H.U. Koop, *Bio/Technology* **11**, 95–97 (1993).

74. J.C. Sanford, T.M. Klein, E.D. Wolf, and N. Allen, *Part. Sci. Technol.* **5**, 27–37 (1987).

75. T.M. Klein, E.D. Wolf, R. Wu, and J.C. Sanford, *Nature, (London)* **327**, 70–73 (1987).

76. T. Klein et al., *Proc. Natl. Acad. Sci. U.S.A.* **85**, 4305–4309 (1988).

77. P. Christou, D. McCabe, and W.F. Swain, *Plant Physiol.* **87**, 671–674 (1988).

78. D.E. McCabe, M.F. Swain, B.J. Martinelli, and P. Christou, *Bio/Technology* **6**, 923–926 (1988).

79. T. Tanaka et al., *Plant Mol. Biol.* **28**, 337–341 (1995).

80. J.M. Vaneck, A.D. Blowers, and E.D. Earle, *Plant Cell Rep.* **14**, 299–304 (1995).

81. J.L. Rasmussen, J.R. Kikkert, M.K. Roy, and J.C. Sanford, *Plant Cell Rep.* **13**, 212–217 (1993).

82. J.C. Sanford, F.D. Smith, and J.A. Russell, *Enzymol.* **217**, 483–509 (1993).

83. Y. Takeuchi, M. Dotson, and N.T. Keen, *Plant Mol. Biol.* **18**, 835–839 (1992).

84. J.J. Finer, P. Vain, M.W. Jones, M.D. Mcmullen, *Plant Cell Rep.* **11**, 323–328 (1992).

85. D.J. Gray et al., *Plant Cell Tissue Organ Cult.* **37**, 179–184 (1994).

86. C. Sautter et al., *Biotechnol.* **9**, 1080–1085 (1991).

87. C. Sautter, *Plant Cell Tissue Organ Cult.* **33**, 251–257 (1993).

88. P. Christou, *Euphytica* **85**, 13–27 (1995).

89. V. Vasil, A.M. Castillo, M.E. Fromm, and I.K. Vasi, *Bio/Technology* **10**, 667–674 (1992).

90. P. Christou, T.L. Fiord, and M. Kofron, *Bio/Technology* **9**, 957–962 (1991).

91. S. Sato et al., *Plant Cell Rep.* **12**, 408–413 (1993).

92. M.F. Jardinaud, A. Souvre, G. Alibert, and M. Beckert, *Protoplasma* **187**, 138–143 (1995).

93. L. Li et al., *Plant Cell Rep.* **12**, 250–255 (1993).

94. D. Becker, R. Brettschneider, and H. Lörz, *Plant J.* **5**, 299–307 (1994).

95. N.S. Nehra et al., *Plant J.* **5**, 285–297 (1994).

96. Y.C. Wan, J.M. Widholm, and P.G. Lemaux, *Planta* **196**, 7–14 (1995).

97. K. Lowe et al., *Bio/Technology* **13**, 677–882 (1995).

98. J.E. Boynton et al., *Science* **240**, 1534–1538 (1988).

99. Z. Svab, P. Hajdukiewicz, and P. Maliga, *Proc. Natl. Acad. Sci. U.S.A.* **21**, 8526–8530 (1990).

100. H. Carrer, T.N. Hockenberry, Z. Svab, and P. Maliga, *Mol. Gen. Genet.* **241**, 49–56 (1993).

101. P.J. Dix and T.A. Kavanagh, *Euphytica* **85**, 29–34 (1995).

102. O.V. Zoubenko, L.A. Allison, Z. Svab, and P. Maliga, *Nucleic Acids Res.* **22**, 3819–3824 (1994).

103. J.M. Staub and P. Maliga, *EMBO J.* **12**, 601–606 (1993).

104. K.E. McBride et al., *Bio/Technology* **13**, 362–365 (1994).

105. R.M. Henke, R.A. Butow, and P.S. Perlman, *EMBO J.* **14**, 5094–5099 (1995).

106. T. Szczepanek and J. Lazowska, *EMBO J.* 3758–3767 (1996).

107. M. Schnorf et al., *Transgenic Res.* **1**, 3–30 (1991).

108. H.A. Verhoeven, J.W. van Eck, J. Blaas, and P. Dijkhuis, *Plant Cell Rep.* **14**, 781–785 (1995).

109. E. Kranz and H. Lörz, *Plant Cell* **5**, 739–746 (1993).

110. P.B. Holm et al., *Plant Cell* **6**, 531–543 (1994).

111. E. Jonesvilleneuve et al., *Plant Cell, Tissue Organ Cult.* **40**, 97–100 (1995).

112. C.M. Laursen et al., *Plant Mol. Biol.* **24**, 51–61 (1994).

113. S.M. Pescitelli and K. Sukhapinda, *Plant Cell Rep.* **14**, 712–716 (1995).

114. X. Xu and B. Li, *Plant Cell Rep.* **13**, 237–242 (1994).

115. A. Arencibia, P.R. Molina, G. Delariva, and G. Selman-housein, *Plant Cell Rep.* **14**, 305–309 (1995).

116. M.F. Jardinaud, A. Souvere, and G. Alibert, *Plant Sci.* **93**, 177–184 (1993).

117. C.R. Smith et al., *Plant Sci.* **104**, 49–58 (1994).

118. J.A. Thompson et al., *Euphytica* **85**, 75–80 (1995).

119. H.F. Kaeppler, D.A. Somers, H.W. Rines, and A.F. Cockburn, *Theor. Appl. Genet.* **84**, 560–566 (1992).

120. W.S. Grayburn and B.A. Vick, *Plant Cell Rep.* **14**, 285–289 (1995).

121. K.A. Feldmann, C. Koncz, N.H. Chua, and J. Schell, eds., *Methods in Arabidopsis Research*, World Scientific, Singapore, 1992, pp. 274–289.

122. M.C.P. Timmermans, O.P. Das, and J. Messing, *Annu. Rev. Plant Physiol. Plant Mol. Biol.* **45**, 79–112 (1994).

123. p. Ahlquist and R.F. Pacha, *Physiol. Plant.* **79**, 163–167 (1990).

124. S. Schlesinger, *Mol. Biotechnol.* **3**, 155–165 (1995).

125. G.P. Lomonossoff, *Agro Food Ind. Hi-Tech* **6**, 7–11 (1995).

126. H. Hamamoto et al., *Bio/Technology* **11**, 930–932 (1993).

127. M.H. Kumagai et al., *Proc. Natl. Acad. Sci. U.S.A.* **92**, 1679–1683 (1995).

128. S. Chapmann, T. Kavanagh, and D.C. Baulcombe, *Plant J.* **2**, 549–557 (1992).

129. D.C. Baulcombe, S. Chapmann, and S. Santa Cruz, *Plant J.* **7**, 1045–1053 (1995).

130. H.B. Scholthof, T.J. Morris, and A.O. Jackson, *Mol. Plant-Microbe Interact.* **6**, 309–322 (1993).

131. H. Albert, E.C. Dale, E. Lee, and D.W. Ow, *Plant J.* **7**, 649–659 (1995).

132. E. Risseeuw, R. Offringa, M.E.I. Frankevandijk, P.J.J. Hooykaas, *Plant J.* **7**, 109–119 (1995).

133. M. Matzke and A.J.M. Matzke, *Annu. Rev. Plant Physiol. Plant Mol. Biol.* **44**, 53–76 (1993).

134. M.K. Bhattacharyya, B.A. Stermer, and R.A. Dixon, *Plant J.* **6**, 957–968 (1994).

135. P. Meyer, *Trends Biotechnol.* **13**, 332–337 (1995).

136. J.E. Bourque, *Plant Sci.* **105**, 125–149 (1995).

137. R. Vanblokland, N. Vandergeest, J.N.M. Mol, and J.M. Kooter, *Plant J.* **6**, 861–877 (1995).

See also GENETIC ENGINEERING: ANIMAL CELL TECHNOLOGY; HERBICIDE-RESISTANT PLANTS, PRODUCTION OF; TOXIN RESISTANT PLANTS FROM PLANT CELL CULTURE AND TRANSFORMATION.

V

VIRAL INACTIVATION, EMERGING TECHNOLOGIES FOR HUMAN BLOOD PRODUCTS

Thomas F. Busby
Shirley I. Miekka
American Red Cross
Rockville, Maryland

OUTLINE

The possible presence of viral pathogens in human blood and plasma poses a major concern for the producers, distributors, regulators, and recipients of human blood products. A continuing long-term effort to ensure the highest level of safety for patients receiving these products has led to the development of a variety of approaches for removing or inactivating potential viral contaminants. In this article we review the issues that are critical for blood product safety. We describe the viruses that can be present in donated blood, plasma, and plasma-derived products. We outline the general guidelines for an optimal method for viral inactivation or removal. Last, we present an overview of current and emerging viral inactivation technologies and point out some advantages and potential difficulties of each method.

HISTORY OF THE USE OF BLOOD PRODUCTS

Although bloodletting was a common practice in the Middle Ages, blood transfusions did not occur until after William Harvey published his discovery of the circulatory system in 1628. Forty years later, the first transfusion of blood into a human was performed with sheep's blood (1). Despite subsequent transfusion reactions, animal-to-human transfusions were continued sporadically for treating mood disorders and insanity. It was not until 1818 that James Blundell, experimenting with dogs, realized that blood transfusions could not cross species lines. Shortly thereafter, he performed the first human-to-human transfusions, several of them successfully. Concerns over transmitting disease by transfusions did not arise until the 1870s when Louis Pasteur and Robert Koch discovered that bacteria could infect people and cause disease. In 1890, serum from animals immunized by serial injections of diphtheria and tetanus bacilli toxins were shown to confer protection against these toxins when injected into other animals. Thus, the precedent was established for a specific therapeutic use of a plasma derivative. In 1900, Walter Reed demonstrated convincingly that yellow fever is caused by a virus. This was the first time a human disease was attributed to a viral agent.

The use of anticoagulants allowed the collection of human blood for transfusion in the early decades of the twentieth century. However, donated whole blood stored poorly because red cells were fragile in the early anticoagulant formulations. Because the fluid component, plasma, was needed for some clinical conditions, the separation of cells and plasma was attempted and was found to significantly improve the stability of plasma. This was the start of component therapy, where a single unit of blood is used for treating different individuals. Transfusions of plasma for volume replacement in hemorrhage, burn, or trauma patients eliminated the adverse clinical reactions that frequently occurred with whole blood transfusions (2). It was soon recognized that patients with thrombocytopenic bleeding had reduced platelet counts and the infusion of platelet-rich plasma improved their condition (3). This led to the development of platelet concentrates to treat related platelet deficiencies.

The first human plasma protein to be used clinically was albumin, purified by Edwin Cohn and co-workers using the ethanol precipitation process (4,5). This product was used extensively during World War II to prevent shock in soldiers wounded or burned on the battlefield. During the purification of albumin, Cohn preserved other protein fractions for future studies. From these fractions, he isolated gamma globulin that contained several common antibodies at 20 to 25 times their concentrations in plasma. Gamma globulin was used to provide passive immunization to children with measles and to prevent infectious or epidemic hepatitis (now known as hepatitis A) in people accidentally exposed to the disease. Both serum albumin and gamma globulin appeared to be safe because none of the recipients of the infused products became infected with hepatitis. By contrast, during the clinical use of human fibrinogen also purified from one of Cohn's plasma fractions, recipients experienced a high incidence of serum hepatitis (now known primarily as hepatitis B and hepatitis C). Because of the expanded use of these and other plasma derivatives and the discovery of additional potential viral contaminants in the blood supply, the need for methods to improve the safety of these products became evident.

THE SAFETY OF BLOOD COMPONENTS

Blood and plasma donors are screened for medical health and lifestyle issues. If it is determined that donors are at risk of infection, their blood is not accepted. All blood or plasma units that have passed this initial screening are subjected to a series of laboratory tests to detect the presence of infective pathogens. Donor selection and laboratory testing have greatly decreased the possibility that an infective unit will be collected and used for component transfusion or included in pools for plasma fractionation. However, if a donation is made between the time of exposure and the appearance of a detectable level of infection, the undetected viral particles could transmit the infection. The frequency of this occurrence in donated blood is very low (6), and it continues to decrease as the sensitivity of laboratory testing is improved. The implementation of nucleic acid testing (NAT) of plasma pools further safeguards against inclusion of viral contaminants in plasma for fractionation. Viral inactivation methods provide added levels of security, decreasing still further the chance that a newly infected donor will compromise the health of patients who receive components or pooled plasma products. In addition, because viral reduction technologies may remove or inactivate unknown viruses, they decrease the risk that new or emerging viral pathogens will be transmitted to blood product recipients at any time in the future.

PLASMA FOR TRANSFUSION AND FRACTIONATION

The components of blood are separated from one another by low-speed centrifugation of whole single-donor blood. The red cells, the densest, sediment to the bottom layer. White cells (leukocytes) are visible as the buffy coat layer immediately above the red cells. Plasma and platelets comprise the top layer, the supernatant fluid. A harder spin will also pellet out platelets, leaving platelet-poor plasma on top. Plasma for transfusion and for fractionation is generally platelet-poor.

Transfusion of single-donor plasma carries a low but measurable risk of disease transmission. Fresh-frozen plasma is transfused to treat patients with a limited number of conditions such as liver disease, multiple coagulation disorders, deficiency of a protein for which no purified derivative is available, and thrombotic thrombocytopenia purpura (7). Plasma is also the starting material for large-scale fractionation to produce several protein products, most notably albumin, gamma globulin, coagulation factors VIII and IX (for treatment of hemophilia A and B), and fibrinogen (for use as a hemostatic tissue sealant). These proteins are purified from pooled plasma from as many as 12,000 donors. The risk of including a contaminated plasma unit increases with increasing pool size. This has prompted a trend toward smaller plasma pools in efforts to increase product safety.

Fresh-frozen plasma is a challenging component to treat for viral contaminants. Any procedure that is used must maintain hundreds of fragile proteins in their native states. The inactivation of an essential protein can severely diminish the efficacy of the treated plasma. In addition, denaturation of any protein may generate neoantigens that can cause a severe reaction in the recipient of the infused plasma. Furthermore, modification of proteins could alter their behavior during fractionation and downstream purification procedures, leading to changes in the purity or characteristics of that protein or of other protein products.

Two inactivation methods have been implemented to decrease the risk of viral transmission through plasma transfusion. Methylene Blue (MB) plus light has been used extensively in Europe to inactivate viruses in single-donor plasma units (8). Solvent/detergent (S/D) treatment is now licensed in the United States (9). Additional methods under development for treating whole plasma include UVC/Rutin (10) and gamma irradiation (11). These methods will be described later in this article.

DESCRIPTION OF BLOOD-BORNE VIRUSES

Before reviewing any of the viral inactivation technologies used for blood products, it will be useful to discuss viruses and their characteristics. The properties of a particular virus (e.g., size, hardiness, outer coat composition, genome structure) determine if it can be successfully inactivated by a given method. A brief review of the pathogenic viruses that can contaminate human blood will set the stage for the subsequent overview of inactivation procedures.

There are two classes of pathogenic viruses found in human blood: enveloped and nonenveloped viruses. In enveloped viruses, a lipid bilayer envelope acquired by budding through the host cell lipoprotein membranes during maturation covers the virions. This envelope is essential for infectivity. The lipid envelope contributes a hydrophobic barrier to the entry of water, salts, and other molecules, thus insulating and protecting the viral interior. Human immunodeficiency virus (HIV), hepatitis B virus (HBV) and hepatitis C virus (HCV) are well-known blood-borne enveloped viruses. HIV is a retrovirus and is the causative agent of AIDS (acquired immunodeficiency syndrome). HBV is responsible for the sometimes fatal hepatitis B. HCV can cause hepatitis C, a milder disease than hepatitis B. Cytomegalovirus and Epstein–Barr virus are less well-known enveloped viruses that can be transmitted in blood. Both viruses can cause mononucleosis, and Epstein–Barr virus is also associated with Burkitt's lymphoma and nasopharyngeal carcinoma.

Nonenveloped viruses are structurally simpler in that the viral genomes are encapsulated in one or more capsid proteins. Nonenveloped viruses are generally smaller than enveloped viruses, and they tend to be very hardy or rugged. These properties make them quite difficult to eliminate by either removal or inactivation methods. The most threatening nonenveloped pathogen is hepatitis A virus (HAV), a small virus that can transmit hepatitis A (infectious hepatitis). Smallest and most resistant to inactivation are the parvoviruses. Human B-19 parvovirus (HPV) infection has been associated with erythema infectiosum (commonly called fifth disease). Infection may be mild or asymptomatic but may result in an intense rash often accompanied by arthritis. It also leads to a cessation of red cell production, which can be a severe problem in anemic or immunocompromised individuals. A few congenital defects have been associated with intrauterine parvovirus infection. Because of its resistance to chemical or physical inactivation methods and its extremely small size, parvovirus is considered to be the most difficult virus to eliminate from plasma products.

Some viral pathogens can be grown in cultured cells and added to (spiked into) starting materials for plasma-derived products to test the effectiveness of removal or viral inactivation procedures. These cultivable human pathogenic viruses include HIV and HAV. However, most human pathogens are not amenable to laboratory culture techniques. Removal/inactivation of HBV, HCV, and HPV, for instance, must be assessed with model viruses that behave similarly to the human pathogen. Model viruses are usually animal pathogens of the same virus family, in which the nucleic acid structure and physicochemical properties are similar to those of the human virus of interest. Table 1 details the properties of the major pathogenic human viruses in blood and some of the model viruses used in laboratory tests or validation studies. Pseudorabies virus (PRV) and vesicular stomatitis virus (VSV) are general models for enveloped viruses. Bovine viral diarrhea virus (BVDV) is a model for HCV. Encephalomyocarditis virus (EMC) is a model for HAV. Simian virus 40 (SV40) is a model for nonenveloped DNA viruses. Two animal parvoviruses, porcine parvovirus (PPV) and canine parvovirus (CPV) are the most common models for HPV and are used in the laboratory to test HPV inactivation techniques.

PRION DISEASES AND THE BLOOD SUPPLY

Another potential type of blood-borne contaminant is the agent of Creutzfeldt–Jakob disease (CJD). This rare, fatal degenerative brain disease is caused by spontaneous mutation (classical CJD), genetic defect (familial CJD), or infectious transmission (iatrogenic CJD). The disease is one of a group of transmissible spongiform encephalopathies (TSEs) that also include kuru, bovine spongiform encephalopathy (BSE or mad cow disease), and sheep scrapie. The TSE diseases are associated with a novel infectious protein or "prion" that is an altered conformation of a normal protein present in essentially all body organs and especially rich in brain and other neurological tissue. In 1997, Stanley Prusiner received a Nobel prize for his proposal that prion proteins are the infectious agents responsible for spreading the disease (12). Others believe that the infectious agent is a nucleic acid containing particle such as an extremely small virus (13). Now it appears that another factor, which may be a protein, is required for infectivity (14). The appearance of a new variant of CJD (vCJD) in the United Kingdom, thought to be caused by eating BSE-infected beef, has amplified concerns about the possibility of transmission through transfusion. Although there are no recorded cases of CJD transmitted to recipients of blood products, there is apprehension that this may occur with vCJD. A recent study by Brown et al. (15) suggests that there may be a potential, albeit minimal, risk of acquiring CJD from administered plasma protein concentrates. No research has been reported on the potential for transmitting vCJD by transfusion.

THE IDEAL VIRAL INACTIVATION METHOD

Before discussing the viral reduction methods in detail, we consider it instructive to envision the desired properties against which any method can be evaluated. The ideal method for eliminating viral infectivity in a therapeutic product would have the following properties:

Table 1. Properties of Human Pathogens and Model Animal Viruses Commonly Used in Viral Validation Studies

Virus Name	Family	Genome	Env.	Size (nm)	Relevant virus or Model for
Human immunodeficiency virus (HIV-1)	Retro	ssRNA (+)	Yes	80–110	Relevant
Bovine viral diarrhea virus (BVDV)	Toga	ssRNA (+)	Yes	40–70	HCV
Pseudorabies virus (PRV)	Herpes	dsDNA	Yes	120–200	Enveloped DNA virus
Vesicular stomatitis virus (VSV)	Rhabdo	ssRNA	Yes	80–100	Enveloped RNA virus
Encephalomyocarditis virus (EMCV)	Picorna	ssRNA (+)	No	22–30	HAV
Hepatitis A virus (HAV)	Picorna	ssRNA(+)	No	27–33	Relevant
Canine parvovirus (CPV)	Parvo	ssDNA	No	18–26	HPV B19
Porcine parvovirus (PPV)	Parvo	ssDNA	No	20–25	HPV B19
Simian virus 40 (SV40)	Papova	dsDNA	No	27–32	Nonenveloped DNA virus

1. It would remove or destroy both enveloped and nonenveloped viruses and would also eliminate the infectivity of prions.

2. It must preserve the biological activity and function of the protein product. All proteins can be inactivated or denatured by extremes in pH, temperature, or harsh chemicals. Clotting factors are especially sensitive to environmental stresses.

3. The process should not create new antigenic sites or expose previously unexposed epitopes through denaturation or chemical modification of the protein. Neoantigens can stimulate the recipient's immune system to produce antibodies to the administered protein, resulting in accelerated clearance from the circulation and decreased product efficacy.

4. It would not require addition of toxic chemicals that would have to be removed by additional process steps. Any additional steps would increase process time and expense, decrease product recovery, and allow for possible reintroduction of bacterial or viral contaminants. Furthermore, sensitive assays would have to be used to show that residual chemical agents were removed to safe levels.

5. There would be no reduction in the yield of the product. During the treatment of a product on a large scale, some product is always lost through handling, and adding the extra viral inactivation step could increase product losses.

6. The procedure should be robust, meaning that it would work effectively under all conditions, such as pH, ionic strength, temperature, and flow rate, that could occur in large-scale processing.

7. It must be possible to scale up for large-scale industrial settings, where solution volumes may be measured in hundreds or thousands of liters.

8. Finally, the ideal process would be simple to use ("idiot-proof"), economical, and readily applicable to a wide diversity of products.

VIRAL INACTIVATION PROCEDURES FOR BLOOD CELLS

Although the risk of transfusion-transmitted viral diseases that remains after screening and testing is very low, nonetheless, there is a perceived need to improve the safety of transfused products. During the last 20 years, several viral inactivation technologies have been developed and implemented to make blood cellular components, plasma, and plasma-derived biological products safer for use in clinical situations. In this section we briefly describe progress being made in improving the safety of cellular components. The increasing use of leukoreduction filters to remove white cells from whole blood and cellular components has diminished the residual risk of viral transmission through transfusion of these products. Blood cells are extremely sensitive to damage, which severely limits the choice of physical or chemical treatments that can be applied to inactivate viruses. The ideal process designed to treat cellular products will attack nucleic acids and halt viral replication without damaging cell function or stability. Red blood cells and platelets are anucleate and

do not contain nucleic acid. Therefore, chemicals targeted at nucleic acids might be expected to have little impact on these cells. No procedure has yet been licensed for use in the United States for treating blood cellular components.

Procedures that look promising for use with cellular concentrates are reviewed here. Some of these methods entail adding a chemical that intercalates into the DNA or RNA helix. It is then activated to form a reactive species that damages and inactivates the nucleic acid. With all chemicals that react with nucleic acids, the possible toxicity or mutagenicity of the reagent is an issue. Residues of the chemical and any toxic reaction products must be removed to levels that have been shown to be safe for the recipient.

Alkylating Agents (Electrostatic)

Positively charged alkylating agents can inactivate viruses by reacting with nucleic acids to form adducts or cross-links. An example is ethylenimine, which has been used for decades to inactivate enveloped and nonenveloped viruses in animal sera. Although there is no decrease in the antibody activity of hyperimmune serum or in the efficacy of the growth-enhancing action of bovine serum in cell culture, ethylenimine does react with some proteins. Selectivity for nucleic acids can be improved by polymerizing ethylenimine to oligomers, which contain periodic positive charges that interact electrostatically with nucleic acid (16). The proprietary compound Inactine™, which has similar charge properties, inactivated $>4 \log_{10}$ of PPV, BVDV, HIV-1, and VSV in red cell concentrates without increasing red cell hemolysis over that of control samples during 28 days of storage (17). Four $\log_{10}$ reduction is equal to 10^4-fold reduction or 0.01% of viral particles remaining.

Dimethylmethylene Blue Plus Light

This photoactivatable phenothiazine compound is 1,9-dimethylmethylene blue (DMMB), a close relative of the well-known dye methylene blue (MB), discussed in a later section of this report. When red cells were treated with $4 \mu M$ DMMB and illuminated with cool-white fluorescent light, inactivation of four extracellular enveloped viruses (VSV, PRV, BVDV, and bacteriophage $\phi 6$) was observed. Intracellular VSV and PRV were also inactivated. The nonenveloped bacteriophage R17 was inactivated, but EMC, a nonenveloped model for HAV, was not affected. Red cell properties were largely maintained by this treatment (18). Virus inactivation required the presence of oxygen. The virucidal activity of DMMB was much greater than that of MB, and dialysis experiments indicate that its affinity for DNA is tenfold higher than that of MB (19). A distinct advantage of DMMB over MB is its ability to enter cells and inactivate intracellular viruses, probably due to the increased hydrophobicity provided by the two additional methyl groups (18).

FRALE Compounds

Frangible anchor linker effector (FRALE) compounds consist of a nucleic acid binding ligand joined by an alkyl chain to an alkylating agent. They inactivate viruses by covalently cross-linking their nucleic acids. The proprietary FRALE compound S-303 has been shown to inactivate $>6 \log_{10}$ of extracellular HIV, duck HBV and BVDV, as well as $>4 \log_{10}$ of two bacteria (*Y. enterocolitica* and *S. epidermidis*) in packed red cells (20,21). In the treated cells, the levels of red cell hemolysis, ATP, glucose, and lactate were the same as the untreated controls throughout 42 days cold storage (20). When treated red cells were transfused into mice and dogs, red cell life span was the same as controls, and no evidence of toxicity was found (21).

Some FRALE compounds such as quinacrine mustard are highly mutagenic at nanomolar concentrations in water or red cells (22). Quinacrine mustard can be degraded by prolonged incubation or reduced in concentration by binding to ion-exchange resins or activated charcoal.

Naphthalene Endoperoxides

Naphthalene endoperoxides (NEs) are prepared by reacting naphthalene compounds with singlet oxygen at low temperature. Upon warming to $25-37\,°C$, NEs release oxygen, half of which is in the singlet state. This virucidal singlet oxygen is generated without forming hydroxyl radicals or superoxide, which can damage cells. The endoperoxide of N,N'-di(2,3-dihydroxypropyl)-3,3'-(1,4-naphthylidene) dipropionamide (DHPNO2) effectively inactivated extracellular and intracellular HIV and extracellular poliovirus in red cell suspensions (23). At 7.5 mM concentration, DHPNO2 inactivated $5 \log_{10}$ of HIV, but higher concentrations (27.5 mM) were required to destroy $6 \log_{10}$ of poliovirus. Although the viral inactivation results are encouraging, these uncharged, hydrophobic NEs may become attached to cell membranes and cause unacceptable levels of red cell hemolysis.

Phthalocyanine Plus Light

Phthalocyanines are a class of photoactivable blue dyes that absorb red light, a color that passes relatively easily through red cell concentrates. Several of these complex heterocyclic organic compounds have been applied to inactivating viruses and parasites in red blood cells. One analog was shown to inactivate HIV infectivity in red cell concentrates (24). A related compound, Pc4, inactivated $\geq 4.6 \log_{10}$ of VSV without damaging red cell circulatory survival in animal tests (25).

Psoralens/UVA Light

This photochemical treatment is being developed for inactivating of viruses and bacteria in platelet concentrates and in plasma. The process uses the proprietary psoralen S-59, a heterocyclic organic compound that intercalates into nucleic acid helices. Upon irradiation with UVA light (320–400 nm), the psoralen is photoactivated and causes cross-linking of the nucleic acid chains (26). When platelet concentrates were spiked with viruses and treated with S-59 (150 µM) and UVA light, inactivation of $>6 \log_{10}$ of three viruses (HIV, duck HBV, BVDV) and two bacteria were obtained under conditions that maintained several platelet functional and biochemical parameters (27).

METHODS FOR REMOVING VIRUSES FROM PLASMA PRODUCTS

Viral reduction technologies can function by one of two routes: the viruses can be physically removed or they can be inactivated. Viruses can be removed from a plasma product by precipitation, chromatography, or nanofiltration.

Precipitation

Protein isolation methods that entail precipitation can separate viral contaminants from the product by partitioning them differentially into precipitate or supernatant compartments. The classic example of this method is the cold ethanol method for fractionating plasma pioneered by Drs. E.J. Cohn and J.L. Oncley in the 1940s (4,5). Using increasing concentrations of ethanol and varying solution pH and salt content, they established conditions to reproducibly precipitate plasma proteins into several enriched mixtures, called Cohn fractions I, II, III, IV-1, IV-4 and V. The largest proteins having the lowest solubility and the bulk of the viruses tend to precipitate at relatively low ethanol concentrations (28), leaving the smaller, more soluble proteins such as serum albumin (Cohn fraction V) largely free of viral contaminants. This plasma fractionation method and variants of it are still used by most of the commercial plasma fractionators today (29). Another precipitating agent used for large-scale plasma protein purification is polyethylene glycol (PEG) (30).

Chromatography

Chromatographic methods are almost universally used for protein purification, especially in downstream processing and polishing of the crude precipitates obtained from Cohn fractionation. Chromatography can be an effective approach for physically removing viruses from plasma protein solutions. However, the effectiveness of viral removal depends on a number of diverse variables, including the nature of the chromatographic matrix, the size and charge of the virus, and the composition of the protein solution, as well as chromatographic conditions of temperature, flow rate, pH, and solution composition. Because of the diversity of possible chromatographic conditions, every separation procedure must be repeatedly tested (validated) to determine its ability to clear relevant model viruses. A virus-contaminated ("spiked") protein solution is passed through a column (i.e., a vertical cylinder) filled with a chromatographic matrix, and the nonbound flow-through solution is collected and saved for analysis. The column is then washed with several column volumes of an appropriate aqueous rinsing buffer to further separate the virus particles from the proteins. Ideally, the protein of interest binds to the matrix, whereas viruses pass unhindered through the column and are further decreased by the rinsing procedure. An elution buffer is then passed through the column to dissociate the bound protein, which is recovered in a separate container. The chromatographic matrix can be an ion-exchange resin, a size-exclusion matrix, a hydrophobic resin, an immobilized monoclonal antibody specific for the protein of interest, or any other type of affinity matrix that binds the desired protein under the selected binding conditions and releases it under nondenaturing elution conditions.

Nanofiltration

Nanofiltration is another viral reduction process that can be effective for removing some viruses from protein solutions. Nanofilters are subbacterial filters with pore diameters of 100 nanometers or less. Bacterial filters have 200-nanometer pore diameters. Large viruses are easily removed from protein solutions, but small viruses require pores smaller than the virus but large enough to allow the protein to pass through. The smallest human pathogenic virus is HPV, which can be removed only with the smallest available pore sizes of 15–20-nm filters. If the protein does not pass unhindered through the nanofilter, protein recovery is compromised. If the pore size of a nanofilter is similar to the diameter of the protein being filtered, the filters can also become clogged, limiting the effectiveness of the process. Therefore, nanofiltration is most useful with small proteins.

One or more of the techniques listed previously may be effective in physically removing viruses during the initial purification of a protein (e.g., ethanol precipitation) or during the final purification and processing steps (chromatography, nanofiltration). The viral load of the starting material may therefore be significantly reduced by the cumulative effect of all of the procedures applied. If the reduction in viral titers is not sufficient to satisfy requirements for product safety, additional processes must be implemented to inactivate viral pathogens by methods such as those described below.

VIRAL INACTIVATION PROCEDURES FOR PLASMA PRODUCTS

This is a compilation of the major viral inactivation methods used for plasma-derived protein products. They are listed alphabetically. Heat and solvent/detergent treatments are the only ones presently used. The other technologies are under development.

Critical Fluids

This novel viral inactivation technique uses high pressure to liquefy gases and force them into the interior of viruses. Ordinary nontoxic gases such as carbon dioxide are used. The important property is the ability to be compressed to a liquid (critical fluid) with appropriate, achievable pressures. The liquefied gas acts somewhat like an organic solvent. When the pressure is rapidly released, the expanding gases destroy the viral envelope, inactivating the virus. This method is reported to be effective against enveloped viruses and many nonenveloped viruses (31).

Gamma Irradiation

Gamma irradiation has long been used to sterilize food, drugs, medical devices, and tissue culture media. Sterilization is brought about by placing the target to be irradiated in the presence of a cobalt-60 or cesium-137 source for a sufficient time to give the desired radiation dose. Whole blood and blood cellular components are commonly irradiated at very low doses of about 0.025 kiloGray (kGy) to inactivate T lymphocytes, the causative agent of graft-versus-host disease in immunocompromised transfusion recipients (32).

There are two types of damage caused by gamma irradiation. Primary damage by direct hits of the target is believed to be the major cause of destruction of viruses. Direct hits on nucleic acids or proteins by gamma rays can cleave and inactivate these molecules. This damage depends on the target size—the larger the target, the greater the damage (33). Secondary damage is caused by chemically reactive free radicals that are generated when gamma rays collide with water molecules. The free radicals can react with and damage proteins or nucleic acids. Secondary damage is independent of target size.

Early attempts to use gamma irradiation to inactivate viruses in plasma and factor VIII concentrates gave mixed results (34,35). Our laboratory has developed a method to successfully treat the blood clotting protein fibrinogen (11). When fibrinogen was gamma irradiated at 40 kiloGray (kGy), the dose needed to inactivate PPV, the fibrinogen was damaged so severely it became insoluble. Upon irradiation at 40 kGy in the presence of certain protein stabilizers, the solubility and clotting function of the fibrinogen were maintained, and viscosity was only slightly increased (Table 2). The stabilizers only slightly decreased viral inactivation. When stabilized, freeze-dried fibrinogen containing PPV was irradiated at 40 kGy, the viral titer was reduced over 4 $\log_{10}$. BVDV was much more sensitive, and was completely inactivated at much lower radiation doses. The added stabilizers are sufficiently nontoxic that they do not need to be removed from the final product. Gamma irradiation has two major advantages: the irradiation procedure can easily be scaled up, and the method can be carried out on freeze-dried products in the final sealed containers.

Table 2. PPV Inactivation, Clotting Time, Solubility, and Viscosity of Unstabilized and Stabilized Fibrinogen before and after Irradiation

Dose (kGy)	Stabilizer Present	Log_{10} PPV Inactivated	Time[a] to Clot (s)	Time to Dissolve (min)	Viscosity
0	−	−	3.5	10.2	Acceptable
40	−	−	Insoluble	Insoluble	Insoluble
0	+	0	3.4	9.3	Acceptable
40	+	4.7	5.4	15.0	Acceptable

[a]Clotting time is for diluted fibrinogen samples (0.6 mg/mL) upon addition of thrombin and calcium.

Heat

Heat can be applied to protein solutions (called "pasteurization") or to freeze-dried proteins in their final sealed vials (termed "dry heat"). Pasteurization, the oldest method used to destroy microbes in plasma products, is traditionally performed by heating the product to 60 °C and holding it at that temperature for 10 hours. Pasteurization has been used for decades to treat human serum albumin, which must be stabilized by sodium caprylate and acetyl-*dl*-tryptophan to prevent heat denaturation and aggregation. Several other plasma derivatives have also been pasteurized, including coagulation factor VIII (36,37), C1-inactivator (38) and α_1-proteinase inhibitor (39). A method has also been developed for pasteurizing human plasma that results in destroying many viruses, with over 80% recovery of most clotting factors and protease inhibitors (40). Pasteurization has the benefit that it can be done with bulk solutions or in final sealed bottles.

An unusual approach to heating protein solutions is to heat them to high temperatures for very short times (41). Short-term heating can be accomplished by applying microwave technology in systems flowing at up to 80 L/h. Temperature profiles for inactivation of enveloped and nonenveloped viruses have been developed (42).

For "dry heat," freeze-dried protein products are heated under more severe conditions, for example, 72 hours at 80 °C. Many commercial plasma derivative processes utilize this type of heat treatment. Procedures describing severe dry heating of coagulation factor VIII concentrates have been reported (43,44).

The use of heat, whether wet or dry, is limited by the ability of the treated proteins to adequately withstand the high temperatures required to inactivate viruses. Protein stabilizers such as sugars, salts, or amino acids can improve protein recovery, but care must be taken to ensure that the stabilizer does not protect the virus from inactivation by the heating procedure.

Inactine

This proprietary, nucleic acid binding compound is being developed to treat plasma and plasma proteins, as well as red cells. The antiviral agent is a family of low molecular weight compounds containing a positively charged nucleic acid binding domain and a self-activating nucleic acid modifying domain (45). Binding to DNA or RNA leads to activation of the modifying group resulting in irreversible covalent modification of the nucleic acid. Inactivation of $4\log_{10}$ of BVDV and PPV in immunoglobulin solutions has been reported, with minimal detectable effect on protein aggregation or antigen binding (45). Because the compound reacts with nucleic acids, the potential for mutagenicity and carcinogenicity must be adequately addressed.

Iodine/Sephadex

Iodine, an element with a long history of use as a disinfectant, can inactivate all known bacterial and viral pathogens. In its free form, iodine is a strong oxidizing agent and can also iodinate proteins, which may be immunogenic or thyrotoxic in transfused individuals. Iodine's compatibility with proteins can be improved by attaching it to a solid support that slowly releases iodine into aqueous solution (46).

One promising method entails binding molecular iodine to the chromatographic matrix Sephadex to form iodine/Sephadex (I_2/S). This process was developed in the authors' laboratory to treat intravenous immunoglobulin (IVIG), an important therapeutic plasma derivative. A virus-spiked IVIG solution is pumped through a chromatographic column containing I_2/S, and the column effluent is then passed immediately through a column of non-iodinated matrix, which captures free iodine. The effluent from the capture column is held at 37 °C for up to 20 hours. During this incubation step, inactivation of both lipid enveloped and nonenveloped viruses occurs. After incubation, any residual traces of iodine can be removed by a diafiltration/dialysis or chromatographic process. We have documented inactivation of $\geq 5\log_{10}$ of two enveloped viruses (BVDV, PRV) and two nonenveloped viruses (EMC and PPV) under conditions that did not detectably damage IVIG (11). Antibody titers to three viral antigens were not affected. The ability of immune complexes to fix complement and to bind natural killer cells was unchanged. The protein was not fragmented or aggregated, and iodination was minimal — under 0.02 molecules of iodine per molecule of immunoglobulin (11). One of the attractive features of this process is that it can be easily scaled up for large industrial applications. The possibility of protein derivatization is its major potential weakness.

Methylene Blue Plus Light

Methylene blue (MB) is a photoreactive dye that penetrates viral envelopes and binds to the nucleic acids. Upon excitation with red light, MB transfers energy to molecular oxygen and produces reactive oxygen radicals that modify nucleic acids into nonfunctional species. MB plus light inactivates enveloped viruses and some nonenveloped viruses. When MB is used in the presence of plasma proteins, the damage to proteins is limited by the lower affinity of the dye for proteins than for the nucleic acids.

Treatment of fresh frozen plasma with MB and light (47) resulted in $>6\log_{10}$ inactivation of six enveloped viruses (HIV, BVDV, VSV, PRV, Sindbis virus, and duck HBV). However, the method was unreliable in inactivating nonenveloped virus. Although SV40 was decreased >5 $\log_{10}$, little HAV was inactivated ($<1\log_{10}$). The effect on plasma proteins was also variable. Recovery of albumin and seven clotting factors was 90% or greater, but 25% or more of the fibrinogen and factor VIII was damaged or destroyed.

Solvent/Detergent

Solvent/detergent (S/D) is a widely used method in which the protein solution is treated with a mixture of the organic solvent tri-*N*-butyl-phosphate (TNBP) and a nonionic detergent (48). The S/D combination disrupts the lipid bilayer coat of enveloped viruses, ruptures the virus particles, and renders them noninfective. The S/D method is used worldwide to treat many purified protein products such as immunoglobulins and coagulation factor VIII. In 1998, S/D-treated pooled normal human plasma was licensed in the United States (9). No reports have been filed of transmission of the enveloped pathogens HIV, HBV, and HCV in products treated by S/D, indicating that any naked nucleic acid released into the product does not transmit disease. S/D is considered to be a very reliable, robust method for inactivating enveloped viruses. It is the only method included in this report that has no impact on nonenveloped viruses such as HAV and HPV.

UVC/Rutin

UVC is short-wavelength ultraviolet light that damages DNA by exciting electrons within these molecules. The product to be treated is exposed to light from a low-pressure mercury lamp that emits 90% of its energy at 254 nm. Because the absorption maximum of nucleic acid is at 260 nm and that of proteins is near 280 nm, nucleic acids adsorb more 254-nm light energy and are therefore damaged more than proteins. One problem is that UVC generates reactive oxygen free radicals that can seriously damage proteins. However if rutin, a plant flavonol glycoside, is added as a protein stabilizer, it neutralizes free radicals and limits protein damage but does not prevent viral inactivation. Because rutin has little or no toxicity, this inactivation method avoids adding toxic (carcinogenic or mutagenic) compounds.

The effectiveness of UVC is illustrated by a series of experiments reported by Chin et al. (49). They illuminated coagulation factor VIII concentrates with varying intensities of UVC light and found that factor VIII clotting activity decreased to <20% at 0.1 Joules per cm^2. When 0.5 mM rutin was present during exposure, factor VIII was protected (>90% recovery). Four viruses (HAV, EMCV, VSV, and PPV) spiked into factor VIII concentrates were inactivated ≥ 5 $logs_{10}$ at 0.1 Joules per cm^2, with or without rutin. Upon treating plasma in the presence of rutin, they obtained $\geq 5 \log_{10}$ inactivation of four viruses and recovered $\geq 70\%$ of the activity of six plasma clotting factors. One weakness of this method is that protein solutions strongly absorb UVC light, and decrease its intensity. To ensure that the contaminating viruses receive a lethal light exposure, the protein solution must be illuminated while flowing through thin transparent sheets. This limits the ability of the process to be scaleup for commercial use.

REGULATORY GUIDELINES FOR VIRAL REDUCTION

It is considered impossible to completely eliminate every viral particle in a product. Regulatory agencies must determine the level of inactivation acceptable for enveloped and nonenveloped viruses. The Committee for Proprietary Medicinal Products (CPMP), a division of the European Agency for the Evaluation of Medicinal Products, has established guidelines for viral validation studies (CPMP 268/95) and for production of plasma-derived medicinal products (CPMP 269/95). CPMP 268/95 states that a process must result in $4 \log_{10}$ reduction of a given virus to be considered effective for that virus. The reduction must be shown to be reproducible and not influenced by process variables (i.e., rugged). A step giving only $2 \log_{10}$ reduction is not considered effective, although it may contribute to product safety. CPMP 269/95 recommends the inclusion of two independent steps that complement one another in their mode of action, so that any virus that survives the first step is inactivated or removed by the second. It is required that one of the steps be effective against nonenveloped viruses.

The goal of plasma fractionators today is implementation of two or more independent viral reduction steps for every plasma-derived product. This can lead to unexpected complications. For example, when a pasteurization step was added to a European S/D-treated factor VIII process, neoantigens were formed, and hemophilic recipients developed inhibitor antibodies to factor VIII (50). Biochemical changes occurred with the combination of pasteurization and S/D that were not seen with either treatment alone.

This illustrates the difficulty facing any manufacturer who wishes to improve product safety by adding a new inactivation step or by combining two viral reduction methods. There are no accepted tests for the presence of new antigenic determinants. Until such methods are developed and shown to be reliable, the implementation of process changes will be hampered by the potential pitfall of undetected neoantigens.

SUMMARY

We have described numerous technologies that are available or are being developed to inactivate viruses in blood components and plasma derivatives. A summary of these methods and their uses is given in Table 3. With the exception of heat and solvent/detergent, none of the methods has been approved for use on clinical products in the United States. Methylene blue has been used in Europe to treat single units of plasma. None of the other methods is yet being used to treat clinical grade material. As they should be, the demands of regulatory agencies are rigorous. Not only must the potential viral contaminants be reduced below critical levels, but the native state and biological activity of the product must be preserved, and any toxic reagent chemicals or by-products must be removed to safe levels. The bottom-line consideration is the safety of the blood product recipient. Short- or long-term exposure of a patient to treated protein or to product additives must not cause harm.

Every viral inactivation method must be tailored to meet the peculiarities of the specific product being treated. Proteins differ tremendously in their properties and stability. Each protein has unique sensitivity or resistance to solution conditions — pH, ionic strength, temperature, or organic solvents — or to chemical antiviral agents. Every treatment and formulation must be chosen to give the maximum viral inactivation with minimum product damage. The method must be optimized and validated with the most relevant model viruses. Whenever possible, the destruction of the actual human viral pathogen should be tested. Even that test, however, is complicated by the fact

Table 3. Summary of Viral Inactivation Methods for Blood Components and Purified Proteins

Method Name	Applications[a]			
	Red Cells	Platelets	Plasma	Proteins
Alkylating Agents	A		P	
Dimethylmethylene blue/Light	P			
FRALE Compounds	A			
Naphthalene endoperoxides	P			
Phthalocyanine/Light	P			
Psoralens/UVA light		P	A	
Critical fluids				A
Gamma irradiation			P	P
Heat			P	P/L
Inactine	A		A	A
Iodine/Sephadex				P
Methylene Blue plus Light			P/L	
Solvent/Detergent			P/L	P/L
UVC/Rutin			P	P

Note: [a]P = publication; A = abstract; L = licensed product.

that laboratory strains of viruses may differ from natural viruses in important respects that can give misleading information about viral sensitivity to a given method.

A plasma product manufacturer must address many process issues when choosing a viral inactivation method. The inactivation process must be scalable from experimental volumes, usually fractions of a liter, to hundreds or thousands of liters. Although this may not appear to be difficult, simply assuring that two large volumes of liquids are adequately mixed can require complex, sophisticated test methods. The process should have little impact on protein quality. Large-scale handling of fragile proteins can cause unacceptable levels of denaturation or loss. The addition of a viral inactivation step to a manufacturing process increases the potential for product loss or damage. Although including two inactivation steps can increase viral safety, it can further compromise product recovery and quality.

A myriad of questions must be answered by a blood product producer in choosing a new viral inactivation method. What is the cost in time, labor, and capital? What is the potential toxicity, mutagenicity, or carcinogenicity of residual antiviral chemicals? Does the process modify the protein in any way? What is the mechanism of viral inactivation? What is the regulatory pathway? Will a large, expensive clinical trial be required? Must a new product license application be submitted, or is the amendment of an existing application sufficient? How much time will this involve? Answers to these and other questions will determine which viral inactivation procedure the manufacturer chooses to implement.

Scientist, clinicians, manufacturers, and regulators may debate the potential threat of a newly discovered infectious agent, whether it is a bacterium, a virus, or a prion. The final judgement as to the seriousness of the problem resides with the national and international regulatory agencies. They may demand elimination of the potential pathogen from clinical products. Conversely, they may consider that the critical shortages that may result from recalls of blood products will be more

devastating than the theoretical risk of an unknown disease agent.

BIBLIOGRAPHY

1. M.M. Wintrobe, *Blood, Pure and Eloquent*, McGraw-Hill, New York, 1980, pp. 659–688.

2. J.A.F. Napier, in J.R. Harris, ed., *Blood Separation and Plasma Fractionation*, Wiley-Liss, New York, 1991, pp. 43–61.

3. H. Krasso, *Wien. Arch. Med.* **14**, 377–404 (1927).

4. E.J. Cohn et al., *J. Am. Chem. Soc.* **68**, 459–475 (1946).

5. J.L. Oncley et al., *J. Am. Chem. Soc.* **71**, 541–550 (1949).

6. R.Y. Dodd, *Immunol. Invest.* **24**, 25–48 (1995).

7. C.R. Colflesh, R. Agarwal, and J.P. Knochel, *Am. J. Med. Sci.* **311**, 167–168 (1996).

8. H. Mohr, *Vox Sang.* **74**(Suppl. 2), 171–172 (1998).

9. B. Horowitz et al., *Vox Sang.* **74**(Suppl. 1), 203–206 (1998).

10. S. Chin et al., *Photochem. Photobiol.* **65**, 432–5 (1997).

11. S.I. Miekka et al., *Haemophilia* **4**, 402–408 (1998).

12. S.B. Prusiner, *Science* **278**, 245–251 (1997).

13. L. Manuelidis, T. Sklaviadis, A. Akowitz, and W. Fritch, *Proc. Natl. Acad. Sci. U.S.A.* **92**, 5124–5128 (1995).

14. G.C. Telling et al., *Cell* **83**, 79–90 (1995).

15. P. Brown et al., *Transfusion* **38**, 810–816 (1998).

16. E.I. Budowsky, M.A. Zalesskaya, N.M. Nepomnyashchaya, and R.G. Kostyanovsky, *Vaccine Res.* **5**, 29–39 (1996).

17. Q.-X. Zhang, C. Edson, E. Budowsky, and A. Purmal, *Transfusion* **38S**, 75S (Abstr. S279) (1998).

18. S.J. Wagner et al., *Transfusion* **38**, 729–737 (1998).

19. S.J. Wagner et al., *Photochem. Photobiol.* **67**, 343–349 (1998).

20. D. Cook et al., *Blood* **90S**, 409a (Abstr. 1820) (1997).

21. D. Cook et al., *Blood* **92S**, 503a (Abstr. 2070) (1998).

22. U.S. Pat. 5,691,132 (Nov. 25, 1997), S. Wollowitz, D. Cook, and A. Nerio.

23. A. Dewilde et al., *Biol. Chem. Hoppe-Seyler* **379**, 1377–1379 (1998).

24. H. Margolis-Nunno et al., *Transfusion* **36**, 743–750 (1996).
25. B. Horowitz et al., *Blood Cells* **18**, 141–150 (1992).
26. D.N. Cook, *Cambridge Healthtech Institute's 5th Annu. Conf. Blood Saf. Screen.*, McLean, Va, February 23–24, 1999.
27. L. Lin et al., *Transfusion* **37**, 423–435 (1997).
28. S. Yei, M.W. Yu, and D.L. Tankersley, *Transfusion* **32**, 824–828 (1992).
29. W.N. Drohan and L.W. Hoyer, in K.C. Anderson and P.M. Ness, eds., *Scientific Basis of Transfusion Medicine: Implications for Clinical Practice*, Saunders, Philadelphia, 1994, pp. 381–402.
30. K.C. Ingham, *Methods Enzymol.* **182**, 301–306 (1990).
31. T. Castor, *Cambridge Healthtech Institute's 5th Annu. Conf. Blood Saf. Screen.*, McLean, Va, February 22–24, 1999.
32. G. Moroff, S.F. Leitman, and N.L. Luban, *Transfusion* **37**, 1084–1092 (1997).
33. D.E. Lea and K.M. Smith, *Parasitology* **34**, 227–237 (1942).
34. H. Hiemstra et al., *Transfusion* **31**, 32–39 (1991).
35. A.D. Kitchen, G.F. Mann, J.F. Harrison, and A.J. Zuckerman, *Vox Sang.* **56**, 223–229 (1989).
36. N. Heimburger et al., *Arzneim-Forschung.* **31**, 619–622 (1981).
37. M.E. Hrinda, F. Feldman, and A.B. Schreiber, *Semin. Hematol.* **27**(Suppl. 2:) 19–24 (1990).
38. C. Williams, M. Wickerhauser, T.F. Busby, and K.C. Ingham, *Vox Sang.* **46**, 260–269 (1984).
39. C.B. Glaser, T.F. Busby, K.C. Ingham, and A. Childs, *Am. Rev. Respir. Dis.* **128**, 77–81 (1983).
40. M. Burnouf-Radosevich, T. Burnouf, and J.J. Huart, *Rev. Fr. Transfus. Hemobiol.* **36**, 93–102 (1993).
41. S.E. Charm et al., *Vox Sang.* **62**, 12–20 (1992).
42. J.K. Walter, B. Heil, U. Striffler, and S. Charm, *Plasma Prod. Biotechnol. Meet.*, Daydream Island, Australia, March, 1999.
43. L. Winkelman et al., *Vox Sang.* **57**, 97–103 (1989).
44. A. Knevelman et al., *Vox Sang.* **66**, 96–103 (1994).
45. C. Edson, A. Purmal, Q.-X. Zhang, and E. Budowsky, *Transfusion* **38S**, 75S (Abstr. S277) (1998).
46. F.A. Highsmith et al., *Transfusion* **34**, 322–327 (1994).
47. J. Chapman, *Transfus. Today* April No. 22 (1995).
48. B. Horowitz, A.M. Prince, M.S. Horowitz, and C. Watklevicz, *Dev. Biol. Stand.* **81**, 147–161 (1993).
49. S. Chin et al., *Blood* **86**, 4331–4336 (1995).
50. S. Raut et al., *Thromb. Haemostasis* **80**, 624–631 (1998).

See also cGMP COMPLIANCE FOR PRODUCTION ROOMS IN BIOTECHNOLOGY: A CASE STUDY; ICH GCP GUIDELINES: PREPARATION, CONDUCT AND REPORTING OF CLINICAL TRIALS; PRODUCT DEVELOPMENT, QUALITY AND REGULATORY ISSUES; VIRUS REMOVAL FROM PLANTS.

VIRAL VACCINE PRODUCTION IN CELL CULTURE

JOHN G. AUNINS
Merck Research Laboratories
West Point, Pennsylvania

OUTLINE

The production of vaccines by animal cell culture was one of the earliest commercial applications of *in vitro* animal cell technology, and despite the recent spotlight accorded recombinant protein products, vaccines remain the most significant application of cell culture in terms of product numbers and societal impact. Vaccine production is also one of the most challenging areas of animal cell culture. One must grow some of the most fastidious host cells in all of animal cell technology, optimize a process of infection that is typically destructive of that host, perform all operations in a very strict processing and regulatory environment, and from this deliver a product at a cost that makes the vaccine affordable enough to distribute millions of doses annually, and at production costs no more than a dollar or two and in many instances much less. Product safety is of paramount concern as well because many of the major viral vaccines are for use in healthy pediatrics. If process economics are critical for the human vaccine industry, they are tenfold as important for veterinary vaccines, which suffer further from the fact that the products are commodities whose prices are measured in pennies. Because of this burden, the veterinary vaccine industry is often a closed-mouth cadre of biotechnologists despite the fact that they have made many of the major advances in vaccine production methods. It is difficult to ascertain modern production methods with a few exceptions. Hence this article will confine its discussion to human vaccines except for literature references and a discussion of the history of the foot-and-mouth disease virus (FMDV) vaccine, which has had a profound influence on the newer recombinant protein biotechnology applications of cell culture.

A general overview of the mechanics of production is given, followed by a discussion of considerations for cell growth and virus production. This is followed by individual sections on the major current human vaccines, FMDV, and potential future cell-culture-derived vaccines. The view is primarily that of a process scientist. However, regulatory considerations (1,2) are also discussed because these have dominated vaccine development historically and will continue to influence various aspects of vaccine development and processing via cell culture technology. The article mainly reflects issues and practices from North America or Europe because these geographical areas have contributed most substantially to recent vaccine development. This article will not address passive antibody-based immunoprophylactics or recombinant DNA subunit vaccines such as the hepatitis B vaccine because the principles of recombinant protein cell culture are described elsewhere in this Encyclopedia. It also does not address the interesting but somewhat arcane applications of cell culture for vaccines against rickettsia (3,4), parasites (5,6), or pathogens of fish (7–11).

MECHANICS OF VIRAL VACCINE PRODUCTION

It is useful to understand the general steps involved in viral vaccine production to appreciate some of the ideas and concerns mentioned in this article. Figure 1 and the following sections illustrate these steps.

Viral Seeds

Once basic research virologists have identified the viral pathogen and host cells that permit its propagation *in vitro*, vaccine development begins in earnest. A viral isolate of interest is grown, screened for adventitious organisms, and grown further to create a Master Virus Seed bank. This culture process can be very straightforward, with the single goal of expanding the amount of virus. However, in the process, the virus may be grown in nonhuman host cells, host cells from a tissue different from the virus' normal target organ, or in cells under altered conditions, for example, low temperature (12–16). Such conditions are usually intended to select for spontaneous viral mutants that are more suited to *in vitro* culture in the host/condition used. In the case of a virus intended for an inactivated-vaccine approach, the goal may simply be to retain the immunogenic epitopes of the virus while adapting it to production conditions for productivity (17–20). In the case of a virus intended for a live vaccine, the goal is to derive an "attenuated" virus that retains the ability to replicate moderately in the host (and thus produce immunizing antigen *in vivo*) without causing clinical disease. Attenuation may alternately be performed for improved manufacturing or clinical safety, even for inactivated vaccines, to avoid potential operator or patient exposure to a pathogen. It is an empirical and uncertain process to arrive at an attenuated vaccine strain with acceptable reactogenicity and immunogenicity (21–25). Because clinical considerations are paramount for the viral

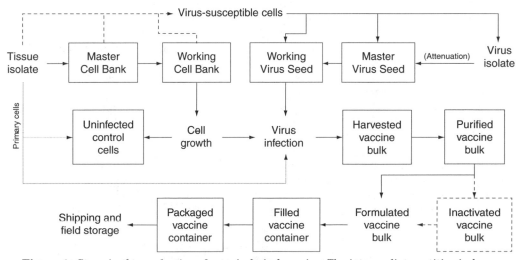

Figure 1. Steps in the production of a typical viral vaccine. The intermediate entities in boxes are those which are typically subject to quality control testing. Dashed lines indicate optional steps or alternative paths which are dependent on the particular vaccine. Dotted lines indicate the processing route for primary cells, that is, no cell banking occurs.

strain derivation, the process scientist is occasionally given a virus–host system where the virus is not fully adapted to the production host cell for optimal productivity, yet the system cannot be changed for regulatory reasons. Most often, though, strain derivation and attenuation conditions adapt the virus toward better replication under production conditions while still satisfying safety and immunogenic goals (15,26).

Working Seeds produced from the Master Seed, are used to manufacture harvested virus bulk lots of vaccine. This scheme forms the classic "two-tier" banking system that is common for both virus and cells and is meant to ensure that the Master Seed lasts for a substantial number of doses (ca. 100 million or more). With this scheme the Master Seed is extensively tested to ensure freedom from adventitious viral contamination (27,28). In the case of attenuated viruses, the Seed is also extensively tested to demonstrate *in vivo* attenuation in a relevant animal model and is usually clinically tested in humans.

Cell Banks

Like the Virus Seeds, the host-cell substrate for viral growth is isolated from tissue and then is placed in a reactor to allow a controlled infection. In the case of primary cells, the isolated tissue is inoculated directly into the reactor, allowed to establish itself, and then is infected with virus. For all other cell types, the cells are usually grown in a two-tier banking system so that exhaustive testing can be applied to the Master and Working Cell Banks. Although attenuation is not an issue here, cell clones with *in vitro* growth advantages can be selected (29). Depending on the cell type, safety assurance by ascertaining the degree of cell "normalcy" is expected to be established (30).

Cultivation

A typical vaccine batch begins with initiating a cell growth train; the biomass is expanded until a sufficient amount is available to produce a substantial batch of virus. At infection, the culture conditions may be altered to promote viral growth rather than cell growth. A portion of the biomass is set aside as uninfected control cultures which are kept for several weeks beyond the infection date. These are examined for cytopathic effect and tested to ensure that no undetected contaminants were present which could have been masked by the intentional infection. Control cells were imperative in the early days of *in vitro* cultured viral vaccines when primary cells were employed and for processes with large numbers of manual aseptic manipulations where environmental contaminants could more readily be introduced. As the industry moves into processes where cells are cultivated from extensively characterized banks and are propagated exclusively in sealed bioreactor systems, the relevance of these cultures may diminish.

Purification

The infected culture is harvested to recover virus, which then is purified. The degree of purification varies substantially depending on viral fragility, the host cell used, and the route of vaccine administration; general purification methods are widely known and practiced (31,32), as well as highly specific modern processes (33–37). The purified vaccine bulk is a typical holding point before formulation and dispensing into filled containers to titrate the potency of the bulk vaccine and to test purity and safety.

Inactivation

For inactivated viral vaccines, the virus may be inactivated either before or after purification by an alkylating (e.g., β-propiolactone) or a cross-linking reagent (e.g., formaldehyde, UV light) (38,39). Care must be taken not to overinactivate, or immunogenicity can be lost (40,41). Provided that there are no substantial process safety issues, the inactivation is preferably done postpurification to avoid modifying nonantigenic proteins. Prepurification inactivation can raise immune responses against the modified proteins (42) or make further purification difficult. Although testing is performed to confirm that the batch has been thoroughly inactivated, due to the statistics of sampling, the guarantee that inactivation has occurred relies on extensive process validation, as well as confirmation of the kinetics and mechanisms of infectivity destruction in the inactivation process (43,44).

Finishing

The finishing steps of vaccine production and distribution are often neglected by those of us who work on the steps closest to cells and virus. However, finishing losses can be important determinants of the amount of virus which must be produced. Beyond creating a purified (inactivated) bulk vaccine, the virus is formulated into a buffer or "stabilizer" that promotes infectivity retention upon long-term storage and dilutes the virus to the appropriate potency for the vaccine dose. Then the formulated bulk is filled into containers and lyophilized in many instances. Labels are applied, and the vaccine is packaged and shipped to clinics and offices for storage before administration. The length of time that can elapse and the thermal conditions under which virus is shipped and stored before administration can lead to substantial infectious viral loss for live vaccines and thus filling to levels higher than the nominal efficacious dose is required. This is not so much a concern for inactivated viral vaccines which tend to be more stable. Development of stable vaccines that can be used in the tropics and less developed countries is a never-ending challenge for vaccine manufacturers (45,46).

HOST CELL SUBSTRATE AND CELL GROWTH

The starting point for any viral vaccine process is the cell substrate because the viruses of interest can replicate only by infecting a eukaryotic host cell. Viral vaccine processing began with *in vivo* (47) and *in ovo* (egg) cultivation, which are still practiced today for Japanese encephalitis virus (48), influenza (49), and yellow fever (50) viruses. *In ovo* propagation remains a mainstay of veterinary vaccines (51). However, it has been recognized that to obtain clean vaccine preparations with superior immunogenicity, minimum side effects (e.g., reactions due to nervous system proteins or egg proteins), and the fewest concerns over adventitious contaminating microorganisms and viruses, *in vitro* growth under controlled conditions is necessary. Safety of the cell substrate has been a major regulatory concern because most viral vaccines are purified partially, if at all, to remove host cell proteins, nucleic acids, and/or any contaminants the cells may harbor. Numerous examples of cell substrate safety failures exist (52).

Primary Cells

During its history, the viral vaccine field has progressed from using whole organisms and organ culture to using cultures of primary cells harvested from an organ. This change occurred in the 1950s and early 1960s after the Enders laboratory's achievement of poliovirus cultivation in primary cells in the 1940s (53). Primary cells are cells derived directly from dissociation of an organism or organ, with minimal or no further propagation. The cells are typically grown only for a limited number of cell divisions in culture. The use of primary cells was initially believed advantageous because they could be cultivated under controlled conditions and extraneous host organism material could be dramatically reduced compared to animal/egg cultures. In addition the process does not grow the cells much beyond tissue explant compared to diploid cell strain cultures, ensuring retention of normal genetics (see below).

Monkey kidney cells and whole chick embryo cells (commonly termed chick embryo fibroblasts or CEFs) are examples of ubiquitously used primary cell types. Sometimes duck (54,55) or quail embryo cells (56,57) have been used as well. The use of primary monkey kidney cells has been discontinued by some of the major poliovirus vaccine manufacturers, in part due to ecological and ethical issues, but mainly due to the adventitious viruses often found in wild-caught monkeys (58–63). CEFs are currently used to produce several vaccines, notably measles and mumps viruses.

For CEFs, the cells are prepared for culture by harvesting the embryo from an egg 10 to 12 days postfertilization, removing the head and feet (and sometimes viscera), mincing the tissue into small pieces, dissociating the soft bits enzymatically using a pancreatin (trypsin) solution, and coarsely filtering out the big and crunchy bits to yield a disperse suspension of cells (64). Similar procedures were initially used for monkey kidney cells, but these gave way to organ perfusion trypsinization techniques that gave a much greater cell yield and allowed an order of magnitude reduction in the number of monkeys used (65–67). The trypsinized suspension is typically placed directly into a bioreactor and cultured as a primary culture, although there has been some exploration of "secondary" and "tertiary" cultures to minimize the initial tissue needs (68,69). Of interest to the process scientist is the spectrum of cell types obtained from this procedure and whether they all retain differentiation characteristics that permit viral replication (70). Little is known regarding these areas, although it is reasonable to expect that because serum is typically employed for

cultivation, rapid loss of cell differentiation and outgrowth of fibroblasts would occur (as suggested by the popular name for these cultures). The culture of virus on CEFs *in vitro* is not necessarily the same as culture *in ovo*, in that viruses injected into the allantoic cavity often replicate in the cells of the chorioallantoic membrane (71–73), which is not part of the embryo harvest.

Because primary cells are not banked, the first line of control for cell properties and contamination is on the animals producing the cells. As mentioned earlier, the use of wild animals is slowing; where still employed, monkeys are quarantined extensively or are captive-bred (69,74,75). The major requirement for using primary cells in vaccine manufacture is to ensure freedom from adventitious agents. For CEFs, the laying flocks are housed specially to prevent infection from wild birds, and the eggs and the chickens are verified to be free of certain common pathogens, hence the term "specific pathogen-free" (SPF) eggs (54,76). These same flocks are used extensively to produce influenza viral vaccines *in ovo* and for safety testing of all viral vaccines. For production, it is incumbent on the manufacturer to demonstrate that the cells are free from adventitious viruses through additional testing of production cultures and uninfected control cells (see above) (77,78). The same types of precautions are also taken for monkeys (79). Oddly enough, in an era when vaccine manufacturers are trying to move away from primary cultures as quickly as possible, a transgenic animal industry is starting up for recombinant protein manufacture (80,81). This is justifiable only for those products where the benefits far outweigh the risks of production in animals and where a feasible alternative technology does not exist.

Human Diploid Cells

Strains of apparently normal diploid cells propagated for more than a few doublings of the population were first practically derived in the early 1960s. These cells from human embryos were termed human diploid cells (HDCs). Their use for vaccine production was surrounded in the early years by vigorous debate over safety because they departed from the accepted primary cell paradigm of being close to the tissue explant in the number of cell divisions. Hence there could be greater opportunity to generate and propagate abnormal cells. The cells were also primate and human. Hence they could conceivably harbor hidden human viruses or be more susceptible to extraneous human pathogens introduced during production. Indeed, they have proven very susceptible to infection by many human and animal viruses and are commonly used in testing vaccine preparations for freedom from adventitious viruses. Nevertheless, as issues emerged with primary primate cells, diploid cells were eventually accepted by industry and the regulatory community and have been proven generally safe during the several decades they have been in use (82). The use of these cells is especially important for those viruses that cannot be readily removed from culture and host-cell contaminants.

The major diploid cell strains used for human vaccines in North America and Europe are the human embryonic lung strains WI-38 (83) and MRC-5 (84) and the fetal rhesus lung strain FRhL-2 (85,86). The history of use and the safety of these particular strains has been accepted to the extent that the most recent regulatory documents concerning cell substrate characterization specifically exempt these cell strains from some of the generally required safety tests (87,88). In general, diploid cell strains grow for a finite lifespan of ca. 50–80 doublings of the population (PDL) before ceasing to divide, a phenomenon called senescence. (The average number of doublings of a population of cells is referred to as the Population Doubling number, or PDL. The doubling number is calculated from tissue explant. A statement of PDL does not imply that each cell in the population has undergone the same number of divisions.) On occasion, mutations occur that cause a cell to become transformed to an immortal growth state and even become aneuploid and tumorigenic. Cells in production are restricted to less than two-thirds of the senescent PDL to ensure that chromosomal abnormalities have not accumulated that might cause such a change to a tumorigenic state. The manufacturer is obliged to demonstrate that diploid cells senesce, fail to cause tumors in immunosuppressed rodents, and have normal karyology at the PDL of use. Manufacturers are encouraged to develop two-tier banking systems for these cells to eliminate reliance on the limited National Institute for Biological Standardization and Control (NIBSC, UK) and American Type Culture Collection Master Banks of these cells.

Continuous Cells

Continuous cell line introduction into vaccine use has been even more controversial than diploid cell introduction, due to real concerns over potential tumorigenic behavior of these cells or their nucleic acid, which can be demonstrated for some continuous cells by injecting the cells or DNA into test animals (30,89,90). As time has gone by, however, the dangers of tumorigenic cellular DNA have become more quantifiable, and it appears that the risk from use of continuous cells is remote (91). To err on the side of safety, there is a requirement for clearance of DNA from the vaccine to a level of typically 100 pg/dose and for negative tumorigenicity testing to ensure safety (87,88). Notably, continuous cell lines are employed for human vaccines, with one exception, for inactivated vaccines where host-cell nucleic acids are likely to be irreparably damaged. The lines are, however, ubiquitous in the recombinant therapeutic protein product area, where nonhuman, nonprimate species are universally used, where purification is always stringent, and where the products are all therapeutics.

The only continuous cell line which has been widely used for human vaccines to date is the Vero cell line (92), which possesses anchorage-dependence and no metastatic tumor-producing potential at the passages used for vaccine production (93). It is used for polio and rabies viral production among others. Stocks are held by the World Health Organization and the American Type Culture Collection. Human vaccines employing Madin–Darby canine kidney (MDCK) cells are in development (20,94,95); this cell line is interesting as one of the few that polarizes upon contiguous monolayer

formation. It too possesses limited tumorigenic potential unless mutated (96,97). The BHK21 cell line has been employed extensively for veterinary FMDV vaccine since the 1960s (98,99), veterinary rabies vaccine (100), and more recently, for producing human recombinant therapeutic proteins such as Factor VIII (101). The use of this continuous tumorigenic line in a veterinary vaccine (along with use of the continuous Namalwa cell line for α-interferon production — this cell line was Epstein–Barr virus transformed and Sendai virus infected/induced, no less!) (102) set the stage for the use of continuous cell lines for human recombinant protein products (103). The cultivation technology developed for Vero and BHK21-cell-derived vaccines laid the foundation for the cell cultivation technology of the therapeutic protein industry (104).

Recombinant Cells

Recombinant cells have not been used for human vaccine production to date. This has been in part because the host cells are diploid with finite life spans prior to senescence, or for Vero, there is a limited number of passages before the cell line becomes tumorigenic. This feature precludes the cell-doubling consuming processes of cloning, expansion into cell banks, and vaccine production while staying within the PDL/tumorigenicity limits mentioned before. It has also been due to the inability to rigorously purify DNA and host protein from the common enveloped vaccine viruses with good retention of infectivity. However, engineered cells will eventually be used if risk–benefit analysis warrants it. Probable situations will be certain new technology platforms based on complementing (105–107) or packaging cells (108,109) for replication-defective virus vectors, or where necessary, for economic production (e.g., metabolic engineering, apoptosis inhibitor gene expression). Like continuous cell use, recombinant cells will incur extra regulatory scrutiny (90).

Cell Growth Considerations

The objectives of the cell substrate growth process for viral production are generally twofold. The first objective is to generate a mass of cells large enough to support production of the necessary viral quantity. The second is to have the cells in a physiological state appropriate to fostering efficient viral propagation.

Culture Hardware. The cell lines employed for human vaccines to date are exclusively anchorage-dependent, and the need to generate large masses of adherent cells has caused a sometimes quixotic quest for the "perfect" attachment-dependent culture hardware (110,111). This is due to the fact that the scale of culture is often in a regime where there is no best choice. If the production scales were slightly smaller, common lab technology such as flasks or roller bottles would prevail. If the scales were very much larger, (microcarrier) suspension cultures would be almost obligatory. Because the intermediate scales and viral characteristics favor no single technology, many alternatives have been developed. Only a few have survived as widespread practical (i.e., idiot-resistant) and economical (i.e., fast time to market and low operating cost) systems for production. These are the culture flask (112), roller bottle (113), disk propagator (114), Cell Factory® (115), certain fixed-bed loop bioreactor systems (116,117), and microcarrier (118,119) or suspension cell culture (120) in stirred tank reactors. There is no best culture system, and hardware selection often depends on the infrastructure and expertise of the manufacturer.

The desired features for culture technology are robustness in manufacturing operations, ease of process development, ease of validation for the system and the process, and an ability to control the environment of the cells. For viruses that are unstable in culture and have rapid replicative cycles, it is sometimes desirable to avoid bioreactor systems that cultivate cells in three-dimensional aggregates or as multilayers (68,116,121). Here, the inner cells have restricted access to the inoculated virus and thus are not infected in synchrony with the rest of the population. A last factor to consider in technology is the virus–host interaction that can affect the ability to harvest the virus. For viruses that accumulate intracellularly or on the cell surface, it is necessary either to lyse or recover the cells (often without resorting to enzymatic means that can destroy virus) to access the virus, and this can influence the choice of bioreactor technology. Some cell lines for future human vaccines will undoubtedly be adaptable to suspension, like BHK21 (120). This will enable the use of stirred, sparging-aerated reactors that will allow, employing standardized and fairly characterized technology. With respect to suspension culturing, there is some evidence that the host-cell growth mode, that is, suspension versus attached, affects viral replication for continuous cell lines and that viruses can adapt to the host growth mode to be more productive (122–126).

Cell Growth up to Infection. Viruses are obligate parasites that use the host-cell machinery to complete their replicative strategy. Thus the cell technologist should seek to elicit a cellular state conducive to viral synthesis immediately before infection for those elements that are not rapidly induced or accumulated from the culture medium. Most viruses have evolved strategies to divert cellular resources away from the host cell's natural program and into the viral synthesis pathway after infection (127). Hence a well-nourished cell with an appropriate growth and enzymatic state (e.g., actively synthesizing DNA in the case of some DNA viruses) (128) and abundant intra- and extracellular substrate pools generally maximizes viral yields (129–131). Note that for low multiplicity infections (much less than one virus per cell), the majority of cells are infected many hours after culture inoculation with virus.

For the relatively few cell lines already adopted for vaccine production (CEF, WI-38, MRC-5, Vero, BHK21, MDCK), their extensive availability and genetic homogeneity relative to recombinant lines have made the optimal nutrient requirements (132–143), feeding regimens (144–150), growth factor requirements (151–155), serum-free (156–163) and low serum (161,164–166)

media fairly well known. Although most vaccines today are derived from cells cultivated from animal products such as serum and trypsin, there is a growing drive to eliminate animal-sourced raw materials from vaccine production, purification, and formulation processes because of real concerns over viral adventitious agents, sometimes from quite unexpected sources (167,168). Theoretical concerns over spongiform encephalopathic agents have also been voiced. In lieu of complete removal, measures are taken to obtain these culture components from known and controlled source animals, to handle the tissues appropriately, to screen them thoroughly for agents, and to treat them before use to inactivate any potentially undetected agents (169–175).

VIRAL GROWTH

Conceptually, viral growth in culture can be broken into a set of events: delivery of virus to the cell, attachment to the cell, penetration into the cytoplasm, uncoating of the genome and delivery of the nucleic acid to the site of transcription, transcription and translation of the genome in one or more cycles of expression, replication of the genome, final production of virion components, virion assembly, and egress from the cell. The discussion following focuses on the principles of the individual events in replication, followed by considerations and general approaches that the cell culture technologist can take to influence the events favorably. The affectors of growth cited following are not inclusive, and those mentioned tend to be more universal or interesting. Perusal of the virological literature will reveal many more effects, often applicable to only certain virus–host cell systems or particular mutant viral strains. Many literature observations are also from contrived situations that are not relevant to industrial viral propagation; they are often intended to establish, via an all-or-nothing condition, that a particular factor plays a role in viral replication. In other words, virologists are usually interested in "how the virus does it," not "how much the virus does it."

Transport

Before a virus can attach to a cell, it needs to be close to the membrane. Hence transport of the virion to the cell is an issue in viral cultivation. Optimizing viral delivery minimizes inoculum degradation and ensures that the infection occurs at a consistent multiple of virions per cell (known as the multiplicity of infection, or MOI). Viruses are typically 20–250 nm in size with Stokesian diffusion coefficients on the order of 10^{-7} to 10^{-8} cm^2/s (176). Hence they possess a diffusion time scale ($\approx L^2/\mathcal{D}$, the diffusion length scale squared divided by the diffusivity) of hours for penetration distances of only 100 μm, about the depth of a typical medium overlay in static culture. Due to this, the virus transport rate to the cell is usually limited by diffusion (177–180). It can be calculated that relatively high shear rates are necessary for convection to dominate viral transport, levels that are about the highest typically encountered in routine stirred cell culture (181). Cell accessibility to a virus is also a consideration for cells that are cultured as aggregates in suspension (182), as multilayers (121,147), or on porous growth supports (183). Because of diffusive transport limitations and blocking by other cells, infection in these situations is not uniform and true MOI and its distribution can vary substantially from theoretical. It is worth noting that not all viruses are inoculated into a culture as individual virions; for some herpesviruses where the virus is strongly cell-associated or labile in the cell-free state, the inoculum can be an infected cell suspension (184–186), and for these cases inoculum diffusion is irrelevant, but transport efficiency of the infected cellular inoculum can still depend on convective transport and reactor considerations (187,188).

Transport speed can be maximized by concentrating cells and virus at the point of inoculation, by reducing the depth of the medium overlay for monolayers, by introducing convection into the system (189,190), or by enhancing the transport of the virus to the cell by other means, for example, centrifugation of virus onto a monolayer (190). Transport speed and its control is important when the virus is labile and/or where the transport phase constitutes a significant portion of the replicative cycle time.

Attachment

Attachment of virions to the cell surface is mediated by specific receptors, and this is a major determinant of tissue tropism of viruses. Receptors can be ubiquitous, as in the case of sialoglycoproteins, or they can be also be relatively rare proteins present on only a few cell types (as in the case of the CD4 receptor for HIV-1) or certain species (191) and at relatively low densities; the receptor density can be determined by Scatchard plots of equilibrium virus binding, usually at low temperatures that preclude viral internalization. (Quotations of receptor number are defined by experimental conditions — the number of viral binding *sites* measured in an experiment is relative and should not be equated with the abundance of receptor *molecules*.) The rate and equilibrium of viral binding is directly related to the availability of receptors and the affinity of the receptor–virus interaction. Several receptor molecule attachments are usually required to achieve the binding energy critical for "irreversible" attachment (192). This is due to low affinity (which does not imply nonselectivity) of single interactions (193) and reflects the evolution of selective target cell infection. For certain viruses, a distinct coreceptor is required after initial binding (194,195); attachment to the coreceptor is often coupled with membrane penetration. Irreversible receptor–virus attachment is not instantaneous. Viral attachment rates to cells are lower than predicted solely by transport considerations in many instances (181,196,197), although attachment rate limitations can be difficult to detect (198,199).

Attachment can be influenced by parameters that affect the availability of receptors. It has been shown experimentally that increasing cell surface receptor density promotes infection in certain instances (200,201). Some viral receptors are obliterated by treatment of the cells with trypsin or other enzymes (202), whereas viral attachment is enhanced by enzymes in other

instances (203). Enhancement could be due to receptor modification or to uncovering of receptors made cryptic by extracellular matrix secretion (204). Receptors can be localized on certain areas of the cell membrane (205–207) and hence can be affected by cell polarization in confluent monolayers of some cell types. Creating artificial binding sites on the cells or virus via chemical addition, for example, addition of polycations to the inoculum, has proven profitable for accelerating infection in many instances (208–210). The latter must be considered cautiously, however, as polycation addition can affect cell health or suppress later replication (211); it may serve to increase infection speed but can lower total yield per cell.

An issue for the practitioner is ensuring a culture milieu that promotes virus–receptor interactions. Although pH optima exist for viral adsorption, with a few exceptions these are quite broad (in the cell culture context) and have maxima in the physiological range (212). Temperature affects binding because it influences cell membrane fluidity and recruitment of receptors or coreceptors, but the effects are typically very weak within the typical range of cell cultivations (213), which can be down to 30 °C for some cold-adapted viral strains. Divalent cations are required for attaching certain viruses to receptors (214–219), and the levels of magnesium and calcium found in typical culture media are usually sufficient for maximal attachment. Polyanions, especially sulfated polysaccharides (181,220–222), are notorious for broad antiviral activity, but Pluronic F68, carboxymethylcellulose (CMC), and polyvinyl alcohol sometimes used for interfacial and shear damage protection do not reportedly affect virus infection. Viscous CMC solutions are sometimes used in plaque assays as inert, diffusion-preventing overlays. It should be noted that for semipurified vaccines, any additives to the culture must be acceptable for clinical administration.

One mechanism by which viral attachment can be hampered is the competition of noninfectious virus particles or viral component proteins in the inoculum for cellular receptors (203). This is a potential issue when trying to assess the amount of replication-competent virus in a semi-inactive preparation where the noninfectious to infectious particle ratio is very high (41,223). With careful propagation, the amounts of defective virus or unassembled components in a typical inoculum should not be large enough to block attachment, although such components can interfere with subsequent replicative steps (224). Viral stocks are typically expanded at low MOI to avoid accumulation of "defective interfering particles" that have acquired mutations (225,226); the mutant viruses cannot grow by themselves, but they can complement each others' mutations at high MOI (multiple infections per cell) or be assisted by functional viruses, leading to packaging and propagation of the defective genomes.

Viral Penetration and Uncoating

A virus penetrates into a host cell by one of two routes: direct penetration of or fusion with the plasma membrane or receptor-mediated endocytosis that leads to penetration of/fusion with an endosomal vesicle membrane. In direct fusion, viral binding to enough plasma membrane receptors or a coreceptor causes a conformational change in the viral envelope or capsid, which then triggers fusion of the viral envelope with the membrane or uncoating of the viral capsid. This spills either a nucleocapsid or the genome with accessory proteins directly into the cytoplasm. As might be imagined, when a nonencapsidated genome is injected into the cytoplasm, this is the site of viral replication, and the accessory proteins in the virion are required to initiate the replicative cycle. When a capsid enters, further events, such as binding of host proteins to the capsid to cause genome release or trafficking of the capsid to nuclear pores where the genome is injected into the nucleus, are often required to initiate replication.

In receptor-mediated endocytosis, the virus and its receptors are phagocytized in a coated pit to form an endosome. The endosome undergoes acidification which triggers conformational change in a viral capsid or envelope protein, and this causes fusion with the vesicle membrane. Thus the rate of fusion and entry into the cytoplasm to begin the intracellular replicative cycle is dictated by the rates of endocytosis and acidification of vesicles. Half-lives of vesicle internalization on the order of 5–30 minutes are common (196,227). As with direct fusion processes, the initial penetration of virus can introduce a genome or can be followed by multistep dismantling and transport of the capsid to the location for transcription (227). Endocytosis does not lead to quantitative delivery of virus because errant endosomal sorting can lead to the destruction of a substantial fraction of the entering virus (228).

Penetration rates can be affected by some cell culture conditions. Penetration and uncoating steps are typically energy-dependent and can be affected by temperature and variables that affect cell metabolism (229). Depending on the cell type and its growth state, the rate of endocytosis can be rapid or slow. Confluent or quiescent primary and diploid cell monolayers can have lowered rates of endocytic activity relative to actively growing cells because of low rates of cellular division and protein synthesis. Endosomal acidification is affected by millimolar quantities of weak bases such as ammonia in the medium, and this can impact fusion and viral replication (230–233) although the phenomenon is not ubiquitous for viruses that use endocytic pathways for entry; this may reflect the use of multiple routes of infection and their predominance in various cell types, differences in the intrinsic endosomal pH of different cells, or the pH required for fusion of different viruses (234–237). The presence of membrane cholesterol is a well-established prerequisite for virus fusion by some enveloped viruses (238). Although it has been suggested that cells cultured under cholesterol-depleted conditions produce lower virus yields (239,240), the effect probably does not persist under prolonged cultivation in these conditions (241). It is probably due to altered membrane fluidity because infection permissivity can be enhanced by fluidity modifiers for many viruses (190,242,243). However, in some instances, fluidity modification by chemicals such as DMSO may be making up for defective viral activation or maturation and/or providing an unnatural infection route of entry.

Considering these data, it is worth adapting cells to serum-free conditions well before infection, although this has not been reported in the literature as beneficial to viral culture.

Animal sera can contain antibodies or other components reactive to viruses (244–248) and can have multiple effects on viral growth. Antibody neutralization of virus in many instances is not directed toward inhibition of receptor-mediated attachment, but toward inhibition of endocytosis, fusion, or uncoating via interference with capsid conformation changes or disassembly (249). Serum also contains complement proteins that can lyse virus or infected cells, and it neutralizes proteases that are sometimes necessary for "activation" or "maturation" of certain viruses (250,251), a prerequisite to penetration and fusion. Because of its interference properties and the inability to purify it thoroughly away from many viruses, serum is usually absent or is employed at the lowest levels possible during infection. When used during infection, it is often from fetal sources that have lower immunoglobulin levels than adult sera and may be either immunoglobulin-depleted or "heat-inactivated" (typically 56 °C for 30 minutes) to ensure destruction of complement components (252).

Replication of Viral Components

A detailed treatment of the different strategies for replicating viral components is not possible in a short article such as this because of the great diversity of genomic structures and replicative strategies (253,254) and the existence of multiple replicative "programs" in cells, for example, latent or persistent infections. The technologist is interested only in productive—and most often lytic—infections for producing vaccine virus, the basic cycle of which is roughly as follows. The viral genome is first transcribed and/or at least partially translated to produce "early" proteins that are necessary to enable one or more of the activities, further viral transcription, genomic replication, or interference with host-cell functions. Then the genome is reproduced, and this event is taken to define a boundary between "early" and "late" life-cycle events. The genome is further transcribed/translated to produce late proteins that incorporate into the virion, chaperone the assembly of the virion, or interfere with host-cell processes to allow for either efficient viral replication or viral egress. Depending on the virus and its genomic structure, there are one, two, or three sequential cycles of early and late transcription and translation in all. In productive infections, the virus immediately initiates its replicative program upon penetration and uncoating, and the earliest events are seen within minutes. The entire replicative program can take from a couple of hours to a day, and it can produce infectious virions ranging from a few to tens of thousands per cell.

Depending on the viral family, the viral genome is translated, transcribed, and replicated in the cytoplasm, the nucleus, or both. The cytoplasmic replicative strategy is most often used by RNA viruses that do not generate DNA and have no need for nuclear involvement. These viruses encode their own RNA polymerases to enable genomic replication. DNA viruses replicate the genome in the nucleus where they have access to cellular machinery, except for the poxviruses and papovaviruses that replicate in the cytoplasm and encode their own polymerases.

Assembly of Viral Components

As the components of the virus are replicated, they are assembled into new virions that may be modified or "matured" and then egress from the cell. These processes also take place by divergent mechanisms (255). Because capsids are composed of several hundred molecules, capsid assembly for viruses takes place in steps. First, individual proteins associate to form "capsomeres," which then are further assembled into more complex structures or into virions. Chaperone proteins may be transiently associated with or incorporated into the structures and then removed at later steps such as genomic encapsidation. The viral genome may begin encapsidation during assembly of the capsomeres or during final virion assembly (255,256), and genomic incorporation relies on specific nucleotide sequences that code for attachment either to capsid proteins or to chaperones. Bases such as polyamines (257–259), histones (260) (or histone-like molecules) are often present in significant quantity, ostensibly to neutralize and condense the nucleic acid and enable packaging it within the confines of the capsid (261,262). As part of the process of capsid formation or maturation, the capsid proteins may be modified, for example, cleaved, to mediate conformational changes that enable final assembly, stability, or infectivity of the capsid (251,263,264).

For enveloped viruses, the envelope around the capsid is acquired via a budding (sometimes a "wrapping") (265) process where the envelope glycoproteins associate with each other to form rafts on a cellular membrane and the capsid is coated in the glycoprotein-lipid envelope as it penetrates through or "buds" from the membrane. In some cases a "matrix" protein or tegument is interposed between the nucleocapsid and the envelope, and these proteins probably facilitate assembly. Viral acquisition of an envelope can occur at the endoplasmic reticulum, Golgi, nuclear, or cytoplasmic membranes (266,267). Acquisition of cytoplasmic membrane can be localized in polarized cells (268). For all but cytoplasmic acquisition, the enveloped virus exits the cell via transport vesicles and an exocytotic pathway. This does not always imply secretion of free virus because some viruses remain associated with the external face of the cytoplasmic membrane after exocytosis. Envelope lipid composition reflects the composition of the compartment membrane through which budding occurs, but host-cell glycoproteins are excluded from the viral envelope by association of the envelope proteins with themselves or with scaffolding, matrix, or tegument proteins. As with capsid proteins for nonenveloped virus, envelope glycoproteins can be matured further by proteolytic cleavage to create the infectious particle (250,269).

Viruses employ varying cellular compartments to replicate components, assemble the virion, and egress from the cell. Capsid proteins that are inside another capsid shell or envelope are non-glycosylated, and are synthesized in the cytoplasm. This is also true of outer capsid proteins of nonenveloped, non-glycosylated

viruses. Glycosylated capsid and envelope proteins are processed through the endoplasmic reticulum (ER) and Golgi-apparatus-like host proteins and are subsequently directed to appropriate transport vesicles via a signal on the protein (270). The same types of post-translational modifications that occur for host proteins are performed on either glycosylated or non-glycosylated viral proteins (e.g., sulfation, carboxylation, phosphorylation, acylation, cleavage). In addition to structural components of the viral capsid, transcription factors, host-affecting proteins, or chaperone proteins that facilitate assembly are also produced (255), and these can be processed through different routes per their genetic sequence. As with viral attachment, egress of virus can take place through preferential locations on the cytoplasmic membrane (271,272).

The cell Growth State, Intracellular Replication, and Assembly. Unlike early infection, owing to the diversity of replicative strategies and to regulation of the intracellular environment, it is not possible to make many generalizations regarding the effect of the cell growth state on replication and assembly. Viruses do certain common things during *in vitro* replication that are of interest to the technologist, however. To a greater or lesser extent, they employ, host-cell machinery for DNA synthesis, transcription, translation, and post-translational protein modifications. It is reasonable to assume that a cell that is generally fit and actively conducting these activities will better replicate virus. The diploid cell types that are the mainstay of vaccine processing exhibit a wide range of activity within the limits of *in vitro* culture conditions; growth can range from rapid cycling to indefinite existence in the G0 state. This is decidedly unlike transformed cells that tend either to unregulated growth at "full throttle" or apoptosis. Knowing which host macromolecular elements are required for viral synthesis and which activities are down- or up-regulated in the cells can inform as to potential effects of the cell state on permissivity and productivity. For example, promoting cell cycling through the S phase increases growth for some DNA viruses that rely on cellular polymerases (273–275). Adding proteolytic enzymes is a well-known tactic to overcome cellular deficiencies in replicative permissivity or viral maturation capability (276,277). Also, knowing which elements are likely to become deficient and limit the host cell's ability to sustain itself and continue viral production can be potentially useful. Serum and most growth hormones generally lack effects that are not attributable to host-cell fitness, under or overdosing relative to typical culture conditions, or highly virally-specific effects (278–283).

In a productive infection, viruses typically compete for host-cell resources by shutting off one or more of the cell's major functions, DNA synthesis, transcription, or translation (127,284–286). Although viruses starve the host cell by these strategies, they also murder cells by inducing apoptosis or torture them by inhibiting apoptosis as the cells attempt suicide. It has been suggested that viral apoptosis strategies have evolved either to maximize productive replication, to enable viral egress, or to enable persistence (287–289). There are hints that inhibition of apoptosis can improve component replication in some virus–host systems (290,291), but utility for increasing virus yields will be system-dependent and is relatively unexplored (292–295). To be useful, any inhibitory strategies (chemical additions, cell or virus genetic modifications) must meet safety expectations.

Culture Conditions, Intracellular Replication, and Assembly. A search of the literature for culture environments or medium conditions that affect viral replication and assembly turns up interesting effects that are sometimes widely, sometimes selectively applicable. It should be noted up front that in studying culture condition effects on viral replication, the timing of the culture perturbation can be critical to experimental success and interpretation because the perturbing agent will often act only on specific steps of the viral cycle and because cellular accumulation, depletion, or adaptation may also play a role. Perturbative timing is often used in conjunction with single-step growth curves (see below) to ferret out the particular replicative step that is being affected. As mentioned in the cell growth section, maintaining healthy, nourished cells in a controlled environment (which should be done for any cell culture process) will foster maximal viral replication. The conditions mentioned below illustrate the boundaries of productive culture conditions.

Nutritional Effects. For some robustly growing viruses, the amount of viral protein expression can be on the order of 10–20% of the total cell protein and is achieved in 24–48 hours (296–298). These levels of replication place a demand on the cell for protein expression that rivals the best of amplified rDNA protein constructs, and they often occur in a disintegrating cell. This emphasizes that the supply of primary building blocks of virus can play a key role in intensive culturing (299–301). Deprivation of essential amino acids ablates viral production in many systems, and less commonly amino acid increases stimulate viral production, emphasizing that their levels are important during infection (130,302–309). The effect of arginine deprivation is particularly widespread (310–316). It will be noted that amino acid deprivation does not necessarily affect polypeptide synthesis because amino acids can be involved in regulation or other functions necessary for viral replication (317–320). Despite these phenomena, however, a few viruses replicate in the absence of common culture nutrients and add-back at infection does not improve titers, lending emphasis to the dependence on intracellular pools and culture state at infection for rapidly replicating viruses that do not place a high metabolic demand on the host cell (321–323). Complete deprivation of energy sources (glutamine, glucose, pyruvate) is detrimental, although there is little information on levels below which viral growth is affected. These are likely to be at or above the levels found for cellular inhibition because viral infection places increased and shifted metabolic demands on cells (324–332). Insulin reportedly negatively influences kinetics (333) or yields (136,334–336) of some viruses, ostensibly through altering intracellular glucose levels. Employing energy sources (fructose, galactose, glutamine) alternative to the lactogenic glucose substrate

can stabilize medium pH better in uncontrolled situations (encountered in roller bottles, Nunc Cell Factories, etc.) (149,337–340); this may be beneficial where infection is affected by pH. Alternatively, buffering can be increased. Compositions that enhance ammonia production should be avoided, as noted before. The addition of nucleic acid bases or nucleosides has reportedly variable effects, either decreasing (137) or enhancing (136) viral output.

General Culture Condition Effects. The degree of culture oxygen saturation does not usually have a strong effect (barring anoxia), although it is generally acknowledged that adequate oxygen is required for optimal viral synthesis (341–349). However, viruses sometimes appear to modulate intracellular redox by promoting reactive oxygen specie generation (350), so culture redox affectors that mediate intracellular redox in turn can modulate some virus–host systems (351,352). Extreme additions or the absence of antioxidants (vitamins A, C, E, selenium, pyruvate, glutathione, N-acetyl cysteine) can either increase or inhibit viral production (273,353–355); these phenomena are possibly related to modulation of the caspase pathway of apoptosis (see above). pH optima for replication in the physiological regime are reported for many viruses (356–364). Temperature often shows an optimum below 37 °C due to more rapid host-cell or viral degradation at higher temperatures (365) or cold adaptation of the virus. The latter is an especially prevalent factor for attenuated vaccine viral strains (13,366–368).

The ionic composition of the medium (K$^+$, Na$^+$, HPO$_4{}^-$, HCO$_3{}^-$, trace metals) does not usually affect viral replication within the normal range, but some salts and other additives can be manipulated to advantage. Calcium is necessary for assembly or capsid stability for a couple of viral families and should optimally be present in millimolar quantities (369). Magnesium sulfate addition of 10–50 mM reportedly enhances viral replication (56,370,371), and speculation is that the effect is due either to enhanced protein synthesis and cell cycling or to enhanced egress. In some cases the effect may be simply one of medium hypertonicity (372,373) because it is replicable using sodium sulfate, sodium chloride, or magnesium chloride (374,375). Hypotonicity is known to suppress replication of certain viruses (376,377), although at osmolarities well below what would normally be used in culture. It is not clear that salts or tonicity act uniformly on component replication; some of the effects may be on viral assembly efficiency (378). Dimethyl sulfoxide addition to cultures reportedly enhances viral production (and/or plaque assay detection) in many systems, and effects are ascribed to enhanced cell cycling, viral or cellular transcriptional activity (379–381), or viral assembly efficiency (382). Substances that affect intracellular compartments involved in viral assembly or maturation can affect productivity by some of the same mechanisms that poison uncoating (113,383).

Antibiotics were one of the great enabling technologies for *in vitro* cultivation of cells for vaccine production. Without them, currently successful vaccines and biologics would not be possible. The Enders group's successful cultivation of poliovirus in nonneural tissue, with which

Sabin had failed a decade earlier (384), was partly due to their ability to maintain cultures longer in the presence of the new antibiotics and thus detect delayed replication (385). Inhibitory effects of aminoglycoside antibiotics occur at high concentrations in several systems (386–390), but effects at the levels used for contamination prophylaxis are not generally documented.

VIRAL PROCESSING

Growth Kinetics and Process Configuration

Without regard to the specifics of viral replication, the process scientist can make many initial decisions about the infection process based on a few simple principles and experiments. Fundamental to the configuration of an infection process is knowledge of the "one-step growth curve" (391) of virus in the host cell of interest. This is illustrated in Figure 2 for a typical lytic viral infection. In this experiment, virus is added to a theoretical MOI greater than one, and the culture is observed for the appearance of new infectious virus or antigen in the cell and supernate fractions. Virus initially disappears from the supernate as it attaches and penetrates the cell. This is followed by the "eclipse" phase during which the infectious virus reaches a minimum in the supernate, when the early events of intracellular replication take place. The infectious virus increases in the cells and/or supernate as the replicative cycle is completed; depending on the system, the virus can be retained in the cell fraction or released to the supernate. Finally, virus infectivity titers typically decrease as production ceases and the newly synthesized

virus decays under culture conditions. "Antigen" (virion structural protein) production accompanies infectivity, and there is always more antigen produced than assembled into infectious particles. It is often more stable than infectivity.

The one-step experiment provides several pieces of useful information. First, the disappearance rate of the virus from the supernate indicates the rapidity of viral transport and attachment. Second, the evolution of either viral components or infectious particles gives an indication of the intrinsic length of time required for the various events in the viral life cycle. Third, the maximum titer achieved gives an indication of the "burst size" or number of infectious virus produced per cell under the most rapid (and presumably most favorable) conditions. Last, measuring the decay phase gives an indication of the stability of the virus produced. Using these pieces of information, infection strategies for production can be devised. Note that for viruses that are not immediately lytic to the cells, the maximum titer may be limited not by cell destruction, but by nutrient depletion or waste product accumulation. In this instance, medium exchanges and further monitoring of viral titers in a one-step experiment give additional information about the intrinsic output and kinetics of an established infection and the evolution of the eventual cytopathic effect.

The rate of viral transport gives an indication of the true MOI and the effectiveness and rate of viral delivery under production conditions (although viral decay may need to be taken into account in some instances) and can guide the researcher as to whether the special measures to enhance the rate or extent of infection discussed before should be employed to benefit the process. Maximizing the

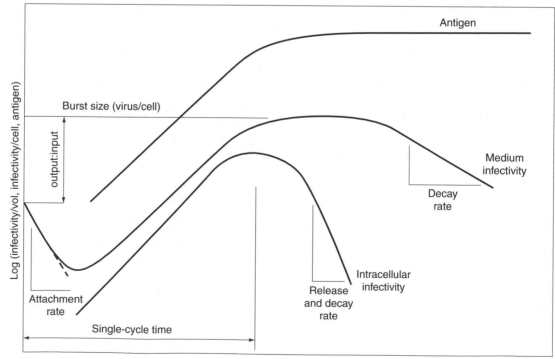

Figure 2. Typical one-step growth curve for a lytic, extracellular, labile virus.

extent of infection for a given viral input can be important for viruses with low output to input ratios.

The maximum titer achieved can be combined with the (effective) MOI to calculate the output to input ratio of a round of infection. This information is used for a couple of items of process configuration. The first consideration is viral supply. As with cell banks, viral stocks for production are usually laid down as two-tier Master and Working Seeds. Because of the extensive adventitious viral testing required of these seeds and the length of time required to perform these tests (some of which last for months), it is convenient to have a Working Seed life span of at least a year in production. To avoid questions of viral mutation that might occur from switching Master Seeds frequently, it is preferred that the Master Seed has a life span that approximates the product's market life span. When the output to input ratio is small (less than ca. 50:1 total), it becomes evident that to preserve Master and Working Seed life spans, a MOI less than one must be used (multiple infection cycles in a culture), the Working Seed to vaccine process scale ratio has to be increased so that the fraction of Working Seed consumed per year is small, or a serial "hot" passage (i.e., not from a cryopreserved stock) must be used in the process (186,392,393). Even if the output to input ratio is very high, it is generally undesirable to propagate virus at high MOI (>1) for multiple passages to avoid defective viral generation and propagation.

The replicative and release time cycle and the maximum viral titer guide the configuration of several parameters for the infection. Given the constraints on MOI above, the process will typically need to support one to three cycles of infection. The total cycle time and the cell concentration at infection dictate the consumption of nutrients and accumulation of waste and thereby impose limits on the maximum profitable cell density for a batch culture process (300,393) or indicate that feeding and/or waste removal should occur during the infection for maximum productivity (117). For low MOI processes, the initially uninfected cells may continue to grow until the first virus burst occurs, and this poses an additional variable to take into account (394). Factored into the decision to use high cell density and to feed during infection are the purity and dose requirements for the vaccine. Most often, uninfected host cells are grown in bovine or equine serum-containing medium or protein hydrolysates. For viruses that are secreted or released by lysis into the medium and are not amenable to purification, a medium exchange to serum-free culture is mandatory to avoid allergic reactions (395,396). A medium exchange to low or zero protein conditions can be required for viruses that require exogenous proteolytic activation (119,251,397,398) to avoid neutralization of added enzyme activity. Many viruses tend to be labile (399–403), especially the secreted, enveloped viruses, and optimization of the mode and frequency of feeding needs to take into account requirements for minimum viral titer (these same viruses are not readily purified or concentrated and are often formulated by simple dilution into a stabilizer) (114) and net culture productivity. Specific experiments independent of one-step growth curves are often required to accurately determine decay kinetics.

To complement the empirical efforts that are always necessary to optimize each new virus–host system, there have been several recent attempts to model various stages of viral propagation to refine the conditions for viral growth (or recombinant protein production from recombinant systems) (196,394,404–406). These models can provide good insight into the influence of variables in infections. In addition, there is a wealth of information on the commonly used insect cell–baculovirus system that illustrates many of the concepts for process optimization discussed in the previous sections (226,299,300,301,407–415).

Viral Assay Considerations

Where viral productivity is reported in the literature, the measure of infection success is often an *in vitro* infectivity assay. For viruses destined for inactivated vaccines, the output of interest may be a measure of the antigen. In the days before *in vitro* culture, virus was titrated by infecting animals, eggs, or chips of eggshell/chorioallantoic membrane with serial dilutions of virus to find a nontoxic end-point dilution. The titration of animal viruses was vastly improved by Dulbecco's translation of the bacteriophage plaque assay on bacterial lawns to the titration of animal viruses on animal cell monolayers (416). This assay, the tissue culture infectious dose ($TCID_{50}$) assay, or indirect immunofluorescence assay is usually employed to titrate cultures (32,417). The plaque assay is conducted by infecting a monolayer of susceptible cells with a dilution of virus sufficient to produce a small number of infection points. After an initial adsorption period, the monolayer is usually covered with a medium containing a gelling polymer to prevent diffusion of viral progeny; the result is that virus grows outward from the initial point of infection and develops a circular "plaque" of cytopathic effect. The plaque can be visualized by a number of different methods. The indirect immunofluorescence assay (focus-forming assay) is a variation of the plaque assay where viral replication is visualized by an immunostaining method in lieu of the cytopathic effect. In the $TCID_{50}$ assay, the virus is serially diluted and inoculated into a multiwell dish containing cells. Cell sheet infection in the wells is assessed as $+/-$ after a period of replication, and the end-point dilution of virus where 50% of the wells would have been infected ($TCID_{50}$) is estimated statistically (418,419). Because of the Poisson distribution involved in this type of end-point dilution assay, the concentration of infectious viral units is $TCID_{50}/0.69$.

Assays to measure antigenic mass for inactivated vaccines vary widely. Hemagglutination assays have been used extensively for influenza (49) and some other viruses (420) which use receptors on red blood cells (RBCs). Here virus is serially diluted into a multiwell plate containing a RBC suspension; at low dilutions, the viruses will cross-link the RBCs. As the virus is diluted across the plate, the end-point dilution at which the cells no longer visibly aggregate can be estimated (as is done for the $TCID_{50}$ assay). It is obvious that a hemagglutination titer obtained by this method does not return the concentration of viral particles because the viruses act in mass to cause the aggregation. ELISA assays are useful to measure antigenic mass and may be related to standard preparations with a known mass concentration (421). However, for vaccine quality control, an ELISA using mono- or polyclonal serum measures *antigenicity* of epitopes that may be irrelevant to *immunogenicity* in man. Because of this situation, inactivated vaccines have historically been potency tested using animal models of immunogenicity (422,423). To employ an ELISA assay, the antibody(ies) must be carefully selected (424). In the future, rapid epitope mapping techniques may be used which may allow eliminating animal potency testing (425). Clearly, a myriad of other measurements can be applied to assess the synthesis and stability of individual viral components (DNA, RNA, proteins, viral particles, and assembly intermediates), and these are highly useful for characterizing the viral life cycle and the manufacturing process, if not directly for the quality control of vaccine.

One main point of mentioning the common assay methods before is that they, too, are biological processes, for example, an infectivity assay is another cell culture process followed by several serial viral infections. Quite understandably, these assays have variable sensitivity and are notoriously imprecise if not performed under strictly controlled conditions and with repetition (419,426). For these reasons, a good fraction of the virological literature quotes infectivity titers in $\log_{10}$ units of virus — modest changes in infectivity (ca. twofold or less) should be particularly scrutinized. The same is true of antigenic content; no less than twofold differences in concentration are often reported. These levels of imprecision render process development very difficult and underscore the need for well-controlled and sensitive assay technology to be successful.

The second main point is that interpretation of biological assay data is often difficult. In particular, it should be recognized that an infectivity titer is always a relative number due to variable assay sensitivity (269,417,426,427), and it cannot be considered to approximate the true number of viral particles in a sample unless confirmed by physical and biochemical measurements of viral particles or components (177). For some viruses, the assembly intermediates are infectious to varying degrees, and this can further complicate interpretation of infectivity data (428–430). Further, it is often an imponderable as to how *in vitro* infectivity, antigenicity, or animal immunogenicity relates to human *in vivo* infectivity or immunogenicity. For adenoviral gene therapies, the U.S. FDA has requested physical measurement of the total of viral particles in infectious preparations as the primary measure for dosing and suggests that infectivity assays be used only to confirm quality; this perhaps indicates a distrust of the accuracy and precision of infectivity assays (431).

In summary, the animal cell technologist must read the literature carefully for the system of interest to divine phenomena relevant and significant to manufacturing. Although infectivity and "antigen" are stressed in the previous discussions, the viral replicative cycle in the host cell of interest must be understood and characterized to understand the bottlenecks in viral replication and to approach optimization rationally. It should not be taken for granted that the general literature pertains to large-scale production systems using selected and sometimes highly altered virus.

VACCINES AND EXAMPLES OF PROCESSES

The following sections give examples of historical and current vaccine processes that have made significant contributions to society or to cell culture technology, are illustrative of the general points in the previous sections, or have set precedent for regulatory issues. It is interesting to contrast the different levels of sophistication for the processes, especially over the course of time as technology matured and as newer vaccines emanated from industry, not public laboratories. Unfortunately, a thorough treatment of all the extant manufacturing processes is not possible because of the lack of a comprehensive and clear public record.

Poliovirus Vaccines

Poliovirus is primarily an enteric virus that infects the intestinal tract via a fecal–oral route. In the process of intestinal infection, viremia occurs which on occasion results in nervous system infection and paralysis. Until the twentieth century, paralytic poliomyelitis disease was relatively infrequent because infection usually occurred early in life when maternal antibody was still present. As sanitation improved, juvenile infections were deferred, causing severe disease with greater frequency. By the late 1940s, epidemics were becoming increasingly devastating, and paralysis afflicted 1 in 5,000 people (432). The creation of a vaccine was enabled by *in vitro* poliovirus cultivation in nonneural tissues in the late 1940s (53), a feat that won Enders, Weller, and Robinson the 1954 Nobel prize for medicine. Previously, it had been possible only to propagate the virus in animals or *in vitro* in nervous system cells, which were known to be unacceptable as a vaccine substrate because of neurological complications which had occurred with myelin protein in brain-derived inactivated rabies vaccines (47,433). Although smallpox (vaccinia/cowpox), rabies, and yellow fever viral vaccines preceded them, polio vaccines were the first biological products from *in vitro* animal cell culture to have a large impact on society and are only the second to drive a human virus to the edge of extinction. Global extermination of poliovirus disease is a goal targeted by the WHO for the year 2000 (434).

The poliovirus has been classified as a picornavirus, and the polio vaccines are two of four major picornavirus vaccines. The virus is a small (ca. 28 nm), single-stranded, (+) sense RNA virus that replicates in the cytoplasm. Entry is via direct membrane fusion, after which the RNA genome is translated, replicated, and the structural proteins and RNA assembled stepwise into icosahedral particles. The assembled capsid is matured by cleavage of the VP0 capsid protein to VP2 + VP4, and the virion exits via cell lysis, which is caused by a combination of host-cell translation inhibition and viral protein expression. For production purposes, the viruses replicate rapidly and to very high levels per cell, so multiplicities of infection are low and the output to input ratio is very high. The virus is released into the culture medium over a period of days, and this is harvested for the vaccine. For vaccination purposes, the fully matured form of the virus (the "D antigen") is infectious and immunogenic and is the desired culture product; the unmatured provirion is not. The virus has three major serological types, designated 1, 2, and 3. These are cultivated individually and combined to construct a trivalent vaccine.

The inactivated Salk vaccine was the first to be introduced in 1955, and only later were the attenuated live Sabin vaccine strains developed and introduced in 1962. The polio vaccines broke acres of new ground in their licensure. Heretofore, there had been no concerns about cell substrate choice, culture media, *in vitro* culture technology, or infection processes — the vaccines of the time were made by propagating virus on calf hides, in animal brains, and in eggs. They are distinctly different vaccines and are discussed separately later.

Inactivated (Killed) Polio Vaccine (IPV/KPV). The Salk inactivated polio vaccine was the first to be mass-produced and was largely responsible for eliminating the disease from North America and parts of Europe (435). The main virtue of IPV lies in its proven safety record during 45 years of use after some initial difficulties with the formaldehyde viral inactivation step (436) and with adventitious viruses in the primary monkey kidney cell substrates (58). The drawback of IPV from a process perspective is that a relatively large amount of virus antigen must be injected to induce immunity, thus the vaccine costs considerably more to manufacture than the attenuated live vaccine. However, this requirement for massive and efficient production of antigen on an anchorage-dependent cell substrate makes IPV processing fascinating to technologists.

As a consequence of the need for multiple producers to achieve a large market supply, a number of labs initially produced virus according to the Salk process. Primary human cells were not desirable. So, monkey cells were employed for virus cultivation because tissues of these animals were known to be susceptible to the virus. Kidney cells in particular were adopted because they produced the highest titers of virus of the various monkey tissues and were large organs (437,438). The Connaught Medical Research Laboratories in Canada developed Medium 199 that allowed maintaining these primary cells without serum for the period of viral infection (439,440). Simple roller tube or static flasks were used as reactors (438,441). The viruses used were the Mahoney, MEF-1, and Saukett strains for types 1, 2, and 3, respectively (441). These strains had been used in the U.S. field trials and were used as standards upon for uniformity of immunogenicity. They are still used today. Because it was known that differences in strain or in the inactivation procedures resulted in an unsafe vaccine (436) or altered D antigen immunogenicity, it was considered imperative early on to fix the strains, the conditions for vaccine production, and the final product potency and safety testing very narrowly (441,442). The current vaccines contain different amounts of D antigen for the three different virus types (a 40–8–32 unit

formula) to optimize the immune response in reduced dosing regimens, and there are still concerns over the fidelity of processing, especially in the inactivation step (443).

After the development of diploid cell lines and continuous cell strains, which were shown to be susceptible to virus and to have no apparent defects, it no longer became tenable to produce in primary monkey cells because of the adventitious agent concerns previously cited. In particular, it was shown that SV_{40}, a tumorigenic virus, was able to survive the prescribed polio inactivation conditions and potentially to contaminate early production lots (444,445). The fact that it was about the fortieth simian virus identified gives an indication of the prevailing situation. The major manufacturers currently produce the virus by modern technology using Vero or MRC-5 cells. The ability to propagate these cells allowed much larger and more economical scales of operation.

Of current manufacturers, the Institute Merieux (now Pasteur Merieux Connaught, PMC) process is perhaps the most impressive and well-published modern IPV process (118,446–449). The PMC process employs Van Wezel's microcarrier technology (450) at the very large scale of 1000 L. The process is based upon a similar one originated by Van Wezel and run by (Rijks Institute Voor Volksgesondheit en Milieu/Stichting tot bevordering van de Volksgezondheid en Milieuhygiene) RIVM/SVM (451) in the Netherlands using primary monkey kidney cells (66,452,453), which was later converted to use diploid MRC-5 cells at Connaught Laboratories (454,455). The process schematic is shown in Figure 3. Cells from a Working Cell Bank are thawed and propagated in stirred tank bioreactors in roughly fivefold scale increments. For passaging, the trypsinized cells are separated from the used microcarrier beads in a special apparatus (69). At the 1000 L scale, the cells are grown to confluent monolayers and then inoculated with virus.

There are several noteworthy features of viral propagation. First, serum is washed from the culture, minimizing its interference with purification. The inoculation volume is roughly one-tenth of the tank operating volume to dramatically compress adsorption time. The infection is rapid and lytic; in a 72-hour period, the cells are destroyed and the culture supernate is harvested; thus the importance of removing serum becomes apparent. Interestingly, the infection is conducted at low dissolved oxygen (DO) concentration. This is perhaps possible because poliovirus can replicate anaerobically (456) and does not place large metabolic demands on the host cell. The low DO may benefit production in that larger scales of operation do not need intensive aeration and agitation to achieve this DO level. The sensitivity of microcarrier cultures to intensive mixing and sparged aeration is wellknown (457). Last, the production scales are dramatic due to the low productivity of the bulk process relative to the dose. The net inactivated vaccine bulk productivity for such a process is on the order of 100 D antigen units/mL of harvested culture volume (455,458), and as mentioned, the vaccine antigen is dosed at 8–40 units. Hence the number of doses per mL of culture is ca. 1–10. For a vaccine of which tens of millions of doses are distributed annually, this translates to millions of liters of culture volume produced.

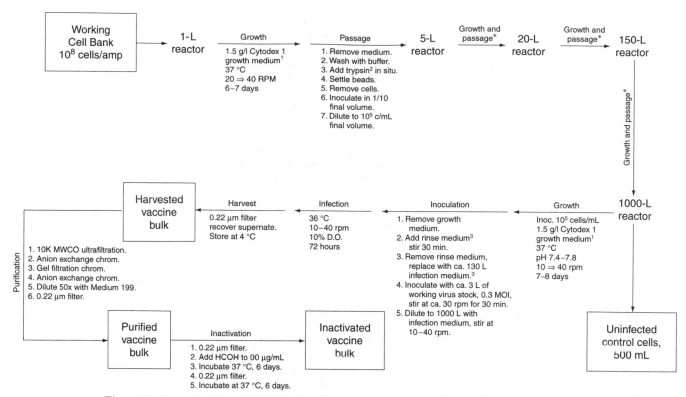

Figure 3. Approximation of the Institute Merieux Vero cell process for inactivated poliovirus vaccine production.

[1]Growth medium: Eagle's Minimal Essential Medium in Earle's salts, 5% newborn calf serum, 1 g/L glucose/fructose, 0.2% lactalbumin hydrolyzate, streptomycin, neomycin, polymyxin B Sulfate.

[2]Trypsin: 0.025% crystalline trypsin in 0.125 M sodium citrate.

[3]Rinse and infection medium: Medium 199, +1 g/L glucose, streptomycin, neomycin, and polymyxin B sulfate.

*Growth and passaging procedures for the intermediate passages are substantially similar to the first. For passaging between larger vessels, the cells may be separated from the used microcarriers in a specialized vibromixed vessel with a retaining screen for the microcarriers.

Oral (Live, Attenuated) Polio Vaccine (OPV). The virtue of Sabin's live polio vaccine lies in its use of the natural route of infection to elicit long-lasting immunity that mimics natural disease. The orally dosed, attenuated virus replicates in the gut, using the body as a bioreactor to produce more immunizing antigen. As a result of the *in vivo* replication, low doses are needed. Hence the vaccine cost is minimal, and production complexity and scale are greatly reduced. Whereas Salk's vaccine immunized the richest countries, the Sabin vaccine is the sine qua non of global poliomyelitis minimization, if not eradication, where the poorest countries must have ready vaccine access (459).

The major issue with the attenuated poliovirus vaccine has always been and continues to be viral genetic stability. Sabin's technical triumph was in achieving reliably attenuated, cloned viral variants by temperature (34 °C) adaptation in monkey kidney culture, cloning, and testing for neurovirulence in a monkey model of disease (14,460–462).

The production of oral poliovirus vaccine is relatively uncomplicated once the hurdles of cell substrate, substrate sourcing, and viral strain selection are overcome. Vaccine was originally made on primary monkey kidney cells, and

it is still produced this way by many manufacturers, but it is also made on diploid WI-38 or MRC-5 cells, and even on Vero cells in one very recent case (449). The monkey kidney cells were obviously chosen because they had been used to attenuate the virus and because there was accumulated experience with Salk vaccine manufacture. The viral strains used are usually the original Sabin strains, the pre-Master Seeds of which are now held in trust by the World Health Organization. Recently, recombinantly derived Type 3 Master Seeds have been adopted to give extra assurance of attenuation (20). Viral cultivation is strictly limited to only a few passages beyond the WHO Seeds, and stringent tests are applied to ensure that reversion to virulence does not occur during the manufacturer's Master Seed, Working Seed, and vaccine passages (20).

The primary monkey kidney process is known from the historical literature and also from regulatory documents (463). From a contemporary viewpoint, it might be thought curious to have governments spell out the conditions of manufacture for public companies. However, when the Sabin vaccine was introduced to Western society in 1962, disease incidence had been greatly reduced by the Salk vaccine, and there was less incentive to assume public risk. In hindsight it seems unlikely that the Sabin vaccine would have been licensed in the United States and Europe at all, had the Union Socialist Soviet Republic of Russia not conducted massive vaccination campaigns which proved the vaccine's utility and safety beyond doubt (464). It was known then that monkey kidney cultures could harbor myriad infectious viruses and that incompletely attenuated virus (caused by extended passaging or incorrect manufacturing conditions) could cause paralytic disease (465). So it was considered necessary to constrain manufacturing practices as tightly as for the inactivated vaccine, if not more so. Just as Salk counseled against alterations of manufacturing technology for IPV, there was considerable reluctance to endorse any kinds of manufacturing changes for oral polio from the original processes and cell substrates from Sabin and others (79,466,467). With the advent of modern molecular biological techniques to ferret out even low levels of virulence-associated mutations, however, process modifications can be undertaken more rationally (24).

An approximation of the historical monkey kidney process (66,79,137,459,468,469) is shown in Figure 4. The process is obviously simple, a reflection of several factors. First, the scale of culture is small, which is a result of the paradigm that only individual kidneys be cultured in a batch; this minimizes the opportunity for cross-contamination and product loss. Overall, the scale of operation is also small because the vaccine bulk is extremely potent. Where the bulk titers are typically 10^8 TCID$_{50}$/mL or higher, the final vaccine follows a 10^6–10^5–$10^{5.5}$ TCID$_{50}$/dose formula, that is, after taking into account processing losses and overfilling the final containers to account for degradation during long-term storage, the number of doses per mL of culture volume is ca. 10–100, and 10 liters of culture make 10^5–10^6 doses! Note that as a result of the small scale, a high technology bioreactor is intentionally avoided because it would only add cost and complexity. Control over the safety of the process comes in specifying the viral passage limits, the cultivation temperature, and the time of harvest. All serve to ensure that the virus goes through only limited rounds of replication and that replication occurs under conditions least likely to favor a revertant virulent strain.

Second, it is immediately obvious that there is no purification, save a sterile filtration to remove cell debris and ensure bacterial absence. This is because kids stick food and far worse things than oral polio in their mouths, but it is also allowable because the cellular material they ingest is from primary cells which should not have oncogenes present. There is a price to pay for the simplicity of the culturing and purification scheme, however, and that is eternal vigilance and testing of the primary cell substrate and the vaccine for adventitious viruses at multiple points through processing (63,470). The cost and overall simplicity of the process explains much of the allure of the Sabin vaccine.

Measles and Mumps Viral Vaccines

"Measles make you mumpy,
Mumps'll make you lumpy,
Chicken pox will make you jump and twitch . . . (471)"

Just before and just after poliovirus was successfully cultivated by Enders, the causative agents of measles

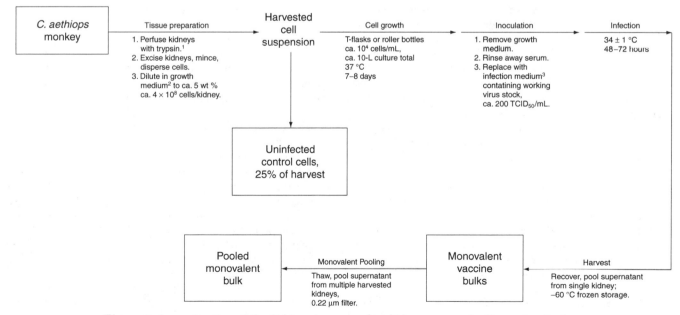

Figure 4. Approximation of the Sabin primary monkey kidney process for live oral poliovirus manufacture.

[1]Trypsin: 0.25% pancreatin in phosphate-buffered saline.

[2]Growth medium: Eagle's Basal Medium, Medium 199 or CMRL-1696, ca. 5% fetal bovine serum, neomycin, strreptomycin, and/or polymyxin B sulfate.

[3]Infection medium: growth medium sans serum.

and mumps disease were also successfully cultivated *ex vivo* (472,473), which led to vaccines for these diseases. The clinical signs of measles virus, a highly contagious virus spread by aerosol, are a high fever and severe rash. These lead to complications with a fairly high frequency, and these complications have a slight degree of associated mortality which is severely exacerbated in developing countries and populations with underlying malnutrition and other disease (474). Of note here, measles is an immunosuppressive virus (475), which is thought to encourage opportunistic infections during the disease. Even recently, measles virus is estimated to cause or contribute to around 1 million deaths per year in young children (476,477). Mumps virus is also spread via droplets, and most often causes infectious parotitis, a fever and swelling of the lower face and jaw. Like measles, it can also have severe complications involving many different organs (478). Also of note, mumps virus can cause aseptic meningitis, as well as other central nervous system complications; these infrequently lead to permanent nervous system damage (478,479). Mumps was the leading viral cause of viral encephalitis in the developed nations until the advent of vaccines against it (25,476,478).

Measles and mumps are paramyxoviruses, a family of (−) sense, single-stranded RNA viruses. These are fairly large viruses, ca. 150–350 nm in diameter, with lipid envelopes and helical nucleocapsids. As suggested by the range of sizes, the viruses are pleiomorphic, that is, they appear in many different forms, usually spherical variants, but sometimes filamentous. Genomic entry into the cell is via direct fusion, which is mediated by the fusion protein on the virus envelope. The (−) genome is transcribed by a virion RNA polymerase complex, and the (+) strands are variously used to synthesize further (−) strands or to be translated into viral proteins. The genome is present in the cytoplasm as an encapsidated complex with the viral nucleoprotein, the "phosphoprotein," and the "large" protein; the "matrix" protein assists assembly of this capsid with the fusion (F) and hemagglutinin-neuraminidase (HN) proteins that have been glycosylated via the Golgi and transported to the cytoplasmic membrane. Rafts of F and HN wrap the nucleocapsid to form completed virus that buds from the membrane of the infected cell. The fusion protein is matured by cellular protease cleavages during processing to form the active protein. These budding viruses are not strongly lytic, possibly due to incomplete host cell shut-off (480) or the method for assembly/egress which requires an intact cell. Infected cultures shed virus into the culture supernate for several days before degenerating. This allows using for low MOI in propagating the viruses (481–484), which avoids defective interfering viral propagation and maximizes titers (365,485,486).

Enders' initial *in vitro* cultivation of the measles virus led to the Edmonston strain B which had been attenuated by passage in human embryonic kidney, human amnion cells, embryonated eggs, and finally CEF culture at 36–37 °C (487,488). This was initially licensed for use with the coadministration of immune globulin because of its incomplete attenuation and high incidence of fever. From the Edmonston A and B strains, further attenuation in CEF cultures at 32 °C resulted in derivative strains with decreased reactogenicity (489). Two of these, Schwarz (490) and Moraten (488) (MOre ATtenuated ENders), licensed in the mid-1960s, are the most prevalent vaccine strains in North America and Europe. In addition to the live vaccines, a formaldehyde-inactivated vaccine was also licensed in the early 1960s (491), but the formaldehyde inactivation conditions altered the immunogenicity of the F protein. This in turn led to an imbalanced immune response in some recipients that caused severe "atypical measles" when the patients were exposed to the wild virus (476,492). Since the early strains, other measles virus vaccine strains have been licensed around the world (493–497). Although many have also been attenuated via avian embryo fibroblast culture, production technology is not as uniform as for the stringently regulated poliovirus vaccines. Because the Moraten and Schwarz strains had been attenuated by cold adaptation on CEFs, this was the cell substrate chosen for production. A particular concern was to ensure that the chicken flocks used to produce eggs for CEF cultures were free of the avian leukosis virus family which was known to contaminate yellow fever virus vaccine preparations from *in ovo* culture and which were tumorgenic in infant monkeys (22,489).

Mumps virus was first cultivated *in ovo* in 1945, but it was the third cell cultured vaccine to obtain licensure, in 1967, in the United States. Like the measles vaccine strains, avian egg embryo attenuation was performed for most isolates; there are diverse vaccine strains in use (25,498–502). Strains are distinct in their immunogenicity (503) and moreover, in their residual ability to cause meningitis (504–507). The high prevalence of meningitis for Urabe Am9 strain mumps compared to the widely used Jeryl Lynn strain caused withdrawal of the Urabe-based vaccines from many countries and spurred a knockoff Jeryl Lynn-based vaccine to replace it (508,509). As with measles, most mumps vaccines are made in avian embryo fibroblast culture; however, a more recent trend has been toward production of mumps and measles in human diploid cells (502,510,511). Despite the extensive passaging in and adaptation to CEF cells, it does not appear that Jeryl Lynn is necessarily as productive in this host cell as some wild type strains (512).

Of the production processes for measles and mumps vaccines, the processes of Merck & Co., Inc. are well known and are fairly representative of primary CEF technology for vaccine production (114,513–520). Approximations of these processes are shown in Figure 5. CEF culture was chosen for these vaccines as opposed to *in ovo* culture because the large numbers of embryos needed for cultivation would make product sterility difficult to guarantee. Because of the larger cell mass used and a desire to minimize aseptic manipulations of vessels, the tissue is placed into a single large reactor rather than a series of flasks or roller bottles. The importance of maintaining asepsis will be seen following. Because a single vessel is employed, better control over the environment is possible via gas exchange and monitoring. Also, unlike poliovirus, degeneration of the infected cells

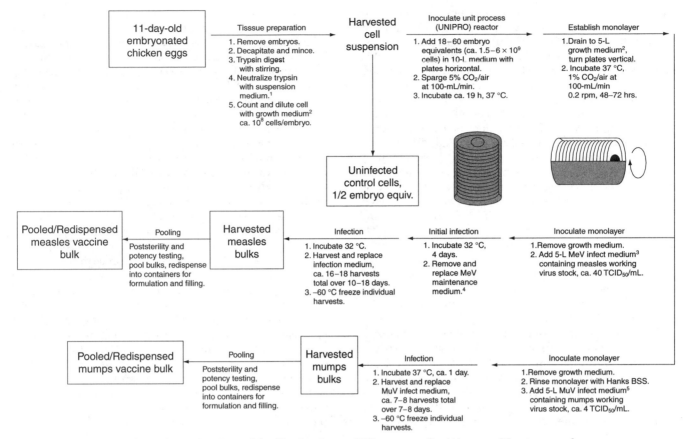

Figure 5. Approximations of the Merck primary CEF processes for Attenuvax Moraten measles vaccine and Mumpsvax Jeryl Lynn mumps vaccine.

[1]Suspension Medium: Medium 199, 10% fetal calf serum, neomycin sulfate.

[2]Growth medium: Medium 199, 2% fetal calf serum, neomycin sulfate.

[3]Me V infect medium: Medium 199, 2.8 g/L sodium bicarbonate, 2% αgamma calf serum, neomycin sulfate.

[4]Me V maintenance medium: Medium 199, 2.8 g/L sodium bicarbonate, 10% SPGA (sucrose, phosphate, glutamate, human albumin), neomycin sulfate.

[5]Mu V infect medium: Medium 199, 2.8 g/L sodium bicarbonate, 25% SPGA (sucrose, phosphate, glutamate, human albumin), neomycin sulfate.

takes place over the course of weeks. This necessitates refeeding the cultures but also allows collection of multiple harvests to maximize productivity. The culture medium during the infection serves as both a crude serum-free medium and a virus stabilizer. Frequency of harvest is an important determinant of culture volumetric productivity because of the rapid infectivity loss of virus in the supernate; despite continued cellular production, viral titer plateaus in long periods between refeeds as a dynamic equilibrium between production and decay is established (365,519).

Establishment of maximum titer is important for these viruses due to two factors. The first factor is the inability of these fragile viruses to be purified and concentrated. Because they are too large ($0.15-0.35$ μm) to be 0.22-μm sterile-filtered without considerable losses (491,521), the viruses are intentionally made on a cell substrate acceptable for injection, and all processing is done aseptically. Only coarse clarification and dilution are contemplated. Second, bulk culture titers are in the range of 10^5-10^7 TCID$_{50}$/mL (513), and the vaccine

dose is about 10^3 and $10^{4.3}$ TCID$_{50}$/0.5 mL for measles and mumps, respectively (522). As with poliovirus, the theoretical number of doses per milliliter of harvest is fairly high, about $10-100$. However, the viruses are fairly susceptible to decay even during storage in the lyophilized state (46,489,521,523). This creates a need for more concentrated virus in the filled container of vaccine to ensure that the minimum dose is present at all times during the product's shelf-life, which reduces the gap between the titers of the bulk and the initially filled containers. In addition, the viruses are most often administered as a trivalent combination measles-mumps-rubella vaccine in a 0.5 mL or smaller dose. In this instance, each virus has only a partial share of the 0.5 mL dose, and thus the vaccine bulk must contain higher virus titers than usual to enable formulation.

Rubella Viral Vaccines

After the introduction of poliovirus, measles, and mumps viruses in the 1950s and 1960s made on primary cell culture substrates, a series of vaccines was made on diploid cells in the late 1960s and the 1970s; these vaccines have much in common technologically because of the characteristics of the cell substrate. They differ mainly in the viral characteristics that affect infection, harvest, and scale of operation. The latter sometimes drives the technology employed. Rubella was the first of the diploid cell vaccines. The serious complication of rubella viral infection is birth defects caused when a woman contracts the virus during pregnancy. The vaccine is universally given to children to provide herd immunity and to ensure that girls are immunized before their childbearing years; this has proven quite successful in reducing rubella and even eliminating it in some places. The elusive causative virus was discovered in 1962 (524,525), and following pandemics in Europe and America from 1963 to 1965 which resulted in tens of thousands of babies with congenital rubella syndrome (526), vaccines were licensed soon thereafter. The early live vaccine strains HPV-77 (527–530) and Cendehill (531–533) were attenuated in primary duck embryo, dog kidney, and rabbit kidney cells, and vaccines using them were initially licensed. They were too reactive, however, and caused transient arthritis in women vaccinated postpartum (534). These early strains gave way to the ubiquitous RA27/3 strain developed by Plotkin at the Wistar Institute and attenuated by adaptation to WI-38 human diploid cells at 30 °C (535).

The rubella virus is a member of the togavirus family (the only member of the rubivirus genera), a single-stranded, (+) sense enveloped RNA virus with an icosahedral capsid; it is about 70 nm in diameter. It enters the cell via endosomal transport and fusion. The genome is uncoated by ribosomal binding to the capsid and is transcribed into (−) sense, (+) subgenomic and (+) genomic species, and translated. The subgenomic specie codes for the virion structural proteins, and the genomic specie encodes regulatory and polymerase proteins. The structural protein is produced as a polyprotein which is proteolytically cleaved to form the nucleocapsid and envelope proteins; the latter are extensively post-translationally modified by N-and O-linked glycosylation, cleavage, and acylation which mediate transport and assembly (536). The nucleocapsid assembles around the genomic RNA in the cytoplasm, and final virus assembly is via budding at the cytoplasmic membrane. Interestingly, rubella alters the composition of the host-cell membrane; the significance of this for viral replication and vaccine production is unknown (537,538). Rubella virus shares many of the practical culturing characteristics with measles and mumps viruses. The virus does not appreciably shut off host-cell protein synthesis (539,540), is not strongly lytic, and establishes persistent infections in some cases (541). It can also form defective interfering particles (542) at high multiplicities.

Propagation of the RA 27/3 strain in diploid cell culture is straightforward, and a representative process is illustrated in Figure 6 (114,543,544). In current vaccines, the virus is made on either MRC-5 or WI-38 cells. The

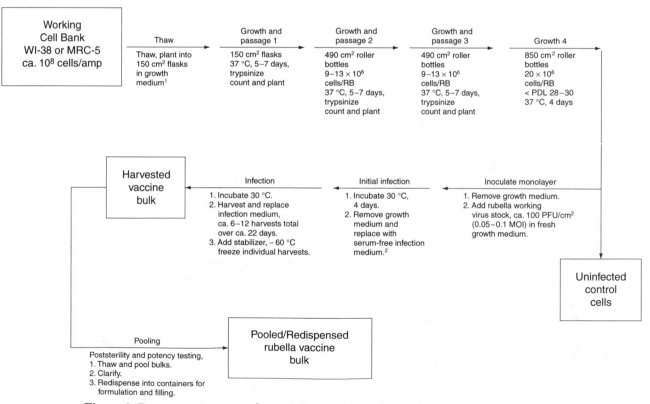

Figure 6. Representative process for a rubella RA 27/3 vaccine made on human diploid cells.

[1]Growth medium: Basal Medium Eagle, 5% calf serum, 1 × amino acids, vitamins, kanamycin, and/or neomycin.

[2]Infection medium: Basal Medium Eagle, ca. 0.2% gelatin or human serum albumin.

process is much like the measles and mumps processes except that a cell number expansion is needed before reaching the amount of biomass needed for industrial-scale viral cultivation. Such a process produces rubella titers in the neighborhood of 10^5 $TCID_{50}$/mL of harvest (544); in this instance, the vaccine strain adapted to the 30 °C culture temperature produces a titer virtually identical to the wild-type parent at 37 °C[535]. These titers are well in excess of the typical dose of 10^3 $TCID_{50}$ (522). The titer combined with the multiple harvests and the good stability of rubella virus (46,545) compared to its measles and mumps vialmates makes the vaccine relatively economical to produce. Like oral polio, this can be done using a fairly small-scale process which does not require high technology equipment.

Rabies Virus

Rabies is almost uniformly fatal if untreated and was one of the most feared viral diseases until the twentieth century. The virus causes encephalitis that has a typical incubation period of 20–60 days (546); this incubation allows time for an immune response to be raised upon therapeutic vaccination with large amounts of antigen. Pasteur and his colleagues, Chamberland and Roux, recognized this incubation period and derived a "fixed" strain of rabies via rabbit intracerebral passage that had high virulence and shorter incubation time than the "street" strains. They also realized that rabies-infected rabbit spinal cords rapidly lost virulence and became inactivated when air-dried. The fixed rabies virus and the variably infectious material enabled conception of both pre- and postexposure prophylactic vaccination. Injecting preparations of increasing infectivity into dogs either before or after street viral exposure showed that the animals could be rendered refractory to disease, and Pasteur translated this result successfully into humans in 1885 (433,547).

If measles, mumps, and rubella vaccines are sagas of viral strain optimization, the history of rabies vaccines is a tale of cell substrate optimization. As can be imagined with such a crude manufacturing process, there were vaccine failures and other drawbacks of the Pasteur vaccine. It subsequently gave way to other physical methods of inactivation and to the Fermi (548) (semi-inactivated) and Semple (549) (inactivated) brain-tissue-based, phenol chemically inactivated vaccines which were more reproducible and stable, and thus amenable to quality control testing. These vaccines were used for most of the twentieth century. However, residual myelin basic protein in the preparations induced an autoimmune response and paralysis in some recipients (550–552). This led to the development of semipurified brain-based vaccines (553,554) (which are still used in many countries) (555), and vaccines based on in ovo duck embryo culture in the 1950s (556). The duck embryo and later chick embryo vaccines had poor immunogenicity, however, because of poor concentration and purity of the material resulting from poor culture productivity (557,558), and they also had side-reaction problems due to large amounts of egg protein present (559,560). These vaccines were supplanted in developed nations in

the early 1970s by diploid-cell-based vaccines (561–565) which are more potent and produce fewer side effects (566,567). They are, however, not especially cost-effective for less developed countries (568,569), and most recently, purified and concentrated duck embryo and chick embryo cell vaccine (PDEV, PCEV or PCEC vaccine) (570–575) and purified Vero cell rabies vaccine (PVRV) (576–579) have been devised to provide widely available, effective, safe, and inexpensive vaccines. The vaccine is primarily used as a therapeutic vaccine for exposed individuals, except for prophylaxis for high risk populations such as rabies vaccine manufacturing personnel and veterinary and animal control professionals. Accordingly, annual treatment requirements are fairly small relative to the vaccines recommended for universal use in children. Total annual vaccinees in the United States and Europe are in the hundreds of thousands, although the total number of doses produced and stockpiled for emergency use is much greater (569).

Rabies virus is a Rhabdovirus (genera Lyssavirus), a large ca. 200 nm long, 75 nm in diameter, bullet-shaped, enveloped, (−) strand RNA virus that replicates mainly in the cytoplasm of infected cells. Defective viruses with truncated genomes are common; these are shorter in length. The virus enters via receptor-mediated endocytosis, uncoats, and the genome is transcribed to mRNA in the cytoplasm via a virion polymerase. The message is subsequently translated into the virion structural proteins. As new copies of the (−) RNA, nucleocapsid (N), and phosphoprotein (P) are made, they are assembled spontaneously into helical ribonucleoprotein particles. The glycoprotein (G)-studded viral envelope is acquired at the cytoplasmic membrane by matrix (M) protein-assisted budding; it does not induce a rapid cytopathic effect in the host cell. The glycoprotein is the major antigenic component of inactivated human vaccines and is the only protein to induce neutralizing antibodies, although the nucleoprotein is also immunogenic.

The most advanced, widely licensed of the processes for producing rabies vaccine for human use is the PVRV process of PMC, which is illustrated in Figure 7 (449,580,581). This process is nearly identical to the PMC-inactivated poliovirus process. The main differences are refinements in the culturing of the earlier polio process and adaptation of the infection and harvest portions of the process to the peculiarities of rabies virus. To achieve a vigorous immune response, large amounts of antigen are included in each dose, 2.5 International Units (582). This translates to ca. $10^{5.5-7}$ infectious viruses, or about 1–10 doses per mL of harvest, given typical titers (576–578). Fortunately, the multiple harvests reduce costs per batch. However, because the number of doses per medium volume harvested is still low and economical production for the intended markets is important, one can see that careful attention has been paid to minimizing medium costs by substituting inexpensive veal serum and lactalbumin hydrolysate for expensive fetal calf serum. (Milk-fed veal calves are iron-starved (this is what makes veal a light pink color), and in response they up-regulate serum transferrin levels. This serum can be backsupplemented

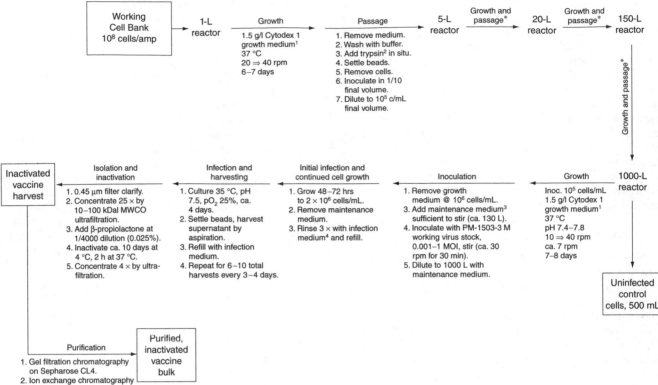

Figure 7. Approximation of the Pasteur Merieux Connaught Vero cell process for inactivated rabies viral (purified Vero rabies vaccine) production.

[1]Growth Medium: Dulbecco's Modified Eagle's Medium or Iscove's Modified Dulbecco's Medium, 5% "veal serium," 1 g/L glucose/fructose, 0.2% lactalbumin hydrolyzate, streptomycin, neomycin, polymyxin B sulfate, HEPES, metal salts.

[2]Trypsin: 0.025% crystalline trypsin in 0.125 M sodium citrate.

[3]Maintenance medium: Minimal Essential Medium, 1% "veal serum."

[4]Infection medium: Minimal Essential Medium, 0.1% human serum albumin.

[*]Growth and passaging procedures for the intermediate passages are substantially similar to the first.

with iron salts to make a reasonable FBS substitute.) There are also indications that the basal medium has been extensively optimized as well (580). An outstanding feature of this versus the previous processes is the β-propiolactone inactivation reaction, which is conducted before purification rather than afterward, as is often the case. This is done to avoid the exposure of production technicians to the virus as much as possible. It is facilitated by the use of the alkylating propiolactone reagent rather than a cross-linking inactivator such as formaldehyde, which would tend to create an unpurifiable and potentially reactogenic product.

Foot-and-Mouth Disease Virus Vaccines

Foot-and-mouth disease virus (FMDV) (583) causes a highly contagious infection of mucosa and other tissues and leads to significant mortality and morbidity among the ruminant animals it infects. Because of the severe economic consequences of FMDV epidemics, vaccination of domestic livestock is nearly universal; vaccines are typically composed of three serotypes, O, A, and C, although locally prevalent strains are routinely cultured.

The virus is a picornavirus (genus aphthovirus) and shares many of the characteristics of poliovirus. The virus has the distinction of being the first recognized filterable agent by Loeffler and Frosch in 1897, and is one of the early major advances in the field of virology (584). The virus was later the subject of some of the earliest practical *in vitro* cell culture work by Hugh and Mary Maitland in the 1920s and 1930s (585,586); the "Maitland technique" for cultivating chick embryo and guinea pig tissues later became the fundamental technique for cultures of monkey kidney tissue for poliovirus vaccine production (438). Before cell culture technology, vaccines were manufactured on bovine tongue epithelium tissue, first *in vivo* (587) and then later *in vitro* in the 1940s using the Frenkel process (588). Because a single tongue could generate only about 200–300 doses of vaccine by this process, it is understandable that improved technology was needed to alleviate tongue shortages (584,589). This problem was solved in the late 1950s by the rapidly advancing cell culture field; it was demonstrated that the continuous, suspension cultivable cell line BHK21, Clone 13, could support growth of the virus (98,590). This led rapidly to the current BHK-based vaccines.

The scope of BHK-based FMDV vaccine manufacture boggles the mind of any biologics developer. Billions of doses have been produced, and the order of magnitude of the culture scale and factory throughput is awesome. A number of processes have been developed for BHK FMDV vaccine (99,124,591–604), but the groundbreaking, and most interesting is the large-scale deep tank process developed by the Animal Virus Research Insitute/Wellcome Foundation in England, shown in Figure 8 (104,120,143,150,393,605–619). What is most special is that to enable this process and its operation on a daily basis, the technology of suspension culture of animal cells at very large scales of 3000–8000 L had to be invented and perfected. This occurred largely in the early 1960s, not very long after submerged antibiotic fermentation first became commonplace and well before the biotechnological revolution. It is the process technology that enabled the recombinant therapeutic protein industry in most respects; the knowledge gained was later transferred to veterinary rabies and α-interferon processing (100,102). The features of the process would be unsurprising today but were pioneering then for industrial practice: a continuous, endogenous retrovirus-containing rodent cell line as production host, cultivated in sparged and stirred suspension culture, controlled for pH and dissolved oxygen concentration, using optimized medium containing protein hydrolysate supplements and Pluronic F68 surfactant to control cell death, and using cell recycling at a scale to accomplish refeed and infection. What is perhaps most impressive is that the process incorporates not just one or two of the features of advanced, modern recombinant protein processing, but most, if not all, of them. It should be noted that

although there is a wealth of information about the general features of the AVRI/Wellcome process, the specifics of the process, for example, the cell expansion train and manufacturing medium composition, are not clear. As a consequence, Figure 8 is somewhat speculative. One noteworthy feature of the process is that to operate at the scales needed, the amount of virus Stock Seed which would need to be banked would be rather large; this is addressed by the use of a "hot" passage of virus, going from a small-scale cryopreserved stock through an intermediate passage, which is then used to infect the final production culture.

Other Vaccines

Other cell culture vaccine processes exist that are either poorly published or are minor in worldwide public significance. The former include varicella zoster virus, hepatitis A virus, and rotavirus vaccines. These are typically newer vaccines whose viruses are all more difficult to culture en masse compared to those previously described, and some were isolated *in vitro* only recently compared to the boom of work in the early 1950s. They are described generally following.

Although not described in this article, there are several examples of the latter, lesser used cell culture vaccines. Adenovirus vaccine is a bivalent type 4 and 7 diploid cell vaccine made in WI-38 cells and is given to military recruits to avoid acute respiratory disease (620–622). A second example is vaccinia virus vaccine against smallpox. Although this vaccine has the greatest claim to fame of the viral vaccines, having successfully eradicated the disease, most of the vaccine for this effort was made from calf

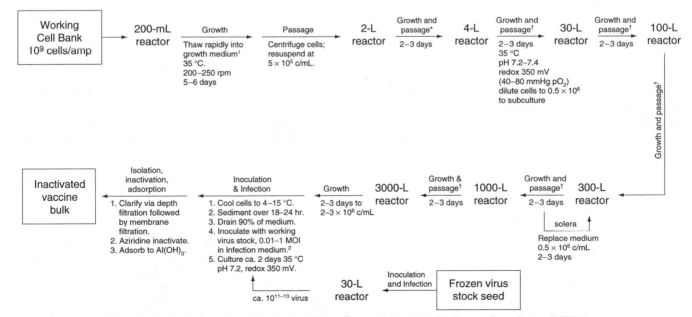

Figure 8. Approximation of the Animal Virus Research Institute/Wellcome Foundation BHK21 suspension cell culture process for veterinary FMDV vaccine.

[1]Growth Medium: Glasgow Modified Eagle's Medium, 7.5% adult bovine serum, 4 g/L peptone, Edifas B50, 1 g/L Pluronic F68 Penicillin, streptomycin, neomycin, polymyxin.

[2]Infection medium: Glasgow MEM, 5% adult bovine serum or horse serum.

*,[†]Growth and passaging procedures for the subsequent passages are substantially similar to the first.

"lymph" or in embryonated eggs (623,624). However, it was obvious from work early in the history of cell culture that the virus could be produced *in vitro* (625–629), and there were smaller quantities of vaccinia made in CEF or rabbit kidney primary cell culture toward the end of the eradication campaign (630–633). Smallpox vaccine is not generally given today except to scientific investigators working with vaccinia (634), although there are renewed efforts to produce a cell-culture-based vaccine for potential monkeypox outbreaks (633,635,636). Last, the self-descriptive tick-borne encephalitis (TBE) virus vaccine is a CEF-cultured vaccine used in parts of eastern Europe and the former Soviet Union where the disease is prevalent (637–641), and Japanese encephalitis virus vaccine is a primary hamster kidney cultured virus used in the Far East (642).

Varicella Zoster Virus. Varicella zoster virus (643–648) (VZV) is a herpesvirus that causes the familiar childhood chickenpox disease. At the initial infection, the virus moves throughout the body, entering the lungs, moving to the liver, spleen, and other organs via T-lymphocytes, and finally to the skin to form vesicular lesions, again via lymphocytes (649); in the process, it integrates its dsDNA genome into neural cells and becomes latent; it can reemerge years later to cause herpes zoster, or "shingles." Although many view chickenpox as a benign rite of childhood, adolescent/adult disease is severe. In addition, pocks are susceptible to secondary bacterial infections, the virus occasionally causes encephalitis, and it can cause (fatal) disseminated chickenpox in immunosuppressed persons. Shingles occasionally causes a persistent, debilitating irritation termed postherpetic neuralgia which can linger for months. Varicella infects about 90% of people in early childhood or adolescence.

Despite early cultivation of the virus by Weller in 1952 (650), Takahashi's Oka strain vaccine (651–653) was licensed for general use in Japan only in 1986, and the Merck/Oka vaccine achieved licensure for general use in the United States only in 1995 after extensive review (654,655). Other Oka strain vaccines have been licensed around the world as well (112,656). This was partly due to the nature of herpesviruses and their propensity to integrate and partly to concerns over postvaccine epidemiology, but in good measure it was due to the difficulties inherent in cultivating VZV (651,654). Infectious virus from *in vitro* culture is almost exclusively associated with cellular membranes (657–659), and very little can be recovered from the culture supernate (660). The literature is full of attempts to improve culture, recovery, and preservation of VZV, especially cell-free virus which would be useful for virological studies or for vaccination (661–675). Although fine details of the licensed manufacturing processes have not been published, one can get a rough picture of the processes from patent and other literature (112,653,673,674,676–680). The virus is generally grown on confluent MRC-5 cells in conventional serum-containing flask or roller bottle cultures. Infection is in a low-serum medium at low MOI, ca. 0.01 infected cell/cell, for a period of ca. 2–3 days. The inoculum is often an infected cell bank for these vaccines.

At harvest, the cell sheet is washed to remove residual serum, and the cell sheet is removed either chemically with EDTA or mechanically by scraping or milling and recovered into a stabilizing buffer. Then the stabilized vaccine harvest is sonicated, and the sonicate is clarified by centrifugation or coarse filtration resulting in the bulk vaccine. It should be noted that because the virus remains closely cell-associated during infection, the term "cell-free virus" applied to the sonicated lysate of the infected cells refers to virus largely associated with cellular debris rather than a monodispersed viral solution (661,663,672). Because of the size of the virus (ca. 200 nm in diameter) and its associated cell debris, clarification is possible only via centrifugation or coarse filtration, and all processing must be conducted aseptically. There is no purification for the vaccines. The virus is unstable throughout cultivation, harvesting, and storage, and consequently, all of the postharvest processing is conducted in stabilizer, and the final vaccine is lyophilized. Because of the low productivity of varicella, the resulting large operating scales, and the need for stringent asepsis, at least one manufacturer has resorted to robotic technology for manipulating the culture vessels (681,682).

Hepatitis A Virus. Hepatitis A virus (HAV) infects the liver and causes a jaundice which is usually mild but can have serious consequences in a fraction of people (683,684). The virus is a picornavirus that eluded *in vitro* cultivation until the late 1970s because of its peculiarly slow growth (685–689). It took 15 years from the initial report of propagation to the licensure of a vaccine. Early attempts were made to devise attenuated live virus vaccines (690,691), partly on the belief that it would be extremely difficult to cultivate the amounts of virus antigen believed to be required for a multidose inactivated vaccine. Although China has pursued the live attenuated approach to licensure (692), it has been possible to devise inactivated vaccines, and several of these have been licensed.

The main virological characteristic of HAV from a cultivation standpoint is the lack of cytopathogenicity *in vitro*. Unlike the poliovirus and FMDV picornaviruses, HAV lacks the ability to shut off host-cell DNA, RNA, or protein synthesis (693), and accumulates only slowly and mainly intracellularly; infection terms of weeks are commonly required to accumulate significant antigen (694). This, it has been suggested, is due to rapid encapsidation of the RNA genome, leaving only a small pool available for further replication (683,686,695). Because of the long cultivation and intracellular disposition of the virus, culture systems that are robust for long-term industrial use and are amenable to recovery of virus from the cell mass are necessary.

Several vaccines are licensed in the United States and Europe for HAV vaccination (696–698); of these, the Merck & Co., Inc. process is the best-published (33,116,699–705). The MRC-5 cell substrate is expanded in Nunc Cell Factories, and the resulting biomass is planted into Costar Cell Cube reactors (a fixed-bed polystyrene reactor), which are at controlled pH and dissolved oxygen at the inlet to the Cube growth elements. The cells are grown until sufficient biomass is attained and then are infected at an

MOI of ca. 0.01. The cultures are continuously perfused to provide nutrients over the long three-week growth period and to enable good antigen accumulation. Then the reactors are drained, the cultures rinsed to remove residual serum, and the intracellular virus is harvested via detergent lysis. The solubilized virus is then taken through extensive purification resulting in a purified bulk virus for inactivation that contains only the virion proteins in detectable amounts. The virus is inactivated using formaldehyde and then is adsorbed onto aluminum hydroxide to result in a final bulk vaccine.

Rotavirus.   Rotavirus (706–708) is an enteric virus that is the most frequent cause of severe dehydrating diarrhea worldwide; it contributes to millions of infant deaths annually (709). Virtually all children have had rotavirus disease by age five. The first commercial oral rotavirus vaccine from Wyeth Lederle Vaccines (American Home Products) was licensed only as recently as 1998 in the United States and 1999 in Europe. This oral vaccine which uses a quasi-Jennerian approach takes advantage of the 11-segment dsRNA genome of rotavirus. Chimeric viruses can be created by coinfecting cells with viruses of different species and then selecting for the desired "reassortant" via antisera against the undesired chimeras. This allows creating a virus that has the gene segment that codes for a human outer capsid antigen mixed in with other segments derived from an animal, either a rhesus monkey (710) or a cow (711–713). The reassortant virus can display the human epitope and induce immunity, but because of the nonhuman virion and accessory proteins, replicates only poorly in the human gut and is thus attenuated. The Wyeth vaccine is a mixture of three rhesus monkey reassortants of human serotypes G1, G2, and G4, and a nonreassortant rhesus rotavirus that shares "G" (glycoprotein) protein homology with human serotype G3.

The licensed rotavirus vaccine from Wyeth is produced in a simple FRhL-2 cell, flask-based, fetal bovine serum-containing process with filtration as the only purification (714,715). The peculiarity of rotavirus infection is that it requires trypsin cleavage of the "P" (protease-sensitive) protein spike on the outer coat to enable membrane fusion (251,716,717). Until this was discovered, it was not possible to propagate rotaviruses readily *in vitro*. Cleavage normally occurs *in vivo* during viral passage through the small intestine. *In vitro*, trypsin must be provided to enable infection spread for inoculations at MOI less than 1 virus/cell (718,719). Thus trypsin is usually provided at a low level during the infection period, and to avoid neutralization, serum and other proteins must be absent. Purification is not required because of both oral vaccine delivery and the diploid host; the lytic virus destroys the cells in 2–3 days, and the whole culture broth can be harvested to give titers of ca. 10^{5-8} PFU/mL (374,718–720). Thus the vaccine concentration of 10^5 PFU/reassortant/dose (714) can be obtained by simple dilution.

FUTURE VACCINE PROCESSES

Although many of the scourges of man have been addressed by the cell-culture vaccines of the past forty-five years, there are more vaccines yet to come. These will arise from three factors: a desire to replace older vaccines with a safer, more efficacious or more economical approach, a refinement of knowledge about existing recalcitrant pathogens that allows constructing of new vaccines, and the emergence of new pathogens.

New Approaches to Old Vaccines

New approaches to older vaccines are contemplated where the existing vaccine has a serious drawback; without such a driver it is difficult to walk away from years and millions of doses worth of experience with a vaccine, even with its known demons, and walk toward a new vaccine and its unknown new demons which cannot be tested before licensure to evaluate side effects that will manifest themselves only in <1 in 10,000 patients. Of the vaccines previously described there are serious replacement efforts for only a couple because these vaccines are for the most part well-established and very safe. Oral poliovirus has recently been phased out in the United States because the only cases of poliomyelitis in the United States are vaccine-induced; the replacement here is IPV/KPV as opposed to a new process. Now, this potentially more economical human rabies vaccines are being considered based on BHK-21 cell culture common to veterinary rabies production (100,122,721–724).

For vaccines currently made *in vivo* or *in ovo*, there are many replacement efforts underway. Cell, culture-based flavivirus vaccines against yellow fever (50,725) and Japanese encephalitis virus (26,642,726–728) are being investigated to replace the current vaccines still made *in vivo, in ovo,* or in primary cells. Serious efforts at replacing egg-based influenza vaccine are also being undertaken to enable more rapid and flexible manufacture, provide a better product, and to expand access to the vaccine (729–739).

New Vaccines

The list of new vaccine targets is potentially infinite and is locally dependent. In the early boom years of virology and viral vaccinology, vaccines were attempted against practically every agent that could be isolated. Many of these came to naught because the biological knowledge was not present or there was not a compelling medical need nor an economic driver for the vaccine. Needless to say, knowledge of viruses and the human immune system has advanced substantially since the 1960s, and this provides new avenues for exploring new vaccine approaches (740,741). In addition, the health-care landscape is moving toward managed care, and with this shift, the role of medical economics is increasing. In the United States, a committee of the National Academy of Sciences recently proposed a model to evaluate cost-benefit for vaccines. The results of the model applied to some 30 potential vaccine targets (not all viral) are shown in Table 1.

Many of these vaccines are in development, for example, the influenza vaccines mentioned previously. It will be noted that HIV-1 vaccine is unranked here because the

Table 1. Vaccine Rankings Produced by the Model of the IOM Committee to Study Priorities for Vaccine Development

Category	Vaccine
Most favorable	Cytomegalovirus for 12-year olds. Influenza for the general populace (current vaccines are targeted for the elderly).
More favorable	Herpes simplex virus for 12-year olds. Human papillomavirus for 12-year olds.
Favorable	Parainfluenza virus vaccine for infants and women in their first pregnancy
Less favorable	Epstein–Barr virus for 12-year olds.

priority of this vaccine was considered unassailable by the committee.

HIV-1 is a good virus to illustrate the cell-culture-based approaches being applied to new viral vaccinations because this vaccine is the current subject of every vaccine scientist's dreams. Classical vaccination using either attenuated (742,743) or inactivated (744–746) virus has been contemplated for this virus. Subunit vaccination using either gp120 (envelope) prepared in recombinant animal cells (747), using fractionated HIV-1 virions (748), or using virus-like particles expressed in a baculovirus system has also been proposed (749,750). The former are adjuvanted to enhance the immune response against the immunity-inducing epitopes, and the latter are an attempt to make the epitope itself presented as naturally and as potently as possible. In addition to these relatively simple approaches, more complex strategies are being developed based on virally vectored HIV-1 genes or combinations of subunit proteins and virally vectored genes (751–756). These latter approaches are intended to mimic an HIV infection as well as possible and to stimulate multiple arms of the immune system against the virus. Unfortunately, not much information on processing is available for many of these approaches because they are in the early stage of development.

CONCLUSIONS

Although often thought of through the 1980s as an intellectual backwater by newcomers to recombinant protein biotechnology, cell-culture-based vaccine manufacturing laid the groundwork that enabled those very products. As the millenium approaches, attention is focusing anew on viral production for new classical vaccines, gene therapy, and genetic vaccination. The demand for viruses will likely be increased dramatically with some of these applications, and it will require ingenuity to meet the production challenges. Many of the approaches that rely on more or less standardized technology, that is, baculovirus production, recombinant vaccinia, adenovirus, retrovirus, should succumb to the weight of concerted effort by scientists and engineers to yield extremely well-characterized processes that are highly economical. The next 45 years promise to be as exciting as the first, as sophisticated engineering and molecular biological and biochemical tools are applied to the vaccine processes to come.

FURTHER READING

This chapter can address only a few of the issues involved in viral vaccine production via cell culture technology. The interested reader is referred to further information on the general aspects of viruses (757), laboratory production of viruses (32,758), and the history of their use in vaccines (759–762). A wonderful illustrated reference to viruses and their life cycles is available that brings pedantic written descriptions to life (763). In addition to these published sources, some superb electronic sources on viruses and vaccines are readily found (764–766). It is imperative to understand the regulatory "rules of the road" from the U.S. Food and Drug Administration (767), the European Medicines Evaluation Agency (EMEA) (768), the European Pharmacopoeia (769), and the World Health Organization (WHO) (770), but inspection of these documents often does not give clues to the origins of the specifications. To understand these regulations and to understand viral vaccines in general, it is highly instructive to read the historical literature on the earlier vaccines, especially the poliovirus vaccines. Much relevant and practically oriented historical literature can be found in the Developments in Biological Standardization series published by the International Association for Biological Standardization and also in the World Health Organization Technical Report Series.

ACKNOWLEDGMENTS

The author would like to express his gratitude to John A. Lewis, Peggy Fahnestock, Charles Goochee, and Anne Aunins for critical reading of this manuscript and many essential comments. Special thanks go to Anne, Emily, Ben, and Tom for their love, support, and patience which allowed completion of this manuscript.

BIBLIOGRAPHY

1. F. Horaud, *Dev. Biol. Stand.* **82**, 113 (1994).
2. L.W. Davenport, in M.F. Powell and M.J. Newman, eds., *Vaccine Design: The Subunit and Adjuvant Approach*, Plenum, New York, 1995, p. 81.
3. WO 97/08296 (March 6, 1997). U.S. Pat. 0,519,599 (August 23, 1996), U.G. Munderloh et al.
4. C. Alloin et al., *Cytotechnology* **21**, 1 (1996).
5. P. Hooshmand-Rad, *Dev. Biol. Stand.* **62**, 119 (1985).
6. E. Pipano, in J.B. Henson and M. Campbell, eds., *Theileriosis: Report of a Workshop held in Nairobi, Kenya*, Int. Dev. Res. Cent., Ottawa, Canada, 1977, pp. 55–65.
7. N.C. Bols, *Biotechnol. Adv.* **9**, 31 (1991).
8. T.P. Evelyn, *Dev. Biol. Stand.* **90**, 3 (1997).
9. A.E. Ellis, ed., *Fish Vaccination*, Academic Press, London, 1988.
10. P. de Kinkelin and M. Le Berre, *Dev. Biol. Stand.* **42**, 99 (1978).
11. B.C. Lidgerding, *Dev. Biol. Stand.* **49**, 233 (1981).
12. U.S. Pat. 3,985,615, (October 12, 1976), T. Kubo.
13. S.A. Plotkin and A.J. Beale, *Dev. Biol. Stand.* **37**, 291 (1977).

14. A.B. Sabin, W.A. Hennessen, and J. Winsser, *J. Exp. Med.* **99**, 551 (1954).

15. A.W. Funkhauser, R.H. Purcell, E. D'Hondt, and S.U.Emerson, *J. Virol.* **68**, 148 (1994).

16. R.M. El Karamany, *Acta Virol.* **31**, 321 (1987).

17. S. Kodihalli, D.M. Justewicz, L.V. Gubareva, and R.G. Webster, *J. Virol.* **69**, 4888 (1995).

18. J.S. Robertson et al., *Vaccine* **12**, 1317 (1994).

19. J.S. Robertson et al., *Virology* **160**, 31 (1987).

20. I.V. Alymova et al., *J. Virol.* **72**, 4472 (1998).

21. B.J. Neff et al., *Proc. Soc. Exp. Biol. Med.* **166**, 339 (1981).

22. M.R. Hilleman, *Pediatrics* **90**, 149 (1992).

23. F. Horaud and B. Albert, *Biologicals* **21**, 311 (1993).

24. D.J. Wood and A.J. Macadam, *Biologicals* **25**, 3 (1997).

25. P.D. Minor, *Biologicals* **25**, 35 (1997).

26. K.H. Eckels et al., *Vaccine* **6**, 513 (1988).

27. *Tests for Extraneous Agents in Viral Vaccines for Human Use*, V2.6.16, European Pharmacopoeia, 1997.

28. *Additional Standards for Viral Vaccines*, 21CFR Ch. 1, Part 630, p. 81, National Archives and Records Administration, Washington, D.C., 1992.

29. M. Rosolowsky, R. McKee, W. Nichols, and B. Garfinkle, *Dev. Biol. Stand.* **93**, 109 (1998).

30. H.E. Hopps and J.C. Petricciani, eds., *Abnormal Cells, New Products and Risk*, In Vitro, Monogr. No. 6, Tissue Culture Association, Gaithersburg, Md., 1985.

31. B.W.J. Mahy and H.O. Kangro, *Virology Methods Manual*, Academic Press, London, 1996.

32. B.W.J. Mahy, ed., *Virology: A Practical Approach*, IRL Press, Oxford, U.K., 1985.

33. WO 94/03589 (February 17, 1994), R. Aboud et al.

34. A.L. Van Wezel, J.A. Van Herwaarden, and E.W. Van de Heuvel de Rijk, *Dev. Biol. Stand.* **42**, 65 (1979).

35. B.G. Huyge et al., *Hum. Gene Ther.* **6**, 1403 (1995).

36. R.S.O'Keeffe, M.D. Johnston, and N.K. Slater, *Biotechnol. Bioeng.* **62**, 537 (1999).

37. U.S. Pat. 5,661,023 (August 26, 1997), M.E. Hrinda et al.

38. S.A. Barteling and R. Woortmeyer, *Arch. Virol.* **80**, 103 (1984).

39. E. Race et al., *Vaccine* **13**, 1567 (1995).

40. M.F. Bachmann, C. Bast, H. Hengartner, and R.M. Zinkernagel, *Med. Microbiol. Immunol.* **183**, 95 (1994).

41. J.E. Salk and J.B. Gori, *Ann. N.Y. Acad. Sci.* **83**, 609 (1960).

42. M.C. Anderson, H. Baer, D.J. Frazier, and G.V. Quinnan, *J. Allergy Clin. Immunol.* **80**, 861 (1987).

43. J.E. Salk et al., *Am. J. Public Health* **44**, 563 (1954).

44. J. Cornfield, M. Halperin, and F. Moore, *Public Health Rep.* **71**, 1045 (1956).

45. J. Peetermans, *Dev. Biol. Stand.* **87**, 97 (1996).

46. C.J. Burke, T.-A. Hsu, and D.B. Volkin, *Crit. Rev. Ther. Drug Carrier Syst.* **16**, 1 (1999).

47. P. Sureau, *Adv. Biochem. Eng. Biotechnol.* **34**, 111 (1987).

48. K. Takaku et al., *Biken J.* **11**, 25 (1968).

49. T. Barrett and S.C. Inglis, in B.W.J. Mahy, ed., *Virology: A Practical Approach*, IRL Press, Oxford, U.K., 1985, pp. 119–150.

50. Fr. Pat. 2,532,548 (March 9, 1984), J.P. Digoutte and V. Deubel.

51. D. Ben-Nathan, *Adv. Biotechnol. Processes* **5**, 123 (1985).

52. P.D. Parkman, *Dev. Biol. Stand.* **88**, 5 (1996).

53. T.H. Weller, F.C. Robbins, and J.F. Enders, *Science* **109**, 85 (1949).

54. A. Gray, *Dev. Biol. Stand.* **25**, 25 (1974).

55. S.A. Plotkin and H. Koprowski, in S.A. Plotkin and E.A. Mortimer, eds., *Vaccines*, Saunders, Philadelphia, 1994, pp. 649–670.

56. Y.S. Boriskin et al., *Arch. Virol.* **101**, 131 (1988).

57. M.S. Bektemirova, E.R. Pille, K.S. Matevosyan, and F.G. Nagieva, *Acta Virol.* **27**, 59 (1983).

58. R.N. Hull, *Virol. Monogr.* **2**, 1 (1968).

59. B.H. Sweet and M.R. Hilleman, *Proc. Soc. Exp. Biol. Med.* **108**, 205 (1961).

60. C.E. Gordon Smith, D.I.H. Simpson, E.T.W. Bowen, and I. Zlonik, *Lancet* **2**, 1119 (1967).

61. R. Siegert, *Virol. Monogr.* **11**, 98 (1972).

62. P.B. Stones, *Dev. Biol. Stand.* **37**, 251 (1976).

63. Committee for Proprietary Medicinal Products (CPMP), *Position Paper on Viral Safety of Oral Poliovirus Vaccine (OPV)*, CPMP/BWP/972/98, European Agency for the Evaluation of Medicinal Products, London, 1998. Available at: *http://www.eudra.org/humandocs/PDFs/PP/097298en.pdf*

64. R.I. Freshney, *Culture of Animal Cells: A Manual of Basic Technique*, Wiley-Liss, New York, 1994, p. 135.

65. H. Kammer, *Appl. Microbiol.* **17**, 524 (1969).

66. A.L. Van Wezel, G. Van Steenis, C.A. Hannik, and H. Cohen, *Dev. Biol. Stand.* **41**, 159 (1978).

67. M.M. Bashor, *Methods Enzymol.* **58**, 119–131 (1979).

68. E.M. Scattergood, A.J. Schlabach, W.J. McAleer, and M.R. Hilleman, *Ann. N.Y. Acad. Sci.* **413**, 332 (1983).

69. A.L. Van Wezel, C.A.M. Van der Velden de Groot, and J.A.M. Van Herwaarden, *Dev. Biol. Stand.* **46**, 151 (1980) (see discussion at the end of this paper, pp. 157–158).

70. A.L. Van Wezel, C.A.M. Van der Velden de Groot, and J.A.M. Van Herwaarden, *Dev. Biol. Stand.* **46**, 151 (1980) (see discussion at the end of this paper, pp. 157–158).

71. C.P. Cerini, J. Arguedas, G. Hernandez, P. Frickey, and A.V. Douglas, *Appl. Microbiol.* **27**, 763–6 (1974).

72. A.M. Woodruff and E.W. Goodpasture, *Am. J. Pathol.* **7**, 209–222 (1931).

73. I. Samuel, E. Tomas, and F. Barnaure, *Virologie* **32**, 145–154 (1981).

74. R. Boot, B.C. Kruijt, G. Van Steenis, and A.L. Van Wezel, *Dev. Biol. Stand.* **47**, 15 (1981).

75. G. Van Steenis, A.L. Van Wezel, I.G. de Groot, and B.C. Kruijt, *Dev. Biol. Stand.* **45**, 99 (1980).

76. R.G. Hein, *Dev. Biol. Stand.* **25**, 31 (1974).

77. A.S. Khan et al., *J. Clin. Virol.* **11**, 7 (1998).

78. J.S. Robertson et al., *Biologicals* **25**, 403–414 (1997).

79. M. Duchene et al., *Viral Immunol.* **3**, 243 (1990).

80. H. Lubon, *Biotechnol. Annu. Rev.* **4**, 1 (1998).

81. A. Colman, *Biochem. Soc. Symp.* **63**, 141 (1997).

82. M.A. Fletcher, L. Hessel, and S.A. Plotkin, *Dev. Biol. Stand.* **93**, 97–107 (1998).

83. L. Hayflick and P.S. Moorehead, *Exp. Cell Res.* **25**, 585 (1961).

84. J.P. Jacobs, C.M. Jones, and J.P. Baille, *Nature (London)* **227**, 168 (1970).

85. R.E. Wallace et al., *In Vitro* **8**, 333 (1973).

86. R.E. Wallace et al., *In Vitro* **8**, 323 (1973).

87. *WHO Requirements for the Use of Animal Cells as in vitro Substrates for the Production of Biologicals*, WHO Tech. Rep. Ser. No. 878, World Health Organization, Geneva, 1998, pp. 20–56. See also *Biologicals* **26**, 175 (1998).

88. *Quality of Biotechnological Products: Derivation and Characterization of Cell Substrates used for Production of Biotechnological/Biological Products*, ICH Harmonized Tripartite Guideline. Reproduced in *Dev. Biol. Stand.* **93**, 223 (1998), and *Fed. Regis.* **63**, (182) 50244 (1998).

89. L. Hayflick and W. Hennessen, *Dev. Biol. Stand.* **70**, 1 (1989).

90. F. Brown, E. Griffiths, F. Horaud, and J.C. Petricciani, *Dev. Biol. Stand.* **93**, (1998).

91. R. Kurth, *Ann. N.Y. Acad. Sci.* **772**, 140 (1995).

92. Y. Yasumura and Y. Kawakita, in B. Simizu and T. Terasima, eds., *Vero Cells—Origin, Properties, and Biomedical Applications*, English translation of original article in *Nihon Rinsho* **21**, 1201 (1963), Chiba University, Chiba, Japan, 1987, pp. 2–19. Note: This book is not commercially available.

93. J. Furesz, R. Bather, G. Contreras, and B. Becker. in *Abnormal Cells, New Products and Risk*. H.E. Hopps and J.C. Petricciani, eds., In Vitro, Monogr. No. 6, Tissue Culture Association, Gaithersburg, Md., p. 57.

94. S.A. Halperin, A.C. Nestruck, and B.J. Eastwood, *Vaccine* **16**, 1331 (1998).

95. A.M. Palache, R. Brands, and G.J. Van Scharrenburg, *J. Infect. Dis.* **176**(Suppl. 1), S20 (1997).

96. H.S. U et al., *J. Cell. Physiol.* **122**, 299 (1985).

97. H. Oberleithner, H.J. Westphale, and B. Gassner, *Pfluegers Arch.* **419**, 418 (1991).

98. P.B. Capstick, R.C. Telling, W.G. Chapman, and D.L. Stewart, *Nature (London)* **195**, 1163 (1962).

99. L. Nardelli and G.F. Panina, *Dev. Biol. Stand.* **37**, 133 (1977).

100. T.W.F. Pay, A. Boge, F.J.R.R Menard, and P.J. Radlett, *Dev. Biol. Stand.* **60**, 171 (1985).

101. H.D. Hoerlein, *Prog. Biotechnol.* **9**, (Pt. 2), 731 (1994).

102. A.W. Phillips, N.B. Finter, C.J. Burman, and G.D. Ball, *Methods Enzymol.* **119**, 35 (1986).

103. P.J. Regan and J.C. Petricciani, *Dev. Biol. Stand.* **68**, 19 (1987).

104. N.B. Finter, A.J.M. Garland, and R.C. Telling, in A.S. Lubiniecki, ed., *Large-scale Mammalian Cell Culture Technology*, Dekker, New York, 1990, pp. 1–14.

105. F.L. Graham, J. Smiley, W.C. Russell, and R. Nairn, *J. Gen. Virol.* **36**, 59 (1977).

106. J.L. Imler et al., *Gene Ther.* **3**, 75 (1996).

107. F.J. Fallaux et al., *Hum. Gene Ther.* **9**, 1909 (1998).

108. N. Inoue and D.W. Russell, *J. Virol.* **72**, 7024 (1998).

109. S.P. Forestell et al., *Gene Ther.* **4**, 600 (1997).

110. A. Prokop and M.Z. Rosenberg, *Adv. Biochem. Eng. Biotechnol.* **39**, 29–71 (1989).

111. S. Agathos, *Cytotechnology* **20**, 173 (1996).

112. E. D'Hondt et al., *Postgrad. Med. J.* **61**(Suppl. 4), 53 (1985).

113. U.S. Pat. 5,360,736 (November 1, 1994), P.J. Provost, D.L. Krah, and P.A. Friedman.

114. A.Y. Elliott, *Manufacture and Testing of Measles, Mumps and Rubella Vaccine*, 19th Immun. Conf. Proc., Boston, 1984, U.S. Department of Health and Human Services, Centers of Disease Control, Atlanta, Ca., 1984, pp. 79–86.

115. N.E. Bishop, D.L. Hugo, S.V. Borovec, and D.A. Anderson, *J. Viral Methods* **47**, 203 (1994).

116. J.G. Aunins et al., in M.J.T. Carrondo, J.-L. Moreira, and J.B. Griffiths, eds., *Animal Cell Technology: From Vaccines to Genetic Medicine*, Kluwer Academic Press, Dordrecht, The Netherlands, 1997, pp. 175–183.

117. W. Noe, R. Bux, W. Berthold, and W. Werz, *Cytotechnology* **15**, 169 (1994).

118. B. Montagnon, J.C. Vincent-Falquet, and B. Fanget, *Dev. Biol. Stand.* **55**, 37 (1984).

119. O. Kistner et al., *Vaccine* **16**, 960 (1998).

120. K.F. Pullen et al., *Dev. Biol. Stand.* **60**, 175 (1985).

121. B.H. Junker et al., *Cytotechnology* **9**, 173 (1992).

122. P. Perrin et al., *Vaccine* **13**, 1244 (1995).

123. M. Amadori, G. Volpe, P. DeFilippi, and C. Berneri, *Biologicals* **25**, 65 (1997).

124. J.P. Whiteside, B.R. Whiting, and R.E. Spier, *Dev. Biol. Stand.* **42**, 113 (1979). (see discussion following this article on p. 137).

125. J.B. Clarke and R.E. Spier, *Dev. Biol. Stand.* **35**, 61 (1977).

126. F. Ciampor, *Acta Virol.* **32**, 168 (1988).

127. R. Schneider and T. Shenk, *Annu. Rev. Biochem.* **56**, 317 (1987).

128. J.M. De Marchi and A.S. Kaplan, *J. Virol.* **23**, 126 (1977).

129. G. Hammer, R.T. Schwarz, and C. Schotissek, *Virology* **70**, 238 (1976).

130. R. Wigand and G. Kumel, *J. Gen. Virol.* **39**, 281 (1978).

131. V. Zaslavsky and P.H. Hofschneider, *Intervirology* **26**, 93 (1986).

132. R.G. Ham, *In Vitro* **10**, 119 (1974).

133. H. Eagle, A.E. Freeman, and M. Levy, *J. Exp. Med.* **107**, 643 (1958).

134. W.L. McKeehan, W.G. Hamilton, and R.G. Ham, *Proc. Natl. Acad. Sci. U.S.A.* **73**, 2023 (1976).

135. R.G. Ham, S.L. Hammond, and L.L. Miller, *In Vitro* **13**, 1 (1977).

136. B. Malewicz, L.E. Anderson, K. Crilly, and H.M. Jenkin, *In Vitro* **21**, 47 (1985).

137. G.M. Healy et al., *Appl. Microbiol.* **21**, 1 (1971).

138. K. Lambert and S.J. Pirt, *J. Cell Sci.* **17**, 397 (1975).

139. K. Lambert and S.J. Pirt, *Dev. Biol. Stand.* **37**, 67 (1976).

140. J.B. Griffiths, *J. Cell Sci.* **6**, 739 (1970).

141. W.L. McKeehan, K.A. McKeehan, S.L. Hammond, and R.G. Ham, *In Vitro* **13**, 399 (1977).

142. M. Butler and W.G. Thilly, *In Vitro* **18**, 213 (1981).

143. W.R. Arathoon and R.C. Telling, *Dev. Biol. Stand.* **50**, 145 (1982).

144. J.B. Griffiths, *J. Cell Sci.* **8**, 43 (1971).

145. C.F. Agostini, G.F. Mann, L.M. Allison, and F.H. Johnson, *Dev. Biol. Stand.* **46**, 51 (1980).

146. G.F. Mann and J. de Mucha, *Dev. Biol. Stand.* **37**, 255 (1976).

147. G.F. Mann and J. de Mucha Macias, *PAHO Bull.* **10**, 205 (1976).

148. G.F. Mann, *Dev. Biol. Stand.* **37**, 149 (1976).

149. A.T. Nahapetian, J.N. Thomas, and W.G. Thilly, *J. Cell Sci.* **81**, 65 (1986).

150. P.J. Radlett, R.C. Telling, C.J. Stone, and J.P. Whiteside, *Appl. Microbiol.* **22**, 534 (1971).

151. J.B. Griffiths, *J. Cell Sci.* **7**, 575 (1970).

152. W.J. Bettger, S.T. Boyce, B.J. Walthall, and R.G. Ham, *Proc. Natl. Acad. Sci. U.S.A.* **78**, 5588 (1981).

153. M. Clynes and J. Keenan, *In Vitro* **32**, 451 (1996).

154. M. Taub, L. Chuman, M.H. Saier, and G. Sato, *Proc. Natl. Acad. Sci. U.S.A.* **76**, 3338 (1979).

155. G.L. Bradshaw, G.H. Sato, D.B. McClure, and G.R. Dubes, *J. Cell Physiol.* **114**, 215 (1983).

156. K. Lambert and S.J. Pirt, *J. Cell Sci.* **35**, 381 (1979).

157. P. Phillips and V.J. Cristofalo, *J. Tissue Culture Methods* **6**, 123 (1980).

158. F.J. Candal, V.G. George, and E.W. Ades, *Biologicals* **19**, 213 (1991).

159. *Int. Pat. Appl.* WO 98/04680 (February 5, 1998), M. Butler and J.M. Berry.

160. *Int. Pat. Appl.* WO 99/21969 (May 6, 1999), S.L. Gould, D.J. Distefano, D.K. Robinson, and T.C. Seamans.

161. J.M. Clark, C. Gebb, and M.D. Hirtenstein, *Dev. Biol. Stand.* **50**, 81 (1981).

162. J. Cinatl et al., *Cell Biol. Int.* **17**, 885 (1993).

163. L. Keay, *Biotechnol. Bioeng.* **17**, 745 (1975).

164. S.P. Forestell, N. Kalogerakis, and L.A. Behie, *Appl. Microbiol. Biotechnol.* **38**, 165 (1992).

165. W.L. McKeehan and R.G. Ham, *Dev. Biol. Stand.* **37**, 97 (1976).

166. E. Kromer, W. Scheirer, and H.W.D. Katinger, *Dev. Biol. Stand.* **50**, 355 (1982).

167. P.F. Nettleton and M.M. Rweyemamu, *Arch. Virol.* **64**, 359 (1980).

168. R.L. Garnick, *Dev. Biol. Stand.* **93**, 21 (1998).

169. F. Brown and A.S. Lubiniecki, eds., Viral safety and evaluation of viral clearance from biopharmaceutical products. Dev. Biol. Std., 88, 1996.

170. C. House, A. House, and R.J. Yedloutschnig, *Can. J. Microbiol.* **36**, 737 (1990).

171. C.R. Rossi, C.R. Bridgman, and G.K. Kiesel, *Am. J. Vet. Res.* **41**, 1680 (1980).

172. D.J. Danner, J. Smith, and M. Plavsic, *Biopharm*, June, p. 50 (1999).

173. G. Hanson and L. Foster, *Art to Science* **16**(2) (1997). (a publication of Hyclone, Inc., Logan, Utah). Available at: *http://www.hyclone.com/ats/atsv16n2.pdf*

174. A. Von Seefried and P. Haffenden, in R.E. Spier, J.B. Griffiths, and B. Meignier, eds., *Production of Biologicals from Animal Cells in Culture*, Butterworth-Heinemann, Oxford, 1991, p. 117.

175. C. Rivat, P. Sertillanges, E. Patin, and J.F. Stoltz, *J. Chromatogr.* **576**, 71 (1992).

176. H.M. Mazzone, *CRC Handbook of Viruses: Mass-Molecular Weight Values and Related Properties*, CRC Press, Boca Raton, Fla., 1998.

177. N. Mittereder, K.L. March, and B.C. Trapnell, *J. Virol.* 70, 7498–7509 (1996).

178. B. Palsson and S. Andreadis, *Exp. Hematol.* **25**, 94–102 (1997).

179. A.C. Allison and R.C. Valentine, *Biochim. Biophys. Acta* **34**, 10–23 (1959).

180. A.C. Allison and R.C. Valentine, *Biochim. Biophys. Acta* **40**, 400–410 (1959).

181. K.U. Dee, H.A. Wood, and M.L. Shuler, *Biotechnol. Bioeng.* **54**, 206 (1997).

182. J.-L. Moreira et al., *Chem. Eng. Sci.* **50**, 2747 (1995).

183. J.M. Berry, N. Barnabe, K.M. Coombs, and M. Butler, *Biotechnol. Bioeng.* **62**, 12 (1999).

184. C.R. Rossi and G.K. Kiesel *Arch. Virol.* **56**, 227 (1978).

185. M. Takahashi, in L.C. Paoletti and P.M. McInnes, eds., *Vaccines: From Clinic to Concept*, CRC Press, Boca Raton, Fla., 1999, pp. 183–198.

186. D. Ben-Nathan and S. Lustig, *Adv. Biotechnol. Processes* **14**, 347–365 (1990).

187. F.J. Muzzio et al., *Biotechnol. Bioeng.* **63**, 185 (1999).

188. D.R. Unger, in M. Flickinger and S. Drew, eds., *The Encyclopedia of Bioprocess Technology*, Wiley, New York, 1999, pp. 2290–2303.

189. B.O. Palsson and A.S. Chuck, *Hum. Gene Ther.* **7**, 743 (1996).

190. J.H. Hughes, *Clin. Microbiol. Rev.* **6**, 150–175 (1993).

191. J.J. Holland, *Virology* **15**, 312 (1961).

192. T.J. Wickham, *Biophys. J.* **58**, 1501 (1990).

193. R. Persson, U. Svensson, and E. Everitt, *J. Virol.* **46**, 956 (1983).

194. H. Deng et al., *Nature (London)* **381**, 661 (1996).

195. P. Mathias, T. Wickham, M. Moore, and G. Nemerow, *J. Virol.* **68**, 6811 (1994).

196. K.U. Dee, D.A. Hammer, and M.L. Shuler, *Biotechnol. Bioeng.* **46**, 485 (1995).

197. T.J. Wickham et al., *J. Gen. Virol.* **73**, 3185 (1992).

198. A.G. Ogston, *Biochim. Biophys. Acta* **66**, 279 (1963).

199. A.L. Koch, *Biochim. Biophys. Acta* **39**, 311 (1960).

200. R.J. Kaner et al., *Am. J. Respir. Cell Mol. Biol.* **20**, 361 (1999).

201. S. Huang, R.I. Endo, and G.R. Nemerow, *J. Virol.* **69**, 2257–2263, (1995).

202. I. Zajac and R.L. Crowell, *J. Bacteriol.* **89**, 574 (1965).

203. L. Philipson, K. Lonberg-Holm, and U. Petterson, *J. Virol.* **2**, 1064 (1968).

204. M. Bisaillon, S. Senechal, L. Bernier, and G. Lemay, *J. Mol. Biol.* **286**, 759 (1999).

205. E.V. Ravkov, S.T. Nichol, and R.W. Compans, *J. Virol.* **71**, 1147 (1997).

206. A. Maisner et al., *J. Biol. Chem.* **271**, 18853 (1996).

207. D.M. Blau and R.W. Compans, *Virology* **210**, 91 (1995).

208. T.J. Wickham, P.W. Roelvink, D.E. Brough, and I. Kovesdi, *Nat. Biotechnol.* **14**, 1570–1578 (1996).

209. L.L. Nisevich, L.A. Konstantinova, and V.M. Stakhanova, *Vopr. Virusolo.* **17**, 344 (1972).

210. S. Nomura, *Proc. Soc. Exp. Biol. Med.* **128**, 163–166 (1968).

211. P.C. Loh, G.M. Hashiro, and J.T. Yau, *Microbios* **19**, 77 (1977).

212. R.L. Crowell, *Bacteriol Proc.* **212**, 180 (1968).

213. N.E. Bishop, and D.A. Anderson, *Arch. Virol.* **142**, 2161 (1997).

214. P. Mathias, M. Galleno, and G.R. Nemerow, *J. Virol.* **72**, 8669 (1998).

215. F. Brown, B. Cartwright, and D.L. Stewart, *Biochim. Biophys. Acta* **55**, 768 (1962).

216. L.C. McLaren, J.J. Holland, and J.T. Syverton, *J. Exp. Med.* **112**, 581 (1960).

217. J.T. Stapleton, J. Frederick, and B. Meyer, *J. Infect. Dis.* **164**, 1098 (1991).

218. N.E. Bishop, and D.A. Anderson, *Arch. Virol.* **142**, 2161 (1997).

219. R. Wyler and W. Wiesendanger, *Arch. Virol.* **47**, 57 (1975).

220. F. Superti, M.L. Marziano, A. Tinari, and G. Donelli, *Comp. Immunol. Microbiol. Infect. Dis.* **16**, 55 (1993).

221. K.K. Takemoto and S.S. Spicer, *Ann. N.Y. Acad. Sci.* **130**, 365 (1965).

222. C.R. Parish, L. Low, H.S. Warren, and A.L. Cunningham, *J. Immunol.* **145**, 1188 (1990).

223. L.D. Dion, J. Fang, and R.I. Garver, *J. Virol. Methods* **56**, 99 (1996).

224. P. von Magnus, *Adv. Virus Res.* **2**, 59 (1954).

225. A.S. Huang and D. Baltimore, in F.-H. Conrat and R.R. Wagner, eds., *Comprehensive Virology*, Plenum, New York, 1977, pp. 73–116.

226. T.J. Wickham et al., *Biotechnol. Lett.* **13**, 483 (1991).

227. U.F. Greber, M. Willetts, P. Webster, and A. Helenius, *Cell* **75**, 477 (1993).

228. Y. Chardonnet and S. Dales, *Virology* 478, (1970).

229. K. Lonberg-Holm and L. Philipson, *Monogr. Virol.* **9**, (1974).

230. A. Helenius, M. Marsh, and J. White, *J. Gen. Virol.* **58**, 47 (1982).

231. M.D. Eaton and A.R. Scala, *Virology* **13**, 300 (1961).

232. E.M. Jensen and O.C. Liu, *Proc. Soc. Exp. Biol. Med.* **107**, 834 (1961).

233. J.S. Oxford and G.C. Schild, *Br. J. Exp. Pathol.* **48**, 235 (1967).

234. C. Kooi, M. Cervin, and R. Anderson, *Virology* **180**, 108 (1991).

235. H. Suzuki et al., *Arch. Virol.* **85**, 25 (1985).

236. J.E. Ludert et al., *Intervirology* **27**, 95 (1987).

237. K.T. Kaljot, R.D. Shaw, D.H. Rubin, and H.B. Greenberg, *J. Virol.* **62**, 1136 (1988).

238. M. Vashishtha et al., *J. Cell Biol.* **140**, 91 (1998).

239. C. Bernardes, A. Antonio, M.C. Pedroso de Lima, and M.L. Valdeira, *Biochim. Biophys. Acta* **1393**, 19 (1998).

240. R. Pal, Y. Barenholz, and R.R. Wagner, *Biochim. Biophys. Acta* **906**, 175 (1987).

241. M.T. Marquardt and M. Kielian, *Virology* **224**, 198 (1996).

242. F. Superti et al., *Comp. Immunol. Microbiol. Infect. Dis.* **18**, 129 (1995).

243. R. Pottathil, P.L. Gutierrez, L.H. Davis, and K.A. Chandrabose, *J. Biol. Chem.* **260**, 5265 (1985).

244. P. Mastromarino, C. Conti, S. Rieti, and N. Orsi, *Arch. Virol.* **103**, 243 (1988).

245. R. Allen, R.A. Finkelstein, and S.E. Suilkin, *Tex. Rep. Biol. Med.* **16**, 391 (1958).

246. M.L. Chapek, L.E. McClaughry, and L.M. Wilkins, *Mod. Vet. Pract.* **59**, 755 (1978).

247. P.A. Offit et al., *J. Clin. Microbiol.* **20**, 266–270, (1984).

248. P.M. Cereda et al., *Microbiologica* **7**, 251 (1984).

249. N.J. Dimmock, *Curr. Top. Microbiol. Immunol.* **183**, 1 (1993).

250. G. Appleyard and H.B. Maber, *J. Gen. Virol.* **25**, 351 (1974).

251. C.F. Arias, P. Romero, V. Alvarez, and S. Lopez, *J. Virol.* **70**, 5832 (1996).

252. W.C. Linscott and W.E. Levinson, *Proc. Natl. Acad. Sci. U.S.A.* **64**, 520 (1969).

253. D. Baltimore, *Bacteriol. Rev.* **35**, 235 (1971).

254. B. Roizman, P. Palese, in B.N. Fields, D.M. Knipe, and P.M. Howley, eds., *Fields Virology*, 3rd ed., Lippincott-Raven, Philadelphia, 1996, pp. 101–111.

255. S. Casjens and J. King, *Annu. Rev. Biochem.* **44**, 555 (1975).

256. L. Philipson, *Curr. Top. Microsc. Immun.* **109**, 1 (1983).

257. S.S. Cohen and F.P. McCormick, *Adv. Virus Res.* **24**, 331 (1979).

258. S.L. Sheppard, A.T. Burness, and S.M. Boyle, *J. Virol.* **34**, 266 (1980).

259. A. Raina, K. Tuomi, and R. Mantyjarvi, *Med. Biol.* **59**, 428 (1981).

260. K.B. Tan, *Proc. Natl. Acad. Sci. U.S.A.* **74**, 2805 (1977).

261. L.C. Gosule and J.A. Schellman, *Nature (London)* **259**, 333 (1976).

262. C.A. Gelfand, Q. Wang, S. Randall, and J.E. Jentoft, *J. Biol. Chem.* **268**, 18450 (1993).

263. H.-D. Klenk and W. Garten, *Trends Microbiol.* **2**, 39 (1994).

264. C. Wallis, J.L. Melnick, and F. Rapp, *J. Bacteriol.* **92**, 155 (1966).

265. M. Schmelz et al., *J. Virol.* **68**, 130 (1994).

266. G. Griffiths and P. Rottier, *Semin. Cell Biol.* **3**, 367 (1992).

267. E.B. Stephens and R.W. Compans, *Annu. Rev. Microbiol.* **42**, 489 (1988).

268. E. Rodriguez Boulan and D.D. Sabatini, *Proc. Natl. Acad. Sci. U.S.A.* **75**, 5071 (1978).

269. Y. Morimoto, Y. Doi, and H. Itoh, *Jpn. J. Med. Sci. Biol.* **23**, 1 (1970).

270. M.G. Roth, J.P. Fitzpatrick, R.W. Compans, *Proc. Natl. Acad. Sci. U.S.A.* **76**, 6430 (1979).

271. R.V. Srinivas, N. Balachandran, F.V. Alonso-Caplen, and R.W. Compans, *J. Virol.* **58**, 689 (1986).

272. R. Harson and C. Grose, *J. Virol.* **69**, 4994 (1995).

273. J.K. Russell and J.E. Blalock, *Biochem. Biophys. Res. Commun.* **122**, 851 (1984).

274. P. Tattersall, *J. Virol.* **10**, 586 (1972).

275. P.J. Durham and R.H. Johnson, *Vet. Microbiol.* **10**, 335 (1985).

276. P.E. Came, A. Pascale, and G. Shimonaski, *Arch. Gesamte Virusforsch.* **23**, 346 (1968).

277. G.E. Gifford and D.G. Klapper, *Arch. Gesamte Virusforsch.* **26**, 321 (1969).

278. D.A. Eppstein et al., *Nature (London)* **318**, 663 (1985).

279. Y.V. Marsh and D.A. Eppstein, *J. Cell. Biochem.* **34**, 239 (1987).

280. L. Korutla and R. Kumar, *Biochem. Biophys. Res. Commun.* **220**, 670 (1996).

281. J.W. Mellors et al., *J. Infect. Dis.* **163**, 78 (1991).

282. R.J. Kaner et al., *Science* **248**, 1410 (1990).

283. R.D. Dix, L. Hurst, and R.W. Keane, *J. Gen. Virol.* **73**, 1845 (1992).

284. H.S. Ginsberg, L.J. Bello, and A.J. Levine, in J.S. Colter and W. Paranchych, eds., *The Molecular Biology of Viruses*, Academic Press, New York, 1967, 547–572.

285. E. Ehrenfeld, *Semin. Virol.* **4**, 199–268 (1993).

286. L. Carrasco, ed., *Mechanisms of Viral Toxicity in Animal Cells*, CRC Press, Boca Raton, Fla., 1987.

287. L.S. Young, C.W. Dawson, and A.G. Eliopoulos, *Br. Med. Bull.* **53**, 509 (1997).

288. D.C. Krakauer and R.J. Payne, *Proc. R. Soc. London, Ser. B* **264**, 1757 (1997).

289. K.B. Schwarz, *Free Radical Biol. Med.* **21**, 641 (1996).

290. A.J. Mastrangelo, J.M. Hardwick, and M.J. Betenbaugh, *Cytotechnology* **22**, 169 (1996).

291. A.J. Mastrangelo and M.J. Betenbaugh, *Trends Biotechnol.* **16**, 88 (1998).

292. M.I. Thoulouze, M. Lafage, J.A. Montano-Hirose, and M. Lafon, *J. Virol.* **71**, 7372 (1997).

293. C.L. Liao et al., *J. Virol.* **71**, 5963 (1997).

294. M. Bitzer et al., *J. Virol.* **73**, 702 (1999).

295. D. Miyamoto et al., *Antiviral Res.* **39**, 89 (1998).

296. V.M. Zaides, L.M. Selimova, O.G. Nikolaeva, and A.G. Bukrinskaia, *Vopr. Virusol.* **1**, 44 (1976).

297. D.D. Patel, D.J. Pickup, and W.K. Joklik, *Virology* **149**, 174 (1986).

298. A. Garnier et al., *Cytotechnology* **15**, 145 (1994).

299. J. Zhang, N. Kalogerakis, L.A. Behie, and K. Iatrou, *Biotechnol. Prog.* **10**, 636 (1994).

300. K.T.K. Wong et al., *Biotechnol. Bioeng.* **49**, 659 (1996).

301. C. Bédard, A. Kamen, R. Tom, and B. Massie, *Cytotechnology* **15**, 129 (1994).

302. N. Hirayama et al., *J. Gen. Virol.* **66** (Pt. 1), 149 (1985).

303. F. Sasao, A. Igarishi, and K. Fukai, *Microbiol. Immunol.* **24**, 915 (1980).

304. P.C. Loh and H.K. Oie, *J. Virol.* **4**, 890 (1959).

305. N. Romano and G. Scarlata, *Arch. Gesamte Virusforsch.* **43**, 359 (1973).

306. V. Stollar, *Virology* **91**, 504 (1978).

307. Y. Ito, H. Okazaki, S. Sakuma, and M. Homma, *Virology* **39**, 277 (1969).

308. A. Igarishi, F. Sasao, and K. Fukai, *Biken J.* **17**, 39 (1974).

309. H.J. Hearn, H.R. Tribble, S.C. Nagle, and O.C. Bowersox, *Appl. Microbiol.* **21**, 342 (1971).

310. C.A. Heilman and H. Rouse, *Virology* **159**, (1980).

311. J.G. Osborn, P.M. Chesters, and J.D. Williamson, *J. Hyg.* **93**, 213 (1984).

312. E. Gonczol, I. Boldogh, and L. Vaczi, *Acta Microbiol. Acad. Sci. Hung.* **22**, 263 (1975).

313. M. Iinuma, K. Maeno, and T. Matsumoto, *Virology* **51**, 205 (1973).

314. R.J. Courtney, R.M. McCombs, and M. Benyesh-Melnick, *Virology* **40**, 379 (1970).

315. J. Aono and Y. Minamishima, *Microbiol. Immunol.* **28**, 129 (1984).

316. L.C. Archard and J.D. Williamson, *J. Gen. Virol.* **12**, 249 (1971).

317. K.J. Auborn and H. Rouse, *Virus Res.* **1**, 615 (1984).

318. J.D. Williamson, *Biochem. Soc. Trans.* **13**, 331 (1985).

319. G.E. Mark, A.S. Kaplan, *Virology* **45**, 53 (1971).

320. S. Gillies and V. Stollar, *Virology* **112**, 318 (1981).

321. H.T. Zwartouw and D.J. Algar, *J. Gen. Virol.* **2**, 243 (1968).

322. H. Eagle, K. Habel, *J. Exp. Med.* **104**, 271 (1956).

323. A. Koch and E. Gyorgy, *Acta Microbiol. Acad. Sci. Hung.* **13**, 85 (1966).

324. A. Mukhopadhyay, S.N. Mukhopadhyay, and G.P. Talwar, *Biotechnol. Lett.* **16**, 339 (1994).

325. C.A.M. Van der Velden den Groot et al., *Adv. Anim. Cell Biol. Technol. Bioprocesses*, p. 404, (1989).

326. B. Schopf, M.W. Howaldt, and J.E. Bailey, *J. Biotechnol.* **15**, 169 (1990).

327. J.D. Ware, W.J. Bellini, and R.J. Ash, *J. Natl. Cancer Inst. (U.S.)* **55**, 1379 (1975).

328. K.T.K. Wong, L.K. Nielsen, P.F. Greenfield, and S. Reid, *Cytotechnology* **15**, 157 (1994).

329. G. Bardeletti, *Intervirology* **8**, 100 (1977).

330. G. Bardeletti, M. Henry, R. Sohier, and D. Gautheron, *Arch. Gesamte Virusforsch.* **39**, 26 (1972).

331. R.A. Chillakuru, D.D.Y. Ryu, and T. Yilma, *Biotechnol. Prog.* **7**, 85 (1991).

332. R. Singhvi et al., *Cytotechnology* **22**, 79 (1996).

333. C. Scholtissek, K. Muller, and S. Herzog, *Virus Res.* **6**, 287 (1986).

334. V. Gauss-Muller and F. Deinhardt, *Proc. Soc. Exp. Biol. Med.* **175**, 10 (1984).

335. V.S. Kokorev and E.G. Kolotvinova, *Vopr. Virusol.* **31**, 623 (1986).

336. P. Gripon, C. Diot, A. Corlu, and C. Guguen-Guillouzo, *J. Med. Virol.* **28**, 193 (1989).

337. C.L. Baugh and A.A. Tytell, *Life Sci.* **6**, 371 (1967).

338. D. Barngrover, J. Thomas, and W.G. Thilly, *J. cell Sci.* **78**, 173 (1985).

339. H. Eagle, S. Barban, M. Levy, and H.O. Schulze, *J. Biol. Chem.* **233**, 551 (1958).

340. L. Fabry, B. Baijot, E. D'Hondt, and M. Duchenne, *Adv. Anim. Cell Biol. Techno. Bioprocesses*, p. 361, (1989).

341. S. Baron, J.S. Porterfield, and A. Isaacs, *Virology* **14**, 444 (1961).

342. A.A. Kamen et al., *Biotechnol. Bioeng.* **50**, 36 (1996).

343. G. Schmid, *Cytotechnology* **20**, 43 (1996).

344. F.E. Wassermann, *Acta Virol.* **13**, 447 (1969).

345. P. Osio, Y. Beaudry, G. Chatot, and R. Fontagnes, *C. R. Hebd. Seances Acad. Sci.* **168**, 550 (1974).

346. D. Bardell, *Microbios* **43**, 87 (1985).

347. G.R. Dubes, M.I. Al Moslih, and A.R. Sambol, **70**, 247 (1981).

348. L.J. Schiff and A.M. Shefner, *J. Clin. Microbiol.* **1**, 44 (1975).

349. A. Naldini, F. Carraro, W.R. Fleischmann, and V. Bocci, *J. Interferon Res.* **13**, 127 (1993).

350. K.B. Schwartz, *Free Radical Biol. Med.* **21**, 641 (1996).

351. A.T. Palamara et al., *Biochem. Biophys. Res. Commun.* **228**, 579 (1996).

352. E. Speir et al., *Circ. Res.* **79**, 1143 (1996).

353. S. Harakeh and R.J. Jariwalla, *Am. J. Clin. Nutr.* **54**(6 Suppl.), 1231S, (1991).

354. C.E. Isaacs et al., *Antiviral Res.* **33**, 117 (1997).

355. Z.A. Lazymova, I.I. Abdullaev, F.I. Abdullaev, and T.A. Asadullaev, *Vopr. Virusol.* **31**, 236 (1986).

356. S.V. Gangodkar, S.P. Paranjape, V.D. Kadam, and R.P. Deolankar, *Curr. Sci.* **73**, 1108 (1997).

357. A. Baghian, M.A. Dietrich, and K.G. Kousoulas, *Arch. Virol.* **122**, 119 (1992).

358. M. Mallo, J. Martinez-Costas, and J. Benavente, *J. Virol.* **65**, 5499 (1991).

359. D.J. Alexander and M.S. Collins, *Arch. Virol.* **49**, 339 (1975).

360. R.I. Podcherniaeva and G.A. Danylbaeva, *Vopr. Virusol.* **36**, 384 (1991).

361. F.B. Johnson and A.S. Bodily, *Proc. Soc. Exp. Biol. Med.* **150**, 585 (1975).

362. O.P. Zhirnov, *Vopr. Virusol.* **31**, 723 (1986).

363. K. Yoshino, T. Kishie, M. Hashimoto, and K. Yanagi, *Arch. Virol.* **47**, 31 (1975).

364. L.L. Moore, D.A. Bostick, and R.F. Garry, *Virology* **166**, 1 (1988).

365. J.V. Scott and P.W. Choppin, *J. Virol. Methods* **5**, 173 (1982).

366. H.F. Maassab, C.A. Heilman, and M.L. Herlocher, *Adv. Biotechnol. Processes* **14**, 203, (1990).

367. M.E. Armstrong et al., *J. Hepatol.* **18**(Suppl. 2), S20 (1993).

368. M.L. Clements et al., *J. Clin. Microbiol.* **29**, 1175 (1991).

369. M.S. Shahrabadi and P.W. Lee, *Virology* **152**, 298 (1986).

370. C. Wallis and J.L. Melnick, *Virology* **16**, 122 (1962).

371. M. Fiala and G.E. Kenny, *J. Virol.* **1**, 489 (1967).

372. E.G. Strauss, E.M. Lenches, and M.A. Stamreich-Martin, *J. Gen. Virol.* **49**, 297 (1980).

373. H. Von Hovel, *Arch. Gesamte Virusforsch.* **43**, 200 (1973).

374. M.E. Begin, *J. Gen. Virol.* **51**, 263 (1980).

375. T. Matsumura, V. Stollar, and R.W. Schlesinger, *J. Gen. Virol.* **17**, 343 (1972).

376. M.R. Waite and E.R. Pfefferkorn, *J. Virol.* **5**, 60 (1970).

377. E.A. Tolskaya, V.I. Agol, M.K. Voroshilova, and G.Y. Lipskaya, *Virology* **29**, 613 (1966).

378. H.A. Blough, J.M. Tiffany, G. Gordon, and M. Fiala, *Virology* **38**, 694 (1969).

379. P.G. West, B. Aldrich, R. Hartwig, and G.J. Haller, *J. Clin. Microbiol.* **26**, 2510 (1988).

380. J. Tanaka et al., *Virology* **146**, 165 (1985).

381. H. Bei, M.M. Monick, and G.W. Hunninghake, *Chin. Med. J.* **111**, 712 (1998).

382. C. Scholtissek and K. Muller, *Arch. Virol.* **100**, 27 (1988).

383. A.H. Koyama and T. Uchida, *Virus Res.* **13**, 271 (1989).

384. A.B. Sabin and P.K. Olitsky, *Proc. Soc. Exp. Biol. Med.* **31**, 357 (1936).

385. F.C. Robbins, in S.A. Plotkin and E.A. Mortimer, eds., *Vaccines*, Saunders, Philadelphia, 1994, pp. 137–154.

386. F.P. Hanssens, H.J. Nauwynck, and M.B. Pensaert, *J. Virol.* **67**, 4492 (1993).

387. G. MacIntyre, D.E. Woods, and R. Anderson, *Antimicrob. Agents Chemother.* **35**, 2630 (1991).

388. M.L. Zapp, S. Stern, and M.R. Green, *Cell* **74**, 969 (1993).

389. D. Garcin, T. Masse, J.J. Madjar, and B. Jacquemont, *Eur. J. Biochem.* **194**, 279 (1990).

390. Yu.Z. Ghendon and T.A. Mikhailovskaya, *Acta Virol.* **26**, 241 (1982).

391. E.L. Ellis and M. Delbruck, *J. Gen. Physiol.* **22**, 365 (1939).

392. U.S. Pat. 4,664,912, (May 12, 1987), T.J. Wiktor, B.J. Fanget, P. Fournier, and B.J. Montagnon.

393. P.J. Radlett, T.W.F. Pay, and A.J.M. Garland, *Dev. Biol. Stand.* **60**, 163 (1985).

394. P. Licari and J.E. Bailey, *Biotechnol. Bioeng.* **39**, 432 (1992).

395. *Part 610—General Biological Products Standards*, Sec. 610.15, 21CFR610.15(b), National Archives and Records Administration, Washington, D.C., 1998. Available at: *http://www.access.gpo.gov/nara/cfr/waisidx/-21cfr610.html*

396. *Varicella Vaccine (Live)*, Monogr. 648, European Pharmacopoiea, 1997.

397. L.H. Uribe et al., *J. Gen. Virol.* **64**, 471 (1983).

398. J.D. Almeida et al., *J. Gen. Virol.* **40**, 213 (1978).

399. M. Bloemraad et al., *Vet. Microbiol.* **42**, 361 (1994).

400. R. Mauler and H. Gruschkau, *Dev. Biol. Stand.* **41**, 267 (1978).

401. I. Slavik, F. Ciampor, and V. Mayer, *Acta Virol.* **27**, 97 (1983).

402. G.M. Lee, J.H. Choi, S.C. Jun, and B.O. Palsson, *Bioprocess Eng.* **19**, 343 (1998).

403. F.L. Black, *Virology* **7**, 184 (1959).

404. K.U. Dee and M.L. Shuler, *Biotechnol. Bioeng.* **54**, 468 (1997).

405. B. Reddy and J. Yin, *AIDS Res. Hum. Retroviruses* **15**, 273 (1999).

406. C.D. De Gooijer et al., *Appl. Microbiol. Biotechnol.* **30**, 497 (1989).

407. B. Maiorella, D. Inlow, A. Shauger, and D. Harano, *Bio/Technology* **6**, 1406 (1988).

408. R.L. Tom et al., *Appl. Microbiol. Biotechnol.* **44**, 53 (1995).

409. C. Bédard, S. Perret, and A.A. Kamen, *Biotechnol. Lett.* **19**, 629 (1997).

410. R. Neutra, B.-Z. Levi, and Y. Shoham, *Appl. Microbiol. Biotechnol.* **37**, 74 (1992).

411. D.A. Lindsay and M.J. Betenbaugh, *Biotechnol. Bioeng.* **39**, 614 (1992).

412. A.W. Caron, J. Archambault, and B. Massie, *Biotechnol. Bioeng.* **36**, 1133 (1990).

413. A. Garnier et al., *Cytotechnology* **22**, 53 (1996).

414. K.U. Dee and M.L. Shuler, *Biotechnol. Prog.* **13**, 14 (1997).

415. P. Licari and J.E. Bailey, *Biotechnol. Bioeng.* **37**, 238 (1991).

416. R. Dulbecco and M. Vogt, *Cold Spring Harbor Symp. Quant. Biol.* **18**, 273 (1953).

417. G. Kado, *Dev. Biol. Stand.* **37**, 261 (1976).

418. L.J. Reed and H. Muench, *Am. J. Hyg.* **27**, 493 (1938).

419. A.J. Darling, J.A. Bose, and J. Spaltro, *Biologicals* **26**, 105 (1998).

420. E.A. Gould and J.C.S. Clegg, in B.W.J. Mahy, ed., *Virology: A Practical Approach*, IRL Press, Oxford, U.K., 1985, pp. 43–78.

421. D.J. Wood et al., *Biologicals* **25**, 59 (1997).

422. G. Van Steenis, A.L. Van Wezel, and V.M. Sekhuis, *Dev. Biol. Stand.* **47**, 119 (1981).

423. T.R. Doel, A.D. Osterhaus, A.L. Van Wezel, and G. Van Steenis, *J. Biol. Stand.* **12**, 93 (1984).

424. L.A. Sawyer et al., *Biologicals* **25**, 299 (1997).

425. G.F. Kersten, W. Jiskoot, T. Hazendonk, and E.C. Beuvery, *Dev. Biol. Stand.* **92**, 295 (1998).

426. M. Valle, *Acta Pathol. Microbiol. Scand., Sect. B, Suppl.* **219**, (1971).

427. P. Albrecht, G. Van Steenis, A.L. Van Wezel, and J. Salk, *Rev. Infect. Dis.* **6**(Suppl. 2), S540 (1984).

428. P.P. Mertens et al., *Virology* **217**, 582 (1996).

429. L.G. Payne and E. Norrby, *J. Virol.* **27**, 19 (1978).

430. S.B. Spring and B. Roizman, *J. Virol.* **2**, 979 (1968).

431. *Guidance for Industry. Guidance for Human Somatic Cell Therapy and Gene Therapy*, U.S. Department of Health and Human Services, Food and Drug Administration, Center for Biologics Evaluation and Research, Washington, D.C., 1998. Available at: *http://www.fda.gov/cber/gdlns/somgene.pdf*

432. J.L. Melnick, in F. Fenner and A. Gibbs, eds., *Portraits of Viruses. A History of Virology*, Karger, Basel, 1988, pp. 147–188.

433. P. Perrin, M. Lafon, and P. Sureau, *Adv. Biotechnol. Processes* **14**, 325 (1990).

434. World Health Organization, *Global Polio Eradication Initiative*, W.H.O., Geneva. Available at: *http://whqsabin.who.int:8082/*

435. J. Salk, J.A. Drucker, and D. Malvy, in E.A. Mortimer and S.A. Plotkin, eds., *Vaccines*, Saunders, Philadelphia, 1994, pp. 205–227.

436. N. Nathanson and A.D. Langmuir, *Am. J. Hyg.* **7**, 16–81 (1963).

437. J.E. Salk et al., *JAMA, J. Am. Med. Assoc.* **151**, 1081 (1953).

438. L.N. Farrell et al., *Can. J. Public Health* **44**, 273 (1953).

439. J.F. Morgan, H.J. Morton, and R.C. Parker, *Proc. Soc. Exp. Biol. Med.* **73**, 1 (1950).

440. H.J. Morton, *In Vitro* **6**, 89 (1970).

441. *Poliomyelitis Vaccination. A Preliminary Review*, W.H.O. Tech. Rep. Ser. No. 101, World Health Organ., Geneva, 1955.

442. *Part 630 - Additional Standards for Viral Vaccines. Subpart A—Poliovirus Vaccine Inactivated*, CFR 21CFR630.1 through 21CFR630.5, National Archives and Records Administration, Washington, D.C., 1992. Note: These regulations are no longer in force, however they are representative of ongoing practice.

443. J. Salk et al., *Dev. Biol. Stand.* **47**, 181 (1981).

444. P. Gerber, G.A. Hottle, and R.E. Grubbs, *Proc. Soc. Exp. Biol. Med.* **108**, 205 (1961).

445. E.A. Mortimer, Jr. et al., *N. Engl. J. Med.* **305**, 1517 (1981).

446. B.J. Montagnon, B. Fanget, and A.J. Nicolas, *Dev. Biol. Stand.* **47**, 55 (1981).

447. B.J. Montagnon, B. Fanget, and J.C. Vincent-Falquet, *Rev. Infect. Dis.* **6**(Suppl. 2), S341 (1984).

448. U.S. Pa. 4,525,349, (June 25, 1985), B.J. Montagnon and B.J.C. Fanget.

449. B.J. Montagnon, *Dev. Biol. Stand.* **70**, 27 (1989).

450. A.L. Van Wezel, *Nature (London)* **216**, 64 (1967).

451. See *http://www.rivm.nl* and *http://www.svm.rivm.nl*

452. P.A. Van Hemert, D.G. Kilburn, and A.L. Van Wezel, *Biotechnol. Bioeng.* **11**, 875 (1969).

453. A.L. Van Wezel, *Prog. Immunobiol. Stand.* **5**, 187 (1972).

454. A. von Seefried and J.H. Chun, *Dev. Biol. (Stand.)* **47**, 25 (1981).

455. A. von Seefried et al., *Rev. Infect. Dis.* **6**(Suppl. 2), S345, (1984).

456. G.E. Gifford and J.T. Syverton, *Virology* **4**, 216 (1957).

457. J.G. Aunins and H.J. Henzler, in H.J. Rehm, *Biotechnology*, 2nd ed., Vol. 3, VCH Verlag, Weinheim, Germany, 1993, p. 219.

458. U.S. Pat. 4,525,349, (June 25, 1985), B.J. Montagnon and B.J.C. Fanget.

459. J.L. Melnick, in S.A. Plotkin and E.A. Mortimer, eds., *Vaccines*, Saunders, Philadelphia, 1994, pp. 155–204.

460. A.B. Sabin and A. Lwoff, *Science* **129**, 1287 (1959).

461. A.B. Sabin, *Virol.* **2**, 99 (1961).

462. A.B. Sabin and L.R. Boulger, *J. Biol. Stand.* **1**, 115 1973.

463. *Manufacture of Poliovirus Vaccine Live Oral Trivalent*, 21CFR630.13. U.S. Department of Health and Human Services, Food and Drug Administration, Center for Biologics Evaluation and Research, Washington, D.C., 1992. Note: these regulations are no longer in force, however are representative of the technology and testing requirements for currently licensed products.

464. V. Agol and S. Drozdov, *Biologicals* **21**, 321 (1993).

465. Refer to paralysis with Koprowski & Cox strains.

466. H.G. MacMorine, G.D. Laurence, W. Parisius, and N.B. Cucakovich, *Dev. Biol. Stand.* **37**, 139 (1977).

467. L. Hayflick, S. Plotkin, and R.E. Stevenson, *Dev. Biol. Stand.* **68**, 9 (1987).

468. M. Ritchey, *Oral poliovirus vaccine*, 19th Immun. Conf. Proc., Boston, 1984. U.S. Department of Health and Human Services, Centers of Disease Control, Atlanta, Ga., 1984, pp. 75–77.

469. *Physicians' Desk Reference*, Medical Economics Company, N.J. Montvale, 1999, pp. 1528–1529.

470. *Poliomyelitis Vaccine (Oral)*, Monogr. 215, European Pharmacopoeia, 1997.

471. J. Leiber and M. Stoller, *Poison Ivy*, Jerry Leiber Music/Mike Stoller Music, 1959.

472. K. Habel, *Public Health Rep.* **60**, 201 (1945).

473. J.F. Enders and T.C. Peebles, *Proc. Soc. Exp. Biol. Med.* **86**, 277 (1954).

474. L.E. Markowitz and S.L. Katz, in S.A. Plotkin and E.A. Mortimer, eds., *Vaccines*, 2nd ed., Saunders, Philadelphia, 1994, pp. 229–276.

475. M.B. McChesney and M.B.A. Oldstone, *Adv. Immunol.* **45**, 335 (1989).

476. E. Norrby, in P. Perlmann and H. Wigzell, eds., *Vaccines*, Springer-Verlag, Berlin, 1999, pp. 93–119.

477. *Reducing Mortality from Major Killers of Children*, Fact Sheet No. 178, World Health Organ. Geneva, 1998. Available at: *http://lynx.who.ch/inf-fs/en/fact178.html*

478. S.L. Cochi, M. Wharton, and S.A. Plotkin, in S.A. Plotkin and E.A. Mortimer, eds., *Vaccines*, 2nd ed., Saunders, Philadelphia, 1994, pp. 277–301.

479. S.A. Rubin, M. Pletnikov, and K.M. Carbone, *J. Virol.* 8037 (1998).

480. S.L. Wechsler and B.N. Fields, *J. Virol.* **25**, 285 (1978).

481. E.S. Sidorenko et al., *Vaccine* **7**, 554 (1989).

482. Ya. Nechaeva et al., *Vestn. Ross. Akad. Med. Nauk* **3**, 29 (1998).

483. Z.G. Peisel et al., *Tr. Inst. Epidemiol. Mikrobiol. Pastera (Proc. Pasteur Inst. Epidemiol. Microbiol.)* **42**, 120 (1973).

484. U.S. Pat. 3,959,074, (May 25, 1976), W.J. Miller, R.E. Spier, and W.J. McAleer.

485. T. Whistler, W.J. Bellini, and P.A. Rota, *Virology* **220**, 480 (1996).

486. C. Bellocq, G. Mottet, and L. Roux, *Biologicals* **18**, 337 (1990).

487. J.F. Enders, S.L. Katz, M.V. Milovanovic, and A. Holloway, *N. Engl. J. Med.* **263**, 153 (1960).

488. M.R. Hilleman et al., *JAMA, J. Am. Med. Assoc.* **206**, 587 (1968).

489. *Measles Vaccines: Report of a WHO Scientific Group*, W.H.O. Tech. Rep. Ser. No. 263, World Health Organ., Geneva, 1963.

490. A.J.F. Schwarz, *Am. J. Dis. Child.* **103**, 216 (1962).

491. J. Warren and M.J. Gallian, *Am. J. Dis. Child.* **103**, 248 (1962).

492. M.R. Hilleman, *Dev. Biol. Stand.* **84**, 107 (1995).

493. A.A. Smorodintsev and L.I. Taros, *Tr. Inst. Epidemiol. Mikrobiol. Pastera (Proc. Pasteur Ins. Epidemiol. Microbiol.)* **67**, 86 (1992).

494. H. Mirchamsky, *Rev. Infect. Dis.* **5**, 491 (1983).

495. M. Hirayama, *Rev. Infect. Dis.* **5**, 495 (1983).

496. S. Makino, *Rev. Infect. Dis.* **5**, 504 (1983).

497. X. Jianzhi and C. Zhihui, *Rev. Infect. Dis.* **5**, 506 (1983).

498. M.R. Hilleman, E.B. Buynak, R.E. Weibel, and J. Stokes, *N. Engl. J. Med.* **278**, 227 (1968).

499. M.A. Afzal et al., *J. Gen. Virol.* **74**, 917 (1993).

500. K. Yamanishi et al., *Biken J.* **13**, 157 (1970).

501. T.I. Kaptsova et al., *Vopr. Virusol.* **6**, 679 (1976).

502. R. Gluck et al., *Dev. Biol. Stand.* **65**, 29 (1986).

503. A.M. Galazka, S.E. Robertson, and A. Kraigher, *Bull. W.H.O.* **77**, 3 (1999).

504. D. Nalin, *Lancet* **299**, 1396 (1989).

505. M. Cizman et al., *Pediatr. Infect. Dis. J.* **8**, 302 (1989).

506. E. Miller et al., *Lancet* **341**, 979 (1993).

507. H. Odisseev and N. Gacheva, *Vaccine* **12**, 1251 (1994).

508. WO 95/14083 (May 26, 1995), N.M. Harford, B.D.A. Colau, and J. Didelez.

509. V. Usonis, V. Bakasenas, K. Chitour, and R. Clemens, *Infection* **26**, 222 (1998).

510. A. Sassani et al., *Biologicals* **19**, 203 (1991).

511. Ya. Nechaeva et al., *Vestn. Ross. Akad. Med. Nauk* **3**, 29 (1998).

512. M. McCarthy, B. Jubelt, D.B. Fay, and R.T. Johnson, *J. Med. Virol.* **5**, 1 (1980).

513. W.J. McAleer et al., *J. Biol. Stand.* **3**, 381 (1975).

514. M.R. Hilleman et al., *JAMA, J. Am. Med. Assoc.* **206**, 587 (1968).

515. U.S. Pat. 3,933,585 (January 20, 1976), W.J. McAleer, R.E. Spier, and K.L. Posch.

516. E.B. Buynak and M.R. Hilleman, *Proc. Soc. Exp. Biol. Med.* **123**, 768 (1966).

517. E.M. Scattergood et al., *Drug Dev. Ind. Pharm.* **9**, 745 (1983).

518. A.Y. Elliott, in A.S. Lubiniecki, ed., *Large-scale Mammalian Cell Culture Technology*, Dekker, New York, 1990, pp. 207–216.

519. E.L. Paul, *Ann. N.Y. Acad. Sci.* **589**, 642 (1990).

520. U.S. Pat. 3,959,074 (May 25, 1976), W.J. Miller, R.E. Spier, and W.J. McAleer.

521. S.J. Musser and G.E. Underwood, *J. Immunol.* **85**, 292 (1960).

522. *Physicians' Desk Reference*, Medical Economics Company, Montvale, N.J., 1999, pp. 1819–1821.

523. G. Colinet and J. Peetermans, *J. Biol. Stand.* **10**, 241 (1982).

524. T.H. Weller and F.A. Neva, *Proc. Soc. Exp. Biol. Med.* **111**, 215 (1962).

525. P.D. Parkman, E.L. Beuscher, and M.S. Artenstein, *Proc. Soc. Exp. Biol. Med.* **111**, 225 (1962).

526. J.J. Witte et al., *Am. J. Dis. Child.* **118**, 107 (1969).

527. H.M. Meyer et al., *Am. J. Dis. Child.* **118**, 155 (1969).

528. E.B. Buynak, M.R. Hilleman, R.E. Weibel, and J. Stokes, *JAMA, J. Am. Med. Assoc.* **204**, 103 (1968).

529. E.B. Buynak et al., *Am. J. Dis. Child.* **118**, 347 (1969).

530. M.R. Hilleman et al., *Am. J. Dis. Child.* **118**, 166 (1969).

531. A. Prinzie et al., *Am. J. Dis. Child.* **118**, 172 (1969).

532. J. Peetermans and C. Huygelen, *Minerva Med.* **61**(Suppl. 30), 1560 (1970).

533. J. Peetermans and C. Huygelen, *Arch. Gesamte Virusforsch.* **21**, 133 (1967).

534. S.A. Plotkin, in S.A. Plotkin and E.A. Mortimer, eds., *Vaccines*, 2nd ed., Saunders, Philadelphia, 1994, pp. 303–336.

535. S.A. Plotkin, J.D. Farquhar, and M. Katz, *Am. J. Dis. Child.* **118**, 178 (1969).

536. T.K. Frey, *Adv. Virus Res.* **44**, 69 (1994).

537. A. Voiland and G. Bardeletti, *Arch. Virol.* **64**, 319 (1980).

538. L.L. Williams et al., *Arch. Virol.* **134**, 379 (1994).

539. M.L. Hemphill, R.-Y. Forng, E.S. Abernathy, and T.K. Frey, *Virology* **162**, 65 (1988).

540. J.K. Chantler, *Virology* **98**, 275 (1979).

541. T.L. Stanwick and J.V. Hallum, *Infect. Immun.* **10**, 810 (1974).

542. T.K. Frey and M.L. Hemphill, *Virology* **164**, 22 (1988).

543. S.A. Plotkin and A.J. Beale, *Dev. Biol. Stand.* **37**, 291 (1977).

544. H. Mirchamsky et al., *Dev. Biol. Stand.* **37**, 297 (1977).

545. J. Peetermans et al., *Dev. Biol. Stand.* **36**, 291 (1976).

546. S.A. Plotkin and H. Koprowski, Rabies vaccine. in S.A. Plotkin and E.A. Mortimer, eds., *Vaccines*, 2nd ed., Saunders, Philadelphia, 1994, pp. 649–670.

547. P. Sureau, *Adv. Biochem. Eng. Biotechnol.* **34**, 111 (1987).

548. C. Fermi, *Z. Hyg. Infektionsks.* **58**, 233 (1907).

549. D. Semple, *Sci. Mem. Med. Sanit. Dep. India*, No. 44, (1911).

550. G. Toro, I. Vergara, and G. Roman, *Arch. Neurol.* **34**, 694 (1977).

551. R.S. Javier, T. Kunishita, F. Koike, and T. Tabira, *J. Neurol. Sci.* **93**, 221 (1989).

552. D. Laouini, M.F. Kennou, S. Khoufi, and K. Dellagi, *J. Neuroimmunol.* **91**, 63 (1998).

553. E. Fuenzalida and R. Palacios, *Bull. Inst. Bacteriol. Chile* **8**, 3 (1955).

554. Y.L. Nogueira, *Rev. Inst. Med. Trop. Sao Paulo* **40**, 295 (1998).

555. O. Perez and C.C. Paolazzi, *J. Ind. Microbiol. Biotechnol.* **18**, 340 (1997).

556. H.M. Powell and C.G. Culbertson, *Public Health Rep.* **65**, 400 (1950).

557. R. Barth, H. Gruschkau, O. Jaeger, and L. Milcke, *Comp. Immunol. Microbiol. Infect. Dis.* **5**, 211 (1982).

558. H. Keller, R. Gluck, A. Wegmann, and A.I. Wandeler, *Schweiz. Med. Wochenschr.* **114**, 648 (1984).

559. R.H. Rubin et al., *Ann. Intern. Med.* **78**, 643 (1973).

560. G. Dempster et al., *Can. Med. Assoc. J.* **120**, 1069 (1979).

561. T.J. Wiktor, M.V. Fernandes, and H. Koprowski, *J. Immunol.* **93**, 353 (1964).

562. A.J. Nicolas et al., *Dev. Biol. Stand.* **40**, 17 (1978).

563. M. Majer, J. Hilfenhaus, R. Mauler, and W. Hennessen, *Dev. Biol. Stand.* **37**, 267 (1977).

564. G.H. Burgoyne, K.D. Kajiya, D.W. Brown, and J.R. Mitchell, *J. Infect. Dis.* **152**, 204 (1985).

565. M. Majer et al., *Dev. Biol. Stand.* **40**, 25 (1978).

566. T.J. Wiktor, S.A. Plotkin, and H. Koprowski, *Dev. Biol. Stand.* **40**, 3 (1978).

567. B. Hafkin et al., *Am. J. Epidemiol.* **107**, 439 (1978).

568. J.F. Bell, *Dev. Biol. Stand.* **40**, 11 (1978).

569. P. Sureau, *Vaccine* **10**, 896 (1992).

570. *Morbid. Mortal. Wkly. Rep.* **47**, 12 (1997).

571. M. Benjavongkulchai et al., *Vaccine* 15, 1816 (1997).

572. R. Barth et al., *J. Biol. Stand.* **12**, 29 (1984).

573. R. Barth, H. Gruschkau, O. Jaeger, and L. Milcke, *Comp. Immunol. Microbiol. Infect. Dis.* **5**, 211 (1982).

574. J. Hilfenhaus et al., *J. Biol. Stand.* **4**, 263 (1976).

575. O. Jaeger and R. Barth, *Arch. Hyg. Bakteriol.* **152**, 379 (1968).

576. C.A.M. Van der Velden den Groot et al., in R.E. Spier, J.B. Griffiths, J. Stephenne, and P.J. Crooy, eds., *Advances in Animal Cell Biology and Technology for Bioprocesses*, Butterworth-Heinemann, London, 1991, pp. 404–407.

577. R.M. El Karamany, *Acta Virol.* **31**, 321 (1987).

578. R.Z. Mendonca et al., *Braz. J. Med. Biol. Res.* **26**, 1305 (1993).

579. C. Wasi et al., *Vaccine* **15**(Suppl. S7), (1997).

580. U.S. Pat. 4,664,912 (May 12, 1987), T.J. Wiktor, B.J. Fanget, P. Fournier, and B.J. Montagnon.

581. A.L. Van Wezel, J.A.M. Van Herwaarden, and E.W. Van de Heuvel-de Rijk, *Dev. Biol. Stand.* **42**, 65 (1979).

582. E.B. Seligmann, in M.M. Kaplan and H. Koprowski, eds., *Laboratory Techniques in Rabies*, World Health Organ., Geneva, 1973, pp. 279–286.

583. R.R. Rueckert, in B.N. Fields, D.M. Knipe, and P.M. Howley, eds., *Virology*, 3rd ed., Lippincott-Raven, Philadelphia, 1996, pp. 609–654.

584. J.B. Brooksby, in F. Fenner and A. Gibbs, eds., *Portraits of Viruses: A History of Virology*, Karger, Basel, 1988, pp. 124–146.

585. S.P. Bedson and H.B. Maitland, *J. Comp. Pathol. Ther.* **40**, 80 (1927).

586. M. Cowan Maitland and H.B. Maitland, *J. Comp. Pathol. Ther.* **44**, 106 (1931).

587. O. Waldmann, Z. Kobe, and G. Pyl, *Zentralbl. Bakteriol., Abt. I: Orig.* **138**, 401 (1937).

588. H.S. Frenkel, *Bull. Off. Int. Epizoot.* **28**, 155 (1947).

589. R.C. Telling, *Process Biochem.*, p. 49 (1969).

590. G.N. Mowat and W.G. Chapman, *Nature (London)* **194**, 253 (1962).

591. R.E. Spier and J.P. Whiteside, *Biotechnol. Bioeng.* **18**, 659 (1976).

592. J.P. Whiteside and R.E. Spier, *Dev. Biol. Stand.* **35**, 67 (1977).

593. L. Nardelli and G.F. Panina, *Dev. Biol. Stand.* **35**, 9 (1977).

594. M.H. Jensen and F.O. Soerensen, *Dev. Biol. Stand.* **35**, 45 (1977).

595. S.J. Barteling, *Dev. Biol. Stand.* **35**, 55 (1977).

596. L. Nardelli and G.F. Panina, *Dev. Biol. Stand.* **37**, 133 (1977).

597. R. Zoletto and G. Gagliardi, *Dev. Biol. Stand.* **35**, 27 (1977).

598. B. Meignier, *Dev. Biol. Stand.* **42**, 141 (1979).

599. H.C. Girard, M. Sutcu, H. Erdom, and I. Gurhan, *Dev. Biol. Stand.* **42**, 127 (1979).

600. B. Meignier, H. Mougeot, and H. Favre, *Dev. Biol. Stand.* **46**, 249 (1980).

601. J.P. Whiteside, B.R. Whiting, and R.E. Spier, *Dev. Biol. Stand.* **46**, 187 (1980).

602. R. Zoletto, *Dev. Biol. Stand.* **60**, 313 (1985).

603. G. Butchaiah and B.U. Rao, *Curr. Sci.* **56**, 346 (1987).

604. L.D. Misra, A.K. Sen, S.P. Nair, and B.U. Rao, *Vet. J.* **62**, 453 (1985).

605. R. Elsworth, G.H. Capel, and R.C. Telling, *J. Appl. Bacteriol.* **21**, 80 (1958).

606. G.N. Mowat, J.B. Brooksby, and T.W.F. Pay, *Nature (London)* **196**, 656 (1962).

607. P.B. Capstick, *Proc. R. Soc. Med.* **56**, 1062 (1963).

608. R.C. Telling and C.J. Stone, *Biotechnol. Bioeng.* **6**, 147 (1964).

609. R.C. Telling and R. Elsworth, *Biotechnol. Bioeng.* **7**, 417 (1965).

610. P.B. Capstick, A.J. Garland, W.G. Chapman, and R.C. Masters, *Nature (London)* **205**, 1135 (1965).

611. P.B. Capstick and R.C. Telling, *Pirbright* **7**, 108 (1966).

612. R.C. Telling, C.J. Stone, and M.A. Maskell, *Biotechnol. Bioeng.* **8**, 153 (1966).

613. P.B. Capstick, A.J.M. Garland, R.C. Masters, and W.G. Chapman, *Exp. Cell Res.* **44**, 119 (1966).

614. P.B. Capstick, A.J.M. Garland, W.G. Chapman, and R.C. Masters, *J. Hyg.* **645**, 273 (1967).

615. P.B. Capstick, R.C. Telling, and A.J.M. Garland, *Prog. Immunobiol. Stand.* **3**, 131 (1969).

616. R.C. Telling, *Process Biochem.* June p. 49 (1969).

617. P.J. Radlett, A.J. Braeme, and R.C. Telling, *Lab. Pract.* **21**, 811 (1972).

618. P.J. Radlett, R.C. Telling, J.P. Whiteside, and M.A. Maskell, *Biotechnol. Bioeng.* **14**, 437 (1972).

619. P.J. Radlett, *Adv. Biochem. Eng. Biotechnol.* **34**, 129 (1987).

620. F.H. Top et al., *J. Infect. Dis.* **124**, 148 (1971).

621. F.H. Top, E.L. Buescher, W.H. Bancroft, and P.K. Russell, *J. Infect. Dis.* **124**, 155 (1971).

622. F.H. Top, B.A. Dudding, P.K. Russell, and E.L. Buescher, *Am. J. Epidemiol.* **94**, 142 (1971).

623. F. Fenner, in M.M. Binns and G.L. Smith, eds., *Recombinant Poxviruses*, CRC Press, Boca Raton, Fla., 1992, pp. 1–43.

624. G.S. Turner, *Lab. Prac.* **19**, 50 (1970).

625. H.B. Maitland and M.C. Maitland, *Lancet* **2**, 596 (1928).

626. H.B. Maitland and A.W. Laing, *Br. J. Exp. Pathol.* **11**, 119 (1930).

627. T.M. Rivers, *J. Exp. Med.* **54**, 453 (1931).

628. H.B. Maitland, A.W. Laing, and R. Lyth, *Br. J. Exp. Pathol.* **13**, 90 (1932).

629. H.B. Maitland and A.W. Laing, *J. Pathol. Bacteriol.* **53**, 419 (1941).

630. V. von Hochstein-Mintzel, *Fortsch. Med.* **95**, 79 (1977).

631. E. Herrero and R. Meggers, *Zentralbl. Bakteriol., Abt. I: Orig.* **209**, 1 (1968).

632. A.C. Hekker, J.M. Bos, and L. Smith, *J. Biol. Stand.* **1**, 21 (1973).

633. H. Mahnel and A. Mayr, *Berl. Muench. Tieraerztl. Wochensch.* **107**, 253 (1994).

634. D. Baxby, *Vaccine* **11**, 395 (1993).

635. D.L. Heymann, M. Szczeniowski, and K. Esteves, *Br. Med. Bull.* **54**, 693 (1998).

636. D.J. McClain et al., *J. Infect. Dis.* **175**, 756 (1997).

637. U. Klockmann, K. Krivanek, J.R. Stephenson, and J. Hilfenhaus, *Vaccine* **9**, 210 (1991).

638. U. Klockmann et al., *J. Biol. Stand.* **17**, 331 (1989).

639. O.V. Popov et al., *Zh. Mikrobio. Epidemio. I Immunobio.* **6**, 34 (1985).

640. F.X. Heinz, C. Kunz, and H. Fauma, *J. Med. Virol.* **6**, 213 (1980).

641. U.S. Pat. 5,719,051, (February 17, 1998), W. Mundt, N. Barrett, F. Dorner, and J. Eibl.

642. G. Peiwei, D. Zhifen, and W. Zhongquan, *Dev. Biol. Stand.* **70**, 223 (1989).

643. T.H. Weller, *J. Infect. Dis.* **166**(Suppl. 1), S1 (1992).

644. R.W. Ellis and C.J. White **10**, 457–691 (1996).

645. J.I. Cohen and S.E. Straus, in B.N. Fields, D.M. Knipe, and P.M. Howley, eds., *Virology*, 3rd ed., Lippincott-Raven, Philadelphia, 1996, pp. 2525–2545.

646. M. Takahashi and A.A. Gershon, Varicella vaccine. in S.A. Plotkin and E.A. Mortimer, eds., *Vaccines*, 2nd ed., Saunders, Philadelphia, 1994, pp. 387–417.

647. M. Takahashi, *Adv. Virus Res.* **28**, 285 (1983).

648. J.M. Ostrove, *Adv. Virus Res.* **38**, 45 (1990).

649. C. Gorse, *Infect. Dis. Clin. North Am.* **10**, 489 (1996).

650. T.H. Weller and M.R. Stoddard, *J. Immunol.* **68**, 311 (1952).

651. M. Takahashi et al., *Biken J.* **18**, 25 (1975).

652. M. Takahashi, *Infect. Dis. Clin. North Am.* **10**, 469 (1996).

653. M. Takahashi, in L.C. Paoletti and P.M. McInnes, eds., *Vaccines: From Concept to Clinic*, CRC Press, Boca Raton, Fla., 1999, pp. 183–198.

654. C. Marwick, *JAMA. J. Am. Med. Assoc.* **273**, 833 (1995).

655. P.R. Krause and S.E. Straus, *Infect. Dis. Clin. North Am.* **13**, 61 (1999).

656. B. Fanget and A. Francon, *Dev. Biol. Stand.* **87**, 167 (1996).

657. A. Gershon, L. Cosio, and P.A. Brunell, *J. Gen. Virol.* **18**, 21 (1973).

658. C. Grose and T.I. Ng, *J. Infect. Dis.* **166**(Suppl. 1), S7, (1992).

659. R. Harson and C. Grose, *J. Virol.* **69**, 4994 (1995).

660. C. Grose, D.M. Perrotta, P.A. Brunell, and G. Con Smith, *J. Gen. Virol.* **43**, 15 (1979).

661. P.A. Brunell, *Virology* **31**, 732 (1967).

662. A.E. Caunt, *Lancet* **2**, 982 (1963).

663. A.E. Caunt and D. Taylor-Robinson, *J. Hyg.* **62**, 413 (1964).

664. M.L. Cook and J.G. Stevens, *J. Virol.* **2**, 1458 (1968).

665. N.J. Schmidt and E.H. Lennette, *Infect. Immun.* **14**, 709 (1976).

666. C. Grose and P.A. Brunell, *Infect. Immun.* **19**, 199 (1978).

667. C. Grose, W.E. Friedrichs, and K.O. Smith, *Intervirology* **15**, 154 (1981).

668. M. Saito et al., *Arch. Virol.* **68**, 59 (1981).

669. B.J. Edmond, C. Grose, and P.A. Brunell, *J. Gen. Virol.* **54** (Part 2), 403 (1981).

670. A. Shimizu, *Uirusu* **32**, 73 (1982).

671. M.J. Levin, S. Leventhal, and H.A. Masters, *J. Clin. Microbiol.* **19**, 880 (1984).

672. K.A. Rekrut, R.A. Levy, and A.L. Warford, *Am. J. Clin. Pathol.* **83**, 500 (1985).

673. U.S. Pat. 5,360,736, (November 1, 1994), P.J. Provost, D.L. Krah, and P.A. Friedman.

674. U.S. Pat. 5,607,852, (March 4, 1997), P.J. Provost, D.L. Krah, and P.A. Friedman.

675. D.R. Harper, N. Mathieu, and J. Mullarkey, *Arch. Virol.* **143**, 1163 (1998).

676. U.S. Pat. 4,000,256, (December 28, 1976), M.R. Hilleman, E.B. Buynak, and B.J. Neff.

677. U.S. Pat. 4,008,317, (Februery 15, 1977), J. Gits.

678. R. Singhvi et al., *Cytotechnology* **22**, 79 (1996).

679. F.J. Muzzio et al., *Biotechnol. Bioeng.* **63**, 185 (1999).

680. J.A. Searles et al., *Abstr. Pap. to 209th Meet., Am. Chem. Soc.*, Pt. 1, BIOT 158 (1995).

681. Anonymous, *The Age of Robotics: Varicella Production at MMD Biological Operations* Merck Manufacturing Division, West Point, N.Y., 1994.

682. R. Archer and L. Wood, *Anim. Cell Technol.*, p. 403 (1992).

683. J.A. Lewis, in S. Specter, ed., *Viral Hepatitis: Diagnosis, Therapy, and Prevention* Humana Press, Totowa, N.J., 199•••, pp. 317–375.

684. W. Jilg, F. Deinhardt, and M.R. Hilleman, in S.A. Plotkin and B.A. Mortimer, eds., *Vaccines*, 2nd ed., Saunders, Philadelphia, 1994, pp. 583–595.

685. P.J. Provost and M.R. Hilleman, *Proc. Soc. Exp. Biol. Med.* **160**, 213 (1979).

686. S.M. Lemon, L. Whetter, K.H. Chang, and E.A. Brown, *FEBS Micross. Lett.* **100**, 455 (1992).

687. B. Flehmig, *Med. Microbiol. Immunol.* **170**, 73 (1981).

688. B. Flehmig, *Med. Microbiol. Immunol.* **170**, 83 (1981).

689. G. Siegl, J. de Chastonay, and G. Kronauer, *J. Virol. Methods* **9**, 53 (1984).

690. P.J. Provost et al., *J. Med. Virol.* **20**, 165 (1986).

691. M.H. Sjögren et al., *Vaccine* **10**(Suppl. 1), S135, (1992).

692. J.S. Mao et al., *Chin. Med. J.* **105**, 189 (1992).

693. V. Gauss-Müller and F. Deinhardt, *Proc. Soc. Exp. Biol. Med.* **175**, 10 (1984).

694. L.N. Binn et al., *J. Infect. Dis.* **153**, 749 (1986).

695. A.W. Funkhauser et al., *Virology* **254**, 268 (1999).

696. J. Peetermans et al., *Vaccine* **10**(Suppl. 1), S99, (1992).

697. R. Gluck et al., *J. Clin. Invest.* **90**, 2491 (1992).

698. D. Garin et al., *Vaccine* **13**, 220 (1995).

699. M.E. Armstrong et al., *J. Hepatol.* **18**(Suppl. 1), S20 (1993).

700. A.J. Hagen, C.N. Oliver, and R.D. Sitrin, *Biotechnol. Prog.* **12**, 406 (1996).

701. A.J. Hagen et al., *Biotechnol. Appl. Biochem.* **23**, 209 (1996).

702. B.H. Junker et al., *Cytotechnology* **9**, 173 (1992).

703. A. Hagen et al., *Bioprocess Eng.* in press, 1999.

704. U.S. Pat. 5,521,082, (May 28, 1996), J.A. Lewis, M.E. Armstrong, and E.A. Emini.

705. D.B. Volkin et al., *J. Pharm. Sci.* **86**, 666 (1997).

706. M.K. Estes and J. Cohen, *Microbiol. Rev.* **53**, 410 (1989).

707. M.K. Estes, in B.N. Fields, D.M. Knipe, and P.M. Howley, eds., *Virology*, 3rd ed., Lippincott-Raven, Philadelphia, 1996, pp. 1625–1655.

708. H.F. Clark and P.A. Offit, in S.A. Plotkin and E.A. Mortimer, eds., *Vaccines*, 2nd ed., Saunders, Philadelphia, 1994, pp. 809–822.

709. I.E. Haffejee, *J. Pediatr. Gastroenterol. Nutr.* **20**, 275 (1995).

710. K. Midthun et al., *J. Virol.* **53**, 949 (1985).

711. H.F. Clark, F.E. Borain, K. Modesto, and S.A. Plotkin, *Vaccine* **8**, 327 (1990).

712. U.S. Pat. 5,626,851, (May 6, 1997), H.F. Clark, P.A. Offit, and S.A. Plotkin.

713. M.L. Clements-Mann et al., *Vaccine* **17**, 2715 (1999).

714. *Physicians' Desk Reference Supplement A*, Medical Economics Company, Montvale N.J., 1999, pp. A80–A84.

715. C.L. Hsieh and W.H. Wainwright, *Abstr. Pap. 213th Meet. Am. Chem. Soc.*, BIOT031 (1997).

716. J.E. Ludert et al., *J. Gen. Virol.* **77**(Part 3), 391, (1996).

717. K. Sato, S. Tokuhisa, and Y. Inaba, *J. Vet. Med. Sci.* **57**, 569 (1995).

718. P.A. Offit et al., *J. Virol. Methods* **7**, 29 (1983).

719. M.K. Estes, D.Y. Graham, C.P. Gerba, and E.M. Smith, *J. Virol.* **31**, 810 (1979).

720. U.S. Pat. 4,636,385, (January 13, 1987), S.A. Plotkin and H.F. Clark.

721. F. Roth and M.W.J. Ullrich, *Berl. Muench. Tieraerztl. Wochenschr.* **108**, 471 (1995).

722. D. Lalosevic et al., *Med. Pregl.* **51**(Suppl. 1), 17 (1998).

723. D. Lalosevic, L. Lazarevic-Ivanc, and S. Stankov, *Med. Pregl.* **50**, 565 (1997).

724. O.W. Merten, J.V. Kieruiff, N. Castignolles, and P. Perrin, *Cytotechnology* **14**, 47 (1994).

725. A.D.T. Barrett, *Biologicals* **25**, 17 (1997).

726. A.D.T. Barrett, *Biologicals* **25**, 27 (1997).

727. WO 97/04803, (February 13, 1997), B. Fanget, A. Francon, and P. Heimendinger.

728. S. Dong et al., *Chin. J. Biotechnol.* **9**, 117 (1994).

729. R. Brands, in M.J.T. Carrondo, J.-L. Moreira, and J.B. Griffiths, eds., *Animal Cell Technology*, Kluwer Academic Press, Dordrecht, The Netherlands, 1997, pp. 165–176.

730. A.M. Palache, R. Brands, and G.J. Van Scharrenburg, *J. Infect. Dis.* **176**(Suppl. 1), S20 (1997).

731. O.W. Merten et al., *Adv. Exp. Biol. Med.* **397**, 141 (1996).

732. E.A. Govorkova et al., *J. Virol.* **70**, 5519 (1996).

733. S.A. Halperin, A.C. Nestruck, and B.J. Eastwood, *Vaccine* **16**, 1331 (1998).

734. O. Kistner et al., *Vaccine* **16**, 960 (1998).

735. WO 96/15231, (May 23, 1996), O. Kistner, N. Barrett, W. Mundt, and F. Dorner.

736. U.S. Pat. 5,756,341 (May 26, 1998), O. Kistner, N. Barrett, W. Mundt, and F. Dorner.

737. U.S. Pat. 5,698,433 (December 16, 1997), O. Kistner, N. Barrett, W. Mundt, and F. Dorner.

738. U.S. Pat. 5,753,489 (May 19, 1998), O. Kistner, N. Barrett, W. Mundt, and F. Dorner.

739. DE 196 12 966 A1 (October 2, 1997), A. Groner and J. Vorlop.

740. R.W. Ellis, *Vaccine* **17**, 1596 (1999).

741. F. Brown, *Dev. Biol. Stand.* **82** 1 (1994).

742. R.C. Desrosiers, *AIDS Res. Hum. Retroviruses* **8**, 411 (1992).

743. J.S. Gibbs, D.A. Regier, and R.C. Desrosiers, *AIDS Res. Hum. Retroviruses* **10**, 343 (1994).

744. C. Prior et al., *Pharm. Technol.* April, pp. 30–52 (1995).

745. WO 95/25789 (September 28, 1995), M.E. Hrinda et al.

746. U.S. Pat. 5,661,023 (August 26, 1997), M.E. Hrinda et al.

747. •••.

748. G.R.B. Skinner, J.A. Davies, M. Sheasby, and Mahmood, *Intervirology* **37**, 259 (1994).

749. P.E. Cruz, C.C. Peixoto, J.-L. Moreira, and M.J.T. Carrondo, *J. Chem. Technol. Biotechnol.* **72**, 149 (1998).

750. S.M. Deutschmann and V. Jaeger, *Anim. Cell Technol.* pp. 425–430 (1992).

751. J.S. Cairns and N. Sarver, *AIDS Res. Hum. Retroviruses* **14**, 1501 (1998).

752. M.D. Lubeck et al., *Nat. Med.* **3**, 651 (1997).

753. A. Schultz, *IAVI Rep.* **3**, 1 (1998). Available at: *http://www.iavi.org/newsletter_winter98_1.html*

754. A.E. Brown and J.G. McNeil, *Southeast Asian J. Trop. Med. Public Health* **29**, 377 (1998).

755. T. Hanke et al., *Vaccine* **16**, 439 (1998).

756. F. Scheiflinger, F. Dorner, and F.G. Falkner, *Arch. Virol.* **143**, 467 (1998).

757. B.N. Fields, D.M. Knipe, and P.M. Howley, eds., *Virology*, 3rd ed., Vols. 1 and 2, Lippincott-Raven, Philadelphia, 1996.

758. A. Cann, ed., *Virology: A Practical Approach*, IRL Press, Oxford, U.K. 1999, in press.

759. S.A. Plotkin and E.A. Mortimer, eds., *Vaccines*, 2nd ed., Saunders, Philadelphia, 1994.

760. A. Chase, *Magic Shots: A Human and Scientific Account of the Long and Continuing Struggle to Eradicate Infectious Disease by Vaccination*, Wm. Morrow, New York, 1982.

761. A. Grafe, *A History of Experimental Virology*, Springer-Verlag, Berlin, 1992.

762. F. Fenner and A. Gibbs, *Portraits of Viruses: A History of Virology*, Karger, Basel, 1988.

763. H.-W. Ackermann, L. Berthiaume, and M. Tremblay, *Virus Life in Diagrams*, CRC Press, Boca Raton, Fla., 1998.

764. D.M. Sander, *All the Virology on the WWW*. Available at: *http://www.tulane.edu/~dmsander/garryfavweb.html*

765. C. Buchen-Osmond, *The Universal Virus Database*. Available at: *http://life.anu.edu.au/viruses/univirdb.htm*

766. D. Radler, ed., *The Vaccine Page*. Available at: *http://www.vaccines.com/*

767. See U.S. Food and Drug Administration regulations and guidance documents at *http://www.fda.gov/cber*

768. See documents of the European Agency for the Evaluation of Medicinal Products at *http://www.eudra.org*

769. See the European Pharmacopoeia, and documents of the European Department for the Quality of Medicines at *http://www.pheur.org*

770. See the World Health Organization Technical Report Series, especially *Reports of the WHO Expert Committee on Biological Standardization*, Tech. Rep. Ser. Nos. 800, 814, 822, 840, 848, 858, 872, 878, W.H.O., Geneva. See also *http://www.who.int*

VIRUS PRODUCTION FROM CELL CULTURE, KINETICS

Lars Keld Nielsen
The University of Queensland
Brisbane, Australia

OUTLINE

INTRODUCTION

While no longer the sole driving force for cell culture technology as it was 40 years ago, viral-based processes continue to represent an important class of cell culture processes. Indeed, the number of viral-based cell culture processes is increasing with (1) viral vaccine production moving from primary cells to continuous cell lines, (2) increased use of viral biopesticides, (3) increased use of viral expression systems, and (4) the use of viral gene therapy vectors. The inherent complexity combined with the problems of working with human or animal pathogens has meant that the academic treatment of viral production kinetics has lagged behind that of other cell culture systems. The emergence of the baculovirus (an innocuous insect virus) for protein expression changed this situation, and baculovirus is used throughout this article to illustrate how to handle complex viral kinetics. Emphasis is placed on the development of mathematical models, which are essential tools when studying viral production kinetics.

HISTORY AND CHALLENGE

From the mid-1950s, when pioneering work of Earle and colleagues (1) enabled routine cell culture, until the emergence of commercial hybridoma and recombinant technologies in the 1980s, cell technology was almost synonymous with viral vaccine production technology. Vaccine production posed a number of unique challenges for research compared to those faced in microbial fermentation, for example:

- The exclusive use of primary cells/tissue and diploid human cell strains rather than cell lines in human vaccine production
- The predominant use of anchorage-dependent cells
- The inherent complexity of cell–virus systems
- The inherent problems of working with human or animal pathogens

As a result, cell technology research followed a path divergent to microbial fermentation research, which in the same period moved towards bioprocess engineering science, including detailed studies of kinetics. Much work in cell technology was related to multiple processes ("scale-out" technology) that is, ways to handle large numbers of small cultures (e.g., Roux or roller bottles), and the technology surrounding the fermentation process (medium preparation, sterile techniques, downstream processing). Notable exceptions were the development of large-scale BHK suspension culture for production of foot-and-mouth and later rabies vaccines (2,3) and the development of microcarrier technology for large-scale propagation of anchorage-dependent cells (4).

The 1980s saw the development of large-scale production of polio and rabies vaccines in Vero cell microcarrier cultures and the development of standards for the use of heteroploid cell lines for human vaccine production (5,6). Economy of scale, quality control issues, and increasing reticence against the use of animal-derived tissue have seen virus production in continuous cell lines move from being limited to animal vaccines to becoming the preferred option for new viral-based vaccines. In the past decade, vaccine production has been joined by protein and biopesticide production in insect cells and production

of gene therapy vectors as bioprocesses relying on virus production.

There is still much to be learned about the kinetics of virus production, even in many of the well-established production systems. This can partly be attributed to a relative lack of academic groups working on the engineering of viral vaccine production and partly due to the inherent complexity of virus processes. Not surprising, most progress has been achieved in the baculovirus–insect cell system, which benefits from baculovirus being nonpathogenic in humans and animals and from insect cells being anchorage independent.

Mathematical modeling plays a crucial role in building an understanding of the kinetics of virus production. Without models it is practically impossible to unveil the kinetics underlying the complex, observed dynamics. Consider a typical production process where cells are infected at a low multiplicity of infection (MOI), where initially only a fraction of cells will be infected. In order to describe the behavior of this process, we need

- A model of noninfected growth
- A model of the physical interaction between virus and cells (attachment and internalization)
- A model of the infection cycle in individual cells to account for changes as cells gradually change from being biomass producers early in the infection cycle to being virus producers late in the cycle
- A population balance model to take into account that cells may be infected at different point in time and thus at any point in time the dynamics of the culture is the cumulative effect of the kinetics shown by the cells in various stages of infection
- A mass balance model to take into account the physical system, for example, describing substrate consumption in a batch culture or the dilution effect in a continuous culture

In addition, depending on the actual system studied, it may be necessary to include

- A model describing genetic stability of the virus, for example, to account for the accumulation of defective viruses observed in continuous culture
- A model to describe the effect of multiple infection, for example, when using multiple virus constructs for multicomponent virus-like particle production or packaging of gene therapy vectors

We recently reviewed the kinetic models developed for baculovirus infection of insect cells (7). Three groups including ours have developed relatively detailed kinetic models of the baculovirus system, and by comparing and contrasting the approaches taken, it is possible to gain insight into what works and what does not. In the remainder of this article, we will describe how to develop kinetic models of virus production using the baculovirus system as the model system. The emphasis is on how to link experiments and model development. The first section provides a brief introduction to baculoviruses. The second section presents the cell yield concept, a highly simplified view of viral processes based on a pseudo mass balance of the process. The cell yield concept provides an objective for process optimization, but does not provide the means for designing the process. For this we need a kinetic model, and this is developed in two stages. First, a model is developed for synchronous infection, and this model is then used together with a population balance model and virus attachment kinetics to formulate a model for asynchronous infection. The usefulness of the developed model is illustrated in the final section, where very low multiplicity of infection is discussed as a possible production strategy.

BACULOVIRUS

Baculoviruses and their use as expression vectors have been described in several excellent books and reviews (8–11). Baculoviruses are rod-shaped viruses with approximately 130 kb of genetic material located on a single double-stranded DNA molecule. Baculoviruses have been isolated from over 500 insect species, mainly of the order of Lepidoptera. The biology of *Autographa californica* nuclear polyhedrosis virus (AcNPV) has been studied in most detail and forms the basis for most recombinant expression systems, while *Helicoverpa zea* NPV (HzNPV) is produced commercially and *H. armigera* NPV (HaNPV) is considered for biopesticide usage.

The individual viruses in NPVs are occluded (embedded) in a paracrystalline matrix composed mainly of a single protein called polyhedrin. The occlusion body, called polyhedron, protects the enclosed virus particles against the environment. Upon digestion by larva, the polyhedron will dissolve in the alkaline gut juices,

and the released viruses will infect midgut epithelium cells. During the ensuing infection cycle nonoccluded viruses (NOV) will be formed in addition to the occluded form. NOVs bud through the cell membrane into the haemolymph, where they become responsible for lateral infection (Fig. 1).

Several cell lines are available for propagating baculoviruses. AcNPV is typically propagated in suspension cultures of Sf-9 cells, a cell line established from ovarian tissue of *S. frugiperda* (fall armyworm), while HzNPV can be propagated in cell lines derived from ovarian tissue of *H. zea* (cotton bollworm). Propagation relies on the lateral infection route, that is, via NOV infection. This is the basis for the baculovirus expression system, where the highly expressed, but nonessential, polyhedrin gene is replaced with a gene of interest through homologous recombination. The model system used by many to study recombinant expression in baculovirus is that of β-galactosidase expression. While ideal for gene expression, the fact that polyhedrin is nonessential for in vitro culture poses stability problems for biopesticide production, where occlusion bodies are essential for delivery. Typically, baculoviruses will degenerate to low producers in five to ten in vitro passages (12), unless a stable isolate has been found (13).

THE CELL YIELD CONCEPT

Baculovirus production is greatly affected by a number of process variables, including: the design of the fermentation system, cell line (14,15), the composition of the medium used for cell growth (16–20), the age and condition of the cell population at time of infection (TOI) (21–25), the

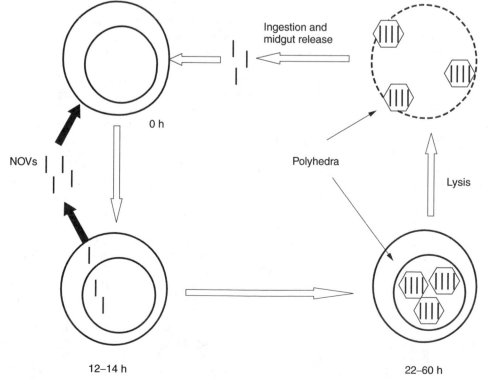

Figure 1. Infection cycle of NPV baculoviruses. The open arrows indicate the virus cycle between larva from ingestion of polyhedra and midgut release of virus to the release by lysis of new polyhedra. The solid arrows indicate lateral infection through nonoccluded viruses (NOVs) released early in the infection cycle.

multiplicity of infection (26–29), and the passage number of virus inoculum (30,31). Most of these variables are set early in process development; for example, we have chosen batch fermentation in serum-free medium using the aforementioned cell lines and a low-passage-number virus stock.

The two remaining parameters, TOI and MOI, are highly correlated and — combined with the variability of cultures and the relative inaccurate assays available for virus determination — it proved to be a nontrivial task to resolve their effect empirically. Indeed, prior to the development of kinetic models descriptions of TOI and MOI effects tended to be inconsistent listings of individual observations. It was only through working with a relatively complex model, we finally developed a conceptual understanding of the system that we termed the *cell yield concept* (32). Like any good concept, it is a simplification with obvious limitations and should only be regarded as a first handle on the system. Importantly, however, it does not rely on baculovirus-specific features and should be applicable to other virus production systems. The cell yield concept is based on an overall pseudobalance for the process:

$$\text{substrate} \longrightarrow \text{cells} + \text{virus/viral products} + \text{waste}$$

The process is catalyzed by cells and — up to a certain point — the yield of virus will increase nearly proportionally with cell yield (i.e., the total number of cells produced in the process). Beyond this point substrate becomes limiting, and any further yield in cells comes at the expense of virus and viral product yield. This is another way of stating that (*1*) each cell can only support the production of a limited number of virus particles and (*2*) the virus yield per cell is highest at low cell density, but remains essentially constant up to the point where substrate becomes limiting.

What is important here is that there is no distinction made of when the cells were produced: whether they all were produced prior to infection, as would be the case at high MOI infection, or whether most were produced in parallel with the infection process, as would be the case at very low MOI. In other words, the outcome is ultimately dictated by the total cell yield in the process, not on the combination of TOI and MOI used to achieve this yield. This point is illustrated in Figure 2 for recombinant baculovirus (a) and for HaNPV production (b). By choosing the appropriate TOI, it is possible to achieve the optimal cell yield for whatever MOI is chosen.

At high MOI (>5 infective viruses per cell) essentially all cells will be infected immediately, and the ensuing infection process will be synchronous. Cell growth halts almost immediately, and thus the cell yield is close to the cell density at TOI. Thus, to achieve optimal production, cells should be infected at a cell density close to the optimal cell yield. At lower MOIs, only a fraction of the cells are initially infected (primary infection). The remainder will continue to grow as noninfected cells. These cells and their progeny will first be infected at some later point (secondary infection) when the cells infected in the primary infection begin to release progeny virus. Hence, the cell yield may

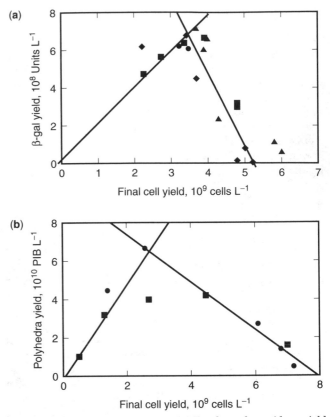

Figure 2. The cell yield concept. (**a**) Total β-galactosidase yield for rβgal-AcNPV infections of Sf9 cells in SF900II medium performed at MOIs of 5 (circle), 0.01 (square), 0.001 (triangle), and 0.0001 (diamond) in shaker flasks. (**b**) Polyhedra yield for HaNPV infections of *H. zea* cells in SF900II+10% serum medium performed at MOIs of 0.5 (circle) and 1–2 (square) in shaker flasks.

be much higher than the cell density at TOI. Thus, to achieve optimal production when using low MOIs, cells should be infected at a cell density lower than the optimal cell yield.

Practically, we obtain the product versus cell yield curve by performing a series of high-multiplicity infections at different cell density. For insect cells, we use a bioreactor for cell growth, harvest 100-mL aliquots into shaker flasks at 6–12 h intervals, infect at MOI 5–10, incubate on a shaker, and follow the ensuing infection process (Fig. 3). Because pH is not a problem in these cultures, the response curve observed in shaker flasks is valid even for controlled bioreactors. In many systems, it may be necessary to perform the infection in bioreactors to match the expected performance in a controlled system.

In suspension insect cell culture, the limiting substrate is a nutrient and the maximum reasonably well defined. In many virus production systems, cells are anchorage dependent and the limiting substrate will be surface area. In such systems, the transition could be broader and the decline is not necessarily linear. In either case, however, the observed optimum cell yield provides an initial goal to aim for in optimizing the process. It does not, however, indicate how to achieve this cell density, if we choose a low MOI. In order to predict this we need a kinetic model.

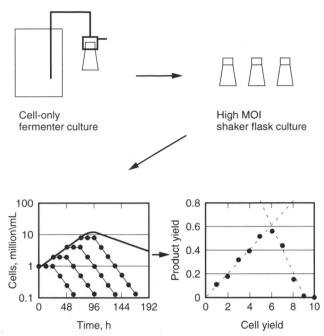

Figure 3. Generating the product versus cell yield curve. During a cell-only bioreactor culture, cells are repeatedly harvested straight into shaker flasks and infected at high MOI and the ensuing infection followed. Maximum product and cell yield are used to generate the product versus cell yield curve and the maximum determined by drawing the supporting lines.

KINETIC MODEL OF VIRAL INFECTION: SYNCHRONOUS INFECTION

All studies of viral kinetics should commence with a study of synchronous infection somewhat below the optimal cell yield. If a batch culture of cells is infected at a high multiplicity (MOI > 5), the ensuing infection process will be essentially synchronous; that is, all cells will go through the infection cycle simultaneously and will — at any given point — be at the same point in the cycle. Under these conditions culture dynamics simply reflects the infection cycle occurring in each cell amplified by the number of cells.

Synchronous cultures are biphasic in nature. We distinguish between the noninfected (cell only) phase and the infection phase. During the noninfected phase, time is the independent variable. During the infection phase, we introduce a new independent variable, *infection time*, denoted τ and measured in hours post infection (hpi). This terminology can cause some confusion. Infection time does not automatically follow true time; rather it relates to a reference infection. The reference infection is typically a high MOI infection (e.g., MOI = 10) of cells in the early to midexponential phase (i.e., relatively low cell density) and in a given medium. When we say that a cell is at 15 hpi, we are actually not saying that the cell has been infected for 15 h; rather we are saying that the cell is at the same point of the infection cycle that a cell would be after 15 h in the reference system.

Infection time can be slower or faster than true time. Infection in late exponential phase, for example, often results in slow progression through the infection cycle (see later); that is, infection time goes slower than real time. For some viral systems, the initial viral load per cell can affect the timing of the infection cycle and in a high multiplicity of infection, *infection time may go faster than real time.* We define the infection velocity, v, as

$$v = \frac{d\tau}{dt} \qquad (1)$$

and note that for the reference system the infection velocity is one hour of infection time (hpi) per one hour of true time (h).

Noninfected Cell Growth

Any traditional cell growth model could be used to describe cell growth prior to infection. Experience tells us, however, that for most virus production systems cells must be infected in optimal health (i.e., in the midexponential phase) in order to achieve a reasonable product yield. Thus all relevant situations can be modeled with a simple exponential growth model

$$\frac{dN_v}{dt} = (\mu_{max} - k_D)N_v \qquad (2)$$

where N_v is the concentration of viable cells, μ_{max} the maximum specific growth rate, and k_D the specific death rate. The noninfected cell parameters, μ_{max} and k_D, can be determined using standard techniques from viable and dead cell numbers during the exponential phase of a noninfected culture.

The Infection Cycle — Qualitative Aspects

Typically, the qualitative aspects (e.g., virus attachment mechanism, molecular biology, and general timing of events), are well established for commercially relevant viruses. This information serves as a sound basis on which mathematical models can be formulated. The starting point may be a graphical representation of the infection cycle, as in Figure 4 for recombinant baculovirus (see also Ref. 33). The first step is virus diffusing to the surface of the cell (1) and attaching to a specific receptor (2). Baculovirus enter the cytosol via random endosomal activity (3) followed by pH-regulated fusion with the endosomal membrane (4). From the cytosol, baculovirus is localized to the nucleus (5), where the outer protein coat dissolves (6). All these processes take place within the first couple of hours of cells being inoculated with virus. Hereafter follows the "genetic" part of the infection, with simultaneous replication of viral DNA (7), transcription (8), and translation of viral proteins (9). The infection cycle is "timed" through sequential protein expression and can be divided into three phases (Ref. 10):

1. Early (0–6 hours post infection). The viral reproduction apparatus is established and the cellular reproduction apparatus switched off.

2. Late (8–18 hours post infection). Synthesis of nonoccluded virions, which are coated in protein (10) and are capable of budding from the cell surface (11).

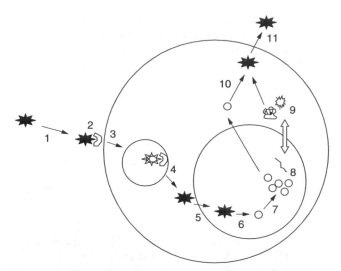

Figure 4. The infection cycle in recombinant baculovirus. 1. Diffusion, 2. attachment, 3. internalization, 4. fusion, 5. nuclear location, 6. uncoating, 7. replication, 8. transcription, 9. translation, 10. encapsulation, and 11. budding.

3. Very late (20–72 hours post infection). Polyhedrin or recombinant product is transcribed using a unique, viral-derived RNA polymerase. In wild-type virus, virions are embedded in occlusion bodies composed primarily of polyhedrin.

The Infection Cycle — Modeling

There are two approaches that can be taken to describe the infection cycle, an unstructured and a structured, mechanistic approach. In the unstructured approach the temporal element of the infection cycle is described by a number of time-varying rates. No attempt is made to follow the internal events of the cell. The three existing full models all employ this approach (29,34,35).

In the structured, mechanistic approach, the infection cycle is described as closely as possible to the true mechanism outlined in Figure 4. For example, separate variables are used to describe virus at the different locations (free, attached, endosomal, cytosolic, and nuclear), and rate equations are expressed in terms of these variables. At present no full mechanistic model exists, though Shuler's group has outlined a possible structure for such a model (33) and has developed detailed models covering up to the point of nuclear location (see later). As a guide to more fundamental research, the mechanistic models obviously excel. Ultimately, they will also prove excellent engineering tools for designing viral production processes. At present, however, the structured models are too cumbersome and require too much effort to develop, and here we will concentrate on the unstructured models.

The modeling approach to be described has three important features:

1. Only directly observable state variables are used
2. All parameters are graphically verifiable
3. All parameters are estimated for high multiplicity of infection

In order to achieve this simplicity, a number of assumptions have been made. It is assumed that there is no growth after infection. In our experience, the total number of cells does increase on average 15% post infection, suggesting that cells may continue to divide through the early phase of infection. Accounting for this growth, however, would involve deciding whether both daughter cells in a division are infected or only one of them. It is possible to determine this based on the multiplicity of infection for individual cells, but introducing this distinction adds substantially to the numerical effort, and the simplifying assumption of no post infection growth is made in most models of infection.

At present, we shall not consider the effects multiple infection and infection with defective virus particles have on the infection cycle. We will only consider a "standard" infection at relatively high MOI (5–10) producing a single type of infected cells. This corresponds to the approach taken in our 1994 model to describe β-galactosidase production using a recombinant AcNPV to infect Sf9 cells in suspension culture (34). More advanced models will be described later. For modeling purposes, the time points of interest are those linked with readily observable events, for example:

- Virus release
- Membrane integrity
- β-Galactosidase production and release

Extracellular virus is not observed in the culture fluid until around the onset of the very late phase. Electron microscopy observations (unpublished) have confirmed that virus progeny is produced from the beginning of the late phase, τ_E. The newly produced virus progeny was observed on the cell surface, and some was observed to readsorb to the cell of origin. Surface presentation of nonoccluded virus in the late phase could be the means by which lateral infection of proximal cells occurs in the gut cells of insects (8). It is not clear if the release rather than surface presentation of virus progeny is linked to the very late phase or simply is a delayed process. Hence, in all three models of baculvirus kinetics the commencement of virus release is designated by its own marker, here designated τ_{VRC}. Virus appears to be released at a relatively constant rate, α_{VR}, and ends after the end of the very late phase at a point designated, τ_{VRE}. Thus the specific rate equation for virus release, r_{VR}, is

$$r_{VR}(\tau) = \begin{cases} 0, & \text{for } \tau \leq \tau_{VRC} \\ \alpha_{VR}, & \text{for } \tau_{VRC} < \tau \leq \tau_{VRE} \\ 0, & \text{for } \tau > \tau_{VRE} \end{cases} \tag{3}$$

Since virus binding has finished when virus release is observed, the virus titre, V, can be described by

$$\frac{dV}{d\tau} = r_{VR}(\tau)N_v - k_v V \tag{4}$$

where the second term accounts for degradation of virus, which is significant for many viruses. Inserting Eq. (3) in to Eq. (4) and integrating, we find the solution

$$V^*(\tau) = \begin{cases} 0, & \text{for } \tau \leq \tau_{VRC} \\ \dfrac{\alpha_{VR}}{k_V}(1 - e^{-k_V(\tau-\tau_{VRC})}), & \text{for } \tau_{VRC} < \tau \leq \tau_{VRE} \\ \dfrac{\alpha_{VR}}{k_V}(1 - e^{-k_V(\tau_{VRE}-\tau_{VRC})})e^{-k_V(\tau-\tau_{VRE})}, \\ & \text{for } \tau > \tau_{VRE} \end{cases} \quad (5)$$

where V^* is the amount of virus per cell. Equation (5) can be used to determine the virus concentration at any given point after infection. For example, when recombinant β-gal-AcNPV is used to infect Sf9 cells, virus release commences at 17 hpi (τ_{VRC}) and ends at 88 hpi (τ_{VRE}). During this period virus is released at a rate of 10 pfu/h/cell. The rate of virus decay is 0.007 l/h (k_V) (i.e., 0.7% of the virus is lost per hour). Inserting these values in Eq. (5), we find that at 60 hpi, for example, the amount of virus per cell is

$$V^*(60 \text{ hpi}) = \frac{10 \text{ pfu/h/cell}}{0.007 \text{ l/h}}(1 - e^{-0.007 \text{ l/h} (60 \text{ h}-17 \text{ h})})$$

$$= 371 \text{ pfu/cell}$$

Membrane integrity can be measured by trypan blue dye exclusion. For noninfected cells, membrane integrity can be used as an indicator of viability. For infected cells, however, membrane integrity gradually decreases during the late part of the infection rather than spontaneously at the end of infection (29). As virus and recombinant product are released gradually as well, there is no particular need for the model to identify the point of death and lysis. The gradual staining of cells is expressed with an empirically fitted equation giving the fraction of stained cells as a function of τ

$$f_U(\tau) = \begin{cases} 1, & \tau \leq \tau_U \\ e^{-\beta_U(\tau-\tau_U)}, & \tau > \tau_U \end{cases} \quad (6)$$

where τ_U is time following infection where staining commences and β_U is the first-order rate of staining hereafter. Using a similar approach, de Gooijer et al. employed the gradual visual changes in infected cells to follow the progression of infection with wild-type virus (35). Equation (6) is used to determine the fraction of unstained cells at any point after infection. For example, when recombinant β-gal-AcNPV is used to infect Sf9 cells staining commences at 43 hpi (τ_U) and occurs at a rate of 0.08 l/h (β_U) (i.e., 8% of unstained cells become stained per hour). Inserting these values in Eq. (6), we find that at 60 hpi, f_U (60 hpi) $= e^{-0.08 \text{ l/h} (60 \text{ h}-43 \text{ h})} = 25.7\%$ of cells remain unstained.

In the baculovirus expression vector system, recombinant protein is expressed under the control of the polyhedrin promoter. Thus recombinant protein expression is directly linked to the expression of the very late genes commencing at τ_L and terminating at τ_{VL}. The production rate is assumed constant, α_{PP}. Both intracellular and extracellular β-galactosidase can be determined experimentally. β-Galactosidase is not a secreted product, and protein release is assumed to be linked to the leakiness of the membrane, as evidenced by trypan blue uptake.

Thus release is assumed to commence at the same time as staining, τ_U. Hereafter, the rate of release is assumed to be proportional to the intracellular concentration (the release constant denoted α_{PR}); that is,

$$r_{PR}(\tau) = k_{PR}(\tau)p_i(\tau) \quad (7a)$$

where

$$k_{PR}(\tau) = \begin{cases} 0, & \text{for } \tau < \tau_U \\ \alpha_{PR}, & \text{for } \tau \geq \tau_U \end{cases} \quad (7b)$$

The intracellular concentration, p_i, is given by

$$\frac{dp_i}{d\tau} = r_{PP}(\tau) - r_{PR}(\tau)p_i; \quad p_i(0) = 0 \quad (8a)$$

where $r_{PP}(\tau)$ is the specific production rate

$$r_{PP}(\tau) = \begin{cases} \alpha_{PP}, & \text{for } \tau_L \leq \tau \leq \tau_{VL} \\ 0, & \text{otherwise} \end{cases} \quad (8b)$$

Solving Eq. (8), the intracellular concentration can be determined

$$p_i(\tau) = \begin{cases} 0, & \text{for } \tau \leq \tau_L \\ \alpha_{PP}(\tau - \tau_L), & \text{for } \tau_L < \tau \leq \tau_U \\ \dfrac{\alpha_{PP}}{\alpha_{PR}} + \alpha_{PP}\left(\tau_U - \tau_L - \dfrac{1}{\alpha_{PR}}\right)e^{-\alpha_{PR}(\tau-\tau_U)}, \\ \qquad\qquad\qquad\qquad \text{for } \tau_U < \tau \leq \tau_{VL} \\ p_i(\tau_{VL})e^{-\alpha_{PR}(\tau-\tau_{VL})}, & \text{for } \tau > \tau_{VL} \end{cases} \quad (9)$$

The extracellular product concentration is given by

$$\frac{dP}{d\tau} = r_{PR}(\tau)N_v - k_P P \quad (10)$$

where the second term accounts for decomposition of extracellular product.

The number of parameters in the preceding model may initially seem large. All parameters, however, can be determined and visually verified using a synchronous infection of cells in the midexponential phase, and several are determined independently of other parameters. Decomposition parameters, k_V and k_P, are determined from the exponential decay curves observed in cultures in which cells are removed after some virus and product have been produced. The membrane integrity parameters, τ_U and β_U, are determined by nonlinear regression from synchronous culture cell viability data.

The three viral production parameters—α_{VR}, τ_{VRC}, and τ_{VRE}—are obtained by nonlinear regression on experimental data using Eq. (4), as illustrated in Figure 5. The timing parameters are visually verifiable, while the production rate is more difficult to confirm due to the effect of degradation. The parameters for product formation are determined in a similar manner.

Substrate Limitation

The simple model outlined previously works well when the cell yield is below the optimal cell yield defined earlier. Near the optimal cell yield, however, it is our experience

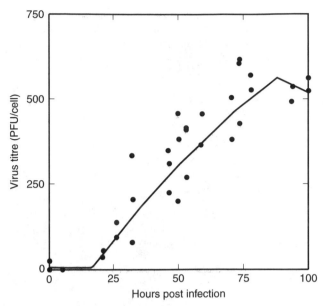

Figure 5. Fitting of virus production parameters. Sf9 cells cultured in serum free Sf900II medium were infected with recombinant baculovirus at a multiplicity of 10 PFU. The data points are from three independent experiments and the solid line represents the model fit to data.

that the infection process slows down and the response is slower than predicted.

In suspension cultures, the limitation appears to be related to the depletion of an essential substrate (24,36). In our 1994 model, we had to overcome several problems in order to describe substrate limitation (34)

1. *Limiting substrate is unknown.* The limiting substrate is still to be identified, and the model had to assume an arbitrary substrate to be present at 1 unit per liter of fresh medium.

2. *Substrate limitation causes complex changes in kinetics.* It has been our experience that substrate limitation causes a general slow down of the growth and infection processes, not only a lowering in production rates as assumed by Licari and Bailey (29). As a simple initial approach, the model was made a simple depletion model; that is, all cellular processes were assumed to occur at maximum rate until depletion of substrate, at which point all cellular processes would stop.

3. *Consumption pattern unknown.* The limiting substrate being unknown, it was not possible to formulate a consumption profile. Instead the specific consumption rate was assumed constant for noninfected and infected cells. The concept was that substrate consumption remained constant while the end product would change from cell mass to viral products over the infection.

With these simplifying assumptions the resulting substrate limitation model only required a single parameter to be obtained, namely, the maximum cell density observed in a noninfected culture, Y_S. Mathematically, the model read

$$\frac{dS}{d\tau} = -\frac{\mu}{Y_S}N_V, \text{ at } \tau = 0 : S = 1 - \frac{N_V}{Y_S} \quad (11)$$

where the boundary condition accounts for the amount of nutrients consumed during the cell growth phase.

While this model captures the essence of the cell yield concept (Fig. 2), the temporal development remains poorly described around the peak, since the model fails to describe the slow down in growth and infection when substrate becomes limiting. Moreover, the assumption of constant substrate consumption before and after infection — while fortuitously correct for β-galactosidase production in Sf9 cells — does not hold for other systems (Table 1) (37). This flaw, however, can be corrected by introducing a separate consumption rate after infection, $q_S \neq \mu/Y_S$.

One possible solution to address the model's inability accurately to describe substrate limitation is to make the maturation velocity, v, a function of substrate concentration, for example,

$$v(S) = \frac{S}{K_S + S} \quad (12)$$

Note that with this definition the "infection time" τ becomes a marker of the progression through the infection cycle rather than a measure of time. At $S = K_s$, for example, the cells progress at $v(K_s) = K_s/(K_s + K_s) = 0.5$, that is, half an "infection hour" for each true hour in culture. If all specific rates also are multiplied with v, the result is to stretch out the infection cycle at lower substrate levels without changing the total yields.

If the limiting substrate is available space, Eq. (12) can be replaced with a spatial saturation model

$$v = \frac{\text{total capacity} - \left(\begin{array}{c}\text{capacity taken by noninfected}\\\text{and infected cells}\end{array}\right)}{\text{total capacity}} \quad (13)$$

as was done by Licari and Bailey (29).

So, if a given surface can support at most 25 million cells and there is 10 million cells present, the rate of infection is $v = (25 \text{ million} - 10 \text{ million})/25 \text{ million} = 0.6$ "infection hour" per true hour.

The approach argued here, however, differs from that used by Licari and Bailey, in that they only took the change in production rate into account, not the prolonging of the infection cycle. The new approach is yet to be tested. The constant K_s will have to be a fitted constant, that is,

Table 1. Specific Consumption Rates (mmol per 10^{12} Cells per Hour) for Five Amino Acids before and after Infection

System phase	Gln	Asn	Leu	Thr	Tyr
Sf9/rAcNPV					
Uninfected	24	2	8	3	13
Sf9/rAcNPV					
Infected	18	13	9	4	14
H. zea/HaNPV					
Uninfected	59	125	16	7	9
H. zea/HaNPV					
Infected	20	37	2	1	2

Note: The comparison shows that while consumption remains essentially constant after infection in the Sf9/rAcNPV system, there is a significant drop in the *H. zea*/HaNPV system (from Ref. 37).

chosen as the value that gives the best description to a series of high-MOI experiments infected at different initial cell density.

Multiplicity of Infection

Infected cells continue to bind virus after the initial infection, yet the proposed model does not take into account possible differences caused by the multiplicity of infection for individual cells. Conceptually, an increase in multiplicity represents an increase in number of viral templates; hence at least the early stages of infection should progress faster at high multiplicity. Indeed, increased rate of RNA synthesis was observed during the 2.5 h after infection when BHK cells were infected with an increasing number of Semliki Forrest Virus (reported in Ref. 38). What remains unclear is to what extent this transient increase affect the overall timing and whether or not total productivity is affected by the multiplicity.

In our experience, the use of an MOI of 10 versus an MOI of 5 in suspension culture does not significantly change the timing of the infection cycle. Furthermore, experiments using two different viruses suggest that any additional virus compete with the existing virus within the cell (Table 2). When recombinant β-galactosidase AcNPV and VP7 AcNPV viruses were added simultaneously (both at an MOI of 5), virus production for each was approximately 50% of that observed in absence of the other virus. When one virus was added earlier, it gained a greater share of the total production at the expense of the other virus, and with 4 hours difference the titer of the second virus would only reach ~10% of the normal level. It follows from these two sets of observations that when a cell is infected with 10 instead of 5 viruses, the productivity *per virus* is essentially halved. Presumably, there is an upper limit on the copy number during the infection cycle, and this limit is reached even if a single virus enters the cell.

Although multiplicity of infection does not appear to affect timing or outcome significantly for baculovirus, there may be other systems where this is an important issue. In particular, timing may be important for viruses with a much shorter cycle than baculovirus. Hence, it may be necessary to model the effect of multiplicity. If

infection occurs over a short period of time (either due to rapid binding of available virus or due to deliberate removal of the viral inoculum after a short contact period), the effect of multiplicity can be accounted for by defining separate cell populations, N_1, N_2, etc., and define separate kinetics for each population. The number of cells in each population can be determined by assuming that virus distribute randomly according to the Poisson distribution with MOI as the parameter (29).

If infection occurs over a longer period of time, it becomes necessary to take into account that the first virus bound may have been replicated before later viruses bind. This situation may occur in a system where binding is intrinsically slow or during secondary infection in low MOI infections (see later), where the primary infected cells continue to release virus gradually throughout the secondary infection. This situation can only be dealt with using highly mechanistic models, as we would need to know not only the amount of DNA/RNA already present in the infected cell to add the contribution from additional infections, but also the delay between virus attachment and release of DNA/RNA into the cytosolic or nuclear pool.

Multiple Virus Infection

The experiment described in Table 2 is an example of viral production systems in which cells are infected by several different viruses. Multiple virus infection can be a deliberate process as in packing of replication-deficient virus for gene therapy or production of multisubunit proteins (e.g., virus-like particles). It may, however, also be the inadvertent outcome of defective virus accumulation.

The latter is an important quality control issue in most viral production systems and is frequently termed the passage effect (31), because serial passage at high multiplicity leads to defective virus accumulation. For baculovirus, we can consider two types of viruses: normal infective particles (I-NOVs) and defective interfering particles that lack about 44% of the virus genome (D-NOVs). There is a third type that leads to an abortive infection, but we will ignore this type here for illustration purposes. With the two virus types, three modes of infection can be envisaged (35):

1. Correct infection arising from entry of at least one I-NOV without any D-NOVs. This infection gives rise to I-NOVs and a small number of D-NOVs.

2. Simultaneous infection of a cell by at least one I-NOV and at least one D-NOV. The genetic advantage of the D-NOV results in production of large quantities of D-NOVs and few I-NOVs.

3. The third mode results from infection of a cell with a D-NOV in the absence of an I-NOV. Without the helper effect of the I-NOV, such infections do not produce any virions.

If we assume that infection occurs over a short period of time, we can again consider the statistics of random virus distribution and calculate the probability for each mode of infection. Because of the vast difference in productivity (a single D-NOV will make the cell produce almost exclusively D-NOV progeny), we do not have to consider

Table 2. The Effect of Co-infection

	Timing VP7 hours	rβgal-AcNPV titre 10^8 pfu/ml (% max)	rVP7-AcNPV titre 10^8 pfu/ml (% max)
Culture 1	−inf	0.00 (0)	0.62 (100)
Culture 2	−4	0.09 (7)	0.55 (89)
Culture 3	−2	0.22 (18)	0.58 (94)
Culture 4	0	0.56 (46)	0.33 (53)
Culture 5	2	0.77 (64)	0.18 (29)
Culture 6	4	0.68 (56)	0.08 (13)
Culture 7	+inf	1.21 (100)	0.00 (0)

Cells were infected with two recombinant AcNPV viruses — one producing β-galactosidase and one producing VP7, a blue tongue virus capsid protein — both at an MOI of 5. The table presents the timing of rVP7-AcNPV virus addition relative to rβgal-AcNPV addition and the resulting virus titers for the two viruses.

exactly how many viruses of each type attaches. Infection results in the formation of three populations, N_I N_{I+D}, and N_D, and we would define a parameter set for each population.

In the general case, it would be necessary to subdivide the N_{I+D} population into many subpopulations to account for differences resulting from different initial amount of the two viruses. In this case, it may again be necessary to consider a structured modeling approach, now with separate pools of DNA and RNA representing each virus. Structured models are also required if the infection process is not instantaneous.

KINETIC MODEL OF VIRAL INFECTION: ASYNCHRONOUS INFECTION

Asynchronous infection represents a significantly more complex problem than synchronous infection. First, it is necessary at any point in time to keep track of cells at any point of the infection cycle. Second, understanding the kinetics of virus attachment and internalization is paramount in asynchronous cultures, whereas it sufficed to assume that all cells were infected simultaneously in the synchronous culture. The complexity of asynchronous culture dynamics, however, is also the main argument for modeling: It is practically impossible to comprehend culture dynamics quantitatively without the aid of a model. This section outlines how to use the behavior observed at high-multiplicity infection—together with a population balance and attachment kinetics—to predict the behavior in low-multiplicity infections, where the infection process is asynchronous.

Population Balance for Asynchronous Infection

When cells are infected at an MOI less than 3–5 in a batch culture, the culture will no longer be synchronous. At any point in time, the culture will be composed of non-infected cells and cells at different points in their individual infection cycle. The culture behavior is the cumulative behavior of these individual cells. In a continuous culture, noninfected cells are added continuously, and the culture will obviously be asynchronously infected.

In order to keep track of the culture, we introduce the cell density function for infected cells, $n(t, \tau)$, where t is true time and τ is time since infection. Note that $n(t, \tau)d\tau$ represents the number of cells at true time t that have been infected for a period between τ and $\tau + d\tau$ hours. Assuming no postinfection growth (as discussed earlier), the law of conservation for cell numbers reads

$$\begin{pmatrix} \text{change in number} \\ \text{of cells in}[\tau, \tau + d\tau] \end{pmatrix} = \begin{pmatrix} \text{number of cells} \\ \text{entering}[\tau, \tau + d\tau] \end{pmatrix}$$
$$- \begin{pmatrix} \text{number of cells} \\ \text{leaving}[\tau, \tau + d\tau] \end{pmatrix}$$

$$n(t + dt, \tau)d\tau - n(t, \tau)d\tau = v(t, \tau)n(t, \tau)dt - v(t, \tau + d\tau)$$
$$\times n(t, \tau + d\tau)dt$$

$$\frac{\partial n}{\partial t} + v\frac{\partial n}{\partial \tau} = 0 \qquad (14)$$

Normally, it will be assumed that $n(0, \tau) = 0$ (i.e., at $t = 0$ no cells are infected). If, furthermore, the infection rate at all times t, $IR(t) = vn(t, 0)$, is specified, then Eq. (14) has a unique solution.

Attachment, Internalization, and Infection

The first event of the infection cycle is the attachment of virus to the cell. Wickham et al. (39) identified three modes of viral attachment for a number of different animal viruses:

Mode 1   Virus attaches to single receptor and is internalized

Mode 2   Initial attachment to receptor is followed by reversible attachment to surrounding receptors and the complex is internalized

Mode 3   As Mode 2, except the number of receptors is so high that spatial saturation of cell surface with virus may occur

Some insect cells, such as *T. ni* cells, do have sufficient number of binding sites to indicate a possible involvement of spatial saturation, while for others, such as *S. frugiperda*, the number of binding sites is too low (31,40). Practically, saturation is likely only to be a factor in low-temperature attachment studies, where very high virus titers are used and internalization is minimal (41). Under standard infection conditions, binding is first order with respect to both virus and receptor number and the depletion of extracellular virus (V) due to binding is (42)

$$\frac{dV}{dt} = -k_aNV \qquad (15)$$

where k_a is the attachment rate constant and N is the total number of cells. Dissociation has been neglected, as it is typically slow relative to multivalent bond formation (stabilization) and internalization.

The infection rate, $IR(t)$, differs from the attachment rate in that the former is only concerned with attachment to previously uninfected cells, N_V, rather than all cells. The infection rate is found as

$$IR(t) = -k_aN_VV\frac{\text{cells}}{\text{PFU}} \qquad (16)$$

where the last part is a unit conversion from virus to cells.

For Sf9 cells propagated in serum free SF900II suspension cultures, we observe attachment rates of $\sim 1.8 \times 10^{-8}$ cm^3 cell^{-1} min^{-1} (k_a); so immediately after infection at the optimal density, 4×10^6 cells cm^{-3}, and at an MOI of 5, the infection rate would be: $IR(t) = (1.8 \times 10^{-8}$ cm^3 cell^{-1} min^{-1}) $(4 \times 10^6$ cells cm^{-3}) $(2 \times 10^7$ PFU cm^{-3}) cells/PFU or approximately 1.4×10^6 cells per min.

The interpretation of k_a depends on whether attachment is diffusion or reaction limited. The maximum rate of attachment occurs when attachment is diffusion limited and every virus collision with the cell surface results in binding (42). This diffusion limited attachment rate can be calculated from a modified Scoluchowski equation (43)

$$k_{a\ (\text{diffusion})} = 4\pi r_{\text{cell}}D_v\eta \qquad (17)$$

where r_{cell} is cell radius, D_{v} is the diffusion coefficient of the virus, and η is an efficiency factor accounting for the fact that virus can only attach to the cell surface where a receptor is present ($\eta \to 1$ as the number of receptors increases). For binding of AcNPV to spodoptera cell lines (e.g., Sf9), typical numbers are $r_{\text{cell}} = 9\,\mu\text{m}$, $D_{\text{v}} = 4 \times 10^{-8}\,\text{cm}^2/\text{s}$ (at $28\,^{\circ}\text{C}$ from the Stokes–Einstein equation corrected for the rod shape of virus, $40\,\text{nm} \times 300\,\text{nm}$), and $\eta = 0.5–1$ (39,42). Inserting these values in Eq. (17), the diffusion-limited rate is found to be $k_{\text{a (diffusion)}} \sim 1 - 3 \times 10^{-8}\,\text{cm}^3\,\text{cell}^{-1}\,\text{min}^{-1}$.

When attachment is reaction limited, k_{a} is equal to $k_{\text{f}}(\alpha N_{\text{r}})$, where k_{f} is the intrinsic forward rate constant for binding of a single viral attachment protein to a receptor, α is the number of attachment proteins per virus, and N_{r} is the average number of receptors per cell.

Equation (16) is for cells in suspension (i.e., spheres) and the corresponding equation for cells in a monolayer is: $k_{\text{a (diffusion)}} = 4r_{\text{cell}}D_{\text{v}}\eta$. Assuming limited spreading in the monolayer and assuming that receptors do not localize on the exposed surface, the theoretical ratio of $k_{\text{a (diffusion)}}^{\text{suspension}}$ to $k_{\text{a (diffusion)}}^{\text{monolayer}}$ is π. For reaction-limited attachment, this ratio is 4, the ratio between exposed surface area in suspension and in monolayer. Hence, $k_{\text{a (diffusion)}}^{\text{suspension}}/k_{\text{a (diffusion)}}^{\text{monolayer}} \sim 3 - 4$ can be used as general correlation and a ratio of ~3 is indeed observed experimentally (42).

The observed attachment rate varies with virus, host, medium, mode of infection, as well as cell density (or "health" of cells). For Sf9 cells propagated in serum-free SF900II suspension cultures, we observe attachment rates of $\sim1.8 \times 10^{-8}\,\text{cm}^3\,\text{cell}^{-1}\,\text{min}^{-1}$ (i.e., around the diffusion limit), up to a cell density of $4 \times 10^6\,\text{cells}\,\text{cm}^{-3}$ (Fig. 6), which corresponds to the optimal cell yield for this system (43). The attachment rate for the same virus and cell line in serum containing IPL-41 suspension cultures is only one-fifth, highlighting the sensitivity of attachment to medium composition (44).

Attachment continues after the initial infection. For baculovirus, the attachment rate remains at the noninfected level for 2–4 h, before falling exponentially until it reaches zero around 15–20 h post infection (Fig. 7) (43). The 2–4 h period is consistent with the time it takes for the virus to internalize and commence transcription (42). The exponential decline may be attributed to the effect of natural protein turnover in the absence of new transcription and translation (the virus takes control over RNA and DNA replication, which is ultimately performed by a virus-specific replication apparatus). Mathematically, we can describe the infection rate for infected cells by

$$k_{\text{ai}}(\tau) = \begin{cases} k_{\text{a}}, & \tau \leq \tau_{\text{IE}} \\ k_{\text{a}}e^{-\beta_{\text{i}}(\tau - \tau_{\text{IE}})}, & \tau > \tau_{\text{IE}} \end{cases} \quad (18)$$

where τ is a measure of how long cells have been infected, k_{a} is the uninfected infection rate, β_{i} is the decline rate, and τ_{IE} is the duration of the immediate early period (i.e., the period postinfection until cell behavior is affected). The fit of Eq. (18) to real data is shown in Figure 5.

Internalization follows different routes for different viruses. Baculovirus enters cells through receptor-mediated endocytosis followed by low-pH-mediated fusion

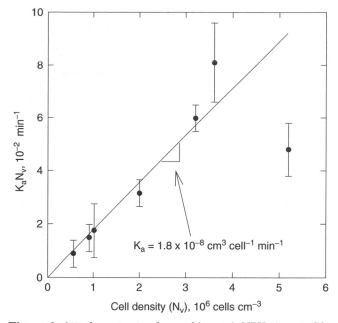

Figure 6. Attachment rate of recombinant AcNPV virus to Sf9 cells in serum-free medium. Suspension cultures were incubated with $\sim$50–100 radioactive labeled virus particles per cell and the attachment rate determined from the exponential decline in free virus concentration.

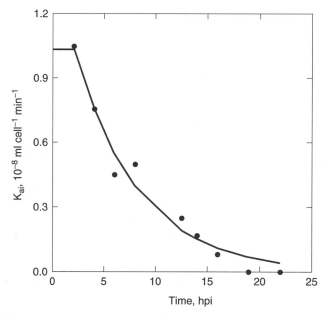

Figure 7. Attachment rate of AcNPV virus to Sf9 cells in serum-free medium following infection. Cells were infected at $2.3 \times 10^6\,\text{cells}\,\text{mL}^{-1}$ at an MOI of 5.

of the viral and endosomal membrane (42). A similar mechanism is used by orthomyxo- (e.g., influenza), toga- (e.g., Semliki Forrest virus, rubella, yellow fever, dengue), and rhabdovirus (e.g., rabies). Internalization is reasonably fast (of the same order as or faster than binding) and will not saturate under normal infection conditions (42). Only 50% of AcNPV virus is effectively internalized, with the remainder found stuck on the outer membrane (42,43). A similar efficiency has been observed for Semliki Forrest virus, and it appears to reflect the efficiency of endosomal fusion rather than defective virus (41). Indeed, Dee and Shuler have presented evidence that low estimates for infective to total virus particles normally observed for AcNPV (typically 1 in 100–300) is caused by inadequate virus assays rather than truly defective viruses (41). It is possible that all virus particles in a low-passage inoculum are fully functional, but half gets randomly routed from endosomes to the lysosomes and released back to the cell surface following partial degradation.

Accurate virus titers are crucial to predict the behavior in low-multiplicity infections. While it probably matters little for kinetics if cells are infected with 5 or 50 infective viruses (the result is a synchronous infection in both cases), an infection at 0.01 virus per cell will behave very differently from an infection with 0.001 virus per cell. For Eq. (16) to make any sense, V must represent the true number of infective viruses.

Mass Balances

Mass balances are formed by combining the population balance model with the virus attachment model and the infection cycle model. For example, the virus titer in a batch culture is described by the ordinary differential equation:

$$\frac{dV}{dt} = -k_aN_VV \qquad \text{attachment to noninfected cells}$$

$$-\int_{\tau=0}^{\infty} k_{ai}(\tau)n(t,\tau)d\tau \quad \text{attachment to infected cells}$$

$$+\int_{\tau=0}^{\infty} r_{VR}(\tau)n(t,\tau)d\tau \quad \text{production} \qquad (19)$$

$$-k_vV \qquad \text{degradation}$$

Where the integrals are used to "sum up" the contribution to binding and production of cells at different stages of infection.

Similarly, for substrate the mass balance for a batch culture is

$$\frac{dS}{dt} = -q_SN_V \qquad \text{consumption by noninfected cells}$$

$$-\int_{\tau=0}^{\infty} q_S(\tau)n(t,\tau)d\tau \quad \text{consumption by infected cells} \qquad (20)$$

Solving the Model

In order to solve the model, the population balance, the virus mass balance, and the substrate mass balance models must be solved simultaneously. If we use a simple substrate depletion model, the maturation velocity is constant, $v = 1$, until depletion, after which all cellular processes are assumed to cease. Prior to depletion the model is:

$$IR(t) = k_aN_VV \qquad (21a)$$

$$\frac{dN_V}{dt} = (\mu - k_d)N_V - IR(t) \qquad (21a)$$

$$\frac{\partial n}{\partial t} + \frac{\partial n}{\partial \tau} = 0 \qquad (21b)$$

$$\frac{dV}{dt} = -k_aN_VV - \int_{\tau=0}^{\infty} k_{ai}(\tau)n(t,\tau)d\tau$$

$$+\int_{\tau=0}^{\infty} r_{VR}(\tau)n(t,\tau)d\tau - k_VV \qquad (21c)$$

$$\frac{dS}{dt} = -q_SN_V - \int_{\tau=0}^{\infty} q_S(\tau)n(t,\tau)d\tau \qquad (21d)$$

$$N_V(0) = N_0; \; n(0,\tau) = 0; \; n(t,0) = IR(t);$$

$$V(0) = V_0; \; S(0) = S_0 \qquad (21e)$$

In this case, Eq. (21b) has the simple solution

$$n(t,\tau) = n(t-\tau, 0) = IR(t-\tau) \qquad (22)$$

that is, the number of cells of infection age τ at true time t is exactly the number of cells infected $(t-\tau)$ hours earlier. If we introduce the variable, $s = t - \tau$, Eq. (21c) is converted to

$$\frac{dV}{dt} = -k_aN_VV - \int_{s=0}^{t} k_{ai}(t-s)IR(s)ds$$

$$+\int_{s=0}^{t} r_{VR}(t-s)IR(s)ds - k_VV \qquad (23)$$

The integrals on the right-hand side of Eq. (23) can be calculated in each time point t by numerical integration using the infection rates $IR(s)$ in previous time points as nodes. Thus the problem can be solved using a standard ODE solver. We use a variable step length, an improved Euler algorithm, and the trapezoidal rule for integration. It should be stressed that Eq. (22) only holds when the infection velocity is constant. If we introduce a more accurate description of infection velocity under substrate limitation, for example, Eq. (12), the solution is nontrivial, requiring a numerical method for solving the first-order partial differential equation and the ODEs simultaneously (e.g., method of lines).

Figure 8 illustrates the model's ability to predict the behavior in low-MOI experiments. All parameters were obtained from high-multiplicity infections in shaker flasks, yet the model adequately predicts the dynamics of a culture infected at an MOI four orders of magnitude lower, in which total infection only occurs after tertiary infections.

USING THE MODEL

Having introduced this relatively complex modeling framework, it is important to return to basics: How does this help us in developing better viral production processes? This final section will illustrate how we have used the model to develop very low-MOI infection processes.

There is substantial commercial incentive to use very low MOIs. The virus titer for a high-yielding recombinant baculovirus is $\sim 2 \times 10^{12}$ PFU/L. Thus, to achieve synchronous infection (MOI = 5) in a 10,000-L

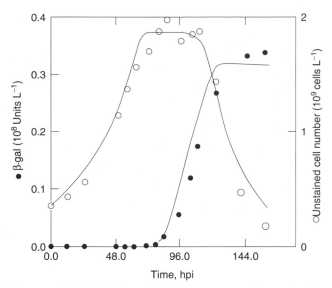

Figure 8. Model fit. The model with parameters determined in high-MOI shaker flask cultures was used to predict the behavior in a bioreactor cultures, where cells were infected at 0.35×10^6 cells mL^{-1} at an MOI of 0.0001.

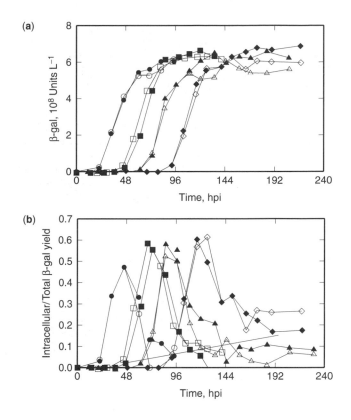

Figure 9. β-gal production profiles for the best infections performed at MOIs of 5 (circle), 0.01 (square), 0.001 (triangle), 0.0001 (diamond) in shaker flasks. The figure shows the total β-gal concentration (**a**) and the ratio of intracellular on total β-gal concentration (**b**).

batch culture infected around the optimal cell yield of 4×10^9 cells/L, we would need 100 L virus stock. Due to the so-called passage effect (31) — serial passage leading to defective viruses — the virus stock should preferably be derived directly from a well-characterized master bank. Assuming that the master virus stock is stored in 10-mL lots, the 100-L virus inoculum could be produced through 2–3 batch scaleup fermentations. In other words, a process relying on synchronous infection will consist of two parallel scaleup processes: one for cells and one for virus.

A more straightforward strategy is to inoculate the 10,000-L batch reactor directly with the 10-mL virus stock. This would obviously lead to an infection at a very low MOI and total infection would rely on secondary and tertiary infections. According to the cell yield concept, if the right cell density at time of infection is chosen the culture will reach the optimal cell density and yield the optimal product titer. That this actually works was illustrated in Figure 2, where MOIs down to 0.0001 were used. Figure 2 does not address two important issues concerning the utility of low-multiplicity infection: dispersion and reproducibility.

Intuitively, low-MOI infection must lead to dispersion in product release and, hence, an undesirable increased exposure of the product to the culture environment (an important issue with labile viral products). Model simulations, however, revealed that low-MOI infections in the baculovirus system do not necessarily result in significant dispersion. The reason for limited dispersion is that only a small fraction of cells are involved in building up the virus titer and that the final surge in virus titer leading to total infection occurs over a short period of time. Interestingly, dispersion does not increase with decreasing MOI. In fact, the highest level of dispersion will occur with an MOI of ~0.7, where half the *final* cell number is infected in first round and the other half (after cell growth) in the second round of infection.

These model predictions were confirmed experimentally (Fig. 9). Except for a delay in the onset of measurable production, lower MOIs did not alter the β-galactosidase concentration profiles [Fig. 9(a)]. For each of the four multiplicities, the production period lasted approximately 36 h, occurred at an identical rate, and yielded approximately the same final β-galactosidase concentration. There is no apparent difference between infecting cells early at a very low MOI or late at a high MOI. This suggests that the final infection in all the experiments infected almost all of the cells and that this infection occurred over a relatively short period. For an MOI of 5, the final infection is also the primary infection and β-galactosidase production commenced at the onset of the very late phase 20–24 hpi. For an MOI of 0.01, only 1% of the cells is infected in the primary infection. The secondary and final infection appears to have occurred around 24 hpi, leaving another 20–24 h until the commencement of the major release period. Similarly, for MOIs of 0.001 and 0.0001 two and three rounds of infections, respectively, seems to have preceded the major final infection. The point is further illustrated by comparing the ratio of intracellular to total β-galactosidase yield for the four MOIs [Fig. 9(b)]. In all four cases, the maximum intracellular β-gal level was 50–60% of the total activity obtained at the end of the culture, and the time to achieve this level was always 24 h after the major onset of production.

The real challenge of performing low-MOI infections is to ensure that the final infection reproducibly occurs when the culture has reached the optimal cell yield. In high-MOI cultures, we can track the cell density all the way and infect when the culture reaches the optimal cell density. In contrast, low-MOI cultures must be infected long before the optimal cell yield, and we rely on virus production and cell growth to reach the optimal cell density. The optimal cell density at infection given the MOI can be predicted using the model, as was done in the preceding experiments, and the main issue is to ensure reproducible behavior of the culture. Inherent variability in cell growth and relatively inaccurate assays makes this a nontrivial task in the laboratory environment. For example, in our experience the specific growth rate of Sf9 cells changes over their useful culture lifespan from $\sim 0.026\ h^{-1}$ one month after thawing to $0.032\ h^{-1}$ $3–5$ month later, before they rapidly degenerate. In an industrial setting, where cells are taken from a well-characterized master bank, this should be less of a problem. Similarly, the low virus inoculum requirement means that virus is taken directly from a well-characterized master bank, avoiding variation caused through scaleup processes.

BIBLIOGRAPHY

1. W.R. Earle, J.C. Bryant, and E.L. Schilling, *Ann. N.Y. Acad. Sci.* **58**, 1000 (1954).

2. P.J. Radlett, *Adv. Biochem. Eng. Biotechnol.* **34**, 129–146 (●●●).

3. T.W. Pay, A. Boge, F.J. Menard, and P.J. Radlett, *Dev. Biol. Stand.* **60**, 171–174 (●●●).

4. A.L. van Wezel, *Nature (London)* **216**, 64 (1967).

5. B. Montagnon, B. Fanget, and J.C. Vincent-Falquet, *Rev. Infect. Dis.* **6**(Suppl 2), S341–S344 (1984).

6. B. Dureux et al., *Lancet* **2**, 98 (1986).

7. J.F. Power and L.K. Nielsen, *Cytotechnology* **20**, 209–219 (1996).

8. R.R. Granados and B.A. Federici, eds., *The Biology of Baculoviruses*, CRC Press, Boca Raton, Fla., 1986.

9. J.M. Vlak, C.D. de Gooijer, J. Tramper, and H.G. Miltenburger, eds., *Insect Cell Culture: Fundamental and Applied Aspects*, Kluwer Academic Publishers, Dordrecht, The Netherlands, 1996.

10. L.K. Miller, *Annu. Rev. Microbiol.* **42**, 177–199 (1988).

11. F.L.J. van Lier, J.M. Vlak, and J. Tramper, *Anim. Cell Biotechnol.* **5**, 169–188 (1992).

12. K.N. Potter, P. Faulkner, and E.A. MacKinnon, *J. Virol.* **18**, 1040–1050 (1976).

13. J.M. Slavicek, M.J. Mercer, M.E. Kelly, and N. Hayes-Plazolles, *J. Invertebr. Pathol.* **67**, 153–160 (1996).

14. W.F. Hink et al., *Biotechnol. Prog.* **7**, 9–14 (1991).

15. J. Wu et al., *J. Ferment. Bioeng.* **70**, 90–93 (1990).

16. G.R. Gardiner and H. Stockdale, *J. Invertebr. Pathol.* **25**, 363–370 (1975).

17. R.H. Goodwin and J.R. Adams, in Kurstak, Maramorosch, and Dubendorfer, eds., *Invertebrate Systems In Vitro*, Elsevier, Amsterdam, 1980, pp. 493–509.

18. J.L. Vaughn et al., *J. Invertebr. Pathol.* **58**, 279–304 (1991).

19. S.A. Weiss et al., *Proc. 9th Aust. Biotechnol. Conf.*, Queensland, Australia, 1990, pp. 220–231.

20. S.A. Weiss, W.G. Whitford, G.P. Godwin, and S. Reid, *Workshop on Baculovirus and Recombinant Protein Production Processes*, Interlaken, Switzerland, 1992, pp. 306–315.

21. A.W. Caron, J. Archambault, and B. Massie, *Biotechnol. Bioeng.* **36**, 1133–1140 (1990).

22. W.F. Hink, E.M. Strauss, and W.A. Ramoska, *J. Invertebr. Pathol.* **30**, 185–191 (1977).

23. K.R. Radford, S. Reid, and P.F. Greenfield, in H. Murakami, S. Shirahata, and H. Tachibana, eds., *Animal Cell Technology: Basic and Applied Aspects*, Kluwer Academic Publishers, Dordrecht, The Netherlands, 1991, pp. 391–396.

24. S. Reuveny, Y.J. Kim, C.W. Kemp, and J. Shiloach, *Biotechnol. Bioeng.* **42**, 235–239 (1993).

25. H. Stockdale and G.R. Gardiner, *J. Invertebr. Pathol.* **30**, 330–336 (1977).

26. M. Brown and P. Faulkner, *J. Invertebr. Pathol.* **26**, 251–257 (1975).

27. E.M. Dougherty, R.M. Weiner, J.L. Vaughn, and C.F. Reichelderfer, *Appl. Environ. Microbiol.* **41**, 1166–1172 (1981).

28. P. Licari and J.E. Bailey, *Biotechnol. Bioeng.* **37**, 238–246 (1991).

29. P. Licari and J.E. Bailey, *Biotechnol. Bioeng.* **39**, 432–441 (1992).

30. M. Kool et al., *Virology* **183**, 739–746 (1991).

31. T.J. Wickham et al., *Biotechnol. Lett.* **13**, 483–488 (1991).

32. K.T.K. Wong et al., *Biotechnol. Bioeng.* **49**, 659–666 (1996).

33. M.L. Shuler et al., *Ann. N.Y. Acad. Sci.* **589**, 399–422 (1990).

34. J.F. Power et al., *Biotechnol. Bioeng.* **44**, 710–719 (1994).

35. C.D. de Gooijer et al., *Biotechnol. Bioeng.* **40**, 537–548.

36. D.A. Lindsay and M.J. Betenbaugh, *Biotechnol. Bioeng.* **39**, 614–618 (1992).

37. S. Chakraborty, Ph.D. Thesis, Queensland University, Brisbane, Australia, 1998.

38. K.U. Dee and M.L. Shuler, *Biotechnol. Bioeng.* **46**, 485–496 (1995).

39. T.J. Wickham et al., *Biophys. J.* **58**, 1501–1516 (1990).

40. T.J. Wickham et al., *J. Gen. Virol.* **73**, 3185–3194 (1992).

41. K.U. Dee and M.L. Shuler, *Biotechnol. Prog.* **13**, 14–24 (1997).

42. K.U. Dee and M.L. Shuler, *Biotechnol. Bioeng.* **54**, 468–490 (1997).

43. T.K. Wong, Ph.D. Thesis, Queensland University, Brisbane, Australia, 1997.

44. J.F. Power, S. Reid, P.F. Greenfield, and L.K. Nielsen, *Cytotechnology* **21**, 155–163 (1996).

See also CELL PRODUCTS — VIRAL GENE THERAPY VECTORS; FLUX ANALYSIS OF MAMMALIAN CELL CULTURE: METHODS AND APPLICATIONS.

VIRUS REMOVAL FROM PLANTS

JOHN L. SHERWOOD
University of Georgia
Athens, Georgia

OUTLINE

Introduction

Heat Treatment of Plants

INTRODUCTION

The losses caused by virus diseases, particularly in vegetatively propagated material, are often not as evident as those caused by other pathogens of plants. Viruses will cause a steady decline in vigor and subsequent loss of yield from the plant. In addition to reductions of yield and quality in field and row crops, viruses may adversely affect the ornamental aspects of plants such as color, shape, and abundance of flowers. The small size of viruses and the variety in type and degree of symptoms caused by virus infection makes detection strictly by visual examination unreliable. Therefore, caution and concern is often expressed about the exchange of germplasm and cultivars between geographical areas where a virus is present in the origin of the material but is absent in the recipient area (1). The lack of inexpensive and reliable curative agents for the elimination of viruses from plants that are growing in the field, orchard, or landscape has resulted in the development of methods for producing virus-free plant materials to replace material that is chronically infected or to assure that newly planted material or plant material exchanged between locations is free of virus.

Much like the therapeutic approaches for elimination of cancerous cells from animals, the approach to remove viruses from plants is to use a treatment that will eliminate the virus but not kill the patient, or plant, in this case. The uneven distribution of virus in plants, particularly the lack of virus in meristematic tissue, the totipotency of most plant cells, and the development of culture media that will result in cellular differentiation and subsequent plant regeneration, has resulted in the use of tissue culture in conjunction with therapeutic measures to develop virus-free plant materials. Unfortunately, the parameters of the chemical or physical treatment that eliminate virus or prevent its movement in the plant, and the specific conditions that result in the selected tissue explant regenerating into a plant, appear to vary with the species or cultivar selected. Thus a singular protocol cannot be developed for virus elimination from plants. As Asjes (2) concluded in trying to develop a uniform method for elimination of viruses from bulbous crops, "the propagation and culture of virus-tested material generally is unpredictable because of the complexity of the factors involved."

Paramount to achieving success is having a reliable way readily to detect the virus. This can range from the use of biological indicators such as a plant that produces localized symptoms (e.g., localized necrotic

lesions) when mechanically inoculated with the virus of concern, serological techniques that detect the viral coat protein or some other protein produced as a result of virus infection, or methods directed at detecting the viral nucleic acid such as hybridization or the polymerase chain reaction. The integration of detection, treatment, and tissue culture has resulted in the production of virus-free plant materials from a vast array of plant species.

HEAT TREATMENT OF PLANTS

Heat treatment, heat therapy, or thermotherapy has long been used to rid plant material, particularly stock plants used in propagation of perennials, of infectious agents. A balance must be struck between conditions that permit plant growth, but maximize virus elimination, because all viruses and all plants do not react similarly to heat treatment. How elevated temperature results in virus elimination is not understood. The effect may be on the virus directly, because many viruses are sensitive to extended periods at elevated temperature, on the movement of the virus in the plant, or on the replication of the virus in the plant. The approaches used to apply heat are an elevated temperature that is maintained or an elevated temperature that is fluctuated with a normal growth temperature for the plant. The amount of temperature elevation, the length of time at the elevated temperature, the intensity of illumination, and the length of illumination in a 24-h period are conditions that have been determined by trial and error to achieve success.

Heat therapy is most routinely applied to whole plants by growing plants for days to months in an incubator or growth chamber maintained at $36-38\,°C$. New growth may be free of virus; so a newly emerged shoot may be grafted onto another plant or directly rooted. Alternatively, plants that have undergone heat treatment may serve as a source of explants for tissue culture, as will be described here. Another approach is to subject tissue explants in culture to elevated temperatures. In doing so, care must be taken to assure adequate humidity is maintained so the tissue explant and the media do not dry out. A fairly comprehensive list has recently been published of genera where heat therapy has been successful (3).

PRODUCTION OF VIRUS FREE PLANTS THROUGH TISSUE CULTURE

Although it has been observed for many years that cultures of tissue from meristematic areas may be free of virus, the mechanism that results in this condition is not known. Speculation on the basis of this phenomenon includes the failure of virus to move into meristematic tissue because of the lack of vascular differentiation in the meristematic areas, the elimination of virus from meristematic areas because virus cannot effectively compete for resources in actively dividing and growing cells, and the detrimental effects of the concentration of plant growth regulators on virus replication in meristematic areas. The optimum parameters leading to production of virus-free plants must be independently determined for each virus–host combination because the specifics of protocols to eliminate virus from different plants vary (4). Factors that must be determined are a method to detect the virus, the type and extent of therapy required to eliminate the virus and maintain tissue viability, and conditions and media for plant culture and differentiation. The historical use of meristem or tip culture to develop virus-free material recently has been reviewed and includes an extensive list of viruses and hosts where meristem tip culture has been used to eliminate virus (5).

The basic facilities and equipment needed for tissue culture are a laminar flow hood with a heat source to sterilize instruments (e.g., Bunsen burner or alcohol lamp), a binocular dissecting microscope (magnification 10–40x) with a fluorescent lamp or fiber optics illuminator to minimize heat to the illuminated area, and instruments for plant dissection (forceps, hemostats, scalpels, or razor blades).

CULTURE OF MERISTEMATIC TISSUE

The true meristem consists only of the cells in the apical dome, and thus from a practical sense it is very difficult to dissect and regenerate plants from the true meristem. Meristematic areas, unlike the true meristem, are not necessarily free of virus. Success of regeneration from meristematic areas of either apical or lateral buds varies, as will the minimum size of the explant that can be successfully cultured. A meristematic tip of 0.5 ± 0.2 mm is commonly used. Generally, the larger the size of tissue removed, the greater the success of regeneration. However, the larger the size of tissue removed, the less the success of regenerating virus-free plants. In garlic, for example, sizes smaller than 0.4 mm resulted in reduced success of regeneration (6). For clover, using shoot tips of 2.4–3 mm resulted in successfully obtaining virus-free plants, but the percentage of plants obtained that were virus free was lower compared to when tips of 0.6 mm were used (7). The growth stage of the plant, the growing conditions, and season also influence the success of regeneration. Well-nourished actively growing shoots are the best sources of meristematic tissue. Although virus-free plants have been obtained from callus cultures, the somaclonal variation in callus makes meristem culture preferable.

Using material from plants grown as cleanly as possible reduces the likelihood of cultured tissue being contaminated. Thus seed germinated under axenic conditions can be a good source of meristematic tissue. Treatment of the shoot prior to dissection reduces the possibility of the meristematic tissue becoming contaminated during dissection. Meristems are covered by developing leaves, and leaf primordia therefore have been found to be aseptic. The need for surface treatment of the shoot depends on the contamination of the shoot and the sensitivity of the tissue. Treatment with 75–95% ethanol or 0.1–0.5% sodium hypochlorite [both amended with a drop of detergent (e.g., Tween 20) to increase wettability] for a few seconds to minutes followed by several rinses in sterile water is generally sufficient. In some cases disinfection by both treatments in succession may be needed.

Dissection is done in the laminar flow hood with the aid of the binocular dissecting microscope that has been wiped with ethanol. Using frequently sterilized instruments, the outer leaves and leaf primordia are carefully removed to expose the meristematic area. The meristematic area is easily injured and quickly desiccates; so instruments sterilized by flaming must be cool and the illumination source must not dry out the tissue. The exposed meristematic area is removed and placed on the surface of the medium in a culture tube.

Basic Culture Media and Conditions

The meristematic area is differentiated; so what is required is elongation of the shoot and development of a root. Each species, and sometimes specific cultivars, will require the appropriate medium (mineral salts, pH, vitamins, organics, hormones) and culture conditions [light (quality and amount), temperature]. There is a wealth of published material on the culture and regeneration of many agronomic and horticultural crops that may provide the necessary infromation on the plant species or cultivar of interest or serve as a starting point for developing the appropriate media and conditions.

Amendment of Culture Media with Chemotherapeutic Compounds

Heat treatment and/or meristem culture alone may not result in obtaining virus-free plants (8). Many chemicals have been added to medium to try to enhance production of virus-free plants. The most commonly used is 1-β-D-1H-ribofuranosyl-1,2,4-triazole-3-caroboxamide (ribavirin, virazole), which, after sterilization by filtration, can be added to cooling media before solidification. Ribavirin is a nucleic acid base analog and becomes incorporated into nascent viral nucleic acid during virus replication, resulting in noninfectious progeny viral nucleic acid. The reaction of a plant species to ribavirin and subsequent success in producing virus-free plants varies. Concentrations ranging from 0 to 100 mg/L and length of time in culture should be tested. Generally, as the concentration of ribavirin and length of time in culture increases, the effectiveness of virus elimination increases. However, concentrations above 20–50 mg/L reduce rate of plant growth and can be phytotoxic. Some other chemicals that have shown utility include flavonoids, glycyrrhizin, and other nucleic acid base analogs (9–11).

Detection of Viruses in Tissues in Culture

Following the establishment of plants from culture in soil, they should be tested for virus (12,13). Because plants may be infected, but assays for virus are negative, some prefer referring to plants taken through this process as being virus tested rather than virus free. When a plant is infected by more than one virus, the plant must be tested for each suspect virus, as some viruses may be more readily eliminated than others. In *Arachis* germplasm, for example, tomato spotted wilt virus and peanut stripe virus were more readily eliminated than peanut mottle virus (14).

An indicator host that produces characteristics symptoms after infection by mechanical inoculation can be very useful, especially if the virus of concern has not been identified. Light or electron microscopy is useful for looking for either inclusion bodies produced as a result of virus infection or for virus particles, respectively. Several types of serological assays, nucleic acid hybridization, and the polymerase chain reaction are used to detect virus components. Their utility depends on the availability of antiserum, cloned virus genes to develop probes, or primers for detection of the specific virus by the polymerase chain reaction. Although these techniques are very sensitive, virus infection can be missed. Thus plants should be assayed several times during growth. It must be remembered that plants obtained through meristem culture and test as virus free are not virus resistant. They can become virus infected as easily as the initial stock plant from whence they originated. Care must therefore be taken to prevent virus infection by mechanical means or by vectors.

CONCLUSIONS

Each parameter for sensitivity to thermotherapy, tissue culture, and chemotherapy may vary with the species and/or cultivar. Thus a range of possibilities may have to be examined to obtain success. Plant material taken through the process of heat therapy, chemotherapy, and/or meristem tip culture is not necessarily virus free and should be tested for virus on several subsequent occasions. A virus-free plant is not virus resistant; so efforts must be taken to prevent subsequent infection of the newly produced plants.

BIBLIOGRAPHY

1. S. Spiegel, E.A. Frison, and R.H. Converse, *Plant Dis.* **77**, 1176–1180 (1993).

2. C.J. Asjes, *Acta Hortic.* **266**, 517–529 (1990).

3. G.I. Mink, R. Wample, and W.E. Howell, in A. Hadidi, R.K. Khetarpal and H. Koganezawa, eds., *Plant Virus Disease Control*, American Phytopathological Society, St. Paul, Minn., 1998, pp. 332–345.

4. R. Stace-Smith, in M. Moo-Young, ed., *Comprehensive Biotechnology: The Principles, Applications and Regulations of Biotechnology in Industry, Agriculture and Medicine*, Pergamon, Oxford, 1985, pp. 69–179.

5. G. Faccioli and F. Marani, in A. Hadidi, R.K. Khetarpal, and H. Koganezawa, eds., *Plant Virus Disease Control*, American Phytopathological Society, St. Paul, Minn., 1998, pp. 346–380.

6. M. Verbeek, P. van Dijk, and P.M.A. van Well, *Eur. J. Plant Pathol.* **101**, 231–239 (1995).

7. P.J. Dale and V.A. Cheyne, *Ann. Appl. Biol.* **123**, 25–32 (1993).

8. K.K. Kartha, in L.A. Withers and P.G. Alderson, eds., *Plant Tissue Culture and Its Agricultural Applications*, Butterworth, London, 1986, pp. 219–238.

9. D. James et al., *Ann. Appl. Biol.* **131**, 459–470 (1997).

10. K.G. Porter and A.R. Kuehnle, *HortTechnology* **7**, 161–164 (1997).

11. E.V. Truskinov and E.V. Rogozina, *Russ. J. Plant Physiol.* **44**, 374–380 (1997).

12. R.E.F. Matthews, *Plant Virology*, 3rd ed., Academic Press, N.Y., 1991, pp. 12–52.

13. T. Candresse, R.W. Hammond, and A. Hadidi, in A. Hadidi, R.K. Khetarpal and H. Koganezawa, eds., *Plant Virus Disease Control*, American Phytopathological Society, St. Paul, Minn., 1998, pp. 399–416.

14. K.B. Dunbar, D.L. Pinnow, J.B. Morris, and R.N. Pittman, *Plant Dis.* **77**, 517–520 (1993).

See also CONTAMINATION DETECTION AND ELIMINATION IN PLANT CELL CULTURE; CONTAMINATION DETECTION IN ANIMAL CELL CULTURE; CONTAMINATION OF CELL CULTURES, MYCOPLASMA; STERILIZATION AND DECONTAMINATION.

INDEX

Page references in **bold** type indicate a main article. Page references followed by italic *t* indicate material in tables.